PHYSICAL METALLURGY

Third, revised and enlarged edition

Edited by

R.W. CAHN

Université de Paris-Sud, France

P. HAASEN

Universität Göttingen, Germany

PART I

1983

NORTH-HOLLAND PHYSICS PUBLISHING

AMSTERDAM – OXFORD – NEW YORK – TOKYO

ISBN: 0444 86 628 0 Set
        0444 86 786 4 Part I
        0444 86 787 2 Part II

PUBLISHED BY:

North-Holland Physics Publishing

a division of

Elsevier Science Publishers B.V.

P.O. Box 103
1000 AC Amsterdam
The Netherlands

SOLE DISTRIBUTORS FOR THE USA AND CANADA:

Elsevier Science Publishing Company Inc.
52, Vanderbilt Avenue
New York, N.Y. 10017
U.S.A.

Library of Congress Cataloging in Publication Data
Main entry under title:

Physical metallurgy.

   Includes bibliographies and indexes.
   1. Physical metallurgy.   I. Cahn, R.W. (Robert W.), 1924–
II. Haasen, P. (Peter)
TN690.P44   1983   669'.94   83-17292
ISBN 0–444–86628–0 (Elsevier : set)
ISBN 0–444–86786–4 (Elsevier : pt. 1)
ISBN 0–444–86787–2 (Elsevier : pt. 2)

Printed in The Netherlands

PREFACE TO THE THIRD EDITION

The first edition of this book was published in 1965 and the second in 1970. The book continued to sell well during the 1970s and, once it was out of print, pressure developed for a new edition to be prepared. The subject had grown greatly during the 1970s and R.W.C. hesitated to undertake the task alone. He is immensely grateful to P.H. for converting into a pleasure what would otherwise have been an intolerable burden!

The second edition contained twenty-two chapters. In the present edition, eight of these twenty-two have been thoroughly revised by the same authors as before, while the others have been entrusted to new contributors, some being divided into pairs of chapters. In addition, seven chapters have been commissioned on new themes. The difficult decision was taken to leave out the chapter on superpure metals and to replace it by one focused on solute segregation to interfaces and surfaces – a topic which has made major strides during the past decade and which is of great practical significance. A name index has also been added.

Research in physical metallurgy has become worldwide and this is reflected in the fact that the contributors to this edition live in no fewer than seven countries. We are proud to have been able to edit a truly international text, both of us having worked in several countries ourselves. We would like here to express our thanks to all our contributors for their hard and effective work, their promptness and their angelic patience with editorial pressures!

The length of the book has inevitably increased, by 50% over the second edition, which was itself 20% longer than the first edition. Even to contain the increase within these numbers has entailed draconian limitations and difficult choices; these were unavoidable if the book was not to be priced out of its market. Everything possible has been done by the editors and the publisher to keep the price to a minimum (to enable readers to take the advice of G.CHR. LICHTENBERG [1775]: "He who has two pairs of trousers should pawn one and buy this book".).

Two kinds of chapters have been allowed priority in allocating space: those covering very active fields and those concerned with the most basic topics such as phase transformations, including solidification (a central theme of physical metallurgy), defects and diffusion. Also, this time we have devoted more space to experimental methods and their underlying principles, microscopy in particular. Since there is a plethora of texts available on the standard aspects of X-ray diffraction, the chapter on X-ray and neutron scattering has been designed to emphasize less familiar aspects. Because of space limitations, we regretfully decided that we could not include a chapter on corrosion.

This revised and enlarged edition can properly be regarded as to all intents and purposes a new book.

Sometimes it was difficult to draw a sharp dividing line between physical metallurgy and process metallurgy, but we have done our best to observe the distinction and to restrict the book to its intended theme. Again, reference is inevitably made occasionally to nonmetallics, especially when they serve as model materials for metallic systems.

As before, the book is designed primarily for graduate students beginning research or undertaking advanced courses, and as a basis for more experienced research workers who require an overview of fields comparatively new to them, or with which they wish to renew contact after a gap of some years.

We should like to thank Ir. J. Soutberg and Drs. A.P. de Ruiter of the North-Holland Publishing Company for their major editorial and administrative contributions to the production of this edition, and in particular we acknowledge the good-humoured resolve of Drs. W.H. Wimmers, former managing director of the Company, to bring this third edition to fruition. We are grateful to Dr. Bormann for preparing the subject index. We thank the hundreds of research workers who kindly gave permission for reproduction of their published illustrations: all are acknowledged in the figure captions.

Of the authors who contributed to the first edition, one is no longer alive: Robert Franklin Mehl, who wrote the introductory historical chapter. What he wrote has been left untouched in the present edition, but one of us has written a short supplement to bring the treatment up to date, and has updated the bibliography. Robert Mehl was one of the founders of the modern science of physical metallurgy, both through his direct scientific contributions and through his leadership and encouragement of many eminent metallurgists who at one time worked with him. We dedicate this third edition to his memory.

April 1983
                                        Robert W. CAHN, Paris
                                        Peter HAASEN, Göttingen

CONTENTS

PART I

Chapter 5. Structure of intermetallic compounds, by K. Girgis 219

6. Metallurgical thermodynamics, by D.R. Gaskell ... 271

Chapter 8. Diffusion in metals and alloys, *by J.L. Bocquet, G. Brébec and Y. Limoge* 385

Chapter 10A. Qualitative and quantitative surface microscopy, by H.E. Exner . .   581

Chapter 11. Transmission electron microscopy, by M. Rühle and M. Wilkens . . . 713

Chapter 13. Interfacial and surface microscopy, by E.D. Hondros and M.P. Seah   855

PART II

Chapter 14. Diffusive phase transformations in the solid state, by Roger D.

Chapter 19. *Mechanical properties, mildly temperature-dependent, by J. Weertman and J.R. Weertman* 1259

Chapter 26. Magnetic properties of metals and alloys, by F.E. Luborsky, J.D. Livingston and G.Y. Chin 1673

Chapter 27. Superconducting materials, by W.L. Johnson

Contents

CHAPTER 1

THE HISTORICAL DEVELOPMENT OF
PHYSICAL METALLURGY

ROBERT F. MEHL [†]

(with a Supplement by Robert W. Cahn)

[†] Deceased

R.W. Cahn and P. Haasen, eds.
Physical Metallurgy; third, revised and enlarged edition
© Elsevier Science Publishers BV, 1983

1.   Introduction

Physical metallurgy as a recognizable discipline is hardly one century old, yet its origins go back far. This chapter will trace its development in its entirety, including the earliest days. The account is divided into four rather roughly separated periods: before the nineteenth century, the nineteenth century, from 1900 to 1940, and from 1940 to the present date.

All antiquity is included in the first period: we know little about it in the present connection; in the last years of that period, however, some of the important ideas in physical metallurgy first appeared. In the second period science and engineering reached an early maturity, and early application of science to physical metallurgy was made; there were heroes in metallurgy toward the end of the 19th century, as we shall see. In the third period, physical metallurgy began to take on its present form; and in the fourth, a great burgeoning occurred, the results of which are so evident in the remarkable liveliness of the subject today.

Physical metallurgy has been and in a measure still is inextricably interwoven with extractive metallurgy, and for a long time, historically, these two branches constituted a common art, practised by the same artisans, and interacting; while the division between the two has become sharper in recent years, it is necessary at the outset to note this close relationship.

2.   Before the nineteenth century

The first step was the development of the smelting of copper. This appears to have occurred before the days of the Sumerians, very likely in the highlands in Western Asia northwest of the Persian Gulf, possibly in the neighborhood of the year 4300 BC (though all dates before 2000 BC are rather uncertain). Native gold and copper had been used earlier, at least by 5000 BC; even then such natural objects were hammered and otherwise formed, and even annealed to provide capacity for further forming; thus some knowledge of work-hardening, of softening by annealing, and of hot-working, all falling within the realm encompassed by physical metallurgy, was available, at a very early date indeed. Smelting led immediately to melting and to casting, and these were widely practised by 3800 BC. Some tabulation of developments will set the scene: silver, gold, copper, lead and iron were all known by 2000 BC; bronze is doubtless older. Itinerant tribes, and merchants and pedlars (for people were on the march) spread this newly developed technology rather quickly, in time to Western Europe. Metal culture was established in Middle Europe in 2000 BC; bronze appeared in England in 1800 BC; iron–nickel meteorites were used in the most ancient days. It is not surprising that the smelting of other metals, especially those easily produced, like lead and zinc, followed shortly after copper. No simple account is possible; new metallurgical methods apparently sprang up in different places independently, and the historical record is too inexact.

Iron smelting (and possibly the manufacture of steel) seems to have appeared at about 2800 BC. Tutankhamen had iron; perhaps the oldest pieces are those from Ur (early third millenium). The oldest iron was, of course, sponge iron, hammered into shape whilst hot. The military power of the Hittites has been attributed to their weapons of iron. As primitive blast furnaces were enlarged, it became possible to produce higher temperatures and thus to melt and to produce cast iron; this, treated by oxidizing flames was converted into wrought iron. The use of this material, as well as the others for that matter, was vastly spurred by the demand for superior weapons. The earliest date for the manufacture of steel is uncertain. Certainly the Romans had steel; the early steel was made from iron by carburizing, and this continued until the eighteenth century, when steel was first melted in crucibles and cast, subsequently to be worked.

Historical evidence and records after the earliest days, from which one might draw evidence of the early knowledge of physical metallurgical operations, are similarly scanty – one can only infer what had been done metallurgically from the composition and the shape of surviving artefacts. The writings of Pliny, 23–79 AD, embodied a number of comments upon metals; but in the long period following, up to the sixteenth century, we have little except, primarily, fragments of information relating to the preparation and treatment of armor and swords. Agricola (who was chiefly though not only an extractive metallurgist) wrote his famous "De Re Metallica" in 1556, dissertating at length and in wonderful detail upon the status of the art (as did others in much the same time period). Although methods of hammering, annealing, and making new alloys were invented during these centuries, by far the greatest emphasis lay on extractive metallurgy. The historical record is clear that chemistry grew out of the arguments about extractive metallurgy, especially the cupellation of lead. Extractive metallurgists and chemists were nearly indistinguishable. The process of oxidation was steadily argued; the phlogiston theory explained the gain in weight on oxidation as the loss of phlogiston, a theory which held sway for a long time, until it was finally overthrown by Lavoisier (1788). The chief progenitor of the scientific era (soon to blossom), Francis Bacon, in the early part of the 17th century, wrote at length on the possibility of alloying, and listed a surprisingly large number of different and even unusual alloys; he commented upon the knowledge that was available on the extent of alloying, on color, on "pliantness", and on stability (volatility). This account suggests (as well as that of Agricola) at least a modicum of growth during these long centuries. As to steel, made of course by carburizing wrought iron, and as to wrought iron itself, much was known in an empirical way, chiefly because of their importance in armor and swords; complex manufacturing processes had been developed to produce steel swords of both beauty and utility, in both the eastern and the western world, of which Damascene steel is the most famous; quaint quenching methods were developed, with much invoking of mysterious powers of odd media.

The development of a science of crystallography and of mineralogy preceded that of the science of solid metals, because of the frequent usefulness of minerals as ores, perhaps because of the extraordinary beauty of many natural minerals, and probably also because the regularity of minerals suggested an order in nature, an intimation of

References: p. 35.

the science to come. The study of mineral crystals and metal crystals have much in common; mineralogical knowledge has often lent essential assistance to the physical metallurgist.

Mineralogists early recognized the existence of polycrystalline aggregates – their task was easy! Some writings in this period are of unusual interest. Hill (1748) thought of freezing as a process of nucleation and growth, an extraordinary example of prescience. He etched rocks in acid, and saw crystalline grains under a microscope; he also recognized, surprisingly, the occurrence of diffusion. Grignon (1775), a blast furnace operator, observed that columnar grains sometimes occur on freezing, and seemed to believe that metals are aggregates of small crystals; he made the famous drawing of a dendrite (from slowly cooled cast iron) that is still so often reproduced; he also etched metals for macroscopic studies, as did Rinmann in Sweden (1774); he seemed to recognize the existence of solid solutions; many workers in this time period observed "grains" in metals, and speculated about them. De Morveau (1776) concluded that solidification is indeed crystallization. It is really surprising to a reader today to observe the extraordinary powers of anticipation these early workers exhibited.

Names often appear of men who are renowned in other fields. Hooke (1665) wrote on micrography, and looked under a low power magnifying glass at the point of a needle and at a razor edge (and made a drawing). Newton (1672) considered surfaces of fracture. Réaumur (1722) was a close student of metals (he played an important part in the development of the French metallurgical industry); using a magnifying glass he noted the grain size of metals; he had proper ideas of the freezing process; and his speculations on the nature of the physical occurrences during the heat-treatment of steel as read today seem remarkably prescient – one merely has to adopt modern nomenclature to make the account quite intelligible and within limits correct; he anticipated the effect of austenite grain size on the hardening process. Such, most briefly, was the status of what we now know as *metallography* before the time of Sorby in the next century.

The occurrence of allotropy in iron, later to prove of fundamental importance, was hypothesized early. Gilbert (1600) discovered that iron loses its ferromagnetism when heated. This presented science with a conception which, confused later with phase-change allotropy, was to create, near the end of the 19th century, the somewhat mischievous beta-iron theory of the hardening of steel. The idea of true phase allotropy was proposed by Bergmann (1781) in Uppsala.

Mechanics saw its early stages of development before 1800. It is said that Galileo measured the tensile strength of a metal by determining the length of a copper rod that would fracture of its own weight. Soon after, of course, Hooke (1660) formulated his famous law, to be followed early in the next century by the formulation of the general equations of elasticity, all of which was to be adopted as part of physical metallurgy.

Speculation on the nature of steel continued after Réaumur. Bergmann (1781) gave a very clear account of the nature of steel, wrought iron, and cast iron as a consequence of the effect of carbon. The ubiquitous phlogiston theory was invoked – steel on quenching (and thus hardening) was thought to gain phlogiston! Very direct evidence of the primary role played by carbon was furnished by Clouet (1798) and by others soon in the next century. The scene was set for the nineteenth century.

3. The nineteenth century

As all know, the nineteenth century saw very great advances in science, in chemistry, physics, and mechanics. This new knowledge found ready application in fields of interest to the physical metallurgist. Here began the marvelously fruitful interplay among the various scientific disciplines. The metallurgist, primarily interested in the solid state, added his bit, a not inconsiderable bit; indeed in many fields of basic science, the metallurgist's contribution was the primary one, and this is as true today as it was then.

Much of the development of metallurgy came about by reason of the rapid development of new methods of preparing metals and alloys, particularly the Bessemer–Kelly and the Siemens–Martin (open hearth) methods of making steel; though Huntsman (1740) had melted steel in a crucible, tonnage (and cheap) steel awaited these two new methods, born shortly after mid-century. Many of the scientific problems which claimed the attention of the metallurgical scientist arose from practical observations in the metallurgical plant; and this remains today a characteristic of metallurgical science even though not so exclusively as in the last century. No clear distinction existed between the extractive and the physical metallurgist during much of the century; the division came toward the end of the century, when a rapidly growing body of knowledge made specialization inevitable (and now observe the remarkable specialization – and fragmentation – in the latter half of the twentieth century, regrettable and unavoidable!).

Methods of measurements, ever important in research, drew attention. Seebeck (1821) discovered *thermoelectricity*, though surprisingly this did not result in the invention of a practical pyrometer until Le Chatelier (1888) devised the platinum/platinum–rhodium thermocouple, which has ever since remained one of the prime tools of the metallurgist. Siemens invented the electrical resistance thermometer in 1877. The development of good microscopes came later in the nineteenth century.

As noted earlier, the work of mineralogists and crystallographers exercised a profound influence on those interested in metals, and it continued to do so. The subject of *crystallography* advanced rapidly in the nineteenth century. Hessel in 1830 demonstrated the thirty-two crystal classes, and Bravais in 1849 devised the fourteen translation lattices. The descriptive knowledge of crystals and their behaviour grew to a large volume. The use of Miller indices (1839) became common in crystallography, even in fields quite closely related to physical metallurgy, for example, in the work of Reusch in 1867 on slip lines and twinning in minerals. Late in the century Federov (1891) in Russia, Schoenfliess (1891) in Germany, and Barlow (1849) in

References: p. 35.

England independently developed the complete lattice structure theory, leading to the derivation of 230 space groups, the maximum possible number of types of arrangements of atoms in three-dimensional space: full experimental confirmation of this had to wait until methods of X-ray diffraction were discovered and elaborated, well in the next century; the theoretical derivation of space groups was a most remarkable tour de force. At the time, however, the space lattices of actual metals were unknown: in the case of iron it was known only that the external symmetry was cubic, thus while the twinning plane in alpha iron was determined in terms of Miller indices, there was no knowledge of the pattern of atoms on this plane.

There was little certainty that the *grains* in common metals, long recognized, were in fact crystallites. As the nineteenth century wore on, uncertainty gradually disappeared. A host of facts reassured the scientist: naturally occurring metal crystals, the geometrical characteristics of the Widmanstätten structure observed in meteorites and later in steels, the preparation of idiomorphic metal crystals, the geometrical regularity of twin bands and of slip bands – and a little scientific comfort descended on this difficult field.

Although Sorby (as we shall see) may well be described as the father of metallography, he was not the first to examine metals under a magnifying glass or microscope. In addition to those noted earlier, we may now note the work of Anosoff who in 1841 studied the watered pattern of Damascene steel under the microscope, and in the course of his work developed etching agents. J.R. von Fuchs (1851) examined cleavage faces on iron, deciding that iron is cubic or rhombohedral.

Sorby created a revolution in the physical metallurgy of his day. As a petrographer he applied petrographic methods to steel, making thin sections (unnecessarily), polishing, etching, and preparing drawings. His first photographs were made in 1864, at a magnification of nine; this work was not published until 1887 (and the subject remained largely dormant in the intervening period); he used a higher magnification in the latter year; he saw and described "the pearly constituent", *pearlite* (named so later by Howe); he realized that pearlite is a structure formed upon the decomposition of a homogeneous high-temperature phase, the formation of which was suppressed by quenching. He thus clearly recognized the occurrence of *allotropy in steels*, comparing it with the recognized allotropy of silver iodide; he saw the ferritic Widmanstätten structure in hypoeutectoid steels as resembling that which Aloys von Widmanstätten had seen in the Agram meteorite in 1808; indeed much of the stimulus behind his work came from a desire to see whether any structures similar to the meteoric Widmanstätten figure could be seen in steels when etched and magnified. It was not published until after the publications of Tchernoff and of Martens.

Sorby's work aroused surprisingly little interest in England. Martens, in 1878, in Germany, undertook the study of metallographic microscopy, including fractured surfaces, methods of polishing and etching, and internal alloy microstructure. This led to Wedding's work (1885) which helped to renew Sorby's interest in the subject for a time, but his interest then wholly lapsed.

Interest in the nature of steel increased rapidly in this century. Following Clouet,

Pepys, working with Davy in 1815, made steel from iron and diamond, and the essential nature of the composition of steel was no longer to be questioned. Karsten (1827) isolated carbide from soft steel, which in 1888 Abel proved to be Fe_3C. But the great excitement (and significance) in the study of steel came, first, with the recognition of the true allotropy of iron and of the associated critical points in steel by Tchernoff. Tchernoff published his classic experimental paper in 1861, showing that steel cannot be hardened unless heated above a certain "critical temperature", Tait demonstrated the allotropy of iron in 1873 by thermoelectromotive force measurements. It cannot be doubted, however, that further advance in the theory of heat-treatment depended, in the first instance, upon the results of metallographic investigations and upon the introduction of the phase rule, even though, as we shall see, these proved a little less than enough.

The theory of the hardening of steel was a favorite subject about which to write in the latter part of this century. Sorby saw the constituent later named *martensite* though he appears to have misinterpreted its nature. Osmond named it in honour of the metallographer Martens; the practice of naming constituents after those who contributed to an understanding of them has continued – e.g. austenite for Roberts-Austen, and lately, bainite for Bain – and it was Howe who instituted the practice of employing the mineralogical suffix "-ite". Some terms, once in general usage, e.g. troostite and sorbite, have fallen out of use primarily because of indefiniteness as to exactly what structure they pertained to; with increase in knowledge, terminology is now much more exact in meaning, though doubtless innovations will occur in time. Osmond, Roberts-Austen, Howe and Sauveur held that retained allotropic phases give martensite its hardness, in particular *beta iron* which, without any direct evidence, was assumed to be especially hard (and to possess some special crystal structure). Others argued for the occurrence of a special carbide, others for great internal stresses. There was to be no relief from this controversy until the following century, when X-ray diffraction proved beta iron to be simply a non-ferromagnetic variety of body-centered cubic alpha iron.

A lack of any understanding of the kinetics of the decomposition of austenite was a serious block to theorizing on the hardening of steel (as we can see now on looking back); mixed microstructures which formed on cooling and thus formed over a range of temperatures, were often thought unique. All became simpler (though not wholly simple!) with the introduction of the technique of isothermal reaction. The study of the nature of plastic deformation of metals, and of the relation of this to crystallography, received great impetus in the latter part of the century. Earlier, mechanical twinning had been observed, first by Neumann in ferritic kamacite in iron–nickel meteorites, and later by Prestel in commercial low-carbon steel. Neumann identified the twinning phase along which mechanical twins form in alpha iron correctly as the {211} plane, and since then these twins have been known as *Neumann bands*.

Especially important was the observation of Ewing and Rosenhain in 1899 that metals – in this case lead – deform by a process of *slip* on internal crystal planes, evidently on equivalent sets of planes, for the "slip lines" were observed to intersect. This provided the first important evidence on the nature of the deformation process

References: p. 35.

in metals. The so-called slip interference theory of hardening (a popular term later) was at least implicit in this observation, for manifestly anything rendering slip more difficult will harden a metal. Shortly thereafter, Mügge studied these slip lines crystallographically and showed them, by geometrical reasoning, to follow the {111} planes in copper, gold, silver and lead. This work was the harbinger of the great volume of work which has appeared since.

Mechanical metallurgy received much attention, chiefly, of course, owing to the construction of steel structures which accompanied the industrial revolution and the consequent need for the testing of materials. In 1807, the English physicist Thomas Young described the *modulus of elasticity*, an early start in the theory of elasticity, to be developed to the full later in the century. Barlow made determinations of the strength of materials, publishing in 1826.

In 1822, Thomas Tredgold published a general treatise on the testing of materials, founded chiefly on Young's work (the testing of materials lay in the hands of civil engineers for a long time, and to a lesser degree still does). The behaviour of iron bridges in that period led first to a study of the behaviour of beams under stress, and then to a study of stresses in framed structures in 1847, especially by Whipple who presented the first correct analysis. The ordinary mechanical testing of materials was well established by 1870.

Mechanical testing revealed new phenomena; *over-strain-aging* in steel, a phenomenon still under intensive investigation, was discovered by Kent; he noted that cold work lowers the elastic limit, removes the yield point and the yield point elongation (and the "drop of the beam"), and that subsequent aging restored these. Martens, in 1890, fully demonstrated the phenomena of *blue brittleness* in steel; the relationship of this to the observation of Kent was not recognized for many years, though both are manifestations of the same phenomenon.

Basic to mechanical testing, and much more so to the subsequently developed theory of plasticity, especially in the advanced form which obtains today, is the understanding of elasticity. Most of the pure theory of elasticity was discovered by Cauchy (1822); he showed that stress may be expressed by six component stresses, and demonstrated the principal planes of stress. For the general elastic anisotropy of crystals he found twenty-one independent constants, of which fifteen are true elastic constants. Werthering, in 1849, showed that the value of Young's modulus is greater in cold-worked copper than in annealed copper. Poisson had obtained earlier (1828) the equations of equilibrium for elastic solids, and these were applied to various problems of vibration and static elasticity. Poisson, in 1829, considered the value of the ratio of lateral contraction to longitudinal extension, and produced what is known as Poisson's ratio. By the year 1871 the theory of elasticity had been practically completely developed. The theory of plasticity, however, remained a mystery and for many later years; various phenomenological theories based on principles of viscous flow were applied; the quite recent development of the dislocation theory promises far more today, but, as we shall see later, the matter is still quite unsettled and even contentious.

The *elastic after-effect* in common, polycrystalline metals, was discovered by

Weber in 1835. Mechanical hysteresis was not discovered until 1881, when Bauschinger demonstrated what is now known as the *Bauschinger effect*.

While most of these effects were difficult, indeed then essentially impossible to rationalize, many basic phenomena were discovered. One example was the discovery of *flow lines* by Lüders, in 1860; subsequently it was shown that these originate in the phenomenon of elongation at the yield point, still later they were shown to be of basic importance in over-strain-aging in steel, and are a point of departure for much of today's work on the nature of the flow process in metals. The effect of repeated stresses, that is, *fatigue*, was discovered and studied early in this century. The classic work, however, is that of Wöhler in Germany, carried out in the years 1860–1870, employing stresses in tension, torsion, and bending: he demonstrated that metals subjected to repeated stresses will fail after a time, developing the first S–N (stress–number of cycles to failure) curve, and he noted the deleterious effect of notches. And thus began this very important field of fatigue testing, of such great importance to industry; since then innumerable S–N curves have been produced, but the mechanism by which fatigue fracture occurs (or indeed any fracture!) has throughout these years quite escaped rigorous proof.

Such observations as were made in those earlier days, chiefly by testing engineers, were largely descriptive, with theory usually only primitive. Little or nothing was known then about the elastic and plastic properties of the single grain in an aggregate; to obtain such knowledge would have required single crystals, and these did not become available until early in the next century.

Although the ancients, after having cold-worked metals, annealed them to soften them for further cold-working, and so in fact *recrystallized* metals, no understanding of this process whatsoever came until the nineteenth century, and this beginning knowledge was most rudimentary; the processes which accompany the annealing of cold-worked metals have indeed proved most complex, and subtle problems remain today. In 1858, Nogues observed that platinum wires heated repeatedly in a reducing gas flame took on a crystalline appearance, perhaps the first observation of grain growth or even of any form of recrystallization. Kalischer (1881–1882) made the first systematic study of the annealing of metals following cold-work: he observed that large grains were developed on heating zinc sheet, thought cold-working destroyed the crystallinity of zinc and heating restored it, and made observations on the concomitant changes in properties. Ledebur (1883) found that the grain size after recrystallization was the greater, the higher the temperature of recrystallization and the longer the time of annealing. Stead (1898) stated that recrystallization proceeds by a process of *nucleation and growth*. Ewing and Rosenhain, and others – including some of the great names in the history of this subject – studied the effect of temperature on grain size, thoroughly appreciating the tremendous effect of temperature but somehow missing the activation concept. All this work was but preliminary.

As one views the diverse events of the nineteenth century, the many strands of new knowledge, from one's present vantage point, one can see how these were to conspire, in the next century, to form the fabric of what we now regard as physical

References: p. 35.

metallurgy; and this is even true of those fields of activity that today are often thought as wholly recent. The beginnings of the "physics of metals", sometimes today broadened to "solid state physics", is an example. Matthiessen in 1867 studied the electrical conductivity of alloys, framing *Matthiessen's Rule*; it is clear that Matthiessen recognized the existence of solid solutions, as others before him had come quite close to doing, anticipating van 't Hoff. Matthiessen recognized also the existence of intermediate phases, and insisted that such phases need not in any way be chemical compounds in the usual sense of the term, i.e. strictly obeying simple valency rules – to us this seems very modern. Kurnakov and Zemczuzny later (1908) used electrical conductivity to study the reactions in the solid state which we now know to be *order–disorder reactions*. It had earlier been suggested by Achard (1784) that there is a close alliance between electrical and thermal conductivity; Wiedemann and Franz (1852) expressed this in the well-known law, later amplified by Lorentz. Seebeck had discovered thermoelectricity earlier, as noted above. These properties, together with thermal analysis which grew out of advances in thermometry, together with common mechanical tests such as hardness, provided the tools which made possible the systematic investigation of the constitution of alloys which was to come in the next century.

A milestone of the greatest possible importance in the development of knowledge of the constitution of alloys was the derivation of the *phase rule* (and of the principles of heterogeneous equilibria in general) by Willard Gibbs. This was published obscurely in the journal of the Connecticut Academy in 1876. It was unearthed later by German physical chemists; its importance to the study of the constitution of alloys was pointed out by Jüptner (1898) and by Le Chatelier. The application to polycomponent systems, and to metal systems in particular, was further extended by Rijn van Alkemade (1893), and especially by Roozeboom (1899). The conditions of equilibrium which Gibbs's phase rule made clear, were of wide application, throughout the field of physical science, and together with the labours of the early chemical thermodynamicists laid the basis for an understanding of the equilibria among all of the phases which matter can exhibit; it thus became the basis of interpreting equilibria in physical metallurgy as well as that in extractive metallurgy. The work of Raoult on the depression of the freezing point by solutes led to the study of amalgams, and shortly afterwards of *alloy systems*. Much work was done at the turn of the century on the initial freezing points of binary alloys: the liquidi provided data useful in applying Raoult's law. Van 't Hoff in 1890 pointed out the analogy between solid solutions and liquid solutions, fully recognizing solid solutions, as indeed Matthiessen had done earlier. Much further development of thermodynamics and of solution theory lay ahead, but the directions were set. Physical chemists, especially Nernst, began to formulate the fundamentals of *electro-chemistry*, which with increasingly sophisticated thermochemistry and thermodynamics provided, in the period to follow, a proper measure of *chemical affinity* in terms of free energy decrease, replacing early vague, qualitative ideas, and the inadequate heat-of-reaction concept.

Roberts-Austen studied the phase constitution of steels, employing the early data on the critical temperature, recognizing the solid solution nature of the phase afterwards to be named after him. Employing this work, and that of Osmond on the thermal examination of steels, Roozeboom applied the phase rule of Gibbs and, in a metallurgical classic, produced an equilibrium diagram for the Fe_3C system. This diagram was of great importance in the development of the study of the constitution of metallic (and other) systems. The work of Roozeboom was followed by that of Heycock and Neville on the constitution of the copper–tin system: the way was clear for a far-flung attack on the constitution of alloy systems, no matter how many components, and in time, as information grew, to a study of the atomic and electronic factors determining alloy constitution, a chapter in science still most active at this writing.

Concomitant with the definition of and the rules of equilibrium, physical chemists, toward the end of the century, laid the basis of kinetics. It has been clear for a very long time that chemical reactions may proceed slowly or rapidly, and clear also that such rates may very greatly with temperature. Even as early as 1896 Roberts-Austen in England measured the rate of diffusion of gold in solid lead (and produced data which in accuracy compare well with much later data); the results came as a surprise to those interested in solids, for the diffusion coefficients were far greater than before supposed; and, most significantly, Roberts-Austen associated the temperature coefficient of the rate with the concept of *activation energy* announced by Arrhenius only a few year before, in 1889, and thus introduced this type of argument, to be of such importance in later years, into the study of solids.

The Reports of the Alloys Research Committee of Roberts-Austen (1891–1899) assisted greatly in the development of physical metallurgy, especially as regards practical problems. Roberts-Austen was much concerned with the effect of small amounts of impurity upon the properties of a metal, and believed this should be studied from the point of view of the periodic table, as opinion so amply and profitably verified in the following half-century. He noted that 0.003% antimony markedly changes the rate of oxidation of molten lead, that 0.05% lead makes gold brittle, that 0.5% of iron reduces the electrical conductivity of copper 60% (which would not have surprised Matthiessen!). He tended to ascribe such effects to ubiquitous allotropy, a view that was to plague physical metallurgy until recent years, and which Le Chatelier opposed with much intelligence, ascribing the effect on mechanical properties to structure instead.

During these years, especially toward the end of the century, new and modified alloy compositions began to appear rapidly. Faraday and Stodart (1820) prepared a number of alloys (by annealing welded wires of the component metals), e.g. iron and platinum. Berthier (1820) made alloys of iron and chromium, and might have become truly famous! Tungsten steel was first made by Jacob (1857) in Austria; Mushet developed tungsten steels and invented air-hardening steels. But the greatest advance was the development of manganese and silicon steels by Robert Hadfield in 1871, with which the great new era of alloy steels was ushered in.

The latter years of the century were active years for those interested in the microstructure of steels. Sauveur in 1893 showed that the grain size of austenite

References: p. 35.

increases as the temperature of austenitizing is increased, thus repeating Réaumur's observation on a metallographic basis. It is most curious that Sauveur's work was not extended, for in this lay the basis for the effect of austenite grain size on hardenability, a subject which was destined to become one of much interest and importance in the 1930s; but then, in those days, with ideas of steel hardening much confused, and with practically nothing known of the kinetics of reaction in the solid state, such foresight could hardly have been hoped for.

The sun in science was rapidly rising as the twentieth century was ushered in.

4.   1900–1940

Physical metallurgy was about to come of age. In the previous century many of the chapters of the subject subsequently to prove to be the most important received their initial impetus, as the reader will observe shortly. A most interesting period began. Not long after the beginning of the period, university departments of metallurgy became substantial; after a few years industry undertook research more seriously; and finally physical metallurgy grew to be important among the professions.

At the very outset, the "Tammann school" at the University of Göttingen came to the forefront. Tammann was a figure long to remain a dominant one. He breathed good science into physical metallurgy; he added fundamental information and theory to a very large number of subjects. One of Tammann's activities should be noted now; he undertook a broad study of the constitution of metal systems, chiefly for the purpose of deriving general rules concerning the constitution of alloys and the nature of alloy phases. The result was a large number of *phase diagrams*. Detailed accuracy was not sought; this came later from other sources.

Although early in the century doubt as to the crystallinity of metals had all but disappeared, little was accomplished until the brilliant discovery of the *diffraction of X-rays* by von Laue in 1912 and the subsequent development by the Braggs (1914) and others. The method was rapidly applied, and brought about a revolution. The determination of the unit cells of all the known and of many of the intermediate alloy phases proceeded rapidly. Westgren (1922) demonstrated that alpha, beta, and delta iron are all body-centered cubic (upon which the beta iron theory of the hardening of steel died a final, reluctant death!) and that gamma iron is face-centered cubic. Bain discovered *superlattices* in 1923; many other examples were discovered, the solid–solid reaction by which they form came to be known as *order–disorder reactions*; Bragg and Williams in 1935 wrote the first theoretical paper on this reaction in terms of interaction energies and the effect of this upon the degree of order and upon the kinetics of ordering. This subject has ever since been a favorite one for physicists interested in the solid state – countless papers have been published. Shortly before, Westgren had discovered the structural analogies which exist in the alloys of copper, silver, and gold, with the metals of the B-subgroups, from which Hume-Rothery was later (1926) to develop the atom : electron ratio theory for similar lattice types. Hume-Rothery's work was remarkable: he showed that the relative atomic size of solvent and solute and electroaffinity play determinative roles in fixing solid solubility. There have been many extensions of this work, especially by Hume-Rothery and by Raynor.

Thus among other factors, atom size was found to be important in determining solid solubility. In 1931, Wever, observing that some elements widen the gamma field in iron alloys while others narrow it, showed that this behaviour was related to atom size. This generalization was of immense help to alloy steel metallurgists who must often deal with complex alloy steels of many components. Shortly afterwards, Laves pointed out that there are compounds (*Laves compounds*) the composition of which is determined only by the possibilities of packing atoms in space; there are intermetallic phases to which one must assign very curious formulae quite at odds with ordinary valency rules.

Solid solutions continued to attract scientific interest. Physical chemists had made great progress in the theory of solutions, and this, together with thermodynamics, was applied to solid solutions. Electrochemical factors were found important. Kremann (1931) showed that liquid metal solutions can be electrolyzed, and shortly after Kubaschewski electrolyzed solid solutions, observing that carbon in austenite moves toward the cathode, that is, solid solutions are effectively ionized.

The amount of X-ray diffraction work in the middle years of this period was very large and crystal structure was a matter of prime interest. A growing belief that electrons must have wave properties led Davisson and Germer in 1927 to attempt to *diffract electrons by crystals* – the experiment worked! Thereby a new method was made available for structural studies, one which owing to the fact that electrons can penetrate but a few atom layers, is ideal for studying surfaces, for example, for studying adsorption.

The beautiful and apparent perfection of crystals was deceptive and forestalled progress to a degree, yet in the middle years of this period, owing to the thoughtfulness of a few workers, particularly Frenkel, Wagner and Schottky (1930-1936) several types of defect were postulated – *vacancies* and *interstitials* in various aspects and combinations, the so-called "point defects" (other imperfections, for example dislocations, will be noted later). Jette (1933) showed that the phase wüstite, "FeO", is an example of a crystal with vacancies (of iron atoms), in this case reaching high concentrations. Point defects were later to prove of importance in a number of connections.

Shortly after the beginning of the century, Tammann published voluminously on the mechanism of *phase transformations*, especially that of freezing, insisting upon the ubiquity of processes of nucleation and growth. This work was extended both theoretically and experimentally by Volmer (1926), who taking Gibbs's concept of capillarity and equilibrium wrote the outline of today's standard *nucleation theory*.

Tammann saw that large crystals could be grown by freezing in such a way that the rate of nucleation is low when the rate of growth is high, and that freezing with the operation of a single nucleus would result in a single crystal. Very satisfactory methods of growing single crystals were developed by Bridgman, Czochralski, and

References: p. 35.

others. Large fields of research on the properties of single crystals were opened, and enthusiasm among metallurgical research workers, faced with fanciful opportunities, became very high.

Among these opportunities lay the great one of studying the *plasticity of the metal crystal* itself apart from the complex and often confusing effect of grain boundaries. The classic work is that of Polanyi, Schmid, and Boas (summarized in the famous book by Schmid and Boas published in 1935). The principle of resolved shear stress for slip was established, the process of recovery recognized in an unambiguous fashion, etc. This remained the basis of the fundamental study of plasticity until the development of dislocation theory, and more especially of experimental methods of detecting and of studying dislocations.

It had long been thought that metal grains in rolled (and otherwise deformed metals) possess some degree of *preferred orientation*. The rotation of single crystals during plastic deformation gave a beginning hint as to how preferred orientations come about; the preferred orientations generated were susceptible to analysis by X-ray diffraction; results were expressed by plotting *pole figures* on the ancient (Alexandrian!) stereographic projection, by Wever in 1925, and this became standard. Many such preferred orientations were determined, together with the correlated physical and mechanical properties.

It is interesting to note that late in this period it became apparent that the yield stress in single crystals is very much less than one would have expected from such calculations of the theoretical strength as were available. To explain this apparent anomaly, Polanyi, Orowan, and Taylor separately and in the same year (1934) postulated the *dislocation*, a type of defect that makes slip a very easy process. Much theorizing followed, but it was not until transmission electron microscopy made actual experimental studies of dislocations possible that real progress was made – then it became possible to have that extraordinary interplay between theory and fact, then modified theory and new fact, that is the beauty of science and which excites the research man.

During these years industry was advancing rapidly, in many directions. Aluminium became available commercially in large tonnages; new and better alloys appeared, especially austenitic stainless steel (Strauss in 1910) and ferritic stainless steel (Brearley in 1912); new mill processes were invented and developed, such as, to take but a single example, the continuous rolling mill. It is not the purpose of this chapter to review these, we should only note here that the development of industry brought to light new information on the behaviour of metals, and created new requirements.

The testing of metals became more searching. Brinell invented the hardness tester that bears his name in 1900. Izod (1903) and Charpy (1904) gave impact testing to the profession; the abrupt decrease in the energy of impact fracture in steels in the neighborhood of room temperature was observed, a subject to become increasingly important with the passage of time. Much data on the fatigue of metals appeared – new and more rapid fatigue testing equipment was invented. Handbooks listed great volumes of test data.

Some workers concerned themselves with the problem of "theoretical strength and practical weakness"; indeed one of the most important papers in this field was published by Griffith in 1920; Griffith considered the low stress for the fracture of glass and postulated minute cracks, which produce stress concentrations under loading (*Griffith cracks*), and postulated also that energy must be expended to produce the surface energy of the fracture surfaces. This became a cornerstone in subsequent theory.

The age-old observation that cold-working hardens metals received new attention in this period, especially in the development of the "amorphous metal theory" by Beilby in 1911. Beilby thought that cold working (of any kind, including polishing) converted metals into an amorphous and more stable state. This theory was an engaging one, and held sway for a long time, even in face of X-ray evidence for crystallinity in cold-worked metals. Rosenhain, in 1913, extended the theory by postulating a layer of amorphous metal at grain boundaries. These ideas were over-simple; in their place we now think of crystalline debris, dislocation structures and internal stresses and strains. The theory, however, had its merits – it provided much opportunity for active argument!

Internal stresses and strains were much argued. New methods appeared by which internal strains can be measured: the broadening of X-ray diffraction lines was taken as a measure of internal strains on a microscopic level. Macrostresses were demonstrated by Heyn in 1911; and Sachs in 1927 devised a sectioning method to analyze the three-dimensional stress system.

Research on the process occurring upon *heating cold-worked metals* produced voluminous new facts and a number of theories. Gerard in 1909 showed that the softening on annealing cold-worked copper occurs at a lower temperature, the greater the degree of cold-work (the idea of a fixed "recrystallization temperature" began ever-so-slowly to disappear). Charpy, and Le Chatelier, and Sauveur (1901–1912) all heated a sample of metal into which a Brinell impression had been made, and observed a region (a circle) in which very large grains resulted from recrystallization, and largely misinterpreted the results! Chappell (1914–1915) showed that this phenomenon is the result of a particular, and low, degree of deformation at which the "rate of nucleation" is low and large grains result, while higher degrees of deformation (near the Brinell impression) produce more and thus smaller grains. This particular degree of deformation became known as the "critical deformation for exaggerated grain growth", an awkward and misleading term. Chappell was quite well aware of the important variables in recrystallization; despite this, in succeeding years it became conventional to plot recrystallization behaviour in three-dimensional diagrams, in which the final grain size was plotted against percentage deformation and temperature, not a happy procedure, for it ignored other important variables, for example, time, initial grain size, etc.

Carpenter and Elam in 1921 published one of the most important papers in this field, reporting on studies of the effect of isothermal annealing of cold-worked aluminium; they observed recovery; they observed the migration of grain boundaries during true grain growth. Schmid demonstrated that the original stress-strain curve could be reproduced after annealing plastically deformed single crystals without

References: p. 35.

recrystallization – an elegant demonstration of recovery.

Some attempts were made at theory. Van Liempt treated recrystallization as an activated process. More definitive experimental work and theory were to follow shortly. In 1939 Johnson provided an analysis of the isothermal recrystallization curve in terms of a rate of nucleation and a rate of growth of new, recrystallized grains. This was later to be applied widely to the analysis of a number of nucleation and growth processes.

Theory and experiment on the nature of steel and the hardening process continued in increasing tempo. The beta iron theory maintained its active, improper life well into this century with contention rife and confusion great. Shortly, however, things were to be set right. In 1916 Howe and Levy studied the Ar_1 point (the lower critical point) and found it to be the lower the greater the rate of cooling. This work, and some other contemporaneous work, was a precursor of the TTT-curve. Dejean (1917) and Portevin and Garvin (1919) extended this to include steels of various carbon percentages; they observed a certain rate of cooling with which two thermal arrests occurred, with the one at high temperatures accompanying the formation of high-temperature reaction products – ferrite (or cementite) and pearlite – and the one at low temperatures registering the formation of martensite; this became known as the "split transformation". The depth of hardening was noted and was defined as that depth in a quenched piece throughout which only martensite appeared, the rest consisting of reaction products formed at a higher temperature.

The extraordinary fruitful work of Bain and his collaborators, especially Davenport, on the isothermal decomposition of austenite appeared in 1929. The progress of isothermal reaction was followed microscopically; the course of the reaction at a series of temperatures was plotted as time versus temperature, giving the "TTT-curve" (originally called the "S-curve"). In these quantitative terms Bain showed the effect of austenite grain size and of alloying elements on the rate of decomposition, and correlated it all with the depth of hardening. Isothermal reaction produced reaction products characteristic of a given temperature of reaction, and not mixed structure such as obtained on cooling; the result was simpler microstructures; and nomenclature, previously a badly muddled subject, became easier and more certain; the structure formed at intermediate temperatures, though it had been seen before, was now recognized safely as unique, and named *bainite*. Some time later Grossmann (1938) subjected the factors of chemical analysis, grain size and quenching velocity to detailed and rigorous mathematical analysis. In the same year Jominy developed the end-quench test for depth of hardening (*hardenability*), now so well known. Thus, finally, the subject of the hardening of steel was placed upon an admirable engineering basis, taking the big step away from art.

It is interesting to note that nearly simultaneously with Bain, Wever also studied the subcritical isothermal reactions in steel, employing magnetic and electrical measurements, as did Robertson. Research simultaneity had begun to appear more frequently – until today it is a serious threat to all those who would be original, and first!

Research in this subject plunged increasingly deeply into more purely scientific aspects. Carpenter and Robertson in 1939 found that martensite does not form isothermally but only athermally – and this remained a firm principle for such diffusionless processes, until, much later, exceptions were found! In a work published in 1929 Fink and Campbell made the very basic discovery that the lattice of martensite is body-centered tetragonal, that it is indeed a transition lattice, the first of many found in solid–solid reactions. In discussing that paper, Bain proposed an atomic–crystallographic mechanism for the martensite transformation, this also a "first".

Studies on the Widmanstätten structure were pursued by Belaiev (1923). He proved that ferrite forms as plates on the octahedral planes of austenite, thinking of this as a cleavage plane, missing the important point that there is a special orientation of ferrite on that plane; we shall return to this subject later. Kurdjumov and Sachs in 1930 analyzed the orientation relationships between austenite and martensite and proposed a crystallographic transformation mechanism. Greninger (1940) proved that the plane along which martensite plates lie, is, in contrast to ferrite, of high index, a complexity of some seriousness to those who like things simple!

The ancient process of tempering of quenched steel did not lack for attention. The long-continued work of M. Cohen began to appear; stages of tempering were formed, and rates measured.

Following the work of Roberts-Austen on diffusion, relatively little was done until the 1920s when von Hevesy's work on the electrical (electrolytic) conductivity of solid salts and on *self-diffusion* with natural radioactive isotopes, galvanized the field into activity. Measurements on self-diffusion produced data later to prove of interest in many another connection, very often in purely metallurgical subjects, such as creep. (For those who are nowadays much taken with the idea of "interdisciplinary science", the whole of this chapter shows that metallurgists have always been "interdisciplinary"!) Grube (1932) published much in the general diffusion field, and Matano (1933) employed the Boltzmann solution to Fick's Law with the result that the variation of the diffusion coefficient with concentration could be calculated. The exponential relationship between the coefficient and temperature was repeatedly confirmed. Following this decade, the treatment of diffusion and other transport phenomena in terms of an activation process became standard. New information followed very rapidly: Seith in 1933 showed the anisotropy of self-diffusion in bismuth; Fonda, Walker and Young (1933) and Langmuir (1934) measured the diffusion of thorium on the surface, at grain boundaries and in the volume of the grain of tungsten, together with the pertinent activation energies. Little was known in the period about the mechanism of diffusion.

The *oxidation of metals and alloys*, and corrosion, had long been of interest to the physical metallurgist. To retrace historically: as early as 1813 Davy stated that the coloured films on tempering metals are in fact oxide films. Barus in 1886 stated that such films grow the more rapidly the higher the temperature and increase in thickness with time, ultimately to true scales. Many other papers appeared on oxide films; shortly Tammann (1922) devised methods to measure the rate of thickening, deriving several analytical relationships, especially the parabolic law for the thickening of scales. The research of Pilling and Bedworth, published in 1923 was one of the most important; these workers showed that the parabolic rate obtains when a given number of metal atoms upon oxidizing form oxide of increased volume, thus forcing further oxidation to proceed by diffusion through the oxide. In the oxidation of iron the phase "FeO" is a defect structure, as noted, that is, there are lattice vacancies where iron atoms should be. In 1929 Pfeil produced indirect but valid evidence indicating that diffusing ion in "FeO" is in fact the iron ion. The formulation by Wagner and Schottky (1930–1936) mentioned earlier, based on selective ion diffusion, subsequently became and remains a classic in the field.

It was shown in 1934 that the lattice of oxide films bears a fixed orientation relationship to the metal lattice upon which it forms. This is *epitaxy*; Widmanstätten figures are also an intergrowth epitaxy phenomenon; indeed it was realized in these years that all solid–solid reactions display epitaxial relationships between reactant and resultant.

The oxidation of solid solutions proved a far more complicated affair. Portevin, Pretel and Jolivet (1934) measured the rates in a series of solid solutions in iron. Although the reates were often approximately parabolic, a great complexity was observed in the microstructure of the oxide layers formed, defying analysis – as it still does!

Age-hardening was essentially discovered by accident, by Wilm in 1906. Wilm quenched an alloy of aluminium–copper–magnesium–manganese, hoping that, somewhat as in steel, this would harden the alloy – it did not! After an intruding, long (and presumably pleasurable) week-end, continued measurements did indeed show substantial hardening. This curious aging phenomenon remained unexplained until Merica, Waltenberg and Scott in 1919 demonstrated the decreasing solubility of copper in aluminium with temperature and proposed that aging was but delayed precipitation of a new phase, microscopically (then) invisible. No finer example occurs in the history of physical metallurgy of the importance of theory to practice; from the time of Wilm to the theory of Merica, no new age-hardening alloys were discovered, for no one knew what alloy compositions to look to; but afterwards, with the guiding principles of delayed precipitation from solid solution, such alloys came forth in abundance.

In 1935 Wassermann and Weerts made the extraordinarily important observation that a transition lattice occurs between the lattice of the matrix and that of the precipitate, accompanying the stages at which the maximum hardening occurs. And then in 1937–1938 Guinier and Preston (independently) observed streaks in Laue photograms indicating an even earlier stage of the decomposition process, perhaps an early stage in the formation of the transition lattice; these have been named *Guinier–Preston zones*.

In the 1930s a series of papers appeared on the nature of the Widmanstätten structure, a microstructure frequently observed in age-hardening systems. These studies demonstrated that precipitate particles, at whatever stage of age-hardening, exhibit an orientation relationship to the matrix, and drew conclusions as to the atomic–crystallographic mechanism of such precipitation reactions. All this has now been built into the theory of age-hardening.

Age-hardening in ferritic alloys, especially low-carbon steels, was discovered and studied; these are typically age-hardening systems. *Over-strain-aging* in similar steels, known for quite a long time, came under extensive study; the phenomenon is of very considerable importance in industry, especially in the sheet-steel industry; steels with diminished strain-aging characteristics were developed and manufactured. Blue brittleness, known earlier, was restudied by Le Chatelier in 1909; the temperature of minimum ductility in the tensile test was shown to depend upon the speed of testing. Fettweiss in 1919 proved that blue brittleness is but strain-aging occurring during the actual course of the tensile test.

Thus, at the end of this period, facts and theories foregathered on a wide front, and physical metallurgy had truly come of age.

5. *1940–1963*

The normal pace of research was disrupted by the world war, yet the exigencies of warfare gave rise to some truly remarkable advances in the physical sciences and in engineering. Chief among these was the invention of atomic energy, which fully convinced a reluctant society that research, if supported, could produce the most exceptional results. All sciences have since profited, including physical metallurgy. Where to start, in this somewhat tempestuous period?

Perhaps it is best to begin with the new research tools. The growing knowledge of particle optics gave birth to several new and extraordinary research instruments. For example. the *field ion emission microscope*, developed by Müller in 1936, made it possible to "see" atoms on the surface of a metal crystal, to observe atoms at grain boundaries, to "see" vacancies and dislocations, to watch the atomic process of vaporization. It had long been the thwarted ambition of the microscopist to determine the chemical composition of microscopic areas – this ambition was consummately realized by Castaing (1956) in the invention of the *electron microprobe analyzer*, a device which furnishes the composition of an area of only one μm^2. Yet, from the physical metallurgical point of view, the *electron microscope* has proved the most valuable by all odds. Developed by Ruska (1931), Zworykin (1938), and others, it was first operated on replicas of metal surfaces; subsequently Heidenreich (1949) and Hirsch (1954) developed the remarkably fruitful method of electron transmission through thin metals foils; a degree of resolution of only a few atom diameters is attained. The method has been employed in many physical metallurgical studies, in nearly every field; we shall have occasion in the following to note these. Other experimental aids must at least be mentioned: the *field electron emission microscope* which, with a very high degree of resolution, is especially suitable for studying adsorbed films on metals; the general availability of artificially produced *radioactive isotopes*; selected-area electron diffraction, permitting the crystal structure and the orientation of exceedingly small areas to be determined, and the general develop-

References: p. 35.

ment of all sorts of electronic laboratory instruments.

Despite the work of Tammann and others no really satisfactory method was devised for determining the rate of nucleation on freezing until Vonnegut (1948) and Pound and LaMer (1952) contrived the volumetric dispersed droplet method which gave valid quantitative measurements. Turnbull (1958) showed how sensitive such values are to layers adsorbed on the droplet surfaces, and thus in general the importance of heterogeneous nucleation. Much has been done by Stranski (1938 et seq.) on the atomic mechanism of crystal growth in nonmetallic systems. In 1949 Frank pointed out that crystal growth will be greatly augmented if a screw dislocation intersects the growing surface, and presented proof of this by finding examples of the resulting growth spirals. Chalmers (1950 et seq.) studied the topography of solid–liquid interfaces by decanting, finding the conditions for sub-grain cell formation and shedding much light on the vexingly complex problem of dendrite formation; he identified *constitutional super-cooling*.

Metallurgists have long known the disproportionately large effects of very small amounts of impurities in metals. When the controlled addition of slight traces to semiconductors became important, Pfann (1952) invented the *zone-refining* and the *zone-levelling* process. Starting with quite pure metals, and by linearly progressive freezing, very great purification was attained. This technique now affords the research man metals the properties of which more nearly approximate the properties of the ideal, truly pure metal and can be used to produce metals with deliberately added impurities in controlled amount; it is applied now to many metals, and is a boon to research.

Microsegregation in alloys, especially in alloy steels, has been a problem of long standing. The electron probe analyzer is the ideal instrument to study this, and is currently heavily used for the purpose. This segregation is dependent upon the distribution coefficient between solid and liquid of a given addition element (the principle that Pfann used) but with so many elements present in steels, nothing is very simple. It is a little surprising that there is, otherwise, so little activity in the study of the mechanism of freezing of steel, or for that matter on iron itself, in view of the huge tonnages frozen every year.

A score or so of years ago little thought was given to the structure and nature of *grain boundaries*; these were thought of merely as planes where two crystals met a random; to be sure much knowledge was available as to the effect of grain boundaries on, for example, plasticity, diffusion, and nucleation. The concept of a grain-boundary energy was old. The first step toward a fuller understanding was taken by Bragg (1940) and by Burgers in 1940, as a result of the development of dislocation theory. Simple grain boundaries, those which may be described by a single angle between the two contiguous grains ("simple tilt boundary") were readily described by an array of edge dislocations; this was confirmed in a most elegant fashion by developing etch pits along low angle boundaries, the spacing of which was proved to be exactly right for the measured orientation difference between the two contiguous grains. This simple structure must be progressively lost as the angular difference becomes greater; and when these orientations involve twist instead of or together with simple tilt, all becomes quite complex. The energy at grain boundaries for simple tilt boundaries was calculated by Shockley and Read (1953) and subsequent measurement of relative boundary energies confirmed this. The pioneer work of C.S. Smith (1948 et seq.) in this field was of the greatest importance; while absolute boundary energies are difficult to measure, relative energies are rather easy. Much has been accomplished in recent years: the relationship between boundary misfit and diffusion coefficients, many plasticity phenomena, the degree of Gibbs' solute adsorption, etc. – a rich field for the physical metallurgist.

The *free surface energy* of metals has been measured by the now well-known method of Udin (1949); in itself it has a basic importance, but since various internal defects, such as a grain boundary, form a groove on the surface, the absolute grain boundary (or twin boundary, or stacking fault) energy can be determined once the reference surface energy is known. Thus the physical metallurgist, through strict scholarship and imaginative experimentation has plunged ever deeper into an understanding of very old, and some very new, problems.

Many new thermodynamic data have been obtained for solid solutions, especially by employing various versions of vapour pressure measurements, but also electromotive force measurements using solid electrolytes. There is quite new evidence (Raynor, 1963) that the effective valency of solute atoms may be quite different from the ordinary valency, indeed can be fractional. New work on the electrolysis of solid solutions shows curious results: in some binary alloys both atoms (ions) move in the same direction but with different velocities, in others in opposite direction; and pure solid copper, electrolyzed, shows a Kirkendall effect, challenging theorists! Silicon and germanium, both having a valency of four, containing small amounts of elements with an element of valency three, or five, show special semiconducting properties; these are the basis of the transistor device; a new special field in electronics has been born, resting upon the behaviour of extremely dilute metallic solid solutions.

The mechanism of diffusion attracted much attention at the beginning of this time period. Huntingdon and Seitz calculated the activation energy (enthalpy) for self-diffusion in copper on the assumption that diffusion proceeds by a vacancy mechanism and found this in agreement with the experimentally determined self-diffusion coefficient. Experimental evidence came from the Kirkendall (1947) experiment, which proved that the two different atoms in a binary solid solution move at different rates, with a net flow of vacancies in one direction, vacancies which in large measure disappear (though in part condensing to porosity), shrinking the volume and thus causing an internal marker to move. Darken (1948) then wrote the classic paper; he pointed out that the driving force behind diffusion must be the partial molal free energy gradient (the chemical potential gradient) and not the concentration gradient and proved it; employing this he analyzed the Kirkendall effect and calculated the separate diffusion coefficients for each of the two elements in binary solid solution. Thus again, as throughout history, physical chemistry and physical metallurgy interplay, as in other connections do physics and mechanics.

References: p. 35.

Various attempts have been made to write a full analytical expression for the diffusion coefficient, involving other factors besides the exponential term (the enthalpy of activation), particularly by Zener (1949). The problem has proved difficult since it is not easy to know what the entropy term should be in alloy diffusion; yet very real progress has been made.

Many research papers in this field have been published: grain-boundary diffusion rates have been determined as a function of grain boundary misorientation; measurements of surface diffusion have been made, with continuing worry about the disturbing effects of gas films adsorbed on the surface; a few measurements have been made of diffusion rates along the edges of dislocations – a diffusion "short-circuit" path; some measurements have been made in an attempt to evaluate the effect of cold-work on diffusion rates, though with uncertain success. The course of true research does not run smooth!

All of the above has related to diffusion in substitutional solid solutions. Diffusion of interstitial atoms is simpler – such atoms simply diffuse along interstitial paths without requiring vacancy intervention, and thus no Kirkendall effect is observed. By combining data from direct diffusion measurements, with those calculated from precipitation reactions and those from Snoek's (1939) *internal friction method*, the diffusion coefficient of carbon in alpha iron is known over fourteen orders of magnitude! An active and important field, this one, still requiring theoretical attention. All this will no doubt one day be associated with the electron theory of metals – but not yet!

Much has been learned about *vacancies* in recent years. They appear to play an important role in the behaviour of metals in many ways. In contrast to other defects, such as dislocations, they are an equilibrium structure, represented by an equilibrium concentration, a "solubility" curve. From electrical resistivity measurements on samples quenched and annealed, this curve has been determined, and the energy of formation and the activation energy of mobility calculated. Vacancies may thus be quenched in – on aging quenched samples of pure metals they precipitate and even harden; on precipitating they finally appear as voids, often of geometrical shape, and this occurs also when vacancies are produced by radiation damage (which hardens metals and produces various, sometimes harmful effects – a large subject in itself); in solid solutions solutes seem to have a special binding energy for vacancies; they interact with dislocations in various ways, and by condensing can themselves produce a form of dislocation; all this has been developed in this period, much in the last few years. Vacancy theory (and fact) has become an important part of many branches of physical metallurgy in this period.

The behaviour of steel has maintained its central position in the science of metals. The very complexity of steel offers much opportunity to the investigator. This is especially true in the field of transformations in the solid state. Many TTT-curves have been determined, each nation jealously guarding its own specifications and producing its own national TTT-curves! Several comprehensive studies have been made of the over-all characteristics of TTT-curves, especially by Hultgren (1947 et seq.) and by Troiano (1946 et seq.). The morphology of the proeutectoid constituents have been classified by Hanemann and Schrader (1933) from samples cooled at different rates; in the early 1940s further studies on isothermally reacted samples gave sufficient information as to identify the chief morphological features – but hardly to explain them satisfactorily.

Bainite has proved interesting, but elusive! Early in the 1940s it was shown that the orientation relationship between ferrite in bainite and the matrix austenite is the same as that for proeutectoid ferrite, and that bainite forms by a nucleation and growth process, chiefly at grain boundaries. In the middle of this period it was found that the formation of bainite produces surface relief effects, somewhat similar to those observed with martensite, and this has been attributed to a supposed semi-coherent interface. Peculiarities have multiplied: the growth rate of a bainite plate is linear with time and different plates grow at different rates. The end is not yet in sight!

The nature and the mechanism of formation of *martensite* has always been an absorbing subject to the physical metallurgist, not only because of the practical importance of martensite but also because scientifically martensite is rather dramatic. M. Cohen and his coworkers, in a long series of papers throughout this period have added much fundamental information: stabilization, the burst phenomenon, factors determining the M_s temperature, stages and rates of tempering. It has become apparent that martensite is representative of a large number of diffusionless transformations; it forms by an intricate shearing process; the velocity of propagation of this process has been measured and found to be about equal to the speed of sound in steel; the electron microscope, performing in its usual spectacular fashion, has shown the presence of extremely thin multiple twins. At about the middle of the period it was observed that martensite in a few alloy steels actually does form isothermally, not as thought before only upon temperature change; shortly isothermal transformations were found in other alloys. A marked increase in the strength of quenched and tempered steel was obtained by working austenite just before quenching; the greatly defective crystallinity produced by working creates a vastly defective martensite, of great strength, both before and after quenching. Thus, where after the discovery of "whiskers" of great strength it was the opinion that greater strength can be attained by greater crystalline perfection, now one believes the opposite – to get great strength, render the crystalline aggregate as imperfect as possible!

Pearlite, and similar, somewhat analogous decomposition products, such as "cellular precipitates" in age-hardening systems (or eutectics) occupy a special place. Early in the 1940s the structure of pearlite was studied in detail, and rates of nucleation and growth were determined in both plain carbon and in alloy steels; pertinent diffusion coefficients were measured, and the interlamellar spacing was measured also – these should be the determinative factors in a diffusion-controlled reaction; yet a fully satisfactory theory of either the rate of growth or the rate of nucleation has escaped us, despite a number of papers notable in effort and in intricacy. The "heroes" of the last century, faced with ever deeper and ever more demanding problems might have become frightened in this century!

The theory of nucleation of Volmer seems, with some slightly modification, to be

References: p. 35.

satisfactory for liquid–liquid transformation and reasonably satisfactory for liquid–solid transformation. For solid–solid transformations however, such as those just discovered, and for the process of precipitation from solid solutions discussed below, the theory needs extensive modification. Becker and Döring (1935) considered the theory for the latter case. But now we know that lattice defects play a very important role, and a varying one. Grain boundaries are ever a place of preferred nucleation; dislocations frequently are – but not always; invisible aggregates of vacancies may act as nucleation inoculants. There has been some theorizing as to the role of defects, and some quantitative predictions; but it is fair to say that no rate of nucleation has as yet been predicted from first principles. One suspects that more quantitatively descriptive information is required.

Large volumes of research have been published in recent years on the age-hardening process. In the preceding period much had been learned about the mechanism of precipitation, but one felt helpless to attack the hardening process itself except most indirectly. Now, however, with the invention of transmission electron microscopy, not only could the details of actual precipitation be directly viewed, but also the behavior of dislocations, that is, the ease of slip, and thus information is gained on the basic mechanism of hardening. In addition to this technique the older ones of X-ray diffraction and of electrical conductivity have been extensively applied. The electron microscope has given visual evidence for concentration fluctuations in some alloys preceding the first stage of precipitation. The studies in the early 1940s of Widmanstätten structures, and of the preceding Guinier–Preston zones have been constantly extended, with interphase interface energies and strain energies brought into consideration. The electron microscope has given proof of the contribution of coherency stresses to the hardening process; it has given evidence as to whether precipitates form on lattice defects (heterogeneous precipitation) or not (homogeneous nucleation) – both have been observed; some precipitates hold up dislocation movement, others do not. Over-aging has been studied; this is an example of pure dispersoid hardening. Wagner (1962) has given a quantitative analysis of the growth of particles (spheroidizing) in a solid matrix. One could go on and on, but this shows the trend.

The plasticity of metals has been a most active field of research, vastly reenergized by the searching power of the technique of transmission electron microscopy with respect to internal defect structures. In an adventurous effort, Hirsch and coworkers proved that this microscope would detect dislocations in all their details. The results of this method, now produced by a host of workers all over the world, have been very rich; simple dislocations were seen early, and their progress through a metal observed as slip progresses; the partial dislocation of Heidenreich and Shockley (1948) and the associated stacking faults are seen; proper electron scattering analysis has provided a method to identify the important vector described by J.M. Burgers (1939); at low degrees of cold-work simple dislocation arrays are evident; at higher degrees of cold-work dislocation tangles, and sub-cells separated by dislocation tangles in walls, are clearly seen; at high degrees of cold-work new dislocations in moving must cut through "forests" of dislocations, and this is observed.

Such observations as these, then, are to be combined with the rates of work-hardening measured, for example, in a simple tensile test of a single crystal. For face-centered cubic metals three stages may be seen in the tensile test, variously associated (presumably) with the types of dislocation array. In this task there is considerable difficulty, and controversy is enjoyed by all! Theories abound, and have a slippery way about them. Many possible events must be considered: what role is played by dislocation pile-ups, by the formation and movement of jogs, by dislocation climb (a self-diffusion phenomenon characterized by an activation energy). The final or perhaps even the penultimate theory has not yet been written; factual knowledge is almost too rich, too easy to get. The theoretical predictions of earlier years, before transmission electron microscopy, have been amply and beautifully confirmed, and unpredicted phenomena have been found in abundance. It was implicit in the original dislocation theory that a sample without properly oriented dislocations should exhibit the supposed theoretical strength of metals; this was confirmed by Galt and Herring in 1952, with the accidental discovery of *metal whiskers*, essentially perfect single crystals of about a micron in diameter; thus, obversely, the dislocation theory was proved again. Dislocations and their study by electron microscopy will appear again in this account.

There are many types of plastic flow in metals; *creep* is another, the interest in which is especially great because of the practical importance of creep behaviour. Studies have been active throughout this period; with many obvious variables studied. Hanson (1939) made a careful evaluation of the effect of grain size, finding that metals with large grains creep more slowly than metals with small grains; the effect of time, temperature and rate of loading have been explored; work by many, especially Dorn (1955), has laid a basis for an activated process, probably self-diffusion; in steels the effect of rather slight degrees of impurity on plastic deformation has proved to be quite great: for example, small amounts of nitrogen have an effect which appears to depend upon whether the nitrogen is bound in a compound or free in a solid solution. Creep has been observed to produce internal cavitation, related presumably to the agglomeration of vacancies originating in the process of slip (a dislocation cutting through a forest of dislocation probably leaves a trail of vacancies or of interstitial atoms). Riches have been invested in a search for ever-better creep-resistant alloys for use at very high temperatures; these are necessarily alloys of high melting point, usually nickel-base, sometimes cobalt-base; and they are alloys often composed of five or six metals, found with only the simplest of theory and with much Edisonian experimentation.

The *yield point* and yield point elongation in steel has long been of interest, both scientifically and practically, and there have been many theories. An historical account cannot, and should not give a full factual treatment. Suffice it to say that this phenomenon is in some way related to an internal reaction; Cottrell (1948) has proposed that carbon (and other) atoms can, be residing upon a dislocation, lock it, so that a stress is required to break a dislocation free. This is the concept of a *Cottrell atmosphere*, now invoked in a number of connections.

Much of today's research follows the outline laid down by Petch (1953) in the

References: p. 35.

so-called *Petch analysis*. This is an expression for the flow stress in terms of the grain diameter, in terms of two stresses, one to move a dislocation along a slip plane normally, and another that probably has to do with the unpinning of a dislocation. Much development along these lines is underway.

Fracture theory remains difficult, yet it is one of the most important in the metallurgical field. Many aspects have been inspected, especially the mechanism, whatever it is, by which cracks initiate, presumably by a special conjunction of moving dislocations, and the mechanism by which cracks propagate, in some way related to the concept of *Griffith cracks*.

The problem of fracture, always upon the mind of the metallurgist, especially the practising metallurgical engineer, received added impetus when catastrophic failures of all-welded ships occurred during the last war. Many tests, more complicated than the Izod and the Charpy, were devised more closely to approximate the mixed stresses in large structures, especially welded structures, with special attention to the transition temperature, the transition from ductile to brittle fracture.

One is much tempted to write the full history of research on the *recrystallization* of metals in this period, for so much has been done. The phenomena which arise on annealing cold-worked metals originate of course in the internal structure produced by cold-working. The first of these is recovery, studied years before, especially by Tammann. If the radiation damage is included, over a wide temperature range at least five stages of recovery obtain; the problem is to identify the separate process; evidently these must be the annealing out of interstitials and of vacancies (or di- or tri-vacancies), rearrangement of dislocations in several possible ways, etc. The formation of sub-grains ("polygons") has engaged the attention of many; it is not easy to identify the discoverer, though Crussard (1944) and Lacombe (1947) have contributed much to this field; it is possible that the first observation was made by Konobeevski and Mirer in 1932 upon annealing bent rock-salt crystals. These subgrains, which often form before primary recrystallization (and have been observed in metals which have been subjected to creep), grow in time; the process often overlaps primary recrystallization; indeed there is much overlap among all of the many ways by which a metal can rid itself of the effects of cold work. It is not entirely clear whether a metal will wholly soften by polygonization (and subsequent growth) or whether the familiar nucleation and growth process is required; various metals behave variously.

Primary recrystallization has long been observed, as the account of the earlier period has shown. This process, of the appearance of essentially stress-free grains which grow, absorbing all of the strained matrix, can be represented in terms of a rate of nucleation and a rate of growth. This is not nucleation in the Gibbsian, poly-phase type, but the isothermal rate closely follows the nucleation and growth mathematics of Johnson. Activation energies are yielded for both rates; but the rates and the activation energies are extremely dependent upon impurities, a phenomenon investigated by many recent workers. The formation of the original nucleus might be merely a process of the coalescence of subgrains which proceeds until a large angle boundary with the matrix obtains whence growth proceeds at a constant rate. There are many workers in this field, and it is difficult today to be certain which of the current points of view will in the end prove to be nearest the truth – a difficulty that plagues all writers of recent history. The development of zone-refining has made metals of great purity available, and these recrystallize at far lower temperatures than ordinary metals. Whatever quantitative values we now have on recrystallization, they certainly cannot be said to be true physical constants of a metal!

Of normal grain growth there is little now to be said: the driving force is the free energy of the grain boundary, and rates of grain growth are in accord with this – except as these are drastically modified by impurities, especially undissolved impurities which anchor grain boundaries, thus interfering with growth. There is little new to be recounted on secondary recrystallization; it was discovered in this period, it follows nucleation and growth kinetics; and the original nucleus of the new grain seems to be minute areas which bear a high-angle relationship to the recrystallization preferred orientation.

Thus the story, in skeleton form. There have been many workers, only a few are mentioned here. The record becomes lengthier, the subject grows, and branches, and grows again. The older generation, in its generosity, leaves much unanswered, undone, to provoke the new!

6. Supplement, circa 1963–1982
(by Robert W. Cahn)

This updating summary must begin with a reference to an important programme of research modestly played down by Prof. Mehl in his chapter: the work of Mehl's research group at Pittsburgh, during the years 1930–1937, on the factors governing the formation of plate-shaped precipitates from metastable solid solutions – a study of the *Widmanstätten structure*. The orientation relationships between the phases were thoroughly explored. This work is briefly mentioned on page 18, but Mehl's name does not appear there. An account of this research will be found in C.S. Smith's pamphlet, listed in the Bibliography, which was published in 1963, the year in which Mehl wrote his historical chapter.

The very rapid developments in physical metallurgy in the past two decades owe much to innovations in instrumentation. The *transmission electron microscope* (TEM), adapted to metallurgical uses, was originally developed by Hirsch and his associates when they were studying dislocation arrangements in deformed metals, and initially the instrument was mostly used to examine cold work, recrystallization and crystal defects. However, as the instrument was progressively improved, and especially as TEM came to be combined with localized chemical analysis, it was increasingly used to study phase transformations of all kinds, to the point where it largely displaced optical microscopy in this enormous field of study. Analytical scanning transmission electron microscopy (STEM), a development of the late 1970s, has further accentuated this trend.

References: p. 35.

The usefulness of Castaing's *electron probe microanalyser* (EPMA) was enhanced by the incorporation of a scanning capacity, which allowed the distribution of an element to be represented pictorially. This improvement, due to Duncumb, went in parallel with the development of the *scanning electron microscope* (SEM) by Oatley at the beginning of the sixties. This instrument, with its ability to represent three-dimensional surface structures in stereoscopic detail and its great depth of focus, was at first used mostly for fractographic studies but quickly developed into a general-purpose (if expensive) rival to the optical microscope; the SEM has a much higher resolving power than the latter. Following the invention of energy-dispersive X-ray wavelength analysis (using a semiconductor detector), the design of SEMs and EPMAs has gradually converged, and before long the instruments may well merge into one.

A number of other instruments combining pictorial representation with analytical capacity have been developed to the point of wide application during the 1970s: they include secondary ion mass spectroscopy (SIMS), Auger electron spectroscopy (AES), Siegbahn's electron spectroscopy for chemical analysis (ESCA, also termed XPS for X-ray photoelectron spectroscopy), and in particular Müller's technique of *field ion microscopy* (FIM) combined with time-of-flight mass spectrometry. All of these, with the aid of ion-beam erosion, can be used to determine very shallow composition profiles, over depths of a micrometre or less. The availability of TEM, STEM, SEM, SIMS, AES, ESCA and FIM has revolutionized the high-resolution study of microstructure and microgradients of composition: collectively they represent an impact on physical metallurgy as great as that of X-ray diffraction between the Wars.

X-ray diffraction has also gained a fresh lease of life since 1950 through the introduction of the X-ray diffractometer, automatic devices for texture determination, proportional and scintillation counters, the position-sensitive X-ray detector (particularly useful for studying internal stresses), and energy-dispersive X-ray diffraction.

The understanding of the mechanisms involved in *solidification* has been transformed by the work of Chalmers and his school, beginning in the early 1950s and continuing until recently. The crucial new element introduced by that research school was the analysis of the stability and morphology of the *interface* between liquid and solid, and the linkage of this to microsegregation on the one hand, and the macroscopic conditions of freezing (thermal gradient, growth rate) on the other. Tiller and Rutter were especially active in the early phases of this work.

Turnbull contributed much over the years to solidification studies, especially the important technique of *droplet solidification*, which allows homogeneous nucleation of solid in liquids to be studied experimentally; this valuable technique has recently been revived and extended by Perepezko.

In recent years, Mullins, Sekerka, Trivedi and Glicksman have contributed much on the lines initiated by the Chalmers school to the understanding of *dendrite* morphology; interface stability has now become a very involved theoretical topic. This in turn has led to much improved structure control in castings and to new processes, especially Fleming's invention of *rheocasting*. The role of trace elements in grain control and in phase-shape control in castings has developed rapidly; an important example is the creation of nodular cast iron by Morrogh and others.

A separate development, starting in Germany (Kofler, Scheil) and continuing in England and America (Hunt, Jackson, Hurle) has increased our understanding of *eutectic solidification*, both coupled and anomalous. The degeneration of rod and lamellar eutectics at high temperatures has been much studied (Cline, Chadwick, McLean among others), especially because of the interest in unidirectionally solidified eutectic structures as materials for gas turbine blades. The stability criterion proved to be related to the general phenomenon of *Ostwald ripening*, i.e. the coarsening of large dispersed-phase particles at the expense of nearby small ones. This crucial exemplar of the "Matthew principle" was clarified by a coarsening theory, published independently and simultaneously by Wagner and by Lifshitz and Slyozov in 1961; these two papers (which have proved to be valid beyond the conditions assumed in the derivation of the theory) are amongst those most cited by physical metallurgists in the past 20 years. The prevention of Ostwald ripening is crucial to the maintenance of finely dispersed microstructures and the good mechanical properties associated with them, and the understanding flowing from the 1961 papers, of the role in coarsening of solubility, diffusion kinetics and interfacial energy, has played an important role in guiding empirical research, especially on refractory alloys.

Phase transformations in the solid state have continued to absorb a large share of the attention of physical metallurgists. In addition to an enormous volume of experimental work in the last 25 years, there has been a growing incursion by physicists – and occasionally chemists – into the very involved theoretical aspects of the subject, so that by now a distinct comprehension gap has developed. In spite of that, the contribution by physicists particularly to the understanding of phase transformations has played an indispensable part in reaching our present level of understanding, as well as creating new uncertainties (an essential role in keeping the research pot boiling).

The current spurt in research on phase transformations started just as the volume of research on age-hardening showed signs of falling away, at the end of the 1950s. The crucial development was the theoretical work on the nature of the *spinodal decomposition*, associated with the names of Hillert, J.W. Cahn and Hilliard. (J.W. Cahn is at intervals blamed – occasionally complimented – for the present book; R.W. Cahn is frequently flattered at being mistaken for the father of the spinodal!) The theoretical ideas which first made sense of modulated microstructures (originally studied in detail in the early 1940s by X-ray diffraction, by Lipson and Daniel, working with Cu–Fe–Ni alloys which were examined fully 25 years later by TEM, by Nicholson and Tufton, and more recently by FIM) reach back to Willard Gibbs and Volmer's nucleation model; for the first time, "uphill diffusion" ceased to be a paradox. The insights created by the spinodal theory have not been exploited as extensively as might have been expected by further experimental work.

The study of *ordered alloys* had passed its first apogee during the 1950s, when

References: p. 35.

much basic work had been done by X-ray and neutron diffraction. A second wave of research, in the 1960s, involved TEM studies of antiphase domain morphology, and then the studies of Amelinckx's school, by high-resolution TEM, of ordered domains of non-cubic symmetry in systems such as Ni–Mo. A third wave of research, during the 1970s, has been based on theoretical ideas concerning the precursor phenomena preceding phase transformations in general, including those involving order. Three concepts are central to these developments: (a) composition or displacement waves, (b) charge density waves and (c) the cluster variation model. These ideas have given fresh life to the old argument as to whether ordered domains are nucleated and grow as a distinct phase, or whether the disordered phase merges continuously into the ordered form. Both models seem to be accepted currently, according to temperature and composition. The formation of certain phases, especially the omega phase in titanium and zirconium alloys, has been explained in great detail, in the light of these precursor models. Physicists who have played a major part in these develop-ments include Kikuchi, Cook, de Fontaine and J.B. Cohen.

The older types of research on phase transformations have not been neglected. Aaronson and his school in particular have been responsible for new insight into diffusion-controlled transformation of the classical nucleation-and-growth variety. A review by Gust on discontinuous phase transformations, published in 1979, cites over 400 papers from the 1960s and 1970s bearing on this "old-fashioned" topic.

The classical task of determining and improving *phase diagrams* has also con-tinued, at a measured pace. The most important development however has been the improvement, to the point of effective application, of phase diagram calculation (Calphad); Kaufman and Petzow have been major contributors to this.

Martensite research has remained active, partly because of a renewed interest in the two-way interplay between stress/strain and transformation. Zackay and Parker exploited this relationship to develop transformation-toughened steels (TRIP steels, from *TR*ansformation-*I*nduced *P*lasticity) in the early 1960s – an innovation which has led on to potentially important related developments for toughening engineering ceramics by incorporating a dispersion of partially stabilized zirconia. In both cases, the stress field of an advancing crack stimulates localized shear transformation, which absorbs energy.

Separately, interest has steadily grown during the 1970s in alloys, such as TiNi, which display a *shape-memory effect* (SME), rather like certain polymers (a return, on warming, of the shape the specimen had before deformation). Unlike polymers, SME alloys owe this behaviour to a special kind of martensitic transformation, which "carries" the whole of the imposed shape change. Wayman in particular has done much to clarify the behaviour of such alloys, as well as the general crystallogra-phy and morphology of martensites. The MIT school has continued to investigate nucleation mechanisms, and has also taken the TRIP concept further.

At a time when the world's steel industry is regarded by some as a spent force, it is salutary to recognize that research on the *physical metallurgy of steels* has never been more active, and very successful in creating useful new products, especially in the past decade. Several investigators, Honeycombe in particular, have remained active in establishing the detailed microstructures resulting from the decomposition of austenite under various circumstances. Improvements to microalloyed and high strength/low alloy steels (the terminology is not as unambiguous as might be wished) and the creation of the entirely new category of *dual-phase* (ferrite + martensite) steels in 1976 by Rashid, has been linked with an ever subtler understanding of the types of microstructure required for high strength or high toughness or high formability or good heat resistance, or appropriate compromises between these desiderata. Much of this research has been done in industrial laboratories, especially in the USA and Japan. It is particularly noteworthy how close, indeed inextricable, is the present symbiosis between, on the one hand, the development of new steel compositions and the study of their microstructures and, on the other hand, the introduction of new processing procedures, of which the most important are controlled rolling mills and continuous annealing lines. In this, as in many other fields of metallurgy, innovations in processes and those in materials continuously stimulate each other.

More and more it is becoming clear that *refinement of grain size*, right down to the micron level, is the key to many desirable properties in steels. For instance, Cuddy in 1981 showed how controlled rolling, by exploiting dynamic recrystallization, could generate an austenite microstructure of a kind which in turn would generate ultrafine ferrite grains; and continuous annealing lines, by rapid cooling of rolled sheet, can generate the same end results. The 1953 Hall–Petch relationship between grain size and flow or fracture strength is still a much used source of understanding – much more recent is the development, to the stage of industrial practice, of *superplastic* forming, which again depends on ultrafine grains, via Herring–Nabarro creep. The metallurgical skill here, built up in particular by Stowell's team, is so to design an alloy composition that the requisite fine grain size is stable at the temperature used for superplastic forming.

The recognition of the central roles of grain size and temperature in determining mechanisms of and resistance to plastic deformation helped to prompt Ashby, in 1972, to the invention of *deformation maps*. (Hints of this important concept appeared earlier in the work of Weertman.) This notion, which is intimately linked with the theoretical derivation of constitutive equations governing various types of deformation, has proved very useful, especially to those involved in the study of creep. Much has been done to improve the creep resistance of superalloys for gas turbines, and physical metallurgical insights have played a steady part. The most impressive use of the theory here has been Sims's application of electron theory, based on Hume-Rothery principles, to predict the formation of the deleterious sigma phase in superalloys of varying compositions: much random empirical work has thereby been saved.

Study of fracture now leans on the science of fracture mechanics which grew in the 1950s and 1960s out of the pioneering ideas of Griffith and Irwin. It is now possible to quantify and test the resistance to fracture of an alloy and thus to predict reliably what kind and size of defect can be safely accepted under specified conditions. Understanding of fatigue failure has not reached a similar level of

References: p. 35.

sophistication, but here also there is a much better knowledge of the physical mechanisms leading to fatigue failure, following the micrographic studies of Forsyth and Brown, among others.

Innovations in dislocation theory passed their apogee in the 1950s, but its present uses are manifold. For instance, ideas based on the climb of dislocation dipoles have been used in the late 1970s to interpret the creep characteristics of dispersion-hardened alloys, especially superalloys with a coherent dispersion. Work-hardening is no longer on the active agenda (the most recent innovation was the study of the asymmetry of work-hardening according to the sense of shear in bcc crystals), but the computation of the Orowan stress governing the form of a dislocation worming its way through a field of particles is still being analyzed and improved upon, by Martin among others.

There has been a great resurgence of research on *grain boundaries*, stimulated by improvements in high-resolution TEM, and many investigators have analyzed the dislocation structure of boundaries of controlled misorientations. As a separate strand, Hondros and Seah have pioneered the examination of the segregation of impurities to grain boundaries, which is the subject matter of chapter 13.

Recrystallization studies also have had something of a revival in the 1970s, after the fallow 1960s. Important contributions include the work of Cotterill and Mould on the nucleation of new grains at large second-phase particles (recently taken on to a very detailed level by Humphreys), and the investigations of Doherty and his school (1971–1979) which have finally established the predominant mechanisms of *nucleation in primary recrystallization*. This in turn has helped to make sense of the genesis of annealing textures. Grain growth has been well served by excellent theorists (Gladman, Hillert) and has also proved an ideal field for the application of modern *stereology* (quantitative metallography), developed in the past two decades by Hilliard, Rhines, Exner and Serra, in particular. The very recent work of Rhines has shown with especial clarity how the study of grain shapes can cast light on the mechanisms of grain growth. The study of *point defects* and their relation to line and planar defects, as well as the associated discipline of diffusion, have received an enormous stimulus from the need to understand radiation damage in metals and ceramics. Non-equilibrium fluxes of point defects under irradiation, first analyzed by Lomer and Anthony, are linked with non-equilibrium diffusion and segregation of solutes, anomalous phase transformation, anomalous irradiation-enhanced creep, the formation of voids with associated swelling (discovered as late as 1969 by Fulton and Cawthorne), formation of bubbles filled with fission gases, and latterly the novel forms of damage associated with the very energetic neutrons formed in thermo-nuclear fusion reactors. Another of the major discoveries in physical metallurgy associated with nuclear energy is the observation, by Barnes and Mazey in the early 1960s, that bubbles and voids can migrate bodily under the influence of a temperature gradient. This migration in turn is controlled by *surface diffusion*, itself very sensitive to the state and composition of a surface: surface diffusion has been an active field of research in recent years, and is in turn linked, through computer modelling, with modern insights in the atomistic structure of crystal surfaces.

Much in the foregoing paragraphs has been connected with the behaviour of unstable or metastable phases. Metastable phases are central to physical metallurgy, and so it is not surprising that very great interest has been aroused by a category of processes which can generate a large family of metastable, metallic phases not previously known. This is *rapid quenching from the melt*, pioneered by Duwez in 1959.

Duwez found methods of cooling metallic melts at a million degrees per second or even more, and thereby he was able to extend solid solubilities, create hitherto unknown crystal structures and even to prevent crystallization altogether, creating thereby *metallic glasses*. Subsequently, improved devices for rapid cooling replaced Duwez's "gun", opening the way to the production of rapidly quenched tapes or powders in large quantities. In the 1970s, attention focused on the glasses, but now that the prospect of improving mechanical properties at both ambient and elevated temperatures by melt-quenching has become clear, crystalline alloys are receiving a large share of attention. Extended solid solubility can lead to more substantial age-hardening, and microsegregation can be eliminated in as-cast alloys. This approach offers most promise in respect of superalloys and tool steels. A whole new technology, starting from rapidly quenched powders – *rapid solidification processing* – is under development.

The most recent innovation is the development of a family of metallic glasses of modest metalloid content which can be crystallized to produce stable ultra fine-grained structures which are strong, tough and heat-resistant.

The physical metallurgy of ferromagnetic materials has developed rapidly in the past two decades. The groundwork was laid in the 1940s and 50s by pioneers such as Bozorth, Néel, Stoner and Wohlfarth who developed a proper understanding of domain wall structure, behaviour of single-domain particles, sources of anisotropy, etc. In the 1950s, domain-wall pinning was believed to contribute little to the achievement of strong permanent magnets, but in the 1960s and 70s this opinion came to be revised. It is now clear that narrow domain walls – which are formed in materials of high anisotropy – intereact strongly with small precipitates, grain boundaries, point defects and even the lattice itself (a parallel to the Peierls force acting on dislocations); in fact, there are many parallels between the behaviour of dislocations and that of narrow domain walls. Kersten, Chikazumi, Kronmüller, Zijlstra are among the many protagonists of these developments.

In the light of this new understanding of domain behaviour, permanent-magnet alloys, the alnicos in particular, have continued to be improved in the past 15 years; ductile permanent magnets (Fe–Cr–Co) were also developed in the 1970s. The main success story, however, is the introduction in 1967 of $SmCo_5$ permanent magnets, the most powerful known, on the basis of the work of Nesbitt and Strnat. This is one form of single-domain magnet, and its behaviour was found to depend intimately on its microstructure; grain boundaries help, surface defects hinder. Another form of single-domain magnet, introduced by Luborsky, entailed the use of iron whiskers.

Soft magnetic materials have also been greatly improved. The long and complex metallurgical history of iron–silicon transformer steel, beginning in the late 19th

References: p. 35.

century, is recounted in detail by Walter in the 1965 Sorby Centennial Symposium (see Bibliography). During the last 15 years, Japanese improvements to the crystallographic textures of these steels have revived research interest in them. The permalloys, based on Ni_3Fe with various additions, have been studied and interpreted more fully than any other alloys (save Fe–Si), and their magnetic behaviour has been minutely mapped in terms of their many forms of anisotropy. Bozorth, Chin and Puzei, starting in the early 1950s, were the principal investigators. During the 1970s, studies of the magnetic properties of metallic glasses, by Luborsky, Graham, Fukamichi and many others, have brought these materials to the point of effective competition with crystalline soft magnetic alloys.

Research on superconductors has been closely linked with magnetics research, especially because superconducting solenoids have recently come to play an important part in high-field magnetism. Superconduction was discovered by Kamerlingh Onnes in 1911, and he discovered the critical temperature and the critical field. Meissner in 1933 found that above the critical field, magnetic flux was excluded from a superconductor. The next 30 years were spent in finding new superconductors (this sport still continues) and in establishing what determines the critical field. This search was complicated by the discovery in the early 1930s by Shubnikov of type-II ("hard") superconductors with a very high critical field. Mendelssohn around 1935 proposed a "sponge" model of superconducting and normal regions to account for the irreversibility of some type-II superconductors, and this model held the field until Abrikosov's crucial paper of 1957 (not widely known in the West until 1962), which established the idea that flux enters a superconductor in the form of quantized flux vortices, which could be pinned at structural defects.

About this time, Rose-Innes, Seraphim and others began to demonstrate the effect of metal and alloy purity on superconducting behaviour; Rose-Innes and Calverley studied the entire range of Nb–Ta solid solutions and showed that the upper critical field was maximized for maximum compositional disorder. Now, at last, metallurgists began to take an interest in the phenomenon. From the early 1960s, Livingston, Evetts, Dew-Hughes and their collaborators began to establish the connections between microstructure (purity, grain size, two-phase morphology, dislocation density and distribution) and critical fields and current densities. Electron microscopy was impressively applied about this time, by Träuble and Essmann, to the imaging of the flux vortices proposed by Abrikosov, and their pinning.

Superconductivity research has increasingly turned, in the past decade, to the study of intermetallic compounds, the A15 family in particular, and of superconduction in metallic glasses, including those which have partially crystallized; Johnson has obtained many of the results on the glasses. Whereas the behaviour of annealed or cold-worked crystalline solid solutions such as Nb–Ti and Pb–Bi has been clearly interpreted, microstructural control of superconducting behaviour in the more novel materials is still the subject of active research.

Further reading

Rosenhain, W., An Introduction to Physical Metallurgy (Constable, London, 1914).

Tammann, G., Lehrbuch der Metallographie (Leopold Voss, Leipzig, 1914).

Sauveur, A., The Metallography of Iron and Steel (McGraw-Hill, New York, 1912).

[The 3 above titles were the first important texts to formulate some of the ideas of physical metallurgy.]

Smith. S.W., Roberts-Austen, a Record of his Work (London, 1914).

Rickard, T.A., Man and Metals (McGraw-Hill, New York, 1932).

Mehl, R.F., A Brief History of the Science of Metals (AIME, New York, 1948).

Aitchison, L., A History of Metals (Interscience, New York; Edward Arnold, London, 1960).

Smith. C.S., A History of Metallography (Univ. Chicago Press, 1960).

Smith C.S., ed., The Sorby Centennial Symposium on the History of Metallurgy (Gordon and Breach, and AIME, New York, 1965).

[These two books of C.S. Smith's together provide the most complete survey of both ancient and more recent movement of ideas as to the structure of metals and alloys.]

Smith, C.S., ed., Sources of the History of the Science of Steel, 1532–1786 (Soc. for the History of Technology, and MIT Press. Cambridge, MA, 1968).

Smith, C.S., Four Outstanding Researches in Metallurgical History (Amer. Soc. For Testing Materials, Philadelphia, PA, 1963).

[This pamphlet includes accounts of Réaumur's early work on iron and steel; experiments by an 18th century scientist, Archard, on physical properties of alloys: the Damascus Sword; structures in partially precipitated alloys.]

Smith, C.S., Metallurgy as a Human Experience (ASM, Metals Park, OH; Metall. Soc. of AIME, New York. Joint publication, 1977).

Mullins, W.W. and M.C. Shaw, eds., Metal Transformations (Gordon and Breach, New York, 1968).

["Transformations" is here used in the sense of "metal-working": historical essays on casting, rolling, machining, etc., are included.]

Mott, Sir Nevill, organizer, The beginnings of Solid State Physics, Proc. R. Soc. 371A (1980) 1–177.

[A series of essays which include accounts of early work on alloy theory, dislocations and electron microscopy.]

Rosenhain Centenary Conference: The Contribution of Physical Metallurgy to Engineering Practice (Royal Society, London, 1976); also published in Phil. Trans. R. Soc. 282A (1976) 1–483.

[This volume, in addition to a detailed scientific biography of Walter Rosenhain, creator of a unified conception of physical metallurgy, contains surveys of the recent history of a number of aspects of applied physical metallurgy.]

Martin, J.W., Precipitation (Pergamon, Oxford, 1978).

[This book includes reprints of a number of the early classical papers on precipitation-hardening.]

Bozorth, R.M., "Basic Research and Applications in Magnetism", IEEE Trans. Magn. MAG-5 (1969) 692.

C.C. Gillispie, ed. in chief, Dictionary of Scientific Biography (Charles Scribner's Sons, New York, 1970–1980, 16 volumes). Biographies of the following physical metallurgists appear in this compendium: N.T. Belaiev, D.K. Chernov, P.A.J.S. Chevenard, J.-F. Clouet, R.A. Hadfield, W. Heyn, W. Hume-Rothery, Z. Jeffries, N.S. Kurnakov, H.C. Le Chatelier, A. Martens, F. Osmond, A.M.G.R. Portevin, R.-A.F. de Réaumur, W.C. Roberts-Austen, H.W.B. Roozeboom, W. Rosenhain, A. Sauveur, H.C. Sorby, J.E. Stead, G.H.J.A. Tammann and A. Wöhler.

CHAPTER 2

STRUCTURE OF THE PURE METALS

H.W. KING

Department of Engineering-Physics
Technical University of Nova Scotia
Halifax, Nova Scotia, Canada

R.W. Cahn and P. Haasen, eds.
Physical Metallurgy; third, revised and enlarged edition
© Elsevier Science Publishers BV, 1983

1. Electronic structure and the Periodic Table

The characteristic physical and chemical properties that distinguish the metals from other elements have their origin in the electronic structures of the different types of atoms. In table 1 the elements are arranged in alphabetical order of their chemical symbols and each is assigned an *atomic number* ranging from H = 1 to Lr = 103.

According to the model first put forward by Rutherford, the atom is pictured as a minute, positively charged nucleus which is surrounded by a cloud of negatively charged electrons. Although the nucleus contributes nearly all the mass of the atom, its diameter of about 10^{-15} m is very small compared to that of the atom as a whole, which is of the order of 10^{-10} m. In an atom of *atomic number* equal to Z the positive charge on the nucleus is equal to $+Ze$ in units of the charge on the electron (1.60209×10^{-19} Coulomb). This charge is carried by Z *protons* each having the same mass as the hydrogen nucleus (1836 times the mass of the electron) and a charge of $+e$.

In the Rutherford model, the nucleus may also contain uncharged particles, which are referred to as *neutrons*. The mass of the neutron (1839 times the mass of the electron) is almost the same as that of the proton and hence neutrons do contribute to the *atomic weights* of the elements which are also given in table 1. Most elements are composed of atoms having different atomic weights but the same atomic number; i.e., although the number of protons is fixed (being equal to the atomic number Z), the number of neutrons may vary from atom to atom giving rise to *isotopes* of different atomic weights. The atomic weights in table 1 indicate the weighted average of the mixture of isotopes found in nature and hence the values often deviate widely from integral numbers. The nearest whole number to the atomic weight is known as the *mass number* and is used to label the isotopes, e.g., ^{235}U and ^{238}U.

Modern nuclear theories recognize three categories of elementary particles:

The first of these are *quarks*, which have spin $1/2$ and can take part in strong interactions. Six types of quarks are postulated, i.e., *up, down, strange, charm, top,* and *bottom*, but not all of these have been found. Quarks can join together to form large composite particles known as *hadrons*, the better known examples of which are protons, neutrons, etc. (which are referred to collectively as *baryons*), and *mesons*, such as *pions, psi mesons*, etc.

The second category of elementary particles are referred to as *leptons*. These also have spin $1/2$ but, in contrast to quarks, leptons do not contribute to strong interactions or aggregate to form composite particles. Six types of leptons are postulated: *electrons, electron neutrinos, muons, muon neutrinos, tau* and *tau neutrinos*. The mass of a lepton is $1/(1.8-1.9 \times 10^3)$ of that of a hadron.

The third category of elementary particles, known as *gauge bosons*, are considered to be the carriers of various physical forces. The *gravitron* is associated with gravity, the *photon* with electromagnetism, W^+, W^- and Z^0 *mesons* with weak nuclear interactions, and *gluons* with strong nuclear intereactions. The gluons can aggregate

Table 1
International atomic weights (1979).

Symbol	Element	Atomic number	Atomic weight	Symbol	Element	Atomic number	Atomic weight
Ac	Actinium	89	227.0278	Mn	Manganese	25	54.9380
Ag	Silver	47	107.880	Mo	Molybdenum	42	95.94
Al	Aluminium	13	26.98154	N	Nitrogen	7	14.0067
Am	Americium	95	(243)	Na	Sodium	11	22.98977
Ar	Argon	18	39.948	Nb	Niobium	41	92.9064
As	Arsenic	33	74.9216	Nd	Neodymium	60	144.24
At	Astatine	85	(210)	Ne	Neon	10	20.179
Au	Gold	79	196.9665	Ni	Nickel	28	58.69
B	Boron	5	10.81	No	Nobelium	102	(259)
Ba	Barium	56	137.33	Np	Neptunium	93	237.0482
Be	Beryllium	4	9.01218	O	Oxygen	8	15.9994
Bi	Bismuth	83	208.9804	Os	Osmium	76	190.2
Bk	Berkelium	97	(247)	P	Phosphorus	15	30.97376
Br	Bromine	35	79.904	Pa	Protoactinium	91	231.0359
C	Carbon	6	12.011	Pb	Lead	82	207.2
Ca	Calcium	20	40.08	Pd	Palladium	46	106.42
Cd	Cadmium	48	112.41	Pm	Promethium	61	(145)
Ce	Cerium	58	140.12	Po	Polonium	84	(209)
Cf	Californium	98	(251)	Pr	Praseodymium	59	140.9077
Cl	Chlorine	17	35.453	Pt	Platinum	78	195.08
Cm	Curium	96	(247)	Pu	Plutonium	94	(244)
Co	Cobalt	27	58.9322	Ra	Radium	88	226.0254
Cr	Chromium	24	51.996	Rb	Rubidium	37	85.4678
Cs	Caesium	55	132.9054	Re	Rhenium	75	186.207
Cu	Copper	29	63.546	Rh	Rhodium	45	102.9055
Dy	Dysprosium	66	162.50	Rn	Radon	86	(222)
Er	Erbium	68	167.26	Ru	Ruthenium	44	101.07
Es	Einsteinium	99	(252)	S	Sulphur	16	32.06
Eu	Europium	63	151.96	Sb	Antimony	51	121.75
F	Fluorine	9	18.998408	Sc	Scandium	21	44.9559
Fe	Iron	26	55.847	Se	Selenium	34	78.96
Fm	Fermium	100	(257)	Si	Silicon	14	28.0855
Fr	Francium	87	(223)	Sm	Samarium	62	150.36
Ga	Gallium	31	69.72	Sn	Tin	50	118.69
Gd	Gadolinium	64	157.25	Sr	Strontium	38	87.62
Ge	Germanium	32	72.59	Ta	Tantalum	73	180.9479
H	Hydrogen	1	1.0079	Tb	Terbium	65	158.9254
He	Helium	2	4.00260	Tc	Technetium	43	(98)
Hf	Hafnium	72	178.49	Te	Tellurium	52	127.60
Hg	Mercury	80	200.59	Th	Thorium	90	232.0381
Ho	Holmium	67	164.9304	Ti	Titanium	22	47.88
I	Iodine	53	126.9045	Tl	Thallium	81	204.383
In	Indium	49	114.82	Tm	Thulium	69	168.9342
Ir	Iridium	77	192.22	U	Uranium	92	238.0289
K	Potassium	19	39.0983	V	Vanadium	23	50.9415
Kr	Krypton	36	83.80	W	Tungsten	74	183.85
La	Lanthanum	57	138.9055	Xe	Xenon	54	131.29
Li	Lithium	3	6.94	Y	Yttrium	39	88.9059
Lr	Lawrencium	103	(260)	Yb	Ytterbium	70	173.04
Lu	Lutetium	71	174.967	Zn	Zinc	30	65.38
Md	Mendeleevium	101	(258)	Zr	Zirconium	40	91.22
Mg	Magnesium	12	24.305				

Values in parentheses refer to the isotope of longest half life which may not be the best known isotope of the element. Data Source: International Union of Pure and Applied Chemistry.

References: p. 71.

to form compound particles, referred to as *glueballs*. The more exotic of these elementary and composite particles have very short lives and hence do not contribute to inter-atomic bonding, crystal structures and the commonly observed chemical and physical properties of materials, all of which have their origins in interactions between the more familiar protons, electrons and photons.

In an electrically neutral atom the Z protons in the nucleus are balanced by Z *orbital* electrons. The latter can be assigned to a series of well-defined *energy levels* referred to by the principal quantum numbers $n = 1, 2, 3 \ldots 7$, or alternatively by the letters K, L, M... Q, in increasing order of distance away from the nucleus. These principal energy levels are composed of one or more *sub-levels* known as s, p, d and f, which can contain 1, 3, 5 or 7 *orbitals* respectively.

Four discrete quantum numbers are thus necessary in order to define the energy state of a particular electron in any given atom. The principal quantum number n is related to the *energy* of the electron in a particular state, the negative energies of the principal shells being inversely proportional to n^2. The second quantum number l is a measure of the *angular momentum* of the electron and may have any value from zero to $(n-1)$. The values of $l = 0, 1, 2$ and 3 are associated with the sub-shells described by the letters s, p, d and f respectively. Hence the K shell can contain only the s type of orbital, the L shell only s and p types, the M shell only s, p and d types and so on, adding an extra sub-shell with each increase in principal quantum number (see table 2). The third quantum number m_l is a measure of the component of the angular momentum in a particular direction (usually that of a very weak applied magnetic field.) This quantum number may have any value from $+l$ to $-l$ including zero, thereby restricting the number of orbitals in the s, p, d and f sub-shells, as mentioned above. The fourth quantum number m_s is related to the direction of the *spin* of the electron and is again determined in the presence of a magnetic field. The spin quantum number can take the values $\pm \frac{1}{2}$ and thus each orbital defined by the quantum numbers n, l and m_l can contain two electrons of opposite spins denoted by the quantum numbers $m_s = +\frac{1}{2}$ and $m_s = -\frac{1}{2}$.

Since each electronic state is associated with a certain energy, the energy of the atom as a whole will be the summation of the energies of the electronic states of the Z orbital electrons. All of the Z electrons are prevented from crowding into the lowest energy states, however, because the Quantum Laws restrict the number of electrons per state. This restriction is expressed by the *Pauli Exclusion Principle* according to which no two electrons may be in exactly the same state as defined by the four quantum numbers n, l, m_l and m_s. In any particular element the Z electrons are therefore distributed among the available states in such a manner as to minimize the total energy of the atom. As may be inferred from the electronic structures of the atoms listed in table 2 it is the distribution of the electrons among the principal and sub-shells which causes the elements to show the well-known periodic variations in valency and properties with increasing atomic number, which are summed up in the Periodic Table in table 3.

The First Period in table 3 is composed of only two elements, hydrogen and helium, which have their orbital electrons in the 1s states of the K shell. The Second

Table 2
The electronic structures of the elements.

Per-iod	Elements	Z	K	L		M			N				O				P			Q
			1s (2)	2s (2)	2p (6)	3s (2)	3p (6)	3d (10)	4s (2)	4p (6)	4d (10)	4f (14)	5s (2)	5p (6)	5d (10)	5f (14)	6s (2)	6p (6)	6d (10)	7s (2)
1	H → He	1 → 2	1 → 2																	
2	Li → Be	3 → 4	2	1 → 2																
	B → Ne	5 → 10	2	2	1 → 6															
3	Na → Mg	11 → 12	2	2	6	1 → 2														
	Al → Ar	13 → 18	2	2	6	2	1 → 6													
4	K → Ca	19 → 20	2	2	6	2	6	–	1 → 2											
	Sc → Ni	21 → 28	2	2	6	2	6	1 → 10	0,1,2											
	Cu → Zn	29 → 30	2	2	6	2	6	10	1 → 2											
	Ga → Kr	31 → 36	2	2	6	2	6	10	2	1 → 6										
5	Rb → Sr	37 → 38	2	2	6	2	6	10	2	6	–		1 → 2							
	Y → Pd	39 → 46	2	2	6	2	6	10	2	6	1 → 10	–	0,1,2							
	Ag → Cd	47 → 48	2	2	6	2	6	10	2	6	10	–	1 → 2							
	In → Xe	49 → 54	2	2	6	2	6	10	2	6	10	–	2	1 → 6						
6	Cs → Ba	55 → 56	2	2	6	2	6	10	2	6	10	–	2	6	–	–	1 → 2			
	La	57	2	2	6	2	6	10	2	6	10	–	2	6	1	–	2			
	Ce → Lu	58 → 71	2	2	6	2	6	10	2	6	10	1 → 14	2	6	0,1	–	2			
	Hf → Pt	72 → 78	2	2	6	2	6	10	2	6	10	14	2	6	1 → 10	–	0,1,2			
	Au → Hg	79 → 80	2	2	6	2	6	10	2	6	10	14	2	6	10	–	1 → 2			
	Tl → Rn	81 → 86	2	2	6	2	6	10	2	6	10	14	2	6	10	–	2	1 → 6		
7	Fr → Ra	87 → 88	2	2	6	2	6	10	2	6	10	14	2	6	10	–	2	6	–	1 → 2
	Ac	89	2	2	6	2	6	10	2	6	10	14	2	6	10	–	2	6	1	2
	Th → Md	90 → 101	2	2	6	2	6	10	2	6	10	14	2	6	10	1 → 12	2	6	1,2	2

Notes:

1. Figures in parentheses denote the number of electrons permitted in the respective subshells.
2. The arrow in a subshell column (→) indicates which particular sub-shell is being filled along the row of elements listed in the elements column.
3. The 3d, 4d, 5d and 6d shells are not occupied until the respective $(n+1)s$ shells outside them have started to fill.
4. The 4f and 5f shells are occupied only after the $(n+1)s$ and $(n+1)p$ shells outside them are filled and the $(n+1)d$ and $(n+2)s$ shells have started to fill.

Table 3
Periodic Table and room-temperature structures of the elements.

	IA	IIA	IIIA	IVA	VA	VIA	VIIA	VIII	VIII	VIII	IB	IIB	IIIB	IVB	VB	VIB	VIIB	0
1st																		1 A3[a] H ; 2 A3[a] He
2nd	3 A2 Li	4 A3 Be											5 T B	6 H C	7 C[a] N	8 M[a] O	9 M[a] F	10 A2[a] Ne
3rd	11 A2 Na	12 A3 Mg											13 A1 Al	14 A4 Si	15 O P	16 O S	17 O[a] Cl	18 A1[a] Ar
4th	19 A2 K	20 A1 Ca	21 A3 Sc	22 A3 Ti	23 A2 V	24 A2 Cr	25 C Mn	26 A2 Fe	27 A3 Co	28 A1 Ni	29 A1 Cu	30 A3 Zn	31 O Ga	32 A4 Ge	33 A7 As	34 A8 Se	35 O[a] Br	36 A1[a] Kr
5th	37 A2 Rb	38 A1 Sr	39 A3 Y	40 A3 Zr	41 A2 Nb	42 A2 Mo	43 A3 Tc	44 A3 Ru	45 A1 Rh	46 A1 Pd	47 A1 Ag	48 A3 Cd	49 A6 In	50 A5 Sn	51 A7 Sb	52 A8 Te	53 O I	54 A1[a] Xe
6th	55 A2 Cs	56 A2 Ba	57 H La	72 A3 Hf	73 A2 Ta	74 A2 W	75 A3 Re	76 A3 Os	77 A1 Ir	78 A1 Pt	79 A1 Au	80 R[a] Hg	81 A3 Tl	82 A1 Pb	83 A7 Bi	84 C Po	85 ? At	86 ? Rn
7th	87 ? Fr	88 A2 Ra	89 A1 Ac															

6th (continued)

58 A1 Ce	59 H Pr	60 H Nd	61 H Pm	62 H Sm	63 A2 Eu	64 A3 Gd	65 A3 Tb	66 A3 Dy	67 A3 Ho	68 A3 Er	69 A3 Tm	70 A1 Yb	71 A3 Lu

7th (continued)

90 A1 Th	91 T Pa	92 O U	93 O Np	94 M Pu	95 H Am	96 H Cm	97 H Bk	98 ? Cf	99 ? Es	100 ? Fm	101 ? Md	102 ? No	103 ? Lr

[a] Low temperatures.

A1 fcc (fig. 3)
A2 bcc (fig. 4)
A3 hcp (fig. 5)
A4 cubic-diamond (fig. 6d)
A5 bc tetragonal
A6 fc tetragonal
A7 rhombohedral (fig. 6c)
A8 trigonal (fig. 6b)

H hexagonal (usually ABAC...
  close-packed)
R rhombohedral
O orthorhombic

C complex cubic
T tetragonal
M monoclinic

Data source: KING [1981]. For
full description of structures
see PEARSON [1958 and
1967].

and Third Periods each contain eight elements and are often referred to as the two *short Periods*. The inner electrons in these elements have either the He or Ne configuration and the outer electrons progressively fill the 2s + 2p and the 3s + 3p orbitals of the L and M shells respectively. The elements which have 1–2 outer electrons in an s orbital are classified into groups IA or IIA, while those which have from 1–6 electrons in a p orbital are placed in the appropriate sub-group from IIIB–0 in table 3. Thus the inert gases in group 0 have eight outer electrons which completely fill the respective ns + np orbitals.

In potassium and calcium, the first two elements of the Fourth Period, the extra electrons outside the argon core enter the 4s orbital of the N shell and hence these elements are assigned to groups IA and ILA respectively. However, the following element, scandium, does not continue the pattern established in the Second and Third Periods since the outer electrons now enter the inner 3d orbitals left over from the M shell, in preference to the 4p orbitals. The 3d orbital is progressively filled from scandium to nickel and the following two elements, copper and zinc, have their outermost electrons in the 4s orbital outside a full 3d sub-shell. Copper and zinc thus have the same valency as potassium and calcium respectively, but because of the full 3d shell they have quite different physical properties from the IA and IIA metals and are usually classified in separate sub-groups IB and IIB respectively. The remaining elements of the Fourth Period, gallium → krypton, reflect the progressive filling up of the 4p sub-shell and are classified in groups IIIB → 0.

The energy difference between the 3d and 4s orbitals is quite small and, as we have seen, in potassium $E_{4s} < E_{3d}$ whereas in copper $E_{3d} < E_{4s}$. This change in the relative energies of the 3d and 4s orbitals occurs gradually over the elements from scandium to nickel which are known as the transition metals and are usually classified into groups IIIA–VIII as in table 3. Throughout this sub-series when the 3d shell is being filled, the number of electrons remaining in the 4s orbital may be equal to zero, one or two, causing the transition metals to have variable ionic valencies and, apart from groups IIIA and IVA, to have very little in common with their opposite numbers in the B sub-groups.

The electronic structures of the elements in the Fifth Period follow the same pattern as described above for Period Four. The 5s orbital of the O shell is filled (outside the krypton core) in rubidium and strontium, and a second transition series extends from yttrium to palladium as the energy of the 4d orbital of the N shell becomes progressively lower than E_{5s}. Outside the full 4d shell the 5s and 5p levels are filled along the elements silver → cadmium and indium → xenon which fall into groups IB–IIB and IIIB–0, zero respectively. However, at xenon there still remains an unfilled inner shell, i.e. the 4f sub-shell of the N shell (see table 2).

The Sixth Period shows a further discontinuity in the pattern of the filling of the electronic states with increasing atomic number. This is brought about because the energies of the 6s, 5d and 4f orbitals are now very close together and the order of the sub-shells in terms of increasing energy changes across the Period. In caesium and barium the 6s orbital has the lowest energy and so these elements are assigned to groups IA and IIA respectively. At lanthanum ($Z = 57$) another series of transition metals is initiated by an electron entering the 5d shell, but almost immediately this process is delayed while the 4f shell is filled from the elements cerium to lutetium ($Z = 58$–91) which are listed in table 3 as a separate sub-period known as the *rare earths* and *lanthanides*. Since the 4f orbitals lie deep within the core of the atom, the outer electronic structures of these elements are very similar (table 2), and hence the physical and chemical properties vary very little along the series. The filling of the 5d shell, which began at lanthanum, is now continued from hafnium to platinum forming a third row of transition elements and thereafter the Sixth Period follows the usual pattern with the filling of 6s and 6p levels from gold → mercury and thallium → radon respectively.

In the Seventh Period the energies of the 5f, 6d and 7s orbitals are all very nearly equal. There is some question as to the precise configuration of the outer electrons in some of the elements but the general pattern is as follows: In francium and radium the outer electrons are in the 7s shell outside the radon core, and hence these elements are classified in groups IA and IIA respectively. The actinium atom has two electrons in the 7s and one in the 6d shell and thus marks the beginning of another possible series of transition elements. The next element thorium, though usually listed among the actinides (as in table 3) has two electrons in both the 7s and 6d orbitals and should therefore be regarded as a group IVA transition metal. In the remaining elements which have so far been identified the filling of the 6d shell is interrupted by the electrons entering the unfilled 5f orbitals of the N shell to form another sub-period similar to the rare earths and known as the *actinides*.

The electronic structures of the elements listed in table 2 are the structures derived for isolated or *free atoms* of the elements for which the various types of orbital have discrete values of energy. When two atoms of an element are brought closer together, however, the outer orbitals no longer have discrete energy values but become spread out over a range of energy known as a *band* (see ch. 3). When the atoms are brought very close together, as for example in a crystal of the element, the spread of the energy bands associated with various orbitals may be so wide that some bands may overlap, giving rise to *hybrid orbitals*. The ns and np orbitals, for example, may hybridize to form (sp) hybrid orbitals, or the ns, np and (n-1)d orbitals may hybridize to form (spd) hybrid orbitals both of which can take part in the interatomic bonding forces in the crystal.

2. Bonding forces in crystals

2.1. The ionic bond

The chemical inactivity of the inert gases demonstrates that an outer electronic structure of eight electrons in completely filled ns and np sub-shells is a particularly stable configuration. Most of the A and B sub-group elements can attain an electronic structure similar to that of one of the inert gases by losing or gaining one or more electrons. In the ionic compounds NaCl and MgS, for example, the Na^+ and Mg^{2+} ions have the electronic configuration of neon, and Cl^- and S^{2-} that of argon. The *ionic bond* (also referred to as *polar, heteropolar* or *electrovalent bond*) in these compounds is the result of an electrostatic attraction between the oppositely charged ions. As the two types of ion are drawn closer together the inner shells of electrons come into contact but interpenetration of the ions is prevented because of the restriction limiting only one electron to a given electronic state (the Pauli Exclusion Principle) thereby giving rise to a repulsive force. The contributions of these two forces to the lattice energy u were summarized by Born and Meyer in the following equation:

$$u = \frac{-Ae^2}{d} + B \exp \frac{d}{\rho},$$
(1)

where e is the electronic charge and d the distance between the ions. The first term represents the contribution of the electrostatic attraction between the oppositely charged ions. The constant A is known as the *Madelung constant* and is related to the crystal structure of the ionic compound. It is usually of the order of unity. The second term is an empirical expression for the repulsive forces between the ions and the quantity ρ is determined from compressibility measurements. For many salts this second term approximates to (B/d^{10}) indicating that the repulsion increases very rapidly at small distances between the ions.

The only restriction on the crystal structure of an ionic compound $A_x B_y$ is that the number of nearest neighbour ions of type A or B maintains the ratio $x : y$. The

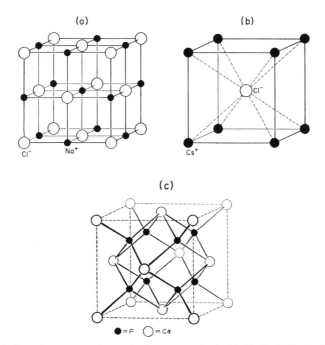

Fig. 1. Crystal structures of some ionic compounds: (a) NaCl; (b) CsCl; (c) CaF$_2$.

References: p. 71.

crystal structures adopted by ionic compounds are therefore governed to a large extent by the relative sizes of the two types of ion. In NaCl the ions differ considerably in size and in the crystal structure each sodium ion has six neighbouring chlorine ions, and vice versa for the chlorine ions, as shown in fig. 1a. In the CsCl structure, where both ions are about the same size, eight chlorine ions are clustered around each ceasium ion as shown in fig. 1b. These examples demonstrate that the number of nearest neighbour ions, i.e. the *coordination* of the crystal, is not a characteristic of the ionic bond. The CaF_2 structure in fig. 1c provides an example of the case when x does not equal y. Each calcium ion has eight fluorine neighbours, whereas each fluorine ion has only four calcium neighbours. The coordination of this crystal may thus be taken as $8:4$.

In general, crystals held together by ionic bonds have high melting points, strength and hardness, and low coefficients of thermal expansion. These properties are indicative of strong interatomic bonding forces. Since all the electrons are bound in the atomic orbitals of the individual atoms, they are unable to contribute to conduction and ionic crystals are therefore insulators. However, it is a characteristic property of ionic crystals that conduction can occur by ion transfer in the molten state.

2.2.   The covalent bond

The stable $(ns + np)$ octet of electrons present in the inert gases may also be obtained by a process in which two atoms share electrons between them. The atom of chlorine, for example, needs one more electron to form the stable argon configuration, and thus two chlorine atoms may share two electrons between them forming the chlorine molecule, Cl_2, as below:

$$:\ddot{\underset{..}{Cl}}. \; + \; \cdot\ddot{\underset{..}{Cl}}: \; \rightarrow \; :\ddot{\underset{..}{Cl}}:\ddot{\underset{..}{Cl}}: \; .$$

The linkage between the two atoms is known as a *single covalent* or *homopolar bond*. The two shared electrons must be of opposite spin and the bond may be pictured as an oscillatory interchange of electrons between the two atoms resulting in a *resonance* effect, the electrons now being a part of both atoms and not associated with either one in particular. In general the number of single covalent bonds which can originate from an atom is equal to the number of electrons required to complete the $(ns + np)$ sub-shells by electron sharing. An element having N electrons in $(ns + np)$ sub-shells will belong to the Nth group of the Periodic Table and can therefore participate in $(8 - N)$ single covalent linkages. Not all of these linkages need be single bonds, however, since double and triple covalent bonds may also be formed, by each atom contributing two or three electrons to the bond respectively. It also follows that the formation of $(8 - N)$ single covalent bonds should result in $(8 - N)$ nearest neighbours in the structure of an element. This so-called $(8 - N)$ rule cannot be applied to the elements in groups I–III however, because even if the coordination number of the structure were to equal $(8 - N)$, there would still be insufficient outer electrons to complete $(ns + np)$ octets around every atom by electron sharing.

The covalent bond differs from the ionic bond in that all covalent linkages originating from any one atom bear a fixed relationship to each other, i.e., they are considered to be *spatially directed*. The precise angular relationships between the bonds depend on both the number and type of electrons involved. The electron clouds of the s orbitals, for example, are known to be spherically symmetrical and those of the three p orbitals to be mutually perpendicular to each other, while the d and f orbitals have even more complicated cloud patterns. In most crystals, however, the bonds involve electrons in hybrid orbitals and the spatial distribution depends on which orbital is predominant. In diamond for instance it is considered that one s electron may be transferred to a p orbital, permitting all four outer electrons to be of unpaired spins, but instead of there being three p orbitals mutually inclined at right angles and one undirected s orbital, the s and p orbitals form four hybrid (sp) orbitals which are directed towards the corners of a regular tetrahedron (see fig. 6d).

Crystals such as diamond which are bound together solely by covalent bonds have high melting points, hardness and strength. Again, like the ionic crystals, they are also insulators since all the outer electrons are closely bound in the covalent linkages. These two types of bonding are distinguishable, however, since whereas on melting the ionic crystals can become conductors (by ion transfer), covalently bonded crystals are insulators in both solid and liquid states.

2.3. The van der Waals bond

All atoms, ions and molecules exhibit weak mutual attraction for each other, referred to as *van der Waals* or *residual* forces, but in most crystals these forces are outweighed by much stronger binding forces, e.g. ionic and covalent bonds, etc. Nevertheless, van der Waals forces do assume a major role in structures of solidified forms of the inert and diatomic gases (where they are the only forces binding the atoms or molecules together in the crystals) and also in some anisotropic structures such as that of selenium (fig. 6b) where they constitute the binding forces along certain directions in the crystal. The origin of the van der Waals forces lies in a polarizing effect caused by the influence of the field associated with the electrons moving round one nucleus on the electrons moving round the nucleus of a neighbouring atom. In an isotropic molecule this effect may result in a permanent dipole moment, but in symmetrical configurations (e.g. crystals of the solid inert gases) no net dipole moment is observed because the polarizing effects are synchronized with the continuously changing fields in neighbouring atoms. The contribution of the van de Waals forces to the lattice energy u is given by,

$$u = 3\hbar\nu_0 - \tfrac{3}{4}\,\frac{\hbar\nu_0\alpha^2}{d^6},\tag{2}$$

where ν_0 is the oscillation frequency of the two atoms (or molecules), α is a constant related to their polarizability, $\hbar$ is Planck's constant and once again d is the distance

References: p. 71.

between the atoms. The first term is related to the energy of the isolated atoms, the second is the interaction energy between neighbouring atoms in the crystal. As may be seen from eq. (2) those forces fall off very rapidly with increasing interatomic distance d, which is consistent with the extreme weakness of the van der Waals bond. The attractive van der Waals forces are of course balanced by repulsive forces which resist the interpenetration of the electron clouds of the atoms or molecules [second term in eq. (1)].

Since no exchange or sharing of electrons is involved in the van der Waals bond, the structures of the resulting crystals are determined primarily by geometrical considerations and thus tend to be close packed. Again because the electrons are closely bound in the $(ns + np)$ octets these crystals are insulators, the electrical properties being those of the individual atoms or molecules and changing very little on passing from the solid to the liquid or gaseous state.

2.4. The metallic bond

The *metallic bond* may be described as an attractive force between an array of positive ions and an intervening gas of "free" electrons. The free electrons are not tied to any atom in particular and their mobility within the lattice of ions contributes towards thermal and electrical conductivity. The concept of the metallic bond was developed primarily to account for these particular physical properties of the metals and an explanation of the strong cohesive forces between the metal atoms has been – until recent times – only a secondary consideration. Since the electronic theory of metals is the subject of the following chapter, in the present section it will be sufficient to note that the various components of the energy of a crystal bound together by metallic bonds may be written as,

$$u = - \frac{Ae^2}{\Omega^{1/3}} + \frac{B}{\Omega^{2/3}} + \frac{Ce^2}{\Omega}, \tag{3}$$

where Ω is the atomic volume (volume of structure per atom) of the crystal. The first of these terms refers to the potential energy of the free electrons, the second to the kinetic energy of the free electrons and the third to the kinetic energy of the electrons in the lower energy states. The sum of these three components results in a distribution of energy as shown in fig. 2, where the minimum energy corresponds to a linear dimension r_0 which may be considered to represent an atomic radius such that $\frac{4}{3}\pi r_0^3 = \Omega$. The energy difference ΔE in fig. 2 represents the work required to convert the metal crystal into a gas of positive ions, and the heat of sublimation of the metal (see §4.1) may be derived from ΔE by subtracting the ionization potential of the free atoms. In addition the curvature of the plot in the region of the minimum may be used to derive the compressibility (see §4.1) of the metal.

Calculations of the lattice constants, heats of sublimation and compressibilities of the alkali metals in group IA show quite good agreement with experimentally determined values, but for copper, silver and gold in group IB the calculated lattice constants are found to be too small and the compressibilities too low. These

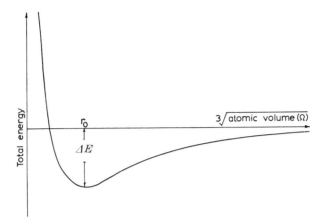

Fig. 2. The total energy of a metal as a function of the separation between the atoms.

discrepancies have been related to the observation that the relative difference between the ionic and atomic radii of the IB metals is much smaller than that for the alkali metals. Hence in copper, silver and gold the ionic cores come into contact before the value of r_0 associated with the minimum in fig. 2 is attained. In order to reduce the interatomic distance as close to r_0 as possible the IB metals therefore crystallize in close-packed structures of high coordination, whereas the alkali metals can assume a less densely-packed structure with interatomic distances compatible with r_0. Similarly, if in the calculation of the compressibility of copper an allowance is made for the repulsive forces preventing interpenetration of the ionic cores, as in the case of the ionic bond [eq. (1)], the values then show good agreement with those determined experimentally. The differences between the structures and properties of the IA and IB metals demonstrate that the metallic bond places no restriction on the number of neighbouring atoms and that the magnitude of the attractive forces between electrons and ions is quite variable.

2.5. Resonance bonding

Studies of the structure of the benzene ring have led to the conclusion that when several different configurations of covalent bonds are possible a structure of lower energy may be formed by a *resonance* between the various configurations. The concept of resonance also introduces the possibility of *one-* and *three-electron covalent bonds* with energies one half of the single and triple bonds respectively. The concept of the resonant bond was applied to the transition metals by PAULING (see for example PAULING [1956]) who suggested that electrons in the $(n - 1)$d shell are divided into *atomic* orbitals and *bonding* orbitals. The electrons in the atomic orbitals are associated with individual atoms and are held responsible for the magnetic properties of the metal. The bonding orbitals on the other hand are considered to form covalent bonds (by hybridizing with the ns and np orbitals) which resonate between a greater number of bond positions. These bonds are assigned a *bond number n* defined as v/L such that v single covalent bonds are assumed to resonate between L positions where L is the coordination number (or *ligand*) of the metal crystal.

The interatomic distances d_n in the three carbon–carbon covalent bonds $[(C-C) = d_1 = 1.54 \text{ Å}, (C=C) = d_2 = 1.33 \text{ Å}, (C\equiv C) = d_3 = 1.20 \text{ Å}]$ may be expressed to a first approximation by the following empirical equation,

$$d_n = d_1 - 0.70 \log n, \tag{4}$$

where n is the bond number as above. PAULING [1956] adapted this equation to the resonant metallic bond by substituting 0.60 for the numerical constant to allow for a shrinkage in bond-length because of the resonance effect, giving

$$d_n = d_1 - 0.60 \log n. \tag{5}$$

This equation indicates that the interatomic distances in metals should become decreased with increasing bond number n, i.e., with increasing number of bonds v or with decreasing coordination number L. Using eq. (5) values of so-called *single-bond metallic radii* $(r_1 = d_1/2)$ have been calculated for the metallic elements (PAULING [1956]). However, the precise values assumed for v and the application of eq. (4) to metals are both the subject of some controversy (see for example HUME-ROTHERY and COLES [1954]).

Although for convenience the particular characteristics of the different types of bond have been studied individually, it is much more the exception than the general rule for the crystalline form of an element to be bound together by only one type of bond. These exceptions concern some, but not all, of the elements from groups IA, IVB and 0 which are bound together by metallic, covalent and van der Waals bonds respectively. In the remainder of the elements a mixture of two or more of these three types of bonding is usually involved. The ionic bond by its nature demands more than one kind of ion (i.e., positive and negative) and hence cannot occur in crystals of the pure elements. However, in many of the intermetallic compounds the bonding is an intimate mixture of ionic and metallic bonds, and resonance between covalent and ionic bonds has also been suggested for the structures of the halogen acids. Thus it often occurs in practice that no clear line of distinction can be drawn between the various types of bond present in crystal.

3. Crystal structures of the metallic elements

3.1. Typical metallic structures

An examination of the Periodic Table given in table 3 shows that (with the exception of manganese and mercury) the A sub-group elements, the transition metals, the later rare earths and the group IB and IIB metals all crystallize into one

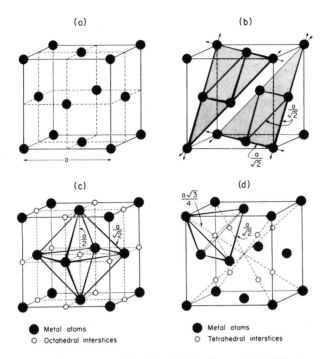

Fig. 3. The face-centred cubic structure: (a) unit cell; (b) close-packed {111} planes; (c) octahedral interstices; (d) tetrahedral interstices.

or more of the following typical metallic structures: face-centred cubic (A_1*, fcc), body-centered cubic (A_2, bcc) and hexagonal close-packed (A_3, hcp). These structures are illustrated in figs. 3–5, respectively.

   In the A_1 *face-centred cubic* structure, atoms are situated at the corners of the unit cell and at the centres of the cell faces (fig. 3a). Each atom has twelve equidistant nearest neighbors situated at a distance of $a/\sqrt{2}$ ($= 0.707\ a$), where a is the side of the unit cell. The second-nearest neighbours, of which there are six, are situated considerably further away at a distance a. The coordination number of the structure is therefore taken as 12. This structure has two types of interstitial positions which may accommodate a smaller atom belonging to another element. The largest interstices are the holes at the centres of the cube and the centres of the cube edges, shown in fig. 3c. Each of these holes is surrounded by six atoms in the fcc lattice situated at the corners of a regular octahedron, and hence the holes are known as *octahedral* interstices. The positions of these interstices are also illustrated by the structure of NaCl in fig. 1a in which the chloride ions may be considered to form a

---

* The symbols "A_1", etc. are part of an internationally agreed scheme for denoting crystal structure types, first introduced in the volumes of Strukturbericht. For a full description see PEARSON [1958 and 1967].

fcc structure while the smaller sodium ions occupy the octahedral interstices. These are also the positions of the interstitial carbon atoms in the austenite phase in steels. A smaller type of interstice is shown in fig. 3d and bears a *tetrahedral* relationship to four of the atoms of the fcc lattice. The positions of the tetrahedral interstices are illustrated by the structure of CaF_2 in fig. 1c, though in this case the larger fluorine ions occupy the tetrahedral interstices of the fcc lattice formed by the smaller calcium ions. In zinc blende on the other hand, only four of the available tetrahedral interstices are occupied resulting in an atomic arrangement which would be the same as diamond (fig. 6d) if all the atoms were identical. If it is considered that the fcc structure is composed of rigid spheres of radius r which are in contact with each other, the maximum radii of the spheres which can be inserted in the interstices are equal to $0.41r$ and $0.225r$ for the octahedral and tetrahedral holes respectively. The most closely-packed planes of the fcc structure are the $\{111\}$ planes within which the atoms are situated at the corners of equilateral triangles as shown in fig. 3b. Each of these planes has three closely-packed directions along which the atoms may be considered to be in contact.

The A_2 *body-centered cubic* structure is less closely packed than the face-centered cubic structure and has an atom at each corner of the unit cell and one in the centre, as illustrated in fig. 4a. Each atom has eight equidistant neighbours at a distance of $\frac{1}{2}a\sqrt{3}$ ($= 0.866a$), where a is the length of the cube edge. Since the six second nearest neighbours are at a distance equal to a, the coordination number of the structure, though usually taken as 8, is sometimes regarded as $(8 + 6)$. The bcc structure also contains two types of interstices. The largest of these are situated at the positions on the cell faces shown in fig. 4d and are surrounded by four atoms of the bcc lattice situated at the corners of a regular tetrahedron. Smaller interstices, which are surrounded by six atoms situated at the corners of an irregular octahedron, are located at the centres of the cell edges and at the face centres, as shown in fig. 4c. If the structure is composed of rigid spheres, the tetrahedral holes will accommodate a sphere of maximum radius equal to $0.291r$, whereas the octahedral holes can only accommodate a sphere of $0.154r$. Hence, the maximum size of sphere which can be accommodated in a rigid bcc lattice is smaller that that accommodated in the more closely-packed face-centered cubic structure. It is of interest to note that the insertion of an atom of radius greater than $0.291r$ into a tetrahedral interstice will cause all four surrounding atoms to be displaced, whereas if an oversize atom is inserted into an octahedral interstice, only the two atoms parallel to the cube edge will be displaced, causing a strain which can be relieved by an expansion of the lattice in this direction only. This situation appears to be responsible for the tendency of the oversized interstitial carbon atoms in bcc α-iron to collect in the smaller octahedral sites, and also for the distortion of the bcc stucture found in the body-centred tetragonal carbon martensites in which the carbon atoms are only to be found in the octahedral sites on cell edges parallel to the c-axis and at the centre of the C faces. The body-centred cubic structure contains no close-packed planes similar to the $\{111\}$ planes of the fcc structure. The most closely-packed planes are the twelve $\{110\}$ planes illustrated in fig. 4b which contain two close-packed

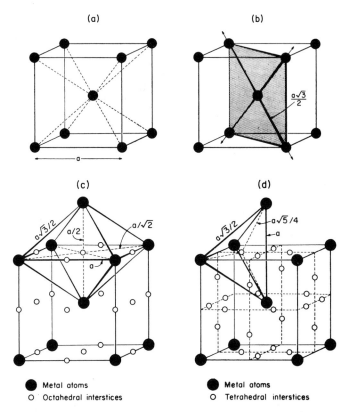

Fig. 4. The body-centred cubic structure: (a) unit cell; (b) close-packed directions in {110} planes; (c) octahedral interstices; (d) tetrahedral interstices.

directions along which rigid spheres would be in contact.

The A_3 *hexagonal close-packed* structure has atoms arranged in hexagonal layers such that each atom has six equidistant near neighbours in the same layer and six other equidistant neighbours, three being in the layer above and three in the layer below, as shown in fig. 5a. The distance between the atoms in the hexagonal layer is referred to as a and the height of the cell as c. The six near neighbour atoms in the adjacent layers are separated by a distance a', given by $\frac{1}{3}a^2 + \frac{1}{4}c^2$. The distance a' will exactly equal a if the axial ratio of the cell (c/a) has the value of $(8/3)^{1/2}$ $(= 1.6330)$. Such a structure is said to be ideally *close-packed* and the coordination number is equal to 12, i.e., the same as that for the fcc structure. Most of the hcp metals have axial ratios in the range from 1.56–1.63, i.e., below the ideal value. Zinc and cadmium form an exception with axial rations of 1.86 and 1.89 respectively. The atomic clouds of the zinc and cadmium atoms are known to be distorted from a spherical shape and this has been attributed to some degree of covalent bonding between the atoms in the (00.1) plane. Although the ideal value of axial ratio is not

References: p. 71.

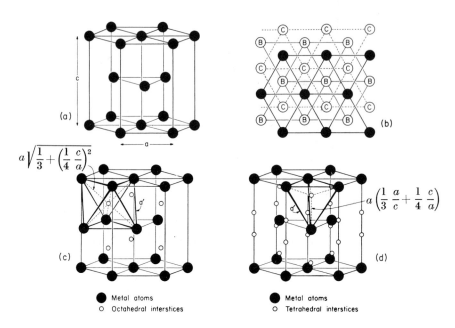

$$a\sqrt{\frac{1}{3}+\left(\frac{1}{4}\frac{c}{a}\right)^2}$$

$$a\left(\frac{1}{3}\frac{a}{c}+\frac{1}{4}\frac{c}{a}\right)$$

● Metal atoms
○ Octahedral interstices

● Metal atoms
○ Tetrahedral interstices

Fig. 5. The hexagonal close-packed structure: (a) unit cell; (b) methods of stacking (00.1) and {111} close-packed planes; (c) octahedral interstices; (d) tetrahedral interstices.

found in pure metals, it has been observed in certain alloy phases (see MASSALSKI and KING [1961]).

The hexagonal close-packed structure also has octahedral and tetrahedral interstices as illustrated in fig. 5c and d. The positions of the octahedral holes are illustrated by the NiAs structure where the arsenic atoms lie on an hcp lattice and the nickel atoms occupy the octahedral interstices which form a simple hexagonal lattice with c half of the total cell height. In the structure of Wurtzite, on the other hand, only selected tetrahedral interstices are occupied, giving a structure related to zinc blende referred to earlier. The diameters of rigid spheres that can be accommodated in these two types of hole are the same as in the fcc structure, i.e. $0.41r$ for the octahedral interstices and $0.225r$ for the tetrahedral interstices [*]. This observation indicates that even though at first sight the hcp and fcc structures appear to be quite different, they are in fact very closely related. As shown in fig. 5b, the atoms in the (00.1) hexagonal layers have the same close packing as the atoms in the {111} planes of the fcc structure (fig. 3b). However, whereas the three-dimensional hexagonal close-packed structure is built up by stacking these planes in alternative

_____

[*] For a detailed description of the effect of c/a on the size and shape of the interstices in the hcp structure, see KING [1971].

positions ABAB..., the face-centered cubic structure is the result of stacking the planes in the sequence ABCABC..., i.e. using the third stacking position labelled C in fig. 5b. The difference in energy between these two structures is quite small, and it is thus possible to disrupt the sequence of stacking by deforming the crystal plastically, or by introducing irregularities during crystal growth, thereby creating so-called *stacking faults*, described in more detail in ch. 4, §9.2, and ch. 18, §3.3.

3.2. Crystal structures of the B-subgroup elements

When the inert gases of group 0 in table 3 are condensed at very low temperatures, they form close-packed cubic structures (A_1), the atoms being bound together by van der Waals forces. The crystal structures of the halogens of group VIIB are composed of diatomic molecules and these are also held together by van der Waals forces because all the outer electrons are tied up in the covalent bonds of the diatomic molecules. However, the structures of the group VIIB elements are more complicated that those of the inert gases since they are concerned with the geometrical problem of close-packing the asymmetrical diatomic molecules, as illustrated by the orthorhombic structure of iodine in fig. 6a.

The $(8 - N)$ rule, referred to previously, permits the elements of group VIB to take part in two single covalent linkages and thus to form tightly bound chains or rings within which the bonds are covalent. These rings or chains may then be

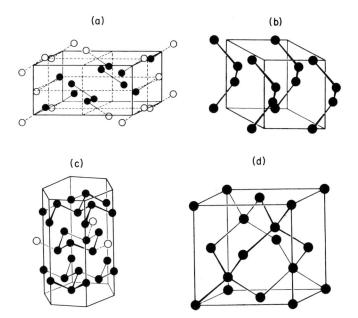

Fig. 6. Crystal structures of B-subgroup elements which conform to the $(8 - N)$ rule: (a) iodine (VIIB); (b) selenium (VIB); (c) antimony (VB); (d) diamond (IVB).

References: p. 71.

assembled into layers to form a three-dimensional structure such as the trigonal A_8 structure of selenium and tellurium shown in fig. 6b. Similarly, the elements in group VB can form double-layer sheets, in which each atom is bound to three close neighbours by covalent bonds, and these sheets may be assembled to form a three-dimensional structure such as the rhombohedral A_7 structure of arsenic, antimony and bismuth illustrated in fig. 6c. The chains in the A_8 structure and the sheets in the A_7 structure are held together by relatively weak bonds composed of van der Waals forces supplemented to a small degree by metallic bonding, and these structures therefore show strong anisotropy in their physical properties. The complexity of such structures also makes deformation processes (such as slip, twinning, etc.) more difficult, causing these elements to be brittle in comparison to those which have the typical metallic structures.

The A_4 diamond structure which is adopted by the group IVB elements carbon, silicon, germanium and grey tin is illustrated in fig. 6d. This structure is relatively open compared with the A_1 and A_2 cubic structures of the typical metals (figs. 3 and 4). Each atom is surrounded by only four nearest neighbours, positioned at the corners of a regular tetrahedron, giving the structure a coordination number of 4. The heavier elements in group IVB tend to have more metallic structures, i.e., white tin has the A_5 body-centred tetragonal structure and lead is a typical metal with the A_1 fcc structure.

The metals in group IIIB do not conform to any general rule with regard to structure. Aluminium has a typical metallic structure (A_1) but gallium, which lies below it in the Periodic Table, crystallizes in a complex orthorhombic structure. Indium shows a return to more metallic structures with the A_6 face-centred tetragonal structure with an axial ratio very nearly equal to unity and the return is complete in thallium which crystallizes in the typical metallic A_2 and A_3 structures.

3.3. The lanthanide and actinide series

The earlier elements of the rare earth group crystallize in one or other of the close-packed metallic structures, or in more complex close-packed structures in which the stacking sequences of the fcc and hcp structures (see fig. 5b) are intermixed, i.e. of the form ABACABAC... as observed in cerium, praseodymium and neodymium, or ABABCBCAC... as observed in samarium. After europium, which has the bcc A_2 structure, all the remaining elements form close-packed A_3 hcp structures with the exception of ytterbium which is fcc.

In the actinide series, thorium exhibits both fcc and bcc structures and protoactinium is body-centred tetragonal. The following three elements, uranium, neptunium and plutonium all form the A_2 bcc structure at high temperatures but, as indicated in table 3, they form complex structures at room temperature. The tetragonal structure of β-uranium is similar to that of the σ phase in the iron–chromium system.

3.4. Allotropy

Many of the elements can transform from one crystalline form to another upon heating or cooling as shown in table 4, in which the allotropic form stable at temperatures just below the melting point is listed above those stable at successively lower temperatures. Two general trends among the metallic elements are apparent from the table: (1) an allotrope with the bcc structure is usually stable at a higher temperature than one with the fcc or hcp structure, and (2) allotropy is most common among the metals for which there is only a very small difference between the energies of the ns, np, $(n-1)$d and $(n-2)$f electronic states, i.e., group IIA, the transition metals, the earlier rare earths and the early actinides.

Although nearest neighbour distances often vary quite markedly from one allotrope to another, the atomic volumes and hence also the total energies (see fig. 2) of the various metallic structures are usually very similar (MOTT [1962]). As discussed more fully in ch. 6, it is usual to compare the relative stability of two competing structures at a given temperature T K in terms of their *free energies*, F, given by the following equation:

$$F = E_0 - \int_0^T dT \cdot \int_0^T \frac{C_p}{T} dT, \tag{6}$$

where E_0 is the *internal energy* of the metal at 0 K and C_p the specific heat at constant pressure of the relevant allotrope. Since the rate of decrease in F with increasing temperature is controlled by the specific heat, the allotrope with the higher specific heat will be expected to have the lower F at high temperatures and conversely the allotrope with the lower specific heat will have the lower F at low temperatures. At some intermediate temperature the free energies will become equal and the metal will transform from one structure to the other.

The major contribution to the specific heat of a crystal comes from the lattice vibrations and hence in general a high value of C_p may be associated with a low vibrational frequency, i.e., with low values for the elastic constants and for the Debye characteristic temperature. Using this correlation between the lattice vibrations and the specific heat, ZENER [1947] has convincingly explained the predominance of the bcc structure at high temperatures by drawing attention to the extremely small resistance of this structure to a shear in the $[\bar{1}10]$ direction in the (110) plane, which gives rise to lattice vibrations of very low frequency and thus a high value for C_p. In the case of transition metals such as iron, the electronic contribution to C_p is quite significant and must therefore be taken into consideration along with the lattice vibrations. Thus SEITZ [1940] has proposed that the transition of bcc α-iron to fcc γ-iron at 930°C occurs because the Debye characteristic temperature of γ is less than that of α, but since in the region of 300°C the electronic specific heat of α becomes greater than that of γ the structure reverts back to bcc when the temperature is raised to 1400°C.

The contribution of the electronic specific heat must also be considered in the early rare earths and actinides in which the energies of the ns, $(n-1)$d and $(n-2)$f

References: p. 71.

Table 4
Allotropic forms of the metallic elements [a].

Element	Z	Allotrope	Crystal system	Structure type [b]	Stability Range (°C)
Am	95	β	cubic	A1	> 605
		α	hexag.	(La)	RT
As	33	ε	ortho.	Blk.P	> 448
		α	rhomb.	A7	RT
Be	4	β	cubic.	A2	> 1250
		α	hexag.	A3	RT
Bk	97	β	cubic	A1	RT(?)
		α	hexag.	(La)	RT
Ca	20	γ	cubic	A2	> 237
		α	cubic	A1	RT
Ce	58	δ	cubic	A2	> 730
		γ	cubic	A1	Rt
		β	hexag.	(La)	< 263 K
		α	cubic	A1	< 95 K
Cm	96	β	cubic	A2	RT(?)
		α	hexag.	(La)	RT
Co	27	β	cubic	A1	> 388
		α	hexag.	A3	RT
Dy	66	β	cubic	A1	> 970
		α	hexag.	A3	RT
Er	68	β	cubic	A2	RT
		α	hexag.	A3	RT
Fe	26	δ	cubic	A2	> 1390
		γ	cubic	A1	> 910
		α	cubic	A2	RT
Gd	64	β	cubic	A2	> 1262
		α	hexag.	A3	RT
Hf	72	β	cubic	A2	> 1995
		α	hexag.	A3	RT
Ho	67	β	cubic	A2	RT
		α	hexag.	A3	RT
La	57	γ	cubic	A2	> 868
		β	cubic	A1	> 340
		α	hexag.	$(A = 4)$	RT
Li	3	α	cubic	A2	RT
		β	hexag.	A3	< 72 K
Lu	71	β	cubic	A2	HT
		α	hexag.	A3	RT
Mn	25	δ	cubic	A2	> 1135
		γ	cubic	A1	> 1095
		β	cubic	$(A = 20)$	> 727
		α	cubic	$(A = 58)$	RT
Na	11	α	cubic	A2	RT
		β	hexag.	A3	< 36 K
Nd	60	β	cubic	A2	> 862
		α	hexag.	(La)	RT
Np	93	γ	cubic	A2	> 577

Table 4 (continued)

Element	Z	Allotrope	Crystal system	Structure type [b]	Stability Range (°C)
Np (cont'd)					
		β	tetrag.	(A = 4)	> 280
		α	ortho.	(A = 8)	RT
Pa	91	β	cubic	A2	> 1170
		α	tetrag.	(A = 2)	RT
Po	84	β	rhomb.	(A = 1)	> 54
		α	cubic	(A = 1)	RT
Pr	59	β	cubic	A2	> 821
		α	hexag.	(La)	RT
Pu	94	ε	cubic	A2	> 476
		δ	tetrag.	(A = 2)	> 450
		γ	cubic	A1	> 319
		α	ortho.	(A = 8)	> 235
		β	mono.	(A = 34)	> 122
		α	mono.	(A = 16)	RT
Sc	21	β	cubic	A2	> 1334
		α	hexag.	A1	RT
Sm	62	β	cubic	A2	> 917
		α	hexag.	(A = 9)	RT
Sn	50	β	tetrag.	A5	RT
		α	cubic	A4	< 18
Sr	38	γ	cubic	A2	> 605
		β	hexag.	A3	> 213
		α	cubic	A1	RT
Tb	65	β	cubic	A2	> 1316
		α	hexag.	A3	RT
		γ	ortho.	(A = 4)	< 220 K
Th	90	β	cubic	A2	> 1400
		α	cubic	A1	RT
Ti	22	β	cubic	A2	> 900
		α	hexag.	A3	RT
Tl	81	β	cubic	A2	> 230
		α	hexag.	A3	RT
Tm	69	β	cubic	A2	RT
		α	hexag.	A3	RT
U	92	γ	cubic	A2	> 772
		β	tetrag.	(A = 32)	> 662
		α	ortho.	(A = 4)	RT
Yb	70	β	cubic	A2	> 732
		α	cubic	A1	RT
		γ	hexag.	A3	< 270 K
Zr	40	β	cubic	A2	> 865
		α	hexag.	A3	RT

[a] Data source: KING [1983].

[b] The structures denoted by the Strukturbericht notation A1, A2, etc. are described in detail by PEARSON [1958 and 1967]. In other cases, the values of A listed in parentheses refer to the number of atoms in the unit cell of the structure.

References: p. 71.

levels are all very nearly equal. However, due to the complexity of the electronic structures a quantitative correlation has not as yet been attempted. KIESSLING [1957] has suggested that the tendency for the rare earths to form structures with various sequences of stacking of close-packed planes may be associated with polarization forces set up by the mutual interaction between the incomplete 4f levels and that if the nature of these forces is diminished or altered at lower temperatures the rare earths may then assume more typical metallic structures.

In contrast to the rare earths, the actinides form typical metallic structures at high temperatures but the low-temperature forms indicate distinct departures from purely metallic bonding. (This change from metallic bonding towards a more covalent type of bonding with decreasing temperature is also evident in manganese and tin.) Plutonium provides an extreme example of allotropy since it forms six different structures. Even though there is a tendency for these to become more metallic with increasing temperature, the δ and δ' structures, which are based on the fcc structure, show the peculiarity of a negative coefficient of thermal expansion and also have high electrical resistivities. There is also a marked change in atomic volume, and hence in density, between the more nonmetallic and the more metallic forms of plutonium.

4. Physical properties related to cohesive forces

4.1. Summary of properties

The interatomic (or intermolecular) cohesive forces which bind a crystal together are very difficult to measure experimentally since, as explained in a later chapter, the elastic limit and tensile strength determined in a mechanical test are governed primarily by the presence of defects in the structure. Nevertheless a general concept of the *strength of cohesion* of the crystalline forms of the elements can be obtained by summing up various pieces of information obtained from such properties as melting points, heats of sublimation, compressibilities, coefficients of thermal expansion and lattice constants.

Strong cohesive forces in crystals are most easily recognized by high melting points and heats of sublimation. Since these properties follow very similar periodic trends with increasing atomic number of the elements, only the melting points need be considered. As shown in fig. 7 the melting points pass through two maxima, one in the middle of the transition metal series and the other at group IVB. When using these properties as an indication of the cohesive strength of an element, however, it is important to bear in mind that the melting point is defined as the temperature at which solid and liquid phases are in equilibrium, and the heat of sublimation is the amount of work required to transform one gram-atom of the solid to a vapour of neutral atoms; i.e., in both cases these physical constants of the elements are not properties of the solid state alone, but of liquid or gaseous phases as well. Hence, any conclusions drawn from these properties must be checked against those drawn

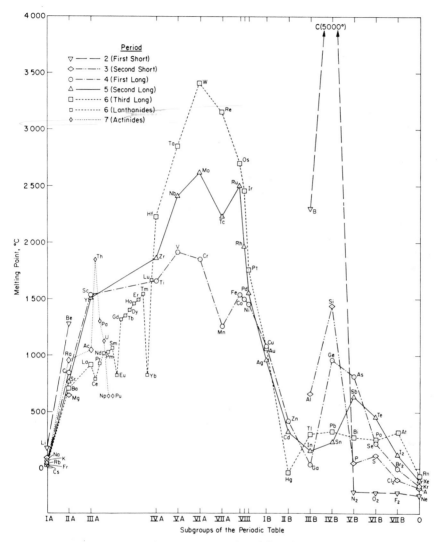

Fig. 7. Melting points of the elements as a function of the subgroup of the Periodic Table.

from properties such as the compressibility or thermal coefficient of expansion which are directly concerned with interatomic forces in the solid state.

The *compressibility* χ of a solid is the fractional decrease in volume per unit of hydrostatic pressure, being a measure of the ease with which the atoms can be pushed closer together. This property bears an inverse relationship to the cohesive forces in a crystal so that the strong cohesive forces in the transition metals and in group IVB are indicated by low values of χ in fig. 8. The *thermal expansion*

References: p. 71.

coefficient of a solid is the fractional change in length (or volume) per unit change in temperature and is thus a measure of the ease with which the amplitude of the thermal vibrations is increased with increasing temperature. A low coefficient of thermal expansion is therefore indicative of strong interatomic forces and the trends with increasing atomic number of the elements are very similar to those of the compressibilities already referred to in fig. 8.

The electron cloud surrounding the nucleus of an atom is not a rigid sphere, and it may vary in both size and shape according to the nature of the interatomic bonding forces to which the outer electrons contribute when the atom forms part of a crystal. In the absence of any other effects, small interatomic distances S_0 may thus be taken to indicate strong cohesive forces. However, a direct comparison of the nearest neighbour distances in the various crystalline structures adopted by the elements is complicated by the general observation that S_0 is decreased with decreasing coordination number of the crystal structure. This may be easily verified by comparing the interatomic distances in various allotropes of an element, e.g., at the transition temperature of 916°C, in fcc γ-iron (coordination 12) $S_0 = 2.578$ Å,

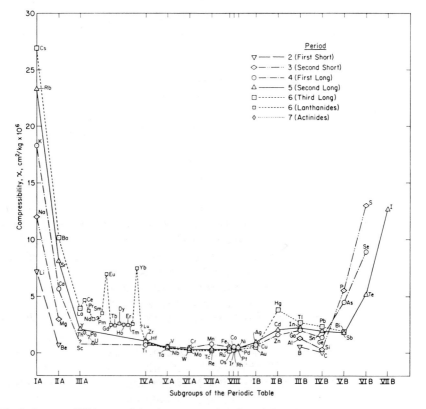

Fig. 8. Compressibilities, χ, of the elements as a function of the subgroups of the Periodic Table.

Table 5
Volumes per atom (Ω), nearest neighbour distances (S_0) and atomic radii (r_0) of crystalline forms of the elements [a].

Element	Z	Str. type	Ω	s_0	r_0
			(Ångström units, conversion factor 1.00202)		
Ac	89	A1	37.451	3.755	2.076
Ag	47	A1	17.056	2.889	1.597
Al	13	A1	16.603	2.864	1.582
Am	95	H	29.27	3.451	1.911
Ar [b]	18	A1	34.473	3.756	2.076
As [d]	33	A7	21.518	2.517	1.726
At	85	?	–	–	–
Au	79	A1	16.959	2.884	1.594
B [d]	5	T	7.786	1.624	1.230
Ba	56	A2	63.367	4.350	2.473
Be	4	A3	8.108	2.225	1.246
Bi	83	A7	35.384	3.071	2.037
Bk	97	H	27.965	3.398	1.883
Br [b,c]	35	O	32.77	2.27	1.99
C [d]	6	H	8.300	1.421	1.281
Ca	20	A1	43.631	3.952	2.184
Cd	48	A3	21.581	2.979	1.727
Ce	58	A1	34.367	3.650	2.017
Cf	98	?	–	–	–
Cl [b,c]	17	O	28.86	1.98	1.90
Cm	96	H	29.984	3.479	1.927
Co	27	A3	11.076	2.497	1.383
Cr	24	A2	12.003	2.488	1.420
Cs	55	A2	115.794	5.318	3.024
Cu	29	A1	11.809	2.238	1.413
Dy	66	A3	31.558	3.504	1.960
Er	68	A3	30.636	3.467	1.941
Es	99	?	–	–	–
Eu	63	A2	48.121	3.969	2.256
F [b,c]	9	M	16.05	1.49	1.97
Fe	26	A2	11.777	2.483	1.411
Fm	100	?	–	–	–
Fr	87	?	–	–	–
Ga	31	O	19.580	2.484	1.672
Gd	64	A3	33.050	3.575	1.991
Ge	32	A4	22.634	2.450	1.755
H [b,c]	1	A3	37.882	3.768	2.083
He [b]	2	A3	32.367	3.577	1.977
Hf	72	A3	22.321	3.127	1.747
Hg [b]	80	R	23.354	2.993	1.773
Ho	67	A3	31.139	3.487	1.952
I [c]	53	O	42.696	2.69	2.168
In	49	A6	26.158	3.252	1.842
Ir	77	A1	14146	2.175	1.500
K	19	A2	75.327	4.608	2.620
Kr [b]	36	A1	44.992	3.992	2.206

References: p. 71.

Table 5 (continued)

Element	Z	Str. type	Ω	s_0	r_0
			(Ångström units, conversion factor 1.00202)		
La	57	H	37.532	3.456	2.077
Li	3	A2	21.609	3.039	1.728
Lr	103	?	–	–	–
Lu	71	A3	29.524	3.434	1.917
Md	101	?	–	–	–
Mg	12	A3	23.239	3.197	1.770
Mn	25	C	12.245	2.258	1.430
Mo	42	A2	15.583	2.745	1.550
N [b,c]	7	C	22.653	1.098	1.755
Na	11	A2	39.493	3.716	2.113
Nb	41	A2	17.980	2.859	1.625
Nd	60	H	34.179	3.322	2.013
Ne [b]	10	A1	22.212	3.155	1.744
Ni	28	A1	10.942	2.492	1.377
No	102	?	–	–	–
Np	93	O	19.224	2.560	1.662
O [b,c]	8	M	17.360	1.15	1.606
Os	76	A3	13.988	2.735	1.495
P [d]	15	O	18.993	2.224	1.655
Pa	91	T	25.212	3.214	1.819
Pb	82	A1	30.326	3.500	1.935
Pd	46	A1	14.717	2.751	1.520
Pm	61	H	33.60	3.30	2.00
Po	84	C	38.137	3.366	2.088
Pr	59	H	34.545	3.338	2.020
Pt	78	A1	15.097	2.774	1.533
Pu	94	M	19.998	2.57	1.684
Ra	88	A2	68.216	4.459	2.535
Rb	37	A2	92.743	4.939	2.808
Re	75	A3	14.7133	2.740	1.521
Rh	45	A1	13.753	2.689	1.486
Rn	86	?	–	–	–
Ru	44	A3	13.568	2.650	1.480
S [d]	16	O	25.754	2.037	1.832
Sb	51	A7	30.201	2.908	1.932
Sc	21	A3	24.974	3.254	1.813
Se	34	A8	27.274	2.374	1.867
Si	14	A4	20.020	2.352	1.684
Sm	62	H	33.202	3.587	1.994
Sn	50	A5	27.049	3.022	1.8622
Sr	38	A1	56.229	4.302	2.378
Ta	73	A2	18.019	2.861	1.626
Tb	65	A3	32.066	3.528	1.971
Tc	43	A3	14.264	2.707	1.505
Te	52	A8	33.969	2.834	2.009
Th	90	A1	32.876	3.596	1.987
Ti	22	A3	17.653	2.986	1.615

Table 5 (continued)

Element	Z	Str. type	Ω	s_0	r_0
			(Ångström units, conversion factor 1.00202)		
Tl	81	A3	28.586	3.408	1.897
Tm	69	A3	30.006	3.4472	1.927
U	92	O	20.747	2.753	1.705
V	23	A2	13.824	2.619	1.489
W	74	A2	15.844	2.741	1.558
Xe [b]	54	A1	54.463	4.336	2.396
Y	39	A3	33.033	3.557	1.991
Yb	70	A1	41.250	3.878	2.143
Zn	30	A3	15.214	2.664	1.537
Zr	40	A3	23.279	3.179	1.771

[a] Data source: KING [1981 and 1982].
[b] Measured at sub-zero temperatures. All other measurements corrected to 25°C.
[c] Diatomic gases based on molecule R_2. Ω and r_0 values not comparable with metallic elements.
[d] Crystal structures based on molecule R_n, which varies with allotrope. Ω and r_0 values not comparable with metallic elements.

whereas in bcc α-iron (coordination 8) $S_0 = 2.515$ Å. Even so the interatomic distances of the metals play an important role in physical metallurgy since the parameter S_0 forms the basis of Hume-Rothery's empirical size factor rule for primary solid solutions (see ch. 4). Values of S_0 for the elements are listed in table 5.

The effect of coordination number on interatomic distances was studied in 1928 by Goldschmidt, according to whom the decrease in interatomic spacing on going from coordination 12 to coordination 8, 6 or 4 is equal to 3%, 4% and 12% respectively. He therefore proposed that for comparative purposes the interatomic distances in crystals of the elements should be expressed in terms of a structure of coordination 12 and that half of this value may be taken as the atomic radius *. Although Goldschmidt's scheme of atomic radii works quite well for the metals with relatively simple structures, it breaks down in the B-subgroup elements many of which have structures of very irregular coordination. Pauling's univalent metallic radii *, calculated according to eq. 5, also make an allowance for the coordination number of the structure; but as mentioned previously the various assumptions involved in this equation have not as yet been justified. Yet another method of eliminating the effects of coordination number on the measured size of an atom is to use the volume of structure per atom (Ω) or, if a linear size parameter is required, an atomic radius r_0 may be calculated such that $\frac{4}{3}\pi r_0^3 = \Omega$. For example, although the

---

* For lists of Goldschmidt's atomic and ionic radii and of Pauling's univalent metallic radii of the elements see TAYLOR [1961].

References: p. 71.

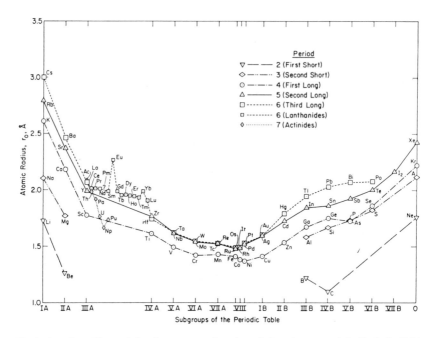

Fig. 9. Atomic radii, r_0, of the elements as a function of the subgroups of the Periodic Table.

interatomic distances in γ- and α-iron at 916°C differ considerably, the values of r_0 are more nearly equal, being 1.425 Å and 1.430 Å respectively. The atomic volume Ω has the additional advantage that it is measurable in any structure, no matter how complex, by dividing the volume of the unit cell by the number of atoms in the unit cell. It also forms the basic parameter in the free-electron approach to metallic cohesion (see eq. (3) and also MOTT [1962]) and has recently been used as the basis for calculating a series of quantitative size-factors for both substitutional and interstitial solid solutions (KING [1966 and 1971]). The values of Ω and r_0 for the elements are included in table 5 and r_0 is plotted as a function of the subgroups of the Periodic Table in fig. 9. It is readily apparent that the periodic variations of the atomic radii in fig. 9 follow a pattern very similar to that of the compressibilities in fig. 8. The significance of these trends, and also of those in the melting points in fig. 7, are considered below for the various sections of the Periodic Table.

4.2. The two short periods

The physical properties plotted in figs. 7–9 indicate that for crystals of the elements in the two short periods the cohesive forces increase from a low value in group IA through group IIA and IIIB to a maximum in group IVB and then fall very steeply over the later B-subgroup elements to another low value in the inert gases. The increase in the strength of cohesion from groups IA to IVB is associated with the increasing p contribution to hybrid (sp) orbitals and a change in the nature of the bonding from purely metallic in group IA to purely covalent in group IVB. The very high melting point, low compressibility and small atomic radius of diamond indicate that the covalent bond is very much stronger than the free-electron metallic bond. The decline in over-all strength of cohesion from group IVB to group 0 is evidenced by the increase in compressibility and atomic radius in phosphorus (VB) and sulphur (VIB) and by the very low melting points of the solid diatomic and inert gases. This does not mean that the interatomic covalent bonds are becoming weaker in groups VB to VIIB, but that the available number of spatially-directed covalent bonds $(8 - N)$ is insufficient to bind together a three-dimensional crystal. The cohesion of these solids is thus determined by the much weaker van der Waals bonds which bind together the layers, chains, diatomic molecules or single atoms in groups VB, VIB, VIIB and 0 respectively. Throughout the two short periods the number of electrons per atom taking part in the bonding progress, i.e., the valency of the element, is the same as its group number N.

4.3. Groups IA and IIA

The very large compressibilities and atomic radii (r_0) of the metals in group IA, and to a lesser extent also in group IIA, arise because in these metals the radius of the entire atom is much greater than that of the ionic core. As mentioned earlier, the group IA metals conform most closely to the free electron model which pictures a metal crystal as an array of small, well separated ions surrounded by a loosely bound electron gas. They are therefore often referred to as "open" metals. There is a general tendency for the compressibilities and atomic radii of the metals in group IA or IIA to become increased with increasing atomic number, i.e., from lithium to caesium or beryllium to barium. This arises because the outer ns electrons become progressively more loosely bound as they are screened from the nucleus by the increasing number of filled inner shells in the ionic core.

4.4. The transition metals and groups IB and IIB

The high melting points and low compressibilities observed in the transition elements indicate that the strength of cohesion of these metals is greater than that of both the IA and the IB metals. It was this observation which led to the concept of the resonant metallic bond in which bonding electrons from the d orbitals are considered to take part in hybrid (sd) and (spd) orbitals. It is of interest to note that, although the melting points of the transition metals decrease after groups VA or VIA (depending on the particular period), the compressibilities remain almost constant from group VA to group VIII confirming that conclusions concerning cohesive strength should not be based on one physical property alone. There is a slight decrease in the magnitude of the cohesive forces on passing from group VIII to group IB which is associated with a decrease in the contribution of the d orbitals,

References: p. 71.

Table 6

Valencies (v) associated with the resonant metallic bond, according to PAULING [1956]

IA	IIA	IIIA	IVA	VA	VIA	VIIA	VIII			IB	IIB	IIIB	IVB	VB	VIB
Li 1	Be 2											B 3			
Na 1	Mg 2											Al 3	Si 2.56	P (3)	S (2)
K 1	Ca 2	Sc 3	Ti 4	V 5	Cr 6	Mn 6	Fe 6	Co 6	Ni 6	Cu 5.56	Zn 4.56	Ga 3.56	Ge 2.56	As 1.56	Se (2)
Rb 1	Sr 2	Y 3	Zr 4	Nb 5	Mo 6	Tc 6	Ru 6	Rh 6	Pd 6	Ag 5.56	Cd 4.56	In 3.56	Sn 2.56	Sb 1.56	Te (2)
Cs 1	Ba 2	La 3	Hf 4	Ta 5	W 6	Re 6	Os 6	Ir 6	Pt 6	Au 5.56	Hg 4.56	Tl 3.56	Pb 2.56	Bi 1.5	
		Ce 3.2	Pr 3	Nd 3	Pn 3	Sm 3	Eu 2	Gd 3	Tb 3.5	Dy 3	Ho 3	Er 3	Tm 3	Yb 2	Lu 3
			Th 4		U 6										

La → Ce

the decrease being strongest in silver, which has a higher compressibility than either copper or gold. A considerable drop in cohesive strength again occurs between groups IA and IIB. PAULING [1956] has attempted to correlate these changes in cohesive strength with the number of electrons per atom v which are available to take part in the resonant metallic bond, arriving at the values listed in table 6. From groups IA–VIA the values of v are the same as the group number N of the element and v then remains constant at 6 until the end of group VIII. In the B-subgroups the numbers of electrons taking part in a resonant bond are considered to be non-integral but to decrease by a whole number in each successive group. It is proper to consider these values of v as the valencies of the metals under these particular bonding conditions, but it is important in the case of the later transition metals and the B-subgroup metals that they should not be confused with the ionic or free electron metallic bond valencies (which are determined by the number of electrons given up by the atom upon ionization). As mentioned earlier, the values of v in table 6 are open to criticism, but the principle of the d orbitals taking some part in the bonding process is beyond dispute.

The low values of compressibilities and atomic radii in the transition and group IB metals are related to the observation that in these metals the ionic cores are very nearly the same size as the entire atoms. The ions may thus be considered as hard spheres which make contact along close-packed directions in the crystal structure, and in contrast to the group IA alkali metals, the metals from groups VA to IB are often referred to as "closed" metals.

There is a general tendency for the atomic radii of the elements to become larger with each successive period as may be seen by comparing the radii of the elements in the first and second long periods in fig. 9. Although in the A-subgroups from IA to IIIA and again in the B-subgroups IIB to 0 the radii of the elements in the third long period are greater than those in the second, the radii of the elements in these two long periods are very nearly the same in the intervening transition metal groups from IVA to IB. This so-called *lanthanide contraction* is attributed to the increased charge on the nucleus, built up across the rare earth series, which is incompletely screened by the inner 4f shell, so 5d electrons are bound closer to the nucleus than the equivalent 3d or 4d shells in the elements of the first two long periods.

4.5. The B-subgroup metals

The B-subgroup elements in the second and third long periods in general tend to be more metallic than those in the first long period and the two short periods. The drop in melting points and rise in compressibilities with increasing atomic number in group IVB reflect the gradual weakening of the covalent bond from diamond → silicon → germanium → grey tin. The weakening of the covalent bond is accompanied by an increase in the degree of metallic bonding, the latter becoming dominant in white tin and lead. In intermediate elements, such as germanium, the bonding is a mixture of both covalent and metallic, causing these elements to behave as semi-conductors (see ch. 3). In groups VB to VIIB, however, the gradual transition from

References: p. 71.

covalent to metallic bonding with increasing atomic number causes an increase in the cohesive forces, i.e., the opposite effect to that observed in group IVB. The contrasting trends are shown most clearly in fig. 8 by the change in the order of the compressibilities of the elements in various periods on going from group IVB to group VB. The increase in cohesive forces occurs because in groups VB–VIIB – although the covalent bonds between the atoms in the layers, chains or diatomic molecules (fig. 6) are weakened – the increasing degree of metallic bonding with increasing atomic number reinforces the relatively weak van der Waals forces which bind together the layers, chains, etc., to form a three-dimensional structure. Since the magnitude of the cohesive forces is determined by the weakest bonds in the crystal, the elements in these groups become stronger as the bonding changes from covalent to metallic, in contrast to those in group IVB.

The atomic radii and the compressibilities of the B-subgroup elements both increase progressively from groups IB to VIIB and the atomic radii of the inert gases are very nearly the same as those of the alkali metals in the respective periods. These changes are associated with the shrinkage of the d shells so that the d orbitals play a rapidly diminishing part in the bonding after group IB, causing the B-subgroup elements to become increasingly more "open" from group IB to VIIB.

4.6. Lanthanides and actinides

A slight fall in cohesive forces occurs between lanthanum in group IIIA and cerium, but thereafter, apart from two very noticeable exceptions (europium and ytterbium, figs. 6–9), there is a small but steady increase in the magnitude of the cohesive forces on going across the lanthanide series. Even so, the melting point of lutetium is still lower than that of the following element hafnium in group IVA. Since most of the rare earths have two outer electrons in the 6s state and one in the 5d state, they are usually trivalent and therefore similar to the group IIIA metals. Although it is possible that some of the inner 4f electrons may take part in the bonding (by hybridizing with the 6s and 5d states) in the earlier metals in the series, in later elements this will be less likely as the 4f electrons are bound much closer to the nucleus. The low melting points and high compressibilities of europium and ytterbium arise because in these elements the outer electron usually present in the 5d state of the free atoms of the lanthanides is drawn into the 4f shell, forming more stable configurations in which the 4f shell is either exactly half-filled or completely full respectively. This leaves europium and ytterbium with only two outer electrons which are both in the 5s state, causing them to be divalent and thus to have melting points and compressibilities resembling those of the alkaline earth metals in group IIA rather than those of the other rare earths.

The high melting point and low compressibility of thorium is due to the presence of two outer electrons in the 6d shell, in addition to two in the 7s shell, which gives this element the properties of a group IVA transition metal. In the following elements protactinium → uranium → neptunium the melting point decreases sharply, indicating a decrease in the strength of the cohesive forces, but the compressibilities also decrease, as shown in fig. 8. This contradictory behaviour is similar to that observed in the later transition elements and, once again, more reliance should be placed on the compressibility data which are dependent on the solid state alone. As there is only a very small difference between the energies of the 5f, 6d and 7s orbitals, it is most likely that the 5f orbitals play an important role in the cohesion of these earlier actinides by hybridizing with the 6d and 7s orbitals. However, a more comprehensive evaluation of the trends in the actinides is prevented at present by a lack of pertinent data.

References

HUME-ROTHERY, W., and B.R. COLES, 1954, Advances in Physics **3**, 149.

KIESSLING, R., 1957, Met. Rev. **2**, 77.

KING, H.W., 1966, J. Mater. Sci. **1**, 79.

KING, H.W., 1971, J. Mater. Sci. **6**, 1157.

KING, H.W., 1981, Bull. Alloy Phase Diagrams **2**, 401.

KING, H.W., 1982, Bull. Alloy Phase Diagrams **2**, 527.

KING, H.W., 1983, Bull. Alloy Phase Diagrams **3**, 276.

MASSALSKI, T.B., and H.W. KING, 1961, Prog. Mater. Sci. **10**, 1.

MOTT, N.F., 1962, Reports on Progress in Physics **25**, 218.

PAULING, L., 1956, Theory of Alloy Phases (Am. Soc. Met., Cleveland, OH).

PEARSON, W.B., 1958 (vol. 1), 1965 (vol. 2), Handbook of Lattice Spacings and Structures of Metals and Alloys (Pergamon Press, New York).

SEITZ, F., 1940, Modern Theory of Solids (McGraw-Hill, New York).

TAYLOR, A., 1961, X-ray Metallography (Wiley, New York).

ZENER, C., 1947, Phys. Rev. **71**, 846.

Further reading

Bowen, H.J.M., Properties of Solids and their Atomic Structure (McGraw-Hill, London, 1967).

Donohue, J., The Structures of the Pure Elements (Wiley, New York, 1974).

Goldschmidt, H.J., International Alloys (Butterworths, London, 1967).

Gschneidner, K.A., and L.R. Eyring, Handbook of the Physical Chemistry of Rare Earths (North-Holland, Amsterdam, 1978).

Hume-Rothery, W., R.E. Smallman and C.W. Haworth, The Structure of Metals and Alloys, 5th Ed. (Institute of Metals, London, 1969).

Kittel, C., Introduction to Solid State Physics. 2nd Ed. (Wiley, New York and London, 1961).

Mott, N.F., and H. Jones, 1936, "Theory of the Properties of Metals and Alloys (Clarendon Press, Oxford; Dover Publications, New York, 1958).

Pauling, L. The Nature of the Chemical Bond, 3rd Ed. (Cornell University Press, Ithaca, New York; Oxford University Press, London, 1960).

Slater, J.C., 1939, Introduction to Chemical Physics (McGraw-Hill, New York and London, 1939).

Spedding, F.H., and A.H. Daane, Met. Rev., **5**, (1960) 349.

Wyckoff, R.W.G., Crystal Structures, vol. I (Interscience, New York and London, 1960).

CHAPTER 3

ELECTRON THEORY OF METALS

D.G. PETTIFOR

Department of Mathematics
Imperial College of Science and Technology
London, UK

R.W. Cahn and P. Haasen, eds.
Physical Metallurgy; third, revised and enlarged edition
© *Elsevier Science Publishers BV, 1983*

1. Introduction

The bulk properties of a metal depend directly on the bonding between the constituent atoms at the *microscopic* level. Thus, in order to provide a fundamental description of metals and alloys, it is necessary to understand the behaviour of the valence electrons which bind the atoms together. The theory which describes the electrons in metals is couched, however, in a conceptual framework that is very different from our everyday experience, since the microscopic world of electrons is governed by *quantum* mechanics rather than the more familiar *classical* mechanics of Newton. Rather than solving Newton's laws of motion the solid state theorist solves the Schrödinger equation,

$$\left(-\frac{\hbar^2}{2m} \nabla^2 + v(\boldsymbol{r}) \right) \psi(\boldsymbol{r}) = E\psi(\boldsymbol{r}), \tag{1}$$

where $\nabla^2 = \partial^2/\partial x^2 + \partial^2/\partial y^2 + \partial^2/\partial z^2$, m is the electronic mass and $\hbar$ is the ubiquitous Planck constant (divided by 2π). $-(\hbar^2/2m)\nabla^2$ represents the *kinetic* energy and $v(\boldsymbol{r})$ the *potential* felt by the electron which has *total* energy E. $\psi(\boldsymbol{r})$ is the wavefunction of the electron where $|\psi(\boldsymbol{r})|^2$ is the probability density of finding the electron at some point $\boldsymbol{r} = (x, y, z)$. The power of the Schrödinger equation is illustrated by solving eq. (1) for the case of a single hydrogenic atom. It is found that solutions exist only if the wavefunction ψ is characterized by three distinct quantum numbers n, l and m whose significance has been discussed at the beginning of the preceding chapter. A fourth quantum number, m_s, representing the spin of the electron results from a relativistic extension of the Schrödinger equation. Thus, the existence of different orbital shells and hence the chemistry of the Periodic Table follows naturally from quantum mechanics through the Schrödinger equation.

WIGNER and SEITZ [1933] were the first to apply the Schrödinger equation to the problem of bonding in metals. In their classic paper they studied the formation of the bond in *monovalent* sodium and obtained the cohesive energy, equilibrium lattice constant, and bulk modulus to within 10% of the experimental values. However, it took nearly another fifty years before the same accuracy was achieved for the *polyvalent* metals. Whereas WIGNER and SEITZ [1933] could assume that the single valence electron on a sodium atom feels only the potential due to the ion core, in a polyvalent metal a given electron will also feel the strong coulomb repulsion from other valence electrons in its vicinity. Thus the problem becomes much more complex. Firstly, the potential $v(\boldsymbol{r})$ must be computed *self-consistently* in that $v(\boldsymbol{r})$ now depends on the coulomb field of valence electrons whose wavefunctions and hence average charge distributions themselves depend on $v(\boldsymbol{r})$ through eq. (1). Secondly, it is necessary in order to obtain bonding to go beyond the *average* self-consistent field of the Hartree approximation and to include the correlations between the electrons. As pointed out in ch. 2, § 1, Pauli's exclusion principle keeps *parallel* spin electrons apart, thereby lessening their mutual coulomb repulsion and lowering the energy by an amount called the *exchange* energy. These *statistical* correlations are described by the Hartree–Fock approximation. In addition, *dynami-*

cal correlations also exist between the anti-parallel spin electrons, which lower the energy of the system by an amount called the *correlation* energy.

During the past ten years a major breakthrough in solid-state physics has occurred with the realization that these very complicated exchange and correlation

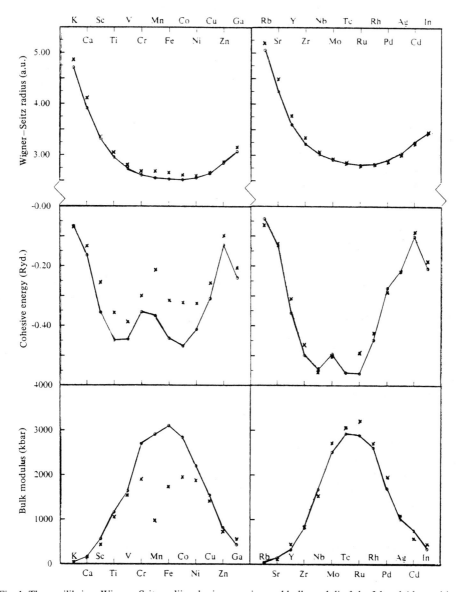

Fig. 1. The equilibrium Wigner–Seitz radii, cohesive energies, and bulk moduli of the 3d and 4d transition series. Experimental values are indicated by crosses and the computed LDF values by the connected points. (From MORUZZI *et al.* [1978].)

References: p. 149.

effects can be accurately modeled by adding a simple local exchange correlation potential $v_{xc}(r)$ to the usual Hartree coulomb potential in eq. (1). The resulting so-called *local density functional* (LDF) equations (HOHENBERG and KOHN [1964] and KOHN and SHAM [1965]) have been shown to yield a surprisingly good description of the energetics of atoms, molecules, and solids (GUNNARSSON and LUNDQUIST [1976], HARRIS and JONES [1978] and MORUZZI *et·al.* [1978]). The success of the LDF scheme is illustrated in fig. 1 by the results of MORUZZI *et al.* [1978] for the cohesive properties of the elemental metals across the 3d and 4d transition series. We see that for the *nonmagnetic* 4d series the equilibrium Wigner–Seitz radius (or lattice constant), cohesive energy and bulk modulus are given to better than 10%. The large deviations in lattice constant and bulk modulus observed amongst the 3d series is due to the presence of *magnetism* and is removed by generalizing the LDF theory to include spin polarization (JANAK and WILLIAMS [1976]). It must be stressed that there are no arbitrary parameters in the theory, the only input being the nuclear charge and crystal structure.

This success of the LDF theory in describing the bonding between atoms allows the interpretation of the results within a *band* framework, since the motion of a given electron is governed by the *one-electron* Schrödinger equation (1). As is well-known, the energy levels, E, of the free atom broaden out into bands of states as the atoms are brought together to form the solid. In this chapter the nature of these energy bands in simple metals, transition metals and binary alloys is discussed, thereby unraveling the microscopic origin of the attractive and repulsive forces in the metallic bond. In §2.1 we begin with a detailed description of the constituent atoms, since we will see that many bulk properties are related to the relative position of the atomic energy levels and to the size of the ionic cores. In §2.2 the diatomic molecule is used to illustrate *bond* formation and in §2.3 the general principle of *band* formation in solids is outlined. The nature of *simple-* and *transition*-metal bands is then discussed in §§3 and 4 respectively, the former being treated within the nearly-free-electron approximation, the latter within the tight-binding approximation. In §5 the knowledge of the energy band behaviour is used to provide a microscopic picture of metallic bonding which is responsible for the cohesive properties of the elemental metals displayed in fig. 1. In §6 *structural* stability is discussed both in the elemental metals and in binary AB compounds. In §7 the ideas on metallic bonding are extended to a discussion of the *heats of formation, ΔH*, of binary alloys. Finally in §8 the band theory of *magnetism* is presented which accounts for the antiferromagnetism of Cr and Mn and the ferromagnetism of Fe, Co, and Ni amongst the 3d transition metals.

2. *Band formation*

2.1. The constituent atoms

The hundred basic building blocks of nature, which are enshrined in the Periodic Table, lead to matter having a wide range and variety of physical properties. This diversity reflects the essential uniqueness of each element in the Periodic Table. For example, even though copper, silver and gold lie in the same noble-metal group, nobody except possibly a theoretician would be prepared to regard them as identical. In this subsection the differences between the elements are *quantified* by discussing the behaviour of the atomic energy levels and the radii throughout the Periodic Table.

The structure of the Periodic Table results from the filling-up of different orbital shells with electrons, as outlined in the previous chapter. The chemical behaviour of a given atom is governed by both the *number* and the *angular-momentum* character of the electrons in the outer partially filled shells. (We shall refer to these electrons as *valence* in contrast to the filled shells of *core* electrons.) The angular-momentum character is determined by the orbital quantum number l, since the *magnitude* of the total orbital angular momentum L is given by quantum theory as:

$$L = \hbar\sqrt{l(l+1)}, \tag{2}$$

where $l = 0, 1, 2,\ldots$ A free-atom electron can, therefore, take only *discrete* values of angular momentum (i.e. $0, \hbar\sqrt{2}, \hbar\sqrt{6},\ldots$) unlike a classical particle which would have a *continuous* spectrum. However, as in the classical case, the angular momentum is *conserved* because the electron is moving in the central spherically symmetric potential of the free atom. Electrons with $l = 0, 1, 2$ and 3 orbital quantum numbers are referred to as s, p, d and f electrons, respectively (after the old terminology of sharp, principal, diffuse and fine spectroscopic lines).

Angular momentum is a vector. Therefore, in addition to the *magnitude* L of the orbital angular momentum L, the electronic state is also characterized by the *components* of the angular momentum. Within quantum theory the component in a given direction (say along the z-axis, specified experimentally by the direction of a very weak applied magnetic field) is quantized and given by

$$L_z = m\hbar, \tag{3}$$

where the magnetic quantum number, m, takes the $(2l + 1)$ values $0, \pm 1,\ldots, \pm(l-1)$, $\pm l$. Because the *energy* of the electron can not depend on the direction of the angular momentum in a spherically symmetric potential, these $(2l + 1)$ states have the same energy and are said to be *degenerate*. Allowing for the additional *spin* quantum number, m_s, which can take two values (corresponding to an up, ↑, or down, ↓, spin electron), each l-state will be $2(2l + 1)$-fold degenerate. Thus an s-shell can hold 2 electrons, a p-shell 6 electrons, a d-shell 10 electrons and an f-shell 14 electrons as discussed in ch. 2, § 1.

The state of angular momentum of the electron determines the *angular dependence* of the wavefunction ψ and hence the angular dependence of the probability-density $|\psi|^2$. The s-state has zero orbital angular momentum corresponding to a spherically symmetric probability density which is illustrated schematically in fig. 2a. The p-state, corresponding to $l = 1, m = 0$, has an angular variation given by $\cos\theta$, where θ is the polar angle. Because the Cartesian coordinates (x, y, z) can be related to the spherical polar coordinates (r, θ, ϕ), and in particular $z = r\cos\theta$, it is customary to

References: p. 149.

refer to the $l = 1$, $m = 0$ state as the p_z *orbital*. Its probability-cloud is illustrated by the left-hand diagram in fig. 2b. We see that it has lobes pointing out along the z-axis, in which direction there is a maximum probability of finding the electron ($\cos^2\theta = 1$ for $\theta = 0, \pi$). On the other hand, there is zero probability of finding the electron in the x–y plane ($\cos^2\theta = 0$ for $\theta = \pi/2$). Since we often deal with atoms in a *cubic* environment in which all three Cartesian axes are equivalent (e.g., fcc or bcc crystals), we form the p_x and p_y orbitals by taking linear combinations of the two remaining states corresponding to $m = \pm 1$. They are illustrated in fig. 2b. The probability clouds of the five d orbitals corresponding to $l = 2$ are shown in fig. 2c. We might expect from fig. 2 that the nature of the bonding between atoms will be very dependent on the angular momentum character of the atomic valence electrons. This will be discussed in §2.2.

Historically it was the discrete lines of the atomic spectra and their ordering

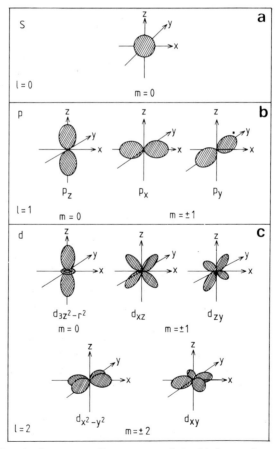

Fig. 2. The probability clouds corresponding to s, p and d orbitals are shown in (a), (b) and (c), respectively.

according to Balmer's formula that led Bohr to postulate his famous model of the hydrogen atom from which he deduced that the *energy* levels were given by

$$E_n = -\left(me^4/32\pi^2\varepsilon_0^2 h^2\right)/n^2, \tag{4}$$

where e is the magnitude of the electronic charge, ε_0 is the permittivity of free space, and n is a positive integer. The corresponding radii of the so-called stationary orbits were given by

$$a_n = \left(4\pi\varepsilon_0 h^2/me^2\right)n^2. \tag{5}$$

Substituting into eqs. (4) and (5) the SI values $m = 9.1096 \times 10^{-31}$ kg, $e = 1.6022 \times 10^{-19}$ C, $4\pi\varepsilon_0 c^2 = 10^7$, $c = 2.9979 \times 10^8$ m/s and $\hbar = 1.0546 \times 10^{-34}$ Js, we have:

$$E_n = 2.1799 \times 10^{-18}/n^2 \quad \text{J} \tag{6}$$

and

$$a_n = n^2 \text{ au.} \tag{9}$$

The *ground state* of the hydrogen atom, which corresponds to $n = 1$, has an energy, therefore, of 2.18×10^{-18} J and an orbital Bohr radius of 0.529×10^{-10} m or 0.529 Å. Because of the small magnitude of the energy in SI units, it is customary for solid-state physicists to work in *atomic units,* where the unit of energy is the Rydberg (Ry) and the unit of length is the atomic unit (au). The former is the ground-state energy of the hydrogen atom, the latter is the first Bohr radius. Thus, in atomic units we have

$$E_n = -n^{-2} \text{ Ry} \tag{8}$$

and

$$a_n = n^2 \text{ au.} \tag{9}$$

It follows from eqs. (4), (5), (8) and (9) that $\hbar^2/2m = 1$ in atomic units. Another frequently used unit is the electron-Volt, where 1 Ry = 13.6 eV. In this chapter *electronic* energy levels, E, will be given in either eV or Ry, whereas *total* energies will be given in either eV/atom or Ry/atom. Conversion to other units may be achieved by using 1 mRy/atom = 0.314 kcal/mole = 1.32 kJ/mole. Length scales will be given either in au or in Å, where 1 au = 0.529 Å.

Solution of the Schrödinger equation (1) for the hydrogen atom leads directly to Bohr's expression (4) for the energy levels, E_n, where n is identified as the *principal* quantum number. For the particular case of the hydrogen atom where the potential $v(r)$ varies inversely with distance r from the nucleus, the energy levels do not depend on the angular-momentum quantum numbers l and m. Figure 3 shows the energy levels of atomic *hydrogen* given by eq. (8), where use has been made of the quantum-theory result that for a given n the orbital quantum number l must be such that $0 \leqslant l \leqslant (n-1)$. The total degeneracy of each orbital including spin, namely $2(2l+1)$, is given at the bottom of the figure and accounts for the structure of the Periodic Table, discussed in the previous chapter. In practice, the energy-level

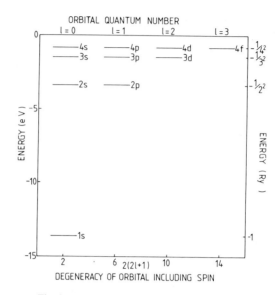

Fig. 3. The energy levels of atomic hydrogen.

diagram of elements other than hydrogen is different from fig. 3, because the presence of more than one electron outside the nucleus leads to the potential $v(r)$ no longer showing a simple inverse distance behaviour, so that states with the same principal quantum number n but different orbital quantum numbers l have their degeneracy lifted. This is illustrated in fig. 4, where it is clear, for example, that the 2s level of the second-row elements B to Ne lies well below that of the corresponding

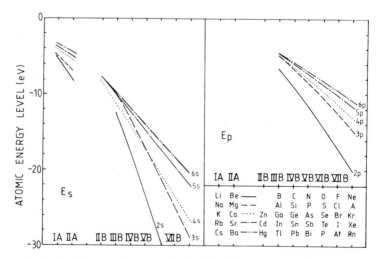

Fig. 4. The valence s and p energy levels (after HERMAN and SKILLMAN [1963]).

2p level. These atomic energy levels were taken from the tables compiled by HERMAN and SKILLMAN [1963] who solved the Schrödinger equation (1) self-consistently for all the elements in the Periodic Table.

Figure 4 illustrates several important features to which we will be returning throughout this chapter. Firstly, the valence energy levels vary *linearly across* a given period. As the nuclear charge Ze increases, the electrons are bound more tightly to the nucleus. However, rather than varying as Z^2, which would be the result for the energy levels of a hydrogenic ion of charge Ze, the presence of the other valence electrons induces the linear behaviour observed. Secondly, the valence s and p energy levels become less strongly bound as one moves *down* a given group, which is to be expected from the hydrogenic energy levels displayed in fig. 3. But there is an exception to this rule: the 4s level has come down and crosses below the 3s level to the left of group VB. This is a direct consequence of the presence of the occupied 3d shell (cf. table 2, ch. 2) whose electrons do not completely screen the core from the valence 4s electrons, which therefore feel a more attractive potential than their 3s counterparts in the preceding row. We will see in §6.2 that this reversal in the expected ordering of the valence s energy levels is reflected in the structural properties of binary AB compounds containing group IIIB elements. Thirdly, it is clear from fig. 4 that the energy *difference* $E_p - E_s$ decreases as one goes from the rare gases to the alkali metals, from right to left across a given period. This will strongly influence the nature of the energy bands and the bonding in the bulk, since if the energy difference is small, s and p electrons will hybridize to form common sp bands.

Figure 5 shows the valence s and d energy levels across the 3d and 4d transition metal series, after HERMAN and SKILLMAN [1963]. The energy levels correspond to the atomic configuration $d^{N-1}s$, where N is the total number of valence electrons,

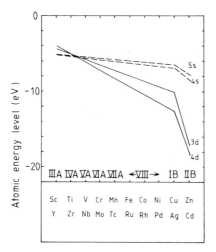

Fig. 5. The valence s and d energy levels across the 3d and 4d transition series (after HERMAN and SKILLMAN [1963]).

References: p. 149.

because this is the configuration closest to that of the bulk metal. Again there are several important features. Firstly, we see that the energy variation is *linear across* the transition metal series as the d shell is progressively filled with electrons. However, once the noble metal group IB is reached the d shell contains its full complement of ten electrons, so that any further increase in atomic number Z adds the additional valence electrons to the sp outer shell and pulls the d energy rapidly down as is evidenced by the change of slope in fig. 5. Secondly, whereas the *valence* s energy level becomes slightly less strongly bound as one moves *down* a given group, the valence 4d energy level becomes more strongly bound than the valence 3d away from the beginning of the transition-metal series. This behaviour appears to be related to the mutual coulomb repulsion between the negatively charged valence electrons. The 3d orbitals are much more compact than the 4d orbitals, so that the putting of electrons into the 3d shell leads to a more rapid increase in repulsive energy than in the 4d shell. The 5d and 6s energy levels have not been plotted in fig. 5 because *relativistic* effects, which are not included in the Schrödinger equation (1), become important for *heavy* atoms in the Periodic Table. Relativistic corrections are discussed in ch. 2 of HERMAN and SKILLMAN [1963]. Thirdly, since $E_s - E_d$ is about 3 eV in copper but 6 eV in silver, it is not surprising that the noble metals display different physical characteristics.

   A concept that is often used in physical metallurgy to discuss and order properties is that of *atomic size*. The microscopic description of the atom, which is provided by quantum mechanics, should be able to give some measure of this quantity. We have seen that quantum mechanics replaces the stationary Bohr *orbits* of radius a_n by orbitals which are not located with a fixed radius but are smeared out in probability-clouds described by $|\psi|^2$. The angular dependence of these probability-clouds has been displayed in fig. 2. We now discuss their radial dependence.

   The solution of the Schrödinger equation for a central spherically symmetric potential can be written in separable form, namely:

$$\psi_{nlm}(r) = R_{nl}(r) Y_l^m(\theta, \phi), \tag{10}$$

where r, θ and ϕ are spherical polar coordinates. As expected, the *angular* distribution depends only on the angular-momentum quantum numbers l and m, the functions $Y_l^m(\theta, \phi)$ being the so-called *spherical harmonics* (see, e.g., SCHIFF [1968]). Y_0^0 is a constant and Y_1^0 is proportional to $\cos\theta$ as we have already mentioned. The *radial* function $R_{nl}(r)$ depends on the principal and orbital quantum numbers, n and l respectively, and therefore changes with energy level E_{nl}. For the hydrogen atom the first few radial functions are (in atomic units)

$$R_{1s}(r) = 2 e^{-r}, \tag{11}$$

$$R_{2s}(r) = \frac{1}{\sqrt{2}} \left(1 - \tfrac{1}{2}r\right) e^{-r/2}, \tag{12}$$

$$R_{2p}(r) = \frac{1}{\sqrt{24}} r e^{-r/2}. \tag{13}$$

A conceptually useful quantity is the probability of finding the electron at some distance r from the nucleus (in any direction), which is determined by the *radial probability density*, $P_{nl}(r) = r^2 R_{nl}^2(r)$.

Figure 6 shows the radial function R_{nl} and the probability density, P_{nl}, as a function of r for the 1s, 2s and 2p states of hydrogen. We see that there is *maximum* probability of locating the electron at the first Bohr radius a_1 for the 1s state and at the second Bohr radius a_2 for the 2p state. The *average* or expectation value of the radial distance r is given by:

$$\bar{r}_{nl} = n^2 \left[1 + \tfrac{1}{2}\left(1 - l(l+1)/n^2 \right) \right], \tag{14}$$

so that $\bar{r}_{1s} = 1.5a_1$, $\bar{r}_{2s} = 1.5a_2$ and $\bar{r}_{2p} = 1.25a_2$. Therefore, the 2s orbital is more extended than the corresponding 2p orbital, as is evident from fig. 6. This is due to the fact that all solutions of the Schrödinger equation must be *orthogonal* to one another, i.e., if ψ_{nlm} and $\psi_{n'l'm'}$ are any two solutions and ψ^* is the complex conjugate of ψ, then

$$\int \psi_{nlm}^* \psi_{n'l'm'} \, d\mathbf{r} = 0. \tag{15}$$

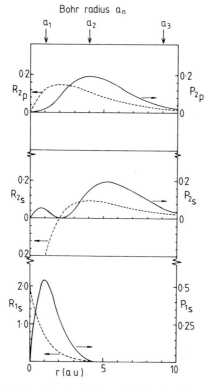

Fig. 6. The radial function R_{nl} (dashed lines) and the probability density, P_{nl} (solid lines) as a function of r for the 1s, 2s and 2p states of hydrogen.

If the states have *different* angular-momentum character then the angular integration over the spherical harmonics [cf. (eq. 10)] guarantees orthogonality. But if the states have the *same* angular-momentum character then the orthogonality constraint implies that:

$$\int_0^\infty R_{nl}(r)R_{n'l}(r)r^2\,\mathrm{d}r = 0. \tag{16}$$

For the orbitals drawn in fig. 6, therefore, we must have

$$\int_0^\infty R_{1s}(r)R_{2s}(r)r^2\,\mathrm{d}r = 0, \tag{17}$$

which can be verified by substituting eqs. (11) and (12) into this equation. This is the origin of the *node* at $r = 2$ au in $R_{2s}(r)$, where the radial function changes sign. The 3s radial function must be orthogonal to the 2s and, therefore, has two nodes, the 4s has three nodes, etc. Just as the energetically lowest 1s state has *no* nodes, so the 2p, 3d and 4f states are nodeless since they correspond to the states of lowest energy for a given l (see fig. 3).

The position of the outer node of the *valence* electron's radial function may be used as a measure of an *l*-dependent core size, since we have seen that the node arises from the constraint that the valence state be orthogonal to the more tightly bound core states. This relationship between node and core size has been demonstrated quantitatively for the case of the sp core of the 4d transition metals (PETTIFOR [1977] and §4.3) and has been discussed for other elements by BLOCH and SCHATTEMAN [1981]. A not unrelated measure of size has been adopted by ZUNGER [1980] who defined *l*-dependent radii R_l by the condition (cf. ST. JOHN and BLOCH

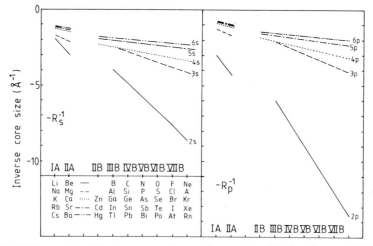

Fig. 7. The negative of the inverse s and p pseudopotential radii (after ZUNGER [1980]).

[1974]) that

$$v_l^{\text{eff}}(R_l) = 0, \tag{18}$$

where $v_l^{\text{eff}}(r)$ is some effective angular-momentum dependent atomic potential (which is given by a first-principles screened pseudopotential, cf. §3.3). Figure 7 shows the resultant values of $-R_s^{-1}$ and $-R_p^{-1}$ for the sp bonded elements. We see a *linear* variation across a given period and a close similarity with the valence energy level behaviour illustrated in fig. 4. As expected, the s and p radii contract *across* a period as the nuclear charge Ze increases, and they expand *down* a column as additional full orbital shells are pulled into the core region. Figure 7 clearly demonstrates that the sizes of the second-row elements B, C, N and O are a lot smaller than those of the other elements in their respective groups, a fact which manifests itself in their different alloying behaviour (cf. fig. 36, below).

2.2. Bond formation

In this subsection we consider what happens to the atomic energy levels and wavefunctions as two atoms A and B are brought together from infinity to form the AB diatomic molecule.

Suppose the A and B valence electrons are characterized by the free atomic energy levels E_A and E_B and wavefunctions ψ_A and ψ_B, respectively. Let us assume, following the experience of theoretical quantum chemists, that the *molecular* wavefunction ψ_{AB} can be written as a *linear combination of the atomic orbitals*,

$$\psi_{AB} = c_A\psi_A + c_B\psi_B, \tag{19}$$

where c_A and c_B are constant coefficients. Let us further assume that the molecular potential v_{AB} that enters the Schrödinger equation can be written as the sum of the spherically symmetric free atom potentials v_A and v_B so that

$$v_{AB} = v_A + v_B. \tag{20}$$

It follows from eq. (1) that the free atom quantities are related by

$$\left(-\nabla^2 + v_A\right)\psi_A = E_A\psi_A, \tag{21}$$

and

$$\left(-\nabla^2 + v_B\right)\psi_B = E_B\psi_B, \tag{22}$$

where we have used the fact that $\hbar^2/2m = 1$ in atomic units.

Substituting eqs. (19) and (20) into eq. (1), the Schrödinger equation for the AB diatomic molecule takes the form

$$\left(-\nabla^2 + v_A + v_B\right)(c_A\psi_A + c_B\psi_B) = E(c_A\psi_A + c_B\psi_B). \tag{23}$$

Multiplying both sides of eq. (23) by ψ_A^* (or ψ_B^*) and integrating over all space, we find, after using eqs. (21) and (22), that

$$(E_A - E)c_A + (h - ES)c_B = 0, \tag{24}$$

and

$$(h^* - ES^*)c_A + (E_B - E)c_B = 0, \tag{25}$$

where the shifts in the atomic energy levels E_A and E_B due to the presence of the neighbouring atomic potential have been neglected. S is the *overlap matrix element* between the atomic orbitals ψ_A on site A and ψ_B on site B, namely:

$$S = \int \psi_A^* \psi_B \, d\mathbf{r}, \tag{26}$$

which in general does not vanish because atomic orbitals on different sites are non-orthogonal [cf. eq. (15)]. h is the *hopping matrix element* which couples the states ψ_A and ψ_B together through the atomic potential and allows the electron on site A to hop to site B and vice versa. As a first approximation it may be written as:

$$h = \int \psi_A^* v \psi_B \, d\mathbf{r}, \tag{27}$$

where v is either the A or B atomic potential. (Strictly, in the final expression (30) it should be taken as the geometric mean of the two matrix elements resulting from the use of v_A and v_B, respectively, in eq. (27).) We may take both S and h to be real so that $S^* = S$ and $h^* = h$. It is apparent from the exponential behaviour of ψ_A and ψ_B in fig. 6 [cf. eqs. (11–13)] that S and h will be very dependent on the internuclear separation R_{AB}, and will decrease rapidly to zero as the atoms are pulled apart.

Equations (24) and (25) may be solved for the unknown molecular energy levels E by writing them in the matrix form of a *secular equation*, namely:

$$\begin{pmatrix} E_A - E & h - ES \\ h - ES & E_B - E \end{pmatrix} \begin{pmatrix} c_A \\ c_B \end{pmatrix} = 0, \tag{28}$$

which has *non-trivial* solutions if the secular determinant vanishes, i.e. if

$$\begin{vmatrix} E_A - E & h - ES \\ h - ES & E_B - E \end{vmatrix} = 0. \tag{29}$$

It is found that the *energy levels* resulting from the quadratic equation (29) do not depend on the overlap matrix element S to first order. Therefore, neglecting S the diatomic energy levels may be written as:

$$E_{AB}^{\pm} = \bar{E} \pm \tfrac{1}{2} \left[4h^2 + (\Delta E)^2 \right]^{1/2}, \tag{30}$$

where $\bar{E} = \tfrac{1}{2}(E_A + E_B)$ and $\Delta E = E_B - E_A$. The corresponding wavefunctions $\psi_{AB}^{\pm}$ may be found by substituting eq. (30) back into eq. (28) and solving for c_A and c_B subject to the *normalization condition*,

$$\int |\psi_{AB}|^2 \, d\mathbf{r} = 1, \tag{31}$$

which states that the *total* probability of finding the electron anywhere in space is unity. The diatomic wavefunctions are given by

$$\psi_{AB}^{\pm} = \left[\left(1 \pm \frac{\varepsilon}{(1+\varepsilon^2)^{1/2}} \right)^{1/2} \psi_A \mp \left(1 \mp \frac{\varepsilon}{(1+\varepsilon^2)^{1/2}} \right)^{1/2} \psi_B \right] / [2(1 \mp S)]^{1/2},$$

(32)

where $\varepsilon = \Delta E/2h$. Solution (32) is for the case $h < 0$ which would correspond, for example, to two spherically symmetric s orbitals overlapping in the presence of an attractive atomic potential v [cf. eq. (27)].

Consider first the simple case of the *homonuclear* diatomic molecule H_2 where $\varepsilon = 0$ and the 1s orbitals $\psi_{A,B}$ are given by the exponential functions $\pi^{-1/2} e^{-r_{A,B}}$ centred on the A, B nuclei respectively [cf. eqs. (10) and (11)]. It follows from eq. (30) that the single atomic 1s energy level splits into a *bonding* and an *antibonding* level, whose energies are separated by $w = 2|h|$ as shown in fig. 8a. The corresponding wave functions,

$$\psi_{AB}^{\pm} = (\psi_A \mp \psi_B)/[2(1 \mp S)]^{1/2},$$

(33)

are illustrated schematically on the right-hand side of the figure. We see that the probability of finding the electron in the bond region between the nuclei is enhanced in the bonding state but reduced in the antibonding state. Moreover, we see that at the *midpoint* between the nuclei the gradient $d\psi/dR$ vanishes in the bonding state

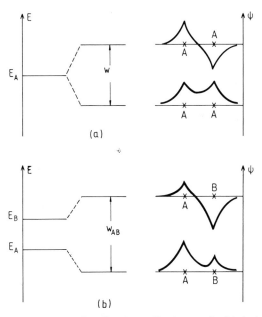

Fig. 8. The bonding (lower lines) and antibonding (upper lines) states for (a) the homonuclear and (b) the heteronuclear diatomic molecule.

References: p. 149.

whereas the wave function ψ vanishes in the antibonding state. We will return to these conditions when discussing metallic bonding.

The ground state of the hydrogen molecule is given by the two valence electrons sitting in the bonding state ψ_{AB}^- with opposite spins in order to satisfy Pauli's exclusion principle. The formation of the bond may be seen more explicitly by looking at the electron *density* $\rho(r) = |\psi(r)|^2$, and writing it in the form

$$\rho_{AB} = \rho_A + \rho_B + \rho_{bond}, \tag{34}$$

where ρ_{bond} represents the *redistribution* of the free-atom probability clouds due to the formation of the covalent bond. It follows from eq. (33) that to first order in the overlap matrix S:

$$\rho_{bond} = \left[(\psi_A^* \psi_B + \psi_B^* \psi_A) - (|\psi_A|^2 + |\psi_B|^2) S \right], \tag{35}$$

where

$$S = e^{-R} \left(1 + R + \tfrac{1}{3} R^2 \right) \tag{36}$$

for the overlap of hydrogenic 1s orbitals.

The formation of the bond at an internuclear separation of 2 au is illustrated in fig. 9 where the middle panel shows how the electrons are drawn into the bond from

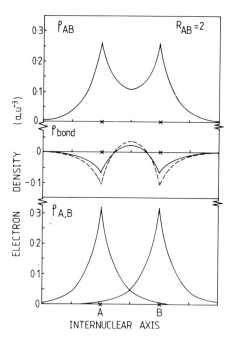

Fig. 9. The electron density of the homonuclear molecule (upper panel) can be regarded as the sum of the *non-interacting* free-atom electron densities (lower panel) and the *quantum-mechanically* induced bond density (middle panel). The dashed curve represents the first-order result, eq. (35), for the bond density.

the outer regions of the molecule. A *bond charge* $Q_{bond}e$ can be defined as the total extra charge in the bond region where the electron density is enhanced. It is clear from the middle panel of fig. 9 that the dashed first-order result, eq. (35), shows some error compared to the result of exact linear combination of atomic orbitals, eqs. (33) and (34), because for $R = 2$ au S equals 0.59 which is not small compared to unity. (This is a typical value for the sp-bonded semiconductors; the d-bonded transition metals have smaller values of S closer to 0.2.) But eq. (35) shows explicitly that the formation of the bond is a *quantum* interference effect, the charge piling up in the bond region because of the interference contribution $\psi_A\psi_B$. In practice, in order to satisfy the virial theorem, the formation of the bond is accompanied by some modification of the free-atom orbitals $\psi_{A,B}$, which has been discussed by RUEDENBERG [1962] and SLATER [1963]. This leads to the energy levels $E_{A,B}$ not being directly identifiable as the *free*-atom energy levels, a point which will be discussed further in § 5.2 on transition-metal bonding.

A diatomic molecule has cylindrical symmetry about the internuclear axis, so that angular momentum is conserved in this direction. Quantum-mechanically this implies that the state of the molecule is characterized by the quantum number m, where $m\hbar$ gives the component of the angular momentum along the molecular axis. However, unlike the free atom where the $(2l + 1)$ different m values are degenerate, the degeneracy is lifted in the molecule. By analogy with the s, p, d,... states of a free atom representing the orbital quantum numbers $l = 0, 1, 2,...$, it is customary to refer to $\sigma, \pi, \delta,...$ states of a molecule as those corresponding to $m = 0, \pm 1, \pm 2,...$ respectively.

Figure 10 illustrates the different characteristics of the σ, π and δ bonds. We have seen from our previous discussion on the homonuclear molecule that a given atomic energy level will split into bonding and antibonding states separated by $2|h|$, where h is the matrix element that couples states ψ_A and ψ_B together through the atomic potential v [cf. eq. (27)]. If $\psi_{A,B}$ are spherically symmetric s orbitals, then a ssσ bond is formed as shown schematically in fig. 10a. If $\psi_{A,B}$ are p orbitals whose probability

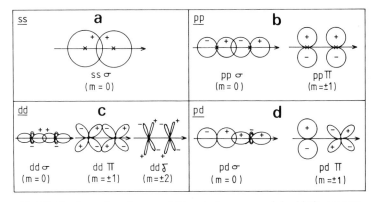

Fig. 10. The formation of σ, π and δ bonds from s, p and d orbitals, see text.

References: p. 149.

clouds are drawn in fig. 2, then the threefold degenerate free atom level (excluding spin degeneracy) splits into the singly degenerate ppσ molecular state ($m = 0$) and the doubly degenerate ppπ molecular state ($m = \pm 1$) shown in fig. 10b. If $\psi_{A,B}$ are d orbitals, whose probability clouds are sketched in fig. 2, then the fivefold degenerate free atom level splits into the singly degenerate ddσ molecular state ($m = 0$) and the two doubly degenerate molecular states ddπ ($m = \pm 1$) and ddδ ($m = \pm 2$) as shown in fig. 10c. For the case of a heteronuclear molecule such as NbC where the carbon p orbitals overlap the niobium d orbitals, a pd bond will be formed from the pdσ and pdπ states illustrated in fig. 10d. It is clear from fig. 10 that the σ bond is relatively strong since the angular lobes point along the molecular axis and can give rise to a large overlap in the bonding region. On the other hand, the ppπ and ddδ bonds will be relatively much weaker since their angular lobes extend in the plane perpendicular to the molecular axis. The importance of σ, π and δ bonding in determining the behaviour of the *bulk* band structure will be demonstrated in §4.1.

Consider now a simple *heteronuclear* diatomic molecule such as LiH where both free atoms have a *single* valence's electron but whose energy levels are not identical (cf. $E_{1s}^H = -13.6$ eV and $E_{2s}^{Li} = -5.5$ eV from figs. 3 and 4). As shown in fig. 8b, bonding and antibonding states are formed whose energies are separated by the amount w_{AB}, where from eq. (30):

$$w_{AB}^2 = w^2 + (\Delta E)^2. \tag{37}$$

Thus, the square of the bonding–antibonding separation is the sum of two contributions, the first arising from the *covalency* and being proportional to the square of the hopping matrix element h, the second arising from the *ionicity* and being proportional to the square of the difference in the atomic energy levels of the two free atoms. The corresponding ground-state electron density can be written from eq. (32), assuming real wavefunctions, as:

$$\rho_{AB} = \frac{\left(1 - \dfrac{\varepsilon}{(1 + \varepsilon^2)^{1/2}}\right)\rho_A + \left(1 + \dfrac{\varepsilon}{(1 + \varepsilon^2)^{1/2}}\right)\rho_B + \dfrac{1}{(1 + \varepsilon^2)^{1/2}}2\psi_A\psi_B}{1 + S}, \tag{38}$$

where $\varepsilon = -\Delta E/w$ for $h < 0$. Comparing this with eq. (34) we see that the formation of the AB heteronuclear molecule is accompanied by a flow of charge Qe from one atom to the other, which is reflected in the behaviour of $\psi_{AB}^{\pm}$ in fig. 8b. It follows from eq. (38) that:

$$Q_A = -Q_B = -\Delta E \big/ \left[w^2 + (\Delta E)^2\right]^{1/2}, \tag{39}$$

where $\Delta E = E_B - E_A$. For large atomic energy level differences such that $\Delta E \gg w$, the B atom loses its single valence electron to the A atom so that a full ionic bond is established: $A^- B^+$.

The *ionicity* of the AB bond may be defined (see, e.g., COULSON et al. [1962], PHILLIPS [1970] and HARRISON [1980]) by:

$$\alpha_I = \Delta E \big/ \left[w^2 + (\Delta E)^2\right]^{1/2}, \tag{40}$$

and the *covalency* of the AB bond by

$$\alpha_c = w / \left[w^2 + (\Delta E)^2 \right]^{1/2},   \tag{41}$$

which are such that

$$\alpha_i^2 + \alpha_c^2 = 1.   \tag{42}$$

The term covalency will be used in this chapter to describe the bonding which arises from the *quantum* mixing of *valence* states on neighbouring sites into the final-state wavefunction. It is not necessarily associated with *pairs* of electrons of opposite spin, as the lone electron in the hydrogen molecular ion H_2^+, for example, shows all the characteristics of the covalent homonuclear bond discussed above. The ideas outlined in this subsection will be taken up and extended to bulk metals in the remaining sections of this chapter.

2.3. Band formation

Figure 11 illustrates how the free-atom energy levels E_s and E_p broaden into *bands* as the atoms are brought together from infinity to form the bulk. Just as the single atomic energy level splits into two energy levels on bringing two atoms together (cf. fig. 8a), so the single level on a free atom splits into N levels on bringing N atoms together, thereby conserving the total number of electronic states. These levels lie between the bottom of the band, which represents the most bonding state, and the top of the band, which represents the most antibonding state. Since $N \approx 10^{23}$ for 1 cm^3 of bulk material, these N levels form a quasi-continuous band of states and it is customary to work with the *density of states*, $n(E)$, where $dN = n(E)\,dE$ gives the number of states in the energy range from E to $E + dE$. The conservation of states requires that:

$$\int_{-\infty}^{\infty} n_\alpha(E)\,dE = \left\{ \begin{array}{c} 2 \\ 6 \\ 10 \end{array} \right. \text{ for } \alpha = \left\{ \begin{array}{c} s \\ p, \\ d \end{array} \right.   \tag{43}$$

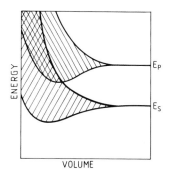

Fig. 11. Energy band formation.

References: p. 149.

where $n_\alpha(E)$ is the density of states *per atom* associated with a given atomic s, p or d level.

In metals at their equilibrium volume, the bands corresponding to different valence energy levels overlap and mix as shown on the left-hand side of fig. 11. The mixing or hybridization in *simple* metals is such as to produce *nearly-free-electron*-like behaviour of the energy bands and density of states, which is discussed in the following section. On the other hand, the density of states in *transition* metals is dominated by a well defined d band, which is accurately described within the *tight-binding* approximation by a linear combination of atomic d orbitals and is discussed in §4.

3. Simple-metal bands

3.1. The free-electron approximation

It had been realized before the advent of quantum mechanics that some metallic properties such as electrical or thermal conductivity could be well understood by regarding the valence electrons as a non-interacting gas of particles which were *free* to travel throughout the metal without being affected by the parent ions. However, it remained for quantum mechanics to remove a striking failure of the classical model, namely its inability to explain the *linear* temperature dependence of the electronic heat capacity, since according to classical statistical mechanics a free particle has a *constant* heat capacity of $\frac{3}{2}k_B$, where k_B is the Boltzmann constant.

The Schrödinger equation for a free-electron gas may be written in atomic units as

$$-\left(\frac{\partial^2}{\partial x^2} + \frac{\partial^2}{\partial y^2} + \frac{\partial^2}{\partial z^2} \right) \psi(r) = E\psi(r). \tag{44}$$

If the electrons are contained within a box of side L then a normalized solution of eq. (44) is the *plane wave*:

$$\psi_k(r) = L^{-3/2} e^{ik \cdot r}, \tag{45}$$

which can be seen by writing $k \cdot r$ as $k_x x + k_y y + k_z z$ and substituting eq. (45) into eq. (44).

This solution corresponds to an electron with kinetic energy E given by:

$$E = k_x^2 + k_y^2 + k_z^2 = k^2. \tag{46}$$

Since the kinetic energy equals $p^2/2m$ where p is the electronic momentum, it follows from eq. (46) that

$$p^2 = 2mE = 2mk^2 = \hbar^2 k^2, \tag{47}$$

using $\hbar^2/2m = 1$. Thus, we have recovered the de Broglie relation

$$p = \hbar k = h/\lambda, \tag{48}$$

because $k = 2\pi/\lambda$ where λ is the wavelength of the plane wave.

The wavelength, λ, of the plane wave is constrained by *boundary conditions* at the surface of the box. For the case of the Bohr orbits in the hydrogen atom, de Broglie had argued that λ must be such that *integer* multiples of the wavelength fit around the circumference of the orbit. Similarly, imposing *periodic* boundary conditions on the box, which in one dimension corresponds to joining both ends in a closed ring, we have that

$$n_x\lambda_x = n_y\lambda_y = n_z\lambda_z = L, \tag{49}$$

where n_x, n_y, n_z are integers. Therefore,

$$k = \frac{2\pi}{L}(n_x, n_y, n_z) \tag{50}$$

so that the allowed values of the wave vector k are discrete and fall on a fine mesh as illustrated in fig. 12.

By Pauli's exclusion principle each state corresponding to a given k can contain *two* electrons of opposite spin. Therefore, at absolute zero all the states k will be occupied within a sphere of radius k_F, the so-called *Fermi sphere*, because these correspond to the states of lowest energy (cf. fig. 13a). The Fermi wave vector k_F may be related to the total number of valence electrons, N, by

$$\tfrac{4}{3}\pi k_F^3 2V/(2\pi)^3 = N, \tag{51}$$

where $V = L^3$, since it follows from eq. (50) that unit volume of k-space contains $V/(2\pi)^3$ states capable of holding two electrons each. Thus,

$$k_F = (3\pi^2 N/V)^{1/3} \tag{52}$$

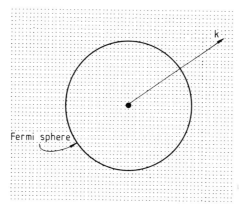

Fig. 12. The fine mesh of allowed k-values. At absolute zero only the states k within the Fermi sphere are occupied.

References: p. 149.

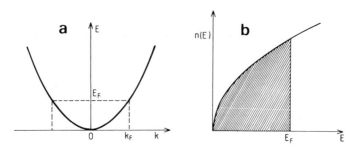

Fig. 13. The free-electron energy dispersion $E(k)$ (a) and density of states $n(E)$ (b).

and the corresponding *Fermi energy*, E_F, is given by

$$E_F = (3\pi^2 N/V)^{2/3}. \tag{53}$$

The electron concentration, N/V, for sodium, magnesium and aluminium at their equilibrium atomic volumes is such that the Fermi energy E_F equals 3.2, 7.1 and 11.6 eV respectively.

The free-electron *density of states* $n(E)$ may be obtained from eq. (51) by writing it in the form

$$N(E) = (V/3\pi^2)E^{3/2}, \tag{54}$$

where $N(E)$ is the total number of states of both spins available with energies less than E. Differentiating eq. (54) with respect to the energy gives the density of states:

$$n(E) = (V/2\pi^2)E^{1/2} \tag{55}$$

which is illustrated in fig. 13b. We can now see why the experimental electronic heat capacity did not obey the classical result of $\frac{3}{2}k_B$. By Pauli's exclusion principle the electrons can be excited only into the *unoccupied* states above the Fermi energy E_F. Therefore, only those electrons within about $k_B T$ of E_F will have enough thermal energy to be excited across E_F. Since $k_B T \approx 0.03$ eV at room temperature, these electrons will comprise a very small fraction, $f \approx k_B T/E_F$, of the total number of electrons N. The classical heat capacity is accordingly reduced by this factor f, as is observed experimentally. Using the correct Fermi–Dirac statistics to describe the occupation of the electron states, we find (see, e.g., KITTEL [1971]):

$$C_V = \frac{\pi^2}{2}k_B(k_B T/E_F) \tag{56}$$

in agreement with the previous qualitative argument.

3.2. Nearly-free-electron approximation

The electrons in a real metal are affected by the *crystalline* lattice, since the potential which they feel is not uniform but varies *periodically* as

$$v(r + R) = v(r) \tag{57}$$

where R is any lattice vector. (For simplicity we will be considering only those crystal structures, such as fcc or bcc, in which there is only *one* atom per primitive lattice site, in contrast to hcp or the diamond structure, for example, which have a basis of *two* atoms, cf. KITTEL [1971].)

Consider first an infinite *one-dimensional* periodic lattice of atoms with repeat distance a such that

$$v(x + na) = v(x). \tag{58}$$

Because all the atoms are equivalent, the probability of locating the electron about a site must be the same for all sites, so that:

$$|\psi(x + na)|^2 = |\psi(x)|^2. \tag{59}$$

For $n = 1$ this implies that

$$\psi(x + a) = e^{ika}\psi(x), \tag{60}$$

where k is a number (in units of $1/a$) which specifies the *phase factor* e^{ika} linking the wavefunctions on neighbouring sites. Repeating eq. (60) n times gives:

$$\psi_k(x + na) = e^{ikna}\psi_k(x), \tag{61}$$

which is the usual statement of *Bloch's theorem* in one dimension. Thus the translational symmetry of the lattice leads to the eigenfunctions being characterized by the Bloch vector, k. However, k is only defined modulo$(2\pi/a)$, since $k + m(2\pi/a)$ results in the same phase factor in eq. (61) as k alone. It is, therefore, customary to label the wavefunction ψ_k by restricting k to lie within the *first Brillouin zone*, defined by

$$-\pi/a \leqslant k \leqslant +\pi/a. \tag{62}$$

We note that in one dimension na is a direct lattice vector, whereas $m(2\pi/a)$ is a *reciprocal* lattice vector. Their product is an integer multiple of 2π.

Extending these ideas to three dimensions, Bloch's theorem, eq. (61), may be written as:

$$\psi_k(r + R) = e^{ik \cdot R}\psi_k(r), \tag{63}$$

where R is any *direct lattice* vector which may be expressed in terms of the fundamental translation vectors a_1, a_2, a_3 as:

$$R = n_1a_2 + n_2a_2 + n_3a_3, \tag{64}$$

where n_1, n_2, n_3 are integers. The corresponding *reciprocal lattice* vectors are defined by:

$$G = m_1b_1 + m_2b_2 + m_3b_3, \tag{65}$$

where m_1, m_2, m_3 are integers and the fundamental basis vectors are *:

---

* Note the additional factor of 2π compared to the definition of reciprocal lattice vectors in the appendix of ch. 11.

References: p. 149.

$$b_1 = (2\pi/\tau) a_2 \times a_3$$
$$b_2 = (2\pi/\tau) a_3 \times a_1 \Big\},$$
$$b_3 = (2\pi/\tau) a_1 \times a_2$$

$$(66)$$

with $\tau = |a_1 \cdot (a_2 \times a_3)|$ being the volume of the primitive unit cell defined by a_1, a_2 and a_3. It is apparent from their definition (66) that

$$a_i \cdot b_j = 2\pi \delta_{ij},$$

$$(67)$$

where $\delta_{ij} = 1$ for $i = j$ but zero otherwise.

The phase factor in eq. (63) only defines the Bloch vector within a reciprocal lattice vector G since it follows from eqs. (64)–(67) that $G \cdot R$ is an integer multiple of 2π. Just as in the one-dimensional case, it is customary to label the wavefunction ψ_k by restricting k to lie within the *first Brillouin zone* which is the closed volume about the origin in reciprocal space formed by bisecting near-neighbour reciprocal lattice vectors. For example, consider the *simple cubic* lattice with basis vectors a_1, a_2, a_3 along the Cartesian axes x, y, z respectively. Because $a_1 = a_2 = a_3 = a$ it follows from eq. (66) that the reciprocal space basis vectors b_1, b_2, b_3 also lie along x, y and z respectively, but with magnitude $(2\pi/a)$. Thus, the reciprocal lattice is also simple cubic and it is shown in fig. 14 in the x–y plane. It is clear that the bisectors of the first nearest-neighbour (100) reciprocal lattice vectors form a closed volume about the origin which is not cut by the second or any further nearest-neighbour bisectors. Hence, the Brillouin zone is a cube of volume $(2\pi/a)^3$. From eq. (50) it

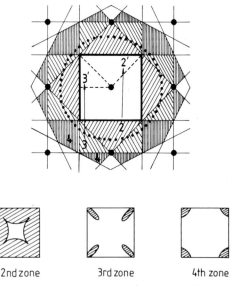

Fig. 14. The first four zones of the simple cubic lattice corresponding to $k_z = 0$. The dotted circle represents the cross-section of a spherical Fermi surface.

contains as many allowed k points as there are primitive unit cells in the crystal. Figure 15 illustrates the corresponding Brillouin zones for the body-centred cubic and face-centred cubic lattices (see, e.g., KITTEL [1971]).

The solutions E_k of the Schrödinger equation for k lying within the Brillouin zone determine the *bandstructure*. Figure 16 shows the bandstructure of aluminium in the $|100\rangle$ and $|111\rangle$ directions, after MORUZZI *et al.* [1978]. It is very similar to the free-electron bandstructure

$$E_k = (k + G)^2 \tag{68}$$

which results from folding the free-electron eigenvalues shown in fig. 13a into the first Brillouin zone. This "folding-in" is illustrated in fig. 14 for the case of the *simple cubic* lattice. For this two-dimensional cross-section we see that the four contributions to the second zone 2 may be translated through (100) reciprocal lattice vectors into the four zones 2', which together completely fill the reduced Brillouin zone in the x–y plane. Similarly, the third and fourth zones shown in fig. 14 may each be translated through reciprocal lattice vectors to fill the first Brillouin zone. For the *fcc* lattice the two lowest eigenvalues given by eq. (68) in the $|100\rangle$ direction are:

$$E_k^{(1)} = k^2, \qquad E_k^{(2)} = (k + g)^2, \tag{69}$$

where $k = (k_x, 0, 0)$ and $g = (2\pi/a)(\bar{2}, 0, 0)$. These two eigenvalues are degenerate at the zone boundary X, where $k = (2\pi/a)(1, 0, 0)$, because from eq. (69) they both take the value $4\pi^2/a^2$. For aluminium $a = 7.60$ au and $4\pi^2/a^2 = 9.3$ eV, so that the two free-electron eigenvalues given by eq. (69) reflect the broad behaviour of the bandstructure shown along ΓX in fig. 16.

However, in order to recover the *energy gap* at the zone boundary X, it is necessary to lift the free-electron degeneracy by perturbing the free-electron gas with the periodic potential of the crystalline lattice. Within the *nearly-free-electron* (NFE) approximation this is achieved by writing the wavefunction ψ_k as a linear combina-

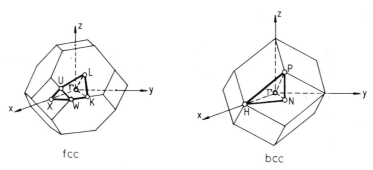

Fig. 15. The fcc and bcc Brillouin zones. Γ labels the centre of the zone. The intersections of the $|100\rangle$ and $|111\rangle$ directions with the Brillouin-zone boundary are labelled X and L in the fcc case and H and P in the bcc case.

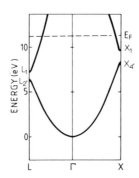

Fig. 16. The bandstructure of fcc aluminium (after MORUZZI *et al.* [1978]).

tion of the plane-wave eigenfunctions corresponding to the two free-electron eigenvalues given by eq. (69); that is:

$$\psi_k = c_1\psi_k^{(1)} + c_2\psi_k^{(2)}, \tag{70}$$

where from eq. (45):

$$\psi_k^{(1)} = V^{-1/2}\exp(i k\cdot r), \tag{71}$$

$$\psi_k^{(2)} = V^{-1/2}\exp[i(k+g)\cdot r]. \tag{72}$$

Substituting eq. (70) into the Schrödinger equation (1), pre-multiplying by $\psi_k^{(1)*}$ or $\psi_k^{(2)*}$ and integrating over the volume of the crystal, V, yields the *NFE secular equation*:

$$\begin{pmatrix} k^2 - E & v(200) \\ v(200) & (k+g)^2 - E \end{pmatrix}\begin{pmatrix} c_1 \\ c_2 \end{pmatrix} = 0. \tag{73}$$

$v(200)$ is the $(2\pi/a)(2, 0, 0)$ Fourier component of the crystalline potential, where

$$v(g) = \frac{1}{V}\int v(r)\, e^{ig\cdot r}\, dr. \tag{74}$$

The energy, E, in eq. (73) is measured with respect to the average potential $v(000)$. Non-trivial solutions exist if the secular determinant vanishes, i.e. if

$$\begin{vmatrix} k^2 - E & v(200) \\ v(200) & (k+g)^2 - E \end{vmatrix} = 0. \tag{75}$$

This quadratic equation has solutions

$$E_k = \tfrac{1}{2}\big[k^2 + (k+g)^2\big] \pm \tfrac{1}{2}\big\{\big[(k+g)^2 - k^2\big]^2 + [2v(200)]^2\big\}^{1/2}. \tag{76}$$

Therefore, at the zone boundary X where $k^2 = (k+g)^2$, the eigenvalues are given by

$$E_X = 4\pi^2/a^2 \pm v(200) \tag{77}$$

and the eigenfunctions are given from eqs. (70) and (73) by:

$$\psi_X = (2/V)^{1/2} \times \begin{cases} \cos(2\pi x/a) \\ \sin(2\pi x/a) \end{cases}. \tag{78}$$

Thus the presence of the periodic potential has opened up a gap in the free electron bandstructure with energy separation

$$E_{gap}^X = 2|v(200)|. \tag{79}$$

Because the energy gap at X in aluminium is about 1 eV (cf. fig. 16), the magnitude of the Fourier component of the potential within this simple NFE treatment is only 0.5 eV. This is small compared to the free-electron Fermi energy of more than 10 eV in aluminium and, therefore, the bandstructure E_k and the density of states $n(E)$ are nearly-free-electron-like to a very good approximation.

The NFE behaviour has been observed experimentally in studies of the *Fermi surface,* the surface of constant energy E_F in k-space, which separates filled states from empty states at $T = 0$. For a free-electron gas the Fermi surface is spherical as illustrated in fig. 12. However, in simple metals we have seen that the free-electron bandstructure is perturbed by the periodic lattice potential, and energy gaps open up across zone boundaries. As illustrated in fig. 14 for the simple cubic lattice, a spherical free-electron Fermi surface (whose cross-section is represented by the circle of solid dots) will be folded into the first Brillouin zone by the relevant reciprocal

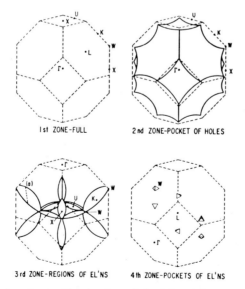

I st ZONE-FULL   2 nd ZONE-POCKET OF HOLES

3 rd ZONE-REGIONS OF EL'NS   4 th ZONE-POCKETS OF EL'NS

Fig. 17. The free-electron Fermi surface of aluminium (after HARRISON [1959]).

References: p. 149.

lattice vectors. The states in the second zone 2, for example, are folded back into 2′ in the reduced zone, thereby giving rise to the shaded occupied regions of k-space and the corresponding Fermi surface indicated in the lower panel of fig. 14. Similarly, the occupied states in the third and fourth zones are folded back into the reduced Brillouin zone as shown. Therefore, even though the crystalline potential may be very weak, it is sufficient to destroy the *spherical* free-electron Fermi surface and to create a new Fermi surface topology, as is illustrated in fig. 14 by the appearance of the electron *pockets* in the third and fourth zones. A very simple procedure for constructing the Fermi surfaces of free-electron-like materials has been suggested by HARRISON [1959, 1960] and fig. 17 shows the resulting Fermi surface of fcc aluminium. A much more detailed treatment of Fermi surfaces may be found in HARRISON [1966], HEINE and WEAIRE [1970] and KITTEL [1971], where the interested reader is also referred for a discussion of transport properties and concepts such as holes and effective mass.

3.3.   Volume dependence

Although the energy bands of simple metals *appear* to be describable by the NFE approximation as discussed in the previous subsection, there is a major difficulty. If the (200) Fourier component of the aluminium lattice potential is estimated from *first principles* using eq. (74), then

$$v(200) \approx -5 \text{ eV}. \tag{80}$$

But the magnitude of this is ten times larger than the value we obtained by *fitting* to the first-principles bandstructure of MORUZZI et al. [1978], namely $|v(200)| = 0.5$ eV. Moreover, by looking at the symmetry of the eigenfunctions at X, we see from fig. 16 that the bottom of the band gap corresponds to $X_{4'}$ or p-like symmetry whereas the top of the band gap corresponds to X_1 or s-like symmetry (see, e.g., TINKHAM [1964]). It follows from fig. 2 and eq. (78) that the NFE states at the bottom and top of the band gap correspond to $\sin(2\pi x/a)$ and $\cos(2\pi x/a)$, respectively. Therefore, in the state with *lower* energy the electron is never located in the planes containing the ion cores, which correspond to $x = na/2$ for the fcc lattice, since $\sin(2\pi x/a)$ vanishes. Instead, the electron has maximum probability of being located midway between these atomic planes. This implies that the relevant Fourier component of the atomic potential is *repulsive*, thereby driving the electrons away from the ion cores, i.e.

$$v^{\text{fit}}(200) = +0.5 \text{ eV}. \tag{81}$$

The origin of the discrepancy between eqs. (80) and (81) is easily found once it is remembered that the NFE bands in aluminium are formed from the *valence* 3s and 3p electrons. These states must be orthogonal to the s and p *core* functions as outlined in §2.1 and they, therefore, contain nodes in the core region as illustrated for the case of the 2s wavefunction in fig. 6. In order to reproduce these very-short-wavelength oscillations, plane waves of *very high* momentum must be included in the plane-wave expansion of ψ_k, so that a linear combination of only the *two* lowest energy plane waves in eq. (70) is an extremely bad approximation. In 1940, HERRING circumvented this problem by starting at the outset with a basis of plane waves that had *already* been orthogonalized to the core states, the so-called orthogonalized plane-wave (OPW) basis. The OPW method led to a secular determinant for the eigenvalues that was identical to the NFE determinant, except that in addition to the Fourier component of the crystal potential $v(G)$ there is also a *repulsive* contribution coming from the core-orthogonality constraint. This tended to cancel the *attractive* coulomb potential term in the core region, thereby resulting in much weaker net Fourier components and hence nearly-free-electron-like behaviour of the bandstructure E_k for the simple metals.

This led to the concept of the *pseudopotential* in which the true potential $v(r)$ in the Schrödinger equation (1) is replaced by a much *weaker* potential $v_{ps}(r)$ which is chosen to preserve the original eigenvalues E_k so that

$$\left(-\nabla^2 + v_{ps} \right)\phi_k = E_k\phi_k \tag{82}$$

(see, e.g., HARRISON [1966] and HEINE and WEAIRE [1970]). The pseudo-*eigenfunctions*, ϕ_k, however, differ from the true eigenfunctions ψ_k because in general they do *not* contain the nodes in the core region as these have been pseudized-away by the inclusion of the repulsive core component in v_{ps}. A plane-wave expansion of ϕ_k, therefore, leads to rapidly convergent eigenvalues E_k in eq. (82). Thus, the NFE approximation will provide a good description of the bandstructure of simple metals provided the Fourier components of the pseudopotential rather than the true potential are taken in the NFE secular equation (75).

Pseudopotentials are not unique, and recently some improved criteria have been given for their choice (see, e.g., BACHELET *et al.* [1982]). However, in this chapter we shall describe only the Ashcroft *empty-core* pseudopotential because of its simplicity. In 1966, ASHCROFT assumed that the cancellation between the repulsive core-orthogonality contribution and the attractive coulomb contribution is exact within some ion core radius R_c, so that:

$$v_{ps}^{ion}(r) = \begin{cases} 0 & r < R_c \\ -2Z/r & r > R_c \end{cases} \quad \text{for} \tag{83}$$

where the *ionic* potential falls off coulombically outside the core (cf. $e^2 = 2$ in atomic units). The Ashcroft empty-core pseudopotential is shown in fig. 18. The resulting ionic lattice has Fourier components given by eq. (74), namely:

$$v_{ps}^{ion}(q) = -\left(8\pi Z/\Omega q^2 \right)\cos qR_c, \tag{84}$$

where Ω is the volume per atom. In the absence of the core $R_c = 0$ and the Fourier components are *negative* as expected. However, in the presence of the core the Fourier components oscillate in sign and may, therefore, take *positive* values. For the case of aluminium the Ashcroft empty-core radius is about 1.2 au (cf. table 16-1 of HARRISON [1980]) and $v_{ps}^{ion}(200)$ will, therefore, be positive. The corresponding

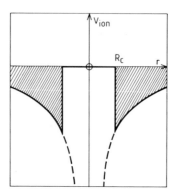

Fig. 18. The Ashcroft empty-core pseudopotential.

Fourier components $v_{ps}(q)$ are obtained from eq. (84) by allowing the free-electron gas to screen the bare ionic lattice. The resulting Fourier components of the aluminium potential are illustrated in fig. 19 for the more sophisticated HEINE–ABARENKOV [1964] pseudopotential. We see that the values of $v_{ps}(111)$ and $v_{ps}(200)$ are in good agreement with the values, 0.17 and 0.53 eV respectively, which are obtained from fitting the first-principles bandstructure within the NFE approximation (cf. fig. 16, eq. (79) and p. 52 of MORUZZI *et al.* [1978]).

Figure 20 shows the densities of states, $n(E)$, of the sp-bonded simple metals, which have been computed from first principles by MORUZZI *et al.* [1978]. We see that Na, Mg and Al across a period and Al, Ga and In down a group are good NFE metals, because their densities of states are only very small perturbations of the free-electron density of states shown in fig. 13b. However, we see that Li and Be display very strong deviations from free electron behaviour. This is a direct consequence of these elements having no p core electrons, so that there is no repulsive core-orthogonality component to cancel the attractive coulomb potential which the valence 2p electrons feel. This leads to sizeable Fourier components of the potential and hence very large band gaps. For example, in fcc Be, $E_{gap}^{L} = 5.6$ eV compared to

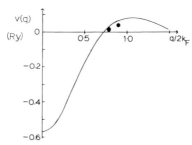

Fig. 19. The HEINE–ABARENKOV [1964] aluminium pseudopotential $v_{ps}(q)$. The two points give the values of $v_{ps}(111)$ and $v_{ps}(200)$ deduced from fig. 16 using eq. (79).

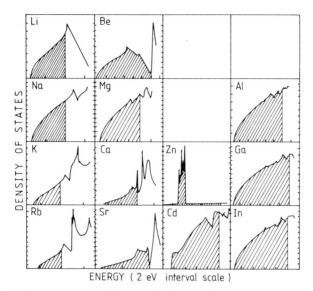

Fig. 20. The density of states, $n(E)$, of sp-bonded metals (after Moruzzi *et al.* [1978]).

the gap of only 0.34 eV in Al, where L is the point $(2\pi/a)(\frac{1}{2},\frac{1}{2},\frac{1}{2})$ in fig. 15. In fact, the band gaps in different directions at the Brillouin zone boundary (cf. fig. 16) are nearly large enough for a gap to open up in the Be density of states, thereby leading to semiconducting behaviour. We note that the effective potential which the valence electrons feel in Li or Be depends on whether they have s- or p-type character, because there *are* 1s core states but no p core states. Such an *l*-dependent potential is said to be *non-local* (cf. Harrison [1966] and Heine and Weaire [1970]), whereas the Ashcroft empty-core pseudopotential of fig. 18 is *local*.

The heavier alkalis K and Rb and alkaline earths Ca and Sr have their occupied energy levels affected by the presence of the respective 3d or 4d band which lies just above the Fermi energy (cf. the relative positions of the s and d free-atom energy levels in fig. 5). This leads to a more than free-electron admixture of $l = 2$ component into the occupied energy states, which requires the use of non-local pseudo-potential theory for accurate agreement with experimental properties (see e.g., Taylor and MacDonald [1980] and Moriarty [1982]). It is clear from fig. 20 that Sr is not a simple NFE metal since the perturbation is very strong and the hybridized bottom of the d band has moved below the Fermi energy. Just as in Be, a gap has nearly opened up at E_F, and theoretically it requires only 0.3 GPa of pressure to turn Sr into a semiconductor, which is in reasonable agreement with high-pressure resistivity data (Jan and Skriver [1981]). The group-IIB elements Zn and Cd, on the other hand, have their valence states strongly distorted by the presence of the *filled* d band. In fig. 5 we see that the 5s–4d energy separation in Cd is larger than the 4s–3d separation in Zn, which results in the Cd 4d band lying

References: p. 149.

about 1 eV below the bottom of the valence 5sp band (p. 152 of MORUZZI *et al.*
[1978]). Figure 20, therefore, demonstrates that not all simple metals display good
NFE behaviour and particular care needs to be taken with Li, Be and the group-II
elements on either side of the transition metal series.

The presence of the ion core in simple metals determines the volume dependence
of the energy bands. Wigner and Seitz had calculated the behaviour of the bottom of
the NFE band in sodium in their classic paper of 1933. They argued that since the
bottom of the band corresponded to the most bonding state, it satisfied the *bonding
boundary condition* implicit in eq. (33), namely that the gradient of the wavefunction vanishes across the boundary of the *Wigner–Seitz cell*. This cell is formed in *real*
space about a given atom by bisecting the near-neighbour position vectors in the
same way that the Brillouin zone is formed in *reciprocal* space. The Wigner–Seitz cell
of the bcc lattice is the fcc Brillouin zone and vice versa (cf. KITTEL [1971]). Since
there are 12 nearest neighbours in the fcc lattice and 14 first and second nearest
neighbours in the bcc lattice, it is a very good approximation to replace the
Wigner–Seitz *cell* by a Wigner–Seitz *sphere* of the same volume (cf. fig. 15).
Imposing the bonding boundary condition across the Wigner–Seitz sphere of radius
S, where

$$\Omega = \tfrac{4}{3}\pi S^3,$$
                                                                                                (85)

the energy of the bottom of the band Γ_1 is fixed by

$$\left[\mathrm{d}R_s(r, E)/\mathrm{d}r \right]_{r=S, E=\Gamma_1} = 0,$$
                                                                                                (86)

where $R_s(r, E)$ is the $l = 0$ solution of the radial Schrödinger equation within the
Wigner–Seitz sphere. The bonding boundary condition is determined by the $l = 0$
radial function because the bottom of the NFE band at Γ_1 is a pure s state (cf. fig.
16).

Figure 21 shows the resulting behaviour of the bottom of the band Γ_1 in sodium
as a function of S after WIGNER and SEITZ [1933]. We see that as the free atoms are
brought together from infinity, the bonding state becomes more and more bonding
until about 3 au when Γ_1 turns upwards and rapidly loses its binding energy. This

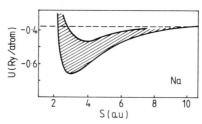

Fig. 21. The total energy, U, as a function of Wigner–Seitz radius, S, for sodium (after WIGNER and SEITZ
[1933]). The bottom of the conduction band, Γ_1, is given by the lower curve, to which is added the average
kinetic energy per electron (the shaded region).

behaviour is well described *at metallic densities* by the Fröhlich–Bardeen expression,

$$\Gamma_1^{\text{WS}} = - (3Z/S)\left[1 - (R_{\text{c}}/S)^2\right] \tag{87}$$

since the single valence electron of sodium is assumed to feel only the potential of the *ion* at the Wigner–Seitz sphere centre so that over the boundary

$$v(S) = -2Z/S, \tag{88}$$

where $Z = 1$ for the monovalent alkali metals (see, e.g., §3.2 of CALLAWAY [1964]). R_{c} may be identified as the radius of an Ashcroft empty-core pseudopotential, because the potential energy of one electron distributed uniformly throughout the Wigner–Seitz sphere with an Ashcroft ionic potential at its centre is given by eq. (87). It follows from eq. (87) that the maximum binding energy of this state Γ_1 occurs for

$$S_{\text{m}} = \sqrt{3}\, R_{\text{c}}. \tag{89}$$

Since for sodium $R_{\text{c}} \approx 1.7$ au (ASHCROFT and LANGRETH [1967] and HARRISON [1980]), eq. (89) predicts that Γ_1 has a minimum at about 2.9 au. This is in good agreement with the curve in fig. 21, which was obtained by solving the radial Schrödinger equation subject to the boundary condition eq. (86).

WIGNER and SEITZ [1933] assumed that the valence electrons of sodium have free-electron-like kinetic energy and density of states, which from fig. 20 is clearly a good approximation. It follows from eqs. (53) and (85) that the Fermi energy E_{F} may be written as:

$$E_{\text{F}} = \Gamma_1^{\text{WS}} + (9\pi/4)^{2/3}/S^2. \tag{90}$$

In §5 we follow up our understanding of the behaviour of the energy bands by discussing the *total* energy of simple metals and the different factors influencing bulk properties such as equilibrium atomic volume and bulk modulus.

4. Transition-metal bands

4.1. Tight-binding approximation

Transition metals are characterized by a partially filled d band, which is well described within the *tight-binding* (TB) approximation by a linear combination of atomic d orbitals. We shall illustrate the TB method (see, e.g., CALLAWAY [1964]) by considering first the simpler case of a lattice of atoms with overlapping *s-state* atomic wavefunctions ψ_{s} and corresponding free atomic energy levels E_{s}. Generalizing eq. (19) for the diatomic molecule to a periodic lattice of N atoms, we can write the crystal wavefunction ψ_k as a linear combination of the atomic orbitals:

$$\psi_k(r) = N^{-1/2}\sum_{R} e^{ik\cdot R}\psi_{\text{s}}(r - R), \tag{91}$$

where the phase factor automatically guarantees that $\psi_k(r)$ satisfies Bloch's theorem, eq. (63). Assuming that the crystal potential is the sum of the atomic potentials $v(r-R)$ and following the method and approximations outlined through eqs. (19)–(30), the eigenvalue E_k may be written as:

$$E_k = E_s + \sum_{R \neq 0} e^{ik \cdot R} \int \psi_s^*(r) v(r) \psi_s(r-R) \, dr, \tag{92}$$

where the non-orthogonality and three-centre contributions have been neglected because they do not contribute to first order. Since the atomic s orbitals are spherically symmetric, the ssσ hopping matrix elements in eq. (92) do not depend on the direction of R but only on the magnitude R (see fig. 10), so that

$$E_k = E_s + \sum_{R \neq 0} e^{ik \cdot R} \text{ss}\sigma_R. \tag{93}$$

The TB bandstructure E_k for a *simple cubic* lattice with s orbitals may now be quickly found. Assuming that the hopping matrix elements couple only to the six *first* nearest-neighbour atoms with position vectors R equal to $(\pm a, 0, 0)$, $(0, \pm a, 0)$ and $(0, 0, \pm a)$, eq. (93) gives

$$E_k = E_s + 2\text{ss}\sigma_1 (\cos k_x a + \cos k_y a + \cos k_z a), \tag{94}$$

where $k = (k_x, k_y, k_z)$. Thus the eigenvalues vary *sinusoidally* across the Brillouin zone. The bottom, E^-, and top, E^+, of the s band correspond to the Bloch states at the centre of the Brillouin zone $(0, 0, 0)$ and at the zone boundary $(\pi/a)(1, 1, 1)$ respectively. It follows from eq. (94) that

$$E^{\pm} = E_s \pm 6|\text{ss}\sigma_1| \tag{95}$$

because ssσ$_1$ is negative as can be deduced from fig. 10 and eq. (92). Comparing E^- with eq. (30) and fig. 8a for the diatomic molecule, we see that the most bonding state in the simple cubic lattice corresponds to *maximum* bonding with all six nearest neighbours simultaneously, which from fig. 10 is only possible for the spherically symmetric s orbital case.

The structure of the TB p band may be obtained by writing ψ_k as a linear combination of the *three* p Bloch sums corresponding to the atomic p_x, p_y and p_z orbitals, where x, y and z may be chosen along the crystal axes for a cubic lattice. That is,

$$\psi_k(r) = N^{-1/2} \sum_{\alpha = x,y,z} c_\alpha \sum_R e^{ik \cdot R} \psi_\alpha(r-R), \tag{96}$$

which leads to the 3×3 TB secular determinant for the p band, namely

$$|(E_p - E_k)\delta_{\alpha\alpha'} + T_{\alpha\alpha'}| = 0, \tag{97}$$

where

$$T_{\alpha\alpha'} = \sum_{R \neq 0} e^{ik \cdot R} \int \psi_\alpha^*(r) v(r) \psi_{\alpha'}(r-R) \, dr. \tag{98}$$

It is clear from fig. 10 that the hopping matrix elements in eq. (98) *do* depend on the direction of R because the p_x, p_y and p_z orbitals are angular dependent. SLATER and KOSTER [1954] showed that they can be written directly in terms of the two fundamental hopping integrals $pp\sigma_R$ and $pp\pi_R$ and the direction cosines (l, m, n) of R.

For a *simple cubic* lattice with only first-nearest-neighbour hopping the matrix elements $T_{\alpha\alpha'}$ may be evaluated to give

$$T_{xx} = 2pp\sigma_1\cos k_x a + 2pp\pi_1(\cos k_y a + \cos k_z a), \qquad (99)$$

with T_{yy} and T_{zz} obtained from T_{xx} by cyclic permutation. The off-diagonal matrix elements vanish for the simple cubic lattice. Therefore, at the centre of the Brillouin zone, Γ, the eigenvalues are *triply* degenerate (if spin is neglected) and given from eqs. (97) and (99) by

$$E_\Gamma^{(3)} = E_p + 2pp\sigma_1 + 4pp\pi_1. \qquad (100)$$

This degeneracy is *partially* lifted along the $|100\rangle$ symmetry direction, because from eq. (99) the bandstructure consists of the *singly* degenerate level

$$E_\Delta^{(1)} = E_p + 4pp\pi_1 + 2pp\sigma_1\cos k_x a \qquad (101)$$

and the *doubly* degenerate level

$$E_\Delta^{(2)} = E_p + 2(pp\sigma_1 + pp\pi_1) + 2pp\pi_1\cos k_x a, \qquad (102)$$

where the former results from the p_x orbitals and the latter from the p_y and p_z orbitals. The degeneracy is *totally* lifted along a general k direction as from eqs. (97) and (99) there will be three distinct non-degenerate energy levels.

Finally, the structure of the TB d band may be obtained by writing ψ_k as a linear combination of the *five* d Bloch sums corresponding to the five atomic orbitals illustrated in fig. 2. This results in a 5×5 TB secular determinant from which the d bandstructure may be computed (SLATER and KOSTER [1954]). Starting from first-principles band theory, ANDERSEN [1973] has shown that within the *atomic sphere approximation* (ASA) *canonical* d bands may be derived which depend neither on the lattice constant nor on the particular transition metal, but only on the crystal structure. This approximation leads to hopping integrals of the form

$$\left.\begin{array}{l} dd\sigma_R = -6 \\ dd\pi_R = 4 \\ dd\delta_R = -1 \end{array}\right\} \times \tfrac{2}{5}W(S/R)^5, \qquad (103)$$

where W is the width of the d band, which is obtained from eq. (33) by imposing the bonding and antibonding boundary conditions over the Wigner–Seitz *sphere* of radius S. It follows from eq. (103) that the hopping integrals scale uniformly with the bandwidth W and do not depend on the lattice constant as it is the ratio S/R that enters. They fall off quickly with distance as the inverse fifth power.

Figure 22 shows the resulting d bandstructure for the fcc and bcc lattices along

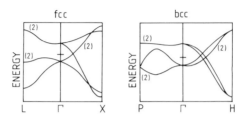

Fig. 22. The fcc and bcc d bandstructure (after ANDERSEN [1973]).

the $|111\rangle$ and $|100\rangle$ directions in the Brillouin zone (ANDERSEN [1973]). We see that at the centre of the Brillouin zone, Γ, there are two energy levels, one of which is *triply* degenerate, the other *doubly* degenerate. The former comprises the xy, yz and xz, T_{2g} orbitals which from fig. 2 are equivalent to one another in a cubic environment. The latter comprises the $x^2 - y^2$, $3z^2 - r^2 E_g$ orbitals which by pointing along the cubic axes are not equivalent to the T_{2g} orbitals. The degeneracy is partially lifted along the $|111\rangle$ and $|100\rangle$ symmetry directions as indicated in fig. 22, because eigenfunctions which are equivalent at $k = 0$ may become non-equivalent for $k \neq 0$ due to the translational phase factor $\exp(i k \cdot R)$ (see fig. 8.8 of TINKHAM [1964]).

The bandstructure of NiO (MATTHEISS [1972]) is shown in fig. 23 because it illustrates s, p and d band behaviour. The three bands arise from the oxygen 2s, 2p and the nickel 3d valence levels, respectively, the ordering being determined by the relative positions of their atomic energy levels in figs. 4 and 5. The Brillouin zone is *face-centred* cubic since the NaCl crystal structure of NiO consists of two inter-penetrating fcc lattices, one containing the sodium atoms, the other the chlorine atoms. In the $|100\rangle$ direction along ΓX the s and p bandstructure is not too dissimilar from that given for the *simple* cubic lattice by eqs. (94), (101) and (102).

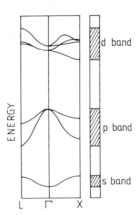

Fig. 23. The bandstructure of NiO (after MATTHEISS [1972]).

The d bandstructure along ΓX in NiO is also similar to that of the fcc canonical d band in fig. 22, except that one level, which joins the upper state at Γ to the *bottom* of the canonical d band at X, has been pushed up and runs across the *top* of the d band in NiO. This is the result of mixing or *hybridization* between the s, p and d blocks in the TB secular determinant (SLATER and KOSTER [1954]), whose strength is determined for example by the non-vanishing pdσ and pdπ hopping matrix elements shown in fig. 10. This mixing can only occur between Bloch states with the same symmetry (TINKHAM [1964]). At the zone boundary X there is only *one* d band state which has the same symmetry X_1 as the s band state. (There are no d band states with the same symmetry as the p band states at X.) The influence of the hybridization on the bandstructure is enhanced by *orthogonality* constraints which can add a further repulsive contribution to the d states because they must be orthogonal to the valence s and p levels lying beneath them in energy.

The bands in fig. 23 illustrate an apparent failure of one-electron theory. NiO is an *insulator*. However, adding the ten nickel and six oxygen valence electrons to the bands shown results in the d band containing only eight of its possible ten electrons [cf. eq. (43)]. Thus, the bandstructure presented in fig. 23 predicts that NiO is a *metal*. The origin of this dramatic failure of band theory was investigated by MOTT [1949], who considered what happens to a lattice of hydrogen atoms as the lattice constant is decreased from some very large value. Initially each atom has a single 1s valence electron associated with it as in the free atom state. The system will, therefore, be *insulating*, because in order for an electron to hop through the lattice it requires an energy given by the difference between the ionization potential of 13.6 eV (corresponding to the atomic 1s level) and the electron affinity of 0.75 eV. This energy difference of about 13 eV is a measure of the coulomb repulsion U between *two* 1s antiparallel spin electrons sitting on the *same* atomic site. However, as the lattice constant decreases the atomic 1s level broadens into a band of states of width W so that the insulating gap will decrease like $U - W$. Therefore, for some sufficiently small lattice spacing W will be large enough for the system to become *metallic* and the hydrogen lattice undergoes a Mott metal–insulator transition.

The very different conducting behaviour of the 3d valence electrons in metallic nickel and insulating nickel oxide can now be qualitatively understood. The width of the d band in NiO is about 2 eV (MATTHEISS [1972]), whereas in pure Ni it is about 5 eV (MORUZZI et al. [1978]) since the Ni–Ni internuclear separation is smaller than in the oxide. Because the value of the screened intra-atomic coulomb integral U in 3d transition metals is about 4 eV, U/W is *greater* than unity for NiO but *less* than unity for Ni. Thus, we expect the former to be insulating and the latter metallic as observed experimentally.

The *breakdown* of conventional band theory at *large* lattice spacings can best be illustrated by considering the hydrogen molecule (cf. fig. 8a). In the ground state the two valence electrons 1 and 2 occupy the same bonding molecular orbital ψ_{AB}^- with opposite spin, so that the total molecular wavefunction may be written within the one electron approximation as

$$\psi(1, 2) = \psi_{AB}^-(1)\psi_{AB}^-(2). \tag{104}$$

Substituting from eq. (33), multiplying through and neglecting the normalization factor $[2(1 + S)]^{-1}$ we have

$$\psi(1, 2) = \left(\psi_A(1)\psi_B(2) + \psi_B(1)\psi_A(2) + \psi_A(1)\psi_A(2) + \psi_B(1)\psi_B(2) \right). \quad (105)$$

The first two contributions correspond to the two possible *neutral* atom states with a single electron associated with each atom, whereas the latter correspond to the two *ionic* states A^-B^+ and A^+B^- respectively. Since the hydrogen molecule dissociates into two *neutral* atoms, we see that $\psi(1, 2)$ gives the wrong behaviour at large separations (see, e.g., SLATER [1963]).

In practice, the Mott transition to the insulating phase is accompanied by the appearance of local *magnetic* moments (BRANDOW [1977]) so that the band model must be generalized to allow for antiferromagnetic solutions of the Schrödinger equation (SLATER [1951a]; cf. §8). Within local spin density functional (LSDF) theory (cf. §1) this leads to a good curve of total energy versus internuclear separation for the hydrogen molecule because the theory now goes over to the neutral free-atom limit (GUNNARSSON and LUNDQVIST [1976]). However, although the antiferromagnetic state leads to a band gap opening up at the Fermi level in NiO (SLATER [1951a]), a proper understanding of CoO and the temperature-dependent properties of these *insulators* can only be obtained by using a more sophisticated *non-local* treatment of exchange and correlation (BRANDOW [1977]). Fortunately, the bulk properties of simple and transition *metals* considered in this chapter can be well understood within the *local* approximation, even though non-locality can play a role in the finer details of the bandstructure (see, e.g., Ni; COOKE *et al.* [1980]).

4.2. Hybrid NFE–TB bands

Transition metals are characterized by a fairly tightly-bound d band that overlaps and hybridizes with a broader nearly-free-electron sp band as illustrated in fig. 24. This difference in behaviour between the valence sp and d electrons arises from the d shell lying *inside* the outer valence s shell, thereby leading to small overlap between the d orbitals in the bulk. For example, from eq. (14) the average radial distance of

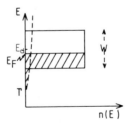

Fig. 24. A schematic representation of transition metal sp (dashed curve) and d (solid curve) densities of states when sp–d hybridization is neglected.

the hydrogenic 3d and 4s wave functions are in the ratio 0.44 : 1. Thus, we expect the bandstructure of transition metals to be represented accurately by a hybrid NFE–TB secular equation of the form (HODGES *et al.* [1966] and MUELLER [1967]):

$$\begin{vmatrix} C - EI & H \\ H^\dagger & D - EI \end{vmatrix} = 0 \tag{106}$$

where C and D are sp-NFE and d-TB matrices respectively [cf. eqs. (75) and (97)]. H is the hybridization matrix which couples and mixes together the sp and d Bloch states with the same symmetry, and I is the unit matrix.

A secular equation of this H–NFE–TB form may be derived (HEINE [1967], HUBBARD [1967] and JACOBS [1968]) by an exact transformation (PETTIFOR [1972a]) of the first-principle bandstructure equations of KORRINGA [1946], KOHN and ROSTOKER [1954] (KKR). They have solved the Schrödinger equation (1) by regarding the lattice as a periodic array of scattering sites which individually scatter the electrons with a change in phase η_l. Transition-metal sp valence electrons are found to be scattered very little by the lattice so that they exhibit NFE behaviour with η_0 and η_1 close to zero. Transition-metal d electrons, on the other hand, are strongly scattered, the $l = 2$ phase shift showing *resonant* behaviour given by

$$\tan \eta_2(E) = \tfrac{1}{2}\Gamma/(E_d - E), \tag{107}$$

where E_d and Γ determine the position and width of the resonance. This allows the KKR equations to be transformed directly into the H–NFE–TB form, in which the two centre TB hopping integrals and hybridization matrix elements are determined explicitly by the two resonant parameters E_d and Γ. The non-orthogonality contributions to the secular equation (MUELLER [1967]) are obtained by linearizing the implicit energy-dependent matrices C, D and H in a Taylor expansion about E_d.

The nonmagnetic bandstructure of fcc and bcc iron is shown in fig. 25, being computed from the H–NFE–TB secular equation with resonant parameters $E_d = 0.540$ Ry and $\Gamma = 0.088$ Ry (PETTIFOR [1970a]). The NFE pseudopotential matrix elements were chosen by fitting the first-principle values of WOOD [1962] at the pure p states $N_{1'}$ ($v_{110} = 0.040$ Ry), $L_{2'}$ ($v_{111} = 0.039$ Ry) and $X_{4'}$ ($v_{200} = 0.034$ Ry). Comparing the bandstructure of iron in the $|100\rangle$ and $|111\rangle$ directions with the canonical d bands in fig. 22, we see there is only the *one* d level with symmetry Δ_1 and Λ_1 respectively which hybridizes with the lowest NFE band, the remaining four d levels being unperturbed. Because of the canonical nature of the pure TB d bands (ANDERSEN [1973]), the bandstructure of all fcc and bcc transition metals will be very similar to that shown in fig. 25 for iron.

The transition-metal density of states, $n(E)$, is not uniform throughout the band as shown schematically in fig. 24 but displays considerable structure that is characteristic of the given crystal lattice. This is seen in fig. 26 for the bcc, fcc and hcp densities of states, which were calculated by the H–NFE–TB secular equation neglecting non-orthogonality contributions with $E_d = 0.5$ Ry and $\Gamma = 0.06$ Ry (PETTIFOR [1970b]). These early histogram densities of states are displayed rather than more accurate recent calculations (see, e.g., RATH and CALLAWAY [1973], JEPSEN *et*

References: p. 149.

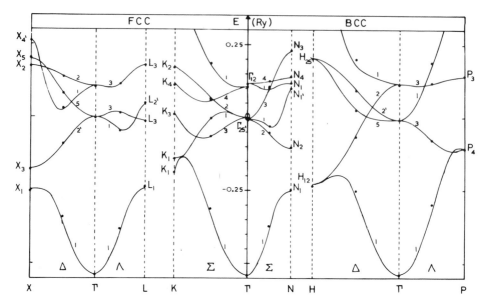

Fig. 25. The H–NFE–TB bandstructure of fcc and bcc iron in the nonmagnetic state. The solid circles represent the first-principle energy levels of WOOD [1962]. (From PETTIFOR [1970a].)

al. [1975] and MORUZZI *et al.* [1978]) because they allow a direct comparison between the bcc, fcc and hcp densities of states for the *same* model element. This will be important when discussing the relative stability of the three different crystal structures in §6.1 and the stability of the ferromagnetic state in the α, γ and ε phases of iron in §8.

The structure in the *calculated* densities of states in fig. 26 is reflected in the behaviour of the *experimental* electronic heat constant, γ, across the nonmagnetic 4d and 5d transition metal series. It follows from eqs. (53), (55) and (56) that the electronic heat capacity may be written as

$$C = \gamma T, \tag{108}$$

where

$$\gamma = \tfrac{1}{3}\pi^2 k_B^2 n(E_F). \tag{109}$$

Therefore, ignoring any renormalization effects such as electron–phonon mass enhancement, the linear dependence of the heat capacity gives a direct experimental measure of the density of states at the Fermi level. Figure 27 shows that the H–NFE–TB densities of states in fig. 26 reflect the experimental variation in γ across the series.

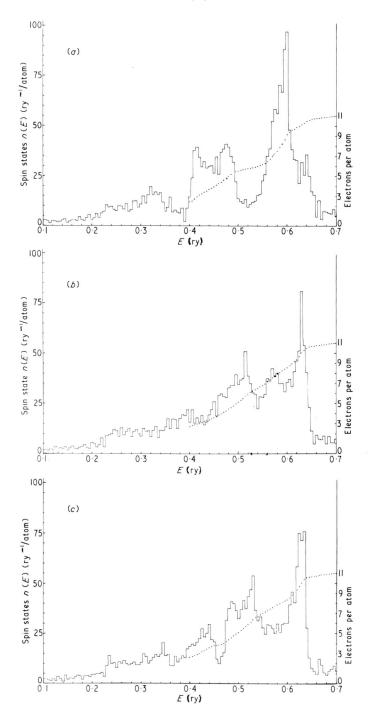

Fig. 26. The density of states for the three structures (a) bcc, (b) fcc, and (c) hcp for a model transition metal. The dotted curves represent the integrated density of states. (From PETTIFOR [1970b].)

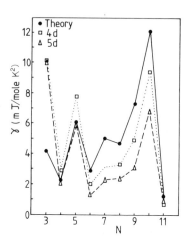

Fig. 27. A comparison of the theoretical and experimental 4d and 5d heat capacities. The theoretical values were obtained directly from eq. (109) and fig. 26, neglecting any changes in the density of states due to bandwidth changes or mass renormalization.

4.3.   Volume dependence

Figure 28 illustrates the volume dependence of the energy bands of the 4d transition metals Y, Tc and Ag, which were calculated by PETTIFOR [1977] within the atomic-sphere approximation of ANDERSEN [1973,1975]. Similar bands have been obtained by GELATT *et al.* [1977] for the 3d metals Ti and Cu with the renormalized-atom approximation of WATSON *et al.* [1970]. We see from fig. 28 that

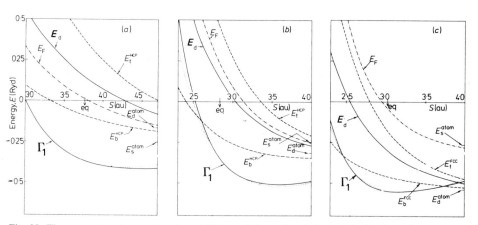

Fig. 28. The energy bands as a function of Wigner–Seitz radius S for (a) Y, (b) Tc, and (c) Ag. The observed equilibrium Wigner–Seitz radii are marked eq. The dotted curve gives the Fröhlich–Bardeen fit (eq. 87) to the bottom of the conduction band Γ_1. E_d, E_t and E_b mark the centre of gravity, and top and bottom of the d band, respectively. (After PETTIFOR [1977].)

the bottom of the NFE sp band Γ_1, which was evaluated within LDF theory, is well fitted by the Fröhlich–Bardeen expression (87). The values of R_c obtained are found to scale *within 1%* with the position of the outer node of the 5s free-atom radial wavefunction. This demonstrates quantitatively that it is the core-orthogonality constraint which is responsible for the rapid turn up in the energy of Γ_1 and that the outer node of the valence s electron is a good measure of the s core size.

The free-atom d level broadens into a band of states of width W as the atoms come together from infinity to form the bulk (see figs. 24 and 28). HEINE [1967] has shown that the Wigner–Seitz boundary conditions imply that W should vary approximately as S^{-5}, where S is the Wigner–Seitz radius. Assuming a power-law dependence of W on S, we can write

$$W = W_0(S_0/S)^n,\tag{110}$$

where W_0 and S_0 are the values of the d-band width and Wigner–Seitz radius respectively at the *equilibrium* lattice spacing of the transition metal. Table 1 gives the values of S_0, W_0 and n for the 4d transition metals (PETTIFOR [1977]). Because of the more extended nature of the d wavefunctions at the beginning of the transition metal series, n takes a value closer to four than to five which we will see in §5.2 is reflected in their bulk properties. Values of the bandwidth W for the 3d, 4d and 5d series may be obtained from the table in ANDERSEN and JEPSEN [1977] and are given explicitly in table 20–4 of HARRISON [1980]. The 3d and 5d bandwidths are approximately 30% smaller and 20% larger respectively than the corresponding 4d widths.

The centre of gravity of the TB-d band, E_d, in fig. 28 rises *exponentially* (PETTIFOR [1977]) as the volume decreases because the potential within the Wigner–Seitz sphere *renormalizes* due to the increase in the electronic charge density (GELATT et al. [1977]). This renormalization in position of the free atomic d level plays an important role in transition-metal energetics and will be discussed further in §5.2.

The different volume dependences of the NFE-sp and TB-d bands displayed in fig. 28 will lead to changes in the relative occupancy of the two bands with volume. This is illustrated in fig. 4 of PETTIFOR [1977] where Y and Zr show a rapid increase in d-band occupancy under compression as the d band widens and the bottom of the

Table 1
Equilibrium values of Wigner-Seitz radius S_0 and d band parameters W, n and n/S_0 for 4d series (from PETTIFOR [1977]).

Quantity	Element								
	Y	Zr	Nb	Mo	Tc	Ru	Rh	Pd	Ag
S_0 (au)	3.76	3.35	3.07	2.93	2.84	2.79	2.81	2.87	3.02
W_0 (eV)	6.3	7.8	9.3	9.5	9.1	8.5	7.6	6.0	3.9
n	3.9	4.0	4.1	4.3	4.5	4.6	4.8	5.1	5.6
n/S_0	1.03	1.19	1.33	1.47	1.58	1.65	1.71	1.77	1.84

References: p. 149.

sp band moves up (cf. fig. 28a). Eventually Γ_1 moves up through the Fermi level E_F at which point all the NFE-sp states have been emptied into the TB-d states and $N_d = N$. On the other hand, the transition metals with more-than-half-filled d bands display a marked degree of constancy in N_d for volumes about their *equilibrium* values, because the sp core effects are largely counter-balanced by the rapid rise in E_d due to the increasing coulomb repulsion between the d electrons (cf. fig. 28c). However, under very high pressures the bottom of the sp band does eventually move up through the Fermi level, and transition metals with *ten* valence electrons (Ni, Pd and Pt) may become semiconducting (McMahan and Albers [1982]). We will return to this dependency of the d-band occupancy on volume and core size when discussing crystal structure stability in §6.

5. Bulk properties

5.1. Simple metals

Within the *free-electron* approximation the total energy per electron may be written (see, e.g., Heine and Weaire [1970]) as:

$$U_{eg} = 2.21/r_s^2 - 0.916/r_s - (0.115 - 0.0313 \ln r_s), \tag{111}$$

where r_s is the radius of the sphere which contains one electron so that

$$r_s = Z^{-1/3}S \tag{112}$$

for a metal with valence Z and Wigner–Seitz radius S. The first term in eq. (111) is the average *kinetic* energy of a free electron gas, namely $\frac{3}{5}E_F$, where E_F is given by eq. (53). The second term is the *exchange* energy which is attractive, because parallel-spin electrons are kept apart by Pauli's exclusion principle, thereby leading to weaker mutual coulomb repulsion. The third term is the *correlation* energy which gives the additional lowering in energy due to the dynamical correlations between the electrons. It follows from eq. (111) that the free electron gas is in equilibrium for $r_s = 4.2$ au with a binding energy per electron of 0.16 Ry or 2.2 eV.

If the electron gas is perturbed to *first order* by the presence of the ionic lattice (Heine and Weaire [1970], Girifalco [1976] and Harrison [1980]), then the total binding energy *per atom* may be written as:

$$U = Z(U_{eg} + U_{ion}), \tag{113}$$

where

$$U_{ion} = -\frac{3Z}{S}\left[1 - \left(\frac{R_c}{S}\right)^2\right] + \frac{1.2Z}{S}. \tag{114}$$

The first and second terms in eq. (114) give the electron–ion [cf. eq. (87)] and the electron–electron potential energies, respectively. The potential energy has been evaluated within the Wigner–Seitz [1933] approximation of neglecting the coulomb interaction between *different* Wigner–Seitz cells as they are electrically neutral. Within the free-electron approximation the ion cores had been smeared out into a uniform positive background so that there was zero net potential energy and U_{ion} vanished.

The equilibrium Wigner–Seitz radius, S_0, which is found from eq. (113) by requiring that U is stationary, depends explicitly on the core radius R_c through the equation

$$\left(\frac{R_c}{S_0}\right)^2 = \frac{1}{5} + \frac{0.102}{Z^{2/3}} + \frac{0.0035 S_0}{Z} - \frac{0.491}{Z^{1/3} S_0}, \tag{115}$$

where the first four terms are coulomb, exchange, correlation and kinetic contributions respectively. GIRIFALCO [1976] has taken the experimental values of the Wigner–Seitz radius S_0 to determine an effective Ashcroft empty-core radius R_c from eq. (115). The resultant values are given in table 2 where, as expected, the core size increases as one goes down a given group in the Periodic Table. It is clear from table 2 that only sodium has an equilibrium value of r_s that is close to the free-electron-gas value of 4.2 au.

The bulk modulus (or inverse compressibility), which is defined by

$$B = V(d^2U/dV^2), \tag{116}$$

may be written from eqs. (113) and (115) in the form

$$B/B_{ke} = 0.200 + 0.815 \, R_c^2/r_s \tag{117}$$

at equilibrium, where the correlation contribution has been neglected since it contributes less than a few percent. B_{ke} is the bulk modulus of the non-interacting free electron gas, namely

$$B_{ke} = 0.586/r_s^5. \tag{118}$$

It follows from eq. (117) and table 2 that the presence of the ion core is crucial for obtaining realistic values of the bulk modulus of simple metals, as was first demonstrated by ASHCROFT and LANGRETH [1967]. However, the simple *first*-order expression eq. (117) is leading to large errors for the polyvalent metals with valence greater than two because the *second*-order contribution is not negligible and must be included (ASHCROFT and LANGRETH [1967]). Table 2 also demonstrates that the noble metals are not describable by the NFE approximation, the theoretical bulk moduli being a factor of five too small. We will return to this point in §5.2.

The *cohesive* energy of the simple metals is observed in table 2 to be about 1 eV *per valence electron*. For example, Na, Mg and Al have cohesive energies of 1.1, 0.8 and 1.1 eV per electron respectively. These are an order of magnitude smaller than the corresponding *binding* energies given by eq. (113), the experimental values being 6.3, 12.1, and 18.8 eV per electron respectively. Although NFE perturbation theory can yield good estimates of *bulk* properties such as the equilibrium atomic volume, structural stability and heat of formation, it can not provide reliable cohesive energies which require an accurate comparison with the *free* atom whose wavefunc-

Table 2
Equilibrium bulk properties of the simple and noble metals.

Metal	Quantity						
	Z	U_{coh}/Z (eV/electron)	S_0 [a] (au)	r_s [a] (au)	R_c (au)	B/B_{ke} (eq. 117)	B/B_{ke} (expt.)
Li	1	1.7	3.27	3.27	1.32	0.63	0.50
Na	1	1.1	3.99	3.99	1.75	0.83	0.80
K	1	0.9	4.86	4.86	2.22	1.03	1.10
Rb	1	0.9	5.31	5.31	2.47	1.14	1.55
Cs	1	0.8	5.70	5.70	2.76	1.29	1.43
Be	2	1.7	2.36	1.87	0.76	0.45	0.27
Mg	2	0.8	3.35	2.66	1.31	0.73	0.54
Ca	2	0.9	4.12	3.27	1.73	0.95	0.66
Sr	2	0.9	4.49	3.57	1.93	1.05	0.78
Ba	2	0.9	4.67	3.71	2.03	1.11	0.84
Zn	2	0.7	2.91	2.31	1.07	0.60	0.45
Cd	2	0.6	3.26	2.59	1.27	0.71	0.63
Hg	2	0.3	3.35	2.66	1.31	0.73	0.59
Al	3	1.1	2.99	2.07	1.11	0.69	0.32
Ga	3	0.9	3.16	2.19	1.20	0.74	0.33
In	3	0.9	3.48	2.41	1.37	0.83	0.39
Tl	3	0.6	3.58	2.49	1.43	0.87	0.39
Cu	1	3.5	2.67	2.67	0.91	0.45	2.16
Ag	1	3.0	3.02	3.02	1.37	0.71	2.94
Au	1	3.8	3.01	3.01	1.35	0.69	4.96

[a] From GIRIFALCO [1976].

tions are not describable by weakly perturbed plane waves. It is necessary, therefore, to perform *similar* calculations in both the free atom and the bulk as, for example, WIGNER and SEITZ [1933] and MORUZZI et al. [1978] have done in their evaluation of the cohesive energies in figs. 21 and 1 respectively. We should point out, however, that eqs. (111)–(114) do yield a *bulk* binding energy for sodium that is very similar to Wigner and Seitz's [cf. eq. (90)], because the additional exchange, correlation and self-energy terms in eqs. (113) and (114) give a net contribution of less than 0.01 eV per sodium atom. Recently, CHELIKOWSKY [1981] has linked the cohesive energy of simple metals to a kinetic-energy change which accompanies the transformation of the exponentially damped free-atom wavefunction to plane-wave bulk states. As expected from table 2 and fig. 20, it is necessary to include an additional *non-local* bulk bonding contribution in order to obtain the stronger cohesion of Li and Be and the weaker cohesion of Zn, Cd and Hg. The anomalously large cohesion of the noble metals Cu, Ag and Au will be discussed in the next subsection.

5.2. Transition metals

The theoretical points in fig. 1 were computed (MORUZZI *et al.* [1978]) by solving the Schrödinger equation (1) with the potential $v(r)$ given by

$$v(r) = v_H(r) + v_{XC}(r),\tag{119}$$

where v_H is the usual Hartree potential and v_{XC} is the exchange-correlation potential evaluated within the local density functional (LDF) approximation of HOHENBERG and KOHN [1964] and KOHN and SHAM [1965], namely

$$v_{XC}(r) = \frac{d}{d\rho}(\rho\varepsilon_{XC}(\rho)).\tag{120}$$

$\varepsilon_{XC}(\rho)$ is the exchange and correlation energy per electron of a homogeneous electron gas of density ρ. It follows from eqs. (111) and (120) that the *exchange* contribution to the potential may be written as:

$$v_X(r) = \tfrac{4}{3}\varepsilon_X(r),\tag{121}$$

where

$$\varepsilon_X(r) = -1.477[\rho(r)]^{1/3}.\tag{122}$$

Thus the exchange potential varies as the third power of the *local* density, due to the exclusion of parallel spin electrons from the immediate neighbourhood (SLATER [1951b]).

The total energy can *not* be written simply as the sum over the occupied one-electron energies E_i of the Schrödinger equation, because the eigenvalue E_i of the ith electron contains the potential energy of interaction with the jth electron and vice versa. Thus, $E_i + E_j$ *double-counts* the coulomb interaction energy between electrons i and j. The total LDF energy is, therefore, given by

$$U = \sum_i E_i - \tfrac{1}{2}\iint \frac{2\rho(r)\rho(r')}{|r-r'|}\,dr\,dr' - \int\rho(r)[v_{XC} - \varepsilon_{XC}]\,dr,\tag{123}$$

where the second and third contributions correct for the "double-counting" of the coulomb and exchange-correlation energies respectively. The potential energy has been written down in eq. (123) within the Wigner–Seitz sphere approximation, the coulomb interaction between neighbouring Wigner–Seitz cells, or Madelung contribution, being neglected. (Note that $e^2 = 2$ in atomic units, which accounts for the factor of two in the integrand of the coulomb integral.)

The presence of the double-counting contribution in eq. (123) does not allow for a direct interpretation of the *total* energy in terms of the one-electron eigenvalues E_i whose behaviour we have studied in the previous sections. For example, as can be seen from fig. 28b the one-electron sum alone would lead to no binding in Tc because the d-electron eigenvalues at the equilibrium atomic volume are everywhere higher than the free-atom d level. The inclusion of the double-counting term is crucial for bonding since it counters to a large extent the shift in the centre of gravity of the d bands E_d due to the *renormalization* of the potential under volume change.

References: p. 149.

In copper, for example, GELATT *et al.* [1977] found that the band-shift energy of 78.6 eV/atom, which accompanies the formation of the bulk metal, is almost totally cancelled by a change in the double-counting term of 77.7 eV/atom. The remaining net repulsive contribution of about 1 eV/atom is typical for the 3d and 4d transition metal series (see fig. 4 of GELATT *et al.* [1977]).

The problems associated with double-counting can be avoided, however, by working not with the total energy, U, but with the *first-order change* in energy, δU, on change in the Wigner–Seitz sphere volume, $\delta\Omega$, for the bulk metal (PETTIFOR [1976]) or change in the internuclear separation, δR, for the diatomic molecule (PETTIFOR [1978a]). By starting either from the virial theorem in the form derived by LIBERMAN [1971] or from the total-energy expression (123) following NIEMINEN and HODGES [1976], PETTIFOR [1976,1978a] showed that the first-order change in *total energy*, δU, may be written, neglecting the Madelung contribution, as:

$$\delta U = \sum_i \delta E_i, \tag{124}$$

where δE_i is the first-order change in the *eigenvalue* which accompanies the first-order volume or distance change *while the potential is kept unrenormalized.* The *general* applicability of this first-order result has been proved by ANDERSEN [1980] for force problems involving arbitrary atomic displacements and by NØRSKOV [1982] for embedding problems involving a change in the local atomic environment (cf. §7). SKRIVER [1982] and McMAHAN and MORIARTY [1983] have demonstrated the applicability of eq. (124) to the evaluation of structural energy differences (cf. §6).

The first-order expression (124) is important because it allows a direct identification of the different roles played by the valence sp and d electrons in bulk transition metal energetics. The eigenstates can be decomposed within the Wigner–Seitz sphere into their different angular momentum components, l, so that eq. (124) may be written as:

$$\delta U = -P\delta\Omega = -\sum_l P_l \delta\Omega, \tag{125}$$

where P is the pressure, given by $P = -\mathrm{d}U/\mathrm{d}\Omega$. By working within the atomic-sphere approximation of ANDERSEN [1973] the *partial pressures* P_l may be expressed (PETTIFOR [1976]) directly in terms of parameters describing the energy bands, namely:

$$3P_{\mathrm{sp}}\Omega = 3N_{\mathrm{sp}}(\Gamma_1 - \varepsilon_{\mathrm{XC}}) + 2U_{\mathrm{sp}}^{\mathrm{ke}}, \tag{126}$$

$$3P_{\mathrm{d}}\Omega = 2N_{\mathrm{d}}(E_{\mathrm{d}} - \varepsilon_{\mathrm{XC}})/m_{\mathrm{d}} + 5U_{\mathrm{d}}^{\mathrm{bond}}, \tag{127}$$

where

$$U_{\mathrm{sp}}^{\mathrm{ke}} = \int^{E_{\mathrm{F}}}(E - \Gamma_1)n_{\mathrm{sp}}(E)\,\mathrm{d}E, \tag{128}$$

$$U_{\mathrm{d}}^{\mathrm{bond}} = \int^{E_{\mathrm{F}}}(E - E_{\mathrm{d}})n_{\mathrm{d}}(E)\,\mathrm{d}E, \tag{129}$$

with $\varepsilon_{\mathrm{XC}} = \varepsilon_{\mathrm{XC}}(S)$. m_{d} is the d-band effective mass which is related to the width W

through $W = 25/(m_d S^2)$. Additional small contributions to eqs. (126) and (127) have been neglected for simplicity in the present discussion (cf. eqs. (13) and (14) of PETTIFOR [1978b]).

The sp partial pressure consists of two terms which give the first-order changes in the *bottom* of the sp band, Γ_1, and in the *kinetic* energy, respectively. In the absence of hybridization with the d band, $n_{sp}(E)$ is free-electron-like and eq. (126) is consistent with the pressure which would be obtained from the simple-metal expression (113) if correlation is neglected. This follows from eqs. (119), (121) and (87) because within LDF theory the bottom of the band is given by

$$\Gamma_1 = \Gamma_1^{WS} + 2.4Z/S + \tfrac{4}{3}\varepsilon_X \qquad (130)$$

since the electron sees the average Hartree field of the valence electrons and the exchange potential v_X in addition to the ion core pseudopotential.

The d partial pressure also consists of two terms which give the first-order changes in the *centre of gravity* of the d band, E_d, and the d *bond* energy, respectively. In the absence of hybridization we may assume that $n_d(E)$ is rectangular as illustrated in fig. 24, so that from eq. (129) the d bond energy may be written

$$U_d^{bond} = -\tfrac{1}{20} W N_d (10 - N_d). \qquad (131)$$

Assuming that $E_d - E_d^{atom}$ and W vary inversely as the fifth power of S, P_d may be integrated with respect to volume to give the d contribution to the *cohesive* energy, namely:

$$U_d = N_d(E_d - E_d^{atom})/4m_d + N_d(\tfrac{4}{3}E_d^{atom} - \varepsilon_{XC})/2m_d + U_d^{bond}. \qquad (132)$$

It follows from fig. 28a that for Tc at its equilibrium volume $E_d - E_d^{atom} = 6$ eV, $\tfrac{4}{3}E_d^{atom} - \varepsilon_{XC} = 1$ eV and $m_d = 5$. Therefore, taking, from table 2, $W = 10$ eV and $N_d = 6$, we have

$$U_d = 1.8 + 0.6 - 12 = -10 \text{ eV/atom}, \qquad (133)$$

which is in reasonable agreement with the LDF value of -8 eV/atom for the Tc cohesive energy in fig. 1.

The dominant contribution to the *cohesive energy* of transition metals is, therefore, the d bond term in eq. (133) as emphasized by FRIEDEL [1964,1969] and illustrated by GELATT *et al.* [1977] in their fig. 4. From eq. (131) it varies parabolically with band filling and accounts for the observed variation of the cohesive energy across the *nonmagnetic* 4d and 5d series shown in fig. 1. It attains a maximum value of $-5W/4$ for $N_d = 5$ when all the bonding and none of the antibonding states are occupied. Equation (132) shows that the shift in centre of gravity of the d band contribution $N_d(E_d - E_d^{atom})$ is reduced by at least an order of magnitude through the factor $(4m_d)^{-1}$, thereby accounting *analytically* for the cancellation arising from the double-counting term in eq. (123).

Figure 29 shows the sp and d partial pressures for Tc. As expected from eq. (131) there is a large *attractive* d bond contribution which is pulling the atoms together in order to maximize the strength of the bond. This is opposed for $S < 4.0$ au by a

References: p. 149.

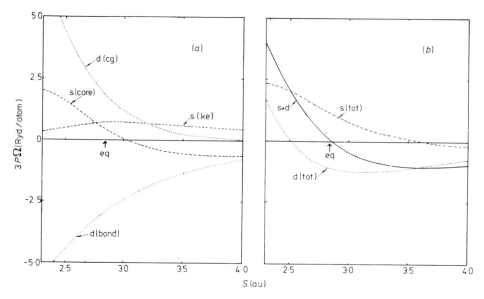

Fig. 29. (a) The *individual* and (b) the *total* sp and d partial pressures as a function of the Wigner–Seitz radius S for Tc. "eq" marks the observed equilibrium Wigner–Seitz radius. (From PETTIFOR [1978b]).

rapidly increasing *repulsive* d centre-of-gravity contribution which reflects the renormalization in E_d. The resulting total d partial pressure is *attractive* at the observed equilibrium volume of Tc (see fig. 29b). As expected from the behaviour of Γ_1 in fig. 28b the bottom of the sp band contribution is attractive for large values of S but becomes *repulsive* in the vicinity of the equilibrium volume as Γ_1 moves up in energy. Thus, whereas in simple metals this contribution is attractive because the ion cores occupy only about 10% of the atomic volume (see fig. 21 and table 3), in transition metals it is repulsive because the ion cores occupy a much larger percentage due to their smaller equilibrium atomic volumes (cf. fig. 1). Together with the sp kinetic energy contribution, the bottom of the sp band contribution provides the necessary repulsion to counter the attractive d partial pressure at equilibrium.

The *size* of a transition-metal atom, which is defined by the equilibrium atomic volume of the pure metal, is not necessarily a helpful quantity for discussing alloy energetics. We have seen that it will be very sensitive to the nature of the local atomic environment, since it is the d bond contribution which is responsible in fig. 1 for the skewed parabolic behaviour of the equilibrium Wigner–Seitz radius across the nonmagnetic 4d series. This may be demonstrated by modifying the simple model of DUCASTELLE [1970] and approximating the total energy of a transition metal by

$$U = U^{\text{rep}} + U_d^{\text{bond}}, \tag{134}$$

Table 3
The values of λ for the 3d, 4d, and 5d transition metal series.

Period	Element and value of λ (in au^{-1})							
	Sc	Ti	V	Cr	Mn	Fe	Co	Ni
3	1.08	1.23	1.37	1.49	1.61	1.74	1.88	2.07
	Y	Zr	Nb	Mo	Tc	Ru	Rh	Pd
4	1.08	1.23	1.37	1.49	1.60	1.72	1.85	2.02
	Lu	Hf	Ta	W	Re	Os	Ir	Pt
5	1.11	1.25	1.38	1.49	1.60	1.72	1.84	2.01

where the Born–Mayer contribution, U^{rep}, is:

$$U^{\text{rep}} = aN^2 e^{-2\lambda S} \tag{135}$$

with a being constant across a given series. This form is suggested by the nature of the repulsive d centre-of-gravity contribution in eq. (132) and fig. 29, although we have assumed that U^{rep} is proportional to N^2 rather than N_d^2 as a reminder that the sp electrons also contribute to the repulsion. The d bond contribution, eq. (131), is proportional to the bandwidth W which is assumed to vary exponentially as

$$W = b\lambda^2 e^{-\lambda S} \tag{136}$$

with b being constant across a given series.

The cohesive energy, equilibrium Wigner–Seitz radius and bulk modulus are given from eqs. (134)–(136) by:

$$U_{\text{coh}} = \tfrac{1}{2} U_d^{\text{bond}}, \tag{137}$$

$$S_0 = \left[\ln\left(-2aN^2/U_d^{\text{bond}}\right)\right]/2\lambda, \tag{138}$$

$$B = -\left(\lambda^2/12\pi S_0\right)U_d^{\text{bond}}. \tag{139}$$

a and b for a given period are obtained from the known bulk modulus and bandwidth of 3d Cr, 4d Mo and 5d W, the values of (a, b) being given in atomic units by (24.3, 11.6), (77.2, 25.8) and (98.9, 31.9) respectively. λ is found by fitting to the *nonmagnetic* Wigner–Seitz radius, assuming that the transition metals have only one sp valence electron. We see from fig. 30 and table 3 that although the equilibrium atomic volume has a minimum in the vicinity of $N = 8$, λ varies nearly *linearly* across the series as expected for a parameter characterizing the free atom (cf. figs. 4, 5 and 7). Thus, although Mo and Ag have almost the same size factors with their equilibrium Wigner–Seitz radii of 2.93 and 3.02 au, respectively, they are immiscible because Mo will lose a large part of its attractive d bond contribution in a Ag environment. The logarithmic derivative of the bandwidth, $-\lambda$, predicted by this model is in good agreement at the equilibrium atomic volume with the first-principles value, $-n/S_0$, as can be seen by comparing tables 1 and 3 for the 4d series.

References: p. 149.

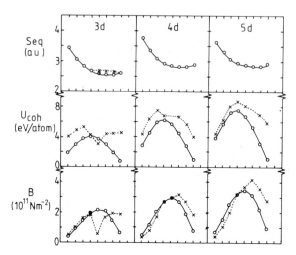

Fig. 30. The theoretical (open circles) and experimental (crosses) values of the equilibrium Wigner–Seitz radius, cohesive energy, and bulk modulus of the 3d, 4d, and 5d transition metals.

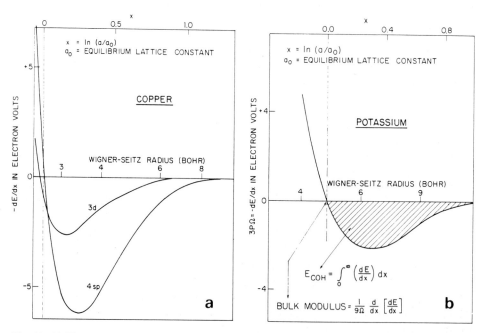

Fig. 31. (a) The sp and d partial pressures for Cu and (b) the sp pressure for K as a function of the Wigner–Seitz radius. The independent variable x is the logarithm of the ratio of the lattice constant a (or Wigner–Seitz radius S) to its equilibrium value a_0 (or S_0), so that equilibrium corresponds to the zero value of x on the upper horizontal axis. The cohesive energy associated with a given pressure curve is the area between the curve and the axis, as illustrated in (b). (From WILLIAMS et al. [1980a].)

The simple model breaks down at the noble-metal end of the series because the Born–Mayer repulsive term in eq. (134) does not describe correctly the d electron behaviour. This can be seen in fig. 31 where the d partial pressure in Cu is *attractive* at the equilibrium atomic volume, the d electrons contributing about 25% to the cohesive energy (WILLIAMS *et al.* [1980a]). Thus, as first pointed out by KOLLAR and SOLT [1974], the filled d shells in copper interact attractively rather than repulsively as assumed by the Born–Mayer contribution (135). This is due to the second term in eq. (132) which dominates at larger atomic volumes. The sp partial pressure of Cu at its minimum is also more attractive than that of K due to the incomplete screening of the Cu ion core by the 3d valence electrons. The net result is that whereas the simple metal K has a cohesive energy of 0.9 eV/atom and a bulk modulus of 0.3×10^{10} N/m^2, the noble metal Cu has a cohesive energy of 3.5 eV/atom and a bulk modulus of 13.7×10^{10} N/m^2, which is reflected by the behaviour of the curves in fig. 31.

6. Structural stability

6.1. Elemental metals

The crystal structure of the *simple* metals can be studied (see, e.g., HARRISON [1966], HEINE and WEAIRE [1970], HAFNER [1974] and MORIARTY [1982]) by perturbing the free electron gas to *second* order in the pseudopotential, thereby extending the first-order expression (113) considered in § 5.1. The resulting binding energy per atom is given in the real-space representation (FINNIS [1974]) by ·

$$U = ZU_{eg} - V\kappa_{eg}^{-1} + \tfrac{1}{2}\phi(\boldsymbol{R}=0; r_s) + \tfrac{1}{2}\sum_{\boldsymbol{R}\neq 0}\phi(\boldsymbol{R}; r_s), \tag{140}$$

where κ_{eg} is the compressibility of the free electron gas. $\phi(\boldsymbol{R}=0; r_s)$ represents the electrostatic interaction between an ion and its own screening cloud of electrons, whereas $\phi(\boldsymbol{R}\neq 0; r_s)$ is a *central* interatomic pair potential which for a local pseudopotential may be written as:

$$\phi(\boldsymbol{R}\neq 0; r_s) = \frac{2Z^2}{R}\left[1 - \frac{2}{\pi}\int_0^\infty \chi(q, r_s)\left[\hat{v}_{ps}^{ion}(q)\right]^2 \frac{\sin qR}{q}\, dq\right]. \tag{141}$$

$\hat{v}_{ps}^{ion}(q)$ is proportional to the Fourier component of the ionic pseudopotential, taking the value $\cos qR_C$ for the Ashcroft potential [cf. eq. (84)]. $\chi(q, r_s)$ is the free-electron-gas response function which screens the ion cores (see, e.g., JACUCCI and TAYLOR [1981]). The first term in eq. (141) gives the direct ion–ion coulomb repulsion, the second the attractive ion–electron contribution.

The interatomic potential (141) may be expressed analytically (PETTIFOR [1982]) at metallic densities as the sum of damped oscillatory terms, namely

$$\phi(\boldsymbol{R}\neq 0; r_s) = (2Z^2/R)\sum_n A_n\cos(2k_nR + \alpha_n)\, e^{-\kappa_nR}, \tag{142}$$

where k_n and κ_n depend only on the density of the free electron gas through r_s,

References: p. 149.

whereas the amplitude A_n and the phase α_n depend also on the ionic pseudopotential (through R_c). The interatomic potentials for Na, Mg and Al are illustrated in fig. 32, where the first three terms in eq. (142) have been retained and an Ashcroft empty-core pseudopotential used (PETTIFOR and WARD [1983]). We see that all three metals are characterized by a repulsive hard-core contribution (dotted–dashed curve), an attractive nearest-neighbour contribution (dashed curve), and an oscillatory long-range contribution (dotted curve). For *very large* interatomic separations the pair potential behaves asymptotically (FRIEDEL [1952]) as

$$\phi(R \neq 0;\, r_s) \sim A\big[v_{ps}(2k_F)\big]^2 \cos(2k_F R)/R^3, \tag{143}$$

where from eqs. (52) and (112) $k_F = (9\pi/4)^{1/3}/r_s$.

A cautionary note must be sounded concerning the use of interatomic pair potentials for describing the energetics of simple metals. It is clear from fig. 32 that

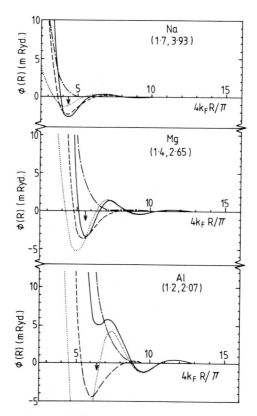

Fig. 32. The analytic pair potential (solid curve) for Na, Mg, and Al, the three individual contributions being given by the dotted–dashed, dashed, and dotted curves respectively. The arrows mark the position of the twelve nearest neighbours in the close-packed fcc and hcp lattices. The values of R_c and r_s are written (R_c, r_s) for each metal. (After PETTIFOR and WARD [1983].)

the pair-potential contribution to the binding energy of sodium and magnesium is
only about 0.25 eV/atom, which is small compared to their cohesive energies of 1.1
and 1.6 eV/atom, respectively. Moreover, in aluminium the pair contribution acts
against cohesion. Thus, there is no microscopic justification for describing the
bonding in simple metals by pair potentials alone. Their cohesion is determined
primarily by the *volume*-dependent terms in eq. (140). However, the pair potential
description is valid for tackling problems concerned with *structural* rearrangement in
which the volume remains fixed, for example in lattice dynamics or in determining
the relative stability of the close- or nearly close-packed fcc, hcp and bcc lattices.

   Figure 33 compares the stability of the fcc, hcp and bcc lattices of Na, Mg and Al
as their volume is reduced from the equilibrium value by nearly an order of
magnitude, which was computed by MORIARTY and MCMAHAN [1982] using a
generalized non-local pseudopotential to second order. We see that under pressure
Na, Mg and Al are predicted to transform from hcp → bcc → hcp, hcp → bcc → fcc
and fcc → hcp → bcc, respectively. The first of these structural transitions occurs at
about 1, 57 and 130 GPa for Na, Mg and Al respectively and should, therefore, be
verifiable by modern high-pressure technology. The trends displayed in fig. 33 may
be understood from the behaviour of the first three contributions to be pair potential
in fig. 32 (PETTIFOR and WARD [1983]; see also MCMAHAN and MORIARTY [1983]).
Because the close-packed structures fcc and hcp have identical first and second
nearest-neighbour distances their relative stability is determined by the position of
their next few neighbours with respect to the long-range oscillatory tail which is
drawn dotted in fig. 32. Since the phase α_3 of this contribution depends on r_s, under
pressure the minima shift with respect to the neighbour positions and the close-packed
phases can reverse their relative stability. On the other hand, the competition
between the close-packed phases and bcc is determined primarily by the contribution from the twelve first nearest neighbours and fourteen first and second nearest
neighbours respectively. Although at their equilibrium volume the first twelve
close-packed neighbours fall at the minimum of the pair potential, thereby favouring
the close-packed structures (cf. fig. 32), under pressure this minimum moves and the
bcc phase may be stabilized (cf. fig. 33).

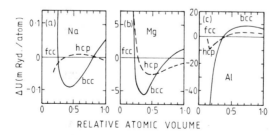

Fig. 33. The energy of the bcc and hcp lattices with respect to the fcc lattice for Na, Mg, and Al as a
function of their atomic volume relative to the observed equilibrium volumes (after MORIARTY and
MCMAHAN [1982]).

References: p. 149.

The *close-packed* metallic behaviour of Na, Mg and Al gives way to the *open* diamond structure of the semiconductor Si as one proceeds *across* the third row of the Periodic Table. This transition from close-packed to open structure is accompanied by a 30% volume expansion so that the volume-dependent term in the binding energy cannot be neglected when determining structural stability. YIN and COHEN [1980] have solved the Schrödinger equation self-consistently for Si using an ionic pseudopotential, and have evaluated the LDF binding energy [cf. eq. (123)] as a function of volume for seven different crystal structures as illustrated in fig. 34a. They find that the diamond structure has the lowest energy with a predicted equilibrium atomic volume, cohesive energy and bulk modulus within 5% of the experimental values. Moreover, the relative ordering of the metallic bcc and hcp phases and their equilibrium energy of about 0.5 eV/atom with respect to the diamond structure is in good agreement with that deduced from experiment (KAUFMAN and NESOR [1973]). The transition to the open semiconducting phase, therefore, contributes about 10% to the total cohesive energy of 4.6 eV/atom.

In moving *down* group IV we see from figs. 4 and 7 that Ge is very similar to Si with about a 10% larger core, whereas Sn and Pb have approximately 30% and 45% larger cores respectively. Thus the binding-energy–volume curves of Ge are found to be almost identical to those of Si except that the close-packed structures move down relative to the diamond structure by about 20% (compare figs. 34a and b; YIN and

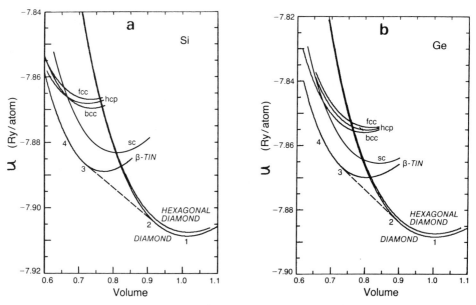

Fig. 34. The binding energy as a function of volume of (a) Si and (b) Ge for seven different crystal structures. The dashed line is the common tangent of the energy curves for the semiconducting diamond phase and the metallic β-tin phase, the system moving from 1 → 2 → 3 → 4 under pressure. (from YIN and COHEN [1980,1981] and YIN [1982].)

COHEN [1980,1981]). The further increase in core size in going from Ge to Sn is probably responsible for the β-Sn structure being stabilized under only 2 GPa of pressure and the still much larger core of Pb at the bottom of group IV leads to the close-packed fcc structure being most stable.

The crystal structure of the *transition* metals can be understood by comparing the d bond contribution eq. (129) to the total energy, because we saw in §5.2 that it dominates the cohesive energy. Figure 35 shows that as the unhybridized tight-binding d band is filled with electrons the structure-trend predicted is hcp → bcc → hcp → fcc → bcc (PETTIFOR [1972b]). Apart from the incorrect stability of the bcc phase at the noble-metal end of the series, this trend agrees with experiment for the *nonmagnetic* 4d and 5d series. The stability of the bcc phase in V and Cr, Nb and Mo, Ta and W, when the d band is nearly half-full, is due to the strong bonding–antibonding separation which is manifest in the bcc density of states compared to the close-packed (cf. fig. 26). The appearance of the bcc phase in iron is due to the presence of *ferromagnetism* (see §8). The stability of different stacking-fault structures shows the same oscillatory behaviour as displayed by the fcc–hcp curve in fig. 35 (PAPON *et al.* [1979]).

The number of d electrons, N_d, also influences the structure of the heavier alkalis and alkaline earths (TAKEMURA *et al.* [1982] and SKRIVER [1982]) and the rare earths (DUTHIE and PETTIFOR [1977]). N_d increases on moving down the *alkaline earth* group as the d band starts to fill (cf. fig. 20) so that Ca, Sr and Ba have 0.51, 0.59

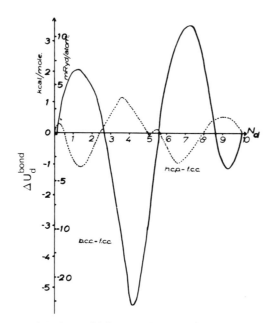

Fig. 35. The d bond energy of the bcc (solid line) and the hcp (dotted line) lattices with respect to the fcc lattice as a function of band filling N_d (from PETTIFOR [1972b]).

References: p. 149.

and 0.87 $l = 2$ electrons within the Wigner–Seitz sphere, respectively (SKRIVER [1982]). Similarly, under pressure N_d increases as the NFE-sp band moves up with respect to the TB-d band (cf. §4.3). SKRIVER [1982] has computed the structural energy differences, using eq. (124), and has found that the trend hcp → fcc → bcc → hcp correlates with increasing N_d in agreement with the observed behaviour down group IIA (Be,Mg: hcp; Ca,Sr: fcc; Ba,Ra: bcc) and under pressure. The trivalent *rare-earth* crystal structure sequence hcp → Sm-type → double hcp → fcc, which is observed for decreasing atomic number and increasing pressure, can similarly be explained in terms of the change in number of d electrons accompanying valence s to d transfer (DUTHIE and PETTIFOR [1977]). Due to the lanthanide contraction of the ion core La has a 20% larger core radius than Lu, which results in La having 0.6 d electrons more than Lu and taking the double-hcp rather than the hcp crystal structure even though they are both trivalent.

6.2. Binary alloys

The most famous example of the crystal structure correlating with the average number of valence electrons per atom, $\bar{Z}$, are the Hume-Rothery alloys of the *noble* metals with the sp bonded elements such as Zn, Al, Si, Ge and Sn (see ch. 4). Assuming that Cu and Ag have a valency of 1, then the fcc α-phase is found to extend to a $\bar{Z}$ of about 1.38, the bcc β-phase to be stabilized around 1.48, the γ-phase around 1.62 and the hcp ϵ-phase around 1.75. MOTT and JONES [1936] pointed out that the fcc and bcc electron-per-atom ratios correlate with the number of electrons required for a free-electron Fermi *sphere* to first make contact with the fcc and bcc Brillouin-zone faces, $\bar{Z} = 1.36$ and 1.48, respectively. This condition corresponds to $2k_F = |G|$ and implies that the long-range Friedel oscillations (143) are in phase with the lattice, thereby giving an additional stabilizing energy. However, as found by STROUD and ASHCROFT [1971] this only leads to the fcc lattice being stabilized in the *immediate* vicinity of $\bar{Z} = 1.36$, the hcp lattice being the most stable for $\bar{Z} < 1.3$. The fcc noble metals with $Z = 1$ can, therefore, *not* be described by the NFE approximation and the $\bar{Z}$ correlation with Fermi-sphere contact must be regarded as fortuitous.

JONES [1937], on the other hand, started with a realistic value for the Cu energy gap at L, namely 4 eV, which is an order of magnitude larger than that expected for simple NFE metals (cf. fig. 16). This large gap, which arises from hybridization and orthogonality constraints with the underlying d band (MUELLER [1967]), leads to a very *non-spherical* Fermi surface which *already* for Cu with $Z = 1$ just makes contact with the fcc Brillouin-zone face in the $\langle 111 \rangle$ direction. Contact is made with the bcc zone for $\bar{Z} = 1.23$. The resulting fcc and bcc densities of states look very similar to those for Be (fcc) and Li (bcc) in fig. 20, because JONES [1937] neglected the presence of the copper d band (cf. fig. 26). Comparing the fcc and bcc band energies JONES [1937] found that the fcc lattice was the more stable for $1 \leqslant \bar{Z} < 1.43$, but since no comparison with the hcp lattice was made, the question as to the origin of the Hume-Rothery rules remains open (HEINE, private communication). A proper treatment of the d band is expected to be essential (cf. fig. 31a). Recently, the non-sphericity of the Fermi surface of noble metal alloys and the implication for long-period superlattices (SATO and TOTH [1961]) have begun to be examined quantitatively by first-principles KKR band calculations (GYORFFY and STOCKS [1983]) assuming total disorder within the coherent-potential aproximation (CPA; see, eg., FAULKNER [1982]).

In addition to the electron-per-atom ratio, atomic size and electronegativity are also recognized as important factors in determining structural stability (see, e.g., ch. 4 and §2 of ch. 5). We saw in the previous subsection that the sp core *size* affects the structure of the elemental metals, because it determines the phase of the oscillations of the simple-metal pair potential and it influences the relative occupancy of the transition-metal d band. Moreover, we saw in §2.2 that the degree of covalency or *ionicity* in an AB bond is measured by $\Delta E/w$ where $\Delta E = E_B - E_A$. Thus, whereas in the elemental metals the coulomb interaction between different Wigner–Seitz cells may be neglected when discussing the relative stability of the close-packed lattices [cf. eq. (123)], in binary compounds the ionic Madelung contribution must be included for sufficiently large values of $\Delta E/w$.

Numerous authors have used the valence, the core-size or the atomic energy level position of the constituent atoms (c.f. figs. 4, 5 and 7) as the basis for constructing two-dimensional *structure maps* which aim to separate into characteristic domains the different crystal structures of binary compounds with a given stoichiometry AB_n. For example, the *valence* has been used by JOHANNES *et al.* [1976], MACHLIN and LOH [1980] and BIEBER and GAUTIER [1981] to plot $\bar{Z}$ vs. ΔZ structure maps for Laves, AB and AB_3 *transition*-metal compounds, respectively. Moreover, JOHANNES *et al.* [1976] showed that the $\Delta Z = 0$ extrapolation of their structure plot could be understood within tight-binding theory, because the TB-d bond contribution gave the observed structure sequence of the Laves phases, namely $MgCu_2 \to MgZn_2 \to MgCu_2 \to MgNi_2$ as $\bar{Z}$ increases. The s and p *core-radii* have been used by ST. JOHN and BLOCH [1974], ZUNGER [1980] and BURDETT *et al.* [1981] to construct structure maps which in the latter two references included compounds with the non-sp elements as well. The metallic radii R_A and R_B have been used by VILLARS *et al.* [1982] to plot R_A/R_B versus $\bar{R}$ diagrams. The relative position of the *atomic energy level* ΔE has been used by BURDETT [1983] to plot ΔE vs. $\bar{Z}$ structure maps for the pd bonded compounds with AB and AB_2 stoichiometry, whilst WATSON and BENNETT [1978] have constructed similar structure maps for the transition-metal compounds but using the difference in their electronegativity scale as one of the coordinates.

A microscopic theory of alloy crystal structure would depend on *all* the above mentioned factors of valence, size and atomic energy level position. For example, the number of valence electrons alone does not differentiate between periods so that the important chemical shifts that take place as one moves down a given group are neglected. On the other hand, the core size by itself overestimates these changes down a group, being more sensitive to a change in row than to a change in column (cf. fig. 7). If, therefore, the aim of structure maps is to provide the best structural

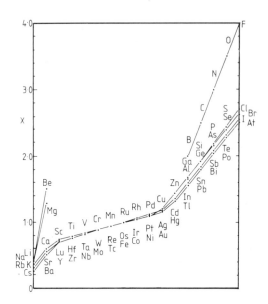

Fig. 36. The chemical scale χ (after PETTIFOR [1983]).

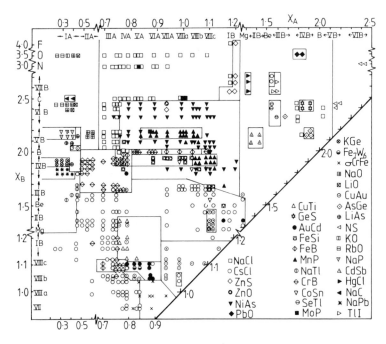

Fig. 37. The (χ_A, χ_B) structure map for 499 AB compounds excluding the sp–sp octets (from PETTIFOR [1983]).

separation of *binary* alloys within a *two-dimensional* plot (χ_A, χ_B), then a new chemical scale χ may be defined to achieve this end. Figure 36 shows such a scale which was set up (PETTIFOR [1983]) by requiring that the variation of chemical coordinate χ *within* a group does not overlap and mix with neighbouring groups (excluding the second-row elements B to F which behave in a chemically distinct fashion from other elements in the same group). χ is also constrained to vary linearly *across* the transition-metal series and again across the sp elements to the right of the noble metals, thereby reflecting the linear behaviour observed in the inverse core size (fig. 7), the s, p and d atomic energy levels (figs. 4 and 5), and the number of valence electrons. The magnitude of the chemical scale is fixed by requiring it to take the Pauling electronegativity values for Be to F.

Figure 37 shows the resulting structure map for 499 binary AB compounds where excellent structural separation is achieved throughout the Periodic Table. The 75 *octet* sp–sp binary AB compounds are not included in fig. 37, but as a group they are separated perfectly by the chemical scale χ into their four structural domains NaCl, CsCl, ZnS and ZnO respectively (PETTIFOR [1983]). The microscopic origin of the different structural domains in fig. 37 remains to be detailed.

7. Heat of formation

A simple and successful *semi-empirical* scheme for calculating the heats of formation of binary alloys has been developed by MIEDEMA *et al.* [1980], who characterized each element in the Periodic Table by two co-ordinates ϕ^* and $\rho^{1/3}$. The heat of formation of a binary AB alloy is then written (in the simplest case) as:

$$\Delta H = -P(\Delta\phi^*)^2 + Q(\Delta\rho^{1/3})^2, \tag{144}$$

where P and Q are positive constants. The attractive term depends on the difference in the elemental work functions, $\Delta\phi$, (later modified to $\Delta\phi^*$) and is similar in spirit to PAULING'S [1960] electronegativity contribution. The repulsive term depends on the difference in the cube root of the electron densities at the elemental Wigner–Seitz sphere boundaries, $\Delta\rho^{1/3}$, and was argued to arise from the distortion of the charge density across the AB interface. Equation (144) has been useful in providing quantitative values for the heats of formation. In this section the *microscopic* origin of the attractive and repulsive contributions to ΔH will be examined in the light of our understanding of the cohesion of the elemental metals (cf. §§ 5 and 6).

Miedema's expression (144) has been most successful in the treatment of binary *transition*-metal alloys, which are well-described by the tight-binding approximation. By analogy with FRIEDEL'S [1964] treatment of pure transition metal cohesion, the AB alloy band may be approximated (PETTIFOR [1979]) by a rectangular density of states of width W_{AB} as shown in fig. 38. It follows from tight-binding theory (CYROT and CYROT-LACKMAN [1976]) that:

$$W_{AB}^2 = W^2 + 3(\Delta E_d)^2, \tag{145}$$

References: p. 149.

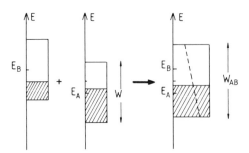

Fig. 38. The rectangular d band model representing AB alloy formation. The dashed line separates the partial density of states associated with atom A from that associated with atom B.

which generalizes the dimer result, eq. (37), to the bulk metal. The first term is the contribution to the square of the alloy bandwidth that arises from nearest-neighbour bonding, whereas the second term reflects the increase in alloy bonding due to the ionicity which is measured by $\Delta E_d = E_d^B - E_d^A$ [cf. eq. (40)]. Thus, the alloy bandwith is given by

$$W_{AB} = \left[1 + 3(\Delta E_d/W)^2\right]^{1/2} W. \tag{146}$$

The heat of formation may now be evaluated explicitly. Filling up the alloy band with the average number of d electrons per atom, $\bar{N}_d$, and comparing the resulting band energy with that obtained from pure metal bands of width W (as illustrated in fig. 38), one finds the contribution to the heat of formation ΔH_0 given by:

$$\Delta H_0/W = -\tfrac{1}{80}(\Delta N_d)^2 - \tfrac{1}{4}\Delta N_d(\Delta E_d/W) - \tfrac{3}{40}\bar{N}_d(10 - \bar{N}_d)(\Delta E_d/W)^2, \tag{147}$$

where eq. (146) has been expanded to second order, and $\Delta N_d = N_d^B - N_d^A$. In addition, there is a further contribution ΔH_1 due to the fact that the elemental equilibrium atomic volumes V_A and V_B are in general different, so that the d bond energy of pure A and B is determined by W_A and W_B, respectively, and not by W as drawn in fig. 38. Assuming that the bandwidth varies inversely with the volume to the five-thirds power (c.f. eq. (110); HEINE [1967]) and that the alloy volume is $V_{AB} = \bar{V} = 1/2(V_A + V_B)$ by Vegard's law, then

$$\Delta W = W_B - W_A = -\tfrac{5}{3}W(\Delta V/\bar{V}). \tag{148}$$

The resulting change in the bond energy due to the change in the bandwidths of the elemental metals from W to W_A, W_B, respectively is given by

$$\Delta H_1/W = -\tfrac{1}{24}(5 - \bar{N}_d)\Delta N_d(\Delta V/\bar{V}). \tag{149}$$

Expressions (147) and (149) may be simplified still further for binary alloys from the *same* transition-metal series. Choosing the 4d series because the 3d row is complicated by the presence of magnetism (cf. §8), we can write $\Delta E_d = -N_d$ eV from fig. 5 and $V = V(N_d)$ from fig. 30. Substituting into eqs. (147) and (149) and taking $W = 10$ eV from table 1, the heat of formation (in eV/atom) is given to second order by

$$\Delta H = \left[f_0(\bar{N}_d) + f_1(\bar{N}_d) \right](\Delta N_d)^2, \tag{150}$$

where

$$f_0(\bar{N}_d) = \tfrac{1}{8}\left[1 - \tfrac{3}{50}\bar{N}_d(10 - \bar{N}_d) \right] \tag{151}$$

and

$$f_1(\bar{N}_d) = -\tfrac{1}{24}(5 - \bar{N}_d)\left(\frac{\mathrm{d}\ln V}{\mathrm{d}N_d} \right)_{\bar{N}_d}. \tag{152}$$

Equation (150) represents the second-order term in a Taylor expansion of $\Delta H(N_d^A, N_d^B)$ in powers of ΔN_d as WILLIAMS *et al.* [1980b] have emphasized.

Figure 39 compares the results of the tight-binding theory with the MIEDEMA *et al.* [1980] semi-empirical values for $\Delta N_d \leqslant 4$, where we see that reasonable agreement is obtained. The more attractive values of ΔH found by MIEDEMA *et al.* [1980] near $\bar{N}_d = 5$ reflect *structural* bonding effects which are not included in the present model with its uniform alloy density of states (c.f. fig. 38). The dependence of the heat of formation on crystal structure has been demonstrated by the first-principles LDF calculations of WILLIAMS *et al.* [1980b] who compared ΔH for the CuAu (fcc) and CsCl (bcc) lattices. It is clear from fig. 39 that the most stable AB alloys will be those for which the average d-band filling is close to 5.5 and ΔN_d is large, for example YPd. On the other hand, for average d-band fillings less than about 4 or greater than 7 the heat of formation will be positive.

The attractive contribution in Miedema's expression (144) may be identified with ΔH_0 provided that ϕ^* is interpreted as the *electronegativity* X rather than the work function ϕ. Within the TB model the charge transfer Q is obtained by assuming partial densities of states $n_A(E)$ and $n_B(E)$ on the A and B sites in the alloy as illustrated in fig. 38. n_A and n_B have been skewed so that their centres of gravity correspond to E_d^A and E_d^B, respectively (PETTIFOR [1980]). The resulting d charge transfer is given by

$$Q_d^B = \tfrac{1}{2}\Delta N_d + \tfrac{3}{10}\bar{N}_d(10 - \bar{N}_d)(\Delta E_d/W_{AB}). \tag{153}$$

The first term reflects the flow of electrons from right to left across the series due to increasing electron density and the second term reflects the flow from left to right due to the increasingly attractive d level as one proceeds across the series (cf. fig. 5). The flow of electrons is, therefore, *not* driven by the difference in the *work functions* $\Delta\phi$ alone, because *all* the electrons throughout the band respond on alloying and not just those in the vicinity of the Fermi level. This can be seen by comparing, in fig. 38, the skewed partial density of states $n_A(E)$ in the AB alloy with the rectangular density of states in the pure metal A.

By implication, the charge transfer is proportional to the difference in the electronegativities, so that we may define a d-electronegativity X_d by

$$\Delta X_d = Q_d. \tag{154}$$

References: p. 149.

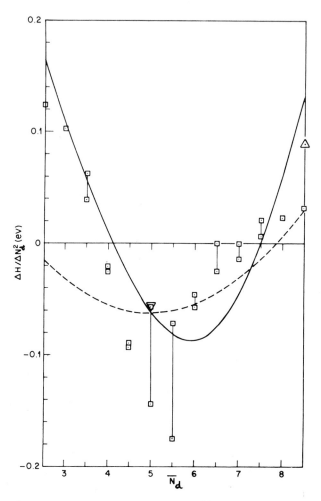

Fig. 39. $\Delta H/(\Delta N_d)^2$ as a function of the average band filling $\overline{N}_d$ for the 4d series. The dashed curve is the ΔH_0 contribution, eq. (151). The squares represent the Miedema values for the 4d alloys with $\Delta N_d \leqslant 4$, the points with common $\overline{N}_d$ being connected by straight lines. (From PETTIFOR [1979].)

Substituting into eq. (153) and integrating for the 4d series with $\Delta E_d/W = -\Delta N_d/10$, the electronegativity is found to be

$$X_d = -\tfrac{1}{2}N_d\left[1 - \tfrac{1}{50}N_d(15 - N_d)\right] + 1.8, \tag{155}$$

where the constant of integration has been chosen so that Mo with $N_d = 5$ takes the PAULING [1960] value of 1.8. Equation (155) is plotted in fig. 40 and compares surprisingly well with the Pauling electronegativities across the 4d series. It follows from eq. (147) and eqs. (153)–(155) that ΔH_0 can be expressed approximately as:

$$\Delta H_0 = -\tfrac{1}{10}W(\Delta X_d)^2 \tag{156}$$

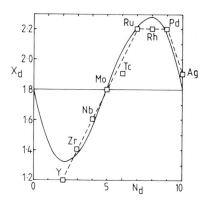

Fig. 40. The d-band electronegativity, X_d, compared to PAULING'S [1960] values (squares) for the 4d series.

for $|\overline{N}_d - 5| \leqslant 5/\sqrt{3}$. Equation (156) gives the correct value of the dashed curve in fig. 39 at the centre of the band and it vanishes at the correct cross-over points $\overline{N}_d = 5 \pm 5/\sqrt{3}$. Since Miedema's final choice of ordinate ϕ^* is very similar to Pauling's electronegativity X (MIEDEMA *et al.* [1980]), the attractive contribution in eq. (144) may be associated with ΔH_0 through eq. (156). The repulsive contribution in the semi-empirical scheme follows ΔH_1 very closely numerically, but conceptually the latter reflects a mismatch in the d band width rather than the electron density (see also WILLIAMS *et al.* [1982]). The heats of formation of 3d, 4d and 5d transition metal AB alloys have been tabulated by WATSON and BENNETT [1981] who used an optimized version of the d band model.

The heats of formation of *simple*-metal binary alloys may be calculated within second-order perturbation theory provided the valence difference $\Delta Z = Z_B - Z_A$ is not too larger (HAFNER [1976] and LEUNG *et al.* [1976]). Neglecting the structurally dependent pair-potential contribution and ignoring the density dependence of $\phi(R = 0; r_s)$ in eq. (140), the heat of formation ΔH will be determined by the volume-dependent free electron gas terms alone. Assuming Vegard's Law with $V_{AB} = \overline{V} = \frac{1}{2}(V_A + V_B)$, these give (PETTIFOR and GELATT [1983]) the contribution (in eV/atom):

$$\Delta H_{eg} = \overline{Z} f_{eg}\left(\overline{\rho^{1/3}}\right)\left(\Delta \rho^{1/3}\right)^2, \tag{157}$$

where

$$f_{eg}\left(\rho^{1/3}\right) = -43.39 + 7.81/\rho^{1/3} + 0.17/\left(\rho^{1/3}\right)^2. \tag{158}$$

The three terms in eq. (158) are the kinetic, exchange and correlation contributions respectively, the flow of charge from the more dense to the less dense atom *lowering* the kinetic energy but raising the exchange and correlation energies. Equation (157) is reminiscent of the MIEDEMA *et al.* [1980] repulsive contribution in eq. (144).

References: p. 149.

However, as is clear from fig. 41 the prefactor f_{eg} is not a positive constant Q but is dependent on the average cube root of the density $\bar{\rho}^{1/3}$. It changes sign from *positive* at low densities (where the exchange and correlation dominate) to *negative* at high densities (where the kinetic energy dominates). The first-principle LDF calculations of ΔH for the Na, Mg, Al, Si, P series with respect to the CsCl (bcc) lattice show the same trend in fig. 41 as eq. (158) although displaced somewhat from the free-electron-gas result because the explicit influence of the core through the last two terms in eq. (140) has been neglected.

Structural effects can be important in determining the sign of ΔH of simple-metal alloys (cf. §2.3.2 of MIEDEMA *et al.* [1980]). This has been demonstrated by the second-order pseudopotential calculations of HAFNER [1977] on binary alkali metal alloys, which are illustrated in fig. 42 for the A_2B stoichiometry. (His values of ΔH for the bcc alloys are approximately four times larger than the experimental, LDF or free-electron gas values, because his calculated density differences are larger than experiment.) Whereas the disordered bcc alloys have *positive* heats of formation, the ordered Laves phases Rb_2Cs, K_2Cs and Na_2K have *negative* heats of formation due to the arrangement of the nearest-neighbour atoms with respect to the minimum in the pair potential. Therefore, provided the volume-dependent contribution to ΔH is not too large and positive, the structural contribution due to the pair potential can

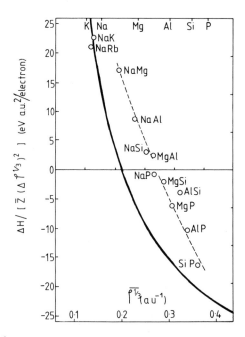

Fig. 41. $\Delta H / [\bar{Z}(\Delta \rho^{1/3})]^2$ as a function of the average cube root of the electron density $\bar{\rho}^{1/3}$ for the 3s and 3p series. The solid curve is the electron-gas contribution, eq. (158). The open circles are the LDF results for the CsCl lattice. (From PETTIFOR and GELATT [1983]).

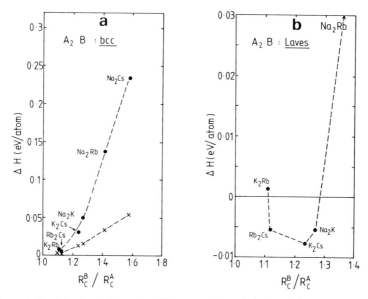

Fig. 42. The *calculated* heats of formation (HAFNER [1977]) of A_2B alkali-metal alloys for (a) the disordered bcc phase and (b) the ordered $MgZn_2$ Laves phase as a function of R_C^B/R_C^A from table 2. The crosses give the electron gas contribution eq. (157) using the *experimental* densities of the elemental metals.

stabilize the phase. If a semi-conducting gap opens up in the alloy density of states, then this will provide additional stability (MIEDEMA *et al.* [1980]), which requires the theory to be extended beyond second order.

The heats of formation of sp elements with transition metals is illustrated by fig. 43 for the Li-row elements with the 4d transition metals. They were calculated by GELATT *et al.* [1983] using LDF theory for the AB stoichiometry with respect to the NaCl lattice. Their theoretical values agree broadly with the semi-empirical values of MIEDEMA *et al.* [1980] who found it necessary to include for sp–d alloys an additional attractive contribution, $-R$, in their expression (144). R is written as the product of two numbers which are determined by the groups in the Periodic Table from which the sp and d constituents are drawn. GELATT *et al.* [1983] have interpreted their results in terms of an *attractive* sp–d bonding contribution, which becomes increasingly ionic on proceeding across the sp series from Li to F, and a *repulsive* d-bond contribution. The latter reflects the loss of d-bond energy due to the narrower alloy d bandwidth, which arises from the larger transition-metal–transition-metal nearest neighbour distance in the alloy as compared to the elemental metal. Curves similar to fig. 43 have been obtained by GELATT *et al.* [1978] for the 3d and 4d transition-metal hydrides.

The heat of *solution* of hydrogen and helium in metals may be calculated within the *effective-medium* approximation of STOTT and ZAREMBA [1980] and NØRSKOV and LANG [1980]. They assumed that the energy required to embed an atom at some

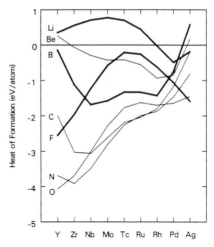

Fig. 43. The heats of formation of 4d transition metals with Li row elements in the NaCl structure (GELATT *et al.* [1983]).

given position R in a host metal which is characterized by an *inhomogeneous* density $\rho(r)$, is the same as that required to embed the atom in a *homogeneous* electron gas of density $\rho = \bar{\rho}(R)$, where $\bar{\rho}(R)$ is the average host electron density seen by the impurity atom at R. Then the energy of the impurity atom at position R in the host lattice is given to lowest order by

$$\Delta U(R) = \left[\Delta U_{\text{hom}}(\rho)\right]_{\rho = \bar{\rho}(R)}. \tag{159}$$

The homogeneous embedding energy $\Delta U_{\text{hom}}(\rho)$ can be evaluated within LDF theory and the results for H and the rare-gas atoms He and Ne are shown in fig. 44a (PUSKA *et al.* [1981]). We see that the rare-gas atoms display a positive embedding energy at all densities because their full electronic shells *repel* the free electron gas through orthogonality constraints. On the other hand, the open-shell hydrogen atom shows a minimum at $\rho = 0.0026$ au^{-3} (i.e., $\rho^{1/3} = 0.138$ au^{-1}) corresponding to an *attractive* embedding energy of -1.8 eV, although it is repulsive for typical transition-metal densities of 0.02–0.03 au^{-3}.

The heats of solution of H and He across the 3d series are shown in fig. 44b after NØRSKOV [1982] and MANNINEN *et al.* [1982], respectively. The results include an important first-order *electrostatic* correction term to eq. (159), which reduces the slope of the He curve in fig. 44a by half and lowers the H curve by -120ρ eV au^3 so that the H embedding energy is attractive throughout the entire range of metallic densities (cf. the solid circles in fig. 44b). The behaviour of the helium heat of solution across the 3d series mirrors that of the host metallic density which varies like the bulk modulus shown in fig. 1. The hydrogen heat of solution is measured with respect to the binding energy of the H_2 molecule, namely -2.4 eV/atom. We see in fig. 44b that agreement with experiments is obtained only if a first-order

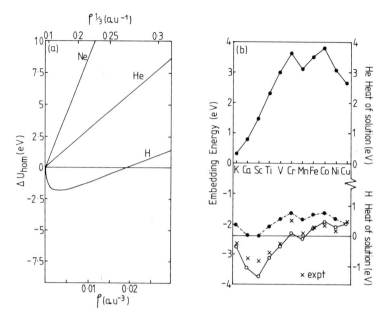

Fig. 44. (a) The homogeneous embedding energy for H and the rare gas atoms He and Ne in a free electron gas of density ρ (after PUSKA *et al.* [1981]). (b) The H and He heats of solution across the 3d series (after NØRSKOV [1982] and MANNINEN *et al.* [1982] respectively). The solid circles include a first-order electrostatic contribution. The open circles include, in addition, a first-order hybridization correction.

hybridization correction is included from eq. (124) which reflects the bonding between the hydrogen impurity and the host nearest neighbour atoms (NØRSKOV [1982]). The effective-medium approximation with first-order electrostatic and hybridization corrections included has been applied successfully to defect problems such as the trapping energies of H and He by interstitials, vacancies and voids (NØRSKOV *et al.* [1982] and MANNINEN *et al.* [1982]). The electron theory of point defects has been reviewed by JENA [1981].

The *ordering* energy of a binary $A_c B_{1-c}$ alloy is defined by

$$\Delta U_{ord} = U_{ord} - U_{dis},\tag{160}$$

where U_{ord} and U_{dis} are the energies in the completely ordered and disordered states respectively. By using second-order perturbation theory for the NFE *simple* metals (HAYES *et al.* [1968] and INGLESFIELD [1969]) or a generalized perturbation theory for the TB *transition* metals (DUCASTELLE and GAUTIER [1976]) the ordering energy eq. (160) can be expressed directly in terms of effective pair interactions ϕ_1, ϕ_2, ϕ_3,... between the first, second, third,... nearest neighbour atoms. ϕ_n depends explicitly on $|\Delta v_{ps}(q)|^2$ for the simple metals and on $|\Delta E_d|^2$ for the transition metals. The ordering energy for $c \leqslant 0.5$ may be written (see, e.g., DE FONTAINE [1979]) as:

$$\Delta U_{ord} = \sum_n \left[p_n - (1-c)^2 z_n \right] \phi_n,\tag{161}$$

References: p. 149.

where z_n and p_n are the number of nth nearest neighbour atoms and B–B atom pairs respectively.

The effective pair interaction in transition metals with respect to an fcc lattice is illustrated by fig. 45a where ϕ_1 and ϕ_2 are plotted as a function of average band filling $\bar{N}_d$ for the TB d band alloy with $c = 0.25$ and $\Delta E_d/W = 0.45$ (BIEBER *et al.* [1983]). As expected from the behaviour of the simple-metal pair potentials in §6.1, the transition-metal pair interactions display oscillations as a function of band filling, $\bar{N}_d$, and nearest neighbour position, n. Figure 45b compares the ordering energy evaluated by the pair interaction of DUCASTELLE and GAUTIER [1976] with the exact TB energy difference from eq. (160). We see that for this particular alloy it is a good approximation in the band-filling region where ordering occurs. Moreover, because the second and further nearest neighbour interactions are at least an order of magnitude smaller than the first nearest neighbour interactions, the ordering energy is dominated by ϕ_1 through eq. (161).

The pair interactions also determine the most stable ordered structure with respect to a given lattice (BIEBER and GAUTIER [1981]). For example, in fig. 46 the Cu_3Au and Al_3Ti structures are shown, which are built on the fcc lattice. They have the same type of first nearest neighbour atoms, so that their relative stability is determined by ϕ_2 and further nearest neighbour interactions. Since ϕ_2 in fig. 45a is negative for $4.4 < \bar{N}_d < 7.3$ when $\Delta E_d/W = 0.45$, the ordered structure with *like* second nearest neighbours will be the more stable, i.e. Cu_3Au. The stability reverses

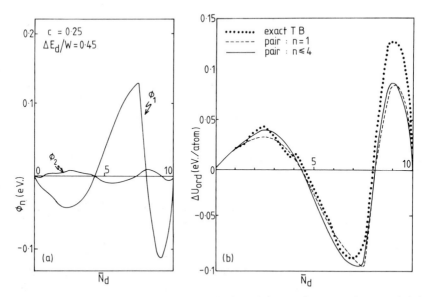

Fig. 45. (a) The first and second nearest neighbour effective pair interrractions, ϕ_1 and ϕ_2, as a function of the average band filling, $\bar{N}_d$, for an AB_3 transition-metal alloy with $\Delta E_d/W = 0.45$ on an fcc lattice. (b) A comparison with the exact result of the ordering energy evaluated using the effective pair interactions. (After BIEBER *et al.* [1983].)

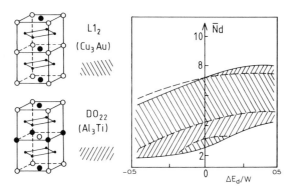

Fig. 46. The relative stability of the Cu_3Au and Al_3Ti structures as a function of the average band filling $\bar{N}_d$, and the renormalized difference in the atomic d levels, $\Delta E_d / W$ (after BIEBER and GAUTIER [1981]).

outside this band-filling region, thereby accounting for the nature of the structure map in fig. 46. This displays only a narrow stability range for the Al_3Ti phase, which is in agreement with empirical structure maps (BIEBER and GAUTIER [1981]).

The ordering energy can be written as the sum of pair interactions, because second-order perturbation theory may be used to expand the energy with respect to the totally disordered state [cf. eq. (160)]. Thus, although the TB d-bond energy *cannot* be expressed as a two-body sum, small energy changes with respect to a given reference may. For example, transition-metal elastic constants (STEINEMANN and FISHER [1981]) and lattice dynamics (VARMA and WEBER [1979]) have been calculated using TB theory to second order in the lattice displacements, thereby leading to explicit force constants between pairs of atoms (FINNIS *et al.* [1983]).

8. *Magnetism*

The magnetic 3d elements have anomalously large equilibrium atomic volumes and small bulk moduli as evidenced by the deviations in fig. 1 between experiment and the non-magnetic LDF theory. In this section we will see that the STONER [1939] theory of band magnetism can explain this anomalous behaviour.

A nonmagnetic system will become magnetic if the lowering in *exchange* energy due to the alignment of the electron spins more than compensates the corresponding increase in kinetic energy. This may be demonstrated by the rectangular d-band model of fig. 47. In the *nonmagnetic* state, the up and down spin electrons are equivalent and, therefore, they have identical density of states $n_\uparrow$ and $n_\downarrow$ as shown in fig. 47a. In the *magnetic* state, the presence of a local magnetic moment, m, produces an exchange field Δ on the atom, of strength

$$\Delta = Im, \tag{162}$$

where I is the Stoner exchange parameter and $m = N_d^\uparrow - N_d^\downarrow$ in Bohr magnetons

References: p. 149.

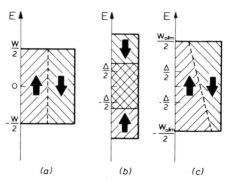

Fig. 47. The rectangular d band model of the (a) nonmagnetic, (b) ferromagnetic, and (c) antiferromagnetic states (after PETTIFOR [1980]).

(μ_B). In the *ferromagnetic* state, all the atomic moments are aligned in the same direction, so that an up-spin electron sees the atomic level E_d shifted by $-\frac{1}{2}\Delta$ on every site, the down-spin electron by $+\frac{1}{2}\Delta$. Therefore, the densities of states $n_\uparrow$ and $n_\downarrow$ are shifted *rigidly* apart by Δ as shown in fig 47 b. On the other hand, in the *antiferromagnetic* state, half the atoms have their moments aligned up, the other half have their moment aligned down, so that an electron sees two types of sites, with energies $E_d \pm \frac{1}{2}\Delta$. The problem is, therefore, analogous to that of the AB alloy discussed in the previous section (cf. fig. 38), and the densities of states $n_\uparrow$ and $n_\downarrow$ (corresponding to an atom with net moment up) are obtained by *skewing* the rectangular nonmagnetic densities of states as shown in fig. 47c.

The magnetic energy which accompanies the formation of a local moment m at each site, may be written as:

$$U_{mag} = \delta T - \tfrac{1}{4} I m^2, \tag{163}$$

where the first term is the change in the kinetic energy and the second is the lowering in energy due to exchange. The *ferromagnetic* (fm) state is created by flipping $\frac{1}{2}m$ down-spin electrons from just below the nonmagnetic Fermi level into the unoccupied up-spin states just above the nonmagnetic Fermi level. This is accompanied by an increase in kinetic energy of $(\frac{1}{2}m)/n(E_F)$ per electron, so that, to second order,

$$U_{fm} = \tfrac{1}{4} m^2 / n(E_F) - \tfrac{1}{4} I m^2 \tag{164}$$

where in this section $n(E_F)$ refers to the nonmagnetic density of states *per spin*. Therefore, the nonmagnetic state will be unstable to ferromagnetism if $U_{fm} < 0$, i.e. if:

$$I n(E_F) > 1 \tag{165}$$

which is the famous *Stoner criterion*. The *equilibrium* value of m in the ferromagnetic state is determined by the condition

$$\overline{In(N_d, m)} = 1, \tag{166}$$

where $\overline{n(N_d, m)}$ is the average of the nonmagnetic density of states per spin between the two energies corresponding to a band-filling of $N_d^{\downarrow}$ and $N_d^{\uparrow}$ respectively (see, e.g., GUNNARSSON [1976]).

The magnetic energy of the *antiferromagnetic* (afm) state can be obtained (PETTIFOR [1980]) by adding up the band energies in fig. 47c and subtracting off the exchange energy which has been double-counted, i.e.:

$$U_{afm} = -\tfrac{1}{20}(W_{afm} - W)N_d(10 - N_d) + \tfrac{1}{4}Im^2, \tag{167}$$

where from eq. (145)

$$W_{afm} = \left\{1 + 3(\Delta/W)^2\right\}^{1/2}W. \tag{168}$$

Expanding eq. (168) to second order and using eq. (162), the nonmagnetic state is found to be unstable to antiferromagnetism if

$$I/W > \left[\tfrac{3}{10}N_d(10 - N_d)\right]^{-1}. \tag{169}$$

This is the rectangular d-band model criterion equivalent to the exact second-order result, namely

$$I\chi_q(E_F) > 1 \tag{170}$$

where $\chi_q(E_F)$ is the response function corresponding to the afm ordering wave vector q (see, e.g., FEDDERS and MARTIN [1966]). The usefulness of the present model is that eqs. (167) and (168) include terms beyond second order so that the *equilibrium* value of the magnetic moment and energy may be obtained explicitly. Equation (167) is stationary for

$$m = (1/\sqrt{3})\left\{\left[\tfrac{3}{10}N_d(10 - N_d)\right]^2 - (W/I)^2\right\}^{1/2} \tag{171}$$

when

$$U_{afm} = \left[\tfrac{1}{20}WN_d(10 - N_d) - \tfrac{1}{6}W^2/I\right] - \tfrac{1}{4}Im^2. \tag{172}$$

The first term in eq. (172) represents the change in kinetic energy, δT. The value of the moment given by eq. (171) is identical to that obtained by filling the up and down spin bands in fig. 47c and solving eq. (162) self-consistently.

Figure 48 shows the regions of stability of the ferromagnetic and antiferromagnetic phases as a function of the renormalized exchange integral, I/W, and band filling, N_d, for the rectangular d-band model (see also PENN [1966]). The fm and afm phases are stable for values of I/W above the critical curves ABC (fm) and DBE (afm), which are defined by eq. (165) with $n(E_F) = 5/W$ and eq. (169), respectively. In the region where both phases are stable, the fm and afm state have the lower energy in region FBE and ABF respectively.

The magnetic behaviour across the 3d series can be accounted for qualitatively

References: p. 149.

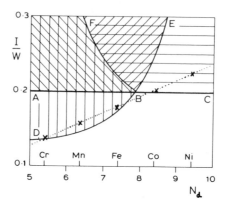

Fig. 48. The regions of stability of the ferromagnetic and antiferromagnetic states as a function of the renormalized exchange integral, I/W, and d band filling, N_d. The crosses mark plausible values of I/W across the 3d series. (After PETTIFOR [1980].)

(see also MORIYA [1965]) by assigning the 3d transition-metals values of N_d in fig. 48 which fix Ni with 0.6 holes. Values of I/W are chosen as marked by the crosses in fig. 48, the numbers lying in the range expected from first-principles LSDF calculations where $I \approx 1$ eV and $W \approx 5$ eV for the 3d series (see, e.g., KÜBLER [1981]). I is approximately constant across the series but W increases from Ni to Cr just as observed in table 1 for the corresponding 4d series from Pd to Mo. Therefore, we expect I/W to decrease in moving from Ni to Cr, as shown in fig. 48. The positions of the crosses in fig. 48 imply that Ni and Co are strong ferromagnets with moments of 0.6 and 1.6 μ_B respectively, whereas Fe ($I/W = 0.180$), Mn($I/W = 0.158$), and Cr ($I/W = 0.136$) are anti-ferromagnets with local moments from eq. (171) of 0.9, 1.6 and 0.7 μ_B, respectively.

In practice, the rectangular d band model is not too bad a description of the *close-packed* fcc and hcp metals whose densities of states are fairly constant away from the top of the d band (c.f. fig. 26). This is demonstrated in fig. 49 by the bandstructure calculations of ASANO and YAMASHITA [1973] who evaluated the fm and afm local moments across the 3d series. Their fcc results are similar to those obtained from fig. 48. In particular, fcc iron is unable to maintain a fm moment, being instead a weak antiferromagnet. However, if I/W were to increase (by volume expansion), then fig. 48 implies that fcc iron eventually stabilizes in the fm state as has been observed experimentally by GRADMANN and ISBERT [1980] and theoretically by the LSDF calculations of KÜBLER [1981].

On the other hand, bcc transition metals have a very non-uniform density of states and are characterized by a very marked antibonding peak for $N \approx 8$ electrons (cf. fig. 26a). $n(E_F)$ is sufficient for the 3d transition metal iron to satisfy the Stoner criterion (165) and the resulting magnetic energy of -0.3 eV/atom (JANAK and WILLIAMS [1976]) stabilizes the bcc lattice with respect to the nonmagnetic or weakly afm close-packed lattices. Under pressure, however, the d band broadens and the

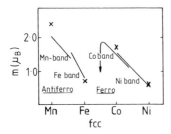 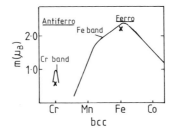

Fig. 49. The magnetic moments of the 3d metals in the ferromagnetic and antiferromagnetic states calculated as a function of band filling by ASANO and YAMASHITA [1973] for the fcc and bcc lattices. The crosses mark the experimental values.

density of states decreases, thereby leading to an increased kinetic-energy contribution in eq. (164). At just over 10 GPa the nonmagnetic structural energy contribution in fig. 35 wins out and ferromagnetic bcc α-iron transforms to the nonmagnetic hcp ε-phase (MADSEN *et al.* [1976]). This is the most stable structure of the isovalent 4d and 5d elements Ru and Os at their equilibrium volume because their wider d bands prevent them from satisfying the Stoner criterion. At atmospheric pressure bcc α-iron transforms to the fcc γ-phase at 1184 K and changes back to the bcc δ-phase at 1665 K just before melting at 1809 K. The occurrence of the α, γ, δ and ε-phases in the temperature–pressure phase diagram of iron can be understood qualitatively (HASEGAWA and PETTIFOR [1983]) within a band theory of magnetism which extends Stoner theory to finite temperatures (CYROT [1970], HASEGAWA [1980] and HUBBARD [1981]).

The simple rectangular d band model of antiferromagnetism presented in fig. 47c does not include any Fermi-surface *nesting* effects which LOMER [1962] argued were responsible for the observed periodicity of the bcc Cr spin density wave. In practice, even though nesting provides only a small contribution to $\chi_q(E_F)$ in eq. (170), it is sufficient to take bcc Cr across the afm stability curve DBE in fig. 48 (WINDSOR [1972] and SKRIVER [1981a]).

The anomalous behaviour of the equilibrium atomic volumes and bulk moduli of the 3d series observed in fig. 1 is due to the *magnetic pressure*, $P_{mag} = -dU_{mag}/dV$, which accompanies moment formation (SHIGA and NAKAMURA [1969] and JANAK and WILLIAMS [1976]). Assuming that I is volume-independent (MADSEN *et al.* [1976]) and W varies inversely with volume to the five-thirds power (HEINE [1967]), it follows from eqs. (164), (167) and (172) that

$$3P_{mag}V = 5\delta T, \qquad (173)$$

because $\delta U_{mag}/\delta m = 0$ at equilibrium.

In particular, for the *ferromagnetic* state the kinetic-energy change, δT, may be approximated by the first term in eq. (164), so that

$$3P_{fm}V = \tfrac{5}{4}m^2/n(E_F). \qquad (174)$$

JANAK and WILLIAMS [1976] have shown that this simple expression accounts for the increase in equilibrium volume on going to the ferromagnetic state which the LSDF results display in fig. 50. For example, iron and nickel have moments of 2.2 and 0.6 μ_B, respectively, and LDF nonmagnetic density of states per spin of 1.5 and 2.2 states per eV atom respectively. Substituting into eq. (174) gives a magnetic pressure for iron and nickel of 21.2 and 1 GPa, respectively, which leads to an increase in the equilibrium volume of 7% and $\frac{1}{2}$%, respectively. The increase in atomic volume reduces the bulk modulus because the valence s electrons are now no longer compressed to the same extent into the core region where they are repelled by orthogonality effects (cf. §5.2).

Figure 50 shows that the experimental *trend* in the equilibrium atomic volume and bulk modulus across the ferromagnetic metals Fe, Co and Ni is well accounted for by the LSDF results (JANAK and WILLIAMS [1976]). Similarly, SKRIVER et al. [1978] have obtained good agreement with experiment across the 5f actinide series, where the LSDF calculations reproduce the sudden 30% volume expansion that is observed in going from Pu to Am, due to the formation of a 5f moment. The 4f rare earths Ce and Pr have also been studied within LSDF theory, by Glötzel [1978] and SKRIVER [1981b] respectively. However, errors remain in figs. 1 and 50 (for the 3d metals in particular) which must be attributed to the *local* approximation to the exchange and correlation energy functional. For example, LDF theory does not position the valence s and d bands in exactly the correct relative position (HARRIS and JONES [1978]) or provide the correct exchange splitting in nickel (WOHLFARTH [1980] and COOKE et al. [1981]). Although the correlations can be treated perturbatively within a TB framework (FRIEDEL and SAYERS [1977]), a simple *non-local* extension of the LDF approximation will be required for the next generation of higher-accuracy first-principles calculations (see, e.g., WILLIAMS and VON BARTH [1983]).

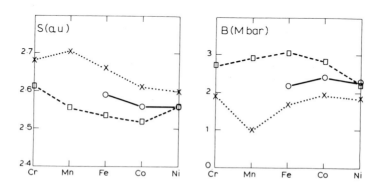

Fig. 50. The equilibrium Wigner–Seitz radius, S, and bulk modulus, B, across the magnetic 3d transition metals. The crosses, circles, and squares are the experimental, spin-polarized LSDF and nonmagnetic LDF results, respectively. (After JANAK and WILLIAMS [1976].)

References

ANDERSEN, O.K., 1973, Solid State Commun. **13**, 133.

ANDERSEN, O.K., 1975, Phys. Rev. **B12**, 3060.

ANDERSEN, O.K., 1980, §5.3 of A.R. MACKINTOSH and O.K. ANDERSEN, in: Electrons at the Fermi Surface, ed. M. Springford (Cambridge Univ. Press).

ANDERSEN, O.K., and O. JEPSEN, 1977, Physica B **91**, 317.

ASANO, S., and J. YAMASHITA, 1973, Prog. Theor. Phys. **49**, 373.

ASHCROFT, N.W., 1966, Phys. Lett. **23**, 48.

ASHCROFT, N.W., and D.C. LANGRETH, 1967, Phys. Rev. **155**, 682.

BACHELET, G.B., D.R. HAMANN and M. SCHLUTER, 1982, Phys. Rev. **B26**, 4199.

BIEBER, A., and F. GAUTIER, 1981, Solid State Commun. **38**, 1219.

BIEBER, A., F. DUCASTELLE, F. GAUTIER, G. TREGLIA and P. TURCHI, 1983, Solid State Commun. **45**, 585.

BLOCH, A.N., and G.C. SCHATTEMAN, 1981, in: Structure and Bonding in Crystals, vol. I, eds. O'Keeffe and Navrotsky (Academic, New York).

BRANDOW, B.H., 1977, Adv. Phys. **26**, 651.

BURDETT, J.K., 1983, J. Solid State Chem., to be published.

BURDETT, J.K., G.D. PRICE and S.L. PRICE, 1981, Phys. Rev. **B24**, 2903.

* CALLAWAY, J., 1964, Energy Band Theory (Academic, London).

CHELIKOWSKY, J.R., 1981, Phys. Rev. Lett. **47**, 387.

COOKE, J.F., J.W. LYNN and H.L. DAVIS, 1980, Phys. Rev. **B21**, 4118.

COULSON, C.A., L.R. REDEI and D. STOCKER, 1962, Proc. Roy. Soc. **A270**, 357.

CYROT, M., 1970, Phys. Rev. Lett. **25**, 871.

CYROT, M., and F. CYROT-LACKMANN, 1976, J. Phys. **F6**, 2257.

DE FONTAINE, 1979, Solid State Physics, vol. 34 (Academic, New York).

DUCASTELLE, F., 1970, J. Physique **31**, 1055.

DUCASTELLE, F., and F. GAUTIER, 1976, J. Phys. **F6**, 2039.

DUTHIE, J.C., and D.G. PETTIFOR, 1977, Phys. Rev. Lett. **38**, 564.

* FAULKNER, J.S., 1982, Prog. Mater. Sci. **27**, 1.

FEDDERS, P.A., and P.C. MARTIN, 1966, Phys. Rev. **143**, 245.

FINNIS, M.W., 1974, J. Phys. **F4**, 1645.

FINNIS, M.W., K. KEAR and D.G. PETTIFOR, 1983, Phys. Rev. Lett., to be submitted.

FRIEDEL, J., 1952, Phil. Mag. **43**, 153.

FRIEDEL, J., 1964, TMS AIME **230**, 616.

FRIEDEL, J., 1969, in: The Physics of Metals, ed. J.M. Ziman (Cambridge Univ. Press, New York) p. 494.

FRIEDEL, J., and C.M. SAYERS, 1977, J. Physique **38**, 697.

GELATT, C.D., H. EHRENREICH and R.E. WATSON, 1977, Phys. Rev. **B15**, 1613.

GELATT, C.D., H. EHRENREICH and J.A. WEISS, 1978, Phys. Rev. **B17**, 1940.

GELATT, C.D., A.R. WILLIAMS and V.L. MORUZZI, 1983, Phys. Rev. **B27**, 2005.

GIRIFALCO, L.A., 1976, Acta Metall. **24**, 759.

GLÖTZEL, D., 1978, J. Phys. **F8**, L163.

GRADMANN, U., and H. ISBERT, 1980, J. Magn. Magn. Mater. **15–18**, 1109.

GUNNARSSON, O., 1976, J. Phys. **F6**, 587.

GUNNARSSON, O., and B.I. LUNDQUIST, 1976, Phys. Rev. **B13**, 4274.

GYORFFY, B.L., and G.M. STOCKS, 1983, Phys. Rev. Lett. **50**, 374.

HAFNER, J., 1974, Phys. Rev. **B10**, 4151.

HAFNER, J., 1976, J. Phys. **F6**, 1243.

HAFNER, J., 1977, Phys. Rev. **B15**, 617.

HARRIS, J., and R.O. JONES, 1978, J. Chem. Phys. **68**, 3316.

HARRISON, W.A., 1959, Phys. Rev. **116**, 555.

HARRISON, W.A., 1960, Phys. Rev. **118**, 1190.

* HARRISON, W.A., 1966, Pseudopotentials in the Theory of Metals (Benjamin, New York).

* HARRISON, W.A., 1980, Electronic Structure and the Properties of Solids (Freeman, San Francisco).
HASEGAWA, H., 1980, J. Phys. Soc. Japan **49**, 963.
HASEGAWA, H., and D.G. PETTIFOR, 1983, Phys. Rev. Lett. **50**, 130.
HAYES, T.M., H. BROOKS and A.R. BIENENSTOCK, 1968, Phys. Rev. **175**, 699.
HEINE, V., 1967, Phys. Rev. **153**, 673.
HEINE, V., and I. ABARENKOV, 1964, Phil. Mag. **9**, 451.
* HEINE, V., and D. WEAIRE, 1970, Solid State Physics, vol. 24 (Academic, New York).
HERMAN, F., and S. SKILLMAN, 1963, Atomic Structure Calculations (Prentice Hall, Englewood Cliffs, NJ).
HERRING, C., 1940, Phys. Rev. **57**, 1169.
HODGES, L., H. EHRENREICH and N.D. LANG, 1966, Phys. Rev. **152**, 505.
HOHENBERG, P., and W. KOHN, 1964, Phys. Rev. **136**, B864.
HUBBARD, J., 1967, Proc. Phys. Soc. **92**, 921.
HUBBARD, J., 1981, Phys. Rev. **B23**, 5974.
INGLESFIELD, J.E., 1969, J. Phys. **C2**, 1285.
JACOBS, R.L., 1968, J. Phys. **C1**, 492.
JACUCCI, G., and R. TAYLOR, 1981, J. Phys. **F11**, 787.
JAN, J-P., and H.L. SKRIVER, 1981, J. Phys. **F11**, 805.
JANAK, J.F., and A.R. WILLIAMS, 1976, Phys. Rev. **B14**, 4199.
JENA, P., 1981, Treatise Mater. Sci. Tech. **21**, 351.
JEPSEN, O., O.K. ANDERSEN and A.R. MACKINTOSH, 1975, Phys. Rev. **B12**, 3084.
JOHANNES, R.L., R. HAYDOCK and V. HEINE, 1976, Phys. Rev. Lett. **36**, 372.
JONES, H., 1973, Proc. Phys. Soc. (London) **49**, 250.
KAUFMAN, L., and H. NESOR, 1973, in: Titanium Science and Technology, vol. 2, eds. R.I. Jaffe and H. Burte (Plenum, New York) p. 773.
* KITTEL, C., 1971, Introduction to Solid State Physics (Wiley, New York).
KOHN, W., and N. ROSTOKER, 1954, Phys. Rev. **94**, 1111.
KOHN, W., and L.J. SHAM, 1965, Phys. Rev. **140**, A1133.
KOLLAR, J., and G. SOLT, 1974, J. Phys. Chem. Solids **35**, 1121.
KORRINGA, J., 1946, Physica **13**, 392.
KÜBLER, J., 1981, Phys. Lett. **81A**, 81.
LEUNG, C.H., M.J. STOTT and W.H. YOUNG, 1976, J. Phys. **F6**, 1039.
LIBERMAN, D.A., 1971, Phys. Rev. **B3**, 2081.
LOMER, W.M., 1962, Proc. Phys. Soc. **A80**, 489.
MACHLIN, E.S., and B. LOH, 1980, Phys. Rev. Lett. **45**, 1642.
MADSEN, J., O.K. ANDERSEN, U.K. POULSEN and O. JEPSEN, 1976, in: Magnetism and Magnetic Materials 1975, Philadelphia, eds. J.J. Becker and G.H. Lander (AIP Conf. Proc. **29**, New York) p. 327.
MANNINEN, M., J.K. NØRSKOV and C. UMRIGAR, 1982, J. Phys. **F12**, L1.
MATTHEISS, L.F., 1972, Phys. Rev. **B5**, 290.
McMAHAN, A.K., and R.C. ALBERS, 1982, Phys. Rev. Lett. **49**, 1198.
McMAHAN, A.K., and J.A. MORIARTY, 1983, Phys. Rev., submitted.
MIEDEMA, A.R., P.F. DE CHATEL and F.R. DE BOER, 1980, Physica B **100**, 1.
MORIARTY, J.A., 1982, Phys. Rev. **B26**, 1754.
MORIARTY, J.A., and A.K. McMAHAN, 1982, Phys. Rev. Lett. **48**, 809.
MORIYA, T., 1965, Prog. Theor. Phys. **33**, 157.
MORUZZI, V.L., J.F. JANAK and A.R. WILLIAMS, 1978, Calculated Electronic Properties of Metals (Pergamon, New York).
MOTT, N.F., 1949, Proc. Phys. Soc. **A62**, 416.
MOTT, N.F., and H. JONES, 1936, Properties of Metals and Alloys (Dover, New York) ch. 7.
MUELLER, F.M., 1967, Phys. Rev. **153**, 659.
NIEMINEN, R.M., and C.H. HODGES, 1976, J. Phys. **F6**, 573.
NØRSKOV, J.K., 1982, Phys. Rev. **B26**, 2875.

Nørskov, J.K., and N.D. Lang, 1980, Phys. Rev. **B21**, 2131.

Nørskov, J.K., F. Besenbacher, J. Bottiger, B.B. Nielsen and A.A. Pisarev, 1982, Phys. Rev. Lett. **49**, 1420.

Papon, A.M., J.P. Simon, P. Guyot and M.C. Desjonqueres, 1979, Phil. Mag. **39**, 301.

Pauling, L., 1960, The Nature of the Chemical Bond (Cornell Univ. Press, New York).

Penn, D.R., 1966, Phys. Rev. **142**, 350.

Pettifor, D.G., 1970a, Phys. Rev. **B2**, 3031.

Pettifor, D.G., 1970b, J. Phys. **C3**, 367.

Pettifor, D.G., 1972a, J. Phys. **C5**, 97.

Pettifor, D.G., 1972b, in: Metallurgical Chemistry, ed. O. Kubaschewski (Her Majesty's Stationery Office, London) p. 191.

Pettifor, D.G., 1976, Commun. Phys. **1**, 141.

Pettifor, D.G., 1977, J. Phys. **F7**, 613.

Pettifor, D.G., 1978a, J. Chem. Phys. **69**, 2930.

Pettifor, D.G., 1978b, J. Phys. **F8**, 219.

Pettifor, D.G., 1979, Phys. Rev. Lett. **42**, 846.

Pettifor, D.G., 1980, J. Magn. Magn. Mater. **15–18**, 847.

Pettifor, D.G., 1982, Phys. Scripta, **T1**, 26.

Pettifor, D.G., 1983, Phys. Rev. Lett., to be submitted.

Pettifor, D.G., and C.D. Gelatt, 1983, fig. 8 of Cohesion and Decohesion in the Metallic Bond, in: Atomistics of Fracture, Proc. Nato Adv. Res. Inst., Corsica, 1981, ed. R. Latanision (Plenum, New York).

Pettifor, D.G., and M.A. Ward, 1983, Phys. Rev. Lett., submitted.

Phillips, J.C., 1970, Rev. Mod. Phys. **42**, 317.

Puska, M.J., R.M. Nieminen and M. Manninen, 1981, Phys. Rev. **B24**, 3037.

Rath, J., and J. Callaway 1973, Phys. Rev. **B8**, 5398.

Ruedenberg, K., 1962, Rev. Mod. Phys. **34**, 326.

St. John, J., and A.N. Bloch, 1974, Phys. Rev. Lett. **33**, 1095.

Sato, H., and R.S. Toth, 1961, Phys. Rev. **124**, 1833.

Schiff, L.I., 1968, Quantum Mechanics, 3rd Ed. (McGraw–Hill, New York).

Shiga, M., and Y. Nakamura, 1969, J. Phys. Soc. Japan. **26**, 24.

Skriver, H.L., 1981a, J. Phys. **F11**, 97.

Skriver, H.L., 1981b, in: Physics of Solids under High Pressure, eds. J.S. Schilling and R.N. Shelton (North-Holland, Amsterdam) p. 279.

Skriver, H.L., 1982, Phys. Rev. Lett. **49**, 1768.

Skriver, H.L., O.K. Andersen and B. Johannsson, 1978, Phys. Rev. Lett. **41**, 42.

Slater, J.C., 1951a, Phys. Rev. **82**, 538.

Slater, J.C., 1951b, Phys. Rev. **81**, 385.

Slater, J.C., 1963, Quantum Theory of Molecules and Solids, vol. I (McGraw–Hill, Maidenhead).

Slater, J.C., and G.F. Koster, 1954, Phys. Rev. **94**, 1498.

Steinemann, S.G., and E.S. Fisher, 1981, Treatise Mater. Sci. Tech. **21**, 223.

Stoner, E.C., 1939, Proc. Roy. Soc. **A169**, 339.

Stott, M.J., and E. Zaremba, 1980, Phys. Rev. **B22**, 1564.

Stroud, D., and N.W. Ashcroft, 1971, J. Phys. **F1**, 113.

Takemura, K., S. Minomura and O. Shimomura, 1982, Phys. Rev. Lett. **49**, 1772.

Taylor, R., and A.H. MacDonald, 1980, J. Phys. **F10**, 2387.

Tinkham, M., 1964, Group Theory and Quantum Mechanics (McGraw–Hill, New York).

Varma, C.M., and W. Weber, 1979, Phys. Rev. **B19**, 6142.

Villars, P., K. Girgis, and F. Hulliger, 1982, J. Solid State Chem. **42**, 89.

Watson, R.E., and L.H. Bennett, 1978, J. Phys. Chem. Solids **39**, 1235; Phys. Rev. **B18**, 6439.

Watson, R.E., and L.H. Bennett, 1981, Calphad **5**, 25.

Watson, R.E., H. Ehrenreich and L. Hodges, 1970, Phys. Rev. Lett. **24**, 829.

Wigner, E.P., and F. Seitz, 1933, Phys. Rev. **43**, 804.

WILLIAMS, A.R., and U. VON BARTH, 1983, in: Theory of the inhomogeneous electron gas, eds. S. Lundquist and N.H. March (Plenum, New York)..

WILLIAMS, A.R., C.D. GELATT and V.L. MORUZZI, 1980a, in: Proc. Metallurg. Soc. AIME, New Orleans 1979, ed. L.H. Bennett (Met. Soc. AIME, Warrendale, PA).

WILLIAMS, A.R., C.D. GELATT and V.L. MORUZZI, 1980b, Phys. Rev. Lett. **44**, 429.

WILLIAMS, A.R., C.D. GELATT and V.L. MORUZZI, 1982, Phys. Rev. **B25**, 6509.

WINDSOR, C.G., 1972, J. Phys. **F2**, 742.

WOHLFARTH, E.P., 1980, in: Ferromagnetic Materials, vol. 1, ed. E.P. Wohlfarth (North-Holland, Amsterdam) ch. 1.

WOOD, J.H., 1962, Phys. Rev. **126**, 517.

YIN, M.T., 1982, Ph.D. thesis, Univ. of California, Berkeley, figs. 5 and 6.

YIN, M.T., and M.L. COHEN, 1980, Phys. Rev. Lett, **45**, 1004.

YIN, M.T., and M.L. COHEN, 1981, Solid State Commun. **38**, 625.

ZUNGER, A., 1980, Phys. Rev. **B22**, 5839.

Further reading

References marked with an asterisk in the list above can also be used for general reading.

CHAPTER 4

STRUCTURE OF SOLID SOLUTIONS

T.B. MASSALSKI

*Department of Metallurgical Engineering
and Materials Science
Carnegie–Mellon University
Pittsburgh, PA, USA*

R.W. Cahn and P. Haasen, eds.
Physical Metallurgy; third, revised and enlarged edition
© *Elsevier Science Publishers BV, 1983*

1. Solid solubility

A *solid solution* is obtained when atoms of different elements are able to share together, and with changing proportions, various sites of a common crystalline lattice. It is now generally recognized that *all* metals and compounds show some solubility in the solid state; a question of great interest is, however, the extent of solid solubility in a given case. For example, only 0.2 wt% of phosphorus can be dissolved in γ-iron, but nearly 39 wt% of zinc can be dissolved in copper without changing its structure. On alloying copper with nickel, on the other hand, the same fcc structure is maintained throughout the entire alloy system (fig. 1a), providing an example of *complete solid solubility*. The Cu–Au alloys have complete solid solubility at high temperatures, but show different behavior at low temperatures (see fig. 1b and § 10). In the great multitude of phase diagrams now known the above cases, and even the case of partial but extensive solid solubility (of several atomic percent), are relatively rare. Complete solid solubility can occur only if the structures of the elements involved are basically the same, but it need not always occur when this condition is fulfilled (i.e., system Cu–Ag). In the case of close-packed hexagonal

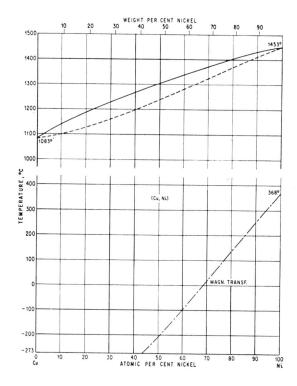

Fig. 1a. Complete solid solubility in the system Cu–Ni which maintains fcc structure throughout the whole composition range (from HANSEN and ANDERKO [1958]).

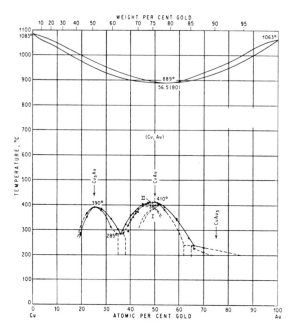

Fig. 1b. The Cu–Au system has complete solid solubility and fcc structure at high temperatures. At low temperatures superlattices form (see §10). (From HANSEN and ANDERKO [1958].)

solid solutions considerable difference between the values of the axial ratio can usually be accommodated on changing from one element to another; for example, the axial ratio, c/a, changes from 1.5873 for Ti to 1.5931 for Zr in the Ti–Zr system, and from 1.6235 for Mg to 1.8856 for Cd in the Mg–Cd system. The phase diagrams of these systems are shown in figs. 1c and 1d. In the case of Ti–Zr the pure elements exist in two allotropic forms (cubic at high temperatures and hexagonal at low temperatures), and complete solid solubility occurs between both modifications on alloying. In the Mg–Cd system, on the other hand, complete solubility occurs only at high temperatures and is interrupted at lower temperatures by the formation of superlattices (see §10).

From the point of view of solid solubility, chemical compounds can be compared with pure metals and may be said to show alloying behaviour if they exhibit wide solid solubility in a phase diagram. Since compounds are usually formed at fixed ratios of the numbers of atoms, the occurrence of solid solubility represents a departure from stoichiometry. If a compound is truly ionic in nature, the extent of such departure may be extremely small, amounting perhaps to a fraction of an at%; and for all practical purposes this is usually ignored and the compound is then drawn as a vertical line in the phase diagram. However, in typical metallic systems a large number of phases have been observed at atomic compositions which bear no

References: p. 214.

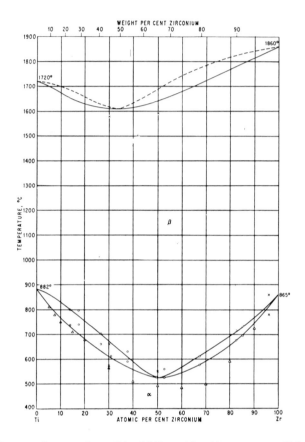

Fig. 1c. The Ti–Zr system has complete solid solubility, with cubic structure at high temperatures and hexagonal structure at low temperatures (from HANSEN and ANDERKO [1958]).

apparent relation to the rules of stoichiometry. Such phases frequently possess wide ranges of solid solubility and resemble the solid solutions obtained on initial alloying of pure metals. To a metallurgist the occurrence of wide solid solubility, both between pure metals and in compounds, is of great practical interest because it is often associated with relatively simple metallic structures which possess desirable mechanical and physical properties.

In this chapter we shall examine some of the factors which determine the limits of solid solubility in metallic systems and then consider some properties of the structure of extended solid solutions, such as lattice spacings, defects, departure from randomness, size effects, etc.

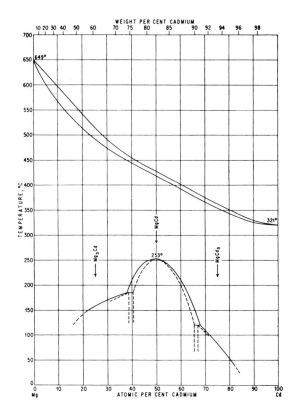

Fig. 1d. In the Mg–Cd system complete solid solubility occurs at high temperatures. Superlattices form at low temperatures (see § 10). (From Hansen and Anderko [1958].)

2. *Terminology (types of solid solutions)*

Solid solutions are phases of variable composition, and in principle any number of components can be alloyed together to form a series of solid solutions. However, for simplicity we shall consider mainly the binary alloys. The replacement of copper atoms by nickel on the lattice of pure copper is an example of a *substitutional* solid solution. Since the two elements can be substituted at all proportions throughout the whole system, they form a *continuous series of solid solutions.* If the solid solubility is limited to only those portions of the phase diagram which are linked to pure elements, the resulting phases are known as *primary (or terminal) solid solutions.* Such solutions have, of course, the same structure as the elements on which they are based. All other phases are usually known as *intermediate phases*; they may be called *intermetallic compounds* or *valence compounds* if their solid solubility is unusually restricted around a stoichiometric composition. Intermediate phases often possess

References: p. 214.

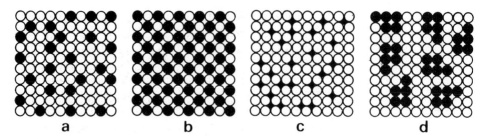

Fig. 2. Schematic models of solid solutions: (a) substitutional random; (b) Substitutional ordered; (c) interstitial random; (d) solute clusters in solid solution.

structures which are different from the structure of either of the component elements.

If the size-difference between the component atoms which participate in forming a solid solution is sufficiently large, it may become possible on alloying for the one kind of atoms to be merely deposited in the holes (or interstices) between the other atoms on their space lattice. An *interstitial* solid solution is then formed. Such solutions can occur for example when nonmetallic elements such as boron, oxygen, nitrogen or carbon are dissolved in a metal lattice.

Both interstitial and substitutional solid solutions can be *random*, with statistical distribution of atoms, or they may be partially or completely *ordered*, in which case the unlike atoms show preference for one another. A fully ordered solid solution is sometimes known as a *superlattice*. Alternatively, the like-atoms may tend to associate together to form clusters within the solid solution. Again, the clusters may be dispersed randomly or they may be ordered or oriented in various ways, producing a variety of complex substructures within the solid solution. A diagrammatical illustration of the various types of solid solution is given in fig. 2.

While it is possible to consider the case of a random solid solution as an idealized example, the mounting experimental evidence, based mainly on diffuse X-ray scattering, suggests that complete randomness (like perfect crystallinity) is probably never found in nature. Hence, solid solutions which are in a thermodynamical equilibrium (ch. 6) may be considered to be truly *homogeneous* on a macroscopic scale, but they need not be homogeneous down to the scale where atoms are considered individually.

3.   Factors governing solid solubility (Hume-Rothery rules for primary solid solutions)

Since all interactions between atoms are a function of electronic forces, they should ultimately be subject to the laws of quantum mechanics. At the present time, however, the available theories of the solid state are unable to incorporate or to account for the many factors which have been known to metallurgists as important in determining the structure and various properties of solid solutions. Such factors, for example, as chemical affinity or the size-difference between atoms can be considered only semi-empirically, and even the electronic structure, for which more elaborate theories exist, has been discussed satisfactorily only in a few rather simple cases. Nevertheless, mainly as a result of studies by Hume-Rothery and his associates (HUME-ROTHERY [1926], HUME-ROTHERY [1961a] and HUME-ROTHERY et al. [1969]), extending over more than thirty years, certain general rules have been formulated concerning the limits of primary solid solubility and, to some measure, also the width and stability of certain intermediate phases. These rules refer to the difference between the relative atomic radii of the participating elements, their electrochemical differences and their relative valencies. *Hume-Rothery rules* may be summarized as follows:

(i) If the difference between the atomic sizes of the component elements forming an alloy exceeds about 14–15%, solid solubility should become restricted. This is known as the *15% rule*. The general concept may be illustrated by reference to fig. 3 (HUME-ROTHERY [1961a]) in which the ranges of favorable atomic sizes with respect to copper, silver and γ-iron are shown diagrammatically. If the atomic diameter of a particular solute element lies outside the favorable size zone for the solvent, the *size factor* is said to be unfavorable and the primary solid solubility will be restricted usually in some proportion to the increasing difference between the two atomic diameters. Within the favorable zone the size factor is only of secondary importance and other factors will determine the total extent of solid solubility. In a sense, therefore, the 15% rule is a negative rule stressing the role of size differences only when they *restrict* alloy formation. In this connection, WABER et al. [1963] have shown that when the size rule alone was applied to 1423 terminal solid solutions, in 90.3% of the systems where little solid solubility was predicted, little solid solubility was in fact observed, but the prediction of extensive solid solubility on the basis of small size difference was only 50% successful. Theoretical justification for the 15% rule has been obtained from considerations of elastic strain energy in a solid solution (see below).

(ii) Formation of stable intermediate compounds will restrict primary solid solubility. The likelihood of the formation of such compounds in an alloy system is related to the chemical affinity of the participating elements and will be increased the more electronegative one of the elements and the more electropositive the other. The general principle leading to the restriction of solid solubility is illustrated in fig. 4 using hypothetical free-energy curves for a primary solid solution and for an intermediate phase. The width of the shaded area represents the extent of primary solid solubility; it becomes more restricted the greater the stability of the intermediate phase. The above principle has become known as the *electronegative valency effect*.

(iii) Empirical studies have shown that in many alloy systems one of the most important factors determining the extent of solid solubility and the stability of certain intermediate phases is *the electron concentration*. This parameter is usually taken to denote the number of all valence electrons per unit cell provided that all

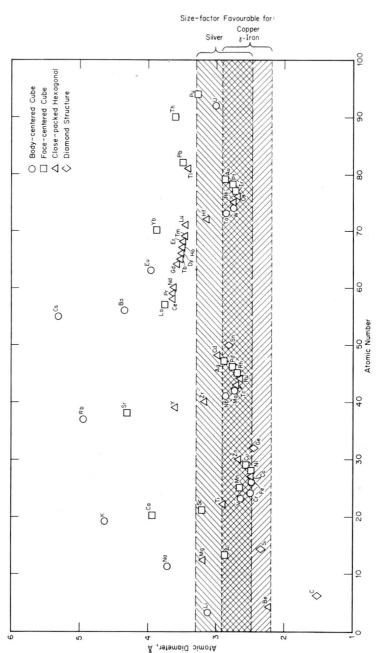

Fig. 3. Illustration of the application of the size-factor principle to solid solutions in copper, silver and γ-iron. The ordinates show the atomic diameters as defined by the closest distance of approach of the atoms in the crystals of elements. The shaded areas show the ranges of favorable size-factor, bounded by the limits ±15% of the atomic diameters of silver, copper, and γ-iron, respectively. The types of structures involved are indicated by different symbols. (After HUME-ROTHERY [1961].)

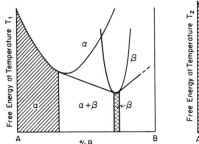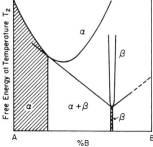

Fig. 4. Restriction of primary solid solubility due to stability of an intermediate phase.

atomic sites within the structure are occupied. Alternatively, electron concentration may be taken as the ratio of all valence electrons to the number of atoms. It is then denoted as e/a.

Following the early investigations by Hume-Rothery and his associates it was also suggested that the mutual solid solubility of two given elements was related to their respective valencies, namely, that the amount of the solid solution in the element of lower valency was always greater than vice versa. This general principle is sometimes known as the *relative valency effect*. It appears to be valid when copper, silver or gold, which are monovalent, are alloyed with the B-subgroup elements of the Periodic Table which possess valencies greater than one. The explanation of this phenomenon is not clear at the moment. It may be associated in part with the fact that the Brillouin zones of the noble metals are only partially filled with electrons; and, although they are touched by the Fermi surface, they are not overlapped as are the Brillouin zones of the B-subgroup elements. A more likely cause, however, has its origin in the long-range charge oscillations around the impurity atoms as discussed by FRIEDEL [1964] and BLANDIN [1965].

Subsequent appraisals by HUME-ROTHERY [1961a] and GSCHNEIDNER [1980] suggest that the relative valency effect is not really a general principle, and that when two elements which are both of high valency are alloyed together it is often not possible to predict which of the two will form the more extensive solid solution with respect to the other.

4.   *The meaning of electron concentration*

In the study of alloys it is often convenient to use the electron concentration, rather than atomic or weight composition, as a parameter against which various properties can be plotted. In the case of the alloys of the noble metals, the use of electron concentration has been particularly successful since it almost never fails to bring about interesting correlations when applied to experimental data. Nevertheless, the physical meaning of electron concentration is by no means as simple as that of chemical composition, and as time progresses it has become increasingly more difficult to "visualize" the process by means of which valence electrons which belong to the solvent and the solute atoms become a common property of the conduction band of an alloy. Usually only the s and p electrons are considered as taking part in such a process, but occasionally the total number of electrons outside the inert-gas core (i.e., s + p + d electrons) has been used to denote the electron concentration (see below). In the B-subgroup elements which follow the noble metals in the respective horizontal rows of the Periodic Table the d bands in the free atoms are fully occupied by electrons. It has been considered for a long time, therefore, that on alloying only the s and p electrons are involved, but the possibility of transfer of electrons from the d band to the conduction band and the s–d hybridization makes the situation more complex. There is no doubt that the presence of d-band electrons sufficiently near the Fermi level in alloys of the noble metals and the changes in the energy of the d-band electrons on alloying constitute an important contribution to the electronic structure. This contribution is at present not fully understood and much work remains to be done to clarify the picture *.

Even if it is assumed that the d band may be ignored and that certain elements possess a well-defined valence (for example, copper = 1, zinc = 2, gallium = 3, etc.), it is not certain whether all of the (s + p) electrons of a solute element go into the conduction band of the alloy. FRIEDEL [1954a] has suggested that in an alloy some of the s + p electrons may lie in bound states near the solute nuclei. According to MOTT [1952] such elements as zinc, gallium, germanium, etc., when disssolved in copper certainly contribute at least one electron to the conduction band. The next electron may or may not be in a bound state, while the additional electrons in gallium and germanium almost certainly are in bound states. Nevertheless, it has been suggested (FRIEDEL [1954a]) that the valence-electron concentration rules may remain valid if one assumes that the potential acting on conduction electrons in an alloy "subtracts" from the bottom of the conduction band as many bound states as there are electrons in the bound atomic orbitals. Hence, the relationship between the effective conduction electrons and the band structure may be such that the Brillouin-zone effects, associated with the stability of phases and certain other alloy properties, may remain relatively unaltered. For further discussion of this and related subjects see references (FRIEDEL [1954a], MOTT [1952] and HUME-ROTHERY and COLES [1954], including proceedings of recent symposia (RUDMAN et al. [1967] BENNETT [1980]).

In alloy systems which involve transition elements, rare earths, actinides, lanthanides and transuranic elements, the assessment of valence and the corresponding changes in electron concentration are open to quite wide speculation. Often they depend on the nature of the particular problem to be considered. Thus, many

---

* Calculations of the cohesive energy of the noble metals using the assumption that only the s electrons are important yield values which are too low when compared with experimental data. The agreement is best in silver, suggesting that the d-band contribution is least important in this case (for further details see MOTT [1962] and ch. 3).

striking regularities are frequently revealed in a group of related elements or alloy systems provided that some valence scheme is adopted against which various properties within the group can be compared. For example, a rather abrupt change occurs in the electronic specific heat, magnetic susceptibility, Hall coefficient, hydrogen absorption, etc., in the transition metals and alloys of the first long period at an electron concentration of about 5.7 (MOTT [1962]) provided that their numbers of electrons outside the inert-gas core are considered to represent their valence, i.e., 4, 5, 6, 7, 8 and 9 for Ti, V, Cr, Mn, Fe and Co respectively (see also for comparison the Pauling scheme of valencies, table 6, ch. 2). At the same time the valencies of these same elements when in dilute solution in the noble metals or aluminium are usually assessed according to a diffferent scheme in which only the predominantly s electrons are included. Considerations of phase stability (EKMANN [1931], RAYNOR [1949]; HUME-ROTHERY [1966] and RAYNOR [1956]) and changes of axial ratio (MASSALSKI [1958], MASSALSKI and KING [1960], COCKAYNE and RAYNOR [1961] and HENDERSON and RAYNOR [1962]) suggest that the above transition elements possess much lower, and possibly variable, valencies in the range between 0 and 2.

In a similar way, valence schemes have been suggested for other alloy groups, but will not be discussed here.

5. *Termination of primary solid solubility*

5.1. **Electronic theories of primary solid solutions based on noble metals**

A survey of binary systems of copper, silver and gold with a large number of elements, and in particular with the B-subgroup elements, has shown that the observed ranges of primary solid solubility may be correlated with electron concentration (HUME-ROTHERY and RAYNOR [1940]). In fig. 5 the maximum ranges * of primary solid solutions based on the three noble metals are indicated as linear plots in terms of e/a for the cases where these solutions are followed by an intermediate phase with a close-packed hexagonal structure (fig. 5a) and, separately, when they are followed by an intermediate phase with the body-centred cubic structure (fig. 5b). Apart from the systems Cu–In and Cu–Sn, the primary solutions follwed by the cubic phase reach somewhat higher values of e/a than when followed by the close-packed hexagonal phase.

Examination of fig. 5 reveals that in silver-based alloys the primary solid solutions terminate within a fairly close range of values near $e/a = 1.4$, whereas in copper-based alloys the e/a values show a wider scatter but the range of maximum

---

* It must be remembered that these maximum ranges occur at different temperatures in each system. Strictly speaking the correlation with e/a should apply only at the absolute zero of temperature. The fact that a significant correlation is observed at relatively high temperatures suggests that the electronic factors play a predominant role even at those high temperatures, although entropy considerations undoubtedly also play a role.

References: p. 214.

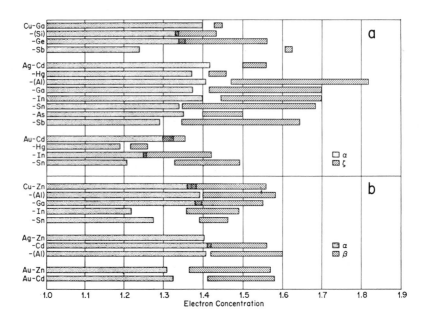

Fig. 5. Extent of the maximum primary solid solubility and of the following intermediate phase in alloys based on the noble metals (see text).

values is again only a little less than 1.4. In the cas of gold-based alloys the primary solid solubility is further restricted ranging between 1.2 and 1.3.

The above correlation between the primary solubility and e/a does not lead to any unique value, but it is quite striking when compared with similar plots drawn as a function of composition. Hence, it has been suspected for a long time that there must be an important link between the primary solid solubility and the electronic structure. During the 1930s an attempt was made by JONES [1937] to calculate the primary solid solubility of alloys based on copper using the theory of Brillouin zones and Bloch functions. This approach, and subsequent developments, are extensively quoted in metallurgical literature and will be discussed briefly below.

The main assumptions of the Jones model were : (i) that the *nearly-free-electron approximation* could be extended from pure metals to random solid solutions, and (ii) that the *rigid-band condition* was applicable on alloying (i.e., that the shape of the density of states curve $N(E)$ for a pure solvent remains unchanged on alloying and that the band gaps in the Brillouin zone do not change in magnitude, the only change being in the number of loosely-bound electrons). The general idea regarding stability of alloy phases was that at certain values of the electron concentration the Brillouin zone of one structure may be associated with a high density of quantum states, $N(E)$, at relatively low values of energy and thus "accommodate" the available electrons within lower total energy than would be possible in the zone of some other structure. This condition is particularly likely to occur in the range of energies associated with contact between the Fermi surface and Brillouin-zone faces since it results in a peak in the density of states. The connection between phase stability and a peak in the density-of-states curve had been established earlier (JONES [1934a]) for the case of the γ-brass structure.

In 1937 JONES considered in detail the theory of the α–β phase boundary in the Cu–Zn system where the face-centred cubic primary solid solution (α) is succeeded by the body-centred cubic intermediate phase (β). Using the same values of the atomic volume for both α and β phases and making them equal to that of copper, and using the same values of energy gaps as those obtained for copper from optical properties ($\Delta E = 4.1$ eV), Jones calculated the density-of-states curves for both phases in terms of energy expressed in electron volts. The result of the calculation is shown schematically * in fig. 6a. The first peak in the density-of-states curve for the α-phase occurs at about 6.6 eV. When compared with the free electron energy at the center of the $\{111\}$ faces in the Brillouin Zone, 6.5 eV, this suggested that the contact between the Fermi surface and these faces should occur in the α-phase already at an early stage of alloying. Many years later PIPPARD [1958] has shown that this contact in fact already exists in pure copper. Interpreted in terms of e/a, the two peaks shown in fig. 6a correspond to $e/a \approx 1.0$ for the α phase and $e/a \approx 1.23$ for the β phase, respectively, and are therefore unlikely to be associated in a simple way with the termination of the primary solid solubility ($e/a \approx 1.4$), or the optimum range of stability for the β phase ($e/a \approx 1.5$). The diagram in fig. 6a is, nevertheless, of interest because of its general emphasis on the relationship between phase stability and the density of states. Actual electronic energy relationships are more likely to be like those shown in fig. 6b, according to which the largest differences between the Fermi energy of free-electron gas and the Fermi energies of electrons in the Brillouin zone of the α and β phases occur at some points to the right of the peaks $\{111\}_\alpha$ and $\{110\}_\beta$ in the density of states (JONES [1962]). The actual α–β phase boundary will then be determined by the common tangent principle (BLANDIN [1965]).

Incorporation of the original Jones model into metallurgical literature has led to a good deal of confusion about the relationship between phase stability and the contact between the Fermi surface and the Brillouin-zone faces. One must appreciate the difference between the attempt by Jones to calculate the relative stability of two adjoining phases in terms of the contact between Fermi surfaces and certain Brillouin-zone faces with assumed large energy gaps and in terms of additional thermodynamic quantities, and similar attempts in terms of *spherical* Fermi surfaces. The use of spherical surfaces amounts to merely calculating the electron concentration at which an inscribed *Fermi sphere* would contact the zone faces. In the latter case, the zone faces by implication should possess zero energy (gaps). As pointed out by HUME-ROTHERY [1964], this important conclusion has been often overlooked in metallurgical literature. Free-electron calculation shows that contact of a Fermi *sphere* with the Brillouin zone would be obtained in the α phase at 1.36 electrons per

---

* For actual curves, reference should be made to the original paper (JONES [1937]). Additional discussion may be found in a recent review article (MASSALSKI and MIZUTANI [1978]).

References: p. 214.

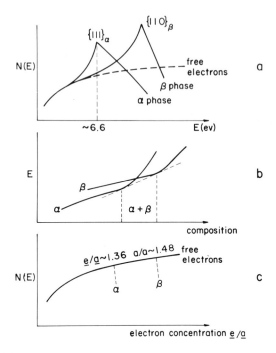

Fig. 6. Schematic models proposed to account for the primary solid solubility of alloys based on copper: (a) Jones model: band gap across the {111} faces of the zone for the fcc structure = gap across the {110} faces of the zone for the bcc structure ≈ 4.1 eV; (b) total electronic energy $E = \int_0^{E_F} N(E) \, dE$, corresponding to the density of states as modified by the interactions with the respective Brillouin zones; (c) density of states for free electrons.

atom and in the β phase at 1.48 electrons per atom (see fig. 6c), and these values are strikingly close to the experimental observation. This, however, must now be regarded as rather fortuitous, at least for the α phases, because it has been proved beyond dispute that the Fermi surface is considerably distorted from a sphere in the [111] direction and touches the set of {111} Brillouin-zone faces in all three noble metals, Cu, Ag and Au (HARRISON and WEBB [1960]). A summary of recent developments in this field may be found in a review article by MASSALSKI and MIZUTANI [1978].

5.2. Primary solid solubility in transition metal alloys

Recent work has shown that electron-concentration principles similar to those established for the noble metals and their alloys apply also to the solid solutions of a number of transition metals, particularly those with the fcc structure (HUME-ROTHERY [1966]). Figure 7 shows the limits of solid solutions in Rh, Pd, Ir and Pt in terms of the *average group number* (AGN) which denotes all electrons outside the

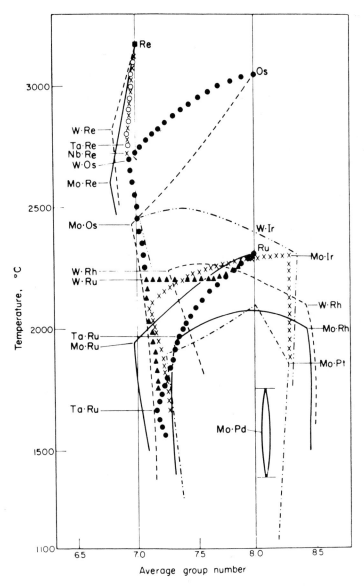

Fig. 7. The composition limits, in terms of AGN, of terminal solid solutions of Nb, Ta, Mo and W in Re, of Mo and W in Os, of Ta, Mo and W in Ru, and of the intermediate ε-phases in the systems Mo–Rh, Mo–Ir, Mo–Pd, Mo–Pt, W–Rh and W–Ir (from HUME-ROTHERY [1966]).

rare-gas shell. The general tendency appears to be for the fcc solid solutions to extend back to an AGN value of about 8.4. A similar effect is found for solid solutions of V and Cr in fcc γ-Fe, and in Ni. The behavior in bcc metals has not

References: p. 214.

been generally examined. However, similar correlations may exist. For example, the solid solubilities of Rh and Ru in bcc Mo terminate at a similar value of AGN of about 6.6 (HUME-ROTHERY [1967]).

5.3. Progress in the electronic theories of alloys *

In the earlier theories of Brillouin zones and Fermi surfaces the Bloch wavefunctions were used as a basis for calculation. Metals and solid solutions were considered as regular arrays of ions immersed in a "sea" of conduction electrons. The potential in a crystal was considered to be a periodically varying quantity corresponding to the periodicity of the ionic lattice and being more or less atomic (i.e. rapidly falling) in character near each ion. Bloch was able to show that wavefunctions of the conduction electrons for which the potential energy was modulated by the periodicity of the lattice were valid solutions of the Schrödinger equation. The resulting Bloch model has served as a very successful basis for discussion of the motion of electrons in metals and alloys. Only the conduction electrons, moving without electrostatic interactions with one another, were considered, and their motion was described by one-particle functions. Hence only the kinetic energy of the electrons was involved.

Subsequent developments in the electron theory have introduced a number of important modifications to the above model. It was found that the description of electronic properties was more consistent with experimental data if only weak *electron–atom* interactions were assumed, i.e., if the periodical potential was not considered to be atomic in character near each ion but only weakly changing from ion to ion. At the same time the additional problem of having to allow for possible strong *electron–electron* interactions was removed by considering that the Bloch model describes the motion, not of one-electron particles but of more complex entities, called *quasi particles*, introduced by Landau. Quasi particles have an electron at the center, surrounded by a region of electron deficiency (correlation hole) and a further region containing electrons that have been pushed out by the Coulombic repulsion away from the central electron and "flow around it much as water flows around a moving particle" (COHEN [1965]).

The problem of looking realistically at electron–atom interactions in order to reconcile the difference between the atomic and the effective potential in a metallic lattice has been tackled by introducing the notion of a *pseudopotential*. In this treatment the electron wavefunctions near the ions are ignored to some extent and substituted by pseudo wavefunctions which have the effect of statistically excluding the valence electrons from regions of space occupied by core electrons. The application of the theory of pseudopotentials has been very useful to the understanding of some problems in the theory of alloys (HEINE [1967] and STROUD [1980]). Other recent developments involve calculations of electronic energies 'ab initio', and

---

* See also ch. 3.

various elaborate treatments of the atomic potentials in solid solutions (see, for example, FAULKNER [1982]).

6.   *The atomic size in solid solution*

On forming a solid solution of element A with element B, two different kinds of atoms come in contact on a common lattice. This inclusion of new centers of disturbance will affect the existing electronic force fields between atoms, both short range and long range; the resulting effects will be of several kinds. On the atomic scale some atoms of the solvent and the solute will be shifted from the mean atomic positions on the lattice and thus suffer a permanent *static displacement*. The resulting average distance between any two neighboring atoms in a solid solution will depend on whether they are of the like kind, either both solvent or both solute, or of the opposite kind. We may thus talk of the average AA, BB or AB *bond distances* which may, even for an identical pair of atoms, depend also on the direction in the lattice.

In addition to local displacements the average distances between lattice planes may also change and we may talk of the change in the *lattice spacings* and, related to them, the volume of the unit cell. Both the lattice spacings and the volume of the unit cell are not related to the actual size of any particular atom.

The relationship between lattice spacings, space lattice and the individual position of atoms may be summarized as follows: the space lattice represents a repetition in space of an elementary unit known as the *unit cell* (fig. 8). The lattice spacings describe the linear dimensions of the unit cell. To a certain extent a unit cell may be chosen quite arbitrarily so that, for example, in the face-centred cubic structure shown in fig. 8b three different unit cells are possible – rhombohedral, face-centred cubic and body-centred tetragonal. The cell which reveals the essential symmetry is cubic; if the X-ray reflections are indexed according to this cell, then the lattice spacing a is associated with the average spacing of atoms located at the corners of the cube and is larger than the spacings between the neighboring atoms within the cube or in other possible unit cells. The a spacing therefore exceeds the *closest distance of approach* of atoms. For example, the closest distance of approach of atoms in fig. 8b is $a/\sqrt{2}$. In a simple structure, one can easily calculate this distance from the known dimensions of the unit cell; but this may be very difficult if the structure is complex as, for example, that of γ brass (fig. 16, below).

In some structures there are considerable variations in the distance between pairs of atoms at their closest distance of approach, according to position and direction in the lattice; and in order to study these a more complex analysis, involving all average interatomic spacings, may become necessary. The *cementite* structure (fig. 9) provides a good example. In this structure the iron–carbon distances vary in the unit cell and the determination of spacings between specified pairs of atoms of iron and carbon requires the knowledge of X-ray line intensities in addition to the Debye–Scherrer analysis.

Throughout a range of solid solutions the average "sizes" of individual atoms

References: p. 214.

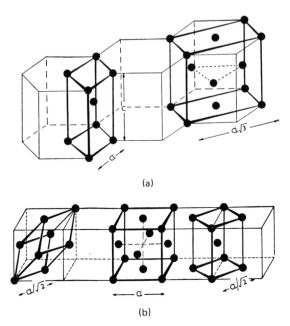

(a)

(b)

Fig. 8. (a) The close-packed hexagonal structure, showing the tetragonal and orthorhombic unit cells, and (b) the face-centred cubic structure, showing the rhombohedral, the face-centred cubic and the body-centred cubic unit cells.

may be expected to change depending on the degree and nature of local displacements. A change in the average lattice spacings may mean a contraction of solute atoms and expansion of solvent atoms or vice versa, and such local changes may bear little relation to the total macroscopic distortion of the unit cell. Therefore it is very desirable to be able to assess the changes in individual atomic sizes in a solid solution, whenever possible. For this purpose methods involving measurement of

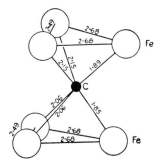

Fig. 9. The variable iron–carbon distances in the structure of cementite, Fe_3C (from GOLDSCHMIDT [1948]).

diffuse X-ray scattering or changes in the intensity of principal (Bragg) reflections have been developed.

From a metallurgical point of view the important questions regarding the atomic size are as follows:

1) What is the actual size of an atom in a pure element and what are the best ways of estimating and defining that size?

2) Having decided upon atomic sizes of pure elements, which is the best method of estimating the influence of atomic sizes in a solid solution?

3) Can one assess this influence of the disparity between initial atomic sizes without additional measurements in a solid solution?

One would like to know, for example, how successful can be the prediction of the influence of the size difference merely from the knowledge of the atomic sizes of the pure elements and perhaps one other physical property, or whether it is always necessary to perform some kind of a measurement in a solid solution before the importance of the atomic size can be assessed more accurately. Yet another question concerns the relationship between the strain in the crystal lattice and the atomic size. The contribution of the strain energy to the total free energy affects the thermodynamical properties, and recently several attempts have been made to estimate the strain energy using methods of continuum elasticity.

The empirical success of the 15% rule (§ 4.3) already suggests that initial sizes of atoms can, in some cases, give a guide to the extent of solid solubility on alloying. However, when formulated in this way the atomic-size difference merely provides a guide to the hindrance which it may cause to the formation of extensive primary solid solubility. In some systems, for example in systems Ag–Sn or Ag–Sb, the limits of primary solid solubility are less than average (for silver-based alloys), yet the widths of the close-packed hexagonal intermediate phases are surprisingly large. In both systems the disparity beween atom radii is within the 0–15% range (i.e., the 15% rule is satisfied), and is appears that the actual value of the size difference may be of importance.

6.1. The size factor

The original formulation of the size-factor concept for binary alloy systems involved the assumption that the *atomic diameter* of an element may be given by the *closest distance of approach* of atoms in its structure * (see ch. 2). This approach to estimating atomic size often meets with difficulties when the structures are anisotropic, or complex, or when the coordination numbers are low. For example, when there are several close distances of approach in the structure (as in gallium with $d_1 = 2.437$, $d_2 = 2.706$, $d_3 = 2.736$ and $d_4 = 2.795$ Å), the closest distance of approach, d_1, does not adequately express the size of the gallium atom when in a solid

---

* The size factor is given by $[(d_B - d_A)/d_A] \times 100$ where d_A and d_B are values of the closest distance of approach of atoms in the solvent and solute respectively. For a detailed account of the possible role of the size factor as defined above reference may be made to a review article by RAYNOR [1956].

References: p. 214.

solution (HUME–ROTHERY and RAYNOR [1954]). A similar consideration may apply even in the case of an element which crystallizes in a typically metallic structure. For example, in zinc, with the close-packed hexagonal structure but a high value of the axial ratio, four possible values can be considered to represent the size of a zinc atom: spacings between atoms in the basal planes which also correspond to closest packing ($d_1 = 2.6649$ Å); spacings between the nearest neighbors of the adjoining basal planes which strongly depend on the axial ratio ($d_2 = 2.9129$ Å); an atomic diameter derived from the average volume per atom of the unit cell of zinc ($d_3 = 3.0762$ Å); and finally an atomic diameter calculated for a hypothetical structure with coordination number 12 ($d_4 = 2.7535$ Å) (see HUME-ROTHERY and RAYNOR [1954] p. 88). For the purpose of the 15% rule, d_1 has been chosen to represent the size of the zinc atom. However, when the behavior of lattice spacings of solid solutions containing zinc is studied in detail, it appears that frequently the lattice spacings expand, or contract, when an opposite behavior might be expected from the value of the closest distance of approach. In fig. 10 the changes with composition in the closest distance of approach, d, and volume per atom in Cu–Zn alloys are shown. Within the primary solid solution based on copper the lattice spacings follow a curve which indicates that zinc behaves as if it possessed larger size than that derived from its a spacing, since the lattice spacings of the alloys show a positive deviation from a line joining the closest distances of approach of copper and

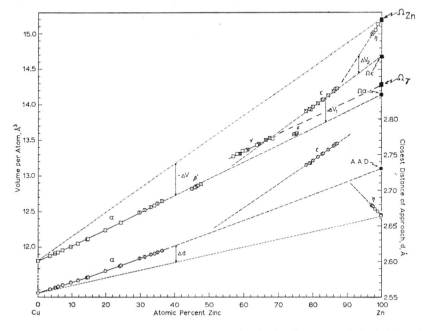

Fig. 10. Trends in lattice spacings and volume per atom in the Cu–Zn system; circles indicate closest distance of approach, d, squares indicate volume per atom. (From MASSALSKI and KING [1961].)

zinc. On the other hand, within the primary solid solution of copper in zinc, addition of copper to zinc again expands the *a* spacing of the latter despite the fact that the value of *d* for copper is indicated to be smaller than that for zinc. Thus, on a finer scale there are often discrepancies between the behavior of lattice spacings in the alloys and the estimated atomic sizes. For such reasons other attempts have been made to derive the average atomic size. For example, in fig. 10 the trend in the *a* lattice spacing within the α phase may be extrapolated towards pure zinc to give a hypothetical size of a zinc atom for the case where the face-centred cubic structure is maintained throughout the Cu–Zn system and on the assumption that the behavior of lattice spacings is linear. The obtained value is marked AAD in the figure, and it is close to the d_4 value mentioned above. This method of estimating *apparent atomic diameters* (AAD), is due to AXON and HUME-ROTHERY [1948]. Another approach makes use of the trend in the volume per atom (MASSALSKI and KING [1961]). Comparison between the atomic sizes estimated from the volume per atom in the pure elements and the behavior of the volume per atom trends in the Cu–Zn system is shown in the upper portion of fig. 10.

6.2. The measurement of atomic size in terms of volume

By analogy to the use of the apparent atomic diameter a measure of the size of a solute atom in any particular primary solid solution or an intermediate phase may be obtained by extrapolating to the solute axis the plot of the mean volume per atom within that phase. In fig. 10 such a procedure is illustrated for the α, γ and ϵ phases of the Cu–Zn system, providing values of the *effective atomic volumes* (MASSALSKI and KING [1961]) or *partial molar atomic volumes*. The different effective atomic volumes estimated in this way for the solute in each phase are independent of the coordination number or the structural anisotropy effects mentioned above. Thus, when the coordination number changes, the atomic volume rather than the inter-atomic distance tends to remain constant (MOTT [1962]). An extensive study of solid solutions of various B-sub-group metals (Zn, Cd, In, Tl etc.) in late transition elements such as Ni, Pd or Pt has shown that often the initial effective atomic volume of a solute, extrapolated to the pure-solute side, is practically the same in a number of different solvents (ELLNER [1978,1980]). A good example is provided by the behavior of Ga, fig. 11. At the same time, it may be seen from fig. 10 that the effective atomic volumes of zinc in the different phases are smaller than the atomic volume of pure zinc. Since these effective volumes are different in each phase, it appears that the *contribution of the atomic size is variable according to composition* and hence it may be desirable to designate several size factors in each binary system. The values of the effective atomic volumes, Ω_α, Ω_β, Ω_ζ, for solutes in several noble metal electron phases are listed in table 1 together with the atomic volumes of pure solvents, Ω_0, and of pure solutes, Ω_S. An examination of the table shows that without exception all solutes show a decrease of the volume per atom on alloying and that this decrease appears to be greatest with solutes of highest valency. Hence, the atomic sizes of such elements as aluminium, indium, thallium or lead, which are

References: p. 214.

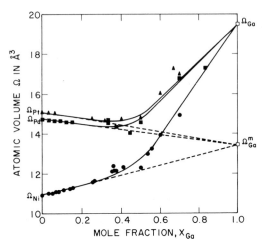

Fig. 11. Changes of atomic volume with composition in the binary Pt–Ga, Pd–Ga and Ni–Ga (from ELLNER [1978]).

Table 1

Effective atomic volume of solutes in electron phases of the noble metals (from MASSALSKI and KING [1961]).

Sub-group	Solute	Ω_s (Å^3)	Effective atomic volume of solute (Å^3)					
			Cu ($\Omega_0 = 11.8$)		Ag ($\Omega_0 = 17.05$)		Au ($\Omega_0 = 16.95$)	
			$\Omega_{(\alpha,\beta',\mu)}$	$\Omega_{(\zeta,\epsilon)}$	$\Omega_{(\alpha,\beta',\mu)}$	$\Omega_{(\zeta,\epsilon)}$	$\Omega_{(\alpha,\beta',\mu)}$	$\Omega_{(\zeta,\epsilon)}$
II B	Zn	15.2	14.15	14.7	14.7	14.8	14.5	14.8
	Cd	21.6	18.8	–	19.95	20.7	19.25	n.m.
	Hg	23.7	n.m.	–	20.75	22.4	20.2	n.m.
III B	(Al)	16.6	14.2	–	15.5	16.1	15.2	–
	Ga	19.6	14.7	n.m.	16.2	16.7	16.2	–
	In	26.15	20.8 [a] 21.3	–	21.4	22.9	21.4 [a] 20.5	n.m.
	Tl	28.6	n.m.	–	23.85	–	n.m.	–
IV B	(Si)	20.0	12.5	n.m.	n.m.	–	n.m.	–
	Ge	22.6	15.1	15.8	17.5	–	17.4	–
	Sn	27.05	21.9	–	22.7	23.3	22.2	22.5
	Pb	30.3	n.m.	–	26.7	–	n.m.	–
V B	As	21.5	16.5	n.m.	18.85	n.m.	n.m.	–
	Sb	30.2	22.3	n.m.	24.8	25.5	23.5	–
	Bi	35.4	n.m.	–	29.3	–	n.m.	–

[a] Alternative data

considered to be an exception when measured in terms of the closest distance of approach, are found to be typical of a general trend for the B-subgroup elements with the noble metals when considered in terms of atomic volume (MASSALSKI and KING [1961]). This generalization does not apply to transition elements and other solvents. MOTT [1962] has pointed out that if the volume of a solute atom in the solid solution is nearly the same as in its own pure metal one can expect the heat of solution to be small. Why a solute atom when placed in a hole similar to its own volume in the solvent tends to retain its original energy, even when the valencies of solvent and solute are different, is not altogether clear.

6.3. Combined effects of size and electronegativity

In the early 1950s, DARKEN and GURRY [1953] suggested that the extent of solid solubility in a given solvent metal may be assessed by testing simultaneously both the size and electronegativity differences between solvent and solute elements. They showed that in a combined plot of electronegativity (ordinate) and size (abscissa), which they called a map (see fig. 12) each element can be represented by a point (see also ch. 5, § 1.5). The closer any two points are on the map, the more likely is a high mutual solid solubility between the elements involved. In a typical Darken–Gurry

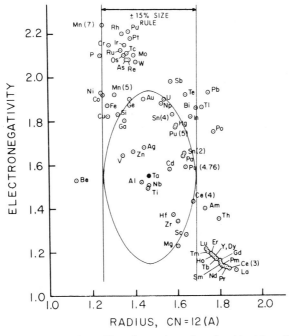

Fig. 12. The Darken–Gurry map with an ellipse drawn about the solvent tantalum. The two vertical lines are the tangents to the ellipse at the termini of the minor axis (±15% of tantalum's radius). (From GSCHNEIDNER [1980].)

References: p. 214.

(D–G) plot, as in fig. 12, substantial solubility is usually indicated by an ellipse drawn around a given solvent point. Waber *et al.* [1963] have shown subsequently, following a statistical survey of 1455 systems for which experimental data exists, that over 75% of the systems obeyed the prediction of solid solubility assessed on the basis of a D–G plot. The usefulness of the D–G method is particularly well demonstrated for the actinide metals and rare-earths (Gschneidner [1980]).

6.4.   Strain in solid solutions

A simple model which takes into account the difference between atomic sizes, and which can yield estimates of lattice strain, may be constructed using basic ideas of continuum elasticity. Several such models have been considered (Lawson [1947], Darken and Gurry [1953], Eshelby [1956] and Friedel [1955]). The general approach is illustrated schematically in fig. 13.

Consider a rubberlike elastic matrix of a large volume V_2 in which a very small cavity has been drilled away of volume V_1. Then, through an infinitesimally small opening (shown as a capillary opening in the figure) an amount of incompressible fluid of volume $(V_1 + \Delta V_1)$ is introduced which, therefore, expands the cavity by the amount ΔV_1. Both the fluid and the matrix are now under stress and the matrix suffers an expansion ΔV_2, shown in the figure by the shaded portion, which is related to the increase in the volume of the cavity by the relationship

$$\Delta V_2 / \Delta V_1 = 3(1 - \nu)/(1 + \nu), \tag{1}$$

where ν is Poisson's ratio. As pointed out by Darken and Gurry [1953], for most metals Poisson's ratio is about 0.3 and hence $\Delta V_2/\Delta V_1$ equals about 1.6, i.e., the volume-increase of a metal bulk will be larger than the increase in the volume of the cavity. The above model can be related to a solid solution in which the expanded cavity is replaced by several solute atoms and the bulk by a metal solvent matrix. In analogy to the expanded volume of the elastic matrix we may expect that in a substitutional solid solution on replacing an atom of the solvent (a cavity) by a

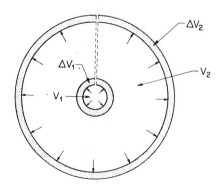

Fig. 13. Model of an incompressible particle in an elastic matrix.

somewhat larger-sized atom of the solute (the incompressible fluid) we should obtain a net expansion of the entire unit cell. The estimates of the strain energy associated with such an expansion have enabled a number of authors (DARKEN and GURRY [1953], ESHELBY [1956]) to show a direct link between the limitation of primary solid solubility and Hume-Rothery's 15% rule. Lattice spacing measurements in solid solutions are also in qualitative agreement with the above model, but sometimes a lattice expansion is observed even if the solute atoms are considered to be smaller than those of the solvent. This discrepancy is usually due to the difficulty of being able to assess correctly the sizes of atoms and to the fact that, on alloying, other factors not included in a crude assessment of size come into play, to mention only that the size of the solute atom in the pure element may differ considerably from its size in solid solution because of such factors as electron concentration, electrochemical effects and static displacements, etc.

Calculations based on simple elastic models permit one to relate the strain energy to composition and atomic volume. A general equation expressing strain energy in a solid solution may be written as (MASSALSKI and KING [1961]):

$$E_S(c) = A\mu\Omega\left(\frac{1}{\Omega}\frac{\partial\Omega}{\partial c}\right)^2 f(c), \qquad (2)$$

where A is a numerical constant, μ is the shear modulus, Ω is the mean atomic volume and c the composition. In many alloy phases the variation of atomic volume with composition is nearly linear and hence for dilute solutions (for which $\Omega_0 \approx \Omega$) one may write:

$$\left(\frac{1}{\Omega}\frac{\partial\Omega}{\partial c}\right) \approx (\Omega_\alpha - \Omega_0)/\Omega_0, \qquad (3)$$

where Ω_0 is the atomic volume of the pure solvent and Ω_α the effective atomic volume of the solute in the α phase. The relationship $(\Omega_\alpha - \Omega_0)/\Omega_0$ represents a measure of a *volume-size-factor* (MASSALSKI and KING [1961]) within a given alloy phase and a comparison of eqs. (2) and (3) shows that the strain energy for dilute alloys is related to the square of the volume-size-factor. Volume-size-factors have been calculated for numerous solid solutions and are available in tabulated form (KING [1966]). It should be pointed out that the use of a volume-size-factor rather than one based on the closest distance of approach necessitates the knowledge of the extrapolated effective atomic volumes of the solute within different phases and hence necessitates additional measurements within solid solutions.

Ellner's studies, for example the plot shown in fig. 11, confirm that in many solid solutions the initial behaviour of the atomic volume with composition is practically linear (usually in the composition range up to about 30–40 at% of solute). The corresponding effective atomic volume obtained from extrapolation to the pure solute side provides a measure of the departure of the atomic volume trend from a possible linear behaviour between the atomic volumes of the pure components. If the difference $(\Omega_{\text{solvent}} - \overline{\Omega}_{\text{solute}})$ is plotted against the difference between the partial molar heats of mixing $(\Delta H_{\text{solvent}} - \overline{\Delta H}_{\text{solute}})$ obtained from measurements (or calculations) a nearly linear relationship is obtained (ELLNER [1978,1980]). Thus, size effects find their expression in the corresponding chemical manifestations.

6.5. Deviation from Vegard's law

A study of available systems based on copper, silver and gold with the B-subgroup elements indicates that, when volume-per-atom trends are considered, alloying between any two elements causes a decrease in the volume per atom from a straight line joining the two values for the pure elements. A similar behavior is observed also when various interatomic spacings are measured and plotted within a solid solution, although in such cases the deviation can have positive or negative sign. The trends usually observed are illustrated in fig. 14.

The expected linear dependence on composition of lattice spacing trends, to follow a line joining the values for the pure elements, has come to be known as *Vegard's Law*, although this law has only been found valid for a number of ionic salts (VEGARD [1921,1928]) and is never quite true in metallic systems. Nevertheless, it is tempting to be able to calculate deviations from assumed linear behavior, without actually performing any measurement in a solid solution, and using solely the knowledge of various parameters in the pure components. Such an attempt has been made by FRIEDEL [1955] for the cases of dilute and concentrated primary solid solutions. Friedel used the atomic volumes, Poisson's ratio, bulk moduli, and compressibilities. The elastic model illustrated in fig. 13 is extended to the case in which both the matrix and the introduced fluid are compressible with compressibility coefficients χ_1 and χ_2. The atoms of solvent and solute are represented by radii r_1 and r_2 which are derived from the atomic volumes of the elements using the

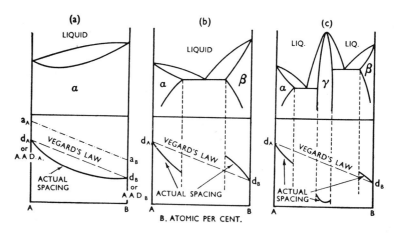

Fig. 14. The commonly observed trends in lattice-spacing–composition curves in three typical binary alloy systems: (a) complete solid solubility; (b) partial solid solubility, A has higher valency than B; (c) presence of an intermediate phase, large electrochemical interaction between A and B. (After MASSALSKI [1958].)

relationship $\Omega = \frac{4}{3}\pi r^3$. The holes in the matrix are represented by the atoms of the solvent with radius r_1 and the introduced distortions by atoms of the solute with radius r_2. On replacing an atom of the solvent by an atom of solute both suffer an elastic adjustment which may be represented by an average radius a common to both. Freidel has shown that at *infinite dilution*

$$(a - r_1)/(r_2 - a) = \alpha = (1 + \nu)\chi_1/2(1 - 2\nu)\chi_2, \tag{4}$$

where ν is again Poisson's ratio and χ_1 and χ_2 are the compressibilities of the solvent and solute respectively. At a finite concentration c the total volume of the solvent will suffer an increase and the average radius of an atom in the solid solution may now be represented by r (derived from average atomic volume) which will be different from the initial radii r_1 and r_2 of both the solvent and solute. Following Friedel, the initial deviation of the average atomic radius r in a solid solution from a line joining the atomic radii of the solvent and solute, may be expressed as follows:

$$\frac{r - r_1}{cr_1} = \frac{r_2 - r_1}{r_1} \frac{\alpha + (\chi_1/\chi_2)}{\alpha + 1}. \tag{5}$$

Comparison between calculated deviations using the above elastic model and the observed deviations (FRIEDEL [1955]) from the assumed Vegard's Law shows a good general agreement for the cases where the solute atoms are considered to be bigger than the solvent atoms, but usually not vice versa.

6.6. Measurement of actual atomic sizes in solid solutions

The static distortions in a solid solution which can be related to the individual atomic sizes may be estimated from a *modulation in diffuse X-ray scattering* (WARREN et al. [1951], ROBERTS [1954] and AVERBACH [1956]) and from a *quasi-temperature reduction in the Bragg reflections* (HUANG [1947], HERBSTEIN et al. [1956] and BORIE [1957, 1959]). In the former case the modulations of the diffuse X-ray intensity diffracted by a solid solution are described by coefficients, α_i, related to the nature of local atomic order of atoms, and by size effect coefficients, β_i, related to the differences in the sizes of the component atoms. According to theory,

$$\alpha_i = 1 - P_A^i/X_A \tag{6}$$

and

$$\beta_i = \left(\frac{1}{\eta - 1}\right)\left[-\left(\frac{X_A}{X_B} + \alpha_i\right)\epsilon_{AA}^i + \left(\frac{X_B}{X_A} + \alpha_i\right)\eta\epsilon_{BB}^i\right], \tag{7}$$

where

$$\eta = f_B/f_A, \qquad \epsilon_{AA}^i = \left(r_{AA}^i - r_i\right)r_i, \qquad \epsilon_{BB}^i = \left(r_{BB}^i - r_i\right)r_i,$$

and P_A^i = probability of finding an A atom in the ith shell about a B atom; X_A = mol fraction of A atoms; f_A, f_B = scattering factors of A and B atoms; r_i = average interatomic distance to the ith neighbor, calculated from lattice spacings; $r_{AA}^i =$

References: p. 214.

distance between two A atoms in the ith shell; r_{BB}^i = distance between two B atoms in the ith shell.

7. Intermediate phases with wide solid solubility

7.1. The electron phases

Of all intermediate phases which possess wide solid solubility the most typically metallic are the electron phases. Their discovery and studies have a historical aspect, and it is of interest to outline this briefly.

Some sixty years ago, even before X-ray analysis had been applied to the study of such phases as the Cu–Al and Cu–Sn β-brasses, HUME-ROTHERY [1926] indicated the possibility that they possessed the same crystallographic structure as that of Cu–Zn β-brass. Systematic and detailed work of Westgren and his collaborators (WESTGREN and PHRAGMEN [1926], WESTGREN [1930]), has subsequently established the validity of this and similar suppositions. The circumstance that the formulas CuZn, Cu_3Al and Cu_5Sn could be ascribed to the three phases with identical β-brass structure caused Hume-Rothery to postulate the principle that the stability of these phases was in some way related to the ratio 3/2 between the number of valence electrons and the number of atoms. Following this empirical formulation many similarities between crystal structures of other intermediate phases have been noted and studied systematically particularly in systems based on copper, silver and gold; and they led to the recognition of the now well-established term *electron compound*. At present it is known that such phases are not compounds in the chemical sense and that they may exist over wide ranges of composition. For this reason they should perhaps be called *electron phases*.

In the Cu–Zn system, which is somewhat typical of systems based on the noble metals, there are three characteristic electron phases commonly known as β-brass, γ-brass and ϵ-brass. Although these phases possess quite wide ranges of homogeneity, it had been thought originally that their ranges of stability were in each case based upon a characteristic stoichiometric ratio of atoms, and the formulae suggested for the β-, γ- and ϵ-brasses were CuZn, Cu_5Zn_8 and $CuZn_3$ respectively. From these formulae one obtains the electron/atom values of 3/2, 21/13 and 7/4 (1.50, 1.62 and 1.75) which have become widely accepted as characteristic of greatest stability of electron phases despite the fact that in some cases these values fall outside the range of stability of known electron phases.

Following mainly the work of JONES [1934a, b, 1937, 1952], the stability of electron phases has been linked via a simple electronic theory of metals with possible interactions between the Fermi surface and the Brillouin zones, with the emphasis on the influence of such interactions on the density of states $N(E)$ at the Fermi surface. The β-, γ- and ϵ-brasses possess the body-centred cubic, complex cubic and hexagonal close-packed structures respectively; and it can be shown that at the onset of contact between the Fermi surface of free electrons and the principal faces of the respective Brillouin zones the zones are relatively full. The values of e/a associated with the free-electron concept of the Fermi surface are: $e/a = 1.48$ for contact between the Fermi surface and the zone for β-brass, $e/a = 1.54$ for contact between the Fermi surface and the $\langle 300 \rangle$ and $\langle 411 \rangle$ faces of the large zone for γ-brass, and $e/a = 1.75$ associated with the filling of the inner zone of ϵ-brass. These electron/atom values based on the Brillouin zone models bear similarity to the original e/a ratios based on chemical formulae (compare 1.5, 1.62 and 1.75 with 1.48, 1.54 and 1.75), but it must be remembered that in both cases the actual values are derived from particular models put forward to interpret the stability of electron phases. The chemical formulae are now known not to be applicable, and the simple Brillouin-zone models suffer from the limitation already mentioned before that for the e/a values quoted above the band gaps across the Brillouin zone must be assumed to be zero or near zero. Thus, as in the case of the theory of primary solid solutions, we are left with two possibilities: (i) The band gaps in the Brillouin zones are relatively large, and the Fermi surfaces are not spherical, but the stability may be described qualitatively by a model as that shown in fig. 6b which points to the existence of a relationship between the density of states and phase stability. (ii) The band gaps in the Brillouin zone are variable with composition and are small in the range of electron phases so that the nearly spherical model of the Fermi surface

Table 2

Typical electron phases based on noble metals, zinc and cadmium, and some transition elements.

Phases with cubic symmetry						Phases with hexagonal symmetry (hcp)	
disordered bcc structure e/a range 1.36–1.59			γ-brass structure e/a range 1.54–1.70		β-Mn structure e/a range 1.40–1.54	$c/a = 1.633$ e/a range 1.22–1.83	$c/a = 1.57$ e/a range 1.65–1.89
β			γ		μ	ζ	ϵ
Cu–Be	Ag–Zn	Au–Al	Cu–Zn	Mn–Zn	Cu–Si	Cu–Ga	Cu–Zn
Cu–Zn	Ag–Cd		Cu–Cd	Mn–In	Ag–Al	Cu–Si	Ag–Zn
Cu–Al	Ag–Al		Cu–Hg	Fe–Zn	Au–Al	Cu–Ge	Ag–Cd
Cu–Ga	Ag–In		Cu–Al	Co–Zn	Co–Zn	Cu–As	Au–Zn
Cu–In			Cu–Ga	Ni–Zn		Cu–Sb	Au–Cd
Cu–Si			Ci–In	Ni–Cd		Ag–Cd	Li–Zn
Cu–Sn			Cu–Si	Ni–Ga		Ag–Hg	Li–Cd
Mn–Zn			Cu–Sn	Ni–In		Ag–Al	
			Ag–Li	Pd–Zn		Ag–Ga	
			Ag–Zn	Pt–Zn		Ag–In	
			Ag–Cd	Pt–Cd		Ag–Sn	
			Ag–Hg			Ag–As	
			Ag–In			Ag–Sb	
			Au–Zn			Au–Cd	
			Zu–Cd			Au–Hg	
			Au–Ga			Au–In	
			Au–In			Au–Sn	
						Mn–Zn	

References: p. 214.

describes the situation adequately. Experimental estimates of the Fermi surfaces in alloys are still limited, but some measurements have been made in both dilute and concentrated solid solutions, and they indicate that the Fermi surface is distorted from the spherical shape, but not substantially (see for example PEARSON [1967], MASSALSKI and MIZUTANI [1978] and KOIKE et al. [1982]). Although the details are still not clear, one is left with indisputable experimental correlations that show e/a to be an important factor in the stability of electron phases. Modelling of such stability in terms of electronic energy alone suggests that very small differences of the order of a few hundred cal/mole are involved between respective competing electron phases (MASSALSKI and MIZUTANI [1978]).

A list of typical electron phases is shown in table 2 in which are also shown the experimentally established ranges of stability of these phases.

7.2. Electron phases with cubic symmetry

The range of stability of the β-phases is shown in fig. 5b, above. The disordered β-phases are stable only at high temperatures and upon cooling or quenching they usually decompose, unless they become ordered as in the Cu–Zn system. In all cases the range of homogeneity of the disordered β-phases decreases with the fall of temperature, causing the phase fields to have the characteristic V-shape as illustrated in fig. 15. The electronic structure of the β-phases appears to be closely linked with the Brillouin zone for the bcc structure formed by 12 {110} faces, which constitute a rhombic dodecahedron. As mentioned in the preceding section, in the free electron approximation a spherical Fermi surface would just touch these faces at $e/a = 1.48$ (see fig. 6c). If the Brillouin-zone faces have a finite discontinuity, the density-of-states curve should show a peak near the value of e/a associated with the contact between the Fermi surface and the Brillouin zone. This possibility has been made the basis of

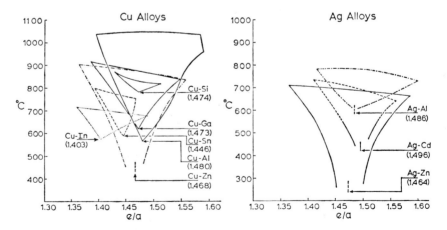

Fig. 15. The typical V-shaped phase fields of the disordered β phases (from MASSALSKI and KING [1961]).

a theory of the occurrence and stability of the β-phases (JONES [1937, 1952]). However, as pointed out above, if the gap across the faces of the Brillouin zone is assumed to be about 4.2 eV, the position in terms of e/a of the calculated peak in the density-of-states curve appears to occur at relatively low values of e/a and bears no relation to the actual ranges of stability. Nevertheless, it is remarkable that the most stable compositions of the β-phases, represented by eutectoid points at the tips of the V-shaped portions of the phase fields (see fig. 15), very nearly correspond to electron-concentration values associated with the free-electron model. More recent developments have centered on the measurement of properties, such as electronic specific heats, or the de Haas van Alphen effect (dHvA), that can be more directly related to the electronic structure. They show that the band gaps in the Brillouin zone are relatively small (~ 3.5 eV), and that the Fermi surface contours approximate a free-electron sphere. However, the stability of the β-phases is undoubtedly related to the total electronic energy integrated from the density-of-states trends from the bottom of the energy band to the Fermi level, and not just to some specific condition such as an initial contact between the Fermi surface and the Brillouin zone (MASSALSKI and MIZUTANI [1978]).

The range of stability of the γ-phases appears to be associated with no particular single value of electron concentration (see table 2) although there does seem to be a strong connection between the stability of γ-phases and the *large (Brillouin) zone*

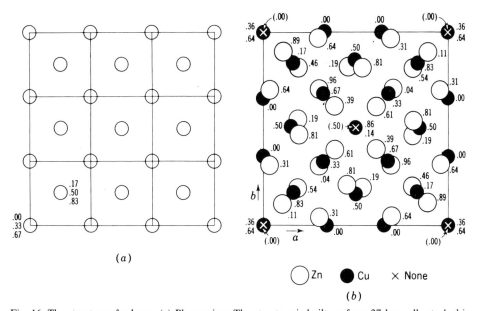

Fig. 16. The structure of γ-brass. (a) Planar view. The structure is built up from 27 bcc cells stacked in three dimensions. Distances above the projection plane are indicated in terms of the large cell edge. (b) The gamma-brass structure derived from (a) by removing the corner and central atoms and displacing others. (From BARRETT and MASSALSKI [1966].)

(see JONES [1934a, b, 1960]). The γ-phases have a complex bcc structure with approximately 52 atoms per cell (see fig. 16). They are usually ordered, certain related atomic sites being occupied by solute atoms and others by solvent atoms. The electronic structure of the γ-phases and certain of their physical properties have been reviewed by MASSALSKI and KING [1961] and MASSALSKI and MIZUTANI [1978]. On the whole, the γ-phases are brittle and they are therefore of no primary metallurgical interest. However, from the point of view of electronic theories the γ-phases are of historical interest because they were the first to be identified with a possible peak in the density-of-states curve associated with the contact of the Fermi surface with the Brillouin zone. Detailed calculations show that actually two closely positioned peaks are involved, corresponding to small band gaps, of the order of 1–2 eV. It is not surprising, therefore, that the Fermi surface associated with the γ-phases appears to be nearly spherical. The interaction of such a spherical Fermi surface with a Brillouin zone which itself resembles a sphere (the zone is bounded by 48 faces), should produce a rapid decrease in the density of states once contact has occurred between the Fermi surface and the zone. This is indeed confirmed by experimental measurements of electronic specific heats which show a rapid decrease of the electronic specific heat coefficient γ with composition. A similar effect is also observed in the cubic μ-phases which possess the β-Mn structure (MASSALSKI and MIZUTANI [1978]).

7.3. Electron phases with hexagonal symmetry

Apart from the more complex σ-, μ- and certain other phases which possess cubic symmetry (see, e.g., MASSALSKI and KING [1961]), the remaining group of electron phases possess the close-packed hexagonal structure. These phases are most numerous of all intermediate phases based on the noble metals, and they may occur anywhere within the electron-concentration range between 1.32 and 2.00 except for the narrow region 1.89–1.93. Together with the close-packed hexagonal primary solid solutions of zinc and cadmium with the noble metals (the η-phases) the close-packed hexagonal phases fall into three natural groups and are usually denoted by the Greek symbols ζ, ε and η on the basis of electron concentration, axial ratio and solute content. The known ε-phases always contain zinc or cadmium as their principal constituents (MASSALSKI and KING [1961]) and their range of stability varies between $e/a = 1.65$ and $e/a = 1.89$ (see table 2). The stability of close-packed hexagonal electron phases again appears to be intimately linked with both contact and overlap of electrons across the Brillouin zone.

The Brillouin zone for the close-packed hexagonal structure is shown in fig. 17 for an ideally close-packed structure. This zone is bounded by twenty faces, six of the {10.0} type, two of the {00.2} type, and twelve of the {10.1} type. The energy discontinuity vanishes across certain lines in the {00.1} faces (JONES [1960]) unless the structure is ordered, and hence these planes do not form a part of the energy zone. However, the {00.1} faces together with the {10.1} faces may be used to obtain a slightly smaller zone for the structure as described by JONES [1960]. Many of the measured electronic properties in hcp structures may be related to the Brillouin zone. The dHvA (de Haas van Alphen) data for pure hcp metals, for instance, are often interpreted in terms of the reduced zone scheme, while the low-temperature specific heat data can be more conveniently discussed in terms of the extended zone. If the extended "roofs" formed beyond the {10.0} planes by the intersection of the {10.1} planes are removed, the resulting zone is still surrounded by energy discontinuities in all directions except along the lines of intersection between the {10.1} and {10.0} zone planes (line HL in fig. 17a). This smaller zone is sometimes known as the *Jones zone* and its electron content per atom is:

$$e/a = 2 - \frac{3}{4}\left(\frac{a}{c}\right)^2\left[1 - \frac{1}{4}\left(\frac{a}{c}\right)^2\right], \tag{8}$$

where c/a is the axial ratio.

The importance of the electron concentration, e/a, as the major parameter controlling the properties and behavior of the hcp phases became clearly evident only after the relationship between c/a and e/a was established in detail. When e/a is constant, for example in a ternary system, c/a also remains constant. However, when e/a is allowed to change c/a changes accordingly. In binary systems, the axial-ratio trends of all known ζ and ϵ phases conform to a general pattern as shown

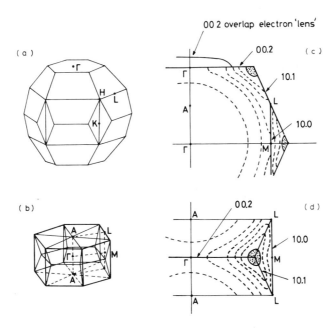

Fig. 17. The Brillouin zone of the hcp structure in the extended scheme (a) and in the reduced scheme (b). The possible contours of the Fermi surface in the vertical section of the corresponding Brillouin zone are shown in (c) and (d). The shaded areas correspond to the holes in pure Zn. The hole in (d) is known as a portion of the "monster". (After MASSALSKI *et al.* [1975].)

in fig. 18. Consideration of this behavior suggests a direct dependence of the structural parameters *a* and *c* on the interaction between Fermi surface and Brillouin zone (FsBz interaction): as the electron concentration increases, the resulting contacts and overlaps of the Fermi surface with respect to different sets of zone planes cause a distortion of the Brillouin zone. This in turn affects the lattice parameters in real space. The earlier models of the electronic structure of the hcp phases have been derived mainly from the interpretation of the trends in lattice parameters, but more recently the electronic structure has also been explored by additional techniques using, e.g., electronic specific heat, superconductivity, magnetic susceptibility, ther-

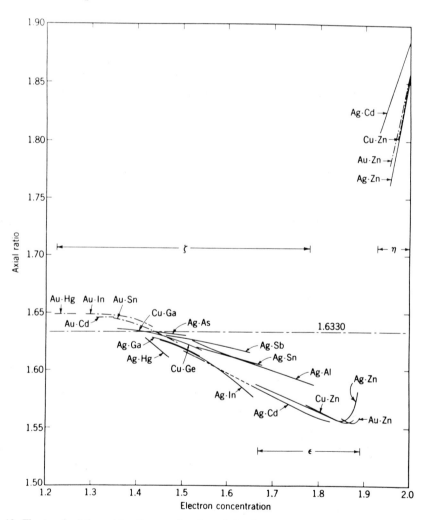

Fig. 18. The trend of the axial ratio as a function of the electron concentration in various hcp alloy systems (from MASSALSKI and MIZUTANI [1978]).

modynamic activity and positron annihilation.

The distance from the origin to the respective zone plane in k-space is given by:

$$k_{10.0} = \frac{2\pi}{\sqrt{3}\,a}, \qquad k_{00.2} = \frac{2\pi}{c} \qquad \text{and} \qquad k_{10.1} = \frac{2\pi}{\sqrt{3}\,a}\left(1 + \frac{3}{4}\left(\frac{a}{c}\right)^2\right)^{1/2}, \qquad (9)$$

and hence depends on the axial ratio. In the range of c/a higher than $\sqrt{3}$, the {00.2} zone planes are closest to the origin, leading to the sequence $k_{00.2} < k_{10.0} < k_{10.1}$ which holds in the η-phases, where c/a exceeds 1.75. The sequence $k_{10.0} < k_{00.2} < k_{10.1}$ holds for all ζ- and ϵ-phase structures. The corresponding Jones zone holds, at most, only 1.75 electrons per atom. Therefore, overlaps of electrons from the Jones zone and higher zones are expected at relatively low values of e/a. The interpretation of the lattice-spacing trends in the ζ-phase Ag-based alloys, whose axial ratios vary between 1.63 and 1.58, strongly suggests that overlaps of electrons across the {10.0} zone planes already occur at about 1.4 electrons per atom. The occurrence of possible overlaps across the {00.2} zone plane within the range of the ϵ-phases has been inferred from measurements of the lattice spacings, electronic specific heat coefficient, the Debye temperature, the superconductivity transition temperature, the magnetic susceptibility and the thermodynamic activity (MASSALSKI and MIZUTANI [1978]). This is shown in fig. 19. In each case the onset of electron overlaps across the {00.2} zone planes has been proposed for the range of e/a exceeding approximately 1.85 electrons per atom. All such measurements imply the occurrence of FsBz interactions that should be reflected also in the corresponding density-of-states changes on alloying.

The available calculated density-of-states curves for the hcp structure are at the moment limited to several pure metals, such as Mg, Zn or Be. All these metals have two valence electrons per atom and may be represented by relatively similar features in the corresponding density-of-state curves. The positions of peaks and subsequent declining slopes occur more or less at the same electron concentration for all three cases, in spite of a large difference in the axial ratios, atomic volumes and electronic interactions. This strongly indicates that the main features of the respective density-of-states curves originate from the FsBz interactions in which e/a plays an essential role. From this, one can conclude that a density-of-states curve for a disordered hcp alloy may also have essentially the same characteristic features. This is confirmed by experiments involving the measurement of electronic specific heats, which are directly proportional to the density of states at the Fermi level (fig. 20).

The experimental coefficients γ plotted in fig. 20 as a function of e/a show that, irrespective of the solute or solvent species, all available γ_{exp} values follow a very similar general trend over a wide range of electron concentrations. An increasing trend is evident in the lower e/a range, culminating in a broad maximum at about 1.5 electrons per atom, and followed by a decreasing trend at higher e/a values. The theoretical density-of-states curve for the hcp Zn, shown in units of mJ/mole K^2 in the same figure allows a direct comparison between a relevant calculation and the experimental data. This shows that the large peak in the theoretical curves more or less coincides with the experimental peak on the abscissa.

References: p. 214.

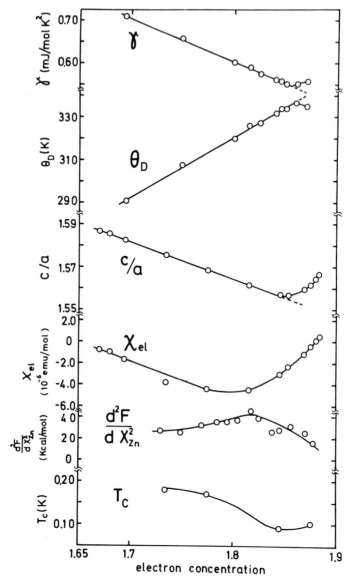

Fig. 19. Behavior of various physical properties in the ε-phase Ag–Zn alloy system: electronic specific heat coefficient γ; Debye temperature θ_D; axial ratio c/a; magnetic susceptibility due to conduction electrons χ_{el}; second derivative of the free energy with respect to concentration (d^2F/dX_{Zn}^2) (in units of 4.2 KJ/mol); superconducting transition temperature T_c. (From MASSALSKI and MIZUTANI [1978].)

The combination of contacts and overlaps with respect to a large number of zone planes is clearly responsible for the large peak in the $N(E)$ curve in hcp metals. The distance of the {10.1} planes from the origin of the zone is relatively insensitive to the

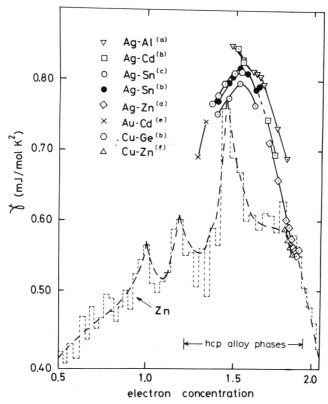

Fig. 20. Trends of electronic specific heat coefficients as a function of electron concentration for hcp Hume–Rothery alloys, shown against the band calculation for pure Zn (from MASSALSKI and MIZUTANI [1978]).

axial ratio (eq. 9). Hence, the large peak may be expected to occur at similar e/a values in most hcp structures. Once contact with the {10.1} planes occurs, additional electrons will be allocated in the remaining hole regions of the Brillouin zone until overlaps across the {10.1} or {00.2} zone planes become possible. Thus, until a sufficiently high e/a is reached, a progressive decrease in the $N(E)$ curve is expected as is actually seen in fig. 20. Based on the above interpretation the likely Fermi surface topography for a typical hcp Hume-Rothery phase may be expected to be like that shown in fig. 21. The recent positron-annihilation studies of the Fermi surface in the ζ-phase Cu–Ge alloys, by SUZUKI *et al.* [1976] and KOIKE *et al.* [1982] are entirely consistent with the conclusions drawn from the electronic specific heat data and earlier work on lattice spacings and axial ratios. Indeed, because of zone contacts and overlaps that are likely to occur in all hcp alloy phases, this particular group of alloys offers a most challenging research area for the positron-annihilation method. For the first time it has become possible to provide a direct evidence for the

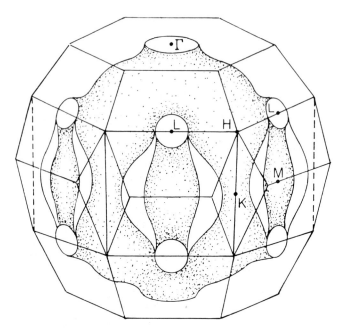

Fig. 21. A very likely Fermi surface topography in an hcp Hume–Rothery electron phase alloy. The 101 contact and 100 overlap are assumed to be present. (From Massalski and Mizutani [1978].)

existence of the Fermi-surface concept in disordered electron phases, precisely along the lines predicted by numerous earlier interpretations based on indirect data.

7.4. Laves phases

An important group of related intermediate phases is obtained by alloying of elements whose atomic diameters, d_{AA} and d_{BB}, are approximately in the ratio 1.2 to 1. The exact lattice geometry requires that d_{AA}/d_{BB} should be 1.225, but in known examples of this type of intermediate phases the ratio varies from about 1.1 to about 1.6. Much of the original work concerning the above phases is due to Laves and his co-workers. For this reason they are often called *Laves phases* (see ch. 5).

Laves phases are close packed, of approximate formula AB_2, crystallizing in one of the three structural types:

1) C_{14} structure, typified by the phase $MgZn_2$, hexagonal, with packing of planes of atoms represented by the general sequence ABABAB etc;

2) the C_{15} structure, typified by the phase $MgCu_2$, cubic, with packing ABCABCABC;

3) the C_{36} structure, typified by the phase $MgNi_2$, hexagonal, with packing ABACABAC.

The main reason for the existence of Laves phases appears to be one of geometrical origin – that of filling space in a convenient way. However, within the given range of atomic diameters which satisfy the space-filling condition, it appears that often the choice as to which particular modification will be stable is determined by electronic considerations. The evidence for this is particularly striking in the magnesium alloys studied by LAVES and WITTE [1935, 1936]. The experimental results concerning the three modifications occurring in several ternary systems based on magnesium are shown in fig. 22 and are plotted in terms of electron concentration. Witte and his co-workers have carried out experiments suggesting that the phase boundaries on the electron-rich side of typical Laves structures occur at very nearly the same e/a, suggesting that the homogeneity of a particular structure may be restricted by an appropriate Brillouin zone. Measurements of the changes in magnetic susceptibility and hydrogen solubility of several alloys within the pseudobinary sections $MgCu_2$–$MgZn_2$, $MgNi_2$–$MgZn_2$, $MgCu_2$–$MgAl_2$ and $MgZn_2$–$MgAl_2$, appear to support this hypothesis. The changes of the magnetic susceptibility in the pseudo-binary $MgCu_2$–$MgZn_2$ system are shown in fig. 23. KLEE and WITTE [1954] proposed that they may be interpreted in terms of interactions between the Fermi surface and the Brillouin zone, the dip in the susceptibility prior to the termination of solid solubility indicating a dip in the density of states.

Measurements of the electronic specific heats, that can be related to the density of states at the Fermi surface, have provided a further evidence of the importance of electronic factors in Laves phases. Examination of the trends of the electronic specific heat coefficient γ, as it varies in pseudobinary systems of $MgCu_2$ with polyvalent metals such as Zn, Al and Si, has shown that a sharp decrease of the

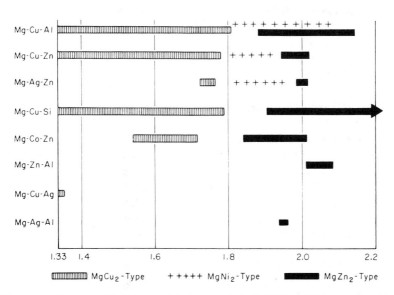

Fig. 22. The ranges of homogeneity in terms of electron concentration of several ternary magnesium alloys which possess the three typical Laves structures (from MASSALSKI [1956] after LAVES and WITTE [1936]).

References: p. 214.

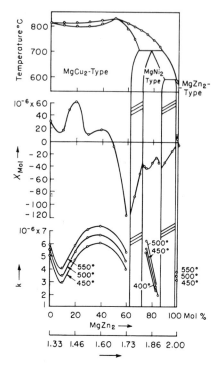

Fig. 23. Variation of hydrogen solubility and magnetic susceptibility with electron concentration in quasi-binary systems $MgCu_2$–$MgZn_2$ (from MASSALSKI [1956] after KLEE and WITTE [1954]).

density of states occurs near the phase boundary before the $MgCu_2$ structure is replaced by a two-phase field. A possible interpretation of this is that an appropriate Brillouin zone becomes filled with electrons. In this respect the electronic specific heat data and the magnetic susceptibility data shown in fig. 23 are very similar (SLICK et al. [1965]).

7.5.   Phases with wide solubility formed by the transition elements

A number of intermediate phases formed by the transition elements possess wide ranges of solid solubility. They are often designated by various Greek or Latin symbols such as σ, μ, δ, χ, P or R. For details reference may be made to TAYLOR [1961], NEVITT [1963] and ch. 5 which deals specifically with alloy compounds.

The σ-phase, the unit cell of which is tetragonal with $c/a \approx 0.52$ and 30 atoms per cell, has received much detailed attention, chiefly because of the detrimental effect which the formation of this phase has on mechanical properties of certain steels. In the system Fe–Cr, for example, the σ-phase separates out of the ferritic matrix and causes brittleness, but in more complex steels such as Fe–Cr–Mn σ-phases can also precipitate from the austenite phase.

X-ray and neutron diffraction studies have shown that many of the phases listed above are structurally related to one another because they can be built up from layers that show close similarities. Thus, undoubtedly, atomic packing plays an important role in determining their stability. At the same time studies of stability ranges, particularly in ternary systems, have shown that the contours of the phase fields of the above phases often bear relation to the value of the average group

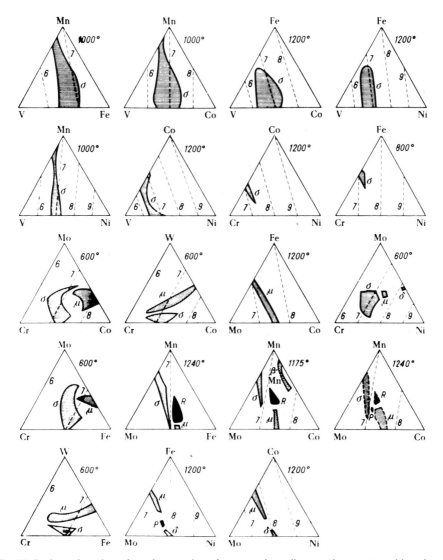

Fig. 24. Isothermal sections through a number of ternary phase diagrams between transition elements showing phase fields of phases with wide solid solubility. Values of average group number are indicated by dashed lines. (From NIEMIEC [1966].)

References: p. 214.

number (AGN). Hence, much speculation has been advanced about the electronic nature of their stability that might be similar to the electron phases of the noble metals. In fig. 24 the ternary phase relationships of some 19 ternary systems are shown at various temperatures as collected by NIEMIEC [1967]. The relationship between AGN and the contours of the σ-phase fields is particularly noticeable. It must be kept in mind however, that since the d-electrons unquestionably contribute to e/a in these phases, and since the d-bands are incompletely filled, the details of possible electronic interactions are bound to be complex and not necessarily related solely to some simple Brillouin zone–Fermi surface effects. For example, some of the bonding forces may be highly directional, or the number of "d-band vacancies" rather than electrons, may play a role.

8. Lattice spacings in solid solutions

The measurement of precise values of lattice spacings in solid solutions has contributed to the understanding of a number of factors which influence their stability and properties. Since the introduction of the Debye–Scherrer powder method some sixty years ago, the interest in the knowledge of lattice spacings in alloys has developed in three distinct directions:

1) in connection with precision measurements of lattice parameters for studies of systematic structural similarities between related alloy phases;

2) in connection with studies of relationships between lattice spacings, composition, electronic structure, size effects, local order, magnetic effects and numerous other properties of solid solutions;

3) in connection with the use of the lattice-spacing method as a tool for determining phase boundaries in alloy systems.

Detailed measurements of lattice spacing trends within individual alloy phases date back to the early 1930s. They were done mostly in terminal solid solutions of the noble metals and a few intermediate phases *. Today the available data fill large volumes (PEARSON [1958,1967]), and further additions are rapidly growing. The importance of the behavior of lattice spacings in hcp electron phases, in connection with their electronic structure, has already been discussed in § 7.3. Some additional aspects are discussed below.

8.1. Lattice spacings in primary solid solutions

The problem of lattice distortion in primary solid solutions of the *monovalent noble metals* has been considered by Hume-Rothery and by Owen and their associates (HUME-ROTHERY [1954] and OWEN [1947]). The relationships obtained by OWEN [1947] between the percentage lattice distortion and the solute valency in binary systems based on a common solvent are shown in figs. 25 and 26. The

---

* For a review of some of these measurements see MASSALSKI [1958].

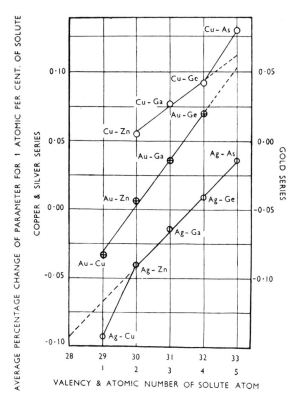

Fig. 25. Percentage lattice distortion as a function of solute valency in solid solutions. Cu, Ag and Au with Zn, Ga, Ge and As. (From PEARSON [1958] after OWEN [1947].)

importance of valence difference is clearly demonstrated in the figures, but there appear to be departures from the general trends which have not been explained. In order to gain further insight into the particular role of the difference beween valencies of the component elements, RAYNOR [1949a] attempted to eliminate size contributions by assuming that the electronic and size effects in certain solid solutions are additive and can be analyzed separately. Raynor's analysis was based on the assumption that a linear Vegard's Law may be applied to the sizes of atoms as given by the closest distance of approach and is therefore open to some doubt (MASSALSKI and KING [1961]).

Nevertheless, a detailed analysis of numerous solid solutions has shown that, after the assumed size contribution has been subtracted, the remaining lattice-spacing variation appears to be proportional to $(V_{su} - V_{sv})^2$ for solutes (su) and solvents (sv) of the same period, and to $(V_{su} - V_{sv})^2 + (V_{su} - V_{sv})$ for solutes and solvents from different periods. Subsequently, PEARSON [1982] has shown that a more general correlation is obtained, valid for a larger number of systems, if a size-effect correction, $\overline{D}$, is calculated from a relationship of the form $a = f\overline{D} + k$, where a is the

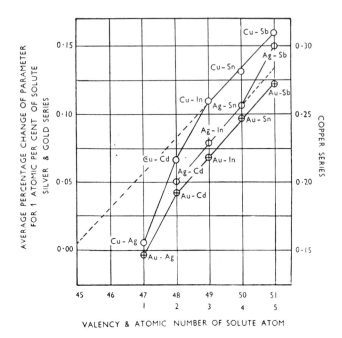

Fig. 26. Percentage lattice distortion as a function of solute valency in solid solutions. Cu, Ag and Au with Ag, Cd, In, Sn and Sb. (From PEARSON [1958] after OWEN [1947].)

lattice parameter, $\bar{D}$ is the average atomic diameter calculated from a linear relationship involving initial atomic diameters based on coordination 12, and f and k are constants. If an additional assumption is made that Ga, Ge, Sn, As, Sb and Bi contribute only two electrons to the conduction-electron concentration when alloyed with the noble metals, fifteen more systems appear to obey a uniform correlation.

Studies of binary systems have been extended to *ternary systems* where it is found that lattice spacings of ternary alloys may often be calculated from binary data using empirical additive relationships. An example of a linear relationship between lattice spacings and composition in the system Cu–Al–In (STIRLING and RAYNOR [1956]) is shown in fig. 27. ARGENT and WAKEMAN [1957] have shown that the expansion of the copper lattice by additions of zinc and gallium or zinc and germanium is additive in the respective ternary systems. Similar results hold also for additions of gallium and germanium to copper. Additive linear behavior suggests that in simple ternary solid solutions there is no appreciable solute–solute interaction, at least in dilute solutions where atoms of copper can effectively prevent contact beween solutes. Even in the system Ag–Mg–Sb (HILL and AXON [1956–7]) the strictly additive behavior of lattice spacings is still observed despite the fact that strong electrochemical differences between magnesium and antimony, and the tendency towards compound formation (Mg_3Sb_2), might be expected to favor clustering of magnesium and antimony atoms which should lead to the contraction of the lattice. However, when

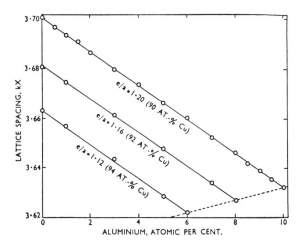

Fig. 27. Lattice spacings of α solid-solution alloys in the Cu–Al–In system along lines of constant copper content (from Massalski [1958] after Stirling and Raynor [1956]).

magnesium and silicon are dissolved in an aluminium lattice, contractions are observed which point to electrochemical interactions (Hill and Axon [1954–5]).

The lattice spacings of solid solutions of lithium, magnesium, silicon, copper, zinc, germanium and silver *in aluminium* have been studied and discussed by Axon and Hume-Rothery [1948] whose data are plotted in fig. 28. It may be seen from the figure that apart from silver, which produces virtually no change of lattice spacings, the aluminium lattice is expanded by magnesium and germanium and contracted by lithium, silicon, copper and zinc. Aluminium is an example of a trivalent solvent with a face-centred cubic structure. The first Brillouin zone can hold only two electrons per atom and must therefore be overlapped; but it has been shown (Harrison [1959] and Harrison and Webb [1960]) that the various portions of the overlapped and unoverlapped Fermi surface, when assembled together, resemble a free electron sphere. Hence, although overlaps exist in the aluminium structure and its alloys, their influence upon lattice spacings may be small.

Axon and Hume-Rothery [1948] have shown that the extrapolated AAD (§6.1) values for various elements dissolved in aluminium are influenced by the interplay of a number of factors such as relative volume per valence electron in the crystals of the solvent and the solute, the relative radii of the ions, and the relative difference in the electrochemical affinities.

The changes in the lattice spacings in the system *magnesium–cadmium* at temperatures at which complete solid solubility occurs in this system (see fig. 1) have been studied by Hume-Rothery and Raynor [1940]. When magnesium is alloyed with cadmium, no change occurs in the nominal electron concentration, both elements being two-valent. The initial additions of cadmium to magnesium cause a contraction of the *a* lattice spacing but only a very slight increase in the axial ratio because

References: p. 214.

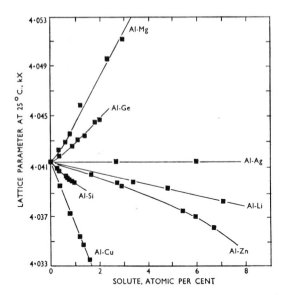

Fig. 28. The lattice-spacing–composition curves of alloys based on aluminium as solvent (from MASSALSKI [1958] after AXON and HUME-ROTHERY [1948]).

the c lattice spacing decreases at about the same rate as does the a lattice spacing. When magnesium is added to cadmium at the opposite end of the phase diagram, both a and c also decrease, but c more rapidly, causing a rapid decrease of c/a. The presence of at least two electrons per atom in this system means that there must exist overlaps from the first Brillouin zone (see fig. 17) since the alloys are conductors of electricity. It is now known from direct measurements of the Fermi surface that in both pure cadmium and pure magnesium overlaps exist across the horizontal and vertical sets of planes in the Brillouin zone, and although the amounts of these overlaps are different in both cases the nature of the overlaps is similar. Hence the relationship between overlaps and trends in the lattice spacings and the axial ratio in the Mg–Cd system is open to speculation.

In a similar way, because of the complexity of factors involved, the interpretation of the lattice spacings of alloys of transition elements may be expected to meet formidable difficulties. The inner-core d-band shells are incomplete, and it is known that electrons from these shells can contribute both to bonding and to conductivity.

The trends in the lattice spacings of the *transition elements* of the Second Long Period (zirconium, niobium, molybdenum, rhodium and palladium), when dissolved in the hexagonal close-packed ruthenium, have been studied by HELLAWELL and HUME-ROTHERY [1954]. In all cases the parameters c and c/a are increased by the formation of a solid solution and, at equal percentages of each solute, the increases are in the order zirconium → niobium → molybdenum → palladium → rhodium. The a parameters are diminished by zirconium and rhodium and increased by palladium, niobium and molybdenum. The axial ratio of ruthenium (1.5824) is considerably less than the ideal value, and the distance in the basal plane is greater than the distance between an atom and its nearest neighbor in the plane above or below. Hellawell and Hume-Rothery interpret the observed lattice spacings on the basis of "size differences" between component atoms as expressed by the minimum distance of approach between atoms in the pure elements and by a possible directional sharing of the electron cloud of zirconium which may take place on alloying.

8.2.　The relationship between lattice spacings and magnetic properties

A survey of the lattice spacings of transition metal alloys as a function of composition shows (PEARSON [1958]) that there are many inflections in the lattice-spacing curves with accompanying inflections in the magnetic properties. The magnetic properties of metals and alloys depend on the arrangement and separation of atoms in a structure, and therefore such changes as the ferromagnetic–paramagnetic transition might be expected to be related to some changes in the lattice spacings and the volume of the unit cell.

The ferromagnetic–paramagnetic changes (F–P) and the antiferromagnetic–paramagnetic changes (A–P) are *second-order transitions* in which the ordering of the spin orientation develops gradually on cooling below the transition temperature, T_c. Such changes are usually accompanied by a sharp change in the slope of the lattice-spacing curve as a function of temperature, such that the derivative da/dT is discontinuous at T_c (WILLIS and ROOKSBY [1954]). Ferromagnetic–antiferromagnetic changes (F–A), on the other hand, are a first-order transition involving a discontinuous change of electron spin orientation and are accompanied by a discontinuous change in lattice spacing (WILLIS and ROOKSBY [1954]). The second order F–P and A–P changes are truly reversible while the first order changes are accompanied by the usual thermal hysteresis in the transition region.

An example of the lattice-spacing changes accompanying an F–P transition is shown in fig. 29a for the system Mn–Sn (WILLIS and ROOKSBY [1954]). In cases of a first-order transition at the Curie point the discontinuous change in the lattice spacings may also be associated with some displacements of the different types of atoms in a structure, so that in such a case the abrupt change in the lattice spacing represents two processes occurring at the same time. According to ROBERTS [1956], the first-order transition at the Curie point is associated with a movement of about 10% of the manganese atoms into interstitial positions. The actual trend in the lattice spacings with temperature in the Mn–Bi system as determined by WILLIS and ROOKSBY [1954] is shown in fig. 29b.

A definite anomaly is found in the temperature variation of the lattice spacings accompanying the F–P transition of pure nickel, but no pronounced anomalies are observed in the slope of the lattice spacings as a function of composition in nickel alloys at compositions at which the F–P change should occur (PEARSON [1958]). COLES [1956] has reported a slight change of slope accompanying the F–P change in

References: p. 214.

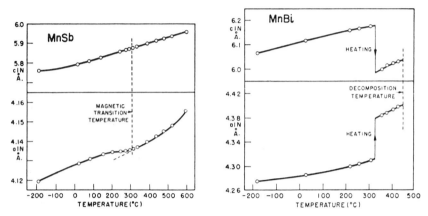

Fig. 29. (a) Lattice spacing of MnSb, which has a B8$_1$ type of structure as a function of temperature. (b) Lattice spacing of MnBi, which has a B8$_1$ type of structure as a function of temperature. (From PEARSON [1958] after WILLIS and ROOKSBY [1954].)

an alloy of nickel–35% copper. This composition corresponds to alloys in which the Curie point occurs at room temperature.

9. Defect structures

In addition to clustering or ordering of atoms, which constitutes a departure from randomness, solid solutions can contain various imperfections which can be of three general types: point-, line- and surface imperfections, according to whether they are vacant sites or interstitial atoms, various types of dislocations, stacking faults, or small-angle boundaries. The nature of dislocations, their interactions and their properties are discussed in ch. 18. Below we shall briefly consider some aspects of vacancies in solid solutions and the presence of various stacking disorders.

From the point of view of energy relationships, the presence of vacant sites in solid solutions may enhance stability, owing to their association with the entropy, the strain energy, or the electronic energy. Vacancies may be introduced by quenching from higher temperatures where their equilibrium number, due to entropy considerations, is higher than at lower temperatures, or they may be introduced by various irradiation processes, plastic deformation or, finally, by alloying. The calculation of the energy associated with the formation of vacancies or interstitials in a solid solution at finite concentrations presents several difficulties (see, for example, FUMI [1955], FRIEDEL [1954b], BROOKS [1955] and MANN and SEEGER [1960]). The subject is presented in some detail in ch. 17.

9.1. Vacancies and vacant sites in structures of alloys

From the point of view of the theory of alloys, vacancies are believed to be produced on alloying under certain conditions when the number of electrons per atom is kept constant or reduced. Evidence of this is provided by terminal solutions or electron phases with lattice defects. With the increase or decrease in the number of solute atoms a change can occur in the number of atoms per unit cell in a way which produces vacant lattice sites. It is believed that this takes place in order to maintain optimum electronic energy. Such vacancy populations, determined by composition and not by temperature, are distinguished as *constitutional vacancies*.

The work of BRADLEY and TAYLOR [1937] and TAYLOR and DOYLE [1972] on Ni–Al, and of LIPSON and TAYLOR [1939] on some ternary alloys based on this phase, are first-known examples of this phenomenon. The Ni–Al alloy may be regarded as an electron phase analogous to β-brass if nickel, a transition element, is assumed to have zero to near zero valency. At 50 at% this phase possesses a CsCl ordered structure in which one kind of atoms, say nickel, occupy cube centers and the other kind of atoms, cube corners. The diameter of a nickel atom is smaller than that of an aluminium atom and hence, if nickel content is increased above 50 at%, the lattice parameter of the structure decreases in the expected manner while the density is increased. However, when the aluminium content is increased above 50 at%, an anomalous behavior is observed since the lattice spacing of the Ni–Al phase does not increase but actually decreases, and the fall in the density is much more rapid than would be expected from the replacement of nickel atoms by aluminium. This behavior is shown in fig. 30 in which the lattice spacing data for Co–Al (BRADLEY and SEAGER as quoted by PEARSON [1958]) are also included. BRADLEY and TAYLOR [1937] concluded that the observed anomalies could be explained if one supposed that in the aluminium-rich alloys there are less than two atoms per unit cell and that omission of atoms occurs from some lattice points with the creation of vacancies. On the nickel-rich side, the extra nickel atoms substitute in the usual way for aluminium atoms on the aluminium sublattice. The aluminium-rich side, however, is quite different: no aluminium substitutes on the nickel sublattice; instead nickel atoms disappear from the nickel sublattice, leaving nickel vacancies. For instance, at 45 at% Ni, 18% of the nickel sites are vacant, all of the aluminium sites are filled. In this way the number of electrons per unit cell is kept constant and equal to approximately 3, corresponding to an *e/a* ratio of 3/2 characteristic of the β-brass structures. Several other studies showed that stoichiometric β–NiAl quenched from a high temperature (as opposed to that slowly cooled) contained a high concentration of *thermal* vacancies; the most recently cited figure is 1.08% of vacancies at 1600°C. This is a very much larger thermal vacancy concentration than is found in other metals or alloys, even just below the melting temperature; so large that on cooling the vacancies will separate out into a population of voids visible in the electron microscope (EPPERSON *et al.* [1978]). 50/50 NiAl containing such vacancies, all on the nickel sublattice, must also contain substitutional defects – that is some nickel atoms in the aluminium sublattice, also called nickel antistructure

References: p. 214.

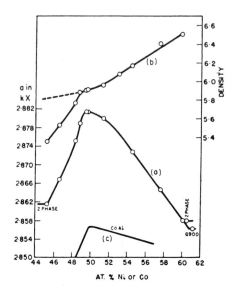

Fig. 30. (a,b) Lattice spacing and density of β-AlNi as a function of composition. (c) Lattice spacing of β-AlCo as a function of composition. (From Pearson [1958] after original work of Bradley and Taylor [1937] and Bradley and Seager [1939].)

atoms – to preserve the overall chemical composition: specifically, two vacancies must be accompanied by one substitutional defect. Such a trio of linked defects is now termed a triple defect. Parallels for the behavior of the NiAl alloys at high temperatures are found in other systems isomorphous with NiAl (see Cahn [1979]).

The conclusion related to the dependence of constitutional vacancies on electron concentration has been criticized on the basis that the omission of atoms could also be interpreted in terms of size-effects. Since there is only one atom of aluminium in the unit cell of the Ni–Al alloy, it appears possible that the omission of atoms with addition of aluminium in excess of 50% occurs as a result of inability to squeeze an additional large aluminium atom in the place of a small nickel atom. A possible differentiation between an interpretation in terms of electronic considerations and one in terms of size considerations could be made by introduction of a further element into the Ni–Al alloy. The size-effect spatial theory requires that the loss of atoms should take place when the concentration of aluminium exceeds more than one per unit cell whereas the electronic theory requires that it should occur when a definite electron concentration, approximately 1.5, is exceeded. Lipson and Taylor [1939] have shown that in two ternary systems, Fe–Ni–Al and Cu–Ni–Al, the general shape of the phase field of the ternary alloys based on Ni–Al falls into the composition regions which indicate that electron concentration, rather than size, is the main factor determining the phase stability.

The interpretation of the lattice spacings and density behavior in alloys based on Ni–Al is limited by the fact that nickel, a transition element, must be assumed to

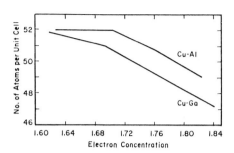

Fig. 31. The number of atoms per unit cell in the γ-phases of the system Cu–Ga and Cu–Al as a function of electron concentration (after HUME-ROTHERY *et al.* [1952]).

possess zero valency in order to make it possible to assume that the above phase is an electron phase of the 3/2 type. However, further evidence of omission of atoms from sites in a unit cell has also been obtained in the study of some γ-brasses (HUME-ROTHERY *et al.* [1952]) and Al–Zn primary solid solutions (ELLWOOD [1948, 1951–2]), in which no transition elements are involved so that the valence of the participating atoms is more definite. In the case of γ-brass two particular binary systems were studied, Cu–Al and Cu–Ga (HUME-ROTHERY *et al.* [1952]). In the former system, lattice spacing work and density data show that the number of atoms in the unit cell of the γ-phase remains constant at about 52 as aluminium is increased to approximately 35.3 at%, after which the number steadily decreases. A similar effect has been observed in the Cu–Ga γ-brass to occur at about 34.5 at% gallium. The data for Cu–Al and Cu–Ga alloys are shown in fig. 31. HUME-ROTHERY *et al.* [1952] have interpreted the creation of vacant sites in γ-brass structures in terms of the Brillouin zone of the γ-brasses, suggesting that both the normal and the defect γ-structures can hold no more than about 87–88 electrons per cell in order not to exceed an electron concentration of about 1.68–1.70. It appears that the high-temperature δ-phase in the Cu–Zn system resembles a defect γ-brass structure in that it possesses numerous lattice defects and vacant atomic sites. Other constitutional vacancies in brass-type alloys have been discussed by NOVER and SCHUBERT [1980].

Creation of lattice defects in which vacancies or excess atoms are involved occurs in intermediate phases probably more frequently than it was thought likely in the past. For example, in intermediate phases which crystallize in structures closely related to the NiAs structure the basic structure, corresponding to the formula AB, can gradually change in the direction of compositions A_2B by a gradual filling of certain vacant spaces * in the structure by the excess atoms of one of the components. In the series of phases such as $NiS \rightarrow NiSe \rightarrow NiAs \rightarrow Ni_3Sb_2 \rightarrow Ni_3Sn_2 \rightarrow Ni_2Ge \rightarrow Ni_2In$ the number of nickel atoms becomes greater than 50 at% and X-ray work has shown that this is accomplished by nickel atoms gradually filling certain

---

* These are analogous to the octahedral, tetrahedral and other vacant spaces which exist in the simple metallic structures as discussed in ch. 2.

References: p. 214.

interstitial positions in the ideal NiAs structure. The typical NiAs structure may be regarded as based on a close-packed hexagonal lattice of metalloid atoms in which the metal atoms occupy the octahedral spaces between the close-packed hexagonal layers (see ch. 5). As the structure becomes filled with the excess of the more metallic atoms, it gradually acquires a pseudo-cubic symmetry and the metallic character increases considerably so that, for example, in the series quoted above the Ni_2In phase is almost indistinguishable from the Cu–Al or Cu–Ca γ-brasses.

Constitutional vacancies in large concentrations have also been found in a number of oxides, especially those of the transition metals, and in some hydrides (e.g., TiH_x) and carbides. In some instances there is evidence of vacancy ordering.

9.2. Stacking faults

The possibility of the formation of stacking faults in typically metallic solid solutions has recently come to play an ever-increasing role in the understanding of many properties of solid solutions, particularly those with the face-centred cubic and the close-packed hexagonal structures. Such phenomena, for example, as the changes in electrical resistivity, work-hardening, recrystallization, creep, deformation texture, crystallography of phase transformations, corrosion, phase morphology and a number of others have been shown to be related to the presence of stacking faults and therefore to the *stacking-fault energy*.

The face-centred cubic and close-packed hexagonal structures are closely related and, being both close packed, differ essentially only in the way in which the closest-packed planes are stacked together. It has been shown originally by BARRETT [1950] that stacking disorders exist in a cold-worked metal. Subsequently, several authors (PATERSON [1952], WARREN and WAREKOIS [1955], WAGNER [1957], WILKENS [1957] and JOHNSON [1963]) developed theories which relate the effect of the presence of various types of stacking faults to the changes in the X-ray diffraction pattern of the face-centred cubic structure. The normal sequence of {111} planes in a face-centred cubic structure can be described as ABCABCABC using the usual A, B, C notation. The three typical stacking errors are illustrated by the characteristic stacking patterns shown in fig. 32. They are: (1) the *intrinsic fault*, corresponding to the removal of a close-packed layer of atoms, (2) the *extrinsic fault*, corresponding to the insertion of an extra close-packed layer of atoms, and (3) the *twin (growth) fault*,

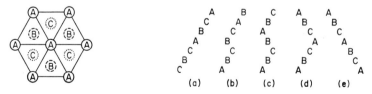

Fig. 32. Planar view of atomic positions and stacking sequences for: (a) perfect fcc crystal; (b) intrinsic fault; (c) extrinsic fault; (d) twin fault; (e) twin crystal. (After JOHNSON [1963].)

produced at the interface between two perfect crystallites which are in twin relation (see READ [1953]). The intrinsic faults have received the most attention, and calculations based upon idealized models suggest that such faults should produce broadening and shifts in X-ray peak positions. This prediction has been verified experimentally in a number of pure metals (Cu, Au, Ag, Pb, Ni, etc.) and alloy systems (mostly based on the noble metals Cu, Ag and Au). Theoretical considerations of the influence of twin faults and extrinsic faults indicate that the corresponding X-ray line-broadening should be asymmetric in both cases and that the peak shifts resulting from the presence of extrinsic faults should occur in a direction opposite to the shift produced by intrinsic faulting (JOHNSON [1963]). Published work to date indicates that in metals intrinsic faults predominate. However in other materials, for example in silicon (AERTS *et al.* [1962a, b]), the stacking-fault energy of intrinsic and extrinsic faults may be of about equal magnitude. If, in addition, one considers the less idealized cases in which the distribution of stacking-fault density is variable in a specimen, the prediction of the over-all X-ray pattern becomes very complex (see for example, BARRETT and MASSALSKI [1966] p. 464). Nevertheless, the X-ray work has served as a useful means for comparison between various metals and alloys and for the studies of trends in faulting probability with composition and temperature.

In addition to the above X-ray analysis a direct estimate of stacking-fault energy γ can also be made by studies of certain annealing or deformation features in metals and alloys and their changes with temperature by studies of twinning frequency in metallographic samples (FULLMAN [1951] and BOLLING and WINEGARD [1958a, b]), by interpretation of dissociated dislocations (nodes) in transmission electron photomicrographs (HOWIE and SWANN [1961] and CHRISTIAN and SWANN [1965]) and other features such as cross-slip, creep, texture etc. [GALLAGHER [1970]).

The possibility of the existence of stacking faults in hcp and bcc structures has been considered in a number of publications both from the experimental and the theoretical point of view. In bcc and hcp metals stacking faults do not produce line shifts (see WARREN [1959a]). In hexagonal metals they produce broadening of certain reflections, which has been observed experimentally, particularly in the case of cobalt (EDWARDS and LIPSON [1942]).

A number of attempts have been made to elucidate the factors which influence the changes of stacking-fault energy upon alloying. Although all such factors must be electronic in nature, it appears at the moment that a detailed interpretation is not possible. In a number of publications the changes of stacking-fault energy have been related to the electron concentration, certain size effects, the changes in the density of states, and the changes in the topology of the Fermi surface. (See GALLAGHER [1970].)

In the case of fcc *metals*, recent measurements of the rate of loop annealing, the stability of tetrahedra introduced by deformation, of faulted dipoles, and of texture developed by rolling have led to the availability of quite precise information on the magnitude of γ for materials in which extended nodes or extrinsic–intrinsic fault pairs cannot be observed. Thus, it is no longer essential to estimate the fault energy of such metals as Cu, Au, Al, and Ni by extrapolating node data or normalized X-ray faulting probability results, although the extrapolation procedures, too, have been improved and now lead to more reliable results. Reasonable estimates of γ, probably accurate to $\pm 20\%$, are: $\gamma_{Ag} = 21.6$ mJ/m^2, $\gamma_{Pb} = 30$ mJ/m^2, $\gamma_{Au} = 50$ mJ/m^2, $\gamma_{Cu} = 55$ mJ/m^2, $\gamma_{Al} = 200$ mJ/m^2 and $\gamma_{Ni} = 250$ mJ/m^2. Estimates of γ in other elements from scaled rolling-texture data are subject to rather larger errors, but are the best values available at the present time: $\gamma_{Ce} < 5$ mJ/m^2, $\gamma_{Yb} < 10$ mJ/m^2, $\gamma_{Th} = 70$ mJ/m^2, $\gamma_{Pt} = 75$ mJ/m^2, $\gamma_{Pd} = 130$ mJ/m^2 and $\gamma_{Rh} = 330$ mJ/m^2 (GAL-LAGHER [1970]). Advances have been made in theoretical estimates of γ for pure materials (BLANDIN et al. [1966]), but difficulties are still experienced in applying the treatments to noble metals on account of their complex electronic structure.

In fcc *solid solutions*, a satisfactory amount of numerically accurate information is now available for the variation of γ (effective) with alloying, particularly in systems with copper, silver, and nickel as solvents. The form of the variation with B-group solutes in all cases follows the pattern established in the earliest studies in that γ decreases with increasing solute concentration, and considerable normalization of the data is achieved in plots with the electron/atom ratio as abscissa.

Several authors have noted that straight-line relationships for the change of γ with alloying can be obtained if γ is plotted on a log scale and the abscissa is expressed in

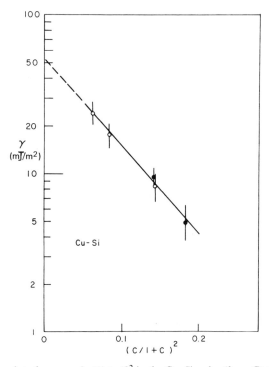

Fig. 33. Semi-log plot of γ versus $[c/(1+c)]^2$ in the Cu–Si series (from GALLAGHER [1970]).

terms of a composition-dependent function $[c/(1 + c)]^2$, where $c = $ (alloying concentration)/(solubility limit) at high temperatures. Expressing the abscissa in this form appears to provide a normalizing effect similar to that which arises by using the e/a ratio, but with the advantage that the solubility limit is in some systems more accurately known than is the effective valence of the solute. The relationship obtained for the fcc Cu–Si alloys is shown in fig. 33. Recent studies also suggest that in alloys of two fcc elements having complete mutual solubility, all compositions have γ intermediate in value between the fault energies of the component metals. Such noble-metal–transition-metal alloys as have been studied have γ of the same order as in the pure noble metal. Contrary to early studies, considerable extrinsic–intrinsic faulting has recently been observed in copper-, silver-, and gold-base alloys, and measurements on fault pairs have revealed that the extrinsic and intrinsic fault energies are approximately equal (GALLAGHER [1970]).

9.3. Metastable structures

Many solid solutions whose properties have been outlined in the preceding sections can exist in a metastable condition at temperatures which fall outside the equilibrium range of stability but at which the rate of approach to equilibrium is so slow as to be negligible. One of the most frequently used methods for producing metastability is rapid quenching from a high temperature. During quenching a single-phase solid solution may be retained untransformed, or it may transform by changing its crystal structure, either by a martensitic or a "massive" process (see BARRETT and MASSALSKI [1966]). Metastable solid solutions have also been obtained by a rapid cooling from the liquid state, using the "splat" or "crusher" cooling techniques (DUWEZ [1965, 1967]), by a rapid cooling from the vapor state, using vacuum deposition techniques (MADER *et al.* [1963]), by various methods involving the quenching of liquid metals on a rapidly revolving copper wheel, and by surface melting methods using laser beams, electron beams, etc. (See DUWEZ [1978] and also ch. 28.)

Following these procedures, enhanced solubilities, non-equilibrium phases and unusual crystalline and amorphous structures have been obtained. For example, a continuous series of *metastable solid solutions* can be obtained in the Cu–Ag system in place of the well-known eutectic phase diagram corresponding to equilibrium conditions. In other instances solid solutions have been obtained that are *amorphous*, resembling a frozen liquid. A large number of metastable phases obtained by the various rapid-cooling techniques have most unusual crystalline (or non-crystalline) electrical, semiconducting, superconducting (ch. 27), magnetic (ch. 26) and thermal properties. The research area of metallic glasses, in particular, has seen very rapid growth during the past decade and numerous symposia on this subject have been published (see, e.g., MASUMOTO and SUZUKI [1982]). In order to produce a metallic glass, crystallization has to be prevented during rapid cooling of the liquid. Cooling rates exceeding 10^6 K/s are usually needed to achieve this, and the most likely regions in phase diagrams where metallic glasses can be produced are the deep

References: p. 214.

eutectic regions. The reason for this has been discussed in numerous publications. One of the possibilities is that, in deep eutectics, the crystallization competing with metallic-glass formation must be of a multi-phase form, which is kinetically difficult. Hence, the chilled liquid becomes more and more viscous without crystallization until a glass transition temperature is reached when the liquid becomes a solid. The subject is discussed more fully in ch. 28.

10.   Order in solid solutions

The phenomena related to order–disorder (O–D) changes in solid solutions comprise a very extensive literature and a detailed review of these is beyond the scope of this chapter. Nevertheless, the tendency for unlike atoms to occupy adjoining sites of a crystalline lattice, leading towards formation of *superlattices*, is a very prominent feature of many solid solutions; and we shall briefly consider this subject from the structural point of view.

On the basis of thermodynamics (see ch. 6) it can be shown that an ordered arrangement of atoms in an alloy may produce a lower internal energy compared to a disordered arrangement, particularly if the segregation of atoms to designated atomic sites occurs at relatively low temperatures where entropy, associated with randomness, plays a lesser role. The condition of perfect order, such that the like atoms are never nearest neighbors, could be achieved only in a perfect single crystal with a simple metallic lattice and at compositions corresponding to stoichiometric ratios of atoms like AB, AB_2, AB_3, etc. Actually, the presence of various imperfections and grain boundaries precludes this possibility in most cases. In addition, it is known that an ordered solid solution consists of *ordered domains* which may be perfectly ordered within themselves but which are *out of step* with one another. This results in more contact between like atoms at the boundaries of adjacent domains. Ordered domains are sometimes called *antiphase domains* and usually their number is quite large within each grain of the material. With the development of electron microscopy techniques, the presence of antiphase domains has been confirmed by direct observation in thin films (GLOSSOP and PASHLEY [1959], SATO and TOTH [1961]).

A further departure from maximum order occurs in solid solutions whose compositions deviate from the optimum stoichiometric ratios of atoms. This is often associated with the fall of the ordering temperature on both sides of the ideal composition and by the change of other properties such as hardness, electrical resistivity, etc.

When the interaction between unlike atoms is very strong, the critical temperature T_c, at which disordering occurs, may lie above the melting point of the material. Alloys with this characteristic closely resemble chemical compounds (see ch. 5). When the interaction forces are less intense, an ordered solid solution may become disordered at a critical temperature even though the composition corresponds to a stoichiometric compound-like formula. Many typical alloy phases show this behavior with temperature. Finally, if the ordering forces are weak, as for example at low atomic concentrations in terminal solid solutions, the critical temperature may lie below the temperature at which attainment of equilibrium is possible within a reasonable time. One may then speak of the disordered state being frozen in. It has been found that the activation energy necessary to switch atoms into disordered positions in a fully ordered alloy is of the same order of magnitude as the heat of activation for diffusion or for recovery from cold work, usually about 1.5–2 eV.

10.1.   Types of superlattices

Simple superlattices in binary alloys with cubic structure occur near compositions corresponding to formulas A_3B, AB and AB_3. The Cu–Au system (see fig. 1b, above) provides a well-known prototype of ordered solid solutions based on the fcc structure. The superlattices Cu_3Au, CuAu and $CuAu_3$ have been investigated in great detail. In the case of Cu_3Au the low-temperature structure, (fig. 34a) is cubic, but in the case of CuAu (fig. 34c) alternate (002) planes contain either all copper or all gold atoms and a contraction occurs in the c direction, presumably as a result of attraction between atoms in these planes. This results in a tetragonal fcc structure with c/a ratio of 0.92.

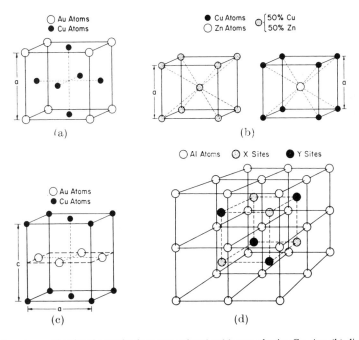

Fig. 34. Various types of ordered superlattices: (a) ordered cubic superlattice Cu_3Au; (b) disordered and ordered structures of β brass; (c) the tetragonal superlattice of AuCu; (d) the structure of Fe_3Al and FeAl: Al atoms fill the X sites in Fe_3Al and the X and Y sites in FeAl.

References: p. 214.

Order in bcc alloys again depends on composition. At 50 at% of solute the AB type of order results in the well-known CsCl structure (fig. 34b) which occurs, for example, in ordered β-brass. When the composition is between approximately 25 and 50 at% of solute, a whole sequence of ordered structures based on the simple body-centred cube becomes sometimes possible and such structures have been studied in much detail. The superlattices that occur in the Fe–Al system (fig. 34d) and the *Heusler alloys* (Cu_2MnAl), which are ordered when in the ferromagnetic condition, have received particular attention (see, for example, TAYLOR [1961]). With solute contents exceeding 50 at% the γ-brass type of order and other more complex superlattices are possible.

By analogy with the cubic structures, ordered superlattices occur frequently in close-packed hexagonal solid solutions. For example, in the Mg–Cd system the continuous series of solid solution at high temperatures is broken at lower temperatures by the formation of ordered superlattices at compositions $MgCd_3$, MgCd and Mg_3Cd (see fig. 1d, above). $MgCd_3$ orders to form the DO_{19} type of structure which is distorted from close-packed hexagonal, while the Mg_3Cd is closepacked hexagonal but with the a axis doubled and the basal layers so arranged that each cadmium atom is in contact with three magnesium atoms in the adjacent layers. Cooling of alloys in the MgCd composition region produces an ordered orthorhombic structure.

10.2. Long-period superlattices

As mentioned in the previous section the low-temperature annealing of CuAu alloys (below 380°C) produces a face-centred tetragonal structure whose unit cell is shown in fig. 34b. This structure is usually referred to as CuAu I. In the temperature interval between 380–410°C another ordered structure has been detected (by JOHANSSON and LINDE [1936]) which is often described as CuAu II. The superlattice CuAu II is a modification of CuAu I and the unit cell of this structure is orthorhombic as shown in fig. 35a. The long cell is obtained by stacking five CuAu I unit cells in a row in the direction of one of the long-cell edges (*b*) and then repeating this unit at five cell intervals with a simultaneous *out-of-step shift* at the boundary through a distance equal to the vectorial distance $\frac{1}{2}(a + c)$. The distance between each antiphase boundary may thus be specified by *Mb* where *M* denotes the domain size or *the period*. For CuAu II, $M = 5$. This superlattice is therefore called a *one-dimensional long-period superlattice* with a period equal to five. OGAWA and WATANABE [1954] have shown that a repulsive force arises at the junction of the long antiphase domains, which leads to a small local lattice-parameter increase in the direction of the long axis. This has the effect of a small periodic error in the diffracting lattice in this direction, and in electron-diffraction patterns it produces "satellite" reflections around the normal reflections.

Many other long-period superlattices have been discovered in cubic alloys, particulary at the A_3B compositions. Long-period superlattices have also been reported in hexagonal alloys (SCHUBERT et al. [1955]). The structure shown in fig. 35b corresponds to the orthorhombic structure Au_3Zn. This long-period superlattice

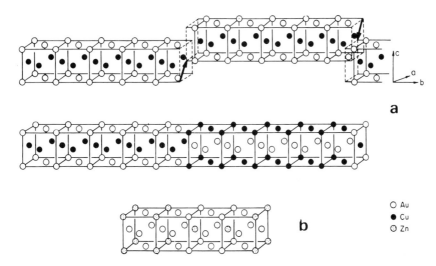

Fig. 35. Long-period superlattices: (a) the structure of CuAu II; (b) the structure of Au–Zn. (After Schubert *et al.* [1955].)

is based on Cu_3Au and consists of four face-centred cells stacked together with a half-diagonal shift as shown in the figure. Most of the long-period superlattices at compositions A_3B retain the cubic symmetry of atomic distribution and they can be either one-dimensional long-period superlattices or two-dimensional superlattices. Much of the recent work in this field is due to Schubert *et al.* [1955] and to Sato and Toth [1961, 1962, 1965].

The discovery of the long-period superlattices has presented a challenge to the theory of alloys because the usual atom-pair interaction models adopted for explanation of the order–disorder phenomena cannot be used unless one assumes extremely long-distance interactions. The most successful interpretation at the moment appears to be that such superlattices are a result of a complex interaction between the Fermi surface and the Brillouin zone (Sato and Toth [1961, 1962, 1965]) and is therefore connected with the collective behavior of the free electrons. The Brillouin zone for the CuAu alloys is shown in fig. 36. The thin lines represent the zone for the disordered fcc structure. This zone is bounded by the octahedral {111} and cubic {200} faces and can hold two electrons per atom. The thick lines represent the zone for the ordered CuAu I superlattice. This zone, as a result of order in the lattice, is now bounded by the {001} and {110} faces and is therefore no longer symmetrical, the {100} faces being much closer to the origin than the {110} faces. The free-electron energies at the centers of the {100} and {110} faces are 2.4 eV and 4.8 eV respectively, while the energy at the Fermi surface corresponding to one electron per atom (Cu–Au system) is 6.5 eV. Therefore electrons should overlap into the larger zone. The existence of "satellite" reflections around the normal reflections in the *b* direction, corresponding to the long-range periodicity in the CuAu II superlattice,

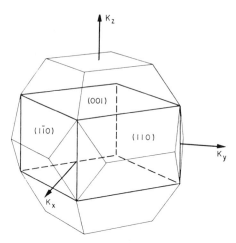

Fig. 36. The Brillouin zone of the disordered (thin lines) and ordered (thick lines) fcc structures (from Sato and Toth [1962]).

suggests that the Brillouin zone would show a slight splitting of certain faces. This is illustrated in fig. 37b and c which represents a horizontal section in the reciprocal lattice throught the zone shown in fig. 36. Sato and Toth [1962] have proposed that at one electron per atom, the Fermi surface comes rather close to the {110} faces and, when the CuAu II superlattice is formed, the interaction between the Fermi surface and these split faces produces extra stabilization of the long-period structure. Since the period M governs the extent to which the satellite spots are separated in the reciprocal lattice, there should be a relationship between M and the electron concentration which governs the volume of the Fermi "sphere". It can be shown that

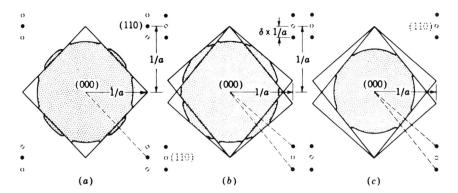

Fig. 37. Horizontal section in reciprocal space through the Brillouin zone of fig. 36, showing possible Fermi surface contours for the Cu–Au superlattice: (a) CuAu I; (b,c) CuAu II. (From Barrett and Massalski [1966].)

as e/a increases, the Fermi "sphere" would fit better with respect to the {110} faces if their splitting were increased. This requires that the period M should decrease. SATO and TOTH [1961] have shown that additions of alloying elements to the CuAu II superlattice, resulting in changes of e/a, also produce changes of the long-range period in the direction suggested by the above model. Furthermore, the model makes also possible the explanation of other characteristics of the long-period superlattices such as the nature of the distortion of the lattice, the concentration and temperature dependence of the distortion and of the periods, and the question whether or not the superlattice will be one-dimensional or two-dimensional.

10.3. Long-range order and short-range order

Attempts to formulate a theory of ordering date back to the 1930s and are associated with the names of Borelius, Johansson and Linde, Dehlinger, Bragg and Williams, Bethe, Peierls, Takagi and others. Several comprehensive reviews exist on both the mechanisms of ordering and on various treatments of the subject, and they may be consulted for details; for example, those of NIX and SHOCKLEY [1938], LIPSON [1950] and GUTTMAN [1956].

The essential condition for a solid solution of suitable composition to become ordered is that dissimilar atoms must attract each other more than similar atoms in order to lower the free energy upon ordering. In terms of *interaction energies* between pairs of atoms of two atomic species A and B this condition is usually expressed as follows:

$$E_{AB} < \tfrac{1}{2}(E_{AA} + E_{BB}), \tag{10}$$

where E_{AA} and E_{BB} represent energies of like pairs of atoms and E_{AB} represents the energy of the unlike pair. If this condition is satisfied for a given alloy of a stoichiometric composition, then at some suitably low temperature the structure will become perfectly ordered, the A and B atoms occupying designated sites in the lattice, which may be called the α and β sites. On warming up the energy will be supplied in the form of heat and will cause some A atoms to migrate into "wrong" β sites and vice versa, causing the atomic distribution to become more *random*. With perfect order at a low temperature the mathematical probability of finding an A atom on an α site and a B atom on a β site is unity. At higher temperatures, however, the probability that an α site is occupied by an A atom will be reduced to a fraction of unity, say p. BRAGG and WILLIAMS [1934] have used this description to define the *long-range order parameter, S,*

$$S = (p - r)/(1 - r), \tag{11}$$

where r is the fraction of A atoms in the alloy. According to eq. (11), S varies from one to zero as order decreases.

The order–disorder change, like the magnetic change, is a *cooperative phenomenon*. As more atoms find themselves in "wrong" atomic sites due to thermal agitation the energy difference indicated by eq. (10) decreases and it becomes easier

References: p. 214.

to produce further disorder. Eventually a critical temperature is reached, T_c, at which all distinction between different sites is lost.

The simple approach as outlined above does not allow for the possibility of the existence of magnetic domains and other types of interruptions in the ordered array of atoms that may cause a departure from perfect order (as mentioned in a previous section) which makes it possible for a high degree of local order to exist even though its perfection is not absolute on a large volume scale. In order to describe such situations an alternative method of defining the state of order is possible which, instead of considering the probability of finding A or B atoms on designated α or β lattice sites, takes into acount the number of unlike nearest neighbors around a given atom. For example, the BETHE [1935] *short-range order parameter*, σ, is defined by:

$$\sigma = (q - q_r)/(q_m - q_r),\tag{12}$$

where q denotes the fraction of unlike nearest neighbors at a given temperature and q_r and q_m correspond to the fractions of unlike nearest neighbors at conditions of maximum randomness and maximum order. As may be seen, σ is defined in such a way that it would become unity for perfect order and zero for randomness.

Actually, instead of reaching zero on disordering σ usually remains a definite value above T_c. In terms of the relationship between atoms σ measures the state of order in the immediate vicinity of a given atom unlike the long-range order parameter, S, of Bragg and Williams which deals with the whole lattice. The description of the immediate surroundings of a given atom can be extended further to include several successive concentric shells corresponding to the first, second, third, etc., nearest neighbors (COWLEY [1950]).

References

AERTS, E., P. DELAVIGNETTE, R. SIEMS and S. AMELINCKX, 1962a, Electron Microscopy (Academic, New York).

AERTS, E., P. DELAVIGNETTE, R. SIEMS and S. AMELINCKX, 1962b, J. Appl. Phys. **33**, 3078.

ARGENT, B.B., and D.W. WAKEMAN, 1956–7, J. Inst. Metals **85**, 413.

AVERBACH, B.L., 1956, in: Theory of Alloy Phases (ASM, Metals Park, OH).

AXON, H.J., and W. HUME-ROTHERY, 1948, Proc. Roy. Soc. **A193**, 1.

BARRETT, C.S., 1950, Trans. AIME **188**, 123.

BARRETT, C.S., and T.B. MASSALSKI, 1966, Structure of Metals, 3rd Ed. (McGraw–Hill, New York).

BENNETT, L.H., ed., 1980, Proc. Conf. on Theory of Alloy Phase Formation (AIME, Warrendale, PA).

BETHE, H.A., 1935, Proc. Roy. Soc. (London) **A150**, 552.

BLANDIN, A., 1965, in: Alloying Behavior and Effects in Concentrated Solid Solutions, ed. T.B. Massalski (Gordon and Breach, New York).

BLANDIN, A., J. FRIEDEL and G. SAADA, 1966, J. Phys. Suppl. C3, **27**, 128.

BOLLING, G.F., and W.C. WINEGARD, 1958a, J. Inst. Metals **86**, 492.

BOLLING, G.F., and W.C. WINEGARD, 1958b, Acta Metall. **6**, 288.

BOLLING, G.F., T.B. MASSALSKI AND C.J. MCHARGUE, 1961, Phil. Mag. **6**, 491.

BORIE, B.S., 1957, Acta Cryst. **10**, 89.

BORIE, B.S., 1959, Acta Cryst. **12**, 280.

BRADLEY, A.J., and A. TAYLOR, 1937, Proc. Roy. Soc. (London) **A159**, 56.

BRAGG, W.L., and E.J. WILLIAMS, 1934, Proc. Roy. Soc. (London) **A145**, 669.

BROOKS, H., 1955, in: Impurities and Imperfections, ASM Seminar (ASM, Metals Park, OH).

CAHN, R.W., 1979, Nature **279**, 579.

CHRISTIAN, J.W., and P.R. SWANN, 1965, in: Alloying Behavior and Effects in Concentrated Solid Solutions, ed. T.B. Massalski (Gordon and Breach, New York) p. 105.

COCKAYNE, B., and G.V. RAYNOR, 1961, Proc. Roy. Soc. **A261**, 175.

COHEN, M.H., 1965, in: Alloying Behavior and Effects in Concentrated Solid Solutions, ed. T.B. Massalski (Gordon and Breach, New York).

COLES, B.R., 1956, J. Inst. Metals **84**, 346.

COWLEY, J., 1950, Phys. Rev. **77**, 669.

DARKEN, L.S., and R.W. GURRY, 1953, Physical Chemistry of Metals (McGraw–Hill, New York).

DEXTER, D.L., 1952, Phys. Rev. **87**, 768.

DUWEZ, P., 1965, in: Alloying Behavior and Effects in Concentrated Solid Solutions, ed. T.B. Massalski (Gordon and Breach, New York).

DUWEZ, P., 1967, Trans. ASM **60**, 607.

DUWEZ, P., ed., 1978, Metallic Glasses, ASM seminar (ASM, Metals Park, OH).

EDWARDS, O.S., and H. LIPSON, 1942, Proc. Roy. Soc. **A180**, 208.

EKMANN, W., 1931, Phys. Chem. **B12**, 57.

ELLNER, M., 1978, J. Less-Common Met. **60**, 15.

ELLNER, M., 1980, J. Less-Common Met. **75**, 5.

ELLWOOD, E.C., 1948, Nature **163**, 772.

ELLWOOD, E.C., 1951–2, J. Inst. Metals **80**, 217.

EPPERSON, J.E., K.W. GERSTENBERG, D. BRENER, G. KOSTORZ and C. ORTIZ, 1978, Phil. Mag. **A38**, 529.

ESHELBY, J.D., 1956, Solid State Phys. **3**, 79.

FAULKNER, J.S., 1982, Prog. Mater. Sci. **27**, 1.

FRIEDEL, J., 1954a, Adv. Phys. **3**, 446.

FRIEDEL, J., 1954b, Les Electrons dans Métaux, 10th Solvay Conference (R. Stoops, Bruxelles, 1955).

FRIEDEL, J., 1955, Phil. Mag. **46**, 514.

FRIEDEL, J., 1964, Trans. AIME **230**, 616.

FULLMAN, R.L., 1951, J. Appl. Phys. **22**, 488.

FUMI, F., 1955, Phil. Mag. **45**, 1007.

GALLAGHER, P.C.J., 1970, Metallurg. Trans. **1**, 2450.

GLOSSOP, A.B., and D.W. PASHLEY, 1959, Proc. Roy. Soc. **A250**, 132.

GOLDSCHMIDT, H.J., 1948, J. Iron Steel Inst. **160**, 345.

GSCHNEIDNER, K.A., 1980, in: Theory of Alloy Phase Formation, ed. L.H. Bennett (AIME, Warrendale, PA).

GUTTMAN, L., 1956, Solid State Phys. **3**, 145.

HANSEN, M., and K. ANDERKO, 1958, Constitution of Binary Alloys (McGraw–Hill, New York).

HARRISON, W.A., 1959, Phys. Rev. **116**, 555; 1960, **118**, 1190.

HARRISON, W.A., and M.B. WEBB, eds., 1960, The Fermi Surface (Wiley, New York).

HEINE, V., 1967, in: Phase Stability in Metals and Alloys, eds. P.S. Rudman, J. Stringer and R.I. Jaffee (McGraw–Hill, New York).

HELLAWELL, A., and W. HUME-ROTHERY, 1954, Phil. Mag. **45**, 797.

HENDERSON, B., and G.V. RAYNOR, 1962, Proc. Roy. Soc. **A267**, 313.

HERBSTEIN, F.H., B.S. BORIE and B.L. AVERBACH, 1956, Acta Cryst. **9**, 466.

HILL, R.B., and H.J. AXON, 1954–5, J. Inst. Metals **83**, 354.

HILL, R.B., and H.J. AXON, 1956–7, J. Inst. Metals **85**, 102.

HOWIE, A., and P.R. SWANN, 1961, Phil. Mag. **6**, 1215.

HUANG, K., 1947, Proc. Roy. Soc. **A190**, 102.

HUME-ROTHERY, W., 1926, J. Inst. Metals **35**, 295.

HUME-ROTHERY, W., 1955, Atomic Theory for the Students of Metallurgy (The Institute of Metals, London); enlarged edition, 1960.

HUME-ROTHERY, W., 1961a, Elements of Structural Metallurgy (The Institute of Metals, London, Monograph and Report Series, no. 26).

HUME-ROTHERY, W., 1961b, J. Inst. Metals **9**, 42.

HUME-ROTHERY, W., 1964, The Metallurgist, p. 11.

HUME-ROTHERY, W., 1966, The Structure of Alloys of Iron (Pergamon Press, Oxford).

HUME-ROTHERY, W., 1967, in: Phase Stability in Metals and Alloys, eds. P.S. Rudman, J. Stringer and R.I. Jaffee (McGraw–Hill, New York).

HUME-ROTHERY, W., and B.R. COLES, 1954, Adv. Phys. **3**, 149.

HUME-ROTHERY, W., and G.V. RAYNOR, 1940, Proc. Roy. Soc. **A174**, 471.

HUME-ROTHERY, W., and D.J. ROAF, 1961, Phil. Mag. **6**, 55.

HUME-ROTHERY, W., J.O. BETTERTON and J. REYNOLDS, 1952, J. Inst. Metals **80**, 609.

HUME-ROTHERY, W., R.E. SMALLMAN and C.W. HAWORTH, 1969, The Structure of Metals and Alloys, 5th Ed. (The Institute of Metals, London) p. 349.

JOHANNSON, C.H., and J.O. LINDE, 1936, Ann. Phys. **25**, 1.

JOHNSON, C.A., 1963, Acta Cryst. **16**, 490.

JONES, H., 1934a, Proc. Roy. Soc. **A144**, 225.

JONES, H., 1934b, Proc. Roy. Soc. **A147**, 396.

JONES, H., 1937, Proc. Phys. Soc. **A49**, 250.

JONES, H., 1952, Phil. Mag. **43**, 105.

JONES, H., 1960, The Theory of Brillouin Zones and Electronic States in Crystals (North-Holland, Amsterdam).

JONES, H., 1962, J. Phys. Radium **23**, 637.

KING, H.W., 1966, J. Mater. Sci. **1**, 79.

KING, H.W., and T.B. MASSALSKI, 1961, Phil. Mag. **6**, 669.

KLEE, H., and H. WITTE, 1954, Z. Phys. Chem. **202**, 352.

KOIKE, S., M. HIRABAYASHI and To. SUZUKI, 1982, Phil. Mag. **45**, 261.

LAVES, F., and H. WITTE, 1935, Metallwirtschaft **14**, 645.

LAVES, F., and H. WITTE, 1936, Metallwirtschaft **15**, 840.

LAWSON, A.W., 1947, J. Chem. Phys. **15**, 831.

LIESER, K.H., and H. WITTE, 1954, Z. Phys. Chem. **202**, 321.

LIPSON, H., 1950, Prog. Metals Phys. **2**, 1.

LIPSON, H., and A. TAYLOR, 1939, Proc. Roy. Soc. (London) **A173**, 232.

MADER, S., H. WIDMER, F.M. D'HEURLE and A.S. NOWICK, 1963, Appl. Phys. Lett. **3**, 201.

MANN, E., and A. SEEGER, 1960, J. Phys. Chem. Solids **12**, 314.

MASSALSKI, T.B., 1956, in: The Theory of Alloy Phases (ASM, Metals Park, OH).

MASSALSKI, T.B., 1958, Met. Rev. **3**, 45.

MASSALSKI, T.B., and H.W. KING, 1961, Prog. Mater. Sci. **10**, 1.

MASSALSKI, T.B., and U. MIZUTANI, 1978, Prog. Mater. Sci. **22**, 151.

MASSALSKI, T.B., U. MIZUTANI and S. NOGUCHI, 1975, Proc. Roy. Soc. **A343**, 363.

MASUMOTO, T., and K. SUZUKI, eds., 1982, Proc. 4th Int. Conf. on Rapidly Quenched Metals (Japan Inst. of Metals, Sendai).

MOTT, N.F., and H. JONES, 1936, The Theory of the Properties of Metals and Alloys (Oxford University Press).

MOTT, N.F., 1952, Prog. Met. Phys. **3**, 76.

MOTT, N.F., 1962, Rept. Prog. Phys. **25**, 218.

NEVITT, M., 1963, in: Electronic Structure and Alloy Chemistry of Transition Elements, ed. P.A. Beck (Wiley, New York).

NIEMIEC, J., 1966, in: Fizykochemia Ciała Stałego, ed. B. Stalinski (Panstwowe Wydawnictwo Naukowe, Warsaw).

NIX, F.C., and W. SHOCKLEY, 1938, Rev. Mod. Phys. **10**, 1.

NOVER, R.G., and K. SCHUBERT, 1980, Z. Metallk. **71**, 329.

OGAWA, S., and D. WATANABE, 1954, Acta Cryst. **7**, 377.

OWEN, E.A., 1947, J. Inst. Metals, **73**, 471.

PATERSON, M.S., 1952, J. Appl. Phys. **23**, 805.

PEARSON, W.B., 1958 and 1967, A Handbook of Lattice Spacings and Structures of Metals and Alloys (Pergamon Press, London and New York) vol. 1, 1958; vol. 2, 1967.

PEARSON, W.B., 1967, in: Phase Stability in Metals and Alloys, eds. P.S. Rudman, J. Stringer and R.I. Jaffee (McGraw–Hill, New York).

PEARSON, W.B., 1982, Phil. Mag. **46**, 387.

PIPPARD, A.B., 1957, Phil. Trans. Roy. Soc. **A250**, 325.

RAYNOR, G.V., 1949a, Trans. Farad. Soc. **45**, 698.

RAYNOR, G.V., 1949b, Prog. Met. Phys. **1**, 1.

RAYNOR, G.V., 1956, The Theory of Alloy Phases (ASM, Metals Park, OH) p. 321.

READ, W.T., Jr, 1953, Dislocations in Crystals (McGraw–Hill, New York).

ROBERTS, R.W., 1954, Acta Metall. **2**, 597.

ROBERTS, B.W., 1956, J. Metals **8**, 1407; Phys. Rev. **104**, 607.

RUDMAN, P.S., J. STRINGER and R.I. JAFFEE, eds., 1967, Phase Stability in Metals and Alloys (McGraw–Hill, New York).

SATO, H., and R.S. TOTH, 1961, Phys. Rev. **124**, 1833.

SATO, H., and R.S. TOTH, 1962, Phys. Rev. Lett. **8**, 239.

SATO, H., and R.S. TOTH, 1965, in: Alloying Behavior and Effects in Concentrated Solid Solutions, ed. T.B. Massalski (Gordon and Breach, New York).

SCHUBERT, K., B. KIEFER, M. WILKENS and R. HAUFLER, 1955, Z. Metallk. **46**, 692.

SLICK, P.I., C.W. MASSENA and R.S. CRAIG, 1965, J. Chem. Phys. **43**, 2792.

STIRLING, P.H., and G.V. RAYNOR, 1956, J. Inst. Metals, **84**, 57.

STROUD, D., 1980, in: Proc. Conf. on Theory of Alloy Phase Formation, ed. L.H. Bennett (AIME, Warrendale, PA) p. 84.

SUTTON, A.L., and W. HUME-ROTHERY, 1955, Phil. Mag. **46**, 1295.

SUZUKI, To., M. HASEGAWA and M. HIRABAYASHI, 1976, J.Phys. **F6**, 779.

TAYLOR, A., 1961, X-Ray Metallography (Wiley, New York).

TAYLOR, A., and N.J. DOYLE, 1972, J. Appl. Cryst. **5**, 201.

VEGARD, L., 1921, Z. Phys. **5**, 17.

VEGARD, L., 1928, Z. Cryst. **67**, 239.

WABER, J.T., K.A. GSCHNEIDNER, A.C. LARSON and M.Y. PRINCE, 1963, Trans. AIME **227**, 717.

WAGNER, C.N.J., 1957, Acta Metall. **5**, 427 and 477.

WARREN, B.E., B.L. AVERBACH and B.W. ROBERTS, 1951, J. Appl. Phys. **22**, 1943.

WARREN, B.E., and E.P. WAREKOIS, 1955, Acta Metall. **3**, 473.

WARREN, B.E., 1959a, Acta Cryst. **12**, 837.

WARREN, B.E., 1959b, Prog. Met. Phys. **8**, 147.

WESTGREN, A., and G. PHRAGMEN, 1926, On the Chemistry of Metallic Compounds, Z. Metallk. **18**, 279.

WESTGREN, A., 1930, Z. Metallk. **22**, 368.

WILKENS, M., 1962, Phys. Stat. Sol. **2**, 692.

WILLIS, M., and H.P. ROOKSBY, 1954, Proc. Phys. Soc. **B67**, 290.

ZIMAN, J.M., 1961, Adv. Phys. **10**, 1.

Further reading

(a) In the present chapter the main emphasis has been placed on solid solutions and structures with wide solid solubility. However, this subject is closely bound with the much wider area of the stability of all alloy phases and crystal structures. Further reading on the theories of alloy phases may be found in: ASM Symp. on The Theory of Alloy Phases (ASM, Metals Park, OH, 1956).

Symp. on Metallic Solid Solutions, Orsay, France, eds. J. Friedel and A. Guinier (Benjamin, New York, 1963).

AIME Symp. on The Alloying Behavior and Effects in Concentrated solid Solutions, ed. T.B. Massalski (Gordon and Breach, New York, 1965).

Battelle Inst. Symp. on Phase Stability in Metals and Alloys, eds. P.S. Rudman, J. Stringer and R.I. Jaffee (McGraw–Hill, New York, 1967).

Structure of Metals, 3rd Ed, C.S. Barrett and T.B. Massalski (McGraw–Hill, New York, 1966).

A discussion of the theories of alloys based on copper is given by:

W. Hume–Rothery, J. Inst. Metals 9 (1961–2) 42. T.B. Massalski and H.W. King, Alloy Phases of the Noble Metals, Prog. Mater. Sci. 10 (1961) 1. T.B. Massalski and U. Mizutani, Prog. Mater. Sci. 22 (1978) 151.

(b) Problems concerning the transition elements and their alloys are discussed in:

AIME Symp. on Electronic Structure and Alloy Chemistry of Transition Elements, ed. P.A. Beck (Wiley, New York, 1963).

Electrons in Transition Elements, by N.F. Mott, Adv. Phys. 13 (1964) 325. Battelle Inst. Symp. on Phase Stability in Metals and Alloys, eds. P.S. Rudman, J. Stringer and R.I. Jaffee (McGraw–Hill, New York, 1967).

(c) Size effects in alloy phases are discussed by:

H.W. King, in: AIME Symp. (1965) listed above.

F. Laves, in: Advances in X-ray Analysis, eds. W.M. Mueller and M.J. Fay, 6 (1962) 43.

(d) Long-period superlattices and stacking faults are discussed by H. Sato and R.S. Toth, and J.W. Christian and P. Swann, respectively, in the AIME Symposium (1965) listed above.

(e) Stability and electronic structure of metallic glasses are discussed by:

U. Mizutani, Prog. Mater. Sci. 28 (1983) in press.

CHAPTER 5

STRUCTURE OF INTERMETALLIC COMPOUNDS

K. GIRGIS

Institut für Kristallographie und Petrographie
Eidgenössische Technische Hochschule
Zürich, Switzerland

R.W. Cahn and P. Haasen, eds.
Physical Metallurgy; third, revised and enlarged edition
© *Elsevier Science Publishers BV, 1983*

1.   Introduction

1.1.   Aim

The aim of this chapter is to work out the systematics of intermetallic compounds on a semi-empirical and a theoretical basis. So one hopes that, in the future, one will be able to answer the following questions:
1. Which phases are expected in a certain system?
2. Why do these phases adopt particular structures?
3. Which are the appropriate definitions and systematics, in general?

1.2.   Definition of intermetallic compounds

An intermetallic compound is a phase which crystallizes with a structure other than those of its components. We differentiate between two types of intermetallic compounds:

(a) Intermetallic phases which possess a homogeneity range are called *Berthollides*. The point position occupation is not restricted to one atomic type, e.g. a point position can be occupied by A as well as by B atoms. Example: $Ta_x Si$, $x = 2.7–3.2$; $Ni_3 Sn$ structure type, $P6_3/mmc$.

6h: $\underline{Ta}$ + Si, mainly Ta occupies 6h;
2a: $\overline{Ta}$ + $\underline{Si}$, mainly Si occupies 2a.

(b) Intermetallic phases without any homogeneity range are called *Daltonides*. Each point position is occupied by one particular atom type. Example: $W_5 Si_3$; $W_5 Si_3$ structure type, $I4/mcm$.

$$4b : W_1, \quad 4a : Si_1,$$
$$16k : W_2, \quad 8h : Si_2. \;\cdot$$

The accurate measurements now available make it less reasonable to differentiate between Berthollides and Daltonides. Even valence compounds show small homogeneity ranges (e.g., the GaP homogeneity range is 10^{-2} at%). The reader who is not familiar with the space-group symbols used above, is referred to appendix A, p. 266, for a brief explanation.

1.3.   Crystal structure data

The structure of an intermetallic compound is defined by the following data:
(a) chemical composition;
(b) structure type;
(c) crystal system and cell constants;
(d) number of atoms per unit cell;
(e) space group, occupied point positions and their atomic parameters.
Other information, such as coordination etc., can be derived from the above data.

1.4. Definition of structure type

Intermetallic compounds with the same (or similar) stoichiometry, crystal system, space group and the same occupied point positions belong to the same structure type. The representatives of a particular structure type can have different atoms, cell constants and different values of the free atomic parameters. The structure type is generally named after the first representative discovered.

1.5. Definition of a solid solution

If one component is dissolved in (an)other component(s) without changing the structure of the host component, the resulting alloy is called a solid solution; it can be binary, ternary, etc.

According to Hume-Rothery, high solubility (more than 5%) occurs if the difference in the atomic radii is less than 15%.

DARKEN and GURRY [1953] introduced an *electronegativity factor* (qualitatively, electronegativity is the power of an atom in a compound to attract electrons to itself; see PAULING [1960] and ch. 4) and developed a diagram for solid solution prediction. In such a diagram, as shown in fig. 1 for coordination number (CN) 12, all elements are included. To determine the solid solubility of a certain element in another, one constructs:

(a) a small ellipse, with the element in the centre, with ± 0.02 electronegativity difference (OC) on one axis and $\pm 8\%$ atomic radius difference on the second axis (OA);

(b) a bigger ellipse, with ± 0.04 electronegativity difference (OD) on one axis and

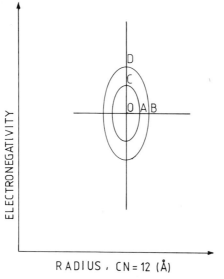

Fig. 1. Darken–Gurry diagram.

References: p. 266.

±15% atomic radius difference on the second axis (OB).

One can subdivide the alloys into three groups:

1) those for which the second element has high solubility (more than 5%) lie inside the small ellipse;

2) those for which the second element has low solubility lie between the two ellipses;

3) those in which the second element tends to be insoluble are outside both ellipses.

2. Factors which govern the structure of intermetallic phases

2.1. Introduction

In general, intermetallic compounds do not follow the general valence rules. For example, in the system K–Na there exists a phase KNa_2, but no phase KNa, although both elements are univalent. Why does KNa not exist?

The reason for this can be found in the different bondings in intermetallic compounds, namely: ionic, covalent, metallic or combinations between these three (see chs. 2 and 3). This section will try to elucidate the factors which influence the structures of the intermetallic phases. First we shall treat the geometrical factors.

2.2. Geometrical principles of metal structures

LAVES [1956] studied the factors which control structures. He found three principles which are valid for structures of metallic elements. In the case of intermetallic compounds these principles are only valid to a certain extent since the situation here is much more complicated. The three geometrical principles are:

(1) space-filling principle;

(2) symmetry principle;

(3) connection principle.

2.2.1. Space-filling principle

The Periodic Table is shown with the Zintl line in fig. 2. 52 out of 91 elements whose structures are known crystallize in the cubic or hexagonal close packed structures with a coordination number of 12. If one allows for 10% distance deviation, 58 elements possess the close-packed arrangement. One should think that metals would tend to higher CN than 12, but 12 is the highest coordination number (CN) where the metal atoms are not distinguished from one another. Assuming that the metal atoms are spherical, then the best space filling will be that of the cubic or hexagonal close packed arrangement, i.e. $CN = 12$.

2.2.2. Symmetry principle

23 of the remaining metals crystallize in a body-centered cubic structure; $CN = 8$. One should therefore assume that there are other factors which operate against the space filling principle, e.g., temperature and binding factors. It is also strange that

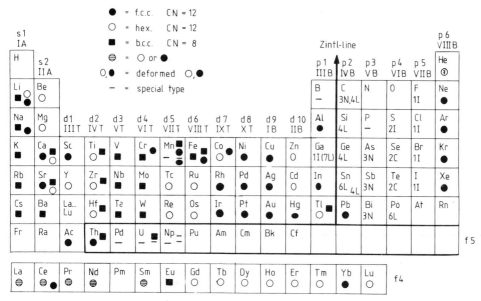

Fig. 2. Structure of the elements. The modifications stable at room temperature are symbolized at the left side of each partition. (After LAVES [1956].)

no coordination numbers 9, 10 or 11 do occur although they show a higher packing density than CN = 8. But arrangements with CN 9, 10 or 11 possess lower symmetry than the 8 coordination.

The tendency to build configurations with high symmetries is obvious and is called the symmetry principle.

2.2.3. Connection principle

Imagine a crystal structure. Connect all atoms with one another. There will be a shortest link between any two atoms. Drop all links except the shortest one. After this procedure the atoms that are still connected form a "connection". The connection is called "homogeneous" if it consists of structurally equivalent atoms, otherwise it is called "heterogeneous". Connections can be finite or infinite, and one-, two- or three-dimensional and are called: islands, chains, nets or lattices. They are symbolized by the letters I, C, N, or L (homogeneous connections) and i, c, n or ℓ (heterogeneous connections) respectively. A glance at the element structures shows that three-dimensional connections are favoured by the elements left of the Zintl line.

This tendency to form multi-dimensional connections is considered to be the influence of a "connection principle".

If one accepts the three above mentioned principles one can understand the occurrence of hcp, ccp (fcc) and bcc structures of metals. These geometrical

References: p. 266.

observations do not allow the prediction of the structure of a certain element. If one alloys two or more metals together and they form an intermetallic compound, one rarely finds hcp, ccp or bcc structures. This may be due to additional interactions present.

2.3.   Ionic and covalent bonding: valence compounds

If all atoms in a compound either accept or provide valence electrons to obtain a stable octet configuration ns^2np^6, i.e., all s and p orbitals are completely filled or completely empty, we get the so called valence compounds group. The octets of the atoms can be completed in two different ways:

1. Electrons are donated to one kind of atoms (anion) by the other one (cation): *ionic interaction (bonding)*.

2. Electrons are shared between the atoms: *covalent interaction (bonding)*.

Most valence compounds are iono–covalent compounds with a bonding intermediate between the two cases; i.e., the electrons are not in the middle of the bond but closer to one of the atoms.

In the following representation, general trends among *valence compounds* are given in table 0. Explanations of symbols and further details are given in § 3.

2.4.   Electrons-per-atom ratio: electron compounds

HUME-ROTHERY [1926] and WESTGREN and PHRAGMÉN [1926] observed that a large number of compounds – now called *electron compounds* – crystallize with the same structure, if they possess the same average number of valence electrons per atom, or *Valence Electron Concentration* (VEC). They found approximately the

Table 0
General trends among valence compounds.

Increase of covalent bonding		Increase of ionic bonding
	Mainly ionic bonding	
	Normal valence compounds	
	Each atom tries to reach a stable octet configuration; general rule: $(VEC)_A = 8 + \dfrac{m}{n} CC - AA$	
	Polyanionic and polycationic valence compounds	
	Defect tetrahedral structure compounds	
	Each atom tries to form tetrahedral orbits sp^3 which overlap with the neighbours sp^3 orbitals; general rule: $ne_A + ne_B = 4(m + n) + (n + m)N_{NBO}$	
	Normal tetrahedral structure compounds	
	Mainly covalent bonding	

following VECs: $\frac{21}{14}$, $\frac{21}{13}$ and $\frac{21}{12}$. Each of these ratios corresponds to certain structures. The VEC also plays a big role in the so called interstitial compounds. These two groups will be treated in some more detail in §4.

2.5. Size factor: size-factor compounds

If the relative atomic volume of the components of a compound governs (beside other factors) the structure formed, we call this the *size factor*. The relative atomic volume plays also a role in the solubility of one element in an other. This group of compounds is treated in some detail in §5. For further discussion of the size factor see ch. 4.

In general, several types of atomic interactions are simultaneously involved in an alloy structure. The ordering of the alloy structures into different categories should therefore be understood only as a guide line or tendency. Figure 3 shows roughly the existence ranges of the three main groups of intermetallic compounds (VILLARS and GIRGIS [1982b]). Figure 4 shows a simplified representation of the different categories of intermetallic compounds.

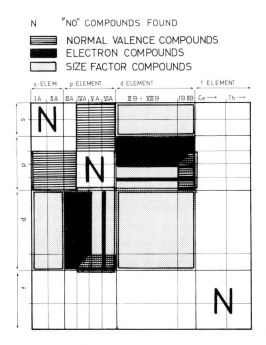

Fig. 3. Existence fields of the intermetallic compounds: normal valence compounds, electron compounds and size-factor compounds.

References: p. 266.

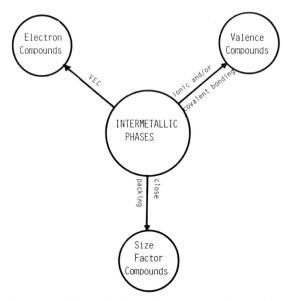

Fig. 4. Simple representation of the three main categories of intermetallic compounds.

3.   Valence compounds

As already mentioned in §2.3, the main factors in valence compounds are ionic and covalent bonding. In the present section, the following compounds will be treated:
3.1. normal valence compounds;
3.2. polyanionic and polycationic compounds (general valence compounds);
3.3. normal tetrahedral structures;
3.4. defect tetrahedral structures.

3.1.   Normal valence compounds

A compound $C_m A_n$ is called a *normal valence compound* (NVC) if the number of valence electrons of the cations is just sufficient to complete the octets of the anions:

$$me_C = n(8 - e_A),\tag{1}$$

where e_C (e_A) is the number of valence electrons of the cation (anion) in the non-ionized state (PARTHÉ [1980]). For the sake of simplicity we shall only consider the A and B group elements of the Periodic System. In this case the number of valence electrons of the elements corresponds to their group number (fig. 2).

Since the elements of groups 1, 2 and 3 do not act as anions, there are only 18 possible solutions of the valence electron equation for normal valence compounds. In any binary system where the electronegativity difference between the elements is

Table 1
The eighteen possible compositions of binary normal
valence compounds [a].

Cations	Anions			
	4	5	6	7
6				$6 7_6$
5			$5_2 6_5$	$5 7_5$
4		$4_3 5_4$	$4 6_2$	$4 7_4$
3	$3_4 4_3$	35	$3_2 6_3$	$3 7_3$
2	$2_2 4$	$2_3 5_2$	26	$2 7_2$
1	$1_4 4$	$1_3 5$	$1_2 6$	17

[a] Elements are indicated by numbers which correspond to
their numbers of valence electrons.

large, a binary normal valence compound is formed with a composition as given in table 1. Examples: Zn_3P_2 $(2_3 5_2)$; NaCl (17); Al_2O_3 $(3_2 6_3)$; $BaCl_2$ $(2 7_2)$. Ternary compositions with two cations are obtained by adding two formulae of the same column:

$$(1_3 5)_5 + 4_3 5_4 = 1_{15} 4_3 5_9 = (1_5 4) 5_3 \ (Li_5 SiP_3).$$

Ternary compositions with two anions are obtained by adding two formulae of the same row:

$$2_3 5_2 + (2 7_2)_3 = 2_6 5_2 7_6 = 2_3 (5 7_3) \ (Zn_3 PI_3).$$

3.2. General valence compounds

Let us consider the more general case where some electrons are also used for bonds between the cations or between the anions. For a compound $C_m A_n$

$$m(e_C - e_{CC}) \quad = \quad n(8 - e_A - e_{AA}). \qquad (2)$$

number of electrons	number of electrons
the m cations provide	the n anions need to
for bonding to n an-	complete the octet
ions.	shell

Here e_{CC} is the average number of valence electrons per cation which remain with the cation, and e_{AA} is the average number of valence electrons per anion that the anions acquire by sharing covalent bonds between themselves.

In the special case that the interatomic bonds consist of electron pair bonds, the experimentally inaccessible e_{CC} and e_{AA} values can be replaced by CC and AA, where CC is the average number per cation of cation–cation bonds and/or the average number of electrons which remain in non-bonding orbitals on the cations, and AA is the average number of anion–anion bonds per anion. Introducing the partial valence electron concentration of the anion:

$$(VEC)_A = \frac{me_C + ne_A}{n}, \tag{3}$$

the above equation can be rewritten as

$$(VEC)_A = 8 + \frac{m}{n}CC - AA. \tag{4}$$

This is the *valence electron equation* * for general valence compounds (PARTHÉ [1973]). The calculation of $(VEC)_A$ allows the classification of the compounds:

$(VEC)_A = 8$: normal valence compound (NVC) with $CC = AA = 0$,

$(VEC)_A < 8$: polyanionic valence compound with $AA > 0$,   (5)

$(VEC)_A > 8$: polycationic valence compound with $CC > 0$.

3.2.1. Polyanionic valence compounds

For *polyanionic valence compounds*, the simplest solution of the general valence compounds equation is:

$$\text{If } CC = 0, \text{ then } \quad AA = 8 - (VEC)_A. \tag{6}$$

The simplest interpretation of the calculated values for AA is:

AA = 0: isolated anions (normal valence compounds);
AA = 1: anion dumb-bells;
1 < AA < 2: finite anion chains;
AA = 2: infinite anion chains or rings;
AA = 3: each anion has three bonds to other anions.

3.2.2. Polycationic valence compounds

For *polycationic valence compounds*, the simplest solution of the general valence compounds equation is:

$$\text{If } AA = 0, \text{ then } \quad CC = \frac{n}{m}[(VEC)_A - 8]. \tag{7}$$

As an example, for GaSe $(VEC)_A = 9$, thus $CC = 1$ if $AA = 0$.

3.3. Normal tetrahedral structures

If each atom in a structure is surrounded by four nearest neighbours at the corners of a tetrahedron, the structure is called *normal tetrahedral structure* (NTS). A

---

* This equation, which relates the number of valence electrons and observable structural features, can only be applied if all bonds are two-electron bonds and additional electrons remain inactive in non-bonding orbitals of the cations or anions. Thus compounds should be semiconductors. If the compounds are of metallic character, this equation is not applicable.

structure where not all the corners are occupied by atoms, i.e., where some atoms have less than four neighbours, is called a defect tetrahedral structure. The general composition formula of the tetrahedral structure for a compound $A_m B_n$ is

$$\frac{(me_A + ne_B)}{(m+n)} = 4. \qquad (8)$$

We can then deduce ten possible combinations:

$$44,\ 35,\ 26,\ 17,\ 3_26,\ 3_37,\ 25_2,\ 2_37_2,\ 15_3,\ 1_26_3.$$

(Notation as in table 1, e.g., 25_2 means: a divalent element is alloyed with two pentavalent elements, as in ZnP_2 or $CdAs_2$.) The composition scheme of 4 valence electrons/atom (average) is a necessary condition for building NTS, but not every compound that fulfills this condition is a NTS. MOOSER and PEARSON [1959] found a relationship between the electronegativity difference, the average principal quantum number and the occurring structures. With the help of a diagram as shown in fig. 5 one can separate the NTS from other structures. PHILLIPS [1970] also succeeded in separating NTS from other structures.

3.4. Defect tetrahedral structures

Compounds in which the atoms still have tetrahedral orbitals but have less than four nearest neighbours are said to have *defect tetrahedral structures* (DTS). Each non-bonding tetrahedral orbital gets a second electron with antiparallel spin to build

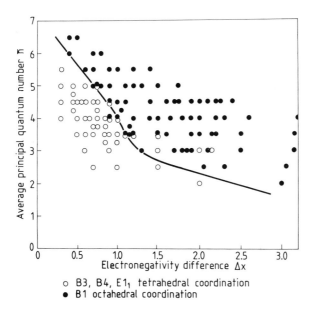

o B3, B4, E1₁ tetrahedral coordination
● B1 octahedral coordination

Fig. 5. Separation between tetrahedral and NaCl-type structures (after MOOSER and PEARSON [1959]).

References: p. 266.

a non-bonding orbital. This means that the number of valence electrons necessary to form DTS is:
- 4 electrons per atom to form 4 tetrahedral orbitals.
- 1 more electron per each non-bonding orbital.

An example is α-Al_2S_3, which crystallizes with a wurtzite-similar structure. The S atoms occupy all the S positions as in wurtzite. The 3 Zn atoms there are replaced by just 2 Al atoms. For each unoccupied point position we should have 4 neighbours with non-bonding orbitals. The symbol for Al_2S_3 is then $3_2 0 6_3$.

The composition formula fulfills eq. (8):

$$\frac{2 \cdot 3 + 1 \cdot 0 + 3 \cdot 6}{2 + 1 + 3} = 4.$$

Generally, for DTS compounds $A_m B_n \ldots 0_p$, where 0 stands for a quadrupole of non-bonding orbitals, the following formula is valid:

$$\frac{me_A + ne_B + \ldots}{m + n + \ldots + p} = 4. \tag{9}$$

The valence electron equation can be rewritten for this case as:

$$me_A + ne_B = 4(m + n) + N_{NBO}(m + n), \tag{10}$$

where N_{NBO} is the average number of non-bonding orbitals per atom. Then

$$VEC = 4 + N_{NBO} \tag{11}$$

is the valence electron equation for tetrahedral structure compounds. If
$\quad$ VEC < 4: no tetrahedral structure is possible,
$\quad$ VEC = 4: normal tetrahedral structure,
$\quad$ VEC > 4: defect tetrahedral structure.

4.   Electron compounds

4.1. Hume-Rothery phases

The average number of valence electrons per atom (valence electron concentration, VEC) can be calculated with the scheme given in table 2. Examples: CuBe has VEC $\frac{3}{2}$, Cu_5Si has VEC $\frac{9}{6} = \frac{3}{2}$ and Ni_5Zn_{21} has VEC $\frac{42}{26} = \frac{21}{13}$.

As mentioned in §2.4, electron compounds with VECs of $\frac{21}{14}$, $\frac{21}{13}$ or $\frac{21}{12}$ crystallize in corresponding structures. The three categories are referred to as the *Hume-Rothery phases*. Table 3 gives a list of different representatives. In practice the given ratios $[\frac{21}{14} (\frac{3}{2}); \frac{21}{13}; \frac{21}{12} (\frac{7}{4})]$ are ranges, which even overlap as is shown clearly in fig. 6 (WITTE [1937]). Moreover the number of valence electrons to be considered is often not clear. The VEC therefore only indicates a range where one of the above mentioned structures may occur. MASSALSKI and MIZUTANI [1978] attempted to summarize some of the main features of the electronic structure of Hume-Rothery phases in the light of more recent research; see chs. 3 and 4.

Table 2
The valence electron concentration calculation scheme.

Element		Valence
Transition elements with nonfilled d-shells		0
Cu, Ag, Au	(d-electrons)	1
Mg	(s-electrons)	2
Zn, Cd, Hg	(d-electrons)	2
Sn, Si, Ge	(p-electrons)	4
Sb	(p-electrons)	5

Table 3
Some representatives of Hume-Rothery phases.

VEC = 3/2			VEC = 21/13	VEC = 7/4
Body-centred cubic structure	Complex cubic "β-manganese" structure	Close-packed hexagonal structure	"γ-brass" structure [c]	Close-packed hexagonal structure
CuBe	Cu_5Si	Cu_3Ga	Cu_5Zn_8	$CuZn_3$
CuZn	Ag_3Al	Cu_5Ge	Cu_5Cd_8	$CuCd_3$
Cu_3Al	Au_3Al	AgZn	Cu_5Hg_8	Cu_3Sn
Cu_3Ga [b]	$CoZn_3$	AgCd	Cu_9Al_4	Cu_3Ge
Cu_3In [a]		Ag_3Al	Cu_9Ga_4	Cu_3Si
Cu_5Si		Ag_3Ga	Cu_9In_4	$AgZn_3$
Cu_5Sn		Ag_3In	$Cu_{31}Si_8$	$AgCd_3$
AgMg		Ag_5Sn	$Cu_{31}Sn_8$	Ag_3Sn
AgZn [b]		Ag_7Sb	Ag_5Zn_8	Ag_5Al_3
AgCd [b]		Au_3In	Ag_5Cd_8	$AuZn_3$
Ag_3Al [b]		Au_5Sn	Ag_5Hg_8	$AuCd_3$
Ag_3In [b]			Ag_9In_4	Au_3Sn
AuMg			Au_5Zn_8	Au_5Al_3
AuZn			Au_5Cd_8	Cu_3Sb & Ag_3Sb [d]
AuCd			Au_9In_4	
FeAl			Mn_5Zn_{21}	
CoAl			Fe_5Zn_2	
NiAl			Co_5Zn_{21}	
NiIn			Ni_5Be_{21}	
PdIn			Ni_5Zn_{21}	
XTl [e]			Ni_5Cd_{21}	
			Rh_5Zn_{21}	
			Pd_5Zn_{21}	
			Pt_5Be_{21}	
			Pt_5Zn_{21}	
			$Na_{31}Pb_8$	

[a] High-temperature X-ray work by W. Hume-Rothery shows that the Cu–In β-phase has a simple bcc structure. It is a solid solution with mean composition more nearly Cu_4In than Cu_3In, but on the In-rich side the solid solution extends nearly to Cu_3In required for a VEC = 3/2.

[b] In certain cases different structures occur at different temperatures for approximately the same VEC. Thus Ag_3Al is bcc at high temperatures, hcp at intermediate temperatures, and of the β-manganese type at low temperatures.

[c] Phases with a distorted γ-brass structure have been reported in the systems Cu–Si, Au–Al and Cr–Al. In Au–Ga and Au–Hg, phases occur at VEC = 21/13 but their structures are not known. Phases of the γ-brass type, but with vacant lattice sites, occur in Pd–In, Ni–In and Ni–Ga.
(HUME-ROTHERY and RAYNOR [1962]).

[d] Sometimes included although VEC = 8/4 really.

[e] Possibly MgTl, CaTl and SrTl as compounds of univalent Tl.

References: p. 266.

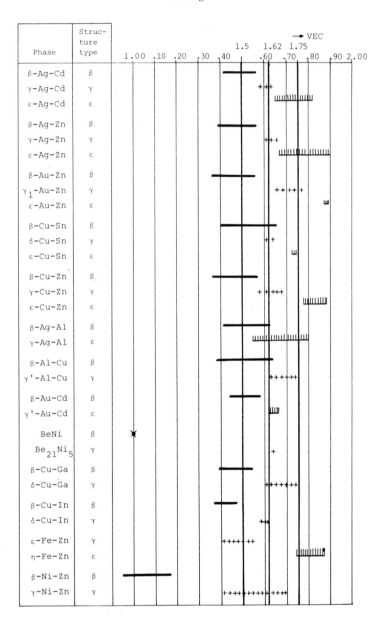

Fig. 6. Existence ranges of some Hume-Rothery phases (after WITTE [1937]).

4.2. Interstitial compounds

This group of compounds is included in the present section dealing with electron compounds, as it was found that the VEC plays an important role in this category. Other factors also play important roles and they will be discussed below.

4.2.1. Definition

Interstitial compounds are generally defined as compounds of the transition metals with relatively large atomic radii (T) with nonmetals with small radii (X = H, B, C, N, O). The X-atoms occupy the interstices of the T-atom host structure. HÄGG [1931] discussed these compounds mainly on a geometrical basis. The favourable radii ratios R_X/R_T for the commonly found interstices are as follows ("Hägg's rule"):

> 0.23:   tetrahedral interstices, CN = 4;
> 0.41–0.59: octahedral interstices, CN = 6.

If the radii of the nonmetal atoms are relatively large compared with those of the transition metal atoms – more than 0.59 as in the case of borides and silicides – complicated structures form. Moreover, if just the geometrical point of view is valid, then we expect the above behaviour in the case of oxygen with the relatively small atomic radius of 0.6×10^{-10} m. This is rarely the case as oxygen tends to form ionic bonds because of its strong electronegativity ($R_{O^{2-}} = 1.32 \times 10^{-10}$ m).

There must therefore be other factors such as VEC, bonding etc., which play an important role in the formation of these compounds.

4.2.2. Correlation between VEC and structure of interstitial compounds

Considering the number of valence electrons per atom, including also the valence electrons of the nonmetal, we observe a clear relationship between the structure and the VEC of these compounds as shown in table 4 (MERZ [1976]).

The table shows that VECs between 4 and 6 favour the bcc; between 7 and 8, the hcp; 8 to 10, fcc. It is worth mentioning that the hcp is characteristic for the T_2X composition in the VEC range 7 to 8. If the VEC is more than 8 as in Mo_2N and W_2N then the structure will be fcc. This is also valid for pure metals. Their stability has been calculated from band structures by PETTIFOR [1970]. See ch. 3, §7.3. This rule is also valid for complicated compositions as shown in fig. 7 (MERZ [1976]) for the quasi-ternary system TiC–TaC–WC, where the stability of the cubic phases *follows lines with constant VEC, even when the atomic radii ratios do not follow Hägg's rule.*

4.2.3. Band models

The properties of a solid are mainly calculated on the basis of the states of the electrons in the crystal. The more information on these we have the more precise are the deduced properties of the material. But in general it is not easy to combine the

References: p. 266.

Table 4
Systematics of the structures of interstitial compounds.

Arrangement of metal atoms in lattice	Metal/interstitial compound		VEC
bcc	Ti [a], Zr [a], Hf [a]		4
	V, Nb, Ta		5
	Cr [a], Mo, W		6
hcp	V_2C, Nb_2C, Ta_2C	/Re	7
	Nb_2N, Ta_2N		7.5
	Mo_2C, W_2C	/Ru, Os	8
fcc	TiC, ZrC, HfC	/Fe [a]	8
	Mo_2N, W_2N		8.5
	VC, NbC,TaC	/Co [a], Rh, Ir	9
	TiN, ZrN, HfN		9
	VN, $NbN_{0.94}$	/Ni [a], Pd, Pt	10
hex. primitive	WC, NbN		10

[a] further modifications are known.

values obtained from a theoretical model with those which are of practical interest (LEHMANN [1974]). The high symmetry of the cubic structure makes it possible to calculate electronic states. The results in the literature are sometimes contradictory, see ch. 3.

The *Rigid Band Model* often gives useful results for homologous and isomorphous materials in which the properties are mainly dependent on the number of electrons contributed by the components (to occupy these states). In the case of cubic

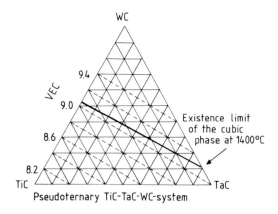

Fig. 7. Stability range of the cubic TiC–TaC–WC solid solution (after MERZ [1976]).

interstitial compounds the valence electrons first occupy an energy band which is formed by a combination of the p-states of the nonmetal and the d-states of the metal atoms. The filling of this energy band at first strengthens the binding. Afterwards these electrons will occupy non-bonding (d) and loosening (p, d) ranges of the band structure. In the transition range, i.e., between 8 and 9 valence electrons, the maximum binding strength is reached. The overlapping of bands is the reason for metallic conduction.

An example for the correlation between the number of electrons and the melting point T_m (MERZ [1976]):
According to the Lindemann equation,

$$(T_m) = K_m M\theta^2 V^{2/3}, \tag{12}$$

where θ is the Debye temperature, K_m a constant, and V the molar volume, the melting point depends on the bonding strength ($M\theta^2$), the atomic and the molar volumina respectively. According to the band model the bonding strength does not vary much for a given VEC. In this case the melting point will be directly correlated to the molar volumina. Figure 8 shows this tendency for VECs 8, 9 and 10 (carbides, borides, nitrides and metals). Similarly one can derive correlations for elasticity and hardness in this group of compounds.

4.2.4. Miedema's model for metal hydrides

Metal hydrides have attracted some interest because of their properties, e.g. as energy storage material. The question arises whether a particular metal would alloy with or absorb hydrogen. *Miedema's model* gives some elucidation concerning this question (MIEDEMA [1976]).

Model for binary compounds. If two elements react with each other, there are two counteracting energy effects. The *Wigner–Seitz-cells* of these elements should inter-

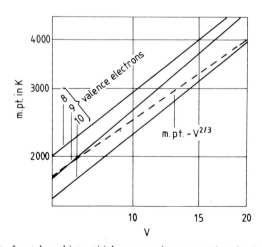

Fig. 8. Melting point of metals and interstitial compounds versus mole volumina (after MERZ [1976]).

References: p. 266.

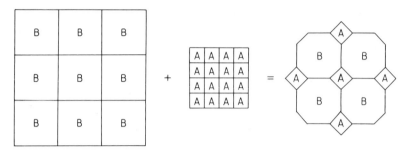

Fig. 9. Atoms in metals A and B. The alloy AB is considered to be composed of atomic cells that resemble those of the pure metals A and B.(After MIEDEMA [1976].)

penetrate as shown in fig. 9. The heat of formation ΔH is

$$\Delta H = -P(\Delta \Phi^*)^2 + Q(\Delta n_{WS}^{1/3})^2, \tag{13}$$

where P and Q are constants. The first term is due to the difference in chemical potential ($\Delta \Phi^*$) of the metals A and B which leads to a charge redistribution, and represents a negative (stabilizing) contribution to ΔH. The second term is due to the discontinuity of the electron density (Δn_{WS}) at the boundary of dissimilar Wigner–Seitz cells, which has to be smoothed, and represents a positive (destabilizing) contribution to ΔH. Using the experimental values of work functions for metals, $\Delta \Phi^*$ has been deduced, and using the bulk moduli, Δn_{WS} has also been derived. Miedema's model succeeded in predicting the correct sign for ΔH for all transition metal hydrides; i.e., in predicting whether a compound could be formed or not. Miedema's model is also valid for systems other than hydrides. With the help of Miedema's deduced parameters ($\Delta \Phi^*$ and Δn_{WS}) one can predict the sign of ΔH for binary systems.

   Application to ternary metal hydrides. Miedema was able to calculate quantitatively the heat of formation of binary as well as ternary metal hydrides. In the case of ternary hydrides the calculated values occasionally show some discrepancies. This is due to the fact that Miedema's model neglects the crystal structure. Efforts to obtain quantitative structural information from Miedema's parameters are in progress (RAJASEKHARAN and GIRGIS [1982]).

4.2.5.   Some important properties of interstitial compounds
– Hardness, brittleness and high melting points of the interstitial compounds are similar to materials with ionic and covalent bonding.
– At high temperatures, the mechanical properties become like those of metals, i.e., they are soft and ductile.
– Their hardness is large, changing strongly with stoichiometry; this is explained as a result of the bonding between the p-electrons of the nonmetal and the d-electrons of the transition metal.
– The mechanical properties indicate covalent bonding between the metalloid p-

and the metal d-electrons. The electronic properties indicate metallic bonding between the d-metal electrons. The d–d-metallic bond is modified compared to that of the metallic element. The metal–metal distances are a little bit larger and the symmetry is also different. It is not clear either, if ionic bonding plays any part.

– Conductivity and luster correspond to those of metals. The electric resistivity at 300 K is the same as that of the transition metals, or lower: for ZrN 7 $\mu\Omega$cm, Zr 42; Al 2.6; Cu 1.7 $\mu\Omega$cm.

– The melting point is generally very high.

– Some compounds show high superconducting temperatures: for $NbC_{0.3}N_{0.7}$ (NaCl type) 17.5 K. Pd, Pd–Ag and Pd–Cu are non-superconductors, but with interstitial H they become superconducting.

– Borides and phosphides of the transition metals, which can be obtained in amorphous form by fast cooling, possess mechanical and electrical properties like those of steel (see ch. 28).

5. Size-factor compounds

5.1. Regularities in intermetallic compounds

As mentioned before, more than one factor influences the structure of inter-metallic compounds. The search for regularities has been carried out by many authors. Most of those studies are valid only for one or a few structure types. VILLARS and GIRGIS [1981, 1982a] examined the 106 known binary structure types containing more than five representatives; 85% exhibit the following regularities:

5.1.1. Correlation between interatomic distance and concentration-weighted mean atomic radius

The *interatomic distance,* d_{AB}, designates the shortest distance between atom A and atom B, which depends on all lattice constants. The concentration-weighted mean atomic radius, $\bar{R}$, is equal to $(mR_A + nR_B)/(m + n)$ for the compound $A_m B_n$, where one takes always $m < n$. Very high correlation factors have been found, e.g., 37 types exhibit correlation factors in the range 0.99 to 1.00.

A similar correlation has been found between the volume of the unit cell V_{uc}, and the *concentration-weighted mean atomic volume,* $\bar{V}$, which is defined by $\bar{V} = (mV_A + nV_B)/(m + n)$ for an $A_m B_n$ compound where V_A and V_B are the atomic volumes of elements A and B respectively.

5.1.2. A narrow range for the values of axial ratios and generalized space-filling factor

The ratios c/a and b/a and the generalized space-filling factor are found to be in narrow ranges for all representatives of a structure type. In certain cases of pronounced scatter of the axial ratios, the structure family may be subdivided. One of the consequences of the above two regularities is the existence of a narrow

References: p. 266.

grouping formed by representatives of a certain structure type in a generalized iso-space-filling-$\bar{R}-R_A/R_B$ diagram. The space filling range for the Si_3W_5 type is 0.75 to 0.76. The mean space filling of 700 compounds of different structure types is 0.74 ± 0.04; (0.74 for ccp or hcp). This demonstrates the close packing in the structure of intermetallic compounds (see §2.2.1., space filling principle).

5.1.3a. Correlation between position of elements in the Periodic Table and their equipoint occupation in the structure

There is a correlation between the position of an element in the Periodic Table (s-, p-, d-, f-element) and its equipoint occupation in the structure; e.g. in the case of Si_3W_5 type (I4/mmm) the point positions 4a and 8h are occupied only by the p-elements, while the 4b and 16k are occupied by d- or f-elements. The ratio of the p- to d- (f-) elements is always 3 : 5 and never 5 : 3.

5.1.3b. Narrow grouping in an isostoichiometric diagram of binary element combinations

In an isostoichiometric diagram we arrange the elements according to their number of s-, p-, d- and f-electrons, the A elements along the vertical axis and the B-elements along the horizontal axis. For each structure type, narrow grouping occurs in the diagram. This diagram has been used to propose one or two possible structure types, with a high probability of existence, for synthesized binary intermetallic compounds (VILLARS and GIRGIS [1982a]).

5.1.4. Grouping in VEC–Δx plot

The electronic characteristics of a structure type are reflected in a grouping in a plot of $\overline{\text{VEC}}$ versus Δx; $\overline{\text{VEC}} = (m\text{VEC}_A + n\text{VEC}_B)/(m + n)$ is the mean valence-electron concentration and $\Delta x = x_A - x_B$ is the *electronegativity difference*.

Notes:
– Using two-dimensional structure maps ZUNGER (1980) has recently reached a relatively successful separation of the known binary AB compounds into different structure domains. PETTIFOR [1983], see ch. 3, presented a single chemical scale χ which characterizes each atom in the Periodic Table. Combining χ_A and χ_B results in crystal structure maps for the binary AB compounds which are more sensitive than the proposed Zunger plots and provide excellent structural separation for 574 compounds.
– RAJASEKHARAN and GIRGIS [1983] show that, notwithstanding the isotropic nature of Miedema's semiempirical theory for the heat of formation of ΔH of intermetallic phases, and contrary to the present view in literature, the parameters $\Delta\Phi^*$ and Δn_{WS} used to predict the sign of ΔH, can contribute quantitatively to our understanding of structural phenomena. In a $(\Delta\Phi^*, \Delta n_{\text{WS}}^{1/3})$ map considerable resolution is obtained among the binary systems in which different structure types occur, showing the importance of the energy of formation of an intermetallic compound in deciding the crystal structure that it adopts. The points corresponding to systems in which Laves phases (MgCu$_2$, MgZn$_2$ and MgNi$_2$ types), SiCr$_3$-type phases, TiAl$_3$-type phases etc. occur, show linear relationships in the $(\Delta\Phi^*, \Delta n_{\text{WS}}^{1/3})$ map, whereas the binary systems with MoSi$_2$-type phases are resolved into two lines corresponding to the two groups of MoSi$_2$-type phases with different c/a ratios and coordinations. The above observations enable us to explain many structural trends that can be noticed from the phase diagrams, for instance the almost total exclusion of SiCr$_3$-type phases from the 250 binary systems in which Laves phases occur and that of Laves phases from the 87 binary systems with SiCr$_3$-type phases.

5.2. Prediction of new intermetallic compounds

Modern industry is highly interested in new materials which possess optimal properties. Certain structure types appear to be favoured for special applications, such as the A15 structure for superconductivity. People engaged in materials research therefore are interested in guide lines for the synthesis of new representatives of particular structure types. For the synthesis of metallic alloy phases about 80 elements have to be considered: If we exclude the halogens, the inert gases and the actinides beyond number 93 (Np) we are left with 84 elements, which for each binary structure type offer the formal possibility of 6972 combinations $A_m B_n$. In choosing the most reasonable candidates one usually has to rely on a mixture of feeling and trial and error.

5.2.1. Savitskii–Gribulya–Kiselyova method

Recently SAVITSKII [1976] and SAVITSKII *et al.* [1972, 1975a, b, 1980] have introduced a method for the prediction of new members of various alloy structure types. For this purpose the properties of the elements as well as of the known representatives of a structure type are represented in a multidimensional diagram. An appropriate computer program has been developed, that is able to recognize a pattern in this space, dividing the element combinations into three categories: Combinations inside the pattern are likely to exist in this structure while those outside will probably adopt another structure, those on the border line are indiscernible.

On the basis of this procedure, the following numbers of probable element combinations have been predicted: $MgCu_2$-type (Laves phase): 2000, $CaCu_5$ type: 1100, $SiCr_3$ (β-W) type: 714, CsCl type: 1500, σ-phase type: 156. Although characteristic data of the elements were used, the resulting numbers of new representatives are surprisingly high. Thus one gets the impression that the extrapolation might have been driven too far.

5.2.2. Villars–Girgis–Hulliger method

Using the regularities in intermetallic compounds (VILLARS and GIRGIS [1981, 1982a]) a method for the prediction of new intermetallic compounds has been developed (VILLARS *et al.* [1980, 1982]). For each structure type a linear relation between the shortest interatomic distance d_{AB} and the concentration weighted mean atomic radius $\bar{R}$ is used to establish a relation between the lattice constants and the radii R_A and R_B of the involved atoms.

A generalized space filling factor can then be formulated as a function of $\bar{R}$ and R_A/R_B. The representatives of a structure type lie in a narrow range. The new expected binary element combinations will also lie in the same range and so a first coarse selection is based on this diagram, excluding those combinations outside this range.

A second reduction of the potential candidates is based on regularity 3a (§5.1), concerning the relation between the position of the elements in the Periodic Table

References: p. 266.

and their equipoint occupation in the structure.

A third reduction is based on the electronic characteristics of a structure type (regularity 4, §5.1).

A further reduction is encountered on the basis of thermodynamic considerations. MIEDEMA [1976] predicted stable element combinations and ruled out unstable combinations.

It is interesting to compare the results of both methods mentioned above. Savitskii *et al.* predicted 714 new $SiCr_3$ type compounds and 156 new σ-phases; Villars *et al.* predicted 93 and 46 respectively, 79% of Villars *et al.*'s candidates are identical with Savitskii *et al.*'s. This fact leaves us with the impression that the methods are reliable. The reasonably small number predicted by Villars *et al.* is encouraging.

5.3. Laves phases

Many binary – as well as ternary – compounds possess one of the three related structures of the general formula AB_2: $MgCu_2$-, $MgZn_2$- and $MgNi_2$-type structures. Much of the original work on these structures is due to LAVES, WITTE and their associates [1936, 1956]. The whole group therefore is frequently called *Laves phases*, as suggested by SCHULZE [1939].

$MgCu_2$ is cubic with 24 atoms per unit cell whereas $MgZn_2$ and $MgNi_2$ are hexagonal, with 12 and 24 atoms per unit cell respectively; for crystal data see table 5. The A and B components may be chosen from any group of the Periodic Table, while in certain cases the same element may act as the A component in association with a metal of smaller atomic diameter, or as the B component in association with a metal of larger atomic diameter (e.g., $MgCu_2$ and $CaMg_2$).

The three structures are closely related: this may be understood if we briefly consider the separate atomic arrangements, as shown in figs. 10 and 11 (A: the bigger atoms, B: the smaller ones). A atoms are arranged in double layers of a hexagonal network, with each A atom of the upper layer directly above one of the lower layers. In the case of $MgCu_2$, looking along the cube diagonal, the different double layers are labelled X, Y and Z for convenience. The B atoms are arranged at the corners of tetrahedra. The arrangement of the double layers and the tetrahedra in space are summarized below. The larger A atoms lie in the holes between the tetrahedra formed by the smaller B atoms.

Structure type	Arrangement	
	A-atom-layers	B-atom-tetrahedra
$MgCu_2$	XYZ XYZ (along [111])	joined point-to-point
$MgZn_2$	XYXY (along [001])	joined point-to-point and base-to-base, alternately
$MgNi_2$	XYXZ XYXZ (along [001])	mixture of the above two arrangements

Table 5
Crystal data [a] of structure types discussed in the present chapter.

Structure type [b]	Crystal system space group CN	Atomic parameters		Element combinations [c]
MgCu$_2$ Laves phase	fcc Fd3m 24	origin at Mg: 8a, Cu: 16d,	$\frac{1}{8}\,\frac{1}{8}\,\frac{1}{8}$ $0\,0\,0;\ \frac{1}{4}\,\frac{1}{4}\,\frac{1}{4}$ $\frac{5}{8}\,\frac{5}{8}\,\frac{5}{8};\ \frac{5}{8}\,\frac{7}{8}\,\frac{7}{8};$ $\frac{7}{8}\,\frac{5}{8}\,\frac{7}{8};\ \frac{7}{8}\,\frac{7}{8}\,\frac{5}{8}.$	s, p–d d, f–p
MgNi$_2$, Laves phase	hexagonal P6$_3$/mmc 24	Mg(1): 4e, Mg(2): 4f Ni(1): 6g, Ni(2): 6h, Ni(3) 4f,	$0\,0\,z;\ 0\,0\,\bar{z};$ $0\,0\,\frac{1}{2}+z;\ 0\,0\,\frac{1}{2}-z,$ $z = 0.094.$ $\frac{1}{3}\,\frac{2}{3}\,z;\ \frac{2}{3}\,\frac{1}{3}\,\bar{z};$ $\frac{2}{3}\,\frac{1}{3}\,\frac{1}{2}+z;\ \frac{1}{3}\,\frac{2}{3}\,\frac{1}{2}-z,$ $z = 0.844.$ $\frac{1}{2}\,0\,0;\ 0\,\frac{1}{2}\,0;$ $\frac{1}{2}\,\frac{1}{2}\,0;\ \frac{1}{2}\,0\,\frac{1}{2};$ $0\,\frac{1}{2}\,\frac{1}{2};\ \frac{1}{2}\,\frac{1}{2}\,\frac{1}{2}.$ $x\,2x\,\frac{1}{4};\ 2\bar{x}\,\bar{x}\,\frac{1}{4};\ x\,\bar{x}\,\frac{1}{4};$ $\bar{x}\,2\bar{x}\,\frac{3}{4};\ 2x\,x\,\frac{3}{4};\ \bar{x}\,x\,\frac{3}{4},$ $x = 0.167.$ as for Mg(2) above, $z = 0.125.$	s–d f–s
MgZn$_2$, Laves phase	hexagonal P6$_3$/mmc 12	Mg: 4f Zn(1): 2a, Zn(2): 6h,	$\frac{1}{3}\,\frac{2}{3}\,z;\ \frac{2}{3}\,\frac{1}{3}\,\bar{z};$ $\frac{2}{3}\,\frac{1}{3}\,\frac{1}{2}+z;\ \frac{1}{3}\,\frac{2}{3}\,\frac{1}{2}-z,$ $z = 0.062.$ $0\,0\,0;\ 0\,0\,\frac{1}{2}.$ as for Ni(2) above, $x = 0.830.$	d–s, p f, d–d
Sigma phase	tetragonal P4$_2$/mnm 30	A: 2a, B: 4g, C: 8i, D: 8i, E: 8j,	$0\,0\,0;\ \frac{1}{2}\,\frac{1}{2}\,\frac{1}{2}.$ $x\,\bar{x}\,0;\ \bar{x}\,x\,0;\ \frac{1}{2}+x\,\frac{1}{2}+x\,\frac{1}{2};$ $\frac{1}{2}-x\,\frac{1}{2}-x\,\frac{1}{2},$ $x = 0.398.$ $x\,y\,0;\ \bar{x}\,\bar{y}\,0;\ \frac{1}{2}+x\,\frac{1}{2}-y\,\frac{1}{2};$ $\frac{1}{2}-x\,\frac{1}{2}+y\,\frac{1}{2};\ y\,x\,0;\ \bar{y}\,\bar{x}\,0;$ $\frac{1}{2}+y\,\frac{1}{2}-x\,\frac{1}{2};\ \frac{1}{2}-y\,\frac{1}{2}+x\,\frac{1}{2},$ $x = 0.537;\ y = 0.132.$ as for C, $x = 0.065;\ y = 0.262.$ $x\,x\,z;\ \bar{x}\,\bar{x}\,z;\ \frac{1}{2}+x\,\frac{1}{2}-x\,\frac{1}{2}+z;$ $\frac{1}{2}-x\,\frac{1}{2}+x\,\frac{1}{2}+z;$ $x\,x\,\bar{z};\ \bar{x}\,\bar{x}\,\bar{z};\ \frac{1}{2}+x\,\frac{1}{2}-x\,\frac{1}{2}-z;$ $\frac{1}{2}-x\,\frac{1}{2}+x\,\frac{1}{2}-z,$ $x = 0.318;\ z = 0.248.$	d–d

References: p. 266.

Table 5 (continued)

Structure type [b]	Crystal system space group CN	Atomic parameters		Element combinations [c]
Cr$_3$Si (A15)	cP Pm3n 8	Cr: 2a, Si: 6c,	$0\,0\,0;\ \frac{1}{2}\,\frac{1}{2}\,\frac{1}{2}.$ $\frac{1}{4}\,0\,\frac{1}{2};\ \frac{1}{2}\,\frac{1}{4}\,0;\ 0\,\frac{1}{2}\,\frac{1}{4};$ $\frac{3}{4}\,0\,\frac{1}{2};\ \frac{1}{2}\,\frac{3}{4}\,0;\ 0\,\frac{1}{2}\,\frac{3}{4}.$	p, d–p
PbMo$_6$S$_8$ Chevrel phase	rh. R$\bar{3}$ ~ 14	0.92Pb: 1a, 6S(1): 6f, 0.75S(2): 2c, 6Mo: 6f,	$0\,0\,0.$ $x\,y\,z;\ z\,x\,y;\ y\,z\,x,$ $\bar{x}\,\bar{y}\,\bar{z};\ \bar{z}\,\bar{x}\,\bar{y};\ \bar{y}\,\bar{z}\,\bar{x},$ $x = 0.383;\ y = 0.126;$ $z = 0.743.$ $x\,x\,x;\ \bar{x}\,\bar{x}\,\bar{x},$ $x = 0.242.$ as for 6S(1), $x = 0.227;\ y = 0.416;$ $z = 0.562.$	
CaCu$_5$	hexagonal P6/mmm 6	Ca: 1a, Cu(1): 2c, Cu(2): 3g,	$0\,0\,0.$ $\frac{1}{3}\,\frac{2}{3}\,0;\ \frac{2}{3}\,\frac{1}{3}\,0.$ $\frac{1}{2}\,0\,\frac{1}{2};\ 0\,\frac{1}{2}\,\frac{1}{2};\ \frac{1}{2}\,\frac{1}{2}\,\frac{1}{2}.$	s, d, f–d d–s
AlB$_2$	hexagonal P6/mmm 3	Al: 1a, B: 2d,	$0\,0\,0.$ $\frac{1}{3}\,\frac{2}{3}\,\frac{1}{2};\ \frac{2}{3}\,\frac{1}{3}\,\frac{1}{2}.$	d, f–p d, f–d
AlCu$_2$Mn Heusler phase	fcc Fm3m 16	Al: 4a, Mn: 4b, Cu: 8c,	$0\,0\,0.$ $\frac{1}{2}\,\frac{1}{2}\,\frac{1}{2}.$ $\frac{1}{4}\,\frac{1}{4}\,\frac{1}{4};\ \frac{3}{4}\,\frac{3}{4}\,\frac{3}{4}.$	
NiAs	hexagonal P6$_3$/mmc 4	Ni: 2a, As: 2c,	$0\,0\,0;\ 0\,0\,\frac{1}{2}.$ $\frac{1}{3}\,\frac{2}{3}\,\frac{1}{4};\ \frac{2}{3}\,\frac{1}{3}\,\frac{3}{4}.$	d–p
Ni$_2$In	hexagonal P6$_3$/mmc 6	Ni(1): 2a, Ni(2): 2d, In: 2c,	$0\,0\,0,\ 0\,0\,\frac{1}{2}.$ $\frac{1}{3}\,\frac{2}{3}\,\frac{3}{4};\ \frac{2}{3}\,\frac{1}{3}\,\frac{1}{4}.$ $\frac{1}{3}\,\frac{2}{3}\,\frac{1}{4};\ \frac{2}{3}\,\frac{1}{3}\,\frac{3}{4}.$	d–p
MnP	ortho-rhombic Pnma 8	Mn: 4c P: 4c	$x\,\frac{1}{4}\,z;\ \bar{x}\,\frac{3}{4}\,\bar{z};$ $\frac{1}{2}-x\,\frac{3}{4}\,\frac{1}{2}+z;\ \frac{1}{2}+x\,\frac{1}{4}\,\frac{1}{2}-z,$ $x = 0.005;\ z = 0.197.$ as for Mn, $x = 0.188;\ z = 0.569.$	d–p

[a] Data from: PEARSON [1967], GIRGIS [1982], VILLARS and GIRGIS [1982a], MAREZIO et al. [1973].
[b] Structure types are ordered according to their sequence in the text.
[c] Minority element first.

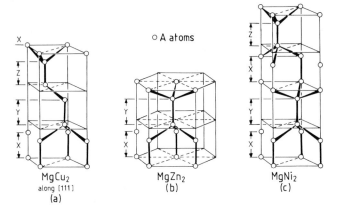

Fig. 10. Arrangement of the bigger A atoms in Laves phases.

It is believed that one of the main factors contributing to the existence of the Laves phases is of *geometrical origin* (size factor), i.e. filling the space in a convenient way. Figure 12 shows that the distance between the A atoms in an $MgCu_2$ structure is $\frac{1}{4}a\sqrt{3}$, and that between the B atoms is $\frac{1}{4}a\sqrt{2}$. If, for maximum filling of space, the A atoms are made to contact each other and the B atoms are also made to contact each other, the ratio of the atomic radii that permits this is $R_A/R_B = (\frac{3}{2})^{1/2} = 1.225$. In practice, the ratio of the Goldschmidt radii of the pure elements, R_A/R_B, for the known Laves phases varies from 1.05 to 1.68. DWIGHT [1961] however, concludes that the Goldschmidt radii of the pure elements are not an important factor in dictating which of the three structures will form; it is only necessary that the A atoms be larger than the B atoms and that they be able to contract or expand to achieve the ideal ratio of 1.225. On the other hand, there are AB_2 combinations whose radius ratios lie well within the typical range which do not form Laves phases.

The role of the *electronic factor* in the formation of the Laves phases is well

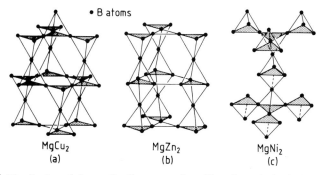

Fig. 11. Distribution of the smaller B atoms and stacking of tetrahedra in Laves phases.

References: p. 266.

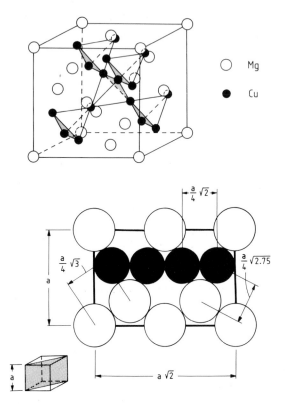

Fig. 12. (top) MgCu$_2$ structure; (bottom) schematic arrangement of the atoms in the (110) plane in the cubic MgCu$_2$ structure: large circles A atoms, small circles B atoms. (After SCHULZE [1939].)

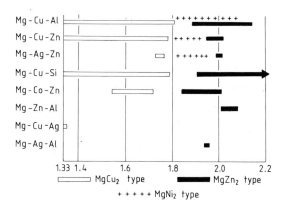

Fig. 13. Homogeneity ranges in terms of valence electron per atom ratios for several ternary Mg alloys (after LAVES and WITTE [1936]).

known (LAVES and WITTE [1936]). KLEE and WITTE [1954], for example, have shown that the electron concentration determines which of the three structures will form in the pseudo-binary systems of $MgCu_2$ and $MgZn_2$ with Al, Ag and Si as shown in fig. 13. This should be considered as a tendency, as "it is impossible to classify the compounds in terms of their electron : atom ratios" (HUME-ROTHERY and RAYNOR, [1962]).

5.4. The sigma phase

The *sigma phase* (σ phase) is hard, brittle and nonmagnetic at ordinary temperatures. In heat-resisting alloys and complex steels containing iron and chromium, the σ phase may be precipitated, owing to faulty composition control or heat treatment, in a form which confers inferior mechanical properties on the material. Therefore many studies of this phase have been carried out.

It is generally found in systems involving the transition elements. Significant features of this phase are that homogeneity ranges are broad and that the temperature ranges of stability are not the same in the different alloy systems. It appears that both the atomic size factor and the electronic factor contribute to the formation and stability of this phase (see also § 5.1).

5.4.1. Crystal structure of the sigma phase

The σ phase belongs to the tetragonal system with 30 atoms per unit cell (table 5). The structure can be described as stacking of Kagomé nets at 0 and 0.5 which are rotated by 90° with respect to each other. Atoms at $z \approx 0.25$ lie in between these nets in their hexagonal cavities as shown in fig. 14. This arrangement repeats itself in the structure along the c axis.

There are five point positions in the structure; the *ordering of the atoms* over the available atomic sites has been described by SHOEMAKER and SHOEMAKER [1969]. The results indicate that the elements to the left of the Mn column in the Periodic Table (A elements) prefer the CN 15 and 16 positions. The elements to the right of Mn (B elements) prefer the CN 12 positions, and either kind or mixtures occupy the CN 14 positions. Mn and Re behave as A or B elements depending on the elements they are alloyed with. Si and Al are found to occupy CN 12 positions. The fact that A elements prefer the higher coordinated positions may be attributed to their large size, but may also be a consequence of their electronic structure.

5.4.2. Electronic factor

Some authors have discussed the σ phase as an *electron compound*. BLOOM and GRANT [1952] assume that the σ-phase compositions are determined by an electron concentration of 210 per unit cell or an average of seven valence electrons per atom, and GREENFIELD and BECK [1954, 1956] have shown that 6.93 electrons per atom can be obtained from the mean composition of the known phases. The second Brillouin zone can contain 6.97 electrons/atom, which is consistent with the above treatment. However, BERGMANN and SHOEMAKER [1954] doubt that the average

References: p. 266.

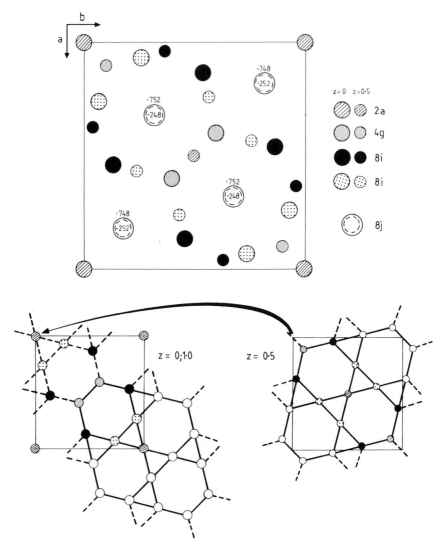

Fig. 14. Description of the structure of the σ phase in terms of Kagomé nets; cell contents (top) as well as stacking of the Kagomé nets (bottom) are shown; projection on (001) plane.

valence of the metal atom can be as high as seven and feel that it is more likely to be closer to 5.76. This latter value is based on the observed interatomic distances.

5.5. Kasper phases

Kasper discovered that some of the known phases (e.g. the sigma phase) can be formed of irregular tetrahedra which fill the space. These phases are called *Kasper*

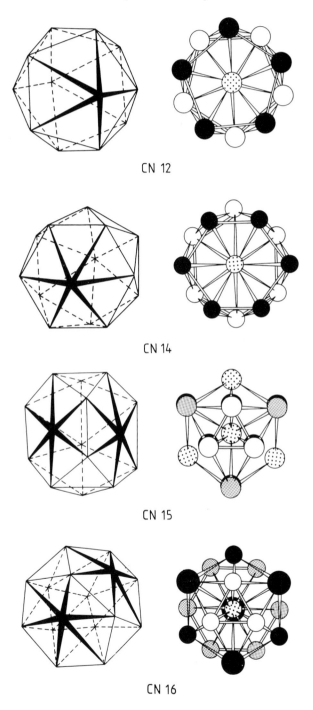

CN 12

CN 14

CN 15

CN 16

Fig. 15. Kasper polyhedra.

References: p. 266.

Table 6
Geometrical characteristics of the Kasper coordination polyhedra.

Type	Coordination			
	12	14	15	16
Ideal point symmetry	$Y_h-\bar{5}3(2/m)$	$D_{6d}-\bar{1}2\cdot2m$	$D_{3h}-\bar{6}m2$	$T_d-\bar{4}3m$
Vertices with surface coordination 5 (6)	12 (–)	12 (2)	12 (3)	12 (4)
Edges	30	36	39	42
Faces (triangular)	20	24	26	28

phases. KASPER [1956] and FRANK and KASPER [1958, 1959] studied polyhedra which have the following features:

(1) The polyhedron has exclusively triangular faces;
(2) The polyhedron is convex;
(3) Five or six edges meet at each corner.

Only four polyhedra do fulfill these conditions; their geometrical characteristics are given in table 6 and fig. 15.

If *each* atom in the structure is surrounded by a Kasper polyhedron, one can connect the central atom to the corners of the triangular faces of these polyhedra. This means that polyhedra will be subdivided into tetrahedra (distorted). These distorted tetrahedra fill the space without vacancies. Examples of these structures are the σ-, μ- and P-phases and Fe_7W_6. The sigma phase possesses five point positions: two of them are surrounded by Kasper-12 polyhedra, two by Kasper-14 polyhedra and one by a Kasper-15 polyhedron. Therefore one can describe this structure as built up of distorted tetrahedra.

5.6. Further phases

There is a large number of structure types which could be discussed in this section. Some of the most frequently occurring are listed here:

Structure type	Space group	Number of atoms per unit cell
$C11_b$, $MoSi_2$	I4/mmm	6
C16, $CuAl_2$	I4/mcm	12
DO_{22}, $TiAl_3$	I4/mmm	8
$D8_8$, Si_3Mn_5	I4/mcm	16
$D8_1$, B_3Cr_5	I4/mcm	32
$D8_m$, Si_3W_5	I4/mcm	32

6. Superconducting materials

A large number of publications currently available reflects the increasing interest in A15 superconductors. The world-wide search to increase T_c above the highest presently obtained value of 23 K continues. MCMILLAN [1968] deduced on a theoretical basis that it should be possible to reach T_c values of 28–40 K. The aim of this section is to give a review of the relationship between structure and superconductivity (see also ch. 27).

6.1. Definitions

6.1.1. Superconductivity
Superconductivity is primarily characterized by the vanishing of electrical resistance below the *superconducting temperature* (T_c). A comparison between the resistance of copper and that of a superconducting material shows that the resistance of the latter is at least 10^{17} times smaller.

The superconducting phenomenon is generally understood. However the calculation of the different parameters necessary for technical applications, e.g. T_c, H_c, J_c, is not yet possible.

6.1.2. The critical magnetic field H_c
A superconducting body below T_c exhibits perfect diamagnetism and excludes a magnetic field up to some *critical magnetic field, H_c*, whereupon it reverts to the normal state. H_c is temperature-dependent.

6.1.3. The critical current density J_c
Above the *critical current density*, J_c, the superconductivity is destroyed and the superconductor reverts to the normal state; J_c mainly depends on the heterogeneity of the material.

6.1.4. Type I (soft) superconductors
Type I superconductors are mostly found among pure metals. Type I exhibits perfect diamagnetism and excludes a magnetic field up to H_c whereupon it reverts to the normal state.

6.1.5. Type II (hard) superconductors
In *type II superconductors* total exclusion of the magnetic field does not take place above a value H_{c1}, where the superconductor exhibits new equilibrium conditions. In parts it is still superconducting, in other parts it does not exclude the magnetic field; this is called the mixed state or *Shubnikov phase*. Superconductivity is destroyed when we reach a higher value, the H_{c2} critical magnetic field, whereupon the superconductor reverts to the normal state.

References: p. 266.

6.2. Superconducting structures

Superconductivity is observed in more than 50 different structure types. Some of the known intermetallic structure types which exhibit superconductivity are shown in table 7.

It is interesting to note that A15 (Cr_3Si) compounds exhibit the highest known superconducting temperatures. The next group with high T_c comprises intermetallic compounds with B1 (NaCl) type structures. The third group, the chalcogenides, exhibit middle T_c but the highest critical magnetic fields H_{c2} found ($H_{c2} = 478$ kA/cm for $PbMo_6S_8$). We shall therefore mainly treat the A15 compound and the Chevrel phases (chalcogenides) in less detail only.

6.3. Structure and superconductivity of A15 compounds

6.3.1. A15 (Cr_3Si) structure description

Most of the representatives of the Cr_3Si structure type crystallize with the composition A_3B. A is a transition metal of the groups IV to VI and B is either a transition or a non-transition metal. The radius ratio of the components lies between 0.84 and 1.12, whereas the mean radius ratio of those phases showing T_c over 10 K is 1.004.

Table 7

Structure types in which compounds showing superconductivity frequently crystallize [a].

Structure type	Bravais type	max. T_c found [K]	Representative	H_{c2} (kA/cm)
A1	fcc	7.19	Pb	~ 1.0
A2	bcc	9.26	Nb	3.4 at 0 K
Solid sol.	bcc	10.00	NbZr	88 at 0 K
Solid sol.	bcc	9.8	NbTi	112 at 0 K
A12(αMn)	bcc	10.5	$NbTc_3$	–
A13(βMn)	c	10.0	Mo_3Al_2C	125 at 1.2 K
A15(Cr_3Si)	c	18.1	Nb_3Sn [b]	196 at 0 K
A15(Cr_3Si)	c	23.2	Nb_3Ge	307 at 0 K
B1(NaCl)	fcc	17.9	Nb(C,N)	127 at 0 K
C15(Laves phase)	fcc	10.4	$(V, Nb)_2Hf_{0.75}$	250 at 0 K
C16($CuAl_2$)	t	11.3	Zr_2Rh	–
C32(AlB_2)	h	11.2	$(MoZr)_2B_5$	–
D5$_c$(Pu_2C_3)	bcc	17.0	$Y_{0.5}Th_{0.3}C_{1.55}$	–
D8$_b$(FeCr; σ)	t	15.8	$Mo_{0.25}Tc_{0.75}$	68
E9$_3$(Fe_3W_3C)	fcc	11.8	Zr_3Rh	–
L1$_2$(Cu_3Au)	c	10.4	La_3In	–
Chalcogenides	rh	15.2	$PbMo_6S_8$	478 at 0 K

[a] This table is taken from RASSMANN and MÜLLER [1976]; some corrections have been inserted by the author.

[b] Nb_3Sn and V_3Si belong to the A15 structure type; their superconducting temperatures are 18.1 and 17 K respectively. Cr_3Si which also belongs to the A15 structure type is not superconducting.

Figure 16 shows the A15 structure, whilst table 8 represents some structural data of V_3Ga as a representative of this structure type. The B atoms build a cubic body-centred lattice complex. The A atoms build three perpendicular chains parallel to the crystallographic axes. These chains are along the face centres of the cube. In the case of a stoichiometric, fully ordered structure, the A atoms occupy the 6c positions and the B atoms the 2a positions in the space group Pm3n–0_h^3 (223).

The B atoms are surrounded by a distorted icosahedron of A atoms (m3–T_h symmetry), fig. 17a, whilst the A atoms are surrounded by a distorted 14-Kasper polyhedron ($\bar{4}$2m–D_{2d} symmetry) of 10 A and 4 B atoms (fig. 17b).

One can describe the structure by packing these Kasper polyhedra. They share triangular faces, building a "sheet of polyhedra". The identical "sheets" above and below are held together by sharing the apices of their Kasper polyhedra in the z-direction; fig. 18 (GIRGIS *et al.* [1976]).

The measured density of the A15 compounds is higher than that of their components, e.g. $\rho_{V_3Ga} = 6.6$ g/cm³; $\rho_v = 6.0$ g/cm³; $\rho_{Ga} = 5.9$ g/cm³ (KUZNETSOVA and ZHDANOV [1972]).

The distance between the A atoms in the chain is 8–14% less than the sum of the radii (SAVITSKII *et al.* [1973]). This indicates the presence of covalent bonding and explains the high density of this structure. This point will be treated later.

Looking at this simple structure one gets the impression that everything is quite clear. The questions which do continually arise are the following:
– What are the factors on which T_c is dependent?
– How can we reach higher T_c values?
– Why is V_3Si superconducting (17 K), whereas Cr_3Si is not, although V and Cr are next to each other in the Periodic Table? Another example: Nb_3Sn, $T_c = 18$ K, and V_3Sn, $T_c = 7$ K, are both isoelectronic; V and Nb belong to the same group. How can we explain the difference?

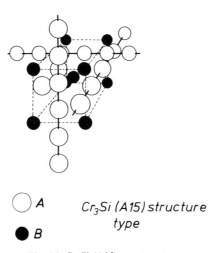

○ A   *Cr_3Si (A15) structure*
● B   *type*

Fig. 16. Cr_3Si (A15) structure type.

References: p. 266.

Table 8
V_3Ga structure data.

Structure type UCD	Crystal system space group CN	Atomic parameters	
A15 (β-W, Cr_3Si) $a = 4.816_{\pm1}$ Å	Cubic Pm3n–O_h^3 (223) 8	V: 6c, Ga: 2a,	$\frac{1}{4}0\frac{1}{2}; \frac{1}{2}\frac{1}{4}0; 0\frac{1}{2}\frac{1}{4};$ $\frac{3}{4}0\frac{1}{2}; \frac{1}{2}\frac{3}{4}0; 0\frac{1}{2}\frac{3}{4}.$ $000; \frac{1}{2}\frac{1}{2}\frac{1}{2}.$

Atoms	Interatomic distance d		$(d_m - d_c)/d_m$ (%)
	calculated, d_c (Å)	measured, d_m (Å)	
V_1–V_1	2.72 [a] (2.676) [b]	0.5a = 2.41	−13 [a] (−11) [b]
V_1–V_2	2.72 [a] (2.676) [b]	$a\sqrt{6}/4$ = 2.95	+8 [a] (+10) [b]
V–Ga	2.75 [a] (2.742) [b]	$a\sqrt{5}/4$ = 2.70	−2 [a] (−2) [b]

[a] Calculated with Goldschmidt radii for CN = 12: R_V = 1.36 Å, R_{Ga} = 1.39 Å.
[b] Calculated with Pauling radii for CN = 12: R_V = 1.338 Å, R_{Ga} = 1.404 Å.

Thus the search for relationships between the superconducting properties and the different physical parameters has proved necessary.

6.3.2.   The search for relations between T_c and different parameters
e/a–T_c **relationship.** MATTHIAS [1953] emphasized the importance of e/a values (number of electrons/atom) for the search of high T_c values. Many superconducting

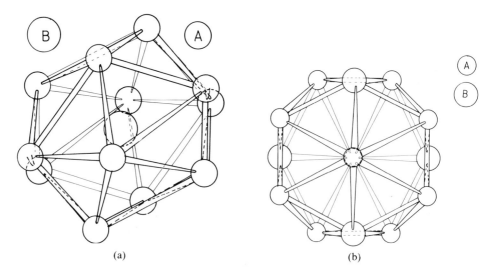

(a)   (b)

Fig. 17. Coordination polyhedra in Cr_3Si-type for A (a) and B (b) atoms, respectively.

V₃Ga

cP8   Cr₃Si type   ◯ V
                          ◯ Ga

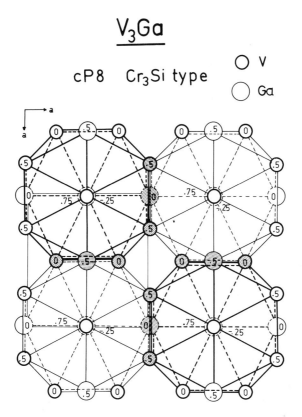

Fig. 18. Cr₃Si structure description in terms of polyhedra packing.

phases have been found with the help of this relation. Our own results (GIRGIS *et al.* [1976], GUBSER *et al.* [1979]) confirm the validity of this relation even for ternary phases (fig. 19).

Again the problem arises that some A15 compounds with favourable e/a values are non-superconductors. Other compounds with the same e/a values show different T_c values; e.g. Nb₃Sn ($T_c = 18$ K) and V₃Sn ($T_c = 7$ K), both compounds being isoelectronic (e/a = 4.75). This demonstrates clearly that superconductivity is influenced by factors other than e/a values.

The e/a ratio does not take into consideration the details of the crystal structure of either the compounds or their components. This may be the reason for the above-mentioned discrepancies.

Cell constants–T_c relationship. TESTARDI [1971] and TESTARDI *et al.* [1971] emphasized the importance of the cell constants. They conclude that T_c is a function of the cell constants alone.

However, SMITH [1972] quickly challenged this belief with high pressure data. GIRGIS [1982] and GUBSER *et al.* [1979] also show its invalidity for ternary phases (fig. 20).

References: p. 266.

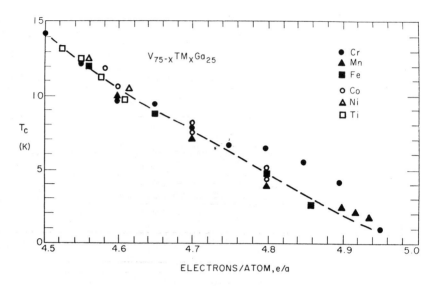

Fig. 19. Dependence of T_c on e/a for ternary A15 compounds ($V_{75-x}TM_xGa_{25}$ phases).

Some other factors on which T_c depends are mentioned in the literature. We discuss some crucial factors, beginning with the dependence of T_c on the long-range order parameter.

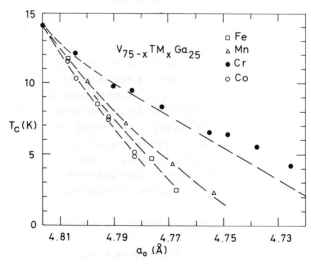

Fig. 20. Dependence of T_c on cell constant (a_0) for ternary A15 compounds ($V_{75-x}TM_xGa_{25}$ phases).

6.3.3. Long-range order parameter (S) and T_c dependence

Many authors have treated this problem: some of the results are mentioned below (see also ch. 4, § 10.3).

– FLÜKIGER *et al.* [1976] have shown that T_c of V_3Ga clearly increases with increasing S by suitable *heat treatment*. One can raise the T_c of V_3Au manifold by increasing the long-range order through annealing the samples at low temperatures (HEIN [1973]).

– BESSLEIN *et al.* [1975] observed a drastic change of T_c following *bombardment* with heavy ions and neutrons, which can be correlated with the long-range order parameter. The following observation is interesting in this context: While compounds like Nb_3Sn, Nb_3Al, Nb_3Ga, Nb_3Ge (thin films), V_3Si and V_3Ga all exhibit large and roughly comparable decreases of T_c with radiation dose, one noticeable exception has been found so far: Mo_3Os. At neutron doses where the afore-mentioned compounds are in the saturation region, T_c of Mo_3Os is only decreasing by 10% (SWEEDLER *et al.* [1977]). This is an indication of the "atypical" A15 group structure.

– V_3Ga shows that the maximum T_c values exist at the *stoichiometric composition*, i.e. maximum long-range order. This is in agreement with Weger's "A-chain integrity" model.

BLAUGHER *et al.* [1969] observed a deviation from this rule in the case of V–Ir, Cr–Ir and V–Os; namely that deviations from the "ideal" composition actually produce an increase in T_c. For the V–Os A15 phase this effect is even more striking since approximately 36% of the A sites are occupied by the B atoms (Os) in a random manner. "These observations contradict the assumption that A-chain integrity is essential to obtain maximum superconducting transition temperatures. If maximum T_c's are obtained through an optimum degree of mixing of the 'd-electrons' however, such behavior would be expected. Thus, it appears that the attainment of specific mixtures of 'd-electron' wave functions may in some cases be more important than maintaining the integrity of the A-atom chains in obtaining desirable superconducting properties".

These conclusions cause some uncertainty in the question of long-range order. The explanation with mixtures of "d-electron" wave functions is unsatisfactory as well. We must not forget the objection raised by WANG and HOLDEN [1975]. They used the measured intensities of BLAUGHER *et al.* [1969] and VAN REUTH and WATERSTRAT [1968] and calculated the long-range order (LRO) parameters of the A and B sites (S_A and S_B are the LRO parameters of the A and B sites respectively). They found that the A sites show a high order parameter, while disorder exists predominantly at the B sites. Wang and Holden have shown that the X-ray powder diffraction data of the above mentioned authors do not indicate disorder in these A15 compounds but, in fact, favour preferential disorder in the B sites. This indicates again the importance of "A-chain integrity". Who is right? Let us take a look at the work done by STAUDENMANN [1977, 1978] and STAUDENMANN *et al.* [1976].

References: p. 266.

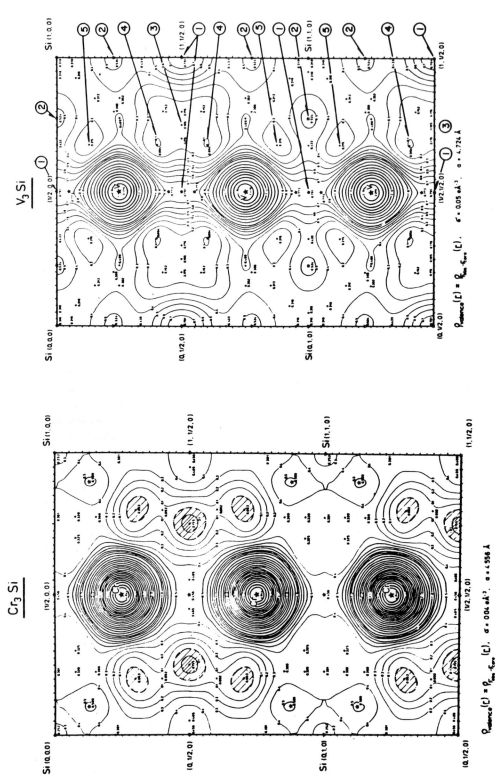

Fig. 21. Valence electron density in the (001) plane of Cr_3Si and V_3Si at room temperature. Negative surfaces are shaded (STAUDENMANN [1977 and 1978]).

6.3.4.   Electron density and bonding in A15 structures

Staudenmann *et al.* studied V_3Si single crystals at room temperature and at 13.5 K as well as Cr_3Si at room temperature. One of the main differences between V_3Si, a high superconductor, and Cr_3Si, a non-superconductor, is that the infinite chain of Cr in Cr_3Si has the appearance of *rows of charged atoms* whereas the V atoms in the analogous chain of V_3Si appear to be *covalently bonded* to one another (fig. 21).

This fact leads us to introduce two classes of A15 structures:

(a) "typical" A15 structures are those with bonding similar to V_3Si (covalent bonding in the chain);

(b) "atypical" A15 structures are those with bonding similar to Cr_3Si (charged atoms in the chain).

FLÜKIGER and JORDA [1977] summarized the optimum conditions in order to obtain T_{cmax} of typical and atypical A15 compounds.

In order to obtain T_{cmax} one should have perfect order and stoichiometric composition in the case of typical A15 compounds; for atypical A15 compounds perfect order and extreme composition are necessary. In the case of segregation the *ordering energy* (ϵ_0) should be lower than the *segregation energy* (ϵ_s), where ϵ_0 is the minimum energy necessary to interchange the A and B atoms and ϵ_s is the lowest energy at which segregation occurs.

6.3.5.   Influence of the atom type on T_c

DEW-HUGHES [1975] puts the different factors influencing the transition temperature, such as atomic weight, atomic radius etc. together in the following formula:

$$T_c = \frac{19.6 \, T_A V_A}{M^{1/2} V_{A15}},$$

where T_A is the transition temperature of the A component, V_A is the atomic volume in pure element A, V_{A15} is the atomic volume in the A15 phase and M is the average atomic mass of the compound.

From a plot of T_c against $T_A V_A / M^{1/2} V_{A15}$ it is surprising to see how suitable this empirical formula is for calculating transition temperatures. According to this, one could expect that a hypothetical stoichiometric Nb_3Si phase would show a yet higher T_c than the stoichiometric Nb_3Ge phase.

One can conclude that in order to obtain maximum T_c values one should consider the following points: stoichiometric composition, perfect order, influence of atom type and favourable e/a ratios.

6.4.   Martensitic transformation

In certain investigations the superconducting properties of these compounds were associated not with a cubic lattice of the Cr_3Si type but with a tetragonal structure formed at low temperatures as a result of a martensitic transformation. Thus, a martensite-type transformation (detected by X-ray diffraction) was observed in V_3Si

References: p. 266.

single crystals at temperatures above the critical point T_c. Below the temperature of the martensitic transformation the degree of tetragonality of the lattice (the axial ratio c/a) became gradually larger, reaching a final value of 1.0025. The structure of Nb_3Sn in the superconducting state is also tetragonal with $c/a = 1.0042$. The martensitic transformation in Nb_3Sn and V_3Si is a phase transformation of the first kind. Several authors have mentioned a sudden change in the specific heat and electrical resistance of the compounds V_3Si, V_3Ga, V_3Ge, V_3Sn and Nb_3Sn at low temperatures. For V_3X compounds with a structure of the Cr_3Si type there is a specific interrelationship between the temperature of the martensitic transformation and the temperature corresponding to the transition into the superconducting state $(T_m/T_c \approx 1.5)$, as may be clearly seen from the following data:

property	compound				
	V_3Si	V_3Ga	V_3Ge	V_3Sn	Nb_3Sn
T_c (K)	16.8	14.1	6.9	3.7	18.0
T_m (K)	23.5–28.6	20.6	10.0	5.4	36.0
T_m/T_c	1.4–1.7	1.5	1.45	1.46	2.0

The relation between the phase transformation and superconductivity is supported by the absence of such a transformation in V_3Ir ($T_c < 0.3$ K) down to 4.6 K. However, in certain superconducting samples of V_3Si also no martensite transformations appear. In tin-enriched samples of Nb_3Sn too, no phase transformation is observed. Thus the question concerning the relation between the superconductivity of Cr_3Si-type compounds and the structural transformation does require a more detailed study. Recent X-ray work established the existence of a martensitic transformation in tin-enriched superconducting $Nb_3(Sn, Sb)$ alloys (SAVITSKII et al. [1973]).

6.5.   Chevrel phases

CHEVREL et al. [1971] reported the preparation of compounds of the type $M_xMo_3S_4$; M = Ag, Sn, Ca, Sr, Pb, Ba, Cd, Zn, Mg, Cu, Mn, Cr, Fe, Co, Ni, Li, Na. MATTHIAS et al. [1972] found that the compounds with M = Pb, Sn, Ag, Cu, Zn, Mg, Cd, Sc, and Y are superconducting; their T_c are 15.2, 14.2, 9.1, 10.9, 3.6, 3.5, 3.5, 3.6 and 3.0, respectively. These are the first non-cubic compounds with relatively high superconducting temperatures.

The structure can be described by a stacking of Mo_6S_8 building blocks. The S atoms lie at the corners of a trigonal distorted cube which contains an octahedron of tightly packed Mo atoms (fig. 22).

This particular arrangement of the Mo_6S_8 units leaves a certain number of cavities. "Big" atoms such as Pb occupy exclusively the larger hole at the origin and yield a stoichiometric compound ($x \approx 1$), whereas small atoms such as Cu may also partially occupy the small interstices and lead to a nonstoichiometric compound

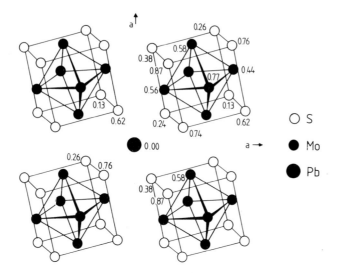

Fig. 22. Projection of the structure of $PbMo_6S_8$ along the rhombohedral axis. The heights of the enumerated atoms are given as fractions of the unit cell parameter.

($x > 1$). Many representatives of this structure type which are superconducting are known today (FISCHER [1978], YVON [1979]).

7. Magnetic structures

7.1. Types of magnetism *

7.1.1. Diamagnetism (atomic or molecular)
Diamagnetic materials possess neither atomic nor molecular permanent magnetic moments, $\chi^{dia} < 0$.

7.1.2. Paramagnetism (atomic or molecular)
Paramagnetic materials possess permanent magnetic moments with random orientation. They may be aligned by means of an external magnetic field, $\chi^{para} > 0$.

7.1.3. Ferromagnetism (structure-dependent)
Ferromagnets exhibit spontaneous long-range order of atomic magnetic moments which are strongly coupled parallel to each other below the *Curie temperature* (T_C). Due to thermal motion the system becomes paramagnetic above T_C (fig. 23).

* See also ch. 26.

Paramagnetism

Spin: disordered

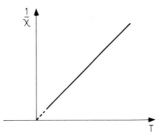

Ferromagnetism

Spin: ↑↑↑↑↑↑ ordered

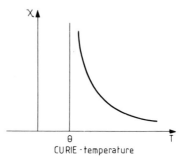

Antiferromagnetism

Spin: ↓↑↓↑↓↑ ordered

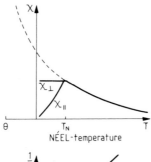

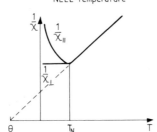

Ferrimagnetism

Spin: ↓↑↓↑↓ ordered

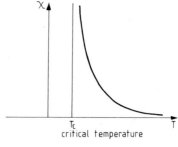

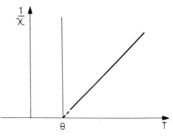

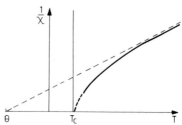

Fig. 23. Types of magnetism.

7.1.4. Antiferromagnetism (structure-dependent)

The simplest *antiferromagnets* are those with two sublattices consisting of magnetic moments of equal magnitude. Below the Néel temperature (T_N) the magnetic moments of each sublattice order themselves parallel to each other and antiparallel to the second sublattice; i.e., long-range order exists. The resulting moment of an antiferromagnetic crystal is zero (fig. 23). There are other configurations of antiferromagnets such as helical, cycloidal spin structures, etc., in general incommensurate (GIRGIS and FISCHER [1979]).

7.1.5. Ferrimagnetism (structure-dependent)

Ferrimagnetic substances possess a spontaneous magnetization below a critical temperature (T_c). The net moment results from incomplete compensation of the magnetic moments of two or more sublattices with antiparallel coupling. It can be understood as a special case of antiferromagnetism. The magnetic moments of the sublattices are antiparallel and not equal in magnitude (fig. 23). Ferrimagnets with spinel structure are known as *ferrites*. They are of technical interest because of their low electrical conductivity which prevents eddy-current losses. They find many technical applications, for example in transformer cores, microwave devices etc.

Some examples of the many structure types which show magnetic properties are discussed below; namely Heusler phases, $CaCu_5$, AlB_2, NiAs, Ni_2In and MnP structure type phases.

7.2. Heusler phases

Magnetic compounds which crystallize with Cu_2MnAl type structure are called *Heusler phases* (fig. 24, table 5).

This structure is stable above 400°C, but it can be frozen by quenching to room temperature. In the case of Cu_2MnAl it is assumed that the whole moment is due to the spin moment of manganese which has an unfilled 3d shell (five electrons). The

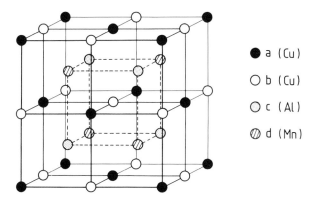

a (Cu)

b (Cu)

c (Al)

d (Mn)

Fig. 24. Crystal structure of the Heusler phases; four point positions are indicated.

References: p. 266.

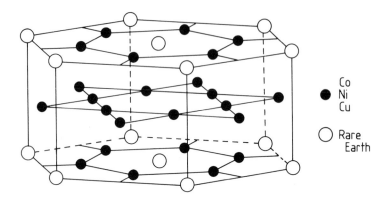

Fig. 25. The CaCu$_5$ structure type.

magnetic properties of Heusler phases are strongly dependent on the ordering of the atoms. CAROLI and BLANDIN [1966] have developed a theory to explain the strong effective magnetic field at the Cu nuclei in Heusler alloys Cu$_2$MnAl and Cu$_2$MnIn, assuming local moments only on the Mn atoms. GOODENOUGH [1963] has treated the magnetism of these Heusler alloys based on the assumption of superexchange via the Cu and Al atoms. This mechanism can explain the large interaction distances of the Mn atoms excluding direct exchange interaction. These distances range from 4.08 to 4.55 Å (HAMES [1960]).

7.3. CaCu$_5$ structure type

The *CaCu$_5$ structure type* crystallizes in the hexagonal space group P6/mmm with one formula per unit cell (figs. 25 and 26 and table 5):

Ca in 1a	0	0	0;						
Cu in 2c	$\frac{1}{3}$	$\frac{2}{3}$	0,	$\frac{2}{3}$	$\frac{1}{3}$	0;			
Cu in 3g	$\frac{1}{2}$	0	$\frac{1}{2}$,	0	$\frac{1}{2}$	$\frac{1}{2}$,	$\frac{1}{2}$	$\frac{1}{2}$	$\frac{1}{2}$.

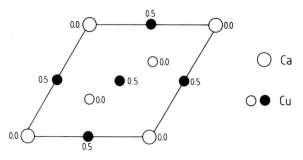

Fig. 26. Projection of the CaCu$_5$ cell in the [001] direction.

One of the important representatives of this structure type is $SmCo_5$ which is a good permanent magnet. The structure is stable in the range from 600° to 1200°C. It melts at higher temperatures and undergoes an eutectoid transformation at lower temperatures. This stability temperature range is smaller for heavy rare earths such as Er and vanishes completely for the Tm–Co compound. $SmCo_5$ magnets are more fully treated in ch. 26, §3.4.1.

7.4. AlB_2 structure type

More than 80 binary compounds as well as many ternary compounds crystallize in the AlB_2 *structure type* (P6/mmm, C32):

A-atoms	in	1a	0	0	0;			
B-atoms	in	2d	$\frac{1}{3}$	$\frac{2}{3}$	$\frac{1}{2}$,	$\frac{2}{3}$	$\frac{1}{3}$	$\frac{1}{2}$.

The small boron atoms form a net of hexagonal rings in the cavities of which the bigger Al atoms lie (fig. 27).

The radius ratio (R_A/R_B) in this structure type lies between 0.97 and 1.81; $c/a = 0.59$–1.27. The large R_A/R_B range causes the occurrence of a wide spectrum of the representatives of this structure type.

Elements which occupy the 1a point position belong to the IA, IIA, IIIB, IVB and

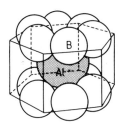

Fig. 27. The AlB_2 structure type, the bigger circle indicates the Al atom, small circles B atoms. In the case of $HoGa_2$ the Al positions are occupied by Ho and the B positions by Ga atoms.

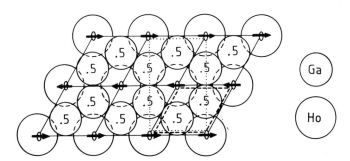

Fig. 28. The $HoGa_2$ structure: arrows indicate magnetic moments; dotted lines: magnetic unit cell; dashed lines: crystallographic unit cell.

References: p. 266.

VIIIT groups. Elements which occupy the 2d positions are Ni and Se or belong to the IB, IIB, IIIT and IVT groups. $HoGa_2$ is one of the representatives of this structure type. This compound is a collinear antiferromagnet. The Ho atoms possess magnetic moments which order antiparallel. The orthohexagonal magnetic cell as well as the crystallographic unit cell are shown in fig. 28 (BARBARA *et al.* [1971]).

7.5. NiAs structure type and related structures

Apart from the above mentioned structure types there exists another class of magnetic materials formed by transition metals with nonmetals. These compounds have the NiAs ($B8_1$), Ni_2In ($B8_2$) or MnP (B31) type structures.

7.5.1. NiAs structure

Crystal data for the *NiAs structure* are given in table 5; figure 29a shows the structure of NiAs; figure 29b shows the position of the octahedral and tetrahedral holes in the structure. There are two tetrahedral holes and one octahedral hole per As atom. The As (B) atoms possess a hexagonal close packing arrangement. The Ni (A) atoms fill the octahedral interstitial holes. The Ni atoms among themselves form a primitive hexagonal lattice and lie in layers in between those of the As (B) atoms. The radius ratios R_A/R_B range from 0.71 to 1.16; $c/a \approx 1/2$–1.96. Elements which occupy the 2c point positions are IIIB to VIB (p1 to p4). The 2a position is occupied by IVT to IB (d2 to d9) elements, see the Periodic Table, fig. 2. The IIA (s2) group does not occupy the 2a position, because its electrons are strongly bound; IIB (d10) elements do occur as B-partners (i.e., 2c position). Some of the representatives of this structure type possess a homogeneity range. NiSb occurs with Ni-content up to 54.5 at%, the excess Ni lies in the trigonal holes as the octahedral holes are already filled. On the Sb-rich side with 46.4 at% Ni, some of the octahedral holes are empty because of Ni deficiency.

The A–B bonding is mainly covalent while the A–A bonding is of metallic character. In the more metallic NiAs type compounds the difference in the A–A and A–B bond lengths is smaller than that in the less metallic ones; e.g. the difference in Fe–S- and Fe–Fe interatomic distances in FeS is equal to 0.44 Å, while the difference between Co–Co- and Co–Sb distances is just 0.02 Å.

7.5.2. Ni_2In structure

As shown in fig. 30, Ni atoms in the *Ni_2In structure* occupy the 2a position (0 0 0, 0 0 $\frac{1}{2}$) but also the 2d position ($\frac{1}{3}$ $\frac{2}{3}$ $\frac{3}{4}$, $\frac{2}{3}$ $\frac{1}{3}$ $\frac{1}{4}$). Crystal data are given in table 5.

7.5.3. MnP structure

Crystal data for the *MnP structure* are given in table 5.

7.5.4. Magnetic properties

In NiAs, Ni_2In and MnP type structures the transition metal atoms are situated close to each other in a linear chain along the *c*-axis, causing the c/a value of these

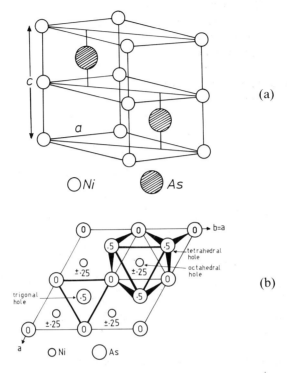

Fig. 29. (a) NiAs structure; (b) The position of the octahedral, tetrahedral and trigonal holes in NiAs structure; projection onto the (001) plane; cell origin shifted.

compounds to be less than the ideal 1.633 for hexagonal close-packing. Magnetic properties of these compounds such as magnetization, characteristic temperatures etc. have been found to be strongly dependent on the interatomic distances along the c-direction.

FORRER [1952] has analyzed the magnetic interactions in B8 type compounds and arrived at some critical values for the distances between the magnetic atoms (Cr: 3.05 Å, Mn: 2.83 Å, Fe: 2.6 Å) beyond which the materials are ferromagnetic (e.g.,

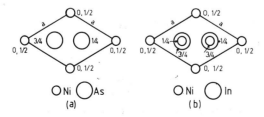

Fig. 30. NiAs and Ni_2In structures projected on the (001) plane; heights given in units of c.

References: p. 266.

MnSb: $c/2 = 2.89$ Å, MnBi: $c/2 = 3.06$ Å) and below which they are antiferromagnetic (e.g., CrSb: $c/2 = 2.72$ Å). However, the conclusions drawn from these structural considerations do not always hold. For example, MnTe with a large $c/2$ value (3.35 Å) is antiferromagnetic. The theoretical model that can explain most of the observations is due to DE GENNES [1960]. In his model, a hopping of electrons between two sorts of ions is assumed by which the ferromagnetic order of the ionic moments is stabilized energetically.

Appendix A.   Brief explanation of space group symbols *

Space groups contain the whole symmetry of a crystal. The symbol order is: first the Bravais Lattice Type (P, A, B, C, I or F), then the symmetry elements for the different directions in the crystal as given in the following table. For example, in the orthorhombic system the symmetry elements along the $\underline{a}$ direction are followed by those along the $\underline{b}$ direction and then those along the $\underline{c}$ direction (4/m: a fourfold rotation axis and mirror plane perpendicular to it).

Crystal system	Symbol position			
	1	2	3	4
triclinic	Type of the	1 or $\bar{1}$	–	–
monoclinic	Bravais Lattice	distinct direction	–	–
orthorhombic		[100]	[010]	[001]
tetragonal		[001]	[100]	[110]
hexagonal		[001]	[100]	[210]
cubic		[001]	[111]	[110]

The symbols 4b, 8h, etc. are called point position symbols. Their occupation by atoms, molecules or any "motifs" gives rise to the crystal structure considered. The number four (8) means that there are four (8) motifs in the considered unit cell; the letter b (h) denotes the ordering of this point position in the given space group.

References

BARBARA, B., C. BÉCLE and E. SIAUD, 1971, J. Physique, Colloq. **32**, C1-1126.
BERGMANN, B.G., and D.P. SHOEMAKER, 1954, Acta Cryst. **7**, 857.
BESSLEIN, B., G. ISCHENKO, S. KLAUMÜNZER, P. MÜLLER, H. NEUMÜLLER, K. SCHMELZ and H. ADRIAN, 1975, Phys. Lett. **53A**, 49.
BLAUGHER, R.D., R.E. HEIN, J.E. COX and R.M. WATERSTRAT, 1969, J. Low Temp. Phys. **1**, 539.
BLOOM, D.S., and N.J. GRANT, 1952, Trans. AIME **197**, 88.

* For more details see: International Tables for X-Ray Crystallography, vol. 1, see HENRY and LONSDALE [1965].

CAROLI, B., and A. BLANDIN, 1966, J. Phys. Chem. Solids **25**, 1217.

CHEVREL, R., M. SERGENT and J. PRINGENT, 1971, J. Solid State Chem. **3**, 515.

DARKEN, L.S., and R.W. GURRY, 1953, Physical Chemistry of Metals (McGraw-Hill, New York) p. 87.

DE GENNES, P.-G., 1960, Phys. Rev. **118**, 141.

DEW-HUGHES, D., 1975, Cryogenics **8**, 435.

DWIGHT, A.E., 1961, Trans. ASM **53**, 479.

FISCHER, Ø., 1978,. Appl. Phys. **16**, 1.

FLÜKIGER, R., and J.L. JORDA, 1977, Solid State Commun. **22**, 109.

FLÜKIGER, R., J.L. STAUDENMANN and P. FISCHER, 1976, J. Less-Common Met. **50**, 253.

FORRER, R., 1952, Ann. Phys. (France) **7**, 605.

FRANK, F.C., and J.S. KASPER, 1958, Acta Cryst. **11**, 184.

FRANK, F.C., and J.S. KASPER, 1959, Acta Cryst. **12**, 483.

GIRGIS, K., unpublished.

GIRGIS, K., and P. FISCHER, 1979, J. Physique Colloq. **40**, C5-159.

GIRGIS, K., W. ODONI and H.R. OTT, 1976, J. Less-Common Met. **46**, 175.

GOODENOUGH, J.B., 1963, Magnetism and Chemical Bond (Wiley, New York) p. 338.

GREENFIELD, P., and P.A. BECK, 1954, Trans. AIME **200**, 253.

GREENFIELD, P., and P.A. BECK, 1956, Trans. AIME **206**, 265.

GUBSER, D.U., H.R. OTT, and K. GIRGIS, 1979, Phys. Rev. **B19**, 199.

HÄGG, G., 1931, Z. Phys. Chem. **B12**, 33.

HAMES, F.A., 1960, J. Appl. Phys. **31** suppl., 370 S.

HEIN, R.A., 1973, Superconducting Intermetallic Compounds – The A15-Story, in: The Science and Technology of Superconductors, vol. 1, eds. W.B. Gregory, W.N. Mathews Jr. and E.A. Edelsack (Plenum, New York, London) p. 333.

HENRY, N.F.M., and K. LONSDALE, 1965, International Tables for X-Ray Crystallography, vol. 1 (Kynoch Press, Birmingham).

HUME-ROTHERY, W., 1926, J. Inst. Metals **35**, 295.

HUME-ROTHERY, W., and G.V. RAYNOR, 1962, The Structure of Metals and Alloys (The Institute of Metals, London) p. 198, 230.

KASPER, J.S., 1956, Atomic and Magnetic Ordering in Transition Metal Structures, in: Theory of Alloy Phases (ASM, Cleveland, OH) p. 264.

KLEE, H., and H. WITTE, 1954, Z. Phys. Chem. **202**, 352.

KUZNETSOVA, S.M., and G.S. ZHDANOV, 1972, Sov. Phys. Crystallogr. **16**, 1077.

LAVES, F., 1956, Crystal Structure and Atomic Size, in: Theory of Alloy Phases (ASM, Cleveland, OH) p. 124.

LAVES, F., and H. WITTE, 1936, Metallwirtschaft **15**, 840.

LEHMANN, G., 1974, Krist. Tech. **9**, 587.

MCMILLAN, W.L., 1968, Phys. Rev. **167**, 331.

MAREZIO, M., P.D. DERNIER, J.P. REMEIKA, E. CORENZWIT and B.T. MATTHIAS, 1973, Mater. Res. Bull. **8**, 657.

MASSALSKI, T.B., and V. MIZUTANI, 1978, Progr. Mater. Sci. **22**, 151.

MATTHIAS, B.T., 1953, Phys. Rev. **92**, 874.

MATTHIAS, B.T., M. MAREZIO, E. CORENZWIT, A.S. COOPER and H. BARZ, 1972, Science **175**, 1465.

MERZ, A., 1976, Hartstoffe und Hartstoff-Verbundwerkstoffe, in: Intermetallische Phasen, eds. Autorenkollektiv (VEB Deutscher Verlag für Grundstoffindustrie, Leipzig) p. 247.

MIEDEMA, A.R., 1976, J. Less-Common Met. **49**, 463.

MOOSER, E., and W.B. PEARSON, 1959, Acta Cryst. **12**, 1015.

PARTHÉ, E., 1973, Acta Cryst. **B29**, 2808.

PARTHÉ, E., 1980, Valence and Tetrahedral Structure Compounds, in: Summer School on Inorganic Crystal Chemistry, Geneva, 1980, ed. E. Parthé (Parthé, Geneva) ch. P.

PAULING, L., 1960, The Nature of the Chemical Bond, 3d Ed. (Cornell Univ. Press, New York) p. 88.

PEARSON, W.B., 1967, Handbook of Lattice Spacings and Structures of Metals and Alloys, vol. 2 (Pergamon Press, Oxford).

PETTIFOR, D.G., 1970, J. Phys. **C3**, 367.
PETTIFOR, D.G., 1983, Electron theory of metals, this volume, ch. 3.
PHILLIPS, J.C., 1970, Rev. Mod. Phys. **42**, 317.
RAJASEKHARAN, T., and K. GIRGIS, 1983, Phys. Rev. **B27**, 909.
RASSMANN, G., and P. MÜLLER, 1976, Supraleitende intermetallische Phasen, in: Intermetallische Phasen, eds. Autorenkollektiv (VEB Deutscher Verlag für Grundstoffindustrie, Leipzig) p. 189.
SAVITSKII, E.M., 1976, Die Prognose anorganischer Verbindungen mit Hilfe von Elektronenrechnern, in: Intermetallische Phasen, eds. Autorenkollektiv (VEB Deutscher Verlag für Grundstoffindustrie, Leipzig), p. 41.
SAVITSKII, E.M., and V.B. GRIBULYA, 1972, J. Phys. Chem. Solids **33**, 1853.
SAVITSKII, E.M., and V.B. GRIBULYA, 1975a, Dokl. Akad. Nauk SSSR **220**, 1066.
SAVITSKII, E.M., and V.B. GRIBULYA, 1975b, Dokl. Akad. Nauk SSSR **223**, 1383.
SAVITSKII, E.M., V.V. BARON, Y.V. EFIMOV, M.I. BYCHKOVA and L.F. MYZENKOVA, 1973, Superconducting Materials (Plenum, New York, London).
SAVITSKII, E.M., V.B. GRIBULYA and N.N. KISELYOVA, 1980, J. Less-Common Met. **72**, 307.
SCHULZE, G.E.R., 1939, Z. Elektrochem. **45**, 849.
SHOEMAKER, C.B., and D.P. SHOEMAKER, 1969, Structural Properties of Some σ-Phase Related Phases, in: Developments in the Structural Chemistry of Alloy Phases, ed. B.C. Giessen (Plenum, New York, London) p. 135.
SMITH, T.F., 1972, J. Low Temp. Phys. **6**, 171.
STAUDENMANN, J.L., 1977, Solid State Commun. **23**, 121.
STAUDENMANN, J.L., 1978, Solid State Commun. **26**, 461.
STAUDENMANN, J.L., P. COPPENS and J. MÜLLER, 1976, Solid State Commun. **19**, 29.
SWEEDLER, A.R., S. MOEHLECKE, R.H. TONES, R. VISWANATHAN and D.C. JOHNSTON, 1977, Solid State Commun. **21**, 1007.
TESTARDI, L.R., 1971, Phys. Rev. **B3**, 95.
TESTARDI, L.R., J.E. KUNZLER, H.J. LEVINSTEIN, J.P. MAITA and J.H. WERNICK, 1971, Phys. Rev. **B3**, 107.
VAN REUTH, E.C., and R.M. WATERSTRAT, 1968, Acta Cryst. **B24**, 186.
VILLARS, P., and K. GIRGIS, 1981, Acta Cryst. **A37**, C-114.
VILLARS, P., and K. GIRGIS, 1982a, Z. Metallk. **73**, 455.
VILLARS, P., and K. GIRGIS, 1982b, unpublished.
VILLARS, P., K. GIRGIS and A. NIGGLI, 1980, Prediction of Expected Binary Compounds in a Certain Structure Type, in: Abstracts Sixth European Crystallographic Meeting, Barcelona, p. 85.
VILLARS, P., K. GIRGIS and F. HULLIGER, 1982, J. Solid State Chem. **42**, 89.
WANG. F.E., and J.R. HOLDEN, 1975, Solid State Commun. **17**, 225.
WESTGREN, A., and G. PHRAGMÉN, 1926, Arkiv Mat. Astron. Fysik **19B**, 1.
WITTE, H., 1937, Metallwirtschaft **16**, 237.
YVON, K., 1979, Bonding and Relationships Between Structure and Physical Properties in Chevrel-Phase Compounds, in: Current Topics in Materials Science, vol. 3, ed. E. Kaldis (North-Holland, Amsterdam) ch. 2.
ZUNGER, A., 1980, Phys. Rev. **B22**, 5839.
ZUNGER, A., 1980, Phys. Rev. Lett. **44**, 582.

Further reading

Beck, P.A., ed., 1963, Electronic Structure and Alloy Chemistry of the Transition Elements (Interscience, New York).
Girgis, K., 1982, Struktur, Kristallchemie und Eigenschaften intermetallischer Verbindungen (ETHZ, Zürich).
Henry, N.F.M., and K. Lonsdale, 1965, International Tables for X-Ray Crystallography, vol. 1 (Kynoch Press, Birmingham).

Hume-Rothery, W.R., R.E. Smallman and C.W. Haworth, 1969, The Structure of Metals and Alloys, 5th Ed. (The Institute of Metals, London).

Pauling, L., 1960, The Nature of the Chemical Bond (Cornell Univ. Press, Ithaca, NY).

Pearson, W.B., 1967, Lattice Spacings and Structures of Metals and Alloys, vol. 2 (Pergamon Press, Oxford).

Pearson, W.B., 1972, The Crystal Chemistry and Physics of Metals and Alloys (Wiley–Interscience, New York).

Schubert, K., 1964, Kristallstrukturen zweikomponentiger Phasen (Springer, Berlin).

Theory of Alloy Phases, 1956 (ASM, Cleveland,OH).

Wells, A.F., 1950, Structural Inorganic Chemistry (Clarendon Press, Oxford).

Westbrook, J.H., ed., 1967, Intermetallic Compounds (Wiley, New York).

CHAPTER 6

METALLURGICAL THERMODYNAMICS

D.R. GASKELL

School of Materials Engineering
Purdue University
West Lafayette, IN 47907, USA

R.W. Cahn and P. Haasen, eds.
Physical Metallurgy; third, revised and enlarged edition
© *Elsevier Science Publishers BV, 1983*

1. Introduction

Metallurgical thermodynamics is concerned with the equilibrium states of existence available to systems, and with the effects of external influences on the equilibrium state. The thermodynamic state of a system is defined in terms of state variables (or *state functions*) and the state variables occur in two categories; *intensive* variables such as pressure, P, and temperature, T, the values of which are independent of the size of the system, and *extensive* variables such as internal energy, U, and volume, V, the values of which are dependent on the size of the system. The simplest equation of state is the ideal gas law,

$$PV = nRT, \tag{1}$$

where n is the number of moles of the gas and R is the universal gas constant. In considering a fixed quantity of ideal gas, only two of the state functions in eq. (1) are independent and the other is dependent. Thus, in a three-dimensional diagram employing P, V and T as ordinates, the equilibrium states of existence of the fixed quantity of gas lie on a definite surface. In any *reversible* change of state of the gas the path of the process lies on this equilibrium surface, such that, in moving from the initial to the final state, the gas passes through a continuum of equilibrium states. Under such conditions the *work, w,* done on or by the gas during the process is given by:

$$w = \int_{V_{\text{initial}}}^{V_{\text{final}}} P \mathrm{d}V, \tag{2}$$

and thus the magnitude of w is dependent on the actual process path taken over the equilibrium surface between the final and initial states. In an *irreversible* process the state of the gas momentarily leaves the equilibrium surface while moving between the initial and final states.

1.1. The First and Second Laws of Thermodynamics

When a system undergoes a process in which it moves from one state to another, the change in the internal energy of the system, ΔU, is given by:

$$\Delta U = U_2 - U_1 = q - w, \tag{3}$$

where q is the heat entering or leaving the system and w is the work done on or by the system during the change of state. For an increment of the process the change is:

$$\mathrm{d}U = \mathrm{d}q - \mathrm{d}w. \tag{4}$$

Equations (3) and (4) are statements of the *First Law of Thermodynamics.* By convention, heat entering the system and work done *by* the system are positive quantities. Equation (3) is remarkable in that, although the individual values of q and w are dependent on the path taken by the system between the initial and final states, their algebraic sum (which is the difference between U_2 and U_1) is independent of the process path. Thus integration of eq. (4) to obtain eq. (3) requires that the process path be known and that the process be conducted reversibly.

The *Second Law of Thermodynamics* states that, for a reversible change of state, the integral of dq/T is independent of the process path. As one of the properties of a state function is that the difference between the values of the function in any two thermodynamic states is independent of the process path taken by the system in moving between the two states, the term dq/T is the differential of a state function. The state function *entropy, S,* is thus defined as:

$$dS = dq_{rev}/T. \tag{5}$$

If change in volume against an external pressure is the only form of work performed during a reversible change of state of a closed system, the work performed is given by eq. (2), and substitution of eqs. (2) and (5) into eq. (4) gives:

$$dU = TdS - PdV. \tag{6}$$

Equation (6), which is a combination of the First and Second Laws of Thermodynamics, gives the variation of U (as the dependent variable) with S and V (as the independent variables).

From consideration of the difference between reversible and irreversible processes and the Second Law, eq. (6) gives the following criteria for thermodynamic equilibrium in a closed system of fixed composition:

(i) S is a maximum at constant U and V;

(ii) U is a minimum at constant S and V.

Equation (6) involves the extensive thermodynamic properties S and U as independent variables. Although it is possible to measure and, with sufficient ingenuity on the part of the experimenter, to control the volume of a system, experimental control of the entropy of a system is virtually impossible, and consequently the criteria for equilibrium obtained from eq. (6) are not of practical use. From the practical point of view it would be desirable to have an equation as simple in form as eq. (6) but in which the independent variables are the intensive properties P and T, both of which are amenable to experimental measurement and control. Such an equation would also provide a criterion for equilibrium in a constant pressure–constant temperature system.

1.2. Auxiliary thermodynamic functions

The required auxiliary state functions are generated by Legendre transformations of U. For example, in eq. (6), written as

$$U = U(S, V),$$

a Legendre transform, H, of U is obtained using:

$$-P = \left(\frac{\partial U}{\partial V}\right)_S = \frac{U - H}{V - 0}. \tag{7}$$

At constant S, the tangent to the variation of U with V passes through the points

References: p. 326.

$U = U$, $V = V$ and $U = H$, $V = 0$. Rearrangement of eq. (7) gives:

$$H = U + PV,$$

which, on differentiation, gives:

$$dH = dU + PdV + VdP. \tag{8}$$

Substitution of eq. (6) into eq. (8) gives:

$$dH = TdS + VdP, \tag{9}$$

in which the extensive variable V has been replaced by the intensive variable P. The transform H is called the *enthalpy*.

Writing eq. (9) as

$$H = H(S, P),$$

a Legendre transform, G, of H is obtained as:

$$T = \left(\frac{\partial H}{\partial S}\right)_P = \frac{H - G}{S - 0}$$

or: $\quad G = H - TS,$ $\hspace{4cm}$ (10)

which, on differentiation, gives:

$$dG = dH - TdS - SdT = -SdT + VdP, \tag{11}$$

in which the extensive variable S has been replaced by the intensive variable T. This transform, G, is called the *Gibbs free energy*. Being dependent on the independent variables T and P, the Gibbs free energy is the most useful of thermodynamic functions and provides the practical criterion that, at constant T and P, thermodynamic equilibrium is established when the Gibbs free energy is minimized.

A third Legendre transform yields the *Helmholtz free energy*, or work function A, defined as

$$A = U - TS.$$

In a multicomponent system containing n_1 moles of component 1, n_2 moles of component 2, n_i moles of component i, etc.:

$$G = G(T, P, n_1, n_2, \ldots, n_i)$$

and thus,

$$dG = \left(\frac{\partial G}{\partial T}\right)dT + \left(\frac{\partial G}{\partial P}\right)dP + \left(\frac{\partial G}{\partial n_1}\right)dn_1 + \cdots \left(\frac{\partial G}{\partial n_i}\right)dn_i. \tag{12}$$

The derivative

$$\left(\frac{\partial G}{\partial n_i}\right)_{T,P,n_j}$$

is of particular significance and is called the *chemical potential*, μ_i, or the partial molar free energy, $\bar{G}_i$, of the component i. Thus, in view of eq. (11), eq. (12) can be written as

$$dG = -S dT + V dP + \sum \bar{G}_i dn_i, \tag{13}$$

and the equilibrium state of any system undergoing any type of reaction at constant temperature and pressure can be determined by application of this equation.

2. Metallurgical thermochemistry

2.1. The measurement of changes in enthalpy

In order to distinguish between the value of an extensive property of a system containing n moles and the molar value of the property, the former will be identified by the use of a prime ('), e.g., with respect to enthalpy, $H' = nH$.

From eqs. (5) and (9), for a process occurring reversibly at constant pressure P:

$$dH' = dq_P,$$

which, on integration, gives:

$$\Delta H' = q_P.$$

Thus, in a system undergoing a process in which the only work performed is the work of expansion or contraction against the constant pressure P, the change in enthalpy, $\Delta H'$, can be measured as the heat q_P entering or leaving the system during the constant pressure process. In the case of heat entering the system the process involves an increase in the temperature of the system and the *constant pressure molar heat capacity*, c_P, is defined as:

$$c_P = \frac{dq_P}{dT} = \left(\frac{\partial H}{\partial T}\right)_P. \tag{14}$$

The constant pressure molar heat capacity of a system can be measured by the methods of calorimetry. In metallurgical applications the measured values are fitted to an equation of the form

$$c_P = a + bT + cT^{-2}.$$

For example, the constant pressure molar heat capacity of solid silver varies with temperature in the range 298–1234 K as:

$$c_{P,Ag(s)} = 21.3 + 8.54 \times 10^{-3}T + 1.51 \times 10^5 T^{-2} \text{ J/K mole}$$

and hence, from eq. (14), the difference between the molar enthalpy of solid Ag at a temperature T and the molar enthalpy at 298 K is

$$\Delta H = \int_{298}^{T} c_{P,Ag} \, dT$$

$$= 21.3(T - 298) + 4.27 \times 10^{-3}(T^2 - 298^2)$$

$$- 1.51 \times 10^5\left(\frac{1}{T} - \frac{1}{298}\right) \text{ J/mole,}$$

References: p. 326.

which is thus the quantity of heat required to raise the temperature of one mole of solid Ag from 298 K to T.

Transformation of a low-temperature phase to a high-temperature phase involves the absorption of the latent heat of the phase change, e.g., the transformation of one mole of silver from the solid to the liquid state at the normal melting temperature of 1234 K requires a heat input of 11.09 kJ. Thus at 1234 K the molar enthalpy of melting of Ag, ΔH_m, is

$$\Delta H_{m,\text{Ag},1234\,K} = H_{\text{Ag}(l),1234\,K} - H_{\text{Ag}(s),1234\,K} = 11.09 \text{ kJ}.$$

The molar heat capacity of liquid Ag is independent of temperature, $c_{P,\text{Ag}(l)} = 30.5$ J/K mole, and the difference between the molar enthalpy of liquid Ag at a temperature T and the molar enthalpy of solid Ag at 298 K is

$$H_{\text{Ag}(l),T} - H_{\text{Ag}(s),298\,K} = \int_{298}^{1234} c_{P,\text{Ag}(s)}\,dT + \Delta H_{m,\text{Ag},1234\,K} + \int_{1234}^{T} c_{P,\text{Ag}(l)}\,dT.$$

As chemical reactions involve the absorption or evolution of heat, they also necessarily involve changes in enthalpy. For example, when conducted at 298 K, the oxidation reaction

$$2\text{Ag}_{(s)} + \tfrac{1}{2}\text{O}_{2(g)} = \text{Ag}_2\text{O}_{(s)}$$

is accompanied by the evolution of 30.5 kJ of heat per mole of Ag_2O produced. Thus,

$$q = \Delta H = -30.5 \text{ kJ},$$

or the system existing as one mole of Ag_2O has an enthalpy of 30.5 kJ less than the system existing as two moles of Ag and half a mole of oxygen gas at 298 K.

As the enthalpies of substances are not measurable quantities, i.e., only changes in enthalpy can be measured (as the evolution or absorption of heat), it is conventional to designate a reference state in which the relative enthalpy is zero. This reference state is the elemental substance existing in its stable form at 298 K and $P = 1$ atm. In practice the designation of $P = 1$ atm is relatively unimportant as the enthalpies of condensed phases are not significantly dependent on pressure and the enthalpy of an ideal gas is independent of pressure. Thus, in the above example:

$$\Delta H_{298} = H_{\text{Ag}_2\text{O}(s),298} - 2H_{\text{Ag}(s),298} - \tfrac{1}{2}H_{\text{O}_2(g),298}.$$

As $H_{\text{Ag}(s),298}$ and $H_{\text{O}_2(g),298}$ are arbitrarily assigned values of zero, the relative molar enthalpy of Ag_2O at 298 K is simply equal to the experimentally-measured molar heat of formation of Ag_2O at 298 K. At any other temperature T:

$$\Delta H_T = H_{\text{Ag}_2\text{O},T} - 2H_{\text{Ag},T} - \tfrac{1}{2}H_{\text{O}_2,T}$$

$$= H_{\text{Ag}_2\text{O},298} + \int_{298}^{T} c_{P,\text{Ag}_2\text{O}}\,dT - 2H_{\text{Ag},298} - 2\int_{298}^{T} c_{P,\text{Ag}}\,dT$$

$$- \tfrac{1}{2}H_{\text{O}_2,298} - \tfrac{1}{2}\int_{298}^{T} c_{P,\text{O}_2}\,dT$$

$$= \Delta H_{298} + \int_{298}^{T} \Delta c_P\,dT,$$

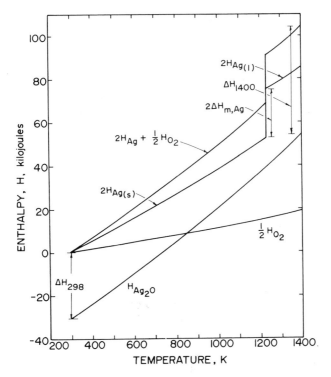

Fig. 1. The enthalpy–temperature diagram for the reaction $2Ag + \frac{1}{2}O_2 = Ag_2O$.

where

$$\Delta c_P = c_{P,Ag_2O} - 2c_{P,Ag} - \tfrac{1}{2}c_{P,O_2}.$$

The enthalpy–temperature diagram for the oxidation of silver is shown in fig. 1.

2.2. The measurement of entropy

From eqs. (5) and (14), we find:

$$dS = \frac{dq_P}{T} = \frac{c_P dT}{T}.$$

Thus, the variation of entropy with temperature at constant pressure is obtained from measured heat capacities as

$$S_T = S_0 + \int_0^T \frac{c_P}{T}\,dT.$$

Nernst's heat theorem, which is also known as the *Third Law of Thermodynamics*, states that all substances at complete internal equilibrium have zero entropy at 0 K,

References: p. 326.

i.e., $S_0 = 0$. Thus, in contrast to enthalpies, the entropies of substances have absolute values.

According to Gibbs, entropy is a measure of the degree of disorder in a system. Thus the entropy of the gaseous state is greater than that of the liquid state, which, in turn, is greater than that of the solid state. The transformation of a solid to a liquid at the normal melting temperature, T_m, involves the absorption of ΔH_m per mole. Thus, at T_m, the molar entropy of the liquid exceeds that of the solid by the molar entropy of fusion, ΔS_m, given by eq. (5) as:

$$\Delta S_m = \Delta H_m / T_m.$$

This corresponds with the fact that the liquid state is more disordered than the solid state, and ΔS_m is a measure of the difference in degree of order. For simple metals, with similar crystal structures and similar liquid structures, ΔS_m lies in the range 8–16 J/K. This correlation is known as *Richard's rule*. Similarly, at the normal boiling temperature, T_b, the molar entropy of boiling, ΔS_b, is obtained from the molar heat of boiling as:

$$\Delta S_b = \Delta H_b / T_b.$$

For simple metals $\Delta S_b \approx 88$ J/K, which indicates that the difference in disorder between the gaseous state at 1 atm pressure and the liquid state significantly exceeds the corresponding difference between the liquid and solid states. The correlation $\Delta H_b = 88 T_b$ is known as *Trouton's rule*.

Although the degrees of disorder, and hence the entropies of condensed states, are not noticeably dependent on pressure, the entropy of a gas is a significant function of pressure. As the internal energy, U', of an ideal gas is dependent only on T, an isothermal compression of an ideal gas from P_1 to P_2 does not involve a change in U'. Thus, from eq. (3), the work of compression, w, equals the heat transferred from the gas to the isothermal surroundings at the temperature T. This transfer of heat from the gas decreases its entropy by the amount

$$\Delta S' = \frac{q}{T} = \frac{w}{T} = \int_1^2 \frac{PdV'}{T},$$

which, from eq. (1), gives:

$$\Delta S' = \int_1^2 \frac{nR\,dV}{V} = -\int_1^2 nR\,d\ln P.$$

Thus

$$S_2' - S_1' = nR \ln(P_1/P_2),$$

which corresponds with the fact that a gas at high pressure is a less disordered state than a gas at low pressure.

As changes in entropy are caused by the transfer of heat, chemical reactions involving heat changes necessarily involve changes in entropy. At 298 K and 1 atm pressure, the molar entropies of $Ag_{(s)}$, $O_{2(g)}$ and $Ag_2O_{(s)}$ are 42.7, 205 and 122 J/K, respectively. Thus the entropy change for the oxidation

$$2Ag_{(s)} + \tfrac{1}{2}O_{2(g)} = Ag_2O_{(s)}$$

at 298 is:

$$\Delta S = 122 - (2 \times 42.7) - (0.5 \times 205) = -65.9 \text{ J/K mole.}$$

This can be viewed in two ways: (i) the entropy decrease is due to the loss of the heat of oxidation from the reacting system, or (ii) the degree of disorder in the system existing as one mole of Ag_2O is less than that when the system exists as two moles of Ag and half a mole of oxygen gas at 1 atm pressure.

The variation, with temperature, of the entropy change for the reaction is determined by the heat capacities of the reactants and products as:

$$\Delta S_T = \Delta S_{298} + \int_{298}^{T} (\Delta c_P/T)dT$$

The entropy–temperature diagram corresponding to fig. 1 is shown in fig. 2.

From the definition of Gibbs free energy, eq. (10), the change in Gibbs free energy due to a chemical reaction occuring at a temperature T, ΔG_T, is

$$\Delta G_T = \Delta H_T - T\Delta S_T$$

$$= \Delta H_{298} + \int_{298}^{T} \Delta c_P \, dT - T\Delta S_{298} - T\int_{298}^{T} (\Delta c_P/T)dT. \tag{15}$$

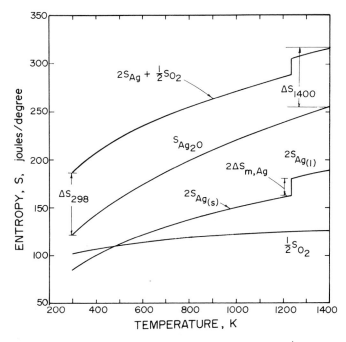

Fig. 2. The entropy–temperature diagram for the reaction $2Ag + \tfrac{1}{2}O_2 = Ag_2O$.

References: p. 326.

Thus, the variation of the change in Gibbs free energy with temperature can be determined from measurement of the variation, with temperature, of the constant pressure molar heat capacities of the reactants and products and measurement of the enthalpy change of the reaction at one temperature. For the oxidation of solid silver, such data give

$$\Delta G_T = -34200 + 87.9T - 1.76T \ln T - 10.8 \times 10^{-3}T^2$$
$$+ 3.2 \times 10^5 T^{-1} \text{ J/mole Ag}_2\text{O}. \tag{16}$$

3. Phase equilibrium in a one-component system

At constant T and P the equilibrium state is that in which the Gibbs free energy has its minimum possible value. In a one-component system the states of existence available are the gaseous and liquid states and the various allotropic or polymorphic forms of the solid state. At any T and P the state with the lowest Gibbs free energy is the stable state. For the transformation

solid → liquid: (17)

$$\Delta G_m(P, T) = G_{(1)}(P, T) - G_{(s)}(P, T) = \Delta H_m(P, T) - T\Delta S_m(P, T).$$

If ΔG_m is negative, the transformation decreases the Gibbs free energy of the system and hence the liquid is stable relative to the solid. Conversely, if ΔG_m is positive the solid is stable relative to the liquid. As absolute values of enthalpy cannot be measured it follows that absolute values of Gibbs free energy cannot be measured. Thus only changes in G can be measured.

The solid and liquid phases coexist in equilibrium with one another in that state at which $\Delta G_m = 0$, i.e., where $G_{(1)} = G_{(s)}$. From eq. (15), at any pressure P this equilibrium occurs at the temperature T_m given by

$$T_m = \Delta H_m / \Delta S_m,$$

and hence T_m is the equilibrium melting temperature of the solid at the pressure P. From eq. (10), G is decreased by decreasing H and increasing S and hence nature prefers states of low enthalpy and high entropy. As $H_{(1)} > H_{(s)}$ and $S_{(1)} > S_{(s)}$ the enthalpy contribution to G favors the solid as the stable state and the entropy contribution favors the liquid as the stable state. In eq. (17) the entropy contribution to ΔG is temperature-dependent and the enthalpy contribution is not. Thus, at high temperatures the former contribution dominates, at low temperatures the latter contribution dominates, and at a unique temperature T_m the two contributions cancel to make $\Delta G = 0$.

For the two-phase equilibrium to exist,

$$G_{(1)} = G_{(s)},$$

and maintenance of the two-phase equilibrium with variation in T and P requires that T and P be varied in such a manner that

$$dG_{(l)} = dG_{(s)}$$

or, from eq. (11), such that

$$-S_{(l)} dT + V_{(l)} dP = -S_{(s)} dT + V_{(s)} dP,$$

i.e.,

$$(dP/dT)_{eq} = (S_{(l)} - S_{(s)})/(V_{(l)} - V_{(s)}) = \Delta S_m / \Delta V_m.$$

As equilibrium between the two phases is maintained, $\Delta H_m = T \Delta S_m$:

$$(dP/dT)_{eq} = \Delta H_m / T \Delta V_m. \tag{18}$$

Equation (18) is the *Clapeyron equation*, which, on integration, gives the variation of T and P required for maintenance of the two-phase equilibrium. Strictly, integration requires knowledge of the pressure and temperature dependences of ΔH_m and ΔV_m. However, for relatively small departures from the state $P = 1$ atm, T_m, ΔH_m and ΔV_m can be taken as constants, in which case:

$$P_2 - P_1 = \frac{\Delta H_m}{\Delta V_m} \ln\left(\frac{T_2}{T_1}\right).$$

Equation (18) can be applied to condensed phase–vapor phase equilibria by making the approximation $\Delta V = V_{(v)} - V_{(condensed\ phase)} \approx V_{(v)}$ and assuming ideal behavior of the vapor phase, i.e., $V_{(v)} = RT/P$, i.e.,

$$(dP/dT)_{eq} = \frac{P \Delta H_b}{RT^2}. \tag{19}$$

Equation (19) is the *Clausius–Clapeyron equation*.

If ΔH_b (the molar enthalpy of boiling) is not a function of temperature (which requires $c_{P(v)} = c_{P(l)}$), integration of eq. (19) gives

$$\ln P = -\frac{\Delta H_b}{RT} + \text{const.},$$

and if ΔH_b is a linear function of T (which requires that Δc_P be independent of temperature) given by $\Delta H_{b,T} = \Delta H_0 + \Delta c_P T$, integration gives

$$\ln P = -\frac{\Delta H_0}{RT} + \frac{\Delta c_P}{R} \ln T + \text{const.}$$

as either (i) the variation of the saturated vapor pressure with temperature or (ii) the variation of the equilibrium boiling temperature with pressure. Experimentally measured vapor pressures are normally fitted by an equation of the type

$$\ln P = -A/T + B \ln T + C.$$

The solid, liquid and vapor states exist on surfaces in G–T–P space. The solid- and liquid-surfaces intersect at a line (along which $G_{(l)} = G_{(s)}$) and projection of this line onto the basal P–T plane of the G–T–P diagram gives the pressure dependence

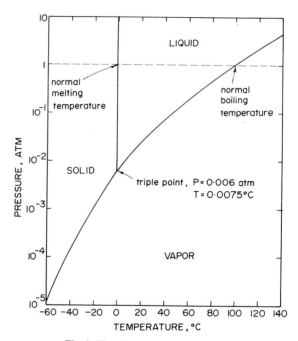

Fig. 3. The phase diagram for H_2O.

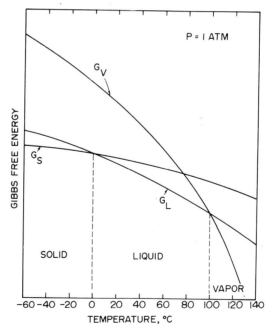

Fig. 4. Schematic representation of the variations of $G_{(s)}$, $G_{(l)}$ and $G_{(v)}$ with temperature at $P = 1$ atm for H_2O.

of T_m. Similarly the vapor- and liquid-surfaces intersect at a line, projection of which onto the basal P–T plane gives the variation, with temperature, of the saturated vapor pressure of the liquid. Similar projection of the line of intersection of the surfaces for the solid and vapor states gives the variation, with temperature, of the saturated vapor pressure of the solid. The three lines of two-phase equilibrium in G–T–P space intersect at a point, called the *triple point*, at which all three phases are in equilibrium with one another. Consideration of the geometry of the intersections of the surfaces in G–T–P space shows that, in a one-component system, a maximum of three phases can exist in equilibrium. Alternatively, as the three phases co-exist in equilibrium at fixed values of T and P the equilibrium is invariant, i.e., has no degrees of freedom. The phase diagram for H_2O is shown in fig. 3 and a schematic representation of the section of G–T–P space at 1 atm pressure is shown in fig. 4. In fig. 4, the slope of any line at any point is $-S$ for that state and hence the "steepness" of the lines increases in the order solid, liquid, vapor. Also the curvatures of the lines are $(\partial^2 G / \partial T^2)_P = -(\partial S / \partial T)_P = -c_P / T$.

4. Chemical reaction equilibrium

From eq. (13), at constant T and P, the Gibbs free energy varies with composition in a chemically reacting system as

$$dG' = \sum \overline{G}_i \, dn_i.$$

The reaction proceeds spontaneously in that direction which involves a decrease in Gibbs free energy, and reaction equilibrium is attained when, thereby, the Gibbs free energy is minimized, i.e., when $dG' = 0$.

Consider the water-gas reaction

$$H_2O_{(g)} + CO_{(g)} = H_{2(g)} + CO_2.$$

At equilibrium:

$$dG = \overline{G}_{H_2} \, dn_{H_2} + \overline{G}_{CO_2} \, dn_{CO_2} - \overline{G}_{H_2O} \, dn_{H_2O} - \overline{G}_{CO} \, dn_{CO} = 0$$

or, in view of the stoichiometry requirement

$$-dn_{H_2O} = -dn_{CO} = dn_{H_2} = dn_{CO_2}:$$

$$dG = \left(\overline{G}_{H_2} + \overline{G}_{CO_2} - \overline{G}_{H_2O} - \overline{G}_{CO} \right) dn_{H_2} = 0.$$

Thus, at equilibrium:

$$\left(\overline{G}_{H_2} + \overline{G}_{CO_2} \right) = \left(\overline{G}_{H_2O} + \overline{G}_{CO} \right). \tag{20}$$

The isothermal transfer of a mole of ideal gas i from the pure state at the pressure P_i and temperature T to an ideal gas mixture at the *partial pressure* p_i involves a change in Gibbs free energy:

$$\Delta G = \overline{G}_i - G_i = RT \ln(p_i / P_i). \tag{21}$$

Again, as only changes in Gibbs free energy can be measured, it is convenient to select a standard state for the gas and consider the Gibbs free energy of the gas in any other state in terms of the difference between the free energy of the gas in this state and the free energy of the gas in the standard state. The standard state for an ideal gas at the temperature T is the pure gas at 1 atm pressure and in this state the Gibbs free energy is the standard free energy, designated G^0. Thus eq. (21) can be written as:

$$\bar{G}_i = G_i^0 + RT \ln p_i. \tag{22}$$

Substitution of eq. (22) into eq. (20) and rearrangement gives:

$$\left(G_{H_2}^0 + G_{CO_2}^0 - G_{H_2O}^0 - G_{CO}^0\right) = -RT \ln \frac{p_{H_2} p_{CO_2}}{p_{H_2O} p_{CO}}. \tag{23}$$

Being the difference between the standard free energies of the products and the standard free energies of the reactants, the left-hand side of eq. (23) is termed the *standard free energy* for the reaction at the temperature T, ΔG_T^0, and, being dependent only on T, it has a definite fixed value at any T. Consequently the quotient of the partial pressures of the reactants and products occurring in the logarithm term on the right-hand side of eq. (23) has a fixed value at any T. This term is called the *equilibrium constant*, K_p, and hence the equilibrium state in any reacting system is such that

$$\Delta G_T^0 = -RT \ln K_p. \tag{24}$$

For the general reaction

$$a\mathrm{A} + b\mathrm{B} = c\mathrm{C} + d\mathrm{D}: \quad K_p = \frac{p_C^c \, p_D^d}{p_A^a \, p_B^b}.$$

Dalton's law of partial pressures in an ideal gas mixture gives

$$p_i = X_i P,$$

where X_i, being the ratio of the number of moles of i in the gas to the total number of moles of all species, is the *mole fraction* of i in the gas and P is the total pressure of the gas.
Thus

$$K_p = \frac{X_C^c \, X_D^d}{X_A^a \, X_B^b} \, P^{c+d-a-b} = K_X \, P^{c+d-a-b}, \tag{25}$$

where K_X is the equilibrium constant expressed in terms of the mole fractions of the reactants and products occurring at reaction equilibrium. From the definition of ΔG_T^0, K_p is independent of pressure and hence, from eq. (25), K_X is only independent of pressure if $c + d - a - b = 0$.
From eqs. (24) and (15):

$$\Delta G_T^0 = -RT \ln K_p = \Delta H_T^0 - T \Delta S_T^0.$$

Thus

$$\ln K_p = -\frac{\Delta H_T^0}{RT} + \frac{\Delta S_T^0}{R},$$

or

$$\frac{\partial \ln K_p}{\partial T} = \frac{\Delta H_T^0}{RT^2}.$$

For the water-gas reaction:

$$CO + H_2O = CO_2 + H_2;$$

$$\Delta G_T^0 = -36400 + 32.0T \text{ J/mole};$$

thus

$$K_p = \exp\left(\frac{36400}{8.3144T}\right)\exp\left(\frac{-32.0}{8.3144}\right).$$

The reaction of a moles of CO with b moles of H_2O produces x moles of each CO_2 and H_2 and leaves $(a - x)$ moles of CO and $(b - x)$ moles of H_2. Thus at any point along the reaction coordinate in a reacting mixture at the constant pressure P:

$$p_{CO} = \frac{a - x}{a + b}P, \qquad p_{H_2O} = \frac{b - x}{a + b}P, \qquad \text{and} \qquad p_{CO_2} = p_{H_2} = \frac{x}{a + b}P,$$

and at reaction equilibrium:

$$\frac{p_{CO_2}p_{H_2}}{p_{CO}p_{H_2O}} = \frac{x^2}{(a - x)(b - x)} = K_p = \exp\left(\frac{36400}{8.3144T}\right)\exp\left(\frac{-32.0}{8.3144}\right)$$

If one or more of the reactants and/or products occurs in a condensed state the attainment of equilibrium involves both phase and reaction equilibrium. For example, at a temperature T the equilibrium

$$2Ag_{(s)} + \tfrac{1}{2}O_{2(g)} = Ag_2O_{(s)} \tag{26}$$

requires the establishment of the phase equilibria

$$Ag_{(s)} = Ag_{(v)} \qquad \text{and} \qquad Ag_2O_{(s)} = Ag_2O_{(v)},$$

and, in the vapor or gas phase, requires establishment of the reaction equilibrium

$$2Ag_{(v)} + \tfrac{1}{2}O_{2(g)} = Ag_2O_{(v)}. \tag{27}$$

Conditions for the phase equilibria are $p_{Ag} = p_{Ag}^0$ (the saturated vapor pressure of solid silver at temperature T) and $p_{Ag_2O} = p_{Ag_2O}^0$ (the saturated vapor pressure of solid Ag_2O at temperature T), and thus, as the equilibrium constant K for the vapor phase reaction, given by eq. (27), has a fixed value at temperature T, the equilibrium oxygen pressure, p_{O_2}, is uniquely fixed by:

$$K = \frac{p_{Ag_2O}^0}{\left(p_{Ag}^0\right)^2 p_{O_2}^{1/2}}.$$

References: p. 326.

Alternatively, reaction equilibrium in the vapor phase requires that:

$$2\overline{G}_{Ag(v)} + \tfrac{1}{2}\overline{G}_{O_2(g)} = \overline{G}_{Ag_2O(v)}, \tag{28}$$

and the two-phase equilibria require that:

$$\overline{G}_{Ag(v)} = \overline{G}_{Ag(s)} \tag{29}$$

and

$$\overline{G}_{Ag_2O(v)} = \overline{G}_{Ag_2O(s)}. \tag{30}$$

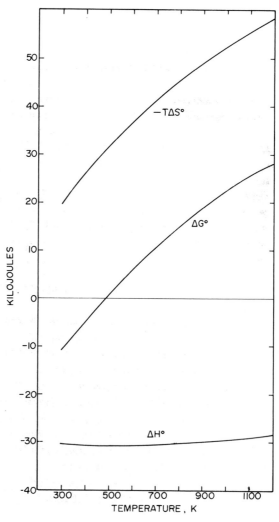

Fig. 5. The variations of ΔH_T^0, $-T\Delta S_T^0$ and ΔG_T^0 with temperature for the reaction $2Ag + \tfrac{1}{2}O_2 = Ag_2O$.

From eq. (11), at constant T, $dG = V dP$, and hence eq. (29) can be written as:

$$G^0_{Ag(v)} + RT \ln p^0_{Ag} = G^0_{Ag(s)} + \int_1^{p^0_{Ag}} V_{Ag(s)} \, dP, \tag{31}$$

where $G^0_{Ag(s)}$ is the standard molar free energy of solid Ag at temperature T. The integral on the right-hand side of eq. (31) is negligibly small and hence eq. (31) can be written as:

$$G^0_{Ag(v)} + RT \ln p^0_{Ag} = G^0_{Ag(s)}. \tag{32}$$

Similarly, eq. (30) can be written as:

$$G^0_{Ag_2O(v)} + RT \ln p^0_{Ag_2O} = G^0_{Ag_2O(s)}. \tag{33}$$

Substitution of eqs. (32) and (33) into eq. (28) gives:

$$2G^0_{Ag(s)} + \tfrac{1}{2} G^0_{O_2(g)} + RT \ln p^{1/2}_{O_2} = G^0_{Ag_2O(s)},$$

$$\text{or} \quad \Delta G^0_T = -RT \ln \frac{1}{p^{1/2}_{O_2(eq,T)}}, \tag{34}$$

where ΔG^0_T is the standard free energy change for the reaction given by eq. (26) and $p_{O_2(eq,T)}$ is the value of p_{O_2} required for equilibrium between $Ag_{(s)}$, $Ag_2O_{(s)}$ and oxygen gas at temperature T. The variations of ΔH^0_T, $-T\Delta S^0_T$ and ΔG^0_T [given by eq. (16)] are shown in fig. 5. Thus, from eq. (34), $p_{O_2(eq,485\,K)} = 1$ atm, at which temperature $\Delta G^0 = 0$. At $T < 485$ K, ΔG^0_T is a negative quantity and hence $p_{O_2(eq,T)} < 1$ atm. At $T > 485$ K, ΔG^0_T is a positive quantity and hence $p_{O_2(eq,T)} > 1$ atm.

5. Ellingham diagrams

In 1944 ELLINGHAM published diagrams showing the variation, with temperature, of the standard free energies of formation of a number of oxides and sulfides, and pointed out that these diagrams "would show at a glance the relative stabilities of the various substances within a given class at any temperature, and would thus indicate, in a direct fashion, the range of conditions required for their reduction to the corresponding elements. It would provide, in fact, what might be described as a ground plan of metallurgical possibilities with respect to the reduction of compounds of the specified class". Such diagrams, which are now available for a wide range of classes of compounds, are known as *Ellingham diagrams,* and the Ellingham diagram for oxides is shown in fig. 6.

In order to facilitate comparison of the stabilities of the various oxides, the standard free energies are for the reaction

$$(2x/y)M + O_2 = (2/y)M_xO_y,$$

i.e., for reactions involving the consumption of one mole of O_2. By choosing this

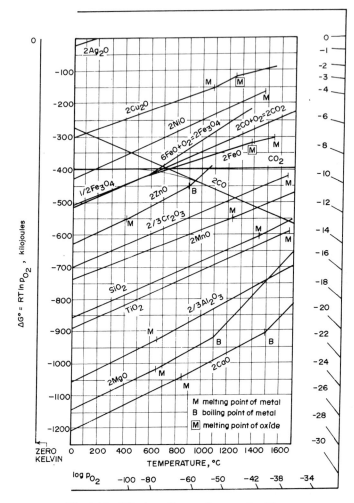

Fig. 6. The Ellingham diagram for several oxides.

basis:

$$\Delta G_T^0 = RT \ln p_{O_2(eq,T)},$$

and hence, in addition to being a plot of ΔG_T^0 versus temperature, the Ellingham diagram is a plot of the variation, with temperature, of the oxygen pressure, $p_{O_2(eq,T)}$, required for equilibrium between the metal and its oxide. The free energy change for the change of state $O_2(T, P = 1 \text{ atm}) \rightarrow O_2(T, P = p_{O_2})$ is:

$$\Delta G_T = RT \ln p_{O_2},$$

and thus, in the Ellingham diagram, lines of constant p_{O_2} radiate from the origin,

$\Delta G^0 = 0$, $T = 0$ K, with slopes of $R \ln p_{O_2}$. Consequently, a nomographic scale of p_{O_2} can be placed on the edges of the diagram and $p_{O_2(eq)}$ at any point on an Ellingham line is obtained as the reading on the nomographic scale which is collinear with the given point and the origin of the diagram. The Ellingham diagram is thus a stability diagram, in that any point in the diagram lying **above** the Ellingham line for a given oxide is a state in which $p_{O_2(T)} > p_{O_2(eq,T)}$ and hence, in all states above the line the oxide is stable relative to the metal. Conversely, any point lying **below** the Ellingham line for the given oxide is a state in which $p_{O_2(T)} < p_{O_2(eq,T)}$ and hence, below the line, the metal is stable relative to the oxide. The Ellingham line thus divides the diagram into stability fields and, if it is required that a given oxide be reduced, the thermodynamic state must be moved from a point above the Ellingham line for the oxide to a point below the line, i.e., must be moved from a position within the oxide stability field to a position within the metal stability field.

The magnitude of ΔG_T^0 is a measure of the relative stability of the oxide and hence, with increasing stability, the Ellingham lines occur progressively lower in the diagram. Consequently, in principle, the element A can reduce the oxide $B_x O_y$ if, in the diagram, the Ellingham line for $A_x O_y$ lies below that for $B_x O_y$.

Over the ranges of temperature in which no phase transitions occur the Ellingham lines are virtually linear, being given by

$$\Delta G_T^0 = A + BT.$$

In this expression A, the intercept of the line with the $T = 0$ K axis, is identified with ΔH^0, the standard enthalpy change for the oxidation, and B, the slope of the line, is identified with $-\Delta S^0$, the standard entropy change for the reaction. The Ellingham lines for the oxidation of solid and liquid metals are more or less parallel with one another, with slopes corresponding to the disappearance of one mole of oxygen gas in the standard oxidation equation. Consequently, the stabilities of these oxides are determined primarily by the magnitudes of their enthalpies of formation.

At the temperature of a phase change the slope of the Ellingham line changes by an amount equal to the entropy change for the phase transition. The slope increases at the transition temperatures of the metal and decreases at the transition temperatures of the oxide. These changes in slope are most noticeable at normal boiling temperatures, e.g., at 1090°C the slope of the Ellingham line for MgO increases by 190.3 J/K, which is the entropy of boiling of 2Mg, and at 1484°C the slope of the Ellingham line for CaO increases by 174.2 J/K, the entropy of boiling of 2Ca.

Carbon is unique in that it forms two gaseous oxides, CO and CO_2, and the positions of the Ellingham lines for these oxides are of particular significance in extraction metallurgy. The Ellingham line for CO has a negative slope due to the fact that the oxidation

$$2C + O_2 = 2CO$$

involves the net production of one mole of gas, and, because the oxidation

$$C + O_2 = CO_2$$

References: p. 326.

does not involve a change in the number of moles of gas, the Ellingham line for CO_2 is virtually horizontal. The enthalpy change for the oxidation of C to form CO as $C + \frac{1}{2}O_2 = CO$ is $-111\,700$ J and the enthalpy change for the oxidation of CO to CO_2 as $CO + \frac{1}{2}O_2 = CO_2$ is $-282\,400$ J. Thus the standard enthalpy change for the Ellingham line for CO is $2 \times (-111700) = -223400$ J and the standard enthalpy change for the Ellingham line for CO_2 is $(-111700) + (-282400) = -394100$ J. Thus, on the basis that the stability of an oxide is determined primarily by the magnitude of ΔH^0, it would appear that CO_2 should be more stable than CO. However, as the Ellingham line for CO has a negative slope, which means that the stability of CO increases with increasing temperature, the Ellingham lines for the two oxides intersect. Consequently, although CO_2 is more stable than CO at lower temperature, the reverse is the case at higher temperatures. The gaseous phase in equilibrium with solid carbon is a $CO-CO_2$ mixture in which the ratio p_{CO}/p_{CO_2} increases with increasing temperature. For a total pressure of 1 atm, the equilibrium gas contains less than 1% CO at temperatures less than 400°C, contains less than 1% CO_2 at temperatures greater than 980°C, and is an equimolar mixture at 674°C. The "carbon line" in the diagram, which is the continuum of states in which carbon is in equilibrium with a $CO-CO_2$ mixture at 1 atm pressure, follows the CO_2 Ellingham line up to about 400°C and then curves down gently to tangentially meet and join the Ellingham line for CO at about 1000°C. Along the carbon line the ratio P_{CO}/P_{CO_2} is fixed by the equilibrium

$$C + CO_2 = 2CO,$$

and, by virtue of the equilibrium

$$CO + \tfrac{1}{2}O_2 = CO_2,$$

the oxygen pressure is also fixed. Thus the carbon line divides the other oxides into two classes, those with Ellingham lines which lie above the carbon line, and those with Ellingham lines which lie below the carbon line. With respect to the former class, the carbon line lies in the stability field of the metal and hence carbon is a potential reducing agent for these oxides, whereas, with respect to the latter class, the carbon line lies in the oxide stability field and hence carbon cannot reduce the oxide. Furthermore, if the Ellingham line for a metal oxide intersects the carbon line, the temperature of intersection is the minimum temperature at which the oxide may be reduced by carbon. Thus, for example, FeO cannot be reduced by carbon at temperatures less than 675°C.

Whether or not carbon can be used as a reducing agent is determined by the stability of any carbide phase which may form, i.e., by the sign of the standard free energy for formation of the carbide from metal and carbon. For example, in the Ellingham diagram the carbon line intersects with the Ellingham line for SiO_2 at 1676°C, and hence above this temperature liquid Si is stable relative to SiO_2 in the presence of C and its equilibrium $CO-CO_2$ gas mixture at 1 atm pressure. However, for the reaction

$$Si_{(l)} + C = SiC,$$

the standard free energy change is $\Delta G_T^0 = -122\,600 + 37.0T$ J and hence SiC is stable relative to liquid Si in the presence of carbon at 1676°C and $P = 1$ atm.

The stability fields in the system Si–O–C at 1676°C are shown in fig. 7 as functions of $\log p_{CO}$ and $\log p_{CO_2}$. Line A is the variation of p_{CO} and p_{CO_2} required for the equilibrium

$$Si_{(l)} + 2CO_2 = SiO_2 + 2CO.$$

Line B is the corresponding variation required for the equilibrium

$$Si_{(l)} + 2CO = SiC + CO_2,$$

and line C is the variation for the equilibrium

$$SiC + 3CO_2 = SiO_2 + 4CO.$$

These lines divide the diagram into stability fields for Si, SiC and SiO_2 and meet at the values of p_{CO} and p_{CO_2} required for the four-phase equilibrium involving the three condensed phases Si, SiC and SiO_2 and the CO–CO_2 gas phase. Line D is the variation of p_{CO} and p_{CO_2} required for the equilibrium between carbon and the gas phase at 1676°C and, as such, represents the compositions of CO–CO_2 gas mixtures which are saturated with carbon. The field below line D is designated "unstable"

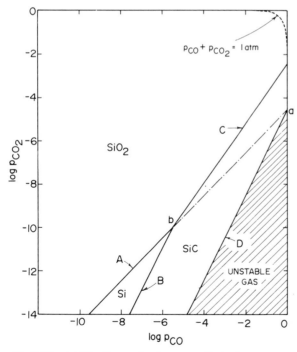

Fig. 7. The stability diagram for the system Si–O–C at 1949 K.

References: p. 326.

gas, as any gas mixture in this field is supersaturated with carbon and hence will spontaneously undergo the carbon deposition reaction

$$2CO \rightarrow C_{(graphite)} + CO_2,$$

until, thereby, the composition of the gas lies on line D. The dashed line is the $(p_{CO} + p_{CO_2}) = 1$ atm isobar. Consequently, the system containing solid carbon and a gas phase at 1 atm pressure exists at the state **a**, and as this state is in the field of stability of SiC, SiO_2 is not reduced to Si by carbon at 1676°. However, if the standard free energy for formation of SiC had been positive, lines B and C would have occurred below line D in the diagram and, as shown by the dashed–dotted extension of line A, the equilibrium Si–SiO_2–C would occur at the state **a**, which is the state of intersection of the carbon line with the Ellingham line for SiO_2 in the Ellingham diagram.

6.   The thermodynamic properties of solutions

6.1.   Mixing processes

The relationship between entropy and the "degree of mixed-up-ness" is quantified by Boltzmann's expression as:

$$S' = k \ln W,$$

where S' is the entropy of the system and W is the number of microstates available to the system *. In the simplest of mixing processes, W is the number of distinguishable arrangements of the constituent atoms on the sites available to them. Consider the mixing of N_A atoms of solid A and N_B atoms of solid B as the process:

state 1 → state 2,

i.e., unmixed A and B → mixed A and B.

In state 1, interchange of the positions of A atoms in the crystal of pure A and/or interchange of the positions of B atoms in the crystal of pure B does not produce a distinguishably different arrangement and hence $W_1 = 1$. However, the N_A atoms of A and N_B atoms of B can be placed on the $N_A + N_B$ lattice sites of the mixed crystal (state 2) in $(N_A + N_B)!$ ways, of which $(N_A + N_B)!/N_A!N_B!$ are distinguishable. Thus

$$W_2 = \frac{(N_A + N_B)!}{N_A!N_B!}.$$

---

* The equivalence between this definition of entropy and the definition in terms of heat flow (§1.1) is demonstrated in general terms in many texts; a particularly clear treatment is provided in ch. 2 of FAST's book (see bibliography).

Thus, for the process:

$$\Delta S' = S_2' - S_1' = k \ln W_2 - k \ln W_1 = k \ln \frac{(N_A + N_B)!}{N_A! N_B!}. \tag{35}$$

If N_A and N_B are sufficiently large numbers, *Stirling's theorem* can be applied as

$$\ln \frac{(N_A + N_B)!}{N_A! N_B!} = (N_A + N_B) \ln(N_A + N_B) - N_A \ln N_A - N_B \ln N_B$$

$$= - N_A \ln X_A - N_B \ln X_B,$$

where, respectively, X_A and X_B are the mole fractions of A and B in the mixed crystal.

Thus, the change in entropy, $\Delta S'^M$, due to mixing, is

$$\Delta S'^M = k \ln(N_A \ln X_A + N_B \ln X_B),$$

and, if $N_A + N_B = N_0$ (Avogadro's number) then the molar entropy of mixing is

$$\Delta S^M = - R(X_A \ln X_A + X_B \ln X_B). \tag{36}$$

This increase in entropy is caused by the increase in the number of spatial configurations made available to the system as a result of the mixing process and, hence, is *configurational* in origin. If there is no change in enthalpy on mixing, the Gibbs free energy change due to the mixing process is given by

$$\Delta G^M = - T\Delta S^M = RT(X_A \ln X_A + X_B \ln X_B). \tag{37}$$

Alternatively, consider the following. Consider that p_A^0 and p_B^0 are the saturated vapor pressures of pure A and pure B at temperature T and that p_A and p_B are the partial pressures of A and B exerted by the mixed crystal (or solid solution) of composition X_A at temperature T. Consider that one mole of A is isothermally evaporated from pure solid A to form A vapor at the pressure p_A^0, that the mole of A vapor is isothermally expanded to the pressure p_A and is then isothermally condensed into a large quantity of the solid solution. As the evaporation and condensation processes are conducted at equilibrium, they do not involve any change in Gibbs free energy and hence the change in Gibbs free energy for the three-step process is simply that caused by the change in pressure from p_A^0 to p_A, i.e.,

$$\Delta G = \overline{G}_{A(in\ the\ solution)} - G_{A(pure)}^0 = RT \ln(p_A / p_A^0).$$

Similarly, for the corresponding three-step process for B,

$$\Delta G = \overline{G}_{B(in\ the\ solution)} - G_{B(pure)}^0 = RT \ln(p_B / p_B^0). \tag{38}$$

Thus, for the mixing of n_A moles of A and n_B moles of B:

$$\Delta G' = G'(\text{solution}) - G'(\text{unmixed A and B})$$

$$= (n_A \overline{G}_A + n_B \overline{G}_B) - (n_A G_A^0 + n_B G_B^0)$$

$$= n_A (\overline{G}_A - G_A^0) + n_B (\overline{G}_B - G_B^0),$$

References: p. 326.

which, from eqs. (37) and (38), can be written for one mole of solution as

$$\Delta G^M = RT\left[X_A \ln\left(p_A/p_A^0 \right) + X_B \ln\left(p_B/p_B^0 \right) \right]. \tag{39}$$

Comparison of eqs. (37) and (39) indicates that, if the mixing process does not involve a change in enthalpy,

$$p_A = X_A p_A^0 \quad and \quad p_B = X_B p_B^0. \tag{40}$$

Equation (40) is an expression of *Raoult's Law* and a solution conforming with this behavior is said to exhibit Raoultian ideal behavior. If the energies of the pure states and the solution are considered to be the sums of the pair-wise bond energies between neighboring atoms, Raoultian ideal mixing requires that:

$$E_{AB} = \left(E_{AA} + E_{BB} \right)/2, \tag{41}$$

where E_{AB}, E_{AA} and E_{BB} are the pair-wise bond energies of A–B, A–A and B–B pairs, respectively. If the condition given by eq. (41) is not met, the isothermal mixing process is accompanied by the evolution or absorption of heat, which, for mixing at constant pressure, represents a change in the enthalpy of the system. In such a situation random mixing of A and B atoms does not occur and hence the entropy of mixing is not longer given by eq. (36).

Any change in the enthalpy on mixing arises from a redistribution of the atoms among their quantized energy levels and this gives rise to a change in the *thermal* (as distinct from the configurational) component of the entropy of the system. Boltzmann's equation can be written as

$$S'_{total} = S'_{conf} + S'_{thermal} = k \ln\left(W_{conf}\, W_{thermal} \right),$$

where W_{conf} is the number of distinguishable ways in which the atoms can be distributed on the available sites and $W_{thermal}$ is the number of ways in which the energy of the system can be distributed among the particles. Thus, for the mixing process,

$$\Delta S' = k \ln\frac{W_{conf(2)}\, W_{thermal(2)}}{W_{conf(1)}\, W_{thermal(1)}},$$

and hence $\Delta S'$ is only given by eq. (35) if $W_{thermal(1)} = W_{thermal(2)}$, i.e., if no redistribution of the energy occurs, and hence no change in enthalpy occurs. This condition is required for Raoultian ideal mixing. If

$$|E_{AB}| > |(E_{AA} + E_{BB})/2|,$$

the solution exhibits a tendency towards *ordering,* i.e., towards maximizing the number of A–B contacts, and if

$$|E_{AB}| < |(E_{AA} + E_{BB})/2|,$$

the solution exhibits a tendency towards *clustering* or phase separation, i.e., towards minimizing the number of A–B contacts.

Configurational entropy is responsible for the occurrence of vacancies in metals.

Consider a perfect single crystal containing N atoms on N lattice sites. If a single atom is removed from a lattice position within the crystal and is placed on the surface of the crystal, random placement of the vacancy on $N + 1$ sites gives rise to a configurational entropy of

$$S = k \ln \frac{(N + 1)!}{N!}.$$

This process involves an enthalpy change ΔH_v and, as the vibration frequencies of the nearest-neighbor atoms to the vacancy are altered, a change occurs in the thermal entropy, ΔS_{th}. Thus, for the formation of N_v vacancies,

$$\Delta G' = \Delta H' - T\Delta S'$$

$$= N_v \Delta H_v - N_v \Delta S_{th} T + kT \ln \frac{(N + N_v)!}{N! N_v!}$$

$$= N_v (\Delta H_v - T\Delta S_{th}) + kT \left[N \ln \frac{N}{N + N_v} + N_v \ln \frac{N_v}{N + N_v} \right]. \tag{42}$$

The formation of vacancies in an initially perfect crystal is thus a spontaneous process which proceeds until, thereby, the Gibbs free energy of the crystal is minimized, in which state

$$\frac{\partial \Delta G'}{\partial N_v} = 0.$$

From eq. (42), this condition occurs when

$$\frac{N_v}{N + N_v} = \exp\left(\frac{-\Delta H_v}{kT} \right) \exp\left(\frac{\Delta S_{th}}{k} \right).$$

The fraction of vacant sites in a crystal can be determined from simultaneous measurement of the thermal expansion of a sample, $\Delta l/l$, and the change in the lattice parameter, $\Delta a_0/a_0$, as measured by X-ray diffraction (see ch. 17, §2.2.1.2). As the former is influenced by both the increase in the average spacing between lattice planes and the creation of vacancies, and the latter is a measure only of the average spacing between planes, the increase in the fraction of vacant lattice sites is proportional to the difference between $\Delta l/l$ and $\Delta a_0/a_0$. Measurements of this type on aluminum give:

$$\frac{N_v}{N + N_v} = 11 \exp\left(\frac{-8820}{T} \right),$$

from which $\Delta H_v = 73.3$ kJ/mole and $\Delta S_v = 20$ J/K mole. At the melting temperature of 660°C this gives the fraction of vacant sites as 9×10^{-4}.

The thermodynamic properties of solutions which do not exhibit Raoultian ideal behavior are dealt with by introducing the concept of activity. The *activity*, a_i, of the component i in a solution is defined as:

$$a_i = p_i / p_i^0 \tag{43}$$

and, from eq. (40), is equal to the mole fraction, X_i, in a Raoultian ideal solution. Thus, the molar free energy of formation of a binary A–B solution, ΔG^M, is given by

$$\Delta G^M = RT(X_A \ln a_A + X_B \ln a_B).\tag{44}$$

The free energy of formation of n moles of a solution, $\Delta G'^M$, can be written in terms of the partial molar free energies of mixing of the components as:

$$\Delta G'^M = n_A \Delta \bar{G}_A^M + n_B \Delta \bar{G}_B^M$$

or, the molar free energy, ΔG^M, as:

$$\Delta G^M = X_A \Delta \bar{G}_A^M + X_B \Delta \bar{G}_B^M,\tag{45}$$

where $\Delta \bar{G}_i^M = \bar{G}_i - G_i^0$ (the difference between the molar free energy of i in the solution and the molar free energy of pure i) is termed the *partial molar free energy of mixing* of i. The partial molar free energy of mixing of i and the molar free energy of formation of the solution are related as:

$$\Delta \bar{G}_i^M = \Delta G^M + (1 - X_i)\left(\frac{\partial \Delta G^M}{\partial X_i}\right)_{T,P}.\tag{46}$$

Comparison of eqs. (39) and (45) shows that in a Raoultian ideal solution

$$\Delta \bar{G}_i^M = RT \ln X_i,$$

and comparison of eqs. (39) and (44) shows that, generally,

$$\Delta \bar{G}_i^M = RT \ln a_i.\tag{47}$$

A typical ideal variation of ΔG^M with composition is shown in fig. 8. In this figure the tangent drawn to the free energy curve at any composition intercepts the $X_A = 1$ axis at $\Delta \bar{G}_A^M$ and intercepts the $X_B = 1$ axis at $\Delta \bar{G}_B^M$. This construction is a geometric representation of eq. (46). Also, as $X_i \to 0$, $a_i \to 0$ and hence, from eq. (47), $\Delta \bar{G}_i^M \to -\infty$, i.e., the vertical axes are tangents to the curve at its extremities. The relationship between the variations of the tangential intercepts with composition is given by the *Gibbs–Duhem equation*:

$$X_A d \ln a_A + X_B d \ln a_B = 0.\tag{48}$$

Usually, the activity of only one component of a solution is amenable to experimental measurement, and the activity of the other component, and hence ΔG^M, are obtained from integration of the Gibbs–Duhem equation.

The *activity coefficient*, γ_i, is defined as $\gamma_i = a_i/X_i$ and hence eq. (44) can be written as:

$$\Delta G^M = RT(X_A \ln X_A + X_B \ln X_B) + RT(X_A \ln \gamma_A + X_B \ln \gamma_B).\tag{49}$$

The first term on the right-hand side of eq. (49) is the molar free energy of formation of a Raoultian ideal solution, $\Delta G^{M,id}$, and the second term, being the difference between the actual molar free energy of solution and the ideal value, is called the *excess molar free energy of mixing*, G^{xs}.

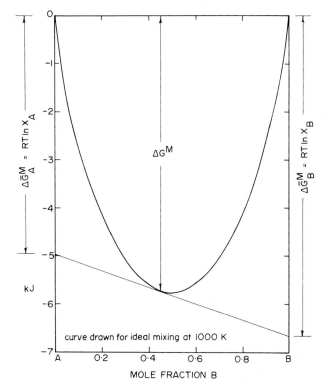

Fig. 8. The variation of ΔG^M with composition in an ideal system at 1000 K.

6.2. Regular solution behavior

A *regular solution* is one which has an ideal entropy of mixing and a nonzero enthalpy of mixing. The properties of such a solution are best examined by means of a simple statistical model of the mixing of N_A atoms of A and N_B atoms of B. If the internal energy, U', of the solution can be taken as the sum of the pair-wise bond energies then

$$U' = P_{AB}E_{AB} + P_{AA}E_{AA} + P_{BB}E_{BB},   \tag{50}$$

where P_{ij} is the number of i–j pairwise bonds and E_{ij} is the energy of the bond relative to i and j at infinite separation. If the coordination number of an atom is z, the number of bonds involving A atoms, $N_A z$, is given by $2P_{AA} + P_{AB}$ and, similarly, the number of bonds involving B atoms, $N_B z$, is given by $2P_{BB} + P_{AB}$. Thus:

$$P_{AA} = \tfrac{1}{2}N_A z - \tfrac{1}{2}P_{AB} \quad \text{and} \quad P_{BB} = \tfrac{1}{2}N_B z - \tfrac{1}{2}P_{AB},$$

substitution of which into eq. (50) gives:

$$U' = \tfrac{1}{2}N_A z E_{AA} + \tfrac{1}{2}N_B z E_{BB} + P_{AB}\left[E_{AB} - (E_{AA} + E_{BB})/2\right].$$

The first two terms on the right-hand side represent the internal energies of N_A atoms of A and N_B atoms of B before mixing and hence, for the mixing process:

$$\Delta U' = P_{AB}\left[E_{AB} - (E_{AA} + E_{BB})/2\right]. \tag{51}$$

If the mixing process, conducted at constant pressure, does not involve a change in volume, then, as $P\Delta V' = 0$, $\Delta H' = \Delta U'$ and eq. (51) is the expression for the enthalpy of mixing. As random mixing of the atoms is assumed, the number of A–B bonds is calculated as the product of the probability of occurrence of an A–B pair and the number of pairs of atoms. The former is given by:

$$2\frac{N_A}{N_A + N_B}\frac{N_B}{N_A + N_B},$$

and the latter is $\frac{1}{2}(N_A + N_B)z$, and hence:

$$\Delta H' = \frac{N_A N_B}{N_A + N_B} z\left[E_{AB} - (E_{AA} + E_{BB})/2\right]. \tag{52}$$

For the mixing of n_A moles of A $(= n_A N_0$ atoms of A) and n_B moles of B $(= n_B N_0$ atoms of B), eq. (52) becomes:

$$\Delta H' = \frac{n_A n_B}{n_A + n_B} N_0 z\left[E_{AB} - (E_{AA} + E_{BB})/2\right]$$

or, per mole of solution:

$$\Delta H^M = X_A X_B N_0 z\left[E_{AB} - (E_{AA} + E_{BB})/2\right].$$

If $|E_{AB}| > |(E_{AA} + E_{BB})/2|$, ΔH^M is negative, which leads to exothermic mixing, and if $|E_{AB}| < |(E_{AA} + E_{BB})/2|$, ΔH^M is positive, which leads to endothermic mixing. On the other hand, if E_{AB} is the average of E_{AA} and E_{BB}, ΔH^M is zero and Raoultian ideal mixing occurs. For any given system,

$$\Omega = N_0 z\left[E_{AB} - (E_{AA} + E_{BB})/2\right]$$

is a constant, and hence, in a regular solution, ΔH^M is a parabolic function of composition, given by:

$$\Delta H^M = \Omega X_A X_B, \tag{53}$$

and $$\Delta S^M = -R(X_A \ln X_A + X_B \ln X_B). \tag{36}$$

For any extensive thermodynamic property Q, the relationship between $\Delta \bar{Q}_i^M$ and ΔQ^M in a binary system is given by:

$$\Delta \bar{Q}_i^M = \Delta Q^M + (1 - X_i)\left(\frac{\partial \Delta Q^M}{\partial X_i}\right),$$

and thus, in a regular solution, from eq. (53):

$$\Delta \bar{H}_i^M = \Omega(1 - X_i)^2,$$

and from eq. (36):

$$\Delta \bar{S}_i^M = -R \ln X_i.$$

The partial molar free energy of mixing of i can be expressed variously as

$$\Delta \bar{G}_i^M = \Delta \bar{H}_i^M - T \Delta \bar{S}_i^M = \Delta \bar{G}_i^{M, \mathrm{id}} + \bar{G}_i^{xs} = RT \ln X_i + RT \ln \gamma_i,$$

and hence, in a regular solution:

$$\bar{G}_i^{xs} = \Delta \bar{H}_i^M = RT \ln \gamma_i = \Omega (1 - X_i)^2.$$

Consequently, the limiting values of γ_i as $X_i \rightarrow 1$ and $X_i \rightarrow 0$ are unity and $\exp(\Omega/RT)$, respectively; i.e., with increasing dilution, the solvent approaches Raoultian ideal behavior and the activity coefficient of the solute approaches a constant value designated γ_i^0. The tendency of γ_i towards a constant value as $X_i \rightarrow 0$ is expressed as *Henry's Law*, i.e.:

$$\gamma_i \rightarrow \gamma_i^0 \text{ as } X_i \rightarrow 0,$$

and if γ_i is constant over some finite range of composition of dilute solution of i, component i is said to exhibit ideal Henrian behavior in this range, its activity being given by:

$$a_i = \gamma_i^0 X_i.$$

Application of the Gibbs–Duhem relation, eq. (48), shows that, over the composition range in which the solute B exhibits ideal Henrian behavior, the solvent A exhibits ideal Raoultian behavior.

The occurrence of Henrian ideal behavior gives rise to the concept of the Henrian standard state, illustrated in fig. 9 which shows the activity of B as a function of composition in the system A–B. The Raoultian standard state is pure B, located at the point R where $a_B = 1$. If, however, pure B behaved as it does in dilute solution in A, extrapolation of its activity along the Henry's Law line would give an activity of γ_B^0 in the hypothetical pure state at $X_B = 1$, relative to the Raoultian standard state. This hypothetical pure state is the Henrian standard state, located at the point H in fig. 9, and, relative to this standard state, the activity of B in any solution, h_B, is

$$h_B = f_B X_B,$$

where f_B is the *Henrian activity coefficient*. In the range of dilute solutions over which B exhibits Henrian ideal behavior, $f_B = 1$ and hence:

$$h_B = X_B.$$

If the vapor pressure of B in the Raoultian standard state is p_B^0, then the vapor pressure of B in the Henrian standard state is $\gamma_B^0 p_B^0$, and hence the change of standard state,

$$B_{(\mathrm{Raoultian\ standard\ state})} \rightarrow B_{(\mathrm{Henrian\ standard\ state})},$$

References: p. 326.

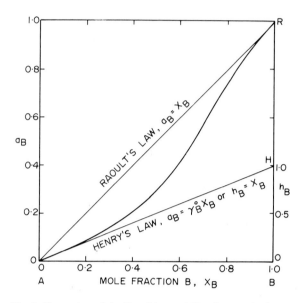

Fig. 9. Illustration of the Raoultian and Henrian standard states.

corresponds to

$$B_{(\text{vapor at pressure } p_B^0)} \rightarrow B_{(\text{vapor at pressure } \gamma_B^0 p_B^0)},$$

with a free energy change of

$$\Delta G_B (R \rightarrow H) = RT \ln \gamma_B^0.$$

7. The thermodynamic origin of phase diagrams

In the definition of activity, given by eq. (43), p_i^0 is the vapor pressure of pure i at the temperature of interest. However, depending on the convenience of the situation, either pure solid i or pure liquid i can be chosen as the standard state. At temperatures below the triple point, $p_{i(\text{solid})}^0 < p_{i(\text{liquid})}^0$, and so the activity of i in a solution, relative to pure solid i as the standard state, is larger than the activity relative to pure liquid i as the standard state. Conversely, at temperatures higher than the triple point temperature the reverse is the case. The activities on the two activity scales are related as

$$\frac{a_{i(\text{relative to solid standard state})}}{a_{i(\text{relative to liquid standard state})}} = \frac{p_{i(\text{liquid})}^0}{p_{i(\text{solid})}^0} = \exp\left(\Delta G_{m,i}^0 / RT\right).$$

Consider the molar free energies of mixing in the system A–B, the phase diagram for which is shown in fig. 10a. For simplicity of discussion it will be assumed that both the solid and liquid solutions exhibit ideal Raoultian behavior. The molar free energies, at temperature T, are shown in fig. 10b. Pure liquid A and pure solid B are chosen as the reference states and are located at points **a** and **b** respectively. $G^0_{A(s)}$ is located at **c**, where $G^0_{A(s)} - G^0_{A(l)} = -\Delta G^0_{m,A}$ at temperature T, and $G^0_{B(l)}$ is located at **d** where $G^0_{B(l)} - G^0_{B(s)} = \Delta G^0_{m,B}$ at temperature T. Thus, relative to unmixed pure liquid A and pure solid B as the reference state, the molar free energy of the unmixed pure liquids (given by line **ad**) is $X_B \Delta G^0_{m,B}$ and the corresponding free energy of the unmixed pure solids (given by line **cb**) is $-X_A \Delta G^0_{m,A}$. Upon mixing to

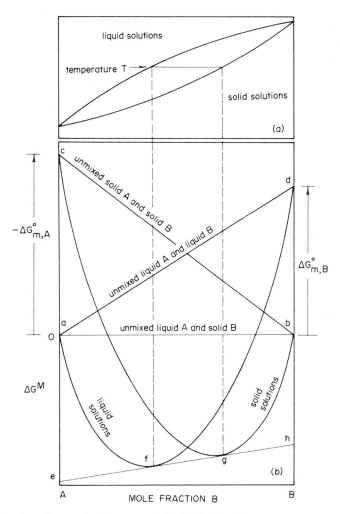

Fig. 10. (a) The phase diagram for the system A–B. (b) The ideal free energy of mixing curves for the system A–B at temperature T.

form Raoultian ideal solutions, the molar free energies decrease by $|RT(X_A \ln X_A + X_B \ln X_B|$ and hence, relative to the chosen reference state:

$$\Delta G^M(\text{solid solutions}) = -X_A \Delta G^0_{m,A} + RT(X_A \ln X_A + X_B \ln X_B),$$

and

$$\Delta G^M(\text{liquid solutions}) = X_B \Delta G^0_{m,B} + RT(X_A \ln X_A + X_B \ln X_B).$$

The double tangent drawn to the two free energy curves touches the curve for the solid solutions at **g** and the curve for the liquid solutions at **f**, with the intercepts at $X_A = 1$ and $X_B = 1$ being **e** and **h** respectively. As the equilibrium state is that of minimum free energy, points **f** and **g** divide the composition range into three regions. At compositions between **a** and **f** the homogeneous liquid solution has the lowest possible free energy and at compositions between **g** and **b** the homogeneous solid solution has the lowest possible free energy. However, at compositions between **f** and **g**, a two-phase mixture of liquid solution of composition **f** and solid solution of composition **g**, the free energy of which lies on line **fg**, has a lower free energy than both the homogeneous solid solution and the homogeneous liquid solution. Thus point **f** is the limit of solution of B in liquid A and **g** is the limit of solution of A in solid B, and so points **f** and **g** are, respectively, the liquidus and solidus compositions at temperature T.

Furthermore, for phase equilibrium:

$$\overline{G}_A(\text{in liquid solution } \mathbf{f}) = \overline{G}_A(\text{in solid solution } \mathbf{g}),$$

and:

$$\overline{G}_B(\text{in liquid solution } \mathbf{f}) = \overline{G}_B(\text{in solid solution } \mathbf{g})$$

or $\quad \Delta \overline{G}^M_A(\text{in liquid } \mathbf{f}) = \Delta \overline{G}^M_A(\text{in solid } \mathbf{g}),$

and:

$$\Delta \overline{G}^M_B(\text{in liquid } \mathbf{f}) = \Delta \overline{G}^M_B(\text{in solid } \mathbf{g}).$$

These requirements state that, for phase equilibrium, the tangent to the molar free energy curve for the liquid solutions at the liquidus composition **f** is also the tangent to the molar free energy curve for the solid solutions at the solidus composition **g**. Geometrically, this condition is such that, simultaneously,

$$\mathbf{ca + ae = ce} \quad \text{and} \quad \mathbf{db + bh = dh}, \tag{54}$$

where: **ce** $= \Delta \overline{G}^M_A$ (relative to solid A as the standard state)
$\qquad\qquad = RT \ln X_A$ (at the composition **g**),

$\qquad$ **ae** $= \Delta \overline{G}^M_A$ (relative to liquid A as the standard state)
$\qquad\qquad = RT \ln X_A$ (at the composition **f**),

$\qquad$ **dh** $= \Delta \overline{G}^M_B$ (relative to liquid B as the standard state)
$\qquad\qquad = RT \ln X_B$ (at the composition **f**)

and **bh** $= \Delta \overline{G}^M_B$ (relative to solid B as the standard state)
$\qquad\qquad = RT \ln X_B$ (at the composition **g**).

Thus eqs. (54) become:

$$\Delta G^0_{m,A} + RT \ln X_A(\text{liquidus}) = RT \ln X_A(\text{solidus}),$$

and

$$- \Delta G^0_{m,B} + RT \ln X_B(\text{solidus}) = RT \ln X_B(\text{liquidus}).$$

As $X_A(\text{liquidus}) + X_B(\text{liquidus}) = 1$ and $X_A(\text{solidus}) + X_B(\text{solidus}) = 1$, the solidus and liquidus compositions (in a Raoultian system) are thus uniquely determined by the values of $\Delta G^0_{m,A}$ and $\Delta G^0_{m,B}$ as:

$$X_{A(\text{liquidus})} = \frac{1 - \exp(-\Delta G^0_{m,B}/RT)}{1 - [\exp(-\Delta G^0_{m,B}/RT)][\exp(\Delta G^0_{m,A}/RT)]} \tag{55}$$

and

$$X_{A(\text{solidus})} = \frac{\exp(\Delta G^0_{m,A}/RT)[1 - \exp(-\Delta G^0_{m,B}/RT)]}{1 - [\exp(-\Delta G^0_{m,B}/RT)][\exp(\Delta G^0_{m,A}/RT)]}. \tag{56}$$

The phase diagram for the system Si–Ge, calculated from eqs. (55) and (56) and the known variations of $\Delta G^0_{m,Si}$ and $\Delta G^0_{m,Ge}$ with temperature, is compared, in fig. 11, with the liquidus and solidus lines determined experimentally by thermal and X-ray analysis. As is seen, the behavior in the system is very close to Raoultian.

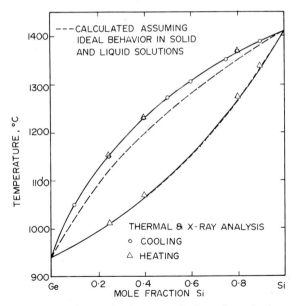

Fig. 11. Comparison of the phase diagram for the system Si–Ge as determined experimentally by X-ray and thermal analysis, with that calculated assuming Raoultian ideal behavior in both the solid and liquid solutions.

Raoultian behavior is very much the exception rather than the rule, and even complete mutual solid solubility between A and B requires that A and B have the same crystal structure, similar atomic sizes, similar electronegativities, and similar valences. The requirement of similar atomic size arises from the introduction of a strain energy into the lattice when the solvent and substitutional solute atoms are of differing size. This strain energy always increases the Gibbs free energy and, hence, can significantly influence the phase relationships in the system. It is found that terminal solid solutions extend only a few atomic percent into a binary system if the

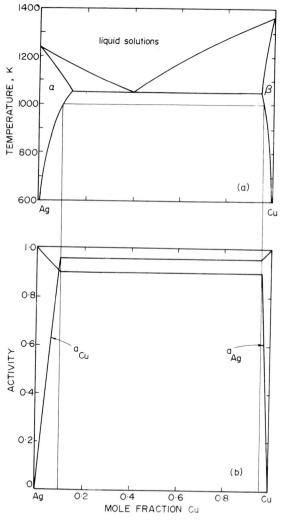

Fig. 12. (a) The phase diagram for the system Ag–Cu. (b) The activities of Ag and Cu in the system Ag–Cu at 1000 K.

atomic diameters differ by more than 14%. Significant differences in electronegativity cause the formation of intermetallic compounds such as Mg_2Si, Mg_2Sn and Mg_2Pb, and differences in valences can cause the formation of electron compounds such as occur in the systems Cu–Zn and Cu–Sn.

Although Cu and Ag are chemically similar, the atomic radius of Ag is 13% larger than than of Cu and hence, as shown in fig. 12a, Cu and Ag form a simple eutectic system. In this system it is presumed that Ag exhibits Raoultian ideal behavior in the Ag-rich α-solid solution and that Cu exhibits Raoultian ideal behavior in the Cu-rich β-solid solution. Consequently Cu in α and Ag in β exhibit Henrian ideal behavior and, at 1000 K, the activities of the components, relative to the pure solids as standard states, are as shown in fig. 12b. At 1000 K, saturation of the α-phase with Cu occurs at $X_{Ag} = 0.9$, and hence, as Ag obeys Raoult's law in the α-phase, $a_{Ag} = 0.9$ at this composition. Phase equilibrium between α saturated with Cu and β saturated with Ag requires that the activities of both Ag and Cu be the same in both phases, and hence $a_{Ag} = 0.9$ in the Ag-saturated β-phase of composition $X_{Ag} = 0.04$. Similarly, $a_{Cu} = 0.96$ in the Ag-saturated β (at $X_{Cu} = 0.96$) and in the Cu-saturated α (at $X_{Ag} = 0.9$). Thus, in the α-phase, Henrian behavior of Cu is given by:

$$a_{Cu} = 9.6 X_{Cu},\tag{57}$$

and in the β-phase, Henrian behavior of Ag is given by:

$$a_{Ag} = 22.5 X_{Ag}.$$

8. Reaction equilibrium involving solutions and the Gibbs phase rule

8.1. The dependence of the equilibrium state on activity

In §4 it was shown that, at constant temperature and pressure, equilibrium is established in the reaction

$$a A + b B = c C + d D,$$

when

$$a\overline{G}_A + b\overline{G}_B = c\overline{G}_C + d\overline{G}_D.\tag{58}$$

As:

$$\overline{G}_i = G_i^0 + RT \ln a_i,$$

eq. (58) can be written as:

$$\Delta G_T^0 = -RT \ln \frac{a_C^c a_D^d}{a_A^a a_B^b},$$

where the quotient in the logarithm term is K_T, the equilibrium constant for the reaction.

Consider the oxidation, at 1000 K, of Cu from an Ag–Cu alloy of $X_{Cu} = 0.08$.

References: p. 326.

From eq. (57), the activity of Cu in this alloy, relative to pure solid Cu as the standard state, is

$$a_{Cu} = 9.6 X_{Cu} = 9.6 \times 0.08 = 0.768.$$

For the reaction:

$$4Cu_{(s)} + O_{2(g)} = 2Cu_2O_{(s)}$$

$$\Delta G_T^0 = -336\,810 + 142.5T \text{ J}.$$

Thus, $\Delta G_{1000}^0 = -194\,300$ J $= -8.3144 \times 1000 \ln K_{1000}$ and so:

$$K_{1000} = 1.41 \times 10^{10} = \frac{a_{Cu_2O}^2}{a_{Cu}^4 \, p_{O_2}}. \tag{59}$$

Oxidation of the Cu occurs when the oxygen pressure in the system has been increased to the level at which $a_{Cu_2O} = 1$. From eq. (59) this oxygen pressure is:

$$p_{O_2} = \frac{1}{(0.768)^4 \times 1.41 \times 10^{10}} = 2.04 \times 10^{-10} \text{ atm}.$$

From eq. (16), ΔG_{1000}^0 for the reaction

$$2Ag_{(s)} + \tfrac{1}{2}O_{2(g)} = Ag_2O_{(s)}$$

has the value 31 062 J. Thus:

$$K_{1000} = \frac{a_{Ag_2O}}{a_{Ag}^2 \, p_{O_2}^{1/2}} = 0.024.$$

Thus, with $a_{Ag} = 0.92$ (Raoultian behavior in the α-solid solution) and $p_{O_2} = 2.04 \times 10^{-10}$ atm:

$$a_{Ag_2O} = 2.9 \times 10^{-7},$$

which shows that the equilibrium oxide is virtually pure Cu_2O. As the oxygen pressure in the system is further increased, the Cu content in the alloy decreases in accordance with eq. (59). Thus the alloy in equilibrium with virtually pure Cu_2O and air (oxygen fraction 0.21) at 1000 K is that in which

$$a_{Cu} = \left[\frac{1}{1.41 \times 10^{10} \times 0.21} \right]^{1/4} = 0.0043,$$

or $X_{Cu} = a_{Cu}/9.6 = 4.5 \times 10^{-4}.$

At this oxygen pressure the activity of Ag_2O in the equilibrium oxide phase, with $a_{Ag} \approx 1$, is:

$$a_{Ag_2O} = 0.024 \times 1 \times 0.21^{1/2} = 0.011,$$

and so the equilibrium oxide phase is still essentially pure Cu_2O.

8.2. The Gibbs phase rule

The complete description of a thermodynamic system containing C components existing in P phases requires specification of the temperatures, pressures and compositions of each of the P phases. As the composition of each phase is defined when the concentrations of $C - 1$ of its components are known, the total number of variables in the description is P pressures $+ P$ temperatures $+ P(C - 1)$ concentrations $= P(C + 1)$. For thermodynamic equilibrium in the system, each of the P phases must be at the same temperature and same pressure and the activity (or partial molar free energy) of each of the individual components must be the same in each of the P phases. Thus, for equilibrium, there are $(P - 1)$ equalities of temperature, $(P - 1)$ equalities of pressure and $(P - 1)C$ equalities of activity, and hence the total number of equilibrium conditions, given as the number of equations among the variables of the system, is $(P - 1)(C + 2)$. The number of *degrees of freedom*, F, which the equilibrium system may have, is defined as the maximum number of variables which may be independently altered in value without disturbing the equilibrium in the system. This number is obtained as the difference between the total number of variables available to the system and the minimum number of equations among these variables that is required for maintenance of the equilibrium, i.e.:

$$F = P(C + 1) - (P - 1)(C + 2)$$
$$= C + 2 - P. \tag{60}$$

Equation (60) is the *Gibbs phase rule* and is a powerful tool in the determination of possible equilibria which may occur in multicomponent, multiphase systems.

In the simplest of applications, i.e., in a one-component system, $F = 3 - P$. Thus, with reference to the phase diagram for H_2O, shown in fig. 3, for the existence of a single phase $F = 2$ and so the pressure and temperature can be varied independently without disturbing the equilibrium, i.e., with $F = 2$ the state of the system can be moved about within the area of stability of the single phase in the pressure–temperature diagram. However, for a two-phase equilibrium the state of the system must lie on one of the lines in fig. 3 and thus only the pressure *or* the temperature can be varied independently. From the phase rule, $F = 1$ and hence the two-phase equilibrium is univariant. The triple point, where the three phases are in equilibrium, occurs at fixed values of temperature and pressure, in accordance with $F = 0$ from the phase rule. The three-phase equilibrium is thus invariant and three is the maximum number of phases which can be in equilibrium with one another in a one-component system.

In a binary system, the inclusion of a second component adds an extra degree of freedom to each equilibrium and hence the maximum number of phases which can be in equilibrium with one another in a two-component system is four. However, phase diagrams for binary systems of metallurgical interest are normally presented for a pressure of 1 atm, i.e., they are the 1 atm isobaric sections of the phase equilibria occurring in pressure–temperature–composition space, and hence one of

References: p. 326.

the degrees of freedom is used in specifying the pressure. Thus, at an arbitrarily selected pressure such as 1 atm, the maximum number of phases which can exist in equilibrium with one another in a binary system is three (unless, by chance, the arbitrarily selected pressure happens to be that at which an invariant four-phase equilibrium occurs). In the binary system A–B, considered at constant pressure, the available variables are T, a_A and a_B. For the existence of a single phase, such as α, β or liquid in fig. 12a, the phase rule gives $F = 2$, and hence any two of T, a_A and a_B may be varied independently. For any two-phase equilibrium, $F = 1$ and hence the specification of any one of the three variables fixes the state of the system. For example, specification of the temperature at which the two-phase equilibrium exists fixes the compositions of the equilibrated phases on the appropriate liquidus, solidus or solvus lines; and specification of the composition of one of the equilibrated phases fixes the temperature at which the chosen composition lies on the appropriate liquidus, solidus or solves line and fixes the composition of the second phase at the other end of the tie-line between the two equilibrated phases. The three-phase equilibrium with $F = 0$ is invariant, and, in fig. 12a, the eutectic equilibrium occurs at a fixed temperature at which the compositions of the α, β and liquid phases are also fixed.

If some, or all, of the components of a system can react chemically with one another to produce new chemical species, a distinction must be drawn between the terms component and species. For example the *components* silver and oxygen in the binary system Ag–O are capable of reacting to form the new *species* Ag_2O, and hence an equilibrium among the three species Ag, Ag_2O and O_2 can occur in the two-component system. The equilibrium among Ag, Ag_2O and O_2 is called an *independent reaction equilibrium*. In a system containing N species and existing in P phases among which there are R independent reaction equilibria, the number of variables is $P(N + 1)$, i.e. P pressures $+ P$ temperatures $+ P(N - 1)$ concentrations. However, if the species i and j react to form the species k, reaction equilibrium requires that

$$\overline{G}_i + \overline{G}_j = \overline{G}_k,$$

and this is an additional equation required among the variables. Thus, if R independent reaction equilibria occur, the number of equations among the $P(N + 1)$ variables, required for equilibrium is $(P - 1)$ equalities of temperature $+ (P - 1)$ equalities of pressure $+ (P - 1)N$ equalities of activity $+ R = (P - 1)(N + 2) + R$, and hence the number of degrees of freedom, F, is

$$F = P(N + 1) - (P - 1)(N + 2) - R$$
$$= (N - R) + 2 - P.$$

Comparison with eq. (60) indicates that

$$C = N - R, \tag{61}$$

i.e., the number of components in a system equals the number of species present minus the number of reaction equilibria. Equation (61) is normally used to calculate the number of independent reaction equilibria from knowledge of the number of components and the number of species. For example, in the two-component system Ag–O, the independent reaction equilibrium among the three species is

$$2Ag + \tfrac{1}{2}O_2 = Ag_2O.$$

For equilibrium among the phases metal, metal oxide and oxygen gas in the two-component system, $F = 1$ and thus only T or p_{O_2} can be selected as the single degree of freedom. Selection of T fixes ΔG_T^0 and hence, via eq. (34), fixes p_{O_2} and vice versa.

• Consider the various equilibria which can occur in the ternary system Si–C–O, for which a stability diagram is shown in fig. 7. It can be considered that this system contains the six species Si, SiO_2, SiC, C, CO and CO_2, and hence $R = 6 - 3$, i.e., there are three independent reaction equilibria. These are derived as follows. The chemical reaction for formation of each compound from its elements is written:

$$Si + O_2 = SiO_2,$$
$$Si + C = SiC,$$
$$C + O_2 = CO_2,$$
$$C + \tfrac{1}{2}O_2 = CO.$$

These equations are then combined in such a way as to eliminate any elements which are not considered as species in the system, and the minimum number of equations so obtained, is the number of independent reaction equilibria, R. In this case oxygen is not considered as species, and elimination of O_2 gives:

$$C + CO_2 = 2CO, \tag{i}$$
$$Si + C = SiC, \tag{ii}$$

and

$$Si + 2CO_2 = SiO_2 + 2CO \tag{iii}$$

as the independent equilibria. From the phase rule, the maximum number of phases which can coexist in equilibrium is five (the condensed phases Si, SiO_2, SiC, C and the gas phase CO–CO_2). This equilibrium is invariant and occurs at the temperature T_{eq} at which $\Delta G_{(ii)}^0 = 0$ and at the pressure $P = p_{CO} + p_{CO_2}$ at which $K_{(i), T_{eq}} = p_{CO}^2/p_{CO_2}$ and $K_{(iii), T_{eq}} = (p_{CO}/p_{CO_2})^2$ are simultaneously satisfied. If the temperature is arbitrarily fixed, as is the case in fig. 7, the maximum number of phases which can coexist in equilibrium is four (three condensed phases and a gas phase). One such equilibrium occurs in fig. 7 at point **b**. For the coexistence of two condensed phases and a gas phase at the arbitrarily selected temperature, $F = 1$, and such equilibria lie on the univariant lines A, B, C and D in fig. 7, and for equilibrium between a single condensed phase and a gas phase, $F = 2$, corresponding to areas of single condensed phase stability in fig. 7.

Occasionally situations are found in which it might appear, at first sight, that the phase rule is not obeyed, and usually, in such situations a degree of freedom is used by a condition of stoichiometry in the system. For example, in the reduction of ZnO by graphite to produce Zn vapor, CO and CO_2, it might appear that the three-phase equilibrium (ZnO, C and the gas phase) in the three-component system (Zn–O–C) has $F = 5 - 3 = 2$ degrees of freedom, and that, with the five species ZnO, C, $Zn_{(v)}$, CO and CO_2, two independent reaction equilibria occur, which can be selected as

$$ZnO_{(s)} + C_{(gr)} = Zn_{(v)} + CO_{(g)} \qquad \text{(iv)}$$

and

$$2ZnO_{(s)} + C_{(gr)} = 2Zn_{(v)} + CO_{2(g)}, \qquad \text{(v)}$$

for which

$$K_{(iv)} = p_{CO} p_{Zn}, \qquad \text{(vi)}$$

and

$$K_{(v)} = p_{Zn}^2 p_{CO_2}. \qquad \text{(vii)}$$

However, selecting T, which fixes the values of $K_{(iv)}$ and $K_{(v)}$, and any one of p_{Zn}, p_{CO} or p_{CO_2} as the two apparent degrees of freedom does not fix the state of the system, i.e., does not allow simultaneous solution of eqs. (vi) and (vii). This difficulty arises because the stoichiometry requirement has not been taken into consideration, i.e. that, as all the Zn and O occurring in the gas phase originates from the stoichiometric ZnO, the condition

$$\frac{n_O}{n_{Zn}} = 1 = \frac{n_{CO} + 2n_{CO_2}}{n_{Zn}} = \frac{p_{CO} + 2p_{CO_2}}{p_{Zn}} \qquad \text{(viii)}$$

must also be satisfied. This stoichiometric requirement decreases F to unity and hence selecting T as the single degree of freedom fixes the partial pressures of Zn, CO and CO_2 as the values required for simultaneous solution of eqs. (vi), (vii) and (viii).

9.   The thermodynamics of surfaces and interfaces

9.1.   The Gibbs adsorption isotherm

In passing from one phase to another in a heterogeneous system, some of the properties undergo significant changes as the boundary between the two phases is traversed. The thin region over which these changes occur is called the *interface,* and a complete thermodynamic analysis of the system requires consideration of the thermodynamic properties of the interface.

Consider fig. 13 which shows the variation of the concentration, c_1, of the component 1 across the interface region in a system comprising equilibrated α and β phases. Calculation of the total number of moles of component 1 in the system as the sum $c_1^\alpha V^\alpha + c_1^\beta V^\beta$, where V^α and V^β are the volumes of the phases, involves the

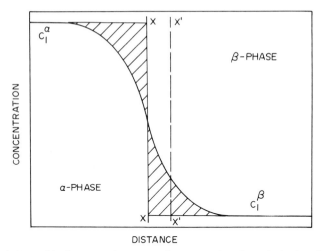

Fig. 13. The variation, with distance, of concentration on passing through the interface between two phases.

assumption that the values c_1^α and c_1^β occur up to some plane in the interface region, and evaluation of $c_1^\alpha V^\alpha + c_1^\beta V^\beta$ requires that a mathematical plane be located somewhere in the interface region. In fig. 13 it is seen that the number of moles of component 1 in the system, calculated as $c_1^\alpha V^\alpha + c_1^\beta V^\beta$, is only equal to the actual number of moles of 1 in the system, n_1, when the boundary plane X–X is located such that the cross-hatched areas in fig. 13 are equal. If the boundary plane is located to the right of X–X, say at X′–X′, then:

$$n_1 < c_1^\alpha V^\alpha + c_1^\beta V^\beta$$

or, if the boundary plane is located to the left of X–X:

$$n_1 > c_1^\alpha V^\alpha + c_1^\beta V^\beta.$$

The difference between n_1 and $c_1^\alpha V^\alpha + c_1^\beta V^\beta$ defines the *surface concentration of component 1*, Γ_1 (moles/cm²), as:

$$\Gamma_1 A_s = n_1 - \left(c_1^\alpha V^\alpha + c_1^\beta V^\beta \right),$$

where A_s is the area of surface between the two phases. Thus, with the boundary located to the left of X–X, Γ_1 is a positive quantity and with the boundary located to the right of X–X, Γ_1 is a negative quantity. In a single-component system where the boundary is between a condensed phase and a vapor phase, it is logical to locate the boundary at X–X so that the surface concentration is zero. However, with two or more components in the system it is not generally possible to locate the interface at a position at which more than one of the surface concentrations are zero. In such a case X–X is located such that the surface concentration of the solvent, Γ_1, is zero and the surface concentration of the solute, Γ_2, is not zero. This is illustrated in fig. 14.

References: p. 326.

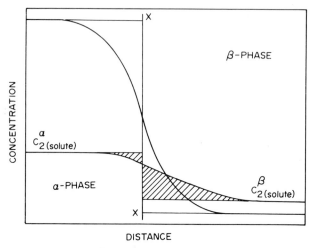

Fig. 14. The variations, with distance, of the concentrations of solvent and solute on passing through an interface, and illustration of the origin of surface concentration of the solute.

The definition of *surface free energy per unit area, G_s,* is analogous to that for the surface concentration, i.e.:

$$G_s A_s = G' - \sum \overline{G}_i^{\alpha} n_i^{\alpha} - \sum \overline{G}_i^{\beta} n_i^{\beta}, \tag{62}$$

where G' is the total free energy of the system.

The *surface tension, σ,* is defined as:

$$\sigma = \left(\frac{\partial G'}{\partial A_s} \right)_{T,P,n_i},$$

and hence, when surfaces are included in the discussion, eq. (13) is written as:

$$dG' = -S'dT + V'dP + \sigma dA_s + \sum \overline{G}_i dn_i. \tag{63}$$

If the surface area is increased by dA_s at constant T, P, and n_i, combination of eqs. (62) and (63) gives:

$$G_s dA_s = \sigma dA_s + \left(\sum \overline{G}_i^{\alpha} n_i^{\alpha} + \sum \overline{G}_i^{\beta} n_i^{\beta} \right). \tag{64}$$

As phase equilibrium is maintained, $\overline{G}_i^{\alpha} = \overline{G}_i^{\beta}$; mass balance requires that:

$$dn_i^{\alpha} + dn_i^{\beta} = -\Gamma_i dA_s,$$

in which case eq. (64) can be written as:

$$G_s dA_s = \sigma dA_s + \sum \overline{G}_i \Gamma_i dA_s$$

or:

$$G_s = \sigma + \sum \overline{G}_i \Gamma_i, \tag{65}$$

i.e., the surface free energy is the surface tension plus the free energy due to the surface concentrations of the components.

Complete differentiation of eq. (65) gives:

$$dG_s = d\sigma + \sum \bar{G}_i d\Gamma_i + \sum \Gamma_i d\bar{G}_i, \tag{66}$$

and the differential of G_s, for conditions of fixed surface area and fixed P gives:

$$dG_s = -S_s dT + \sum \bar{G}_i d\Gamma_i. \tag{67}$$

Combination of eqs. (66) and (67) gives:

$$d\sigma = -S_s dT - \sum \Gamma_i dG_i, \tag{68}$$

which is *Gibbs' equation for surface tension*. At constant T, eq. (68) gives, for the binary system A–B in which $\Gamma_A = 0$:

$$\Gamma_B = -\left(\frac{\partial \sigma}{\partial \bar{G}_B}\right)_T = -\left(\frac{\partial \sigma}{RT \partial \ln a_B}\right)_T$$

$$= -\frac{1}{RT}\left(\frac{d\sigma}{d \ln a_B}\right). \tag{69}$$

Equation (69), which is known as the *Gibbs adsorption isotherm*, indicates that any solute which lowers the surface tension has a positive value of Γ and hence is concentrated in the surface, and, conversely, any solute which raises the surface tension has a lower concentration in the surface than in the bulk phase.

The influence of dissolved oxygen on the surface tension of liquid iron at 1550°C is shown in fig. 15 as the variation of σ with the activity of oxygen relative to the 1

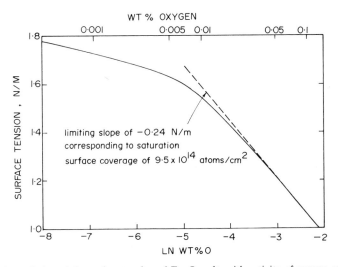

Fig. 15. The variation of the surface tension of Fe–O melts with activity of oxygen at 1550°C.

References: p. 326.

weight percent standard state. The surface concentration of oxygen at any concentration of oxygen in the bulk phase is obtained from the slope of the line and the Gibbs adsorption isotherm. At high oxygen contents the slope of the line approaches the constant value of -240 dyne/cm, which corresponds to saturation coverage of the surface by adsorbed oxygen. From the Gibbs adsorption isotherm this saturation coverage is calculated as

$$\Gamma_0 = 6.023 \times 10^{23} \times \frac{240}{8.3144 \times 10^7 \times 1823} = 9.5 \times 10^{14} \text{ atoms/cm}^2.$$

9.2.   The Langmuir adsorption isotherm

Consider the equilibrium between the component i in a vapor phase and i adsorbed on the surface of a condensed phase. If is is considered that the atoms of i are adsorbed on specific adsorption sites on the surface of the condensed phase, the limit of adsorption occurs when all of the available sites are occupied by adsorbed atoms. This limit corresponds to the surface being covered by a monolayer of adsorbed atoms at the surface concentration Γ_i^0. At surface concentrations, Γ_i, less than that corresponding to monolayer coverage, the fraction of surface sites occupied, θ_i (or the fractional saturation of the surface) is defined as:

$$\theta_i = \frac{\Gamma_i}{\Gamma_i^0}. \tag{70}$$

At equilibrium, the rates of adsorption and desorption of i are equal, the former being proportional to the pressure of i in the vapor phase, p_i, and the fraction of unoccupied surface sites, $(1 - \theta_i)$, and the latter being proportional to the fraction of surface sites occupied by i, i.e.:

$$k_a p_i (1 - \theta_i) = k_d \theta_i,$$

where k_a and k_d are the rate constants for the adsorption and desorption reactions, respectively. Thus:

$$p_i = K_i \frac{\theta_i}{1 - \theta_i}, \tag{71}$$

where

$$K_i = k_d/k_a = \exp(-\Delta G_i^0/RT),$$

and ΔG_i^0 is the change in molar free energy accompanying the transfer of one mole of i from the vapor state at 1 atm pressure to the adsorbed layer on the surface at the surface concentration Γ_i^0. Equation (71), which is *Langmuir's adsorption isotherm*, shows that θ_i is proportional to p_i at small θ_i and $(1 - \theta_i)$ is inversely proportional to p_i at large θ_i.

Alternatively, eq. (71) can be written as:

$$a_i = K_i' \frac{\theta_i}{1 - \theta_i}. \tag{72}$$

BELTON has combined the Gibbs and Langmuir adsorption isotherms by substitution of eqs. (70) and (72) into eq. (69) to give:

$$\frac{d\sigma}{d \ln a_i} = -RT\Gamma_i = -RT\theta_i\Gamma_i^0 = -RT\Gamma_i^0 \frac{K_i'a_i}{1 + K_i'a_i},$$

which, on integration between the composition limits X_i' and X_i'', becomes:

$$\sigma'' - \sigma' = -RT\Gamma_i^0 \ln\frac{1 + K'a_i''}{1 + K'a_i'}. \tag{73}$$

If Langmuir's isotherm holds at all compositions, one limit can be taken as the pure solvent, in which case eq. (73) becomes

$$\sigma^P - \sigma = RT\Gamma_i^0 \ln(1 + K'a_i), \tag{74}$$

where σ^P refers to the surface tension of the pure solvent. Curve-fitting of eq. (74) with the experimental data shown in fig. 16 and $\sigma^P = 1788$ dyne/cm, $\Gamma_O^0 = 240$ dyne/cm, gives $K' = 220$. Thus, if oxygen adsorbed on liquid iron exhibits ideal Langmuir behavior:

$$\theta_O = \frac{220 \cdot [\text{wt\%O}]}{1 + 220 \cdot [\text{wt\%O}]}. \tag{75}$$

Equation (75) is shown in fig. 16 in comparison with the variation of θ_O obtained from the slopes in fig. 15 as $\theta_O = \Gamma_O/\Gamma_O^0$.

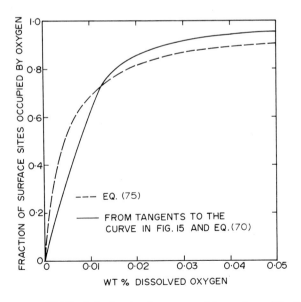

Fig. 16. The variation, at 1550°C, of the fractional coverage of the surface of liquid iron by adsorbed oxygen with concentration of oxygen in the melt.

References: p. 326.

A number of applications of the Gibbs and Langmuir absorption isotherms will be found in ch. 13, §§ 2 and 4.

9.3. Curved interfaces

The existence of surface tension gives rise to the interesting phenomenon that the equilibrium vapor pressure exerted by a spherical droplet is a function of the radius of curvature of the droplet. This phenomenon, which was first discussed by Kelvin in 1871, is of importance with respect to the dependence of the limit of solid solution of one component in another on the particle size of the second phase.

The general equation

$$dG' = -S'dT + V'dP + \sigma dA_s + \sum_i \overline{G}_i dn_i \tag{63}$$

was tacitly applied to systems containing flat interfaces. However, provided that σ is not a function of the radius of curvature of the interface, and that the interface within the system does not influence the exterior pressure, eq. (63) can be applied to the transfer of matter across curved interfaces. The *partial molar free energy*, $\overline{G}_i^*$, defined from eq. (63) as:

$$\overline{G}_i^* = \left(\frac{\partial G'}{\partial n_i} \right)_{T,P,A_s,n_i},$$

pertains to the addition of i to the system in such a manner that A_s remains constant. However, in a process involving the transfer of matter to a small spherical droplet, A_s, being dependent on the volume, and hence on the amount of matter in the droplet, is not an independent variable. The incremental increase in volume of a droplet caused by the addition of dn_i moles of the various components is:

$$dV' = \sum_i \overline{V}_i dn_i,$$

where $\overline{V}_i$ is the partial molar volume of i in the system. From the relationship between the surface area and the volume of a sphere,

$$dA_s = \frac{2dV'}{r} = \sum_i \frac{2\overline{V}_i}{r} dn_i,$$

substitution of which into eq. (63) gives:

$$dG' = -S'dT + V'dP + \sum_i \left(\overline{G}_i^* + \frac{2\overline{V}_i\sigma}{r} \right) dn_i.$$

Comparison with eq. (63) gives the identity

$$\overline{G}_i = G_i^* + \frac{2\overline{V}_i\sigma}{r} \tag{76}$$

as the variation of partial molar free energy with spherical particle size. From the relationship between partial molar free energy and activity, eq. (76) can be written as

$$\ln a_i = \ln a_i^* + \frac{2\bar{V}_i\sigma}{RT_r} . \tag{77}$$

In a limited terminal solid solution of B in A, in which B obeys Henry's Law, the activity of B at the limit of solubility is:

$$a_B = \gamma_B^0 X_{B(sat)},$$

and hence, from eq. (77), the solubility limit varies with particle size of the second phase as

$$\ln \frac{X_{B(sat,r)}}{X_{B(sat)}^*} = \frac{2\sigma\bar{V}_B}{RT_r} , \tag{78}$$

where $X_{B(sat,r)}$ is the solubility limit when the second phase occurs as a dispersion of spherical particles of radius r and $X_{B(sat)}^*$ is the solubility limit when the second phase is massive. Equation (78), which is known as the *Thomson–Freundlich equation*, provides a thermodynamical explanation of the phenomenon of *Ostwald ripening* (see ch. 10B, §3.2.2). When the second phase, precipitating from a primary solid solution, occurs in a range of particle sizes, it is observed that the particles of radius greater than some average value grow and that the smaller particles redissolve in the matrix. As the concentration of solute in the matrix at the interface between the matrix and a small precipitate is greater than that at the interface between the matrix and a large precipitate, a concentration, and hence activity, gradient exists between the two interfaces. This, in turn, provides the driving force for the diffusion of dissolved solute from one interface to the other, with the overall result that the larger particle grows and the smaller particle dissolves. Equation (78) is also of interest in that it indicates that no such quantity as "maximum solubility" exists.

10. *The measurement of thermodynamic activity*

Although activities are thermodynamic functions of state, their magnitudes and variations are determined by the interactions among the constituent particles of the system, which, in turn, determine bond energies and influence the spatial configurations assumed by the particles. Thus measurement of activities within a class of similar simple systems can be expected to provide, at best, some fundamental understanding of the natures of these interactions or, at least, a basis for correlation of the behavior, which can then be used for extrapolation of the behavior of more complex systems.

The molar free energy of formation of a solution or compound from its pure components is obtained from the activities via eq. (44) and as the various phase equilibria occurring in a materials system are determined by the variations, with composition, temperature and pressure, of the relative free energies of the various

References: p. 326.

phases, such equilibria can be most precisely determined by accurate measurement of activity. Also, the activity of a component in a solution is a measure of the minimum free energy required to convert the component from its state in solution to the pure state in any proposed extraction or refining process.

In the majority of the experimental methods the activity of only one component is measured. In such cases the activities of the other components can be obtained by integration of the Gibbs–Duhem equation. For constant temperature and total pressure this expression is $\sum X_i d \ln a_i = 0$ or, in a more convenient form, $\sum X_i d \ln \gamma_i = 0$ where $\gamma_i = a_i/X_i$ is the activity coefficient of i. Applied to the binary system A–B in which the variation of γ_A is known across the entire range of composition:

$$\ln \gamma_B \ (\text{at } X_B) = - \int_{X_B=1}^{X_B} \frac{X_A}{X_B} \, d \ln \gamma_A. \tag{79}$$

10.1. Determination of activity by experimental measurement of vapor pressure

The experimental technique for the measurement of vapor pressure is determined by the magnitude of the pressure to be measured, and the various techniques which have been developed can be classified as *absolute methods* (direct and indirect static methods) and *indirect methods* (effusion and transpiration methods).

The earliest activity measurements were made on binary alloys of Hg with Zn, Au, Ag and Tl at temperatures near the boiling point of Hg. The partial pressure of Hg exerted by an amalgam is so much greater than the partial pressure of the other component that the former can be equated with the total vapor pressure of the amalgam. In the first studies the alloy was used as the sealing liquid in a U-tube null-point manometer. The vapor in equilibrium with the alloy is contained in the closed arm of the manometer, and hydrogen, the pressure of which is measured at a second manometer, is introduced to the other arm until the meniscuses in both arms are at the same level. The vapor pressures of amalgams at lower temperatures have been measured using various devices such as membrane manometers, quartz spiral manometers and ionization gages.

The partial pressures of Zn and Cd over α-Ag–Zn–Cd alloys and of Zn over α-brasses have been measured by resonance absorption spectroscopy. In studying the Zn alloys, light produced by a spark between Zn electrodes, is passed through a sample of vapor in equilibrium with the alloy, and the absorption of the 3076 Å resonance line is measured. As absorption of the 3035 Å resonance line does not occur, it is used as an internal standard and the vapor pressure, p, of Zn is obtained from Beer's Law as $-\ln(I_{3076}/I_{3035}) = Kpd/T$ where I is the intensity of the transmitted light, K is the absorption coefficient, T is the absolute temperature and d is the distance travelled by the light through the sample of vapor.

The *dew point method* is well-suited to systems containing a distinctly volatile component and has been applied to measurement of the activity of Zn in binary alloys containing Cu, Al, Ag, Au, Zr, Th, U, and Y, and the activity of Cd in Ag–Cd alloys. Experimentally, the alloy is placed at one end of a long initially evacuated tube which is heated to the desired temperature T_1. The temperature of the other end of the tube is lowered until condensation of the volatile component is observed at the temperature T_2. As the pressure within the tube is uniform, the partial pressure of the volatile component exerted by the alloy at T_1 equals the saturated vapor pressure of the pure volatile component at T_2. The use of fused silica tubes, which permits visual observation of condensation at the cooler end, has limited the temperature to less than $1100°C$ and, generally, measurements have been made in the range 400-$900°C$. In a similar *isopiestic technique,* the pure volatile component is placed in the cool end of an initially evacuated tube maintained in a known temperature gradient, and weighed quantities of the pure second component are placed at intervals along the temperature gradient. The volatile component is transferred from the vapor phase to the specimens of nonvolatile component until the alloys in equilibrium with the prevailing pressure of the volatile component are formed. In this technique, which has been applied to measurement of the activities of Al in solid Al–Fe and Al–Ni alloys, the compositions of the equilibrated alloys are determined gravimetrically.

Application of the dew point and isopiestic techniques to measurement of activity requires knowledge of the temperature dependence of the saturated vapor pressure of the volatile component.

In the *transpiration technique,* an inert carrier gas is passed over a sample at a flow rate which permits evaporation of the alloy to occur to the extent necessary to saturate the carrier gas. This technique has been used to measure the activities in liquid Fe–Cu and Fe–Ni alloys. The material evaporated from the sample is condensed downstream and is chemically analyzed. The total amount of evaporation into unit volume of the carrier gas at the total pressure P is determined by measuring the weight loss of the sample or by quantitative analysis of the amount of condensate recovered from a known volume of gas. If n_{Fe}, n_{Cu} and n_{He} are the numbers of moles of Fe, Cu and He carrier gas in the sampled volume, the partial pressure of Fe is calculated, from the ideal gas law, as $p_{Fe} = Pn_{Fe}/(n_{Fe} + n_{Cu} + n_{He})$. An advantage of this technique is that the activities of both components are measured and hence internal consistency of the results can be checked using the Gibbs–Duhem equation. However, in order that surface depletion of the more volatile component be avoided, the rates of diffusion in the alloy must be faster than the rates of evaporation.

In the *effusion technique* the alloy to be studied is placed in a *Knudsen cell* (a sealed crucible containing a small orifice in its lid) and the crucible is heated in vacuum to the desired temperature. Phase equilibrium is established between the vapor phase and the condensed phase in the cell and, if the dimensions of the orifice are small in comparison with the mean free path of the vapor species, the passage of vapor species through the orifice is not disturbed by collisions. Thus the rates of effusion of the vapor species are proportional to their vapor pressures within the cell. From gas kinetic theory, the number of particles in a vapor phase striking unit area of the containing wall in unit time is $0.25n\bar{c}$, where n is the density of vapor species and $\bar{c} = (8RT/\Pi M)^{1/2}$ is the average speed of the particles. Consequently, the

References: p. 326.

weight loss, W, due to effusion through an orifice of area A in time t is $pAt/(2\Pi MRT)^{1/2}$ and hence the pressure, p, of the species in the cell is $p = (W/At)(2\Pi RT/M)^{1/2}$. If a radioactive tracer is added to the alloy, very small amounts of effusing substance can be detected. For example, gamma-ray spectrometry of neutron-irradiated Au–Cu alloys has facilitated estimation of quantities as small as 10^{-10} g.

The transpiration and effusion techniques require that the molecular weights of the vapor species be known and hence they can only be used to study systems in which no complex vapor molecules are formed.

The problems caused by complex molecule formation can be eliminated by mass-spectrometric analysis of the vapor effusing from the Knudsen cell. In the *Knudsen cell–time of flight mass-spectrometer* combination, the beam of particles effusing from the cell is introduced to the ionization chamber of the mass-spectrometer through a slit. Ionization is produced by a pulsing electron beam and after each pulse the ionization chamber is cleared of ions by a pulse of small negative potential. The ions are then subjected to a continuously maintained high negative potential which accelerates them into a field-free drift tube, and the time required for a given ion to traverse the drift tube and be detected is proportional to $(m/e)^{1/2}$. The ion current, I_i^+, measured for the species i is related to the vapor pressure of i as:

$$p_i = KI_i^+ T, \tag{80}$$

where the constant K is determined by the ionization cross-section of the ion, the detector sensitivity and the geometry of the Knudsen cell–ion source. The application of the technique to measurement of activities in binary systems was greatly facilitated by a manipulation of the Gibbs–Duhem equation which allows the variations, with composition, of the activity coefficients of the individual components to be obtained from the corresponding measured ratio of the activity coefficients as:

$$\ln \gamma_B \left(\text{at } X_B \right) = - \int_1^{X_B} X_A \mathrm{d} \ln \frac{\gamma_A}{\gamma_B}. \tag{81}$$

From eq. (80):

$$\frac{I_A^+}{I_B^+} \propto \frac{p_A}{p_B} \propto \frac{a_A}{a_B} = \frac{\gamma_A X_A}{\gamma_B X_B},$$

substitution of which into eq. (81) gives:

$$\ln \gamma_B \left(\text{at } X_B \right) = - \int_1^{X_B} X_A \mathrm{d} \left(\ln \frac{I_A^+}{I_B^+} - \ln \frac{X_A}{X_B} \right).$$

Use of a mass-spectrometer requires that a pressure of less than 10^{-8} atm be maintained in the areas of the ion source, analyzer and detector. This technique has been applied to measurement of activities in a large number of binary and ternary systems containing V, Cr, Fe, Co, Ni, Cu, Ag, Au, Al, Tl, Pb, Sn, Bi, Sb, and In.

10.2.   Determination of activity by establishing heterogeneous equilibrium

Heterogeneous equilibrium at constant temperature and pressure requires that the partial molar free energy, and hence activity, of each component of the system be the same in each of the phases present, i.e., a_i (in phase I) $= a_i$ (in phase II) $= a_i$ (in phase III) $= \cdots$. Thus, if the activity of a component can be fixed at a known value in any one of the phases, its value in every other phase is known.

One of the more simple heterogeneous equilibria involves a binary liquid, saturated with one of its components. In a simple binary eutectic system exhibiting virtually complete mutual immiscibility in the solid state, the saturated liquids on the liquidus lines are in equilibrium with virtually pure solids. Thus, in the melt of A-liquidus composition at the liquidus temperature T, the activity of A relative to pure liquid A as the standard state equals the activity of pure solid A relative to liquid A as the standard state, both being given by $a_A = \exp(-\Delta G^0_{m,A}/RT)$ where $\Delta G^0_{m,A}$ is the molar free energy of melting of A at temperature T. Activities have been calculated in this manner along liquidus lines in such systems as Ag–Si and Ag–Pb.

Fe and Ag are virtually immiscible in the liquid state, and when Si is added as a solute to coexisting liquid Fe and Ag it is distributed between the two liquids such that its activity is the same in both phases. The activities of Si in liquid Fe and liquid Fe–C alloys have been determined by chemical analysis of equilibrated Fe and Ag liquids containing Si, and knowledge of the activity of Si in Ag–Si alloys. In a similar manner the activity of Ag in Al–Ag alloys has been determined from measurement of the equilibrium partitioning of Ag between the virtually immiscible liquids Al and Pb, and the activity of Al in Al–Co alloys has been determined by partitioning Al between the virtually immiscible liquids Ag and Co.

The respective equilibrium constants for the reactions $CO_2 + C_{(graphite)} = 2CO$ and $CO + \frac{1}{2}O_2 = CO_2$ are:

$$K_4 = \frac{p^2_{CO}}{p_{CO_2}a_C} \tag{82}$$

and

$$K_5 = \frac{p_{CO_2}}{p_{CO}p^{1/2}_{O_2}}. \tag{83}$$

Thus, at a fixed temperature, which determines the values of K_4 and K_5, a CO–CO$_2$ gas mixture of known p_{CO} and p_{CO_2} has an activity of carbon given by eq. (82) and a partial pressure of oxygen given by eq. (83). Similarly, by virtue of the equilibrium $H_2 + \frac{1}{2}O_2 = H_2O$, an H_2–H_2O mixture of known p_{H_2} and p_{H_2O} exerts a unique partial pressure of oxygen at any temperature; by virtue of the equilibrium $H_2 + \frac{1}{2}S_2 = H_2S$, an H_2–H_2S mixture of known p_{H_2} and p_{H_2S} exerts a unique partial pressure of sulfur at any temperature; and, by virtue of the equilibrium $C_{(graphite)} + 2H_2 = CH_4$, a CH_4–H_2 mixture of known p_{CH_4} and p_{H_2} has a unique activity of carbon at any temperature. Consequently, CO–CO$_2$ and CH$_4$–H$_2$ mixtures can be used as gas phases of fixed activity of carbon for use in the establishment of heterogeneous equilibria between a gas phase and a condensed phase. Similarly, $CO-CO_2$ and H_2-H_2O mixtures can be used as gas phases of fixed oxygen pressure and H_2-H_2S mixtures can be used as gas phases of fixed sulfur pressure. The activities of carbon in liquid and solid iron have been determined by equilibrating iron with $CO-CO_2$ and CH_4-H_2 mixtures and measuring the equilibrium carbon content of the metal phase, and the activities of oxygen and sulfur in liquid iron have been determined by equilibrating iron with H_2O-H_2 and H_2S-H_2 mixtures, respectively. In more simple gas–metal equilibria the activities of hydrogen and nitrogen in iron have been determined by measuring the solubilities of the gases as functions of gas pressure. Activities in the system $Fe-Fe_2O_3$ have been determined by experimental observation of the variation of the composition of small samples of condensed phases with temperature and oxygen pressure imposed by an equilibrating gas phase. The variation, with composition, of the activity of Fe in the system is determined by Gibbs–Duhem integration of the corresponding measured variation of the equilibrium partial pressure of oxygen. The oxygen content of liquid iron in equilibrium with pure liquid iron oxide at 1600°C is 0.23 wt%. If the oxide of a less noble metal than iron is dissolved in the liquid iron oxide, the activity of iron oxide, and hence the equilibrium oxygen content of the liquid iron are decreased. If the latter is x wt%, the activity of FeO, relative to pure Fe-saturated iron oxide as the standard state, in the oxide solution is $x/0.23$. This technique has been used to determine the activity of FeO in $CaO-FeO$ and $CaO-FeO-SiO_2$ melts saturated with liquid iron.

One step more complex is the establishment of equilibrium between a gas phase and two condensed phases. The equilibrium between manganese, manganous oxide and a $CO-CO_2$ mixture, expressed as $Mn + CO_2 = MnO + CO$ requires:

$$K = \frac{p_{CO} a_{MnO}}{p_{CO_2} a_{Mn}}. \tag{84}$$

Thus, at a given temperature, the equilibrium between pure Mn (at unit activity) and Mn-saturated pure MnO (at unit activity) occurs at a unique value of the ratio p_{CO}/p_{CO_2} given by eq. (84). If a metal more noble than Mn is embedded in an excess of MnO and subjected to a lower p_{CO}/p_{CO_2} ratio, manganese is transferred from the MnO to the metal phase until the activity of Mn required by eq. (84) and the imposed p_{CO}/p_{CO_2} is established. The manganese content of the alloy corresponding to the imposed activity is determined by chemical analysis. The other component of the alloy must be sufficiently more noble than Mn that formation and solution of its oxide in the MnO phase is negligible. The activity of Mn in Mn–Pt alloys has been determined in this manner. Having determined this relationship, the activity of MnO in oxide melts containing oxides more stable than MnO can be determined by equilibrating a small sample of Pt with an excess of oxide melt and a $CO-CO_2$ gas mixture. Again, as Mn is distributed between the Pt–Mn alloy and the oxide melt in accordance with eq. (84) and the imposed p_{CO}/p_{CO_2}, chemical analysis of the equilibrated Pt–Mn alloy yields a_{Mn} and hence, from eq. (84), the value of a_{MnO} in the oxide melt. In this application the other oxide component must be of a metal which is sufficiently less noble than Mn that the extent of its solution in the Pt–Mn phase is negligible. This technique has been used to determine the activity of MnO in systems such as $MnO–SiO_2$, $MnO–TiO_2$, $MnO–Al_2O_3$, $MnO–B_2O_3$ and $MnO–CaO–SiO_2$.

Other examples of determination of activities by establishing equilibrium between a binary alloy, a nonmetallic phase of known composition and a gas phase include:

$$Fe(\text{in Fe–Ni alloys}) + H_2O = FeO + H_2;$$

$$2Cr(\text{in Cr–Ni alloys}) + 3H_2O = Cr_2O_3 + 3H_2;$$

$$3Mn(\text{in Mn–Cu alloys}) + CH_4 = Mn_3C + 2H_2;$$

$$2Cu(\text{in Cu–Au alloys}) + H_2S = Cu_2S + H_2;$$

$$3Si(\text{in Si–Ag alloys}) + N_2\,(\text{in } N_2–H_2 \text{ mixtures}) = Si_3N_4. \tag{85}$$

Again, in this application, the "inert" metal must be sufficiently more noble than the primary component metal that its occurrence in the equilibrium nonmetallic phase is negligible. Corrections are required in systems where the nonmetallic phase is not a line compound. Thus, for example, in eq. (85), the activity of FeO is that in the wustite equilibrated with the imposed partial pressure of oxygen, relative to Fe-saturated wustite as the standard state. Equation (85) has also been used to determine the activity of FeO in $FeO–SiO_2$ melts by establishing the equilibrium $Fe + H_2O = FeO$ (in $FeO–SiO_2$ melts) $+ H_2$.

If the difference between the nobilities of the metals is small enough that an oxide solution is produced in equilibrium with the binary alloy phase a different approach is taken. For example, if a small specimen of an Fe–Mn alloy is equilibrated with an excess of an FeO–MnO solid solution, the exchange equilibrium $Fe + MnO = Mn + FeO$ is established, wherein $K = a_{Mn}a_{FeO}/a_{Fe}a_{MnO}$. From chemical analysis of the equilibrated Fe–Mn alloy and knowledge of the activities in the system Fe–Mn, the ratio $\gamma_{FeO}/\gamma_{MnO}$ in the equilibrating oxide solution is obtained as:

$$\frac{\gamma_{FeO}}{\gamma_{MnO}} = K \frac{a_{Fe}X_{MnO}}{a_{Mn}X_{FeO}},$$

and Gibbs–Duhem integration of the variation of this ratio with composition in the oxide solution according to eq. (81) yields the individual activity coefficients, and hence activities, of the components of the oxide solution. This technique has been used to determine activities in the systems $Fe_2SiO_4–Co_2SiO_4$ and $Fe_2SiO_4–Mn_2SiO_4$.

Activities have been determined by establishing equilibrium among three condensed phases and a gas phase. As an example, the activity of SiO_2 in $CaO–MgO–Al_2O_3–SiO_2$ melts has been determined by establishing the equilibrium

$$SiO_2 + 2C = Si + 2CO \tag{86}$$

in systems comprising a silicate melt, solid graphite, liquid iron and CO gas at 1 atm pressure, and by establishing the equilibrium

$$SiO_2 + 2SiC = 3Si + 2CO \tag{87}$$

References: p. 326.

in systems comprising a silicate melt, solid SiC, liquid iron and CO gas at 1 atm pressure. The activity of SiO_2 is obtained from chemical analysis of the equilibrated liquid phases, knowledge of the equilibrium constants for the reactions given by eqs. (86) and (87) and knowledge of the activity of Si in Fe–Si–C melts. Gibbs–Duhem integration of the results yielded activities in the systems $CaO–SiO_2$, $CaO–Al_2O_3$, $MgO–SiO_2$, $CaO–Al_2O_3–SiO_2$, $MgO–CaO–SiO_2$ and $MgO–Al_2O_3–SiO_2$.

10.3. Electrochemical measurement of activity

The EMF of a reversible galvanic cell, ε, is related to the free energy change, ΔG, for the cell reaction as $\Delta G = -zF\varepsilon$ where F is Faraday's constant and z is the number of Faradays required for the cell reaction. Thus, in a concentration cell of the type

pure metal A |ionic conductor containing metal A ions of valence z_A| alloy A–B,

the cell reaction is A(pure) → A(in the A–B alloy) for which $\Delta G = RT \ln a_A$ (in the A–B alloy). Thus the activity of A in the alloy is obtained as $\ln a_A = -(z_A F\varepsilon/RT)$. The determination of activity by measurement of the EMF of an electrochemical cell requires that the electrolyte be a purely ionic conductor and that the valency z_A be defined. A further requirement is that the extent of the exchange reaction at the cathode–electrolyte interface between B in the alloy and A in the electrolyte be negligible. If this condition is not met, the measured EMF contains a contribution of unknown magnitude arising from the transfer of electrolyte between regions of different composition. In practice the extent of the exchange reaction is rendered negligible by ensuring that B is significantly more noble than A. Molten chlorides are purely ionic conductors and hence these melts are popular as liquid electrolytes. The concentrations of low valent cations in the electrolyte are minimized by dissolving the chlorides in mixtures of alkali chlorides.

The activity of Al in Al–Ag melts in the range 700–800°C has been obtained from measurement of the EMFs of cells of the type

$$Al_{(1)} \,|\, Al^{3+} (in \; KCl–NaCl) \,|\, Al–Ag_{(1)}.$$

Similarly the activities of Cd in Cd–Pb, Cd–Bi, Cd–Sb and Cd–Sn alloys, and the activities of Cu in Cu–Au melts and Ag in Ag–Au melts have been determined from concentration cells with liquid chloride electrolytes.

The cell

$$Mg_{(1)} \,|\, MgCl_{2(1)} \,|\, Cl_{2(g,1\,atm)}$$

is a formation cell in which the cell reaction is $Mg + Cl_2 = MgCl_2$. With pure liquid Mg, pure liquid $MgCl_2$ and Cl_2 at 1 atm pressure, the free energy change is the standard free energy change, ΔG^0, and the EMF is the standard EMF, $\varepsilon^0 = -\Delta G^0/2F$. Alloying the anode with a more noble metal such as Al alters the free energy change for the cell reaction to $\Delta G = \Delta G^0 - RT \ln a_{Mg}$ (in the alloy) and hence the cell EMF to

$$\varepsilon = \varepsilon^0 + \frac{RT}{2F} \ln a_{Mg} \text{ (in the alloy)}. \tag{88}$$

Equation (88) has been used to determine the activities of Mg in Mg–Al melts from EMF measurements in the range 700–880°C.

Similarly, the formation cell

$$Pb_{(1)} \mid PbO_{(1)} \mid O_{2(g,1 \, atm)}$$

has a standard EMF of $\varepsilon^0 = -\Delta G^0/2F$. Alloying the PbO electrolyte with the oxide of a less noble metal, such as SiO_2, changes the cell EMF to:

$$\varepsilon = \varepsilon^0 - \frac{RT}{2F} \ln a_{PbO} \text{ (in PbO–SiO}_2\text{)},$$

and this has been used as the basis for electrochemical determination of the activities in the system PbO–SiO$_2$ in the range 850–1050°C.

Within wide ranges of temperature and oxygen pressure, ZrO_2 and ThO_2 in the fluorite structure, stabilized by solid solution with CaO and Y_2O_3, respectively, exhibit unusually high conductivities and transport numbers for O^{2-} of essentially unity. Consequently CaO–ZrO$_2$ and Y$_2$O$_3$–ThO$_2$ have been used as solid electrolytes in oxygen concentration cells of the type

$$Pt, O_{2(g,at \, pressure \, P_1)} \mid CaO\text{–}ZrO_2 \mid O_{2(g,at \, pressure \, P_2)}, \; Pt,$$

in which the cell reaction is $O_{2(g,at \, pressure \, P_1)} \rightarrow O_{2(g,at \, pressure \, P_2)}$ and the cell EMF is $\varepsilon = -\Delta G/4F = -(RT/4F) \ln P_2/P_1$. The oxygen pressure at the electrodes can be fixed by using equilibrated metal–metal-oxide couples, e.g., with Fe–FeO and Ni–NiO the cell becomes

$$Fe, FeO \mid CaO\text{–}ZrO_2 \mid Ni, NiO,$$

with a cell reaction of NiO + Fe = FeO + Ni. With the electrodes Fe–FeO and (Fe–Ni)–FeO, the cell reaction is $Fe_{(pure)} \rightarrow Fe_{(in \, the \, Fe-Ni \, alloy)}$ and the cell EMF is

$$\varepsilon = -\frac{RT}{2F} \ln a_{Fe} \text{ (in the alloy)}. \tag{89}$$

This method is similar to that discussed in connection with eq. (85). In the chemical equilibration technique the oxygen pressure is imposed, and the Fe–Ni alloy in equilibrium with FeO and the imposed oxygen pressure is produced in the experimental apparatus. In the EMF technique the oxygen pressure in equilibrium with a given Fe–Ni alloy and FeO is measured. Equation (89) has been used as the basis for electrochemical determination of the activities in a large number of solid and liquid binary alloy systems, the majority of which contained Fe, Co, Ni or Cu as the less noble metal. The activity of Si in Fe–Si alloys at 1550°C and 1600°C has been determined with electrodes of Cr, Cr$_2$O$_3$ and SiO$_2$, Fe–Si and activities in the systems Ta–W and Ta–Mo have been determined with a Y$_2$O$_3$–ThO$_2$ electrolyte and Ta, Ta$_2$O$_5$ and Ta–X, Ta$_2$O$_5$ electrodes. The activities of SnO in SnO–SiO$_2$ melts

References: p. 326.

and PbO in PbO–SiO$_2$ melts have been determined from cells of the type M, MO | CaO–ZrO$_2$ | M, MO–SiO$_2$.

Other solid electrolytes which have been used include β-alumina and soft soda glass for measurement of the activity of sodium in alloys, and glasses containing K$^+$ and Ag$^+$ for study of K and Ag alloys, respectively. It can be expected that, as new solid state electrolytes are developed for possible use in fuel cells, they will be applied to the determination of activities by EMF measurements.

Bibliography

ALCOCK, C.B., Principles of Pyrometallurgy (Academic Press, London, 1976).

BELTON, G.R., Langmuir Adsorption, the Gibbs Adsorption Isotherm and Interfacial Kinetics in Liquid Metal Systems, Metallurg. Trans. **B7** (1976) 35.

BELTON, G.R., and R.J. FRUEHAN, The Determination of Activities by Mass-Spectrometry – Some Additional Methods, Metallurg. Trans. **2** (1971) 291.

CALLEN, H.B., Thermodynamics (Wiley, New York, 1960).

CHANDRASEKHARAIAH, M.S., O.M. SREEDHARAN and E. CHATTOPADHYAY, Thermodynamic Studies of Alloys and Intermetallic Compounds, in: Solid Electrolytes and Their Applications, ed. E.C. Subbarao (Plenum, New York, 1980).

ELLINGHAM, H.J.T., Reducibility of Oxides and Sulfides in Metallurgical Processes, J. Soc. Chem. Ind. **63** (1944) 125.

ELLIOTT, J.F., Physical Chemistry of Liquid Metal Solutions, in: Metallurgical Treatises, eds. J.F. Elliott and J. Tien (The Metallurgical Society of AIME, Warrendale, PA, 1981).

ELLIOTT, J.F., M. GLEISER and V. RAMAKRISHNA, Thermochemistry for Steelmaking (Addison–Wesley, Reading, MA, 1963).

FAST, J.D., Entropy (McGraw–Hill, New York, 1962).

GASKELL, D.R., Introduction to Metallurgical Thermodynamics, 2nd Ed. (McGraw–Hill, New York, 1981).

GOKCEN, N.A., Thermodynamics (Techscience, Hawthorne, CA, 1977).

HULTGREN, R., P.D. DESAI, D.T. HAWKINS, M. GLEISER and K.K. KELLEY, Selected Values of the Thermodynamic Properties of Binary Alloys (American Society for Metals, Metals Park, OH, 1973).

KUBASCHEWSKI, O., and C.B. ALCOCK, Metallurgical Thermochemistry, 5th Ed. (Pergamon Press, New York, 1979).

LEWIS, G.N., and M. RANDALL, Thermodynamics, 2nd Ed., revised by K.S. Spitzer and L. Brewer (McGraw–Hill, New York, 1961).

ROSENQUIST, T., Principles of Extractive Metallurgy (McGraw–Hill, New York, 1974).

STEINER, A., and K.L. KOMAREK, Thermodynamic Activities in Solid Ni–Al Alloys, Trans. Metallurg. Soc. AIME **230** (1964) 786.

SWALIN, R.A., Thermodynamics of Solids, 2nd Ed. (Wiley, New York, 1972).

TURKDOGAN, E.T., Physical Chemistry of High Temperature Technology (Academic, New York, 1980).

WAGNER, C., Thermodynamics of Alloys (Addison–Wesley, Reading, MA, 1952).

CHAPTER 7

PHASE DIAGRAMS

ARTHUR D. PELTON

Département de Génie Métallurgique
Ecole Polytechnique Montréal, Québec, Canada

R.W. Cahn and P. Haasen, eds.
Physical Metallurgy; third, revised and enlarged edition
© *Elsevier Science Publishers BV, 1983*

1. Introduction

The study of phase equilibria and phase transformations is central to nearly all branches of metallurgy and materials science. Although departures from equilibrium will occur in any real system, a knowledge of the equilibrium state under a given set of conditions is the starting point for the understanding of most processes.

A phase diagram is a graphical representation of the loci of thermodynamic variables when equilibrium among the phases of a system is established under a given set of conditions. The phase diagrams most familiar to the metallurgist are those for which temperature and composition are the axes. These are discussed in §§2 and 3 for binary (two-component) and ternary (three-component) systems. However, the effect of other variables such as total pressure and chemical potential of the components (e.g., the partial pressure of oxygen) may often be of interest. In §4, different types of phase diagrams are discussed along with the general rules governing their construction.

Throughout the chapter, the thermodynamic origin of phase diagrams is stressed. With the advent of modern computer techniques, the relationship between phase diagrams and the thermodynamic properties of the system has become of increasing practical importance. As discussed in §2.10, a quantitative coupling of the two is now possible. Furthermore, as discussed in §3.5, the computer-assisted thermodynamic approach often permits good estimates of unknown multicomponent phase diagrams to be made, and can often significantly reduce the experimental effort required to measure the phase diagram of a system.

2. Binary phase diagrams

The temperature–composition (T–X) phase diagram of the Bi–Sb system is shown in fig. 1 (HULTGREN et al. [1963]). The abscissa is the composition, expressed as *mole fraction* of Sb, X_{Sb}. Note that $X_{Sb} = 1 - X_{Bi}$. Phase diagrams are also often drawn with the composition axis expressed as weight percent.

At all compositions and temperatures in the area above the line labelled *liquidus*, single-phase liquid alloys will be observed, while at all compositions and temperatures below the line labelled *solidus*, alloys exist as single-phase solid solutions. An alloy sample at equilibrium at a temperature and overal composition between these two curves will consist of a mixture of solid and liquid phases, the compositions of which are given by the liquidus and solidus compositions at that temperature. For example, a Bi–Sb sample of overall composition $X_{Sb} = 0.60$ at $T = 700$ K (at point R in fig. 1) will consist, at equilibrium, of a mixture of liquid alloy of composition $X_{Sb} = 0.37$ (point P) and solid alloy of composition $X_{Sb} = 0.82$ (point Q). The line PQ is called a *tie-line* or *conode*. As the overall composition is varied at 700 K between points P and Q, the compositions of the liquid and solid phases remain fixed at P and Q, and only the relative proportions of the two phases change. From a simple mass balance, one can derive the *lever rule* for binary systems: (moles of liquid)/(moles of solid) = RQ/PR. Hence, at 700 K a sample of Bi–Sb alloy with overall composition $X_{Sb} = 0.60$ consists of liquid and solid phases in the molar ratio $(0.82 - 0.60)/(0.60 - 0.37) = 0.96$. Were the composition axis expressed as weight percent, then the lever rule would give the weight ratio of the two phases.

Suppose that a liquid Bi–Sb alloy with composition $X_{Sb} = 0.60$ is cooled very slowly from an initial temperature of 900 K. When the temperature has decreased to the liquidus temperature of 780 K (point A) the first solid appears, with a composition at point B ($X_{Sb} = 0.93$). As the temperature is decreased further, solid continues to precipitate with the compositions of the two phases at any temperature being given by the liquidus and solidus compositions at that temperature and with their relative proportions being given by the lever rule. Solidification is complete at 630 K, the last liquid to solidify having composition $X_{Sb} = 0.18$ (point C).

The process just described is known as equilibrium cooling. At any temperature during equilibrium cooling the solid phase has a uniform (homogeneous) composition. In the preceding example, the composition of the solid phase during cooling varies along the line BQD. Hence, in order for the solid particles to have a uniform composition at any temperature, diffusion of Sb from the center to the surface of the growing particles must occur. Since solid state diffusion is a relatively slow process, equilibrium cooling conditions are only approached if the temperature is decreased very slowly. If a Bi–Sb alloy of composition $X_{Sb} = 0.60$ is cooled very rapidly from the liquid, concentration gradients will be observed in the solid grains, with the concentration of Sb decreasing towards the surface from a maximum of $X_{Sb} = 0.93$ (point B) at the center. Furthermore, in this case solidification will not be complete at 630 K since at 630 K the average concentration of Sb in the solid particles will now be greater than $X_{Sb} = 0.60$. These considerations are discussed more fully in ch. 9.

At $X_{Sb} = 0$ and $X_{Sb} = 1$ in fig. 1 the liquidus and solidus curves meet at the equilibrium melting points, or *temperatures of fusion*, of Bi and Sb, which are: $T^0_{f(Bi)} = 544.5$ K, $T^0_{f(Sb)} = 903$ K.

The phase diagram is influenced by the total pressure, P. Unless otherwise stated, T–X diagrams for alloy systems are usually presented for $P = \text{const.} = 1$ atm. However, for equilibria involving only solid and liquid phase the phase boundaries are typically shifted only by the order of a few hundredths of a degree per

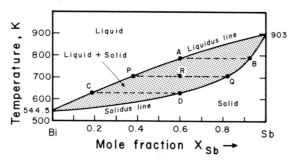

Fig. 1. Phase diagram of the Bi–Sb system (after HULTGREN *et al.* [1963]).

References: p. 382.

atmosphere change in P (see ch. 6, §3). Hence, the effect of pressure upon the phase diagram is generally negligible unless the pressure is of the order of hundreds of atmospheres. On the other hand, if gaseous phases are involved then the effect of pressure is very important (§2.12).

2.1.   The thermodynamic origin of phase diagrams

In this section we shall consider first of all the thermodynamic origin of simple "lens-shaped" phase diagrams in binary systems with complete liquid and solid miscibility. (This subject is also treated in ch. 6, §7.)

An example of such a diagram was given in fig. 1. Another example is the Ge–Si phase diagram in the lowest panel of fig. 2 (HANSEN [1958]). In the upper three

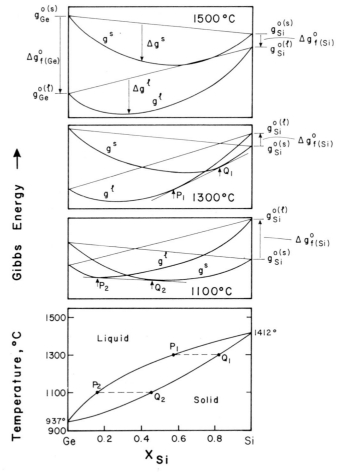

Fig. 2. Ge–Si phase diagram (after HANSEN [1958]) and Gibbs energy–composition curves at three temperatures, illustrating the common tangent construction.

panels of fig. 2 are shown, to scale, the molar Gibbs energies of the solid and liquid phases, g^s and g^l, at three temperatures. As illustrated in the top panel, g^s varies with composition between the standard molar Gibbs energies of pure solid Ge and of pure solid Si, $g_{Ge}^{0(s)}$ and $g_{Si}^{0(s)}$, while g^l varies between the standard molar Gibbs energies of the pure liquid components $g_{Ge}^{0(l)}$ and $g_{Si}^{0(l)}$. The molar *Gibbs energies of mixing* of the solid and liquid phases, Δg^s and Δg^l, are negative and are equal to the difference between the Gibbs energy of the solution and a simple weighted average of the Gibbs energies of the pure unmixed components in each phase.

The difference between $g_{Si}^{0(l)}$ and $g_{Si}^{0(s)}$ is equal to the standard molar Gibbs energy of fusion (melting) of pure Si, $\Delta g_{f(Si)}^0 = (g_{Si}^{0(l)} - g_{Si}^{0(s)})$. Similarly for Ge, $\Delta g_{f(Ge)}^0 = (g_{Ge}^{0(l)} - g_{Ge}^{0(s)})$. The Gibbs energy of fusion of a pure component may be written as:

$$\Delta g_f^0 = \Delta h_f^0 - T\Delta s_f^0, \tag{1}$$

where Δh_f^0 and Δs_f^0 are the standard molar enthalpy and entropy of fusion. Since, to a first approximation, Δh_f^0 and Δs_f^0 are independent of T, Δg_f^0 is approximately a linear function of T. If $T > T_f^0$, then Δg_f^0 is negative. If $T < T_f^0$, then Δg_f^0 is positive. Hence, as seen in fig. 2, as T decreases, the g^s curve descends relative to g^l. At 1500°C, $g^l < g^s$ at all compositions. Therefore, by the principle that a system always seeks the state of minimum Gibbs energy at constant T and P, the liquid phase is stable at all compositions at 1500°C. At 1300°C, the curves of g^s and g^l cross. The line P_1Q_1, which is the *common tangent* to the two curves, divides the composition range into three sections. For compositions between pure Ge and P_1, a single-phase liquid is the state of minimum Gibbs energy. For compositions between Q_1 and pure Si, a single-phase solid solution is the stable state. Between P_1 and Q_1, total Gibbs energies lying on the tangent line P_1Q_1 may be realized if the system adopts a state consisting of two phases with compositions at P_1 and Q_1 and with relative proportions given by the lever rule. Since the tangent line P_1Q_1 lies below both g^s and g^l, this two-phase state is more stable than either phase alone. Furthermore, no other line joining any point on g^l to any point on g^s lies below the line P_1Q_1. Hence, this line represents the true equilibrium state of the system, and the compositions P_1 and Q_1 are the liquidus and solidus compositions at 1300°C.

It may be shown that the common tangency condition also results in equal *activities* of each component in the two phases at equilibrium. That is, equality of activities and minimization of total Gibbs energy are equivalent criteria for equilibrium between phases.

As T is decreased to 1100°C, the points of common tangency are displaced to higher concentrations of Ge. For $T < 937$°C, $g^s < g^l$ at all compositions.

It should be noted that absolute values of Gibbs energies cannot be defined. Hence, the relative positions of $g_{Ge}^{0(l)}$ and $g_{Si}^{0(l)}$ in fig. 2 are completely arbitrary. However, this is immaterial for the preceding discussion, since displacing both $g_{Si}^{0(l)}$ and $g_{Si}^{0(s)}$ by the same arbitrary amount relative to $g_{Ge}^{0(l)}$ and $g_{Ge}^{0(s)}$ will not alter the compositions of the points of common tangency.

It should also be noted that in the present discussion of equilibrium phase

References: p. 382.

diagrams we are assuming that the physical dimensions of the single-phase regions in the system are sufficiently large that surface (interfacial) energy contributions to the Gibbs energy can be neglected. For very fine grain sizes in the sub-micron range however, surface energy effects can noticeably influence the phase boundaries.

The shape of the two-phase (solid + liquid) "lens" on the phase diagram is determined by the Gibbs energies of fusion, Δg_f^0, of the components and by the mixing terms, Δg^s and Δg^l. In order to observe how the shape is influenced by varying Δg_f^0, let us consider a hypothetical system A–B in which Δg^s and Δg^l are ideal Raoultian (§2.2). Let $T_{f(A)}^0 = 800$ K and $T_{f(B)}^0 = 1200$ K. Furthermore, assume that the entropies of fusion of A and B are equal and temperature-independent. The enthalpies of fusion are then given from eq. (1) by the expression $\Delta h_f^0 = T_f^0 \Delta s_f^0$ since $\Delta g_f^0 = 0$ when $T = T_f^0$. Calculated phase diagrams for $\Delta s_f^0 = 3$, 10 and 30 J/mol K are shown in fig. 3. A value of $\Delta s_f^0 \simeq 10$ is typical of most metals (*Richard's rule*). However, when the components are ionic compounds such as ionic oxides, halides, etc., then Δs_f^0 can be significantly larger since there are several atoms per formula

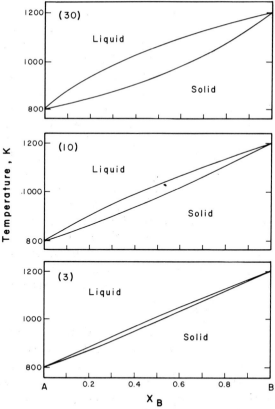

Fig. 3. Phase diagrams for a system A–B with ideal solid and liquid solutions with $T_{f(A)}^0 = 800$ K and $T_{f(B)}^0 = 1200$ K, calculated for entropies of fusion $\Delta s_{f(A)}^0 = \Delta s_{f(B)}^0 = 3$, 10 and 30 J/mol K.

unit. Hence, two-phase "lenses" in binary ionic salt or oxide phase diagrams tend to be "fatter" than those encountered in alloy systems. If we are considering vapour–liquid equilibria rather than solid–liquid equilibria, then the shape is determined by the entropy of vaporization, Δs_V^0 (§2.12). Since $\Delta s_V^0 \approx 10 \Delta s_f^0$, two-phase (liquid + vapour) lenses tend to be very wide.

2.2. Minima and maxima in two-phase regions

As discussed in ch. 6, §6, the Gibbs energies of mixing, Δg^s and Δg^l, may each be expressed as the sum of an ideal (Raoultian) term which is purely entropic and which is given by the Boltzmann equation for a random substitutional solution of A and B particles, and an *excess* term, g^E (sometimes written g^{xs}):

$$\Delta g = RT(X_A \ln X_A + X_B \ln X_B) + g^E, \tag{2}$$

where X_A and X_B are the mole fractions of the components. An *ideal* or *Raoultian* solution is defined as one in which $g^E = 0$. Both the solid and liquid phases in the Ge–Si system (fig. 2) are approximately ideal. With two ideal solutions, a "lens-shaped" two-phase region always results. However, in most alloy systems, even approximately ideal behaviour is the exception rather than the rule.

If $g^E > 0$ then the system is said to exhibit positive deviations from ideality. If $g^E < 0$, then we speak of negative deviations.

Curves of g^s and g^l for a hypothetical system A–B are shown schematically in fig. 4 at a constant temperature below the melting points of pure A and B such that the solid state is the stable state for both pure components. However, in this system $g^{E(l)} < g^{E(s)}$ so that g^s presents a flatter curve than does g^l and there exists a central composition region in which $g^l < g^s$. Hence, there are two common tangent lines, P_1Q_1 and P_2Q_2. Such a situation gives rise to a phase diagram with a minimum in the two-phase region as observed in the Au–Cu system shown in fig. 5 (HULTGREN *et al.* [1963]). At a composition and temperature corresponding to the minimum point, liquid and solid of the same composition exist in equilibrium.

A two-phase region with a minimum point as in fig. 5 may be thought of as a two-phase "lens" which has been "pushed down" by virtue of the fact that the

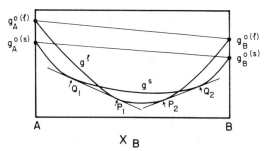

Fig. 4. Isothermal Gibbs-energy–composition curves for solid and liquid phases in a system A–B in which $g^{E(l)} < g^{E(s)}$. A phase diagram of the type in fig. 5 results.

References: p. 382.

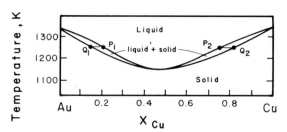

Fig. 5. Phase diagram of the Au–Cu system (after HULTGREN et al. [1963]).

liquid is relatively more stable than the solid. Thermodynamically, this relative stability is expressed as $g^{E(l)} < g^{E(s)}$.

Conversely, if $g^{E(l)} > g^{E(s)}$ to a sufficient extent, then a two-phase region with a maximum will result. In alloy systems, such maxima are nearly always associated with the existence of an intermetallic phase, as will be discussed in §2.8.

2.3. Miscibility gaps

If $g^E > 0$ for a solution, then the solution is thermodynamically less stable than an ideal solution. In an alloy system this can result from a too large difference in atomic diameter of the components, which will lead to a (positive) lattice strain energy, or from differences in valence, or from other factors (see ch. 4).

In the Au–Ni system, g^E is positive in the solid phase. In the top panel of fig. 6 is plotted $g^{E(s)}$ at 1200 K (HULTGREN et al. [1963]) as well as the ideal Gibbs energy of mixing, Δg^{ideal}, also at 1200 K. The sum of these two terms is the Gibbs energy of mixing $\Delta g^s = \Delta g^{ideal} + g^{E(s)}$, which is plotted at 1200 K as well as at other temperatures in the central panel of fig. 6. Now,

$$\Delta G^{ideal} = RT(X_{Au} \ln X_{Au} + X_{Ni} \ln X_{Ni})$$

is always negative and varies directly with T, whereas g^E varies less rapidly with temperature. As a result, the sum, $\Delta g^s = \Delta g^{ideal} + g^E$, becomes less negative as T decreases. However, the limiting slopes to the Δg^{ideal} curve at $X_{Au} = 1$ and $X_{Ni} = 1$ are both infinite

$$\left(\lim_{X_{Au} \to 1} d(\Delta g^{ideal})/d X_{Au} = \lim_{X_{Ni} \to 1} d(\Delta g^{ideal})/d X_{Ni} = \infty \right),$$

whereas the limiting slopes of g^E are always finite (Henry's Law). Hence, Δg^s will always be negative as $X_{Au} \to 1$ and $X_{Ni} \to 1$ no matter how low the temperature. As a result, below a certain temperature the curves of Δg^s will exhibit two negative "humps". Common tangent lines P_1Q_1, P_2Q_2, P_3Q_3 to the two humps define the ends of tie-lines of a two-phase solid–solid *miscibility gap* in the Au–Ni phase diagram which is shown in the lower panel in fig. 6 (HULTGREN et al. [1963]). The peak of the gap occurs at the *critical* or *consolute* temperature and composition, T_c and X_c.

When $g^{E(s)}$ is positive for the solid phase in a system it is usually also the case

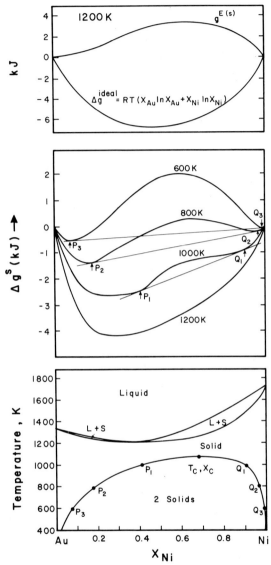

Fig. 6. Phase diagram and Gibbs energy curves of solid solutions for the Au–Ni system (after HULTGREN *et al.* [1963]).

that $g^{E(l)} < g^{E(s)}$, since the unfavourable factors (such as a difference in atomic dimensions) which are causing $g^{E(s)}$ to be positive will have less of an influence upon $g^{E(l)}$ in the liquid phase owing to the greater flexibility of the liquid structure to accommodate different atomic sizes, valencies, etc. Hence, a solid–solid miscibility gap is often associated with a minimum in the two-phase (solid + liquid) region as in the Au–Ni system.

References: p. 382.

2.4. Simple eutectic systems

The more positive g^E in a system is, the higher is T_c and the wider is the miscibility gap at any temperature. Suppose that $g^{E(s)}$ is sufficiently positive that T_c is higher than the minimum in the (solid + liquid) region. The result will be a phase diagram such as that of the Ag–Cu system shown in fig. 7 (HULTGREN et al. [1963]).

In the upper panel of fig. 7 are shown the Gibbs energy curves at 1100 K. The two common tangents define two two-phase regions. As the temperature is decreased below 1100 K, the g^s curve descends relative to g^l, and the two points of tangency, P_1 and P_2, approach each other until, at $T = 1052$ K, P_1 and P_2 become coincident at the composition E. That is, at $T = 1052$ K there is just one common tangent line contacting the two portions of the g^s curve at compositions A and B and contacting the g^l curve at E. This temperature is known as the *eutectic temperature*, T_E, and the composition E is the *eutectic composition*. For temperatures below T_E, g^l lies completely above the common tangent to the two portions of the g^s curve and so, for $T < T_E$ a solid–solid miscibility gap is observed. The phase boundaries of this two-phase region are called the *solvus* lines. The word eutectic is from the Greek for

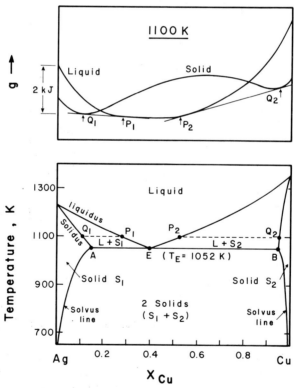

Fig. 7. Phase diagram and Gibbs energy curves at 1100 K of the Ag–Cu system (after HULTGREN et al. 1963). Solid Ag and Cu are both fcc.

"to melt well" since an alloy has the lowest melting point at the eutectic composition E.

This description of the thermodynamic origin of simple eutectic phase diagrams is strictly correct only if the pure solid components A and B have the same crystal structure (see §2.6).

Suppose a Ag–Cu alloy of composition $X_{Cu} = 0.28$ (composition P_1) is cooled from the liquid state very slowly under equilibrium conditions. At 1100 K the first solid appears with composition Q_1. As T decreases further, solidification continues with the liquid composition following the liquidus curve from P_1 to E and the composition of the solid phase following the solidus curve from Q_1 to A. The relative proportions of the two phases at any T are given by the lever rule. At a temperature $T = (T_E + \delta)$ just above T_E, two phases are observed: a solid of composition A and a liquid of composition E. At a temperature $T = (T_E - \delta)$ just below T_E, two solids with compositions A and B are observed. Therefore, at T_E, during cooling, the following *binary eutectic reaction* occurs:

$$\text{liquid} \rightarrow \text{solid}_1 + \text{solid}_2. \tag{3}$$

Under equilibrium conditions the temperature will remain constant at $T = T_E$ until all the liquid has solidified, and during the reaction the compositions of the three phases will remain fixed at A, B and E. For this reason the eutectic reaction is called an *invariant* reaction.

The morphologies of two-phase grains resulting from the co-precipitation of two solids during eutectic reactions are discussed in detail in ch. 9.

2.5. Binary phase diagrams with no intermediate phases

2.5.1. Thermodynamic origin illustrated by simple regular solution theory

Many years ago VAN LAAR [1908] showed that the thermodynamic origin of a great many of the observed features of binary phase diagrams can be illustrated at least qualitatively by simple regular solution theory. As discussed in ch. 6, §6.2, a *regular* solution is one in which:

$$g^E = \Omega X_A X_B, \tag{4}$$

where Ω is a parameter independent of temperature and composition.

In fig. 8 are shown several phase diagrams calculated for a hypothetical system A–B containing a solid and a liquid phase with melting points of $T_{f(A)}^0 = 800$ K and $T_{f(B)}^0 = 1200$ K and with entropies of fusion of both A and B set to 10 J/mol K, which is a typical value for metals. The solid and liquid phases are both regular with $g^{E(s)} = \Omega^s X_A X_B$ and $g^{E(l)} = \Omega^l X_A X_B$. The parameters Ω^s and Ω^l have been varied systematically to generate the various panels of fig. 8.

In panel (n) both phases are ideal. Panels (l–r) exhibit minima or maxima depending upon the sign and magnitude of $(g^{E(l)} - g^{E(s)})$, as has been discussed in §2.2. In panel (h) the liquid is ideal but positive deviations in the solid give rise to a

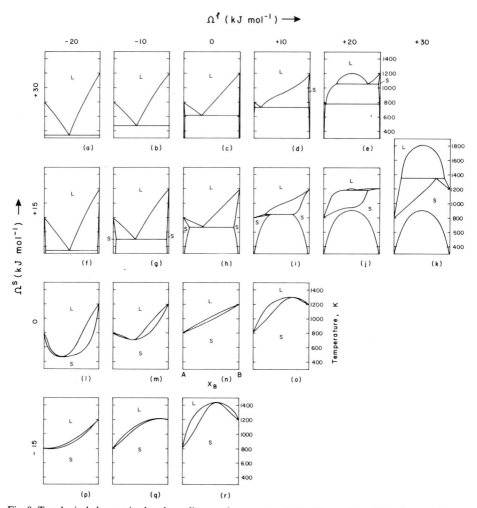

Fig. 8. Topological changes in the phase diagram for a system A–B with regular solid and liquid phases, brought about by systematic changes in the regular solution parameters Ω^s and Ω^l. Melting points of pure A and B are 800 K and 1200 K. Entropies of fusion of both A and B are 10.0 J/mol K. (PELTON and THOMPSON [1975].)

solid–solid miscibility gap as discussed above in §2.4. On passing from panel (h) to panel (c), an increase in $g^{E(s)}$ results in a widening of the miscibility gap so that the solubilities of A in solid B and of B in solid A decrease. Panels (a–c) illustrate that negative deviations in the liquid cause a relative stabilization of the liquid with resultant lowering of the eutectic temperature.

Eutectic phase diagrams are often drawn with the maximum solid solubility occurring at the eutectic temperature (as in fig. 7). However fig. 8d, in which the maximum solubility of A in the B-rich solid solution occurs at approximately $T = 950$ K, illustrates that this need not be the case even for simple regular solutions.

2.5.2.   Liquid–liquid immiscibility – monotectics

In fig. 8e, positive deviations in the liquid have given rise to a *liquid–liquid miscibility gap*. An example of a real system with such a phase diagram is the Cu–Pb system shown in fig. 9 (HULTGREN *et al.* [1963]). If a Cu–Pb alloy with $X_{Pb} = 0.10$ is cooled slowly from the liquid state, solid Cu begins to appear at 1260 K. Upon further cooling the liquid composition follows the liquidus curve to point A at $T = 1227$ K. The following invariant *monotectic reaction* then occurs:

$$liquid_A \rightarrow liquid_B + Cu_{(solid)}, \tag{5}$$

where $liquid_A$ and $liquid_B$ are liquids with compositions at points A and B. The temperature remains constant at the monotectic temperature and the compositions of all phases remain fixed until $liquid_A$ is completely consumed. Cooling then continues with precipitation of copper with the liquid composition following the liquidus line from B to the eutectic E.

Returning to fig. 8, we see that in panel (d) the positive deviations in the liquid are not large enough to produce immiscibility but they do result in a flattening of the liquidus which is often described as a "tendency to immiscibility". An example of such a flattened (or "S-shaped") liquidus resulting from a positive $g^{E(l)}$ is shown later for the Cd–Pb system in fig. 12.

2.5.3.   Peritectics

The invariant which appears in fig. 8i is known as a *peritectic*. The Au–Fe system shown in fig. 10 (HULTGREN et al. [1963]) exhibits a peritectic PQR at 1441 K as well as another at about 1710 K. The Gibbs energy curves, g^l and g^{fcc}, of the liquid and solid face-centred cubic phases are shown schematically at the peritectic temperature of $T_p = 1441$ K in the upper panel of fig. 10. One common tangent line PQR to g^l and to the two portions of g^{fcc} can be drawn.

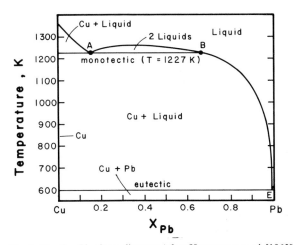

Fig. 9. The Cu–Pb phase diagram (after HULTGREN *et al.* [1963]).

References: p. 382.

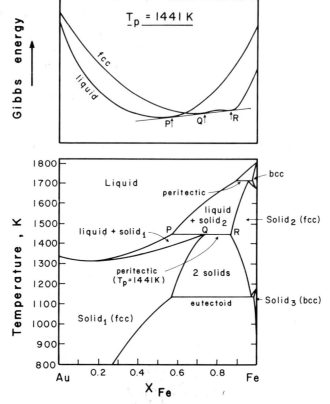

Fig. 10. Phase diagram and Gibbs energy curves at the peritectic temperature of 1441 K for the Au–Fe system (after HULTGREN *et al.* [1963]).

Suppose that a Au–Fe alloy of composition $X_{Fe} = 0.65$ is cooled very slowly from the liquid state. At a temperature $(T_p + \delta)$ just above 1441 K, a liquid phase of composition P and an fcc phase of composition R are observed at equilibrium. At a temperature $(T_p - \delta)$ just below 1441 K, the two phases at equilibrium are liquid and solid with compositions P and Q respectively. The following invariant *binary peritectic reaction* thus occurs upon cooling:

$$\text{liquid} + \text{solid}_2 \rightarrow \text{solid}_1. \tag{6}$$

This reaction occurs isothermally with all three phases at fixed compositions (at points P, Q and R). In the case of an alloy with overall composition between P and Q, the reaction occurs isothermally until all solid$_2$ is consumed. In the case of an alloy with overall composition between Q and R, it is the liquid which will first be completely consumed.

A peritectic reaction between a liquid and solid$_2$ occurs on the surface of the particles of solid$_2$ which can rapidly become coated with solid$_1$. By preventing contact between liquid and solid$_2$, this coating may greatly retard further reaction to such an extent that equilibrium conditions can only be achieved by extremely slow cooling.

2.5.4. Syntectics

The invariant in fig. 8k in which a solid decomposes upon heating into two liquids is known as a *syntectic*. It is rarely observed in alloy systems. Examples are found in the K–Pb and K–Zn systems (HANSEN [1958]). A phase diagram similar to fig. 8j, although without the tiny miscibility gap, is exhibited by the Au–Pt system (HANSEN [1958]).

2.6. Limited mutual solid solubility

In §2.4 the region of two solids in the Ag–Cu phase diagram of fig. 7 was described as a miscibility gap in the solid phase. That is, only one g^s curve was drawn. If, somehow, the appearance of the liquid phase could be suppressed, then the two solvus lines in fig. 7, when projected upwards, would meet at a critical point (as in the Au–Ni system in fig. 6) above which one continuous solid solution would exist at all compositions.

Such a description is justifiable as long as the pure solid components have the same crystal structure (i.e., belong to the same space group). This is the case for Ag–Cu since solid Ag and Cu are both fcc. The same assumption was made in our treatment of the peritectic Au–Fe system (fig. 10) in which the region of two solids was treated as a miscibility gap. Again in this case this description is permissible since Au and Fe are both fcc in this temperature range.

However, consider the simple eutectic system A–B in fig. 11 in which pure solid A and B are hcp (hexagonal close-packed) and fcc respectively. In this case, if the formation of the liquid phase could be suppressed the two solvus lines could not project upward to meet at a critical point, since this would imply that above this critical temperature a continuous series of solid solutions varying smoothly from hcp to fcc could exist. Such a situation is prohibited by symmetry conditions. That is, one continuous curve for g^s cannot be drawn. Each solid phase must have its own separate Gibbs energy curve, as shown schematically in the upper panels of fig. 11. In this figure, $g_A^{0(fcc)}$ is the *standard molar Gibbs energy of pure fcc A* and $g_B^{0(hcp)}$ is the standard molar Gibbs energy of pure hcp B. Such quantities may be defined in a number of different and non-equivalent ways as will be discussed below.

A real system with a phase diagram similar to fig. 11 is the Cd–Pb system shown in fig. 12 (ASHTAKALA *et al.* [1981]). Gibbs energy curves at a temperature below the eutectic are shown schematically in the upper panel. Let us derive an expression for g^{fcc} under the assumption that the Pb-rich fcc solid solution is a *Henrian solution*. As discussed in ch. 6, §6.2, when a solution is sufficiently dilute in one component, Henrian behaviour may be assumed. That is, the activity of the solvent is ideal ($a_{solvent} = X_{solvent}$; $\gamma^0_{solvent} = 1$), while for the solute, $a_{solute} = \gamma^0_{solute} X_{solute}$, where the *Henrian activity coefficient*, γ^0_{solute}, is independent of composition. At $T_E = 247.8°C$ in fig. 12, Cd in the Pb-rich fcc solution at $X_{Pb} = 0.940$ exists in equilibrium with

References: p. 382.

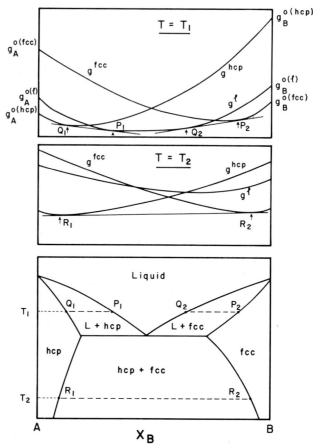

Fig. 11. Phase diagram and Gibbs energy curves at two temperatures for a simple eutectic system A–B in which pure solid A and B have different crystal structures.

virtually pure solid hcp Cd. Thus, in the fcc solution, $a_{Cd} \approx 1.0$ with respect to pure solid hcp Cd as standard state. Hence, $\gamma^0_{Cd} = a_{Cd}/X_{Cd} = 1.0/0.060 = 16.67$ at 247.8°C. We can now express g^{fcc} as:

$$g^{fcc} = \left(X_{Cd} g_{Cd}^{0(hcp)} + X_{Pb} g_{Pb}^{0(fcc)} \right) + RT\left(X_{Cd} \ln a_{Cd} + X_{Pb} \ln a_{Pb} \right)$$

$$= \left(X_{Cd} g_{Cd}^{0(hcp)} + X_{Pb} g_{Pb}^{0(fcc)} \right) + RT\left(X_{Cd} \ln\left(\gamma^0_{Cd} X_{Cd} \right) + X_{Pb} \ln X_{Pb} \right). \quad (7)$$

However, since γ^0_{Cd} is independent of composition we can combine terms as follows:

$$g^{fcc} = \left[X_{Cd}\left(g_{Cd}^{0(hcp)} + RT \ln \gamma^0_{Cd} \right) + X_{Pb} g_{Pb}^{0(fcc)} \right]$$

$$+ RT\left(X_{Cd} \ln X_{Cd} + X_{Pb} \ln X_{Pb} \right). \quad (8)$$

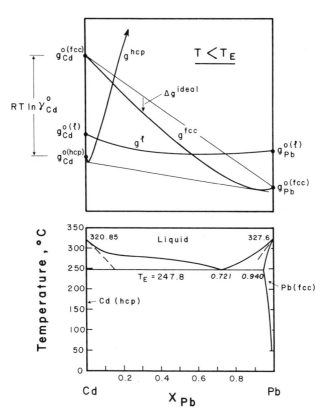

Fig. 12. Phase diagram of the Cd–Pb system (after ASHTAKALA *et al.* [1981]) and Gibbs energy curves (schematic) at a temperature below the eutectic. Dashed lines indicate limiting liquidus slopes calculated for zero solid solubility.

Let us now define:

$$g_{Cd}^{0(fcc)} = \left(g_{Cd}^{0(hcp)} + RT \ln \gamma_{Cd}^0 \right).$$

From eq. (8) it can be seen that relative to $g_{Cd}^{0(fcc)}$ defined in this way and to $g_{Pb}^{0(fcc)}$, the fcc solution is ideal. This is illustrated in fig. 12.

At 247.8°C in Cd–Pb, $(g_{Cd}^{0(fcc)} - g_{Cd}^{0(hcp)}) = RT \ln \gamma_{Cd}^0 = R(247.8 + 273.15) \ln 16.67 = 12.19$ kJ/mol. As a first approximation we could take this value to be independent of T, or as a second approximation we could evaluate γ_{Cd}^0 at other temperatures along the solidus and express $(g_{Cd}^{0(fcc)} - g_{Cd}^{0(hcp)})$ as, say, a linear function of T.

Although the above treatment has the advantage of numerical simplicity, it suffers from the difficulty that the numerical value of $(g_{Cd}^{0(fcc)} - g_{Cd}^{0(hcp)})$ is solvent-dependent and will be different for, say, solutions of Cd in fcc Cu and Cd in fcc Pb. For purposes of predicting binary phase diagrams from first principles (§2.11) or for estimating ternary phase diagrams from binary phase diagrams (§3.5) it would be desirable if $g_{Cd}^{0(fcc)}$ could be defined to be system-independent so as to be truly the "standard molar Gibbs energy of metastable fcc Cd". A great deal of effort has been expended by the international CALPHAD group under the impetus of Kaufman (KAUFMAN and BERNSTEIN [1970]) and co-workers to compile tables of *lattice stabilities* for metals in the fcc, hcp, bcc, and liquid states (that is, to obtain a set of relative values of $g^{0(fcc)}$, $g^{0(hcp)}$, $g^{0(bcc)}$ and $g^{0(l)}$ for every metal). In some cases, these can be calculated by extrapolating thermodynamic data from regions of T and P where the phases are stable. In other cases, lattice stabilities can be estimated partly from theoretical calculations and partly from the analysis of a large number of binary phase diagrams followed by a judicious choice of the "best" values which most closely fit the greatest number of systems. Tabulations of lattice stabilities are now available for many metals (KAUFMAN [1977, 1978, 1979]; KAUFMAN and NESOR [1978]; MACHLIN [1981]).

2.7. Calculation of limiting slopes of phase boundaries

In fig. 12 we see that the solubility of Pb in solid Cd is very small. The actual solubility at T_E is about 0.14 mol% (HANSEN [1958]). In thermodynamic terms this means that g^{hcp} increases very rapidly as Pb is added to solid Cd (see fig. 12), or that the Henrian activity coefficient γ_{Pb}^0 is very large. The fact that the solubility of Cd in solid Pb is much greater than that of Pb in solid Cd can be understood in terms of the Hume-Rothery rule (ch. 4) that solubilities are greater when the solute atoms are smaller than the solvent atoms, since the lattice strain energy will be less and hence g will rise less rapidly upon addition of solute.

As discussed later in §5, it is usually more difficult experimentally to determine a solidus than it is to measure liquidus temperatures. However, if the liquidus has been measured in the limit as $X_{solvent} \rightarrow 1$, then the limiting slope of the solidus can be calculated. Let component B be the solvent in a system A–B. The partial Gibbs energies of B along the liquidus and solidus are equal ($g_B^l - g_B^s = 0$). Hence:

$$\left(g_B^l - g_B^{0(l)}\right) - \left(g_B^s - g_B^{0(s)}\right) = -\left(g_B^{0(l)} - g_B^{0(s)}\right). \tag{9}$$

But: $(g_B^l - g_B^{0(l)}) \equiv RT \ln a_B^l$ and $(g_B^s - g_B^{0(s)}) \equiv RT \ln a_B^s$, where a_B^l and a_B^s are activities of B on the liquidus and solidus with respect to the pure liquid and pure solid standard states respectively. Hence, eq. (9) may be written as:

$$RT \ln a_B^l - RT \ln a_B^s = -\Delta g_{f(B)}^0. \tag{10}$$

In the limit $X_B \rightarrow 1$, Raoult's Law holds for both phases. That is, $a_B^l \rightarrow X_B^l$ and $a_B^s \rightarrow X_B^s$. Hence, in the limit, eq. (10) may be written as:

$$RT \ln X_B^l/X_B^s = -\Delta g_{f(B)}^0. \tag{11}$$

Furthermore, in the limit, $T \rightarrow T_{f(B)}^0$ and from eq. (1) $\Delta g_{f(B)}^0 \rightarrow \Delta h_{f(B)}^0(1 - T/T_{f(B)}^0)$. Finally, $\lim_{X_B \rightarrow 1}(\ln X_B) = (X_B - 1)$. Substituting these limiting values into eq. (11) we obtain:

$$\lim_{X_B \rightarrow 1} \left(d X_B^l/dT - d X_B^s/dT\right) = \Delta h_{f(B)}^0/R\left(T_{f(B)}^0\right)^2. \tag{12}$$

If the limiting slope of the liquidus, $\lim_{X_B \to 1}(\mathrm{d}\,X_B^l/\mathrm{d}T)$, is known, then the limiting slope of the solidus can be calculated via eq. (12) if the enthalpy of fusion is known.

For the Cd–Pb system, limiting liquidus slopes were calculated for both components from eq. (12) under the assumption that there is no solid solubility (that is, that $\mathrm{d}\,X_B^s/\mathrm{d}T = 0$). These are shown as the dashed lines on fig. 12. In Cd-rich solutions, agreement with the measured *limiting* liquidus slope is very good, but in Pb-rich solutions the poor agreement indicates the existence of appreciable solid solubility as has been confirmed by direct measurement.

2.8. Intermediate phases

The phase diagram of the Ag–Mg system (HULTGREN *et al.* [1963]) is shown in fig. 13. An *intermetallic phase,* β', is seen centered approximately about the composition $X_{Mg} = 0.5$. The Gibbs energy curve for such an intermetallic phase has the form shown schematically in the upper panel of fig. 13. $g^{\beta'}$ rises quite rapidly on either side of its minimum which occurs near $X_{Mg} = 0.5$. As a result, the β' phase appears on the phase diagram only over a limited composition range. This form of the curve $g^{\beta'}$ results from the fact that when $X_{Ag} \approx X_{Mg}$ a particularly stable crystal structure exists in which Ag and Mg atoms preferentially occupy different sites. The two common tangents P_1Q_1 and P_2Q_2 give rise to a maximum in the two-phase (β' +

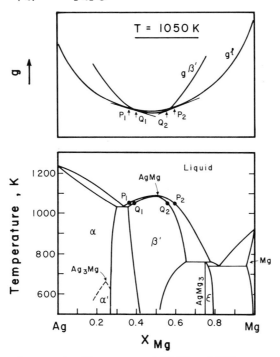

Fig. 13. Ag–Mg phase diagram (after HULTGREN *et al.* [1963]) and Gibbs energy curves (schematic) at 1050 K.

References: p. 382.

liquid) region in the phase diagram. (Although the maximum is observed very near $X_{Mg} = 0.5$, there is no thermodynamic reason for the maximum to occur exactly at this composition.)

The Na–Bi phase diagram is shown in fig. 14 (HANSEN [1958]). Gibbs energy curves at 700°C are shown schematically in the upper panel. $g(Na_{3/4}Bi_{1/4})$ rises extremely rapidly on either side of its minimum which occurs at $X_{Na} = 3/4$, $X_{Bi} = 1/4$. (We write $g(Na_{3/4}Bi_{1/4})$ rather than $g(Na_3Bi)$ in order to normalize to a basis of one mole of metal atoms.) As a result, the points of tangency Q_1 and Q_2 of the common tangents P_1Q_1 and P_2Q_2 are nearly (but not exactly) coincident. Hence, the composition range over which single-phase Na_3Bi exists (sometimes called the *range of stoichiometry* or *homogeneity range* of Na_3Bi) is very narrow (but never zero). The two regions labelled (Na_3Bi + liquid) in fig. 14 are the two sides of a two-phase region which passes through a maximum just like the (β' + liquid) regions in fig. 13. Because the Na_3Bi single-phase region is so narrow we refer to Na_3Bi as an *intermetallic compound*. In the case of Na_3Bi, any slight deviation from the stoichiometric composition causes a very large increase in Gibbs energy. Owing to the large difference in electronegativities of Na and Bi, Na_3Bi could be considered to

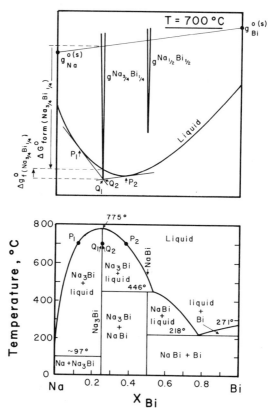

Fig. 14. Na–Bi phase diagram (after HANSEN [1958]) and schematic Gibbs energy curves at 700°C.

be a semi-ionic compound. Deviations from stoichiometry would require the substitution of Na on Bi sites or vice versa which would be energetically very unfavourable.

If stoichiometric Na_3Bi is heated, it will melt isothermally at 775°C to form a liquid of the same composition. That is, the melting behaviour of Na_3Bi is similar to that of a pure element. Such intermetallic compounds are called *congruently melting* or simply *congruent compounds*. The β' phase in fig. 13 might also be called a congruent intermetallic compound AgMg (or $AgMg_{1\pm\delta}$). It is debatable, however, whether a phase with such a wide range of composition should really be called a *compound*.

It should be noted with regard to the congruent melting of Na_3Bi in fig. 14 that the limiting slopes dT/dX of the two liquidus curves at the congruent melting point (775°C) are both zero, since we are really dealing with a maximum in a two-phase region and not with the melting of an element.

Another intermetallic phase (or compound) labelled ε is also seen in fig. 13. This phase has a narrow range of stoichiometry around the composition $AgMg_3$. Also, in fig. 14 there is another intermetallic phase (or compound) NaBi with a very narrow range of stoichiometry. Both these phases decompose peritectically upon heating. That is, if stoichiometric solid NaBi is heated, it does not melt isothermally to form a liquid of the same composition, but rather it decomposes at the peritectic temperature of 446°C to form another solid, Na_3Bi, and a liquid of composition $X_{Bi} \approx 0.53$. Such compounds are known as *incongruently melting* or simply *incongruent compounds*. An incongruent compound is always associated with a peritectic. (The word peritectic comes from the Greek for, (loosely) "to melt in a round-about way".)

For purposes of phase diagram computations involving very stoichiometric compounds such as Na_3Bi, we may, to a good approximation, consider the Gibbs energy curve, $g(Na_{3/4}Bi_{1/4})$, to have zero width. Then all we need is the numerical value of $g(Na_{3/4}Bi_{1/4})$ at the minimum. This value is usually expressed in terms of the *Gibbs energy of fusion of the compound*, $\Delta g^0_{f(Na_{3/4}Bi_{1/4})}$, or in terms of the "*Gibbs energy of formation*", $\Delta g^0_{form(Na_{3/4}Bi_{1/4})}$, of the compound from solid Na and Bi according to the reaction: $\frac{3}{4}Na_{(s)} + \frac{1}{4}Bi_{(s)} = Na_{3/4}Bi_{1/4(s)}$. Both these quantities are interpreted graphically in fig. 14.

2.9. Topology of binary phase diagrams

In ch. 6, §8 the *Gibbs phase rule* was derived:

$$F = C - P + 2, \tag{13}$$

where C is the number of components, P the number of phases in equilibrium, and F the number of degrees of freedom. That is, F is the number of parameters which can be independently varied without affecting the state of the system. In the present context, the thermodynamic parameters are temperature, total pressure, and the compositions of the phases at equilibrium. Since binary temperature–composition phase diagrams are plotted at constant pressure, usually 1 atm, we have already eliminated one degree of freedom. In a binary system, $C = 2$. Hence, for binary

References: p. 382.

isobaric T–X diagrams the phase rule reduces to:

$$F = 3 - P. \tag{14}$$

Binary T–X diagrams contain single-phase areas and two-phase areas. In the single-phase areas, $F = 3 - 1 = 2$. That is, temperature and composition can be varied independently. These regions are thus called *bivariant*. In two-phase regions, $F = 3 - 2 = 1$. If, say, T is chosen, then the compositions of both phases are fixed by the ends of the tie-lines. Two-phase regions are thus termed *univariant*. Note that the overall composition can be varied within a two-phase region at constant T, but the overall composition is not a parameter in the sense of the phase rule. Rather, it is the compositions of the individual phases at equilibrium that are the parameters to be considered in counting the number of degrees of freedom.

When three phases are at equilibrium in a binary system at constant pressure, $F = 3 - 3 = 0$. Hence, the compositions of all three phases as well as T are fixed. There are two general types of three-phase *invariants* in binary phase diagrams. These are the *eutectic-type* and *peritectic-type* invariants as illustrated in fig. 15. Let the three phases concerned be called α, β and γ with β as the central phase as shown in fig. 15. α, β and γ can be solid, liquid or gaseous phases. At the eutectic-type

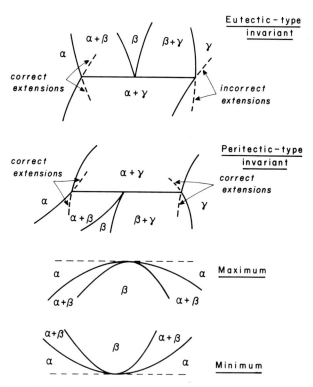

Fig. 15. Some topological units of construction of binary phase diagrams illustrating rules of construction.

invariant, the following invariant reaction occurs isothermally as the system is cooled:

$$\beta \rightarrow \alpha + \gamma, \tag{15}$$

whereas, at the peritectic-type invariant the invariant reaction upon cooling is:

$$\alpha + \gamma \rightarrow \beta. \tag{16}$$

Some examples of eutectic-type invariants are: (i) *eutectics* (fig. 7) in which $\alpha = $ solid$_1$, $\beta = $ liquid, $\gamma = $ solid$_2$. The eutectic reaction is $l \rightarrow s_1 + s_2$; (ii) *monotectics* (fig. 9) in which $\alpha = $ liquid$_1$, $\beta = $ liquid$_2$, $\gamma = $ solid. The monotectic reaction is $l_2 \rightarrow l_1 + s$; (iii) *eutectoids* (fig. 10) in which $\alpha = $ solid$_1$, $\beta = $ solid$_2$, $\gamma = $ solid$_3$. The eutectoid reaction is $s_2 \rightarrow s_1 + s_3$.

Some examples of peritectic type invariants are: (i) *peritectics* (fig. 10) in which $\alpha = $ liquid, $\beta = $ solid$_1$, $\gamma = $ solid$_2$. The peritectic reaction is $l + s_2 \rightarrow s_1$; (ii) *syntectics* (fig. 8k) in which $\alpha = $ liquid$_1$, $\beta = $ solid, $\gamma = $ liquid$_2$. The syntectic reaction is $l_1 + l_2 \rightarrow s$; (iii) *peritectoids* in which $\alpha = $ solid$_1$, $\beta = $ solid$_2$, $\gamma = $ solid$_3$. The peritectoid reaction is $s_1 + s_3 \rightarrow s_2$.

An important rule of construction which applies to invariants in binary phase diagrams is illustrated in fig. 15. This *extension rule* states that at an invariant the extension of a boundary of a two-phase region must pass into the adjacent two-phase region and not into the single-phase region. Examples of both correct and incorrect constructions are given in fig. 15. To understand why the "incorrect extension" shown is not correct, consider that the $(\alpha + \gamma)$ phase boundary line indicates the composition of the γ-phase in equilibrium with the α-phase as determined by the common tangent to the Gibbs energy curves. Since there is no reason for the Gibbs energy curves or their derivatives to change discontinuously at the invariant temperature, the extension of the $(\alpha + \gamma)$ phase boundary also represents the composition of the γ-phase in equilibrium with the α-phase. Hence, for this line to extend into a region labelled as single-phase γ is incorrect.

Two-phase regions in binary phase diagrams can terminate: (i) on the pure component axes (at $X_A = 1$ or $X_B = 1$) at a transformation point of pure A or B; (ii) at a critical point of a miscibility gap; (iii) at an invariant. Two-phase regions can also exhibit maxima or minima. In this case, both phase boundaries must pass through their maximum or minimum at the same point as shown in fig. 15.

All the *topological units* of construction of binary phase diagrams have now been discussed. The phase diagram of a binary alloy system will usually exhibit several of these units. As an example, the Fe–Al phase diagram (neglecting the order–disorder transition in Fe-rich alloys) is shown in fig. 16 (HANSEN [1958]). Eutectics are observed at 1165°C and 655°C. There are peritectics at 1232°C and 1160°C. A eutectoid is seen at 1103°C and a peritectoid at 1158°C. The η-phase ("Fe$_2$Al$_5$") is congruent, while the θ-phase ("FeAl$_3$") melts incongruently. The stoichiometric ζ-phase (FeAl$_2$) decomposes before melting into ε and η at 1158°C. The ε-phase exists only over the temperature range 1103–1232°C.

Between 910°C and 1390°C in fig. 16 is seen a two-phase $(\alpha + \gamma)$ γ-*loop*. Pure Fe

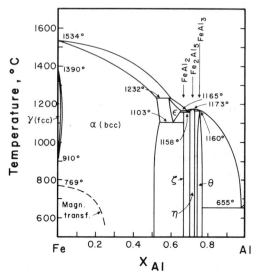

Fig. 16. Fe–Al phase diagram (after HANSEN [1958]).

adopts the fcc γ(austenite) structure between 910°C and 1390°C, but exists as bcc α(ferrite) above and below this temperature range. Aluminum, however, enters more easily into the bcc α than into the fcc γ structure, such that small additions of Al to Fe stabilize the α phase at all temperatures. Such γ-loops are common in systems with Fe as one component.

2.9.1. Order–disorder transformations

In fig. 13 for the Ag–Mg system, a transformation from an α′ to an α phase is shown occurring at approximately 390 K at the composition Ag₃Mg. This is an *order–disorder* transformation. Below the transformation temperature, *long-range ordering* (superlattice formation) is observed. An *order parameter* may be defined which decreases to zero at the transformation temperature. This type of phase transformation is not a first-order transformation like those considered so far in this chapter. Unlike first-order transformations which involve a change of state (solid, liquid, gas) and also involve diffusion over distances large compared with atomic dimensions, order–disorder transformations, at least at the stoichiometric composition (Ag_3Mg in this example), occur by atomic rearrangement over distances of the order of atomic dimensions. The slope of the curve of Gibbs energy versus T is not discontinuous at the transformation temperature. As we deviate from the stoichiometric Ag_3Mg composition in fig. 13, the transformation temperature decreases. Whether a two-phase ($\alpha + \alpha'$) region exists with a maximum at the stoichiometric composition just as in the case of first-order transformations, or whether a single line should be drawn separating the α and α′ regions as in fig. 13 is beyond the scope of the present chapter. For a detailed discussion see ch. 4, §10, and INDEN [1982].

A type of phase transformation of importance in ferrous metallurgy is the magnetic transformation. Below its *Curie temperature* of 769°C, Fe is ferromagnetic. Above this temperature it is not. The transformation involves a change in ordering of the magnetic domains and is not first-order. Additions of alloying elements will change the temperature of transformation as shown in fig. 16. Magnetic transformations are treated in ch. 26. See also MIODOWNIK [1982] and INDEN [1982].

2.10. Computer-coupled thermodynamic / phase diagram analysis

So far in this chapter we have used thermodynamics qualitatively or semi-quantitatively to explain the observed features of binary phase diagrams. However, in recent years a rapid development of analytical techniques and of computer software has permitted a truly quantitative coupling of thermodynamics and phase diagrams in a great many systems. That is, it is now possible to carry out a simultaneous critical analysis of available experimental thermodynamic data (calorimetric measurements of enthalpies of mixing, activity data from vapour pressures or electrochemical measurements, etc.) and of available phase diagram measurements on a binary system with a view to obtaining mathematical expressions for the Gibbs energy of each phase which best reproduce all the available data.

The phase diagram is a rich source of thermodynamic data which is often overlooked or not fully exploited. The coupled thermodynamic/phase diagram analysis permits full utilization of all available information while permitting the data to be checked for internal consistency. Furthermore, the results are then in a compact analytical form which can be easily stored in computer data banks. Proper thermodynamic smoothing of the experimental phase diagram points is obtained. Metastable phase boundaries can easily be calculated. Finally, such an analysis is the first step in the estimation of a ternary phase diagram from data on its binary sub-systems, as will be discussed in §3.5.

The computer coupling of thermodynamics and phase diagrams is a growing field of much current research interest. An international journal, CALPHAD, published by Pergamon Press, and an annual international meeting, the CALPHAD Conference, are now devoted to this subject.

In order to indicate what is involved in such a coupled analysis, an example will now be outlined for the K–Na system. For complete details of this system see BALE [1983].

The K–Na phase diagram is shown in fig. 17. Liquidus temperatures to approximately ±0.25° and solidus compositions to approximately ±0.1–0.4 at% have been measured (OTT *et al.* [1969]). Enthalpies of mixing in the liquid have been measured calorimetrically to approximately ±100 J (YOKOKAWA and KLEPPA [1964]). Activities in the liquid have been measured by vapour-phase absorption spectrophotometry (CAFASSO *et al.* [1968]). Finally, the Gibbs energies of fusion of K and Na are known, but that of the compound KNa_2 is not known.

References: p. 382.

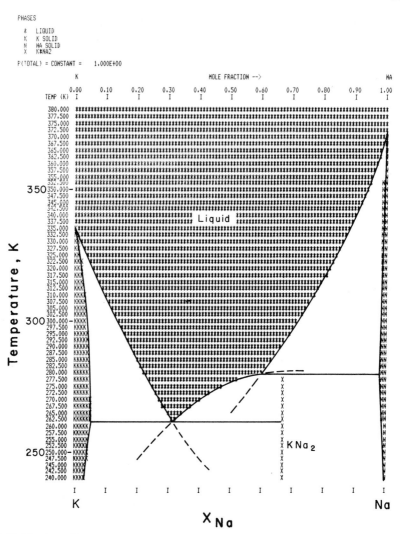

Fig. 17. K–Na phase diagram, computer-generated from optimized thermodynamic equations. Dashed lines are calculated metastable extensions.

The excess molar Gibbs energy of a solution phase may be expressed as:

$$g^{E} = \Delta h - T s^{E} \tag{17}$$

where Δh is the molar enthalpy of mixing and s^{E} is the molar excess entropy. For a binary system A–B, these may be conveniently expressed as polynomials in the mole fractions:

$$\Delta h = X_{A} X_{B} \left(h_{0} + h_{1} X_{B} + h_{2} X_{B}^{2} + h_{3} X_{B}^{3} + \cdots \right), \tag{18}$$

$$s^{E} = X_{A} X_{B} \left(s_{0} + s_{1} X_{B} + s_{2} X_{B}^{2} + s_{3} X_{B}^{3} + \cdots \right), \tag{19}$$

where the coefficients h_i and s_i are found empirically. The number of terms required in these expansions to yield a satisfactory "fit" to experimental data varies from system to system. It has been found that the thermodynamic properties of a great many binary alloy phases are adequately represented by 2- to 5-member polynomial series.

If we let $s^E = 0$, and if we let all coefficients $h_i = 0$ for $i \geqslant 1$, then $g^E = \Delta h = h_0 X_A X_B$, which is the regular solution expression, eq. (4). Polynomial expansions as in eqs. (18) and (19) can thus be considered as extensions of regular solution theory.

Differentiation of eqs. (18) and (19) yields the following expressions for the partial molar excess Gibbs energies of components A and B:

$$g_A^E = \sum_{j \geqslant 0} \left(h_j - Ts_j \right)\left(X_B - jX_A \right) X_B^{j+1}, \tag{20}$$

$$g_B^E = \sum_{j \geqslant 0} \left(h_j - Ts_j \right)\left(j + 1 \right) X_A^2 X_B^j. \tag{21}$$

Equation (10) relates the activities of a component along its liquidus and solidus to its Gibbs energy of fusion. Since the ideal activity equals the mole fraction, eq. (10) can be written as:

$$RT \ln X_B^l / X_B^s + g_B^{E(l)} - g_B^{E(s)} = -\Delta g_{f(B)}^0, \tag{22}$$

where X_B^l and X_B^s are the liquidus and solidus compositions at T, and where $g_B^{E(l)}$ and $g_B^{E(s)}$ are the partial molar excess Gibbs energies of the component on the liquidus and solidus.

In the K–Na system, solubilities in the two terminal solid solutions are sufficiently small that Raoult's Law may be assumed to hold for the solvent in each case. Hence, for Na-rich solid solutions, we set $g_{Na}^{E(s)} = 0$, and experimental liquidus/solidus points can then be used to calculate values of $g_{Na}^{E(l)}$ along the Na-liquidus via eq. (22).

Similarly, $g_K^{E(l)}$ can be calculated along the measured K-liquidus. For these calculations, Gibbs energies of fusion of K and Na taken from the literature were expressed (BALE [1983]) as functions of T as follows:

$$\Delta g_{f(K)}^0 = -2.533 + 0.16317\, T + 4.5518 \times 10^{-5}\, T^2$$

$$-2.0530 \times 10^{-9}\, T^3 - 2.934 \times 10^{-2}\, T \ln T \text{ kJ/mol}, \tag{23}$$

$$\Delta g_{f(Na)}^0 = -1.638 + 0.12706\, T + 3.1690 \times 10^{-5}\, T^2$$

$$-1.7726 \times 10^{-9}\, T^3 - 2.268 \times 10^{-2}\, T \ln T \text{ kJ/mol}. \tag{24}$$

The experimental calorimetric values of Δh for the liquid phase, the liquid activity data, and the values of $g_{Na}^{E(l)}$ and $g_K^{E(l)}$ calculated from the measured phase diagram may now be combined in a least-squares "optimization" analysis to obtain numerical values of the coefficients h_i and s_i which best fit all these data. Such optimization procedures are described by LUKAS et al. [1977] and by BALE and PELTON [1983].

References: p. 382.

The optimized equations for the liquid K–Na phase as found by BALE [1983] are:

$$\Delta h^{l} = X_{K} X_{Na} (2.2510 + 1.4058\, X_{Na})\ \text{kJ/mol}, \tag{25}$$

$$s^{E(l)} = X_{K} X_{Na} (-0.6309 + 1.3004\, X_{Na} + 5.0957\, X_{Na}^{2} - 5.8522\, X_{Na}^{3})\ \text{J/mol K}. \tag{26}$$

Next, the terminal solid solutions are treated as Henrian solutions (see §2.6). Best fits to the measured phase diagram were obtained with the following expressions for the Henrian activity coefficients:

$$RT \ln \gamma_{Na}^{0} = 5.535\ \text{kJ/mol}, \tag{27}$$

$$RT \ln \gamma_{K}^{0} = 9.996\ \text{kJ/mol}, \tag{28}$$

where the standard state is the pure liquid in each case. Finally, the experimental liquidus of the compound KNa_{2} can now be used to determine the Gibbs energy of fusion of the compound (for details see BALE and PELTON [1982] and BALE [1983]). The optimized expression is:

$$\Delta g_{f(Na_{2}K)}^{0} = 11.295 - 40.229\, T\ \text{kJ/mol of Na}_{2}\text{K}. \tag{29}$$

Equations (23)–(29) now give a complete description of the thermodynamic properties of all the phases. Equation (25) reproduces the calorimetric data to ± 20 J. Liquid activity data are reproduced within experimental error limits. The phase diagram shown in fig. 17 is a computer-generated diagram calculated by computing the common tangent lines to the Gibbs energy curves defined by eqs. (23)–(29). The agreement between the calculated and measured diagrams is within 1 K everywhere and is generally better than 0.5 K.

Recent reviews of computer-assisted calculation and analysis of phase diagrams have been written by ANSARA [1979] and by SPENCER and BARIN [1979].

2.10.1. Calculation of metastable phase boundaries

First-order phase transformations involve the nucleation and growth of the new phase. In many cases, nucleation and/or growth may be slow processes. For example, many liquids can be undercooled many degrees below their melting points before solidification begins. When such kinetic effects play a significant role, metastable phase boundaries become important. For example, in fig. 17, the K- and KNa_{2}-liquidus lines are shown extended below the eutectic temperature by the dashed lines. These metastable extensions indicate the temperatures at which metastable solidification of each solid would commence if the formation of the other solid were suppressed. Similarly, the Na- and KNa_{2}-liquidus lines are shown extended metastably on either side of the peritectic. Metastable phase boundaries may be quite difficult to measure directly. However, the analytical technique described above is well suited to their calculation. The metastable boundaries shown in fig. 17 were computer-calculated from the thermodynamic equations (23)–(29) by simply suppressing one of the solid phases in the calculation. In this way, for example, a metastable congruent melting point of KNa_2 of 281 K was calculated. If the formation of all solids is suppressed, then the positive deviations in the liquid phase give rise to a liquid–liquid miscibility gap with $T_C = 175$ K at $X_{C(Na)} = 0.64$. Although such submerged miscibility gaps are of very limited practical importance in most alloy systems, they are of much interest in certain glass-forming systems such as SiO_2–Al_2O_3.

2.11. Ab-initio calculation of phase diagrams

In principle, alloy phase diagrams could be calculated *ab initio* from (i) a set of lattice stabilities of the elements and intermetallic compounds, and (ii) a means of predicting Gibbs energies of mixing of alloy phases. The present state of the art has been reviewed by MACHLIN [1981].

As discussed in §2.6, semi-empirical lattice stabilities for several metals, each in several crystal structures, have been devised by Kaufman and coworkers as well as by Machlin and others. In the next decade, pseudo-potential theory (COHEN *et al.* [1982]; also ch. 3, §§3.3 and 6.1) holds promise as a means of calculating lattice stabilities from first principles.

Means of predicting Gibbs energies of mixing by empirical methods and from first principles have recently been developed. However, agreement with measured values is still no better than several kJ. These methods are reviewed by MACHLIN [1981].

Brewer and co-workers have also presented procedures for prediction of binary phase diagrams (see, e.g., BREWER and LAMOREAUX [1980]).

Although much progress is being made, the complexity of atomic interactions in alloys is such that there is still a long way to go before accurate phase diagrams calculated from first principles become available.

2.12. Binary phase diagrams involving a gaseous phase

The effect of total pressure, P, upon the Gibbs energy change for the transformation of one mole of pure component A from the α- to the β-phase is given by:

$$\Delta g_A^{\alpha \to \beta} = \Delta g_A^{0(\alpha \to \beta)} + \int_{P=1}^{P} \left(v_A^\beta - v_A^\alpha \right) dP, \tag{30}$$

where $\Delta g_A^{0(\alpha \to \beta)}$ is the standard (i.e. at $P = 1$ atm) molar Gibbs energy of transformation and where v_A^α and v_A^β are the molar volumes of the phases. For solids and liquids, molar volumes are sufficiently small that the final term in eq. (30) is negligible unless P is very large. If a gaseous phase is involved, however, this is no longer the case. If gaseous A is ideal and monatomic, and since $v_A^g = RT/P \gg v_A^l$, the molar Gibbs energy of vaporization is given by

$$\Delta g_A^{(v)} = \Delta g_A^{0(v)} + RT \ln P. \tag{31}$$

The phase diagram of the Cd–Zn system at $P = 1$ atm is shown in fig. 18a. This

References: p. 382.

diagram was calculated by computer from optimized expressions for the Gibbs energies of the phases as discussed in §2.10. Cd and Zn boil at 1 atm pressure at their standard boiling points of 1038 K and 1181 K respectively.

As the pressure is lowered, the boiling points decrease. With $\Delta g^{(v)}$ of Cd and Zn given by eq. (31), the phase diagram was recalculated at $P = 10^{-3}$ atm and $P = 10^{-4}$ atm as shown in figs. 18b and c. At 10^{-4} atm, pure solid Cd and Zn sublime directly to gas, but there is still a liquid region in the center of the phase diagram.

As shown by this example, when gaseous phases are involved there is a great advantage in calculating phase diagrams from the optimized Gibbs energy curves.

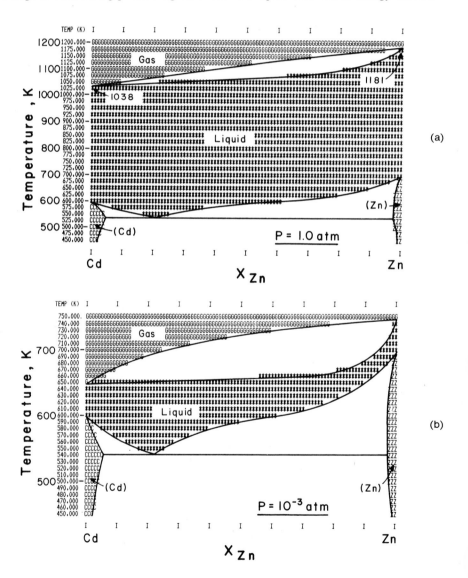

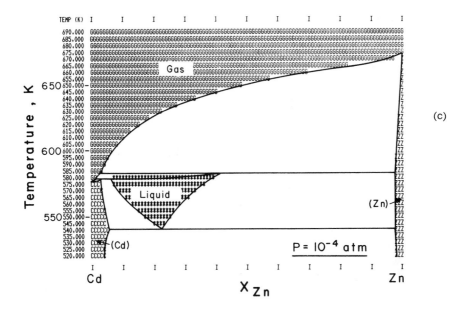

Fig. 18. Computer-generated temperature versus composition phase diagrams of the Cd–Zn system at constant total pressures of (a) 1 atm, (b) 10^{-3} atm, and (c) 10^{-4} atm.

2.12.1. Binary pressure–composition phase diagrams

Rather than plotting T–X phase diagrams at constant P, it is often desirable to plot P–X phase diagrams at constant T. Examples for the Cd–Zn system at $T = 1100$ K and $T = 575$ K are shown in figs. 19a and b. Such P–X diagrams obey exactly the same geometrical rules of construction as T–X diagrams. That is, they consist of the same topological units as discussed in §2.9 and fig. 15.

3.   *Ternary phase diagrams*

In this section, an introduction to ternary phase diagrams will be given. A complete discussion of the subject is beyond the scope of this chapter. For a more detailed treatment, see PRINCE [1966], RICCI [1964], FINDLAY [1951] or WEST [1965].

For systems of four or more components, graphical representation of phase equilibria becomes increasingly difficult because of the large number of composition variables. In general, the type of two-dimensional section or projection of the multi-dimensional phase diagram which best presents the phase equilibria will vary depending upon the particular system and composition region in question. In the study of multicomponent phase equilibria, the Gibbs phase rule, eq. (13), is an

References: p. 382.

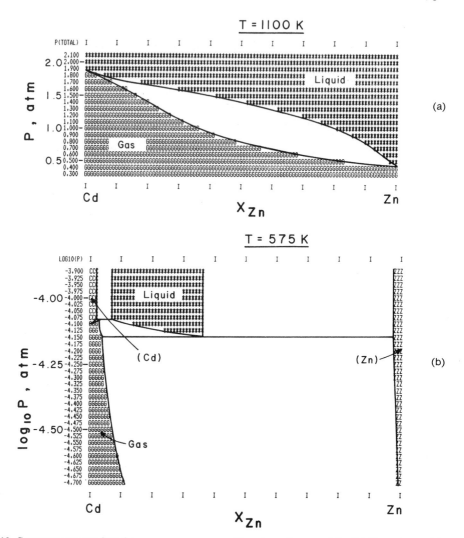

Fig. 19. Computer-generated total pressure versus composition phase diagram of the Cd–Zn system at (a) $T = 1100$ K and (b) $T = 575$ K.

invaluable guide. Multicomponent phase diagrams and phase equilibria are discussed by PRINCE [1966] and by FINDLAY [1951].

3.1. The ternary composition triangle

In a ternary system with components A–B–C, the sum of the mole fractions is unity. $(X_A + X_B + X_C) = 1$. Hence, there are two independent composition variables. A representation of composition, symmetrical with respect to all three components

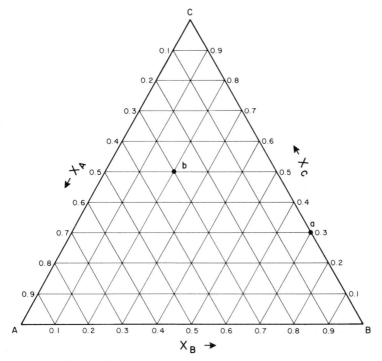

Fig. 20. The equilateral ternary composition triangle.

may be obtained with the equilateral "composition triangle" as shown in fig. 20. Compositions at the corners of the triangle correspond to the pure components. Along the edges of the triangle are found compositions corresponding to the three binary subsystems A–B, B–C and C–A. Lines of constant mole fraction X_A are parallel to the B–C edge, while lines of constant X_B and X_C are parallel to the C–A and A–B edges respectively. For example at point **a** in fig. 20, $X_A = 0$, $X_B = 0.7$ and $X_C = 0.3$. At point **b**, $X_A = 0.3$, $X_B = 0.2$ and $X_C = 0.5$.

   Similar equilateral composition triangles can also be drawn with coordinates in terms of weight% of the three components.

3.2.   Ternary space model

   A ternary temperature–composition "phase diagram" at constant total pressure may be plotted as a three-dimensional "space model" within a right triangular prism with the equilateral composition triangle as base and temperature as vertical axis. Such a space model for a simple eutectic ternary system A–B–C is illustrated in fig. 21. On the three vertical faces of the prism we find the phase diagrams of the three binary subsystems, A–B, B–C and C–A which, in this example, are all simple eutectic binary systems. The binary eutectic points are at e_1, e_2 and e_3. Within the prism we see three *liquidus surfaces* descending from the melting points of pure A, B and C. Compositions on these surfaces correspond to compositions of liquid in equilibrium with A-, B- and C-rich solid phases.

In a ternary system at constant pressure, the Gibbs phase rule, eq. (13), becomes:

$$F = 4 - P. \tag{32}$$

When the liquid and one solid phase are in equilibrium, $P = 2$. Hence, $F = 2$, and the system is bivariant. A ternary liquidus is thus a two-dimensional surface. We may choose two variables, say T and one composition coordinate of the liquid, but then the other liquid composition coordinate and the composition of the solid are fixed.

The A- and B- liquidus surfaces in fig. 21 intersect along the line e_1E. Liquids with compositions along this line are therefore in equilibrium with A − rich and B-rich solid phases simultaneously. That is, $P = 3$ and so $F = 1$. Such "valleys" are thus called *univariant lines*. The three univariant lines meet at the *ternary eutectic point* E at which $P = 4$ and $F = 0$. This is an invariant point since the temperature and the compositions of all four phases in equilibrium are fixed.

3.3. Polythermal projections of liquidus surfaces

A two-dimensional representation of the ternary liquidus surface may be obtained as an orthogonal projection upon the base composition triangle. Such a *polythermal projection* of the liquidus of the Bi–Sn–Cd system (BRAY *et al.* [1961–62]) is shown in fig. 22. This is a simple eutectic ternary system with a space model like that shown in fig. 21. The constant temperature lines on fig. 22 are called *liquidus isotherms.* The univariant valleys are shown as the heavier lines. By convention, the large arrows indicate the directions of decreasing temperature along these lines.

Let us consider the sequence of events which occur during the equilibrium cooling from the liquid of an alloy of overall composition **a** in fig. 22 ($X_{Bi} = 0.05$, $X_{Sn} = 0.45$, $X_{Cd} = 0.50$). Point **a** lies within the *field of primary crystallization* of Cd. That is, it lies within the composition region in fig. 22 in which Cd-rich solid will be

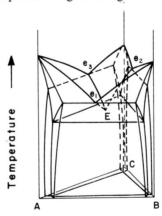

Fig. 21. Perspective view of ternary space model of a simple eutectic ternary system. e_1, e_2, e_3 are the binary eutectics and E is the ternary eutectic. The base of the prism is the equilateral composition triangle.

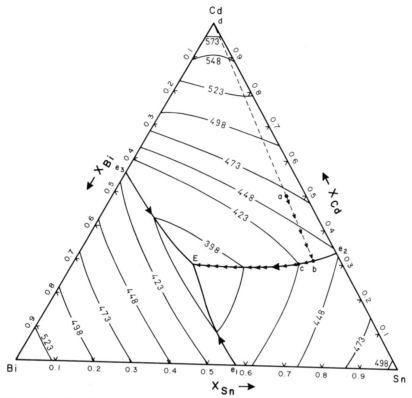

Fig. 22. Projection of the liquidus surface of the Bi–Sn–Cd system (after BRAY *et al.* [1961–62]). Small arrows show crystallization path of an alloy of overall composition at point **a**.

the first solid to precipitate upon cooling. As the liquid alloy is cooled, the Cd-liquidus surface is reached at $T \approx 465$ K (slightly below the 473 K isotherm). A solid Cd-rich phase begins to precipitate at this temperature. Now, in this particular system, Bi and Sn are nearly insoluble in solid Cd, so that the solid phase is virtually pure Cd (note that this fact cannot be deduced from fig. 22 alone). Therefore, as solidification proceeds, the liquid becomes depleted in Cd, but the ratio X_{Sn}/X_{Bi} in the liquid remains constant. Hence, the composition path followed by the liquid (its *crystallization path*) is a straight line passing through point **a** and projecting to the Cd-corner of the triangle. This crystallization path is shown on fig. 22 as the line **ab**.

In the general case in which a solid solution rather than a pure component or stoichiometric compound is precipitating, the crystallization path will not be a straight line. However, for equilibrium cooling, a straight line joining a point on the crystallization path at any T to the overall composition point **a** will extend through the composition, on the solidus surface, of the solid phase in equilibrium with the liquid at that temperature.

When the composition of the liquid has reached point **b** in fig. 22 at $T \approx 435$ K,

References: p. 382.

the relative proportions of the solid Cd and liquid phases at equilibrium are given by the *lever rule* applied to the *tie-line* **dab**: (moles of liquid)/(moles of Cd) = **da/ab**. Upon further cooling the liquid composition follows the univariant valley from **b** to E while Cd and Sn-rich solids co-precipitate as a binary eutectic mixture. When the liquidus composition attains the ternary eutectic composition E at $T \approx 380$ K the invariant *ternary eutectic reaction* occurs:

$$\text{liquid} \rightarrow s_1 + s_2 + s_3, \tag{33}$$

where s_1, s_2 and s_3 are the three solid phases and where the compositions of all four phases as well as T remain fixed until all liquid is solidified.

In order to illustrate several of the features of polythermal projections of liquidus surfaces, a projection of the liquidus of a hypothetical system A–B–C is shown in fig. 23. For the sake of simplicity, isotherms are not shown, but only the univariant lines with arrows to show the directions of decreasing temperature. The binary subsystems A–B and C–A are simple eutectic systems, while the binary subsystem B–C contains one congruent binary phase, ε, and one incongruent binary phase, δ,

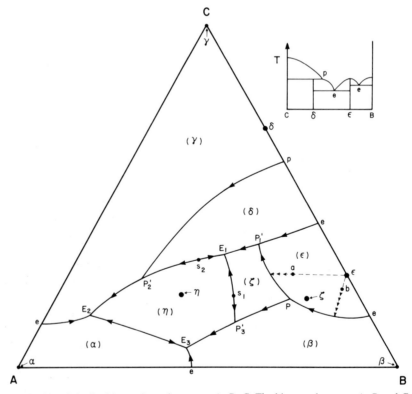

Fig. 23. Projection of the liquidus surface of a system A–B–C. The binary subsystems A–B and C–A are simple eutectic systems. The binary phase diagram B–C is shown in the insert. All solid phases are assumed pure stoichiometric components or compounds. Small arrows show crystallization paths of alloys of compositions at points **a** and **b**.

as shown in the insert in fig. 23. The letters **e** and **p** indicate binary eutectic and peritectic points. The ε and δ phases are called *binary compounds* since they have compositions within a binary subsystem. Two *ternary compounds,* η and ζ, with compositions within the ternary triangle as indicated in fig. 23, are also found in this system. All compounds as well as pure solid A, B and C (the "α, β and γ" phases) are assumed to be stoichiometric (i.e. there is no solid solubility). The fields of primary crystallization of all the solids are indicated in parentheses in fig. 23. The composition of the ε phase lies within its field, since ε is a congruent compound, while the composition of the δ phase lies outside of its field since δ is incongruent. Similarly for the ternary compounds, η is a congruently melting compound while ζ is incongruent. For the congruent compound η, the highest temperature on the η-liquidus occurs at the composition of η.

The univariant lines meet at a number of *ternary eutectics* E_i (three arrows converging), a *ternary peritectic* P (one arrow entering, two arrows leaving the point), and several *ternary quasi-peritectics* P_i' (two arrows entering, one arrow leaving). Two *saddle points* **s** are also shown. These are points of maximum T along the univariant line but of minimum T on the liquidus surface along a section joining the compositions of the two solids. For example, s_1 is at a maximum along the univariant $E_1 P_3'$, but is a minimum point on the liquidus along the straight line $\zeta s_1 \eta$.

Let us consider the events occurring during the cooling from the liquid of an alloy of overall composition **a** in fig. 23. The primary crystallization product will be the ε phase. Since this is a pure stoichiometric solid the crystallization path of the liquid will be along a straight line passing through **a** and extending to the composition of ε as shown on the figure.

Solidification of ε continues until the liquid attains a composition on the univariant valley. Then the liquid composition follows the valley towards the point P_1' in co-existence with ε and ζ. At point P_1' the invariant *ternary quasi-peritectic reaction* occurs isothermally:

$$\text{liquid} + \varepsilon \rightarrow \delta + \zeta. \tag{34}$$

Since there are two reactants in a quasi-peritectic reaction, there are two possible outcomes: (i) The liquid is completely consumed before the ε-phase; in this case, solidification will be complete at the point P_1'. (ii) ε is completely consumed before the liquid; in this case, solidification will continue with decreasing T along the univariant line $P_1' E_1$ with co-precipitation of δ and ζ until, at E, the liquid will solidify eutectically (liquid $\rightarrow \delta + \zeta + \eta$). To determine whether condition (i) or (ii) occurs, we use the mass balance criterion that, for three-phase equilibrium, the overall composition **a** must always lie within the *tie-triangle* formed by the compositions of the three phases. Now, the triangle joining the compositions of δ, ε, and ζ does not contain the point **a**, but the triangle joining the compositions of δ, ζ, and liquid at P_1' does contain the point **a**. Hence, case (ii) occurs.

An alloy of overall composition **b** in fig. 23 solidifies with ε as primary crystallization product until the liquid composition contacts the univariant line. Thereafter, co-precipitation of ε and β occurs with the liquid composition following the

References: p. 382.

univariant valley until the liquid reaches the peritectic composition P. The invariant *ternary peritectic reaction* then occurs isothermally:

$$\text{liquid} + \varepsilon + \beta \rightarrow \zeta. \tag{35}$$

Since there are three reactants, there are three possible outcomes: (i) Liquid is consumed before either ε or β and solidification terminates at P. (ii) ε is consumed first; solidification then continues along the path PP$_3'$. (iii) β is consumed first and solidification continues along the path PP$_1'$. Which outcome occurs depends on whether the overall composition **b** lies within the tie-triangle (i) $\varepsilon\beta\zeta$, (ii) $\beta\zeta$P, or (iii) $\varepsilon\zeta$P. In the example shown, case (i) will occur.

3.4. Ternary isothermal sections

Isothermal projections of the liquidus surface do not give information on the compositions of the solid phases at equilibrium. However, this information can be presented at any one temperature on an *isothermal section* such as that shown for the Bi–Sn–Cd system at 423 K in fig. 24. This phase diagram is a constant temperature slice through the space model of fig. 21.

The liquidus lines bordering the one-phase liquid region of fig. 24 are identical to the 423 K isotherms of the projection in fig. 22. Point **c** in fig. 24 is point **c** on the univariant line in fig. 22. An alloy with overall composition in the one-phase liquid region of fig. 24 at 423 K will consist of a single liquid phase. If the overall composition lies within one of the two-phase regions, then the compositions of the two phases are given by the ends of the *tie-line* containing the overall composition. For example, a sample with overall composition **p** in fig. 24 will consist of a liquid of composition **q** on the liquidus and a solid Bi-rich alloy of composition **r** on the solidus. The relative proportions of the two phases are given by the lever rule: (moles of liquid)/(moles of solid) = **pr/pq**.

In the case of solid Cd, the solid phase is nearly pure Cd, so all tie-lines of the (Cd + liquid) region converge nearly to the corner of the triangle. In the case of Bi- and Sn-rich solids, some solid solubility is observed. (The actual extent of this solubility is somewhat exaggerated in fig. 24 for the sake of clarity of presentation.) Alloys with overall compositions rich enough in Bi or Sn to lie within the single-phase (Sn) or (Bi) regions of fig. 24 will consist at 423 K of single-phase solid solutions. Alloys with overall compositions at 423 K in the two-phase (Cd + Sn) region will consist of two solid phases.

Alloys with overall compositions within the three-phase triangle **dcf** will, at 423 K, consist of three phases: solid Cd- and Sn-rich solids with compositions at **d** and **f**, and liquid of composition **c**. To understand this better, consider an alloy of composition **a** in fig. 24, which is the same composition as the point **a** in fig. 22. In §3.3 we saw that when a alloy of this composition is cooled, the liquid follows the path **ab** on fig. 22 with primary precipitation of Cd and then follows the univariant line with co-precipitation of Cd and Sn so that at 423 K the liquid will be at the composition point **c**, and two solid phases are in equilibrium with the liquid.

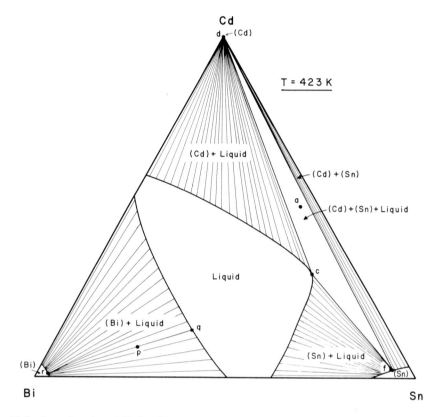

Fig. 24. Isothermal section of Bi–Sn–Cd system at 423 K (after BRAY *et al.* [1961–62]). Extents of solid solubility in Bi and Sn have been exaggerated for clarity of presentation.

3.4.1. Topology of ternary isothermal sections

At constant temperature the Gibbs energy of each phase in a ternary system is represented as a function of composition by a surface plotted in a right triangular prism with Gibbs energy as vertical axis and the composition triangle as base. Just as the compositions of phases at equilibrium in binary systems are determined by the points of contact of a common tangent line to their isothermal Gibbs energy curves, so the compositions of phases at equilibrium in a ternary system are given by the points of contact of a common tangent plane to their isothermal Gibbs energy surfaces. A common tangent plane can contact two Gibbs energy surfaces at an infinite number of pairs of points, thereby generating an infinite number of tie-lines within a two-phase area on an isothermal section. A common tangent plane to three Gibbs energy surfaces contacts each surface at a unique point, thereby generating a three-phase tie-triangle.

Hence, the principal topological units of construction of an isothermal ternary phase diagram are three-phase $(\alpha + \beta + \gamma)$ tie-triangles as in fig. 25 with their

References: p. 382.

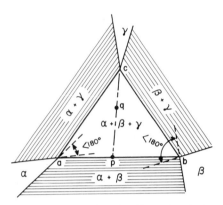

Fig. 25. A tie-triangle in a ternary isothermal section illustrating the lever rule and the extension rule.

accompanying two-phase and single-phase areas. Each corner of the tie-triangle contacts a single-phase region, and from each edge of the triangle there extends a two-phase region. The edge of the triangle is a limiting tie-line of the two-phase region.

For overall compositions within the tie-triangle, the compositions of the three phases at equilibrium are fixed at the corners of the triangle. The relative proportions of the three phases are given by the lever rule of tie-triangles which can be derived from mass balance considerations. At an overall composition **q** in fig. 25, for example, the relative proportion of the γ-phase is given by projecting a straight line from the γ-corner of the triangle (point **c**) through the overall composition **q** to the opposite side of the triangle, point **p**. Then: (moles of γ)/(total moles) = **qp/cp** if compositions are expressed in mole fractions, or (weight of γ)/(total weight) = **qp/cp** if compositions are in weight percent.

Isothermal ternary phase diagrams are generally composed of a number of these topological units. An example for the Al–Zn–Mg system at 25°C is shown in fig. 26 (KÖSTER and DULLENKOPF [1936]). The β, γ, δ, θ, η and ζ phases are binary intermetallic compounds with small (~ 1%) ranges of stoichiometry which can dissolve a limited amount (~ 1–6%) of the third component. The T phase is a ternary phase with a single-phase region existing over a fairly extensive oval-shaped central composition range. Examination of fig. 26 shows that it consists of the topological units of fig. 25.

An *extension rule* for ternary tie-triangles is illustrated in fig. 25. At each corner, the extension of the boundaries of the single-phase regions, indicated by the dashed lines, must either **both** project **into** the triangle as at point **a**, or must **both** project **outside** the triangle as at point **b**, and furthermore the angle between these extensions must be less than 180°. For a proof, see LIPSON and WILSON [1940].

Many published phase diagrams violate this rule. For example, it is violated in fig. 26 at the δ-corner of the (ε + δ + T) tie-triangle.

Another important rule of construction, whose derivation is evident, is that within any two-phase region tie-lines must never cross each other.

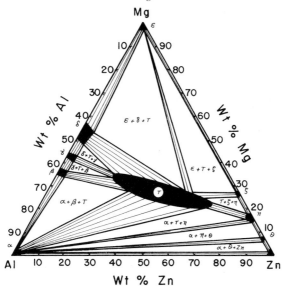

Fig. 26. Ternary isothermal section of the Al–Zn–Mg system at 25°C (after Köster and Dullenkopf [1936]).

3.5. Calculation of ternary phase diagrams from binary data

Among 70 metallic elements are formed 70! / 3! 67! = 54 740 ternary systems and 916 895 quaternary systems. In view of the amount of work involved in measuring even one isothermal section of a relatively simple ternary phase diagram, it is very important to have means of estimating ternary and higher-order phase diagrams.

The most fruitful approach to such predictions is via thermodynamic methods. In recent years, large advances have been made in this area by the international CALPHAD group. Many key papers have been published in the CALPHAD Journal.

As a first step in the thermodynamic approach, one critically analyzes the experimental phase diagrams and thermodynamic data for the three binary subsystems of the ternary system in order to obtain a set of mathematical expressions for the Gibbs energies of the binary phases as was discussed in §2.10. Next, interpolation procedures based on solution models are used to estimate the Gibbs energies of the ternary phases from the Gibbs energies of the binary phases. Finally, the ternary phase diagram is computer-calculated from these estimated ternary Gibbs energies by means of common tangent plane or total Gibbs energy minimization algorithms.

As an example of such an estimation of a ternary phase diagram, the experimental (Bray *et al.* [1961–62]) and estimated (Ansara and Bonnier [1971]) liquidus projections of the Bi–Sn–Cd system are shown in fig. 27. The estimated phase diagram was calculated from the thermodynamic properties of the three binary subsystems under the assumption that solid solutions are Henrian and with the

References: p. 382.

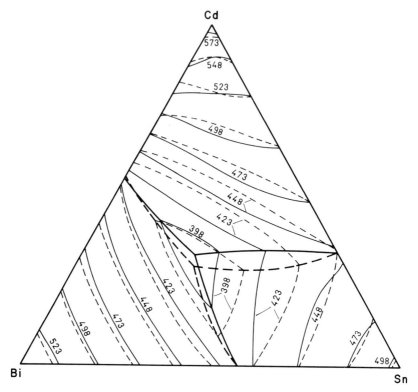

Fig. 27. Projection of liquidus of the Bi-Sn-Cd system; dashed line: experimental (after BRAY *et al.* [1961–62]); solid line: estimated from binary data (ANSARA and BONNIER [1971]).

Gibbs energy of the ternary liquid approximated via the interpolation equation suggested by KOHLER [1960] and by OLSON and TOOP [1966]:

$$g^{E} = (1 - X_{Cd})^{2} g^{E}_{Bi/Sn} + (1 - X_{Bi})^{2} g^{E}_{Sn/Cd} + (1 - X_{Sn})^{2} g^{E}_{Cd/Bi}. \tag{36}$$

In this equation, g^{E} is the excess molar Gibbs energy at a composition point in the ternary liquid phase and $g^{E}_{Bi/Sn}$, $g^{E}_{Sn/Cd}$ and $g^{E}_{Cd/Bi}$ are the excess Gibbs energies in the three binary systems at the same ratios X_{Bi}/X_{Sn}, X_{Sn}/X_{Cd} and X_{Cd}/X_{Bi} as at the ternary point. If the ternary liquid phase as well as the three binary liquid phases are all regular solutions, then eq. (36) is exact. In the general case, a physical interpretation of eq. (36) is that the contribution to g^{E} from, say, pair interactions between A and B particles is constant at a constant ratio X_{A}/X_{B} apart from the dilutive effect of the C particles which is accounted for by the term $(1 - X_{C})^{2}$ taken from regular solution theory.

As a second example, the experimental isothermal section at 923 K of the Cr–Ni–Fe phase diagram is compared in fig. 28 with the diagram calculated solely from optimized binary thermodynamic properties (CHART *et al.* [1979]).

From figs. 27 and 28 it can be seen that the estimated phase diagrams are quite

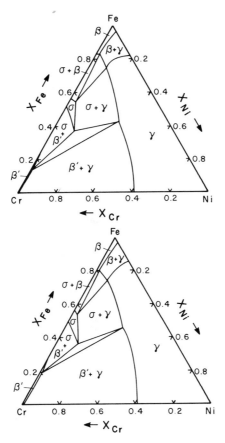

Fig. 28. Isothermal section at 923 K of the Cr–Ni–Fe phase diagram from CHART *et al.* [1979]. Lower diagram is experimental; upper diagram is calculated from binary data.

acceptable for many purposes. The agreement between the experimental and calculated diagrams can be greatly improved by the inclusion of one or two "ternary terms" with adjustable coefficients in the interpolation equations for g^E.

For example, the ternary term $aX_{Bi}X_{Sn}X_{Cd}$, which is zero in all three binaries, could be added to eq. (36) and the value of the parameter a which gives the "best" fit to the measured ternary liquidus could be determined. This, of course, requires that ternary measurements be made, but only a very few (even one or two in this example) experimental liquidus points will usually suffice rather than the large number of measurements required for a fully experimental determination. In this way, the coupling of the thermodynamic approach with a few well chosen experimental measurements holds promise of greatly reducing the experimental effort involved in determining multicomponent phase diagrams.

Reviews of the various interpolation procedures and computer techniques for estimating and calculating ternary and higher-order phase diagrams are given by ANSARA [1979] and by SPENCER and BARIN [1979].

References: p. 382.

4. Different types of phase diagrams

In general, a phase diagram represents the geometrical loci of thermodynamic parameters when equilibrium between phases under a given set of conditions is established. Since variables such as total pressure, molar volume, chemical potentials of components, etc. may be considered, there are many kinds of phase diagrams of metallurgical interest other than the isobaric temperature–composition phase diagrams which we have mainly considered so far. For example, binary isothermal pressure–composition phase diagrams have been shown in fig. 19. These various phase diagrams can be classified into geometrical types according to their topological rules of construction. For instance, binary isothermal $P-X$ diagrams as in fig. 19 are members of the same type as binary isobaric $T-X$ diagrams since they are both formed from the same topological units of construction.

Another useful kind of phase diagram belonging to this same geometrical type are isothermal chemical-potential–composition diagrams for ternary systems. An exam-

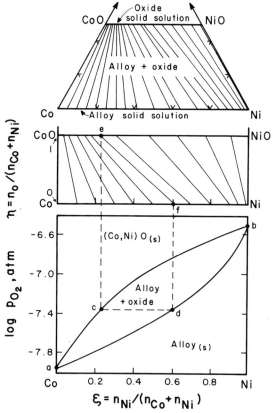

Fig. 29. Corresponding type-2 and type-3 phase diagrams for the Co–Ni–O system at 1600 K (from PELTON and THOMPSON [1975]).

ple is shown in the lowest panel of fig. 29 (PELTON and THOMPSON [1975]) for the
Co–Ni–O system at T = 1600 K (and at a constant total hydrostatic pressure of 1
atm). Here the logarithm of the partial pressure of O_2 is plotted versus the metal
ratio $\xi = n_{Ni}/(n_{Co} + n_{Ni})$, where n_i = number of moles of i. There are two phases in
this system under these conditions, a solid alloy solution stable at lower p_{O_2}, and a
solid solution of CoO and NiO stable at higher p_{O_2}. For instance, point **a** gives p_{O_2}
for the equilibrium between pure Co and pure CoO at 1600 K. Between the two
single-phase regions is a two-phase (alloy + oxide) region. At any overall composition on the tie-line **cd** between points **c** and **d**, two phases will be observed, an alloy
of composition **d** and an oxide of composition **c**. The lever rule applies just as for
binary T–X diagrams.

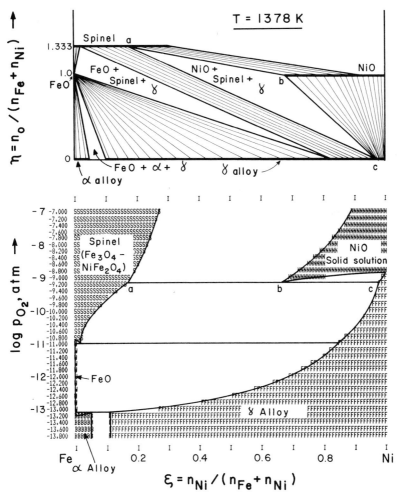

Fig. 30. Corresponding type-2 and type-3 phase diagrams for the Fe–Ni–O system at 1378 K (PELTON *et
al.* [1979]).

References: p. 382.

The isothermal section of the ternary Co–Ni–O system at 1600 K is shown in the top panel of fig. 29. There are two single-phase regions with a two-phase region between them. The single-phase areas are very narrow since oxygen is only very slightly soluble in the solid alloy and since CoO and NiO are very stoichiometric oxides. In the central panel of fig. 29 this same diagram is shown but with the composition triangle "opened out" by putting the oxygen corner at infinity. This can be done if the vertical axis becomes $\eta = n_O/(n_{Co} + n_{Ni})$ with the horizontal axis as $\xi = n_{Ni}/(n_{Co} + n_{Ni})$. These are known as *Jänecke coordinates*. It can be seen in fig. 29 that each tie-line, **ef**, of the isothermal section corresponds to a tie-line, **cd**, of the log p_{O_2}–ξ diagram. This underscores the fact that every tie-line of a ternary isothermal section corresponds to a constant chemical potential of each of the components.

Another example of a log p_{O_2}–ξ diagram is shown for the Fe–Ni–O system at 1378 K in the lower panel of fig. 30 (PELTON *et al.* [1979]). The corresponding ternary isothermal section in Jänecke coordinates is shown in the upper panel. Each of the invariant three-phase tie-triangles in the isothermal section corresponds to an invariant line in the log p_{O_2}–ξ diagram. For example, the (NiO + spinel + γ) triangle with corners at points **a**, **b** and **c** corresponds to the "eutectic-like" invariant with the same phase compositions **a**, **b** and **c** at log $p_{O_2} \approx -9.2$. We can see that within a three-phase tie-triangle, p_{O_2} is constant.

An example of yet another kind of phase diagram which is a member of this same geometrical type is shown in fig. 31. For the quaternary Fe–Zn–S–O system at $T = 1260$ K and at constant $p_{SO_2} = 1$ atm, fig. 31 is a plot of log p_{O_2} versus the molar metal ratio ξ (PONCET [1981]). Since log p_{O_2} varies as $-\frac{1}{2}$log p_{S_2} when p_{SO_2} and T are constant, fig. 31 is also a plot of log p_{S_2} versus ξ.

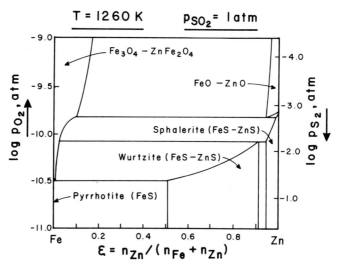

Fig. 31. Type-2 diagram of log p_{O_2} (and log p_{S_2}) versus the molar metal ratio ξ at $p_{SO_2} = 1$ atm and $T = 1260$ K in the Fe–Zn–S–0 system (after PONCET [1981]).

It can be seen that all the different kinds of diagrams discussed above are of the same geometrical type as binary $T-X$ diagrams since they are all composed of the same topological units of construction (as in fig. 15). Their interpretation is thus immediately clear to anyone familiar with binary $T-X$ diagrams. Log $p_{O_2}-\xi$ diagrams (figs. 29–31) are useful in the study of high temperature oxidation of alloys, metallurgical roasting processes, etc.

The log $p_{O_2}-\xi$ diagram for Fe–Ni–O in fig. 30 is a computer output calculated by means of the same computer program which produced the binary phase diagrams of figs. 17–19. This program operates by computing common tangent lines to the Gibbs energy–composition curves of the phases. That is, with the aid of log $p_{O_2}-\xi$ diagrams, the calculation of a ternary phase diagram can be reduced to the same algorithms as required to calculate a binary phase diagram. The diagram in fig. 30 was calculated from optimized mathematical expressions for the Gibbs energy curves of all the phases. With these same optimized equations, log $p_{O_2}-\xi$ diagrams at other temperatures can be calculated as can $T-\xi$ diagrams at constant p_{O_2} which are also of the same geometrical type. For details see PELTON *et al.* [1979].

Another important geometrical type of phase diagram is exemplified by $P-T$ phase diagrams for one-component systems as shown for H_2O in fig. 32. In such diagrams, which are discussed in ch. 6, §3, bivariant single-phase regions are indicated by areas, univariant two-phase regions by lines, and invariant three-phase regions by *triple points*. The most important rule of construction is the *extension rule*. As illustrated by the dashed lines in fig. 32, at a triple point the extension of any two-phase line must pass into the single-phase region of the third phase.

Another kind of phase diagram of the same geometrical type is shown in fig. 33. For the Fe–S–O system at $T = 800$ K, the axes of the diagram are the equilibrium partial pressures of S_2 and O_2. Single-phase areas indicate which pure compounds of Fe are stable under the given conditions. Two-phase regions are lines. Three phases can co-exist only at triple points. The extension rule given above applies at all triple points. Such *stability diagrams* or *predominance diagrams* are very useful in the study of oxidation, corrosion, roasting, etc. They have been treated in ch. 6, §5 and were discussed by PELTON and THOMPSON [1975] and by BALE *et al.* [1979]. They lend

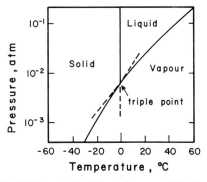

Fig. 32. Type-1 $P-T$ phase diagram of H_2O.

References: p. 382.

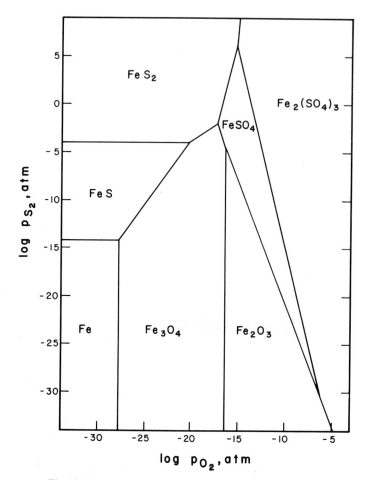

Fig. 33. Type-1 predominance diagram for Fe–S–O at 800 K.

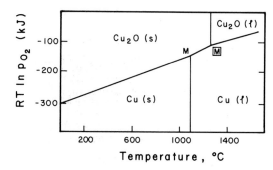

Fig. 34. Ellingham diagram for Cu_2O plotted as a type-1 phase diagram.

themselves to rapid computer calculation by Gibbs energy minimization from thermodynamic data stored in computerized data banks (BALE *et al.* [1979]). Their usefulness is by no means restricted to metal–sulphur–oxygen systems or even to systems of three components.

In ch. 6, §5 a number of *Ellingham Diagrams* are shown. These are plots of the standard Gibbs energy of formation of oxides, $\Delta G^0 = RT \ln p_{O_2}$, versus temperature. Consider the curve for Cu_2O, and place vertical lines at the melting points of Cu and of Cu_2O as shown in fig. 34. We then have, in this figure, a phase diagram of $RT \ln p_{O_2}$ versus T which is of the same geometrical type as those in figs. 32 and 33. The diagram is divided into phase fields, or regions of stability or predominance, of solid Cu, liquid Cu, solid Cu_2O and liquid Cu_2O. Two phases can co-exist along the lines of the diagram and three phases can co-exist at the triple points.

As a final example of this same geometrical type of diagram, a plot of $RT \ln p_{O_2}$ versus T for the Fe–O system is shown in fig. 35b. Again, one-, two-, and three-phase regions are indicated by areas, lines and triple points respectively. In fig. 35a is the binary T–X phase diagram for the Fe–O system. The correspondence

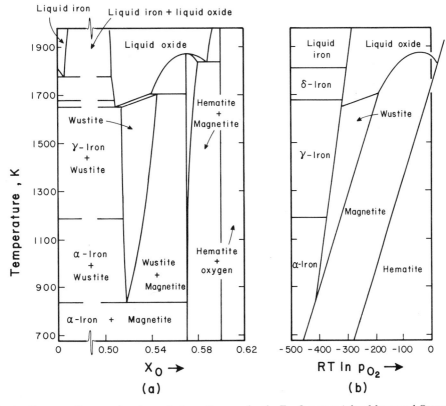

Fig. 35. Corresponding type-1 and type-2 phase diagrams for the Fe–O system (after MUAN and OSBORN [1965]).

References: p. 382.

between figs. 35a and 35b is evident. Each two-phase tie-line of fig. 35a corresponds to a constant p_{O_2} in fig. 35b. Invariants such as eutectics and peritectics in fig. 35a become triple points in fig. 35b.

4.1. Classification of phase diagrams

Phase diagrams of the geometrical type exemplified by one-component $P-T$ diagrams were called *type-1 phase diagrams* by PELTON and SCHMALZRIED [1973]. Examples of type-1 diagrams were given in figs. 32–34 and 35b. Those of the type exemplified by isobaric binary temperature–composition diagrams were termed *type-2 phase diagrams*. Examples of various kinds of type-2 diagrams were given in figs. 19, 29–30 (lower panels), 31 and 35a. Diagrams of the type exemplified by ternary isothermal sections (figs. 24, 26, 28, and upper panels of figs. 29 and 30) were called *type-3 phase diagrams*. Many more examples of different kinds of useful phase diagrams of each type have been given by PELTON and SCHMALZRIED [1973] and by PELTON and THOMPSON [1975].

We may speak of "corresponding" type-1, -2 and -3 phase diagrams. For example, figs. 35a and 35b are corresponding type-2 and type-1 phase diagrams, respectively, for the Fe–O system. The upper and lower panels of figs. 29 and 30 are corresponding type-2 and type-3 phase diagrams. In a system of C components we may define *thermodynamic potentials* ϕ_i $[i = 1, 2, \ldots, (C + 2)]$. These are T, P, μ_1, $\mu_2, \ldots, \mu_C$ (where μ_j is the chemical potential of component j). For each potential ϕ_i we may define a "corresponding" extensive variable Q_i. For the potentials T, P and μ_j the corresponding extensive variables are S, $-V$, and n_j respectively (n_j is the number of moles of component j). If we choose any three potentials, designated ϕ_1, ϕ_2, ϕ_3 and if we hold ϕ_4, $\phi_5, \ldots, \phi_{C+2}$ constant, then a plot of ϕ_1 versus ϕ_2 will be a type-1 phase diagram. If we now replace ϕ_2 by the ratio ϕ_2/ϕ_3, then we obtain a corresponding type-2 diagram. If, further, we also replace ϕ_1 by ϕ_1/ϕ_3 then we obtain the corresponding type-3 phase diagram. For a detailed discussion see PELTON and SCHMALZRIED [1973] and PELTON and THOMPSON [1975].

5. Experimental techniques of measuring phase diagrams

It is beyond the scope of the present article to give a complete discussion of experimental techniques. Only a brief survey of the major techniques will be presented with a view to providing the reader with some insight into the difficulties involved. More detailed discussions are given by RAYNOR [1970], MacCHESNEY and ROSENBERG [1970], BUCKLEY [1970], and HUME-ROTHERY et al. [1952].

As has been discussed in §§2.10 and 3.5, modern techniques of computer coupling of thermodynamics and phase diagrams hold much promise in significantly reducing the amount of experimental effort required to characterize a phase diagram completely, particularly in the case of multicomponent systems.

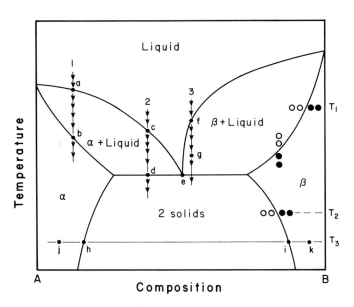

Fig. 36. Binary phase diagram to illustrate some experimental techniques; solid circles: single-phase alloy, open circles: two-phase alloy.

5.1. Thermal analysis

Liquidus temperatures are commonly determined by the measurement of *cooling curves*. Consider the binary alloy A–B of composition 1 in fig. 36. A sample of liquid alloy, of the order of 50 g, is held in a crucible in a furnace. The furnace temperature is then decreased slowly at a uniform rate, usually not exceeding 1°C per minute, while the temperature of the alloy is measured by a calibrated recording thermocou-

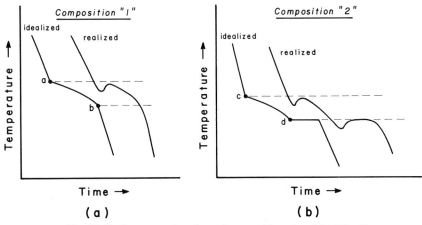

Fig. 37. Cooling curves for alloys of compositions 1 and 2 of fig. 36.

References: p. 382.

ple. A graph of sample temperature versus time (the *cooling curve*) is shown in fig. 37a. At the liquidus temperature (point **a** in fig. 36), solidification commences with the evolution of heat. This causes a decrease in the cooling rate of the specimen with, ideally, a resultant abrupt change of slope of the curve as shown in fig. 37a. When solidification is complete at the solidus composition (point **b** in fig. 36), heat evolution ceases and, ideally, another change of slope of the cooling curve is observed. From the "idealized" cooling curve of fig. 37a, one can then read the liquidus and solidus temperatures. For an alloy of composition 2, the idealized cooling curve is shown in fig. 37b. There is a change of slope at the liquidus, and a plateau at the eutectic temperature since, ideally, the sample temperature remains constant until the invariant eutectic solidification reaction is complete.

In a real experiment, however, cooling curves of the type labelled "realized" in fig. 37 are usually obtained. Some degree of undercooling (or *supercooling*) is almost always observed. The sample must be cooled below the transformation temperature before nucleation of the new phase occurs. The temperature then rises again. However, at a liquidus the temperature will never rise all the way back up to the liquidus, so that some extrapolation technique must be used to estimate the liquidus temperature. At a eutectic, the equilibrium eutectic temperature may be regained by the sample after supercooling provided that the quantity of material solidifying eutectically is large enough to yield a sufficient evolution of heat. Supercooling may be minimized by stirring or by constantly jolting the sample to induce nucleation.

It is important that temperature gradients within the sample be eliminated by stirring and by the use of a furnace with a good constant temperature zone. Otherwise, part of the sample will start to solidify before the rest and the cooling curve will show a rounded rather than an abrupt change of slope.

At compositions where the liquidus is steep, such as the composition 3 in fig. 36, the rate of heat evolution is small. That is, on descending from the liquidus at point **f** to a point **g** an appreciable distance below the liquidus, only a small amount of heat is evolved since, as can be seen from the lever rule, only a small amount of solid is precipitated. Hence, it is more difficult to determine the exact temperature of the change in slope of the cooling curve, and the technique of thermal analysis is less precise. For very steep liquidus lines, a method of segregation and sampling or quenching may be preferable, as will be discussed below.

For liquidus temperatures below about $1000°C$, absolute accuracies of the order of $\pm 1°C$ can be obtained by cooling curve methods under optimal conditions. For temperatures of the order of $100°C$ or lower, accuracies of $\pm 0.25°C$ may be obtained.

In principle, solidus temperatures can be determined by the method of cooling curves as shown for the idealized curve in fig. 37a. In certain very favourable cases, with very slow cooling rates, this may be possible. However, in most cases a curve such as the "realized" curve of fig. 37a will be observed, in which determination of the solidus temperature is extremely imprecise. The reasons for this are, firstly, that the solid phase will contain concentration gradients so that solidification will not be complete at the equilibrium solidus temperature; secondly, that the precipitated solid phase will insulate the thermocouple from the sample thereby reducing sensitivity; and thirdly, that by the time the solidus temperature is approached the sample temperature will have lagged well behind the furnace temperature so that the cooling rate will start to accelerate rapidly. For these reasons, solidus temperatures are better measured by *heating curves* which are, in most respects, analogous to cooling curves. An important precaution here is to ensure, by means of a long anneal, that the solid sample is homogeneous before commencing the experiment. In general, it is more difficult to measure solidus temperatures with accuracy than it is to measure liquidus temperatures.

In principle, a peritectic invariant can also be evidenced by a plateau on a cooling curve. However, as discussed in §2.5.3, peritectic reactions are frequently greatly retarded kinetically so that only a weak short thermal arrest may actually be observed.

In general, the precision of thermal analysis experiments may be increased by the use of Differential Thermal Analysis (DTA) in which two thermocouples, connected in opposition, are placed, respectively, in the sample and in a standard specimen which undergoes no phase transformation in the temperature range of study.

5.2.   Sampling techniques and quenching techniques

As discussed above, thermal analysis may be inaccurate for determining the position of a steep liquidus. In such a case, a segregation and sampling technique may prove best. Suppose an alloy of overall composition and temperature in the (liquid + solid) region at point **g** in fig. 36 is held at temperature until equilibrium is established. A specimen of the liquid phase is then obtained, perhaps by suction in a ceramic tube. Chemical analysis will then give the composition of the liquidus at this temperature. A similar technique might be used to measure the compositions of the boundaries of a liquid–liquid miscibility gap. Clearly these methods depend for accuracy on a clean separation of the phases and on the prevention of oxidation and of volatilization losses while the sampling device is inserted into the container.

The principle of *quenching techniques* for solidus determinations is illustrated at temperature T_1 in fig. 36. Samples at each of the four overall compositions shown at T_1 are held at temperature long enough for equilibrium to be attained. They are then quenched rapidly. When examined microscopically, samples from the two-phase zone will exhibit regions of rapidly quenched liquid which can be distinguished from the solid grains. In this way the solidus composition can be bracketed. Alternatively, one could quench samples of the same composition annealed at different temperatures, thereby bracketing the solidus temperature as is also illustrated in fig. 36.

Because of the slowness of solid state reactions, thermal analysis is rarely a useful technique for locating phase boundaries involving two solid phases. However, in such cases annealing and quenching followed by microscopic observation to determine whether one or two phases are present can often be used to bracket the phase boundary as illustrated for the solvus line in fig. 36 at T_2.

Another method of determining phase boundaries in the solid state involves the

References: p. 382.

annealing of a sample in a two-phase (solid$_1$ + solid$_2$) region followed by quenching and subsequent quantitative analysis by any of several techniques to determine the compositions of the two phases present. The relevant techniques of quantitative metallography are discussed in ch. 10, §2.4.3, where several examples are quoted of the use of such techniques to determine solid solubility limits.

In all techniques involving quenching, it is essential that the quench be as rapid as possible so as to avoid any diffusion, segregation or reaction during cooling.

5.3. Other techniques

Suppose that one wishes to determine the compositions (points **h** and **i**) of the phase boundaries at T_3 in fig. 36. Samples at a number of compositions at T_3 between points **j** and **k** are annealed and quenched. The lattice spacings of the α and β phases are then measured by X-ray techniques. The lattice spacings, when plotted versus composition, vary continuously in the single-phase regions, but remain constant in the two-phase region. Extrapolation of the single-phase and two-phase portions of the lattice spacing versus composition curve to their point of intersection then gives the composition of the phase boundary. If too much decomposition occurs upon quenching, then high-temperature X-ray techniques may be required to perform the measurements at temperature.

A technique which is similar in principle consists in measuring the electrical conductivity of specimens at various compositions at T_3 along the line between points **j** and **k**. Again, sharp breaks in the plot of conductivity versus composition are noted at the phase boundaries. This technique is often quite rapid, and can be carried out at elevated temperatures without the necessity of quenching.

In the interdiffusion technique, polished pellets of compositions **j** and **k** are clamped together and annealed at T_3. Following quenching, a composition versus distance scan is performed across the specimen by, say, microprobe analysis. A sharp discontinuity in the curve is observed at the interface, the compositions at either side being the phase boundary compositions **h** and **i**. This technique can also often be used to indicate the presence and compositions of one or more intermediate phases in one single experiment (see for example, SCHMALZRIED [1974]).

A great many other techniques of phase diagram measurement exist, such as dilatometric (HUME-ROTHERY et al. [1952], SINHA et al. [1967]), hardness (BARREAU and CIZERON [1979]), and magnetic measurements (ch. 26, §6, also SUCKSMITH [1939]). The complete determination of an alloy phase diagram usually requires a combination of several techniques (e.g., a combination of dilatometry and magnetic measurements (SERVANT et al. [1973])).

6. Bibliography

6.1. Compilations of phase diagrams

An extensive critical compilation of binary alloy phase diagrams was started by HANSEN [1958] and continued by ELLIOTT [1965] and SHUNK [1969]. This remains a classic work in the field. In the last few years, W.G. Moffatt of the General Electric Company, Schenectady, NY has been compiling the "Handbook of Binary Phase Diagrams", in loose-leaf form. A continual up-dating service is available to subscribers.

A comprehensive, non-critical compilation of binary and ternary phase diagrams in 22 volumes has been edited, in Russian, by AGEEV [1959–1978]. HULTGREN *et al.* [1973] have critically evaluated the phase diagrams and thermodynamic properties of a large number of binary alloy systems. The ASM "Metals Handbook", edited by HAWKINS *et al.* [1973], contains approximately 450 binary and ternary phase diagrams. An index to all the above as well as to many more general and specialized compilations has recently become available (MOFFATT [1979]).

Ternary alloy phase diagrams have been compiled by AGEEV [1959–1978] and by GUERTLER *et al.* [1969], among others. PRINCE [1978] has prepared a multicomponent alloy constitution bibliography for the period 1955–1973.

An international program aimed at a comprehensive critical compilation of all available binary and ternary alloy phase diagrams, often coupled with thermodynamic data, has been undertaken by the American Society for Metals and the National Bureau of Standards. It is planned to make the compiled diagrams available from computer storage as well as in printed form. The "Alloy Phase Diagram Bulletin" is a new journal devoted mainly to reporting the results of the evaluations, system by system, as they become available.

For phase diagrams of nonmetallic systems of interest to metallurgists (such as oxides, halides, etc.), "Phase Diagrams for Ceramists" is an extensive compilation of several thousand binary, ternary and higher-order systems, in four volumes, prepared by LEVIN and co-workers [1964–1981].

6.2. Texts

A large number of texts covering all aspects of the theory, measurement, and uses of phase diagrams are available. Only a selected few are listed here.

FINDLAY [1951] gives a comprehensive introduction to phase diagrams, although more from a chemist's than a metallurgist's viewpoint. RHINES [1956] gives a detailed classical discussion of the interpretation and uses of phase diagrams in metallurgy. Good discussions of the interpretation of binary and ternary diagrams are given by RICCI [1951,1964] and WEST [1965]. GORDON [1968] gives a simple introduction to the thermodynamic origin of binary phase diagrams. PRINCE [1966] treats the interpretation of phase diagrams in much detail, and gives some thermodynamic

References: p. 382.

background. A series of five volumes edited by ALPER [1970–1978] treats many aspects of the theory, interpretation, measurement, and uses of phase diagrams in materials science.

Acknowledgments

I should like to express my appreciation to Mr. J. Desrochers who made all the drawings.

References

AGEEV, N.V., ed., 1959–1978, Phase Diagrams of Metallic Systems, vol. 1–22 (Academy of Sciences of USSR, Moscow).

ALPER, A.M., ed., 1970–1978, Phase Diagrams – Materials Science and Technology, vol. 1–5 (Academic, New York).

ANSARA, I., 1979, Internat. Met. Rev. Review 238, no. 1, 20.

ANSARA, I., and E. BONNIER, 1971, Monatsh. Chemie **102**, 1855.

ASHTAKALA, S., C.W. BALE and A.D. PELTON, 1981, Bull. Alloy Phase Diagrams **2**, 83.

BALE, C.W., 1983, Bull. Alloy Phase Diagrams, in press.

BALE, C.W., and A.D. PELTON, 1982, Metallurg. Trans., **14B**, 77.

BALE, C.W., A.D. PELTON and W.T. THOMPSON, 1979, F*A*C*T (Facility for the Analysis of Chemical Thermodynamics) Users' Instruction Manual (McGill University/Ecole Polytechnique, Montreal).

BARREAU, O., and G. CIZERON, 1979, Mém. Sci. Rev. Mét. **76**, 729.

BRAY, H.J., F.D. BELL and S.J. HARRIS, 1961–62, J. Inst. Metals **90**, 24.

BREWER, L., and R.H. LAMOREAUX, 1980, Phase Diagrams, in: Atomic Energy Rev., Special Issue no. 7 (Molybdenum: Physicochemical Properties of its Compounds and Alloys), ed. L. Brewer (Atomic Energy Agency, Vienna).

BUCKLEY, R.A., 1970, in: Techniques of Metals Research, ed. R.A. Rapp (Interscience, New York) vol. IV, part 1.

CAFASSO, F.A., V.M. KHANNA and H.M. FEDER, 1968, in: Proc. Internat. Conf. on Properties of Liquid Metals, Brookhaven, 1966 (U.S. Dept. of Commerce, Washington) p. 531.

CHART, T., F. PUTLAND and A. DINSDALE, 1979, in: Proc. Calphad VIII Conference, Stockholm, 1979, eds. B. Uhrenius and M. Hillert (Royal Institute of Technology, Stockholm) p. 183.

COHEN, M.L., V. HEINE and J.C. PHILLIPS, 1982, Scientific American **246**, 82.

ELLIOTT, R.P., 1965, Constitution of Binary Alloys, First Supplement (McGraw–Hill, New York).

FINDLAY, A., 1951, The Phase Rule, 9th Ed., revised by A.N. Campbell and N.O. Smith (Dover, New York).

GORDON, P., 1968, Principles of Phase Diagrams in Materials Systems (McGraw–Hill, New York).

GUERTLER, W., M. GUERTLER and E. ANASTASIADIAS, 1969, A Compendium of Constitutional Ternary Diagrams of Metallic Systems, WADC Technical Report 58-615 (Parts I, II, III) (U.S. Dept. of Commerce, Springfield, VA).

HANSEN, M., 1958, Constitution of Binary Alloys, 2nd Ed. (McGraw–Hill, New York; 1st Ed.: Springer, Berlin, 1936).

HAWKINS, D.T., R. HULTGREN, L. BREWER and S.-G. CHANG, 1973, Metals Handbook, 8th Ed., vol. 8 (ASM, Metals Park, OH).

HULTGREN, R., R.L. ORR, P.D. ANDERSON and K.K. KELLEY, 1963, Selected Values of Thermodynamic Properties of Metals and Alloys (Wiley, New York).

HULTGREN, R., P.D. DESAI, D.T. HAWKINS, M. GLEISER, K.K. KELLY and D.D. WAGMAN, 1973, Selected Values of the Thermodynamic Properties of the Elements and Binary Alloys, vol. 1, 2 (ASM, Metals Park, OH).

HUME-ROTHERY, W., J.W. CHRISTIAN and W.B. PEARSON, 1952, Metallurgical Equilibrium Diagrams (Inst. of Physics, London).

INDEN, G., 1982, Bull. Alloy Phase Diagrams **2**, 412.

KAUFMAN, L., 1977, Calphad J. **1**, 7.

KAUFMAN, L., 1978, Calphad J. **2**, 117.

KAUFMAN, L., 1979, Calphad J. **3**, 45.

KAUFMAN, L., and H. BERNSTEIN, 1970, Computer Calculation of Phase Diagrams (Academic, New York).

KAUFMAN, L., and H. NESOR, 1978, Calphad J. **2**, 59, 81, 295, 325.

KOHLER, F., 1960, Monatsh. Chemie **91**, 738.

KÖSTER, W., and W. DULLENKOPF, 1936, Z. Metallk. **28**, 309.

LEVIN, E.M., C.R. ROBBINS and H.F. MCMURDIE, 1964, Phase Diagrams for Ceramists; 1969, Supplement; LEVIN, E.M. and H.F. MCMURDIE, 1975, Supplement; R.S. ROTH, T. NEGAS and L.P. COOK, 1981, Supplement (Am. Ceramic Soc., Columbus, OH).

LIPSON, H., and A.J.C. WILSON, 1940, J. Iron Steel Inst. **142**, 122.

LUKAS, H.L., E.Th. HENIG and B. ZIMMERMANN, 1977, Calphad J. **1**, 225.

MACCHESNEY, J.B., and P.E. ROSENBERG, 1970, in: Phase Diagrams – Materials Science and Technology, ed. A.M. Alper (Academic, New York) vol. 1, ch. 3.

MACHLIN, E.S., 1981, Prediction of Alloy Phase Stability, in: Metallurgical Treatises, ed. J.K. Tien and J.F. Elliott (Metallurg. Soc. AIME, New York) p. 409.

MIODOWNIK, A.P., 1982, Bull. Alloy Phase Diagrams **2**, 406.

MOFFATT, W.B., 1979, The Index to Binary Phase Collections (General Electric, Schenectady, NY).

MUAN, A., and F. OSBORN, 1965, Phase Equilibria Among Oxides in Steelmaking (Addison–Wesley, Reading, MA).

OLSON, N.J., and G.W. TOOP, 1966, Trans. Met. Soc. AIME **236**, 590.

OTT, J.B., J.R. GOATES, D.R. ANDERSON and H.T. HALL, Jr., 1969, Trans. Farad. Soc. **65**, 2850.

PELTON, A.D., and H. SCHMALZRIED, 1973, Metallurg. Trans. **4**, 1395.

PELTON, A.D., and W.T. THOMPSON, 1975, Prog. Solid State Chem. **10**, Part 3, 119.

PELTON, A.D., H. SCHMALZRIED and J. STICHER, 1979, J. Phys. Chem. Solids **40**, 1103.

PONCET, G., 1981, Master's thesis (Ecole Polytechnique, Montréal).

PRINCE, A., 1966, Alloy Phase Equilibria (Elsevier, Amsterdam).

PRINCE, A., 1978, Multicomponent Alloy Constitution Bibliography 1955–73 (The Metals Society, London).

RAYNOR, G.V., 1970, Phase Diagrams and Their Determination, in: Physical Metallurgy, 2nd Ed., Ed. R.W. Cahn (North-Holland, Amsterdam) ch. 7.

RHINES, F.N., 1956, Phase Diagrams in Metallurgy (McGraw–Hill, New York).

RICCI, J.E., 1951, The Phase Rule and Heterogeneous Equilibrium (Van Nostrand, New York).

RICCI, J.E., 1964, Phase Diagrams of Fused Salts, in: Molten Salt Chemistry, ed. M. Blander (Interscience, New York) ch. 4.

SCHMALZRIED, H., 1974, Solid State Reactions (Academic, New York), ch. 7.

SERVANT, C., O. CIZERON and P. LACOMBE, 1973, J. Iron Steel Inst. **211**, 75.

SHUNK, F.A., 1969, Constitution of Binary Alloys, Second Supplement (McGraw-Hill, New York).

SINHA, A.K., R.A. BUCKLEY and W. HUME-ROTHERY, 1967, J. Iron Steel Inst. (London) **205**, 191.

SPENCER, P.J., and I. BARIN, 1979, Mater. Eng. Appl. * **1**, 167.

SUCKSMITH, W., 1939, Proc. Roy. Soc. [A] **170**, 551.

VAN LAAR, J.J., 1908, Z. Phys. Chem. **63**, 216; **64**, 257.

WEST, D.R.F., 1965, Ternary Equilibrium Diagrams (McMillan, New York).

YOKOKAWA, T., and O.J. KLEPPA, 1964, J. Chem. Phys. **40**, 46.

Further reading: see §6

* Sci. & Tech. Press, Reigate, U.K.

CHAPTER 8

DIFFUSION IN METALS AND ALLOYS

J.L. BOCQUET, G. BRÉBEC, Y. LIMOGE

Centre d'Etudes Nucléaires de Saclay
Département de Technologie
Section de Recherches de Métallurgie Physique
91191 Gif sur Yvette, France

R.W. Cahn and P. Haasen, eds.
Physical Metallurgy; third, revised and enlarged edition
© Elsevier Science Publishers BV, 1983

1.   Macroscopic and microscopic theories of diffusion

In this section we will present the macroscopic and microscopic theories of diffusion. The former provides a description of the observed phenomena (which are fluxes), starting from the formalism associated with the thermodynamics of irreversible processes; one then obtains a formal expression of these fluxes as a function of thermodynamic forces and of parameters which are called the *phenomenological coefficients*. In the latter approach the fluxes are calculated by starting from atomic mechanisms. The parameters used in this case are the jump frequencies; they have a clear physical meaning, as opposed to the phenomenological coefficients which are only coefficients of proportionality. For both formalisms, however, a knowledge of the underlying atomic mechanisms is required in order to describe the diffusion phenomena properly. Thus we begin with a brief review of the possible mechanisms; then we recall the main results obtained with the macroscopic and microscopic theories; finally we show how diffusion coefficients depend on temperature and pressure and on the mass of the jumping atom.

1.1.   The mechanisms of diffusion

In crystalline solids, the atoms occupy well defined equilibrium positions (regardless of thermal vibrations); they move by jumping successively from an equilibrium site to another site. The different possible mechanisms for dense structures are schematized in fig. 1.

1.1.1.   Exchange mechanisms

In the *direct exchange mechanism* (fig. 1a) two neighbouring atoms exchange their positions. This mechanism is unlikely for dense structures, for it would involve large distortions and would then entail too large activation energies.

In the *cyclic exchange mechanism* as proposed by ZENER [1951], N atoms exchange themselves simultaneously (in fig. 1b, $N = 4$); the energy involved is much lower than in the direct exchange, but this mechanism remains unlikely, because of the constraint imposed by a collective motion.

At the present time there are no experimental supports for any such mechanisms in crystallized metals and alloys. In metallic liquids, and maybe in amorphous alloys, cooperative motions are more likely operating.

1.1.2.   Mechanisms involving point defects

In thermal equilibrium a crystal always contains point defects. The best known are vacancies, divacancies and interstitials. The presence of these defects in the crystals will allow the atoms to move without too large lattice distortions. The properties of these point defects are described in ch. 17.

1.1.2.1.   Interstitial mechanisms.   In the *interstitial mechanism* (fig. 1d) the atoms move from interstitial sites to interstitial sites. Usually small interstitial atoms, like hydrogen or carbon in metals, diffuse through the lattice by this mechanism.

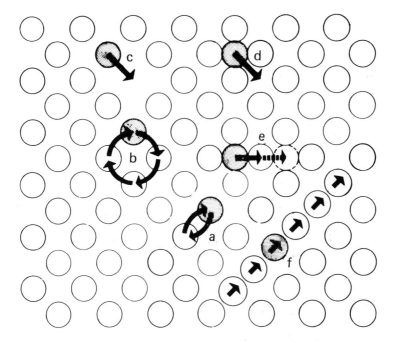

Fig. 1. Mechanisms of diffusion in crystals after ADDA and PHILIBERT [1966]: (a) direct exchange, (b) cyclic exchange, (c) vacancy, (d) interstitial, (e) interstitialcy, (f) crowdion.

The *interstitialcy mechanism* is somewhat more complex; as sketched in fig. 1e, the atoms move from interstitial to substitutional sites and vice-versa. At higher temperatures, this mechanism contributes to silver diffusion in the silver halides. In metals and alloys with a dense structure the interstitial formation energy is so large that the concentration of these defects is completely negligible at thermal equilibrium. The situation is quite different when the material is out of equilibrium (for instance when it is plastically deformed or irradiated); under these conditions one can create *Frenkel pairs*, namely, an equal number of vacancies and interstitials, which will both contribute to the diffusion. In metals and alloys the interstitial atom is not centred on the interstitial site: it has a dumbbell split configuration around a stable position. It is generally recognized that the self-interstitial is split along a $\langle 100 \rangle$ direction in fcc and along a $\langle 110 \rangle$ in bcc materials (SCHILLING [1978]; ch. 17, §3.3.2.2). The case of the mixed dumbbell (one solute + one solvent) is not so simple (see for example LAM *et al.* [1981]). The elementary jumps for these split interstitials are shown in fig. 2. At low temperatures, under irradiation, the interstitial would have a *crowdion* configuration (SEEGER [1976]; fig. 1f); at a higher temperature this crowdion would convert into a split interstitial.

1.1.2.2. Vacancy mechanisms. In metals and alloys, near the melting point, the vacancy concentration is about 10^{-3} to 10^{-4} site fraction. These vacancies allow the

References: p. 466.

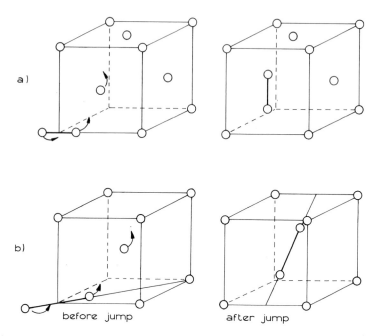

Fig. 2. Elementary jumps of the split interstitials (a) in fcc metals and (b) in bcc metals.

atoms to move rather easily, and this mechanism is operating in most cases.

Besides monovacancies there are *vacancy aggregates*: divacancies, trivacancies, etc... which can contribute to the diffusion (ch. 17, §2.2.1.1). The ratio divacancies/monovacancies generally increases with temperature, so that the divacancy contribution to the diffusion also increases. We will see that numerous anomalies observed at high temperature (leading to curvature of the Arrhenius plot) are attributed to the divacancies. In dilute alloys there is often a binding energy between solutes and vacancies, and the resulting solute–vacancy pairs (complexes) also contribute to the diffusion. The *relaxation mechanism* which is a variant of the vacancy mechanism has been proposed by NACHTRIEB and HANDLER [1954]. The underlying idea is that a large relaxation around a vacancy distorts its surroundings to such an extent that a liquid-like diffusion mechanism can take place; this idea has now been abandoned.

Molecular dynamics calculations by DAFANO and JACUCCI [1977] have shown that at high temperatures, when the atom jump frequency becomes large, a dynamical correlation between successive jumps can occur so that a vacancy can move more than one jump distance; these *vacancy double jumps* are an alternative explanation for the observed curvature of the Arrhenius plot.

1.1.2.3. Mixed mechanisms. For some systems it has been necessary to devise more complex mechanisms in order to account for abnormally fast diffusion. The dissociative model by FRANK and TURNBULL [1956] is the first attempt at explanation. It assumes that the fast diffusing solute dissolves both substitutionally and interstitially; the mass transport is then due to a mixed vacancy and interstitial mechanism. MILLER [1969] has improved this mechanism by introducing the idea of vacancy–interstitial pairs. For more details see §4.2.

1.1.3.   Mechanisms involving extended defects

Linear defects (dislocations) and planar defects (surfaces, interfaces, grain boundaries, etc.) are disordered regions in which the atomic migration is easier than in the bulk. These preferential paths of diffusion are called *short-circuits*. The diffusion mechanisms are not yet well known but it is a topic where one is expecting rapid theoretical advances owing to the increasing power of computers. For more details see §7.

1.2.   The macroscopic theory of diffusion

1.2.1.   Generalities

Diffusion is an irreversible phenomenon; it is thus necessary to use the proper formalism, namely *thermodynamics of irreversible processes* (TIP), to describe it.

We refer the reader, for a detailed discussion of the subject, to the following specialized books and articles: PRIGOGINE [1947], HOWARD and LIDIARD [1964], MÜNSTER [1966] and DE GROOT and MAZUR [1969].

For measuring a flux, it is necessary to define a frame of reference; for the crystallized solid there are two preferred reference frames: the *laboratory reference frame* which is bound to the ends of the sample (we will neglect the sample size variation) and the *lattice reference frame* which is rigidly bound to the atomic planes. It is possible to mark this lattice reference frame with inert markers such as very thin wires, oxide particles, scratches on the surface etc. These inert markers neither contribute nor alter the diffusion but "follow" the motion of the neighbouring atomic planes. Hereafter we will denote fluxes measured with respect to the laboratory frame by J^0 and fluxes measured with respect to the lattice frame by J.

The vacancy mechanism most commonly operates in metals and alloys; we will present the TIP formalism with this assumption. We assume further that the medium is isotropic; no chemical reactions take place; no viscous phenomena and no size variations occur; and, last, that mechanical equilibrium is achieved. We will restrict the discussion to the case of a binary alloy since only these alloys have been widely studied theoretically and experimentally.

1.2.2.   Binary alloys and vacancy mechanism

In a binary alloy there are three species: A, B and vacancies V; there will then be three fluxes, J_A, J_B and J_V in the lattice reference frame or J_A^0, J_B^0 and J_V^0 in the laboratory frame. For a sample subjected to a concentration gradient, ∇n, a temperature gradient, ∇T, and an electric field, E, it has been shown (BRÉBEC

[1978]) that:

$$J_A = -D_A \nabla n_A + (L_{AA} Z_A^* + L_{AB} Z_B^*)eE - (L_{AA}\bar{Q}_A + L_{AB}\bar{Q}_B)\frac{\nabla T}{T}, \tag{1}$$

$$J_B = -D_B \nabla n_B + (L_{BA} Z_A^* + L_{BB} Z_B^*)eE - (L_{BA}\bar{Q}_A + L_{BB}\bar{Q}_B)\frac{\nabla T}{T}, \tag{2}$$

$$J_V = -(J_A + J_B), \tag{3}$$

$$v = \frac{J_V}{n} = -\frac{J_A + J_B}{n}, \tag{4}$$

$$J_A^0 = J_A + n_A v \quad \text{and} \quad J_B^0 = J_B + n_B v. \tag{5}$$

We have omitted the vector notation for simplicity but we must keep in mind that J_i, ∇n_i, ∇T, E and v are vectors. Symbols are defined in what follows.

D_A and D_B are the *intrinsic diffusion coefficients*; they are given by:

$$D_A = kT\varphi \left(\frac{L_{AA}}{n_A} - \frac{L_{AB}}{n_B} \right), \qquad D_B = kT\varphi \left(\frac{L_{BB}}{n_B} - \frac{L_{BA}}{n_A} \right), \tag{6}$$

where k is the Boltzmann constant and L_{AA}, L_{AB}, L_{BA} and L_{BB} are the *phenomenological coefficients* which depend on the intensive quantities such as temperature, concentration, etc.; further they verify the *Onsager reciprocity relation* $L_{ij} = L_{ji}$ (here $L_{AB} = L_{BA}$); φ is the *thermodynamic factor* of the A–B solution; it is given by:

$$\varphi = 1 + \frac{\partial \log \gamma_A}{\partial \log C_A} = 1 + \frac{\partial \log \gamma_B}{\partial \log C_B}, \tag{7}$$

where γ_A and γ_B are the thermodynamic activity coefficients. n_A, n_B and n_V are the numbers of A and B atoms and vacancies per unit volume, respectively.

The number of sites per unit volume is equal to:

$$n = n_A + n_B + n_V.$$

We now define the *atomic fractions*, taking into account the three species:

$$N_A = \frac{n_A}{n}, \qquad N_B = \frac{n_B}{n} \quad \text{and} \quad N_V = \frac{n_V}{n},$$

or, taking into account only the A and B atoms:

$$C_A = \frac{n_A}{n_A + n_B} \quad \text{and} \quad C_B = \frac{n_B}{n_A + n_B}.$$

Since n_V is always small ($n_V \ll n_A + n_B$), the two definitions are practically equivalent.

Z_A^* and Z_B^* are the *effective valences* for A and B and e the absolute value of the charge of an electron. If the material is an insulator or an ionic conductor, these effective valences are equal to the ionic valences z_A and z_B. In a metallic alloy for which the electrical conductivity is due to the electronic carriers there is a momentum transfer from these carriers (electrons or holes) to the A and B atoms. This is equivalent to a force which has to be added to the electrostatic force; as a consequence an effective valence can be defined (see §6).

$\bar{Q}_A$ and $\bar{Q}_B$ are energies per mole and are related to the *heats of transport* Q_A^* and Q_B^*. Physically these heats of transport define the *heat flux*, J_q, associated with the matter fluxes J_A and J_B when there is no thermal gradient. Actually it can be shown that:

$$J_q = Q_A^* J_A + Q_B^* J_B + \alpha \frac{\nabla T}{T},$$ (8)

which implies:

$$J_q = Q_A^* J_A + Q_B^* J_B \quad \text{when } \nabla T = 0.$$

In metals and alloys the assumption is often made that the vacancies are in thermal equilibrium everywhere in the sample; this implies that the vacancy sources and sinks (dislocations, grain boundaries, etc.) are effective enough to fulfill this assumption. When this equilibrium condition is well obeyed we have:

$$\bar{Q}_A = Q_A^* - \Delta H_{FV} \text{ and } \quad \bar{Q}_B = Q_B^* - \Delta H_{FV}.$$

ΔH_{FV} is the *vacancy formation enthalpy* in the alloy.

When the requirement of local equilibrium is not met, no simple relation holds between $\bar{Q}$ and Q^*.

Finally, v is the lattice velocity measured with respect to the laboratory frame. The physical reason for the lattice displacement is related to the fact that vacancies are not conservative species (they can be created or destroyed at certain lattice sites). In fig. 3 we have sketched the process responsible for the inert marker displacement; we see, in this simple example, that the lattice moves to the right because the vacancies created on the left are eliminated on the right.

We notice from equations (1)–(5) that the fluxes measured in the laboratory

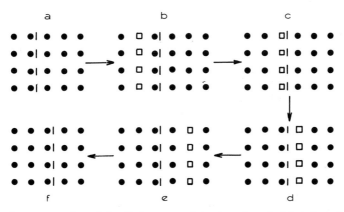

Fig. 3. Schematic representation of the displacement of inert markers (solid circles: atoms; squares: vacancies; dashes: inert markers: (a) initial state; (b) creation of a plane of vacancies; (c, d, e) displacement of the vacancy plane towards the right; (f) elimination of the vacancies. Comparison between (a) and (f) shows that the inert markers are displaced to the right.

References: p. 466.

frame are equal to:

$$J_A^0 = C_B J_A - C_A J_B, \qquad J_B^0 = -(C_B J_A - C_A J_B),$$

so that $\quad J_A^0 + J_B^0 = 0.$

1.2.3. Some special cases

1.2.3.1. Chemical diffusion. In the absence of electric fields and thermal gradients. eqs. (1)–(5) become:

$$J_A = -D_A \, \nabla n_A, \qquad J_B = -D_B \, \nabla n_B, \qquad v = (D_A - D_B) \, \nabla N_A. \tag{9}$$

In the laboratory frame we have:

$$J_A^0 = -J_B^0 = -\tilde{D} \, \nabla n_A, \tag{10}$$

where:

$$\tilde{D} = N_B D_A + N_A D_B, \tag{11}$$

$\tilde{D}$ is the *chemical diffusion coefficient*.

We see that, for binary alloys, the fluxes have the form of *Fick's first Law*:

$$J_i = -D_i \, \nabla n_i.$$

In the lattice frame there are two independent fluxes and thus two intrinsic coefficients, whereas in the laboratory frame there is only one flux and one chemical diffusion coefficient.

1.2.3.2. Dilute systems. For dilute alloys n_B (or C_B) $\to 0$ and $\varphi \to 1$; on the other hand it can be shown (§4.1.2.1) that L_{BB}/n_B tends to a finite value, whereas L_{BA}/n_A, which is of the order of n_B, tends towards zero. So:

$$D_{B, n_B \to 0} = kT \frac{L_{BB}}{n_B} = D_{B*}. \tag{12}$$

This coefficient is the *solute diffusion coefficient at infinite dilution*. It will be denoted by D_{B*} to distinguish it from D_B and to recall that diffusion is generally studied with radioactive isotopes which are used at great dilution; then we will also replace n_B by n_{B*}. D_A does not become as simple as D_B because the cross-term L_{AB}/n_B does not tend to zero with n_B (§4.1.2.1).

For these dilute systems the flux of solute is equal to:

$$J_B = -D_{B*} \, \nabla n_{B*} + \frac{n_{B*} D_{B*}}{kT} Z_B^{**} eE - \frac{n_{B*} D_{B*}}{kT^2} Q_B^{**} \, \nabla T, \tag{13}$$

where:

$$Z_B^{**} = Z_B^* + \frac{L_{AB}}{L_{BB}} Z_A^* \quad \text{(the } apparent \; effective \; valence\text{)},$$

$$Q_B^{**} = \bar{Q}_B + \frac{L_{AB}}{L_{BB}} \bar{Q}_A \quad \text{(the } apparent \; heat \; of \; transport\text{)}.$$

Equation (13) has the generalized form of Fick's first Law:

$$J_i = -D_i \nabla n_i + \langle v \rangle_i n_i.$$

When B atoms are isotopes A* of the element A, eq. (13) becomes:

$$J_{A^*} = -D_{A^*} \nabla n_{A^*} + \frac{n_{A^*} D_{A^*}}{kT} Z_A^{**} eE - \frac{n_{A^*} D_{A^*}}{kT^2} Q_A^{**} \tag{14}$$

Because $Z_{A^*}^* = Z_A^*$ and $Q_{A^*}^* = Q_A^*$ we have dropped the asterisk on A in Z_A^{**} and Q_A^{**}. These are given by:

$$Z_A^{**} = \frac{Z_A^*}{f_0} \quad \text{and} \quad Q_A^{**} = \frac{\overline{Q}_A}{f_0},$$

where f_0 is the *correlation factor for self-diffusion*; its presence stems from the non-random character of the tracer atom displacements by a vacancy mechanism. It can be shown that:

$$\frac{1}{f_0} = 1 + \frac{L_{A^*A}}{L_{A^*A^*}}. \tag{15}$$

D_{A^*} is the *self-diffusion coefficient*, given by:

$$D_{A^*} = kT \frac{L_{A^*A^*}}{n_{A^*}}. \tag{16}$$

1.2.4. The various diffusion coefficients

Diffusion coefficients have the dimensions $L^2 T^{-1}$. In the international system of units they are expressed in $m^2 s^{-1}$. The CGS system ($cm^2 s^{-1}$) is still widely used. We will show now which experimental situations correspond to these various coefficients.

The *chemical diffusion coefficient* $\tilde{D}$ describes the interdiffusion of A and B (fig. 4a); it can be measured from the curve C_A (or C_B) versus x; in general it depends on the concentration.

The *intrinsic coefficients* D_A and D_B correspond to a similar experiment; but to obtain them it is necessary to determine $\tilde{D}$ and v [see eqs. (9) and (11)]. v is obtained from the displacement of inert markers (see *Kirkendall effect*, §5.3.1.1). These coefficients depend also on the concentration.

The *solute diffusion coefficient at infinite dilution* D_{B^*} corresponds to the experimental situation shown in fig. 4b. A thin layer of B* atoms has been deposited on the A surface so that $C_{B^*} \approx 0$ and B* diffuses in pure A.

The *self-diffusion coefficient* D_{A^*} corresponds to a similar situation when B* is replaced by A*.

Two other diffusion coefficients are defined as shown in fig. 4c; they are the *self-diffusion coefficients in an homogeneous alloy* AB which are denoted by $D_{A^*}^{AB}$ and $D_{B^*}^{AB}$. The B* (or A*) concentration is always negligible so that the alloy composition is not modified by the diffusing species. These coefficients depend on the concentra-

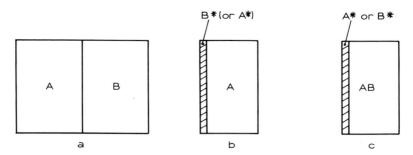

Fig. 4. Different types of diffusion experiments: (a) chemical diffusion → $\tilde{D}$; (b) self or solute diffusion in pure metals → D_{A^*} or D_{B^*}; (c) self-diffusion in homogeneous alloys → $D_{A^*}^{AB}$ or $D_{B^*}^{AB}$.

tion. An alternative notation often used for dilute alloys is:

$$D_{A^*}(C_B) \equiv D_{A^*}^{AB}, \qquad D_{B^*}(C_B) \equiv D_{B^*}^{AB},$$

where C_B is the concentration of B.

The macroscopic description presented above cannot account for the A* and B* diffusion into AB alloys; it would be necessary to derive the flux equations for four species A, A*, B, B* (plus vacancies); this is beyond the scope of this review and we refer the reader to HOWARD and LIDIARD [1964] for more details. Thus it is possible to show that the self-diffusion coefficients in the alloy and the intrinsic diffusion coefficients are related by:

$$D_A = D_{A^*}^{AB} \, \varphi \, r_A, \qquad D_B = D_{B^*}^{AB} \, \varphi \, r_B, \tag{17}$$

where φ is the thermodynamic factor and r_A and r_B are terms which will be made explicit in § 5.3.1.2. These relations, (17), were first established by DARKEN [1948] in a simplified form for the case when $r_A = r_B = 1$.

1.2.5. Fick's second Law

We have seen that the fluxes in a binary alloy have the form:

$$J_i = -D_i \, \nabla n_i \quad \text{or} \quad J_i = -D_i \, \nabla n_i + n_i \langle v \rangle_i.$$

By using the *conservation equation*:

$$\frac{\partial n_i}{\partial t} = -\operatorname{div} J_i$$

we obtain *Fick's second Law*; this partial differential equation can be solved for given initial and boundary conditions. D_i and $\langle v \rangle_i$ can then be obtained from a comparison between the experimental and the calculated concentration curve $C(x)$.

When D_i and $\langle v \rangle_i$ are constant and the diffusion is along the x direction Fick's second Law has the form:

$$\frac{\partial n_i}{\partial t} = D_i \frac{\partial^2 n_i}{\partial x^2}, \tag{18}$$

or
$$\frac{\partial n_i}{\partial t} = D_i \frac{\partial^2 n_i}{\partial x^2} - \langle v \rangle_i \frac{\partial n_i}{\partial x}. \tag{19}$$

The geometry which is most commonly used for measuring D_i is a thin layer deposited onto an "infinite sample" (see fig. 4b and 4c); in this case the solution of eq. (18) has the well-known form:

$$n_i(x,t) = \frac{Q}{\sqrt{\pi D_i t}} \exp\left(-\frac{x^2}{4 D_i t}\right), \tag{20}$$

where Q is the quantity of the diffusing species deposited per unit surface, so that D_i is obtained from the slope of the straight line: log n_i versus x^2.

In the presence of an electric field, the equation to be solved is eq. (19); very often the geometry used is a thin layer sandwiched between two infinite samples. The solution is then:

$$n_i(x,t) = \frac{Q}{2\sqrt{\pi D_i t}} \exp\left[-\frac{(x - \langle v \rangle_i t)^2}{4 D_i T}\right]. \tag{21}$$

$\langle v \rangle_i$ is obtained from the displacement of the maximum of the curve $n_i(x)$ with respect to the origin (defined by the welding interface).

For chemical diffusion (see fig. 4a), $\tilde{D}$ is not constant, we have then to solve:

$$\frac{\partial n_i}{\partial t} = \frac{\partial}{\partial x}\left(\tilde{D}_i \frac{\partial n_i}{\partial x}\right). \tag{22}$$

MATANO [1933] has shown that, when $\tilde{D}_i$ depends on x through n_i:

$$\tilde{D}_i(n_i) = -\frac{1}{2t} \frac{\int_0^{n_i} x \, dn_i}{(dn_i/dx)}. \tag{23}$$

The x origin must be chosen so that:

$$\int_0^{n_{i,\,max}} x \, dn_i = 0. \tag{24}$$

This origin lies in the *Matano plane*. In fig. 5 the different terms of eqs. (23) and (24) are illustrated.

Numerous solutions of the diffusion equation can be found in CRANK [1956] and CARSLAW and JAEGER [1959]. We will see that in some cases Fick's equation is not valid; the first restriction is related to the discontinuous nature of crystals (lattice effect) and will be discussed in § 1.3.5. The second restriction is met in chemical diffusion (spinodal decomposition: CAHN [1967]; ch. 14, § 3.1). In both cases the discrepancy with Fick's law becomes only noticeable for harmonics of concentration with short wavelengths.

References: p. 466.

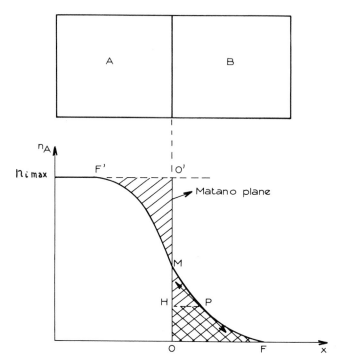

Fig. 5. Matano method for the calculation of $\tilde{D}$. The Matano plane is defined by the equality of the two areas F'O'M and FOM (hatched surfaces). $\int_0^{n_i} x \, dn_i$ is equal to the area HPFO (doubly hatched surface), dn_i/dx is the slope of the tangent to the concentration curve in P.

1.3. The microscopic theory of diffusion

The aim of the microscopic theory is to describe the observed macroscopic effects from the atomic jumps which are the elementary processes in diffusion.

1.3.1. Einstein relation and flux expression

For a *random walk motion*, Einstein [1905] has shown that the diffusion coefficient of species i along the x direction is given by:

$$D_i = \frac{\overline{X^2}}{2\tau},\tag{25}$$

where $\overline{X^2}$ is the mean square displacement along the x direction for the duration τ. If X_k is the displacement of the kth atom along the x direction during τ, we have:

$$\overline{X^2} = \frac{1}{N}\sum_{k=1}^{N} X_k^2,\tag{26}$$

where N is the number of diffusing atoms of species i.

In many cases the motion is not random but the expression (25) still holds provided that $\tau \to 0$.

According to LE CLAIRE [1958] and MANNING [1968], the flux J_i measured with respect to the lattice reference frame is equal to:

$$J_i = \langle v \rangle_i n_i - D_i \frac{\partial n_i}{\partial x} - n_i \frac{\partial D_i}{\partial x}, \tag{27}$$

where:

$$\langle v \rangle_{i,\tau \to 0} = \frac{\overline{X}}{\tau}, \tag{28}$$

D_i is given by eq. (25) when $\tau \to 0$, $\overline{X}$ is the mean displacement during τ for species i.

These relations, (25), (27) and (28), are valid for anisotropic media but to save space we have omitted the more precise notation D_{ix}, $\langle v \rangle_{ix}$ etc.

1.3.2.   Calculation of $\overline{X}$ and $\overline{X^2}$ in terms of jump frequencies

It is easy to show that:

$$\overline{X} = \sum_{i=1}^{n} \overline{x_i}, \tag{29}$$

$$\overline{X^2} = \sum_{i=1}^{n} \overline{x_i^2} + 2 \sum_{i=1}^{n-1} \sum_{j=i+1}^{n} \overline{x_i x_j}, \tag{30}$$

where x_i is the ith displacement along x and n is the mean number of atomic jumps during τ. The overbar denotes an average over a large number of atoms.

1.3.2.1.   Expression for $\overline{X^2}$. *For a truly random walk motion the last term in eq.* *(30), $P = 2 \Sigma\Sigma \overline{x_i x_j}$, vanishes.* When $\overline{X}$ differs from zero (chemical diffusion, electro and thermal diffusion, etc.) this term P is also different from zero but it has been shown that the $\overline{X}$ contribution to P is of the order of τ^2 whereas the $\Sigma \overline{x_i^2}$ term, eq. (30), is of the order of τ; as a consequence the $\overline{X}$ contribution to P is negligible when $\tau \to 0$.

But even if $\overline{X} = 0$, the P term is not necessarily equal to zero, owing to the mechanism of diffusion. We will see later that for most diffusion mechanisms the successive atomic jumps are not independent of each other, and *that the motion is not a truly random walk*. This can be easily understood for the vacancy mechanism: the vacancy concentration is so low ($\approx 10^{-4}$ to the melting point) that two consecutive atomic jumps are likely due to the same vacancy and it is then obvious that after one jump an atom has a greater than random probability of making a reverse jump; there is *correlation*. This correlation between the directions of two successive jumps initiated by the same vacancy reduces the efficiency of the walk with respect to a truly random walk. Correlation occurs for all defect-assisted diffusion mechanisms except for the purely interstitial and exchange mechanisms; it is related to the low concentration of point defects (vacancies, divacancies, interstitials, etc...) and decreases when this concentration increases (WOLF [1980]).

References: p. 466.

How to take this effect into account will be reported in § 1.3.4. *To summarize, we can always calculate* $\overline{X^2}$ *by assuming* $\overline{X} = 0$, *because when* $\tau \to 0$, $\overline{X^2}$ *does not depend on* $\overline{X}$.

For a truly random walk motion, $P = 0$ and we have:

$$\overline{X^2} = \tau \sum_{k=1}^{z} \Gamma_k x_k^2, \tag{31}$$

where z is the number of jump directions, Γ_k the mean atomic jump frequency for the kth direction and x_k the displacement along x for a k-jump. Hence:

$$D_i = \frac{1}{2} \sum_{k=1}^{z} \Gamma_k x_k^2. \tag{32}$$

For cubic lattices all the frequencies Γ_k are equal, and:

$$D_i = \frac{\Gamma l^2}{6}, \tag{33}$$

where $\Gamma = \Sigma_k \Gamma_k$ is the total jump frequency and l is the jump distance ($\frac{1}{2} a \sqrt{2}$ for fcc, $\frac{1}{2} a \sqrt{3}$ for bcc).

1.3.2.2. Expression for $\overline{X}$. With the same notation as for $\overline{X^2}$ we have:

$$\overline{X} = \tau \sum_{k=1}^{z} \Gamma_k x_k. \tag{34}$$

For the case that $\overline{X}$ is not zero, the potential energy of the atoms versus their position is schematized in fig. 6 (for simplicity we have shown regular energy barriers which correspond to a mean displacement $\overline{X}$ independent of x). The shape of this energy diagram is due to a force F_i acting on the atoms such that (see fig. 6):

$$\Delta W = \frac{F_i x_j}{2}.$$

The atom jumps are easier towards the right than towards the left (in fig. 6) and if $\Delta W \ll kT$ we have:

$$\Gamma(\rightarrow) = \Gamma_0 \left(1 + \frac{F_i x_j}{2 kT}\right), \qquad \Gamma(\leftarrow) = \Gamma_0 \left(1 - \frac{F_i x_j}{2 kT}\right), \tag{35}$$

where Γ_0 is the jump frequency when $F_i = 0$; $\rightarrow$ denotes jumps towards the right and $\leftarrow$ jumps towards the left.

We then obtain, with eqs. (34) and (35):

$$\langle v \rangle_i = \frac{\overline{X}}{\tau} = \frac{F_i D_i}{kT}. \tag{36}$$

This expression is the *Nernst–Einstein relation*.

F_i has the following forms, according to the nature of the field acting on the atoms:

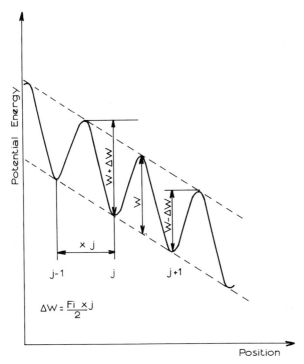

Fig. 6. Schematic representation of the potential energy diagram of the atoms when a constant force is present.

$F_i = Z_i^* eE$ for an electric field,

$$= -\frac{\overline{Q_{i\alpha}}}{T}\frac{dT}{dx} \quad \text{for a thermal gradient,}$$

$$= -k\frac{\partial \log \gamma_i}{\partial x} \quad \text{for a concentration gradient,} \tag{37}$$

where Z_i^* is the effective valence, $\overline{Q_{i\alpha}} = Q_{i\alpha}^* - h_{f v \alpha}$, $Q_{i\alpha}^*$ is the heat of transport for an α-type jump of the species i, $h_{f v \alpha}$ is the vacancy formation enthalpy on a site from which an α type jump is possible, γ_i is the coefficient of activity of species i in the alloy at the position x; this last term can be evaluated from a thermodynamical study of the alloy; we will see in §6 how it is possible to measure and calculate Z^* and Q^*. We observe that with the microscopic approach there are as many heats of transport as there are different types of jumps, whereas with the macroscopic approach the number of the heats of transport is equal to the number of species.

The expression for $\overline{X}$, eq. (36), is not complete because the diffusion mechanism can give rise to an additional term; in order to go further it is thus necessary to adopt a particular model for diffusion. We will consider the case of a binary alloy and a vacancy mechanism.

References: p. 466.

1.3.3. Binary alloys and vacancy mechanism

In the case of a vacancy mechanism there is a coupling between the A and B fluxes through the vacancy flux. This coupling, known as the *vacancy flow effect*, contributes to $\langle v \rangle_i$ in addition to the force F_i. The calculation of this term is rather tedious and for more details we refer the reader to MANNING [1968]. Two cases have to be considered, depending on whether it is a dilute or a concentrated alloy. The diffusion models and results (expressions for L_{AA}, L_{AB} and L_{BB}) are given in §4 for dilute alloys and §5 for concentrated alloys.

1.3.4. Correlation effects

For most diffusion mechanisms the successive atomic jumps are not independent; as a result, the last term of eq. (30), $P = 2 \, \Sigma\Sigma \, \overline{x_i x_j}$, does not vanish. The *correlation factor f* is defined as:

$$f = \frac{D_{\text{actual}}}{D_{\text{random}}}, \tag{38}$$

and from eq. (30) we obtain:

$$f = 1 + \left(2 \sum_{i=1}^{n-1} \sum_{j=i+1}^{n} \overline{x_i x_j} \right) \Big/ \sum_{i=1}^{n} \overline{x_i^2}. \tag{39}$$

Thus, the expression for D, eq. (33), becomes:

$$D = f \frac{\Gamma l^2}{6}. \tag{40}$$

In order to calculate f we have then to evaluate the term $P = 2 \, \Sigma\Sigma \, \overline{x_i x_j}$, which will depend on the mechanism of diffusion. BARDEEN and HERRING [1951] were the first to point out that point-defect diffusion mechanisms involve a non-random-walk motion for the atoms, and they calculated the correlation factor f for a vacancy mechanism. Since this pioneer work, several studies have been published on this topic; we refer the reader to the books or articles by ADDA and PHILIBERT [1966], MANNING [1968] and LE CLAIRE [1970a].

The principal techniques used for the calculation of f are:

(i) *Computer simulations*; $\overline{X_{\text{actual}}^2}$ is obtained by Monte Carlo simulations and compared to $\overline{X_{\text{random}}^2}$. For more details see for instance WOLF [1980].

(ii) *The pair association method*; this technique is described in §4; the fluxes are calculated from the diffusion model and by comparing with the macroscopic expressions we obtain D_{actual} and then f with eq. (38). This technique can only be used for dilute alloys.

(iii) *The random walk method*; this is the calculation of f from the expression (39). In this type of calculation it is necessary to evaluate the return probabilities of the defect on the neighbouring sites of the atom after the first exchange with this atom. To obtain these probabilities, several methods can be used:

– The BARDEEN and HERRING [1951] technique;

References: p. 466.

– the matrix method (Le Claire and Lidiard [1956], Mullen [1961], Howard [1966];
– the electrical analogue method (Compaan and Haven [1956,1958];
– the Benoist et al. [1977] method.
In this last reference a clear comparison is made of these different techniques.

For self-diffusion, f is independent of temperature in isotropic materials (for vacancy mechanism $f = 0.72$ for bcc, 0.78 for fcc and hcp, 0.5 for diamond lattice; for divacancy mechanism $f = 0.475$ for fcc and hcp lattice). For impurity diffusion see §4.

In some cases the knowledge of the correlation factor can allow us to choose among several of the mechanisms of diffusion; it is then a very useful quantity, but as we will see later, experiment does not yield f alone. What is measured is the *isotope effect, E,* from which it is not obvious how to extract f (§ 1.4.3).

1.3.5. The limitation of Fick's Law

We present here a first restriction of Fick's Law, which is related to the discontinuous nature of the lattice (Martin and Benoist [1977]). Let us consider the case of one-dimensional diffusion; the rate equations for an atomic plane n are:

$$\frac{dC_n}{dt} = \Gamma(C_{n+1} - 2C_n + C_{n-1}), \tag{41}$$

where Γ is the atomic jump frequency and C_i the concentration for the ith plane.

We have to compare the solution of this rate equation, which takes into account the discontinuous nature of the lattice, with the macroscopic equation:

$$\frac{\partial C}{\partial t} = D\frac{\partial^2 C}{\partial x^2}. \tag{42}$$

Let us suppose an infinite medium with an initial concentration variation according to a sine form:

$$C_{(0)} = C_1 + (C_2 - C_1)\sin\frac{2\pi x}{\lambda}.$$

The solution will be:

$$C(t) = C_1 + (C_2 - C_1)\left(\sin\frac{2\pi x}{\lambda}\right)e^{-\alpha t}; \tag{43}$$

when $t \to \infty$, the concentration becomes homogeneous, $C \to C_1$.

By substituting eq. (43) in eqs. (41) and (42), we obtain:

$$\alpha_R = 2\Gamma\left[1 - \cos\frac{2\pi a}{\lambda}\right], \qquad \alpha_F = \left(\frac{2\pi}{\lambda}\right)^2 D, \tag{44}$$

where a is the interatomic distance, subscript R stands for the solution of eq. (41) and F for the solution of Fick's Law, eq. (42).

In expanding $\cos(2\pi a/\lambda)$ and taking into account the fact that $D = \Gamma a^2$ for this

References: p. 466.

one-dimensional diffusion, we obtain:

$$\alpha_R = \left(\frac{2\pi}{\lambda}\right)^2 D\left[1 - \frac{2}{4!}\left(\frac{2\pi a}{\lambda}\right)^2 + \frac{2}{6!}\left(\frac{2\pi a}{\lambda}\right)^4 \dots\right]. \tag{45}$$

We clearly see by comparing eqs. (44) and (45) that the solutions of the rate equations and of Fick's equation are only identical when $2\pi a/\lambda \ll 1$, i.e., for large wavelengths. Since a concentration profile can be expanded in a Fourier series, the short-wavelength components will evolve in a different manner than predicted by Fick's Law. This effect will be noticeable only for very short wavelengths (α_R and α_F differ by 3% for $\lambda = 10a$ and by 0.03% for $\lambda = 100a$).

1.4. The diffusion coefficient

In this section we will examine the variations of D with the temperature T and pressure P of the experiment and the mass M of the jumping atom.

For a cubic structure and a diffusion mechanism which involves point defects, it has been shown (see FLYNN [1972]) that:

$$D = \nu\, a^2 f \exp\left(\frac{\Delta S_F + \Delta S_M}{k}\right) \exp\left(-\frac{\Delta H_F + \Delta H_M}{kT}\right), \tag{46}$$

where ΔS_M and ΔS_F are the defect migration and formation entropies, respectively, ΔH_M and ΔH_F the corresponding enthalpies, a is the lattice parameter and ν the atomic vibration frequency (about $10^{13}/s$ in solids).

1.4.1. Variation with temperature

For self-diffusion in isotropic media, f is independent of T, so that from eq. (46), D has the well-known *Arrhenius form*:

$$D = D_0 \exp\left(-\frac{Q}{kT}\right), \tag{47}$$

with $D_0 = \nu\, a^2 f \exp\left(\dfrac{\Delta S_F + \Delta S_M}{k}\right)$ and $Q = \Delta H_F + \Delta H_M.$ \tag{48}

D_0 is the *frequency factor* and Q the *activation energy*.

For impurity diffusion, f depends on T and, strictly speaking, D has no longer the Arrhenius form, but if we want still to recast its variation into the form of an Arrhenius law, we define Q as:

$$Q = -k\frac{\partial \log D}{\partial(1/T)} \qquad [\text{see (47)}];$$

hence we obtain:

$$Q = \Delta H_F + \Delta H_M - C, \tag{49}$$

and $D_0 = \nu\, a^2 f \exp\left(\dfrac{\Delta S_F + \Delta S_M}{k}\right)\exp\left(-\dfrac{C}{kT}\right),$

where $C = k\dfrac{\partial \log f}{\partial (1/T)}.$

If C depends on T, Q and D_0 will also depend on T but it is experimentally observed that C is small and more or less constant so that impurity and self-diffusion behaviour is qualitatively similar.

As a matter of fact, the Arrhenius plot (log D versus $1/T$) is often curved; the departure from a straight line is more or less substantial (curvature only at high temperature, continuous curvature, two straight lines with different slopes); in general, the activation energy increases with T. Several explanations are possible:

(1) The enthalpy and entropy terms depend on T (GILDER and LAZARUS [1975]).

(2) Diffusion occurs by more than one mechanism; this is the case
- for non-homogeneous media; e.g. grain boundary + volume diffusion;
- when several types of jumps occur (DAFANO and JACUCCI [1977]);
- when several defects contribute to the diffusion. Monovacancies are responsible for most of the diffusion processes and at the present time, the curvatures at high temperature are generally ascribed to the increasing contribution of the divacancies (SEEGER and MEHRER [1970]). If several defects contribute to the diffusion we have:

$$D = \sum_i D_i;$$

D is the measured diffusion coefficient and D_i the contribution to the diffusion of the ith defect.

(3) There is an intrinsic domain at high temperature and an extrinsic domain at low temperature; this is mainly the case for semiconductors and ionic crystals. At high temperature (*intrinsic* region) the point-defect concentration is only a function of the temperature, whereas at low temperature (*extrinsic* region) the defect concentration is mainly controlled by the impurity content.

Typically, for metals and alloys, D_0 is in the range of 10^{-6}–10^{-4} m^2/s and Q in the range of 100–600 kJ/mole ($\approx$ 1–6 eV), depending on the melting point of the material.

1.4.2. Variation with pressure

We know from thermodynamics that:

$$\left(\frac{\partial G}{\partial P}\right)_T = -V,$$

where P is the pressure, G the free enthalpy ($G = H - TS$) and V the volume. We obtain from eq. (46):

$$\left(\frac{\partial \log D}{\partial P}\right)_T \approx -\frac{\Delta V_F + \Delta V_M}{kT}. \tag{50}$$

We have neglected the $\partial \log f/\partial P$ and $\partial \log \nu/\partial P$ terms; the former is strictly zero for self-diffusion and the latter is small. $\Delta V = \Delta V_F + \Delta V_M$ is the *activation volume*, where ΔV_F and ΔV_M are the *defect formation* and *migration volumes*, respectively. In general, ΔV_M is small so that ΔV_F is not very different from ΔV. Typically ΔV varies from 0.5 to 1.3 Ω (Ω is the atomic volume); in some cases ΔV is negative, which can be an indication of an interstitial-type mechanism.

References: p. 466.

1.4.3. Variation with atomic mass

From an experimental point of view the *isotope effect* is obtained by measuring simultaneously the diffusion coefficients D_α and D_β of isotopes α and β of the same element with masses m_α and m_β. It can be shown that:

$$E = \frac{D_\alpha/D_\beta - 1}{\left(m_\beta/m_\alpha\right)^{1/2} - 1} = f\,\Delta K \tag{51}$$

where E is the isotope effect, f the correlation factor and ΔK a number ranging between 0 and 1, which allows for the fact that during the jump neighbouring atoms move a little, so the jump becomes an N-body problem.

The relation (51) is only valid when the correlation factor f has the form:

$$f = \frac{u}{u + v},$$

where u is a term which depends on all the frequencies involved except v which is the isotope jump frequency. For fcc materials BAKKER [1971] has shown that eq. (51) is valid for vacancy, divacancy and impurity–vacancy pair mechanisms. For the more complicated mechanisms such as the Miller mechanism, eq. (51) is no longer valid (see LE CLAIRE [1970a] and PETERSON [1975]).

Isotope effect measurements can contribute to identification of the diffusion mechanism through the correlation factor; but we have to know ΔK. Unfortunately ΔK is not often well known; an expression has been established by LE CLAIRE [1966], which allows ΔK to be estimated if the defect formation volume ΔV_F has been measured or calculated:

$$\Delta K \approx \left(1 + \frac{\xi}{3}|(1 - \Delta V_F)|\right)^{-1}. \tag{52}$$

In this expression, ξ is the number of neighbouring atoms when the jumping atom is in saddle-point position and ΔV_F is expressed as a fraction of the atomic volume. For more details about the isotope effect we refer the reader to LE CLAIRE [1970a] and PETERSON [1975].

2. Experimental methods

We shall review the different techniques which allow the diffusion coefficients D to be measured; for the heats of transport and effective valence measurements the reader is referred to §6. Two kinds of methods are used to measure D: macroscopic methods which are based on Fick's first Law and microscopic methods. With the former, we compare the experimental concentration profiles (or a quantity which depends on the concentration) with the appropriate solution of Fick's Law. The latter takes advantage of the fact that many physical phenomena depend on the atomic jumps (for instance, NMR or Mössbauer signals) and can be used to measure atomic jump frequencies. For the microscopic methods it is, in general, necessary to know the diffusion mechanism precisely in order to be able to deduce the jump frequency from the measured signal, whereas the macroscopic methods yield D without any assumption on the diffusion mechanism; but the macroscopic methods entail a macroscopic displacement of the atoms and thus a large number of jumps. At low temperature, for small values of D, it is then necessary to perform long anneals. Conversely, because they only involve a small number of jumps, the microscopic methods require much shorter durations and they allow the variation of D with time to be studied for systems which are not in equilibrium (systems under irradiation, after quenching, during plastic deformation, etc.). For a given system the combination of both kinds of techniques can help to determine the diffusion mechanism (see for instance BRÜNGER *et al.* [1980]). We shall successively discuss these two types of techniques.

2.1. Macroscopic methods

Most frequently the quantity which is measured is the concentration $C(x)$ at point x, and the resulting concentration profile is compared with the appropriate solution of Fick's Law; but any quantity which depends on the concentration or on the flux can allow the determination of the diffusion coefficient. In the first part we focus on methods which determine the profile $C(x)$; in the second part we briefly discuss other macroscopic techniques. For more details see ADDA and PHILIBERT [1966].

2.1.1. *D* from the *C(x)* curve
2.1.1.1. *C(x)* by sample sectioning. Generally the $C(x)$ profile is obtained by sectioning the diffusion zone and measuring the quantity of the diffusing species in each slice (thickness Δx).

For *sectioning*, several techniques can be used:
Mechanical sectioning with precision lathe (10 μm, 5×10^{-16} m²/s), microtome (1 μm, 5×10^{-18} m²/s) or grinding machine (1 μm, 5×10^{-18} m²/s).
Chemical or electrochemical attack (50 Å, 10^{-22} m²/s).
Sputtering by ionic bombardment (10 Å, 5×10^{-24} m²/s).
The numbers in parentheses indicate, respectively, the minimum thickness of the slices and the minimum diffusion coefficient which can be obtained in practice.

The slice thickness, Δx, and the values of x can be measured by weighing; when Δx is too small, weighing becomes inaccurate and other techniques (optical methods, Talystep) have to be used. The techniques most frequently employed for the *determination of the concentration C(x)* are activity counting (for the radioactive species) and mass spectrometry. Each of them can, in principle, be utilized with one of the sectioning methods described previously. They are very sensitive, especially activity counting which allows the detection of atomic fractions as small as 10^{-10}. Ionic sputtering is associated with mass spectrometry in commercial apparatus (ionic analyzers or SIMS, i.e. secondary ion mass spectrometry, see ch. 10A, §3.7) and with activity counting in several devices (see for instance GUPTA [1975]); both allow the determination of diffusion coefficients as small as 5×10^{-24} m^2/s.

2.1.1.2.   Non-destructive techniques. As a matter of fact all these techniques are methods of analysis which could be associated with the sectioning of the sample but they also allow the determination of the profiles without sectioning.

The Castaing microprobe (electron microprobe analyzer). A thin electron beam ($\phi \approx 1$ μm^2; analyzed zone ≈ 1 μm^3) stimulates the X-fluorescence radiation of the element to be studied (ch. 10A, §3.5.2); the profile $C(x)$ can be obtained by analyzing the sample along the diffusion direction. This technique is convenient for studying chemical diffusion. The sensitivity is of the order of 10^{-3} and it is not possible to measure diffusion coefficients smaller than 10^{-15} m^2/s.

Nuclear reactions. The surface of the sample is bombarded with particles (α, protons, etc.) which induce a nuclear reaction with the element to be studied; the energy spectrum of the out-going particles created by this nuclear reaction allows the determination of the concentration profile $C(x)$. These techniques are convenient for the analysis of light nuclei.

Back-scattering. As previously, the surface of the sample is bombarded and one studies the energy spectrum of the elastically back-scattered particles, from which it is possible to obtain the concentration profile. In contrast with nuclear reaction methods, the back-scattering method is convenient for the analysis of heavy nuclei.

For more details about these two last methods we refer the reader to the writings of ENGELMANN [1977], PHILIBERT [1976] and CHU *et al.* [1978].

2.1.2.   Other macroscopic methods

There are numerous macroscopic techniques which allow the determination of diffusion coefficients from measurements of properties depending on matter transport; the most important are the following:

– Measurement of the quantity of matter leaving or crossing a sample. This method is much employed for gases and volatile products.

– Measurement of the growth rate of a new phase. When the growth is controlled by diffusion it is possible to calculate D from the growth kinetics. This is fully explained by SCHMALZRIED [1974].

– Measurements of compaction and deformation kinetics. Sintering of powders and creep of crystals are in some cases controlled by bulk diffusion; it is then possible to deduce D from compaction or deformation kinetics (ch. 20, §1.10; ch. 30, §2.2).

– Measurements of the evolution of the concentration modulation by X-rays (or electrical resistance). This method was initially developed by COOK and HILLIARD [1969] and used for amorphous systems by ROSENBLUM *et al.* [1980]. A film of periodic composition is deposited by evaporation or sputtering; this film tends to homogenize on heating, according to the solution given in §1.3.5. The kinetics can be followed by X-rays and

$$D = -\frac{\lambda^2}{8\pi^2} \frac{\mathrm{d}}{\mathrm{d}t}\left(\ln \frac{I(t)}{I_o} \right),$$

where I is the intensity of the satellite peak in the neighbourhood of the central spot (it is also possible to follow this kinetics by the measurement of the electrical resistance of the sample).

This technique allows the determination of very small coefficients of diffusion ($\sim 10^{-27}$ m^2/s).

The *Gorsky effect*, in spite of its being a macroscopic method, will be described in the next section, together with relaxation phenomena.

2.2. Microscopic (or local) methods

The methods described here pertain to two groups: on the one hand, studies of relaxation kinetics in out-of-equilibrium samples, on the other hand various spectroscopic methods involving transition matrices disturbed by atomic jumps.

2.2.1. Relaxation methods

The reader can find a very detailed theory of relaxation properties in solids as well as experimental results in NOWICK and BERRY [1972].

2.2.1.1. Thermodynamic aspects of relaxation.
The internal energy of a system is defined by the state variables, stresses, temperature, fields, etc., and by a set of n internal variables, labelled v_i, the equilibrium values of which, v_i^e, are fixed by the values of the state variables. These internal parameters can be, for example, the order parameters in an alloy or the populations of the various energy levels that a system can occupy. If one of the state variables changes suddenly, the various internal variables which are coupled with it will relax to the new equilibrium values. In the cases of interest here, the diffusional mobility D controls the relaxation towards equilibrium. We can then measure a relaxation time τ, related to D by

$$D = k \frac{a^2}{\tau},$$

where a is a distance characteristic of the lattice, and k is a constant depending on the specific model involved.

The internal energy varies according to:

$$dU = T\,dS + dU_{\text{ext}} - \sum_i U_i\,dv_i, \tag{53}$$

where dU_{ext} is the energy supplied by the external forces and the dv_i stand for the variations of the internal variables. U_i is the ordering energy associated with the ith internal variable.

If the deviations from equilibrium, $v_i - v_i^e$, are not too large, the U_i can be expanded as

$$U_i = - \sum_j U_i^j \left(v_j - v_j^e \right). \tag{54}$$

When the time evolution of the v_i's is first-order, one speaks of relaxation phenomena. In this case:

$$\frac{dv_i}{dt} = - \sum_j w_i^j \left(v_j - v_j^e \right). \tag{55}$$

One sees easily that it is always possible to find a set of n normal modes V_i evolving in time as:

$$V_i(t) = V_i^e + \left[V_i(t=0) - V_i^e \right] \exp(-t/\tau_i). \tag{56}$$

In eq. (56), τ_i is the relaxation time of the ith normal mode. In many cases the homogeneity of the sample is not perfect and, instead of a single-valued τ_i, we observe a distribution $\pi(\tau_i)$ of times, corresponding either to the distribution of atomic environments or to the various relaxation paths.

In diffusion studies of metals and alloys, the most frequently used external influences are mechanical stresses, magnetic field or temperature jumps.

2.2.1.2. Anelasticity. In the case of mechanical stresses one speaks of *anelasticity*. Two solicitation modes are used in these studies. The first one is the *mechanical after-effect*: a static stress (or strain) is applied and the strain (stress) relaxation is followed in time. The application for example of a constant stress leads to an instantaneous elastic response defining the *unrelaxed modulus* M_0. Afterwards the system displays a relaxation of the strain which corresponds at infinite time to the *relaxed modulus* M_∞. The after-effect anelasticity is then defined by three physical quantities:

 – the relaxation intensity: $\Delta = (M_0 - M_\infty)/M_\infty$;
 – the mean relaxation time $\bar{\tau}$;
 – the width of the relaxation time spectrum β.

In many cases the experimental data are well fitted with a Gaussian spectrum (NOWICK and BERRY [1972]):

$$\pi(\tau) = \left(\beta \sqrt{\pi} \right)^{-1} \exp - \left(\ln(\tau/\bar{\tau})/\beta \right)^2.$$

The second mode is the *internal friction mode*. In this case, stress and strain are periodic with a frequency ω according to:

$$\sigma = \sigma_0 \exp i\omega t, \qquad \epsilon = \epsilon_0 \exp i(\omega t - \varphi).$$

The *phase factor* φ between stress and strain expresses the energy dissipation due to anelasticity. One can show that φ is related to $\bar{\tau}$ by:

$$\tan \varphi \sim \frac{\omega \bar{\tau}}{1 + \omega^2 \bar{\tau}^2}. \tag{57}$$

The phase factor displays a Debye resonance versus ω, or versus temperature variation through the temperature dependence of $\bar{\tau}$; the maximum value is obtained for $\omega \bar{\tau} = 1$. In real experiments the measurements are made either in forced, or in free, damped oscillations. One can then measure the energy absorbed per cycle, $\delta w/w$, or the magnification factor at the resonance Q (inverse of Full Width at Half Maximum (FWHM) of the ϵ_0^2-versus-ω curve) as a function of temperature. In the free case one measures the logarithmic decrement $\delta = \ln[\epsilon(t)/\epsilon(t+T)]$, where T is the oscillation period.

All these physical quantities are related by:

$$2\pi \sin \varphi \sim \frac{\pi \Delta}{(1+\Delta)^{1/2}} \sim \frac{2\pi}{Q} \sim 2\delta \sim \frac{\delta w}{w}. \tag{58}$$

The study of the value of φ versus ω, at various temperatures, gives the relaxation time $\bar{\tau}$ versus temperature. We deduce D, the diffusion coefficient, as

$$D = \frac{k\,a^2}{\bar{\tau}}.$$

A great variety of experimental set-ups have been used. The reader will find many references in NOWICK and BERRY [1972]. The most commonly used are the torsion pendulum, in either internal friction or after-effect mode, and the resonant bar at higher frequency. The corresponding D's which can be measured are given in table 1.

2.2.1.3. Snoek relaxation. In body-centered cubic metals the interstitial defect has a tetragonal symmetry, in both octahedral and tetrahedral sites. Owing to this lower symmetry it can give rise to an anelasticity effect, the so-called *Snoek effect* (SNOEK [1939]). In most cases experimental results are, in bcc metals, in good agreement with the octahedral model (see fig. 7 and §4.2.1). Under a uniaxial tensile stress σ along the Oz axis, there is a splitting of the energy levels of the three kinds of sites S_x, S_y, S_z, in favor of S_z sites. The ordering energy [eqs. (53) and (54)] is: $U_i = \gamma\sigma$, where γ is the lattice parameter variation along Oz axis due to the redistribution from S_x and S_y to S_z sites. The associated internal variable is $v = (n_z - n/3)$, n and n_z being the total atomic fraction and the atomic fraction of solute on S_z sites, respectively. Taking Γ as the total solute frequency jump, one easily shows that $\Gamma = 2/3\bar{\tau}$, and D is given by

$$D = \frac{a^2}{36\bar{\tau}}, \tag{59}$$

where a is the lattice parameter. (See also ch. 20, §4.3.)

Table 1
Diffusion coefficient ranges accessible through different techniques.

Method	Relaxation time τ or Frequency ω	Range of D_{B*} accessible (m²/s)
Elastic after-effect (Zener or Snoek)	$10 < \tau < 10^5$ s	$10^{-25} < D_{B*} < 10^{-21}$
Internal friction (Zener or Snoek)	1 Hz $< \omega < 10^5$ Hz	$10^{-20} < D_{B*} < 10^{-15}$
After-effect and internal friction in Gorsky relaxation	Approximately same as above	$10^{-12} < D_{B*} < 10^{-8}$
Torque measurement (magnetic anisotropy method)	$10 < \tau < 10^5$ s	$10^{-25} < D_{B*} < 10^{-21}$
NMR, field gradient Pulsed NMR	– $10^{-7} < \tau < 0.1$ s	$10^{-13} < D_{B*} < 10^{-8}$ $10^{-19} < D_{B*} < 10^{-13}$
Mössbauer	–	$10^{-15} < D_{B*} < 10^{-11}$
Neutron scattering	–	$10^{-11} < D_{B*} < 10^{-9}$

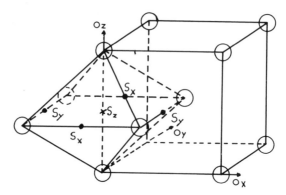

Fig. 7. Characteristics of octahedral interstitial sites in bcc lattices. There are three kinds of sites, S_x, S_y and S_z. For a S_z site the first-neighbour distance in the z direction is $a/2$, and $a/\sqrt{2}$ in the $x0y$ plane.

2.2.1.4.   Zener relaxation. In face-centered cubic metals, an interstitial solute has the same symmetry as the lattice. Therefore there is no anelasticity associated with interstitial solute. On the other hand, a pair of substitutional solute atoms B of non-zero size effect in an A solvent metal represents a defect of orthorhombic symmetry. Their reorientation under stress then gives rise to an anelastic relaxation which can be seen in all lattices of higher symmetry. ZENER [1943, 1947] was the first to point out the existence of an internal friction peak in a 70 : 30 α-brass, which he further analyzed as the effect of the reorientation of solute pairs (now called the *Zener effect*). LE CLAIRE [1951] has analyzed the kinetics of their reorientation and shown how it allows the solute jump frequencies to be determined. Nevertheless this model in terms of solute pairs suffers from several weaknesses:
– Contrary to Snoek relaxation, the Zener effect can be observed only in con-centrated alloys, because of its dependence on the square of the B concentration. The description in terms of isolated pairs therefore becomes less satisfactory.
– Several parameters of the relaxation (the anisotropy, the temperature dependence of Δ) are badly accounted for by the pair model.
– The solute mobility alone is involved in Le Claire's analysis of the kinetics. However, NOWICK [1952] has shown that the mobility of both species is needed to produce a relaxation.

Clearly we need a full description of the ordering under stress to give a good account of the Zener effect. LE CLAIRE and LOMER [1954] and WELCH and LE CLAIRE [1967] have given a solution to this problem in the framework of Cowley's order parameters (up to the second-nearest neighbours for the latter authors). The most elaborate analysis of the kinetics for the first model is due to RADELAAR [1970]. He simultaneously calculated τ_R, the relaxation time for ordering, and D_{A*}^{AB} and D_{B*}^{AB}, the tracer diffusion coefficients of respectively A* and B* in the alloy:

$$\tau_R \sim a^2 \, g(\alpha) \left(C_A / D_{B*}^{AB} + C_B / D_{A*}^{AB} \right), \tag{60}$$

where $g(\alpha)$ is a smooth function of α, the short range order parameter. No equivalent analysis exists for Welch and Le Claire's model.

One clearly sees that the (approximate) formula (60) does not allow one diffusion coefficient alone to be deduced from τ_R values. The relaxation time appears to be a "Zener-averaged" function of various atomic jump frequencies, and not the particular arrangement which gives the diffusion coefficients. For example, τ_R frequently appears to be a thermally activated quantity, the activation energy of which is lower than the activation energy of either D_{B*}^{AB} or D_{A*}^{AB} (NOWICK and BERRY [1972]).

Nevertheless, while the use of Zener relaxation in measuring diffusion coefficients is a delicate task, this effect is of paramount interest in studies of the behaviour of point defects in alloys in, or out of, equilibrium (BERRY and OREHOTSKY [1968], BALANZAT and HILLAIRET [1980]).

2.2.1.5. Gorsky effect. Any defect B which produces a lattice dilatation is also able to give rise to an anelastic relaxation. This is the well known *Gorsky effect* (GORSKY [1935]) the complete theory of which was given by ALEFELD *et al.* [1970]. Indeed, the migration of positive (resp. negative) dilatation centers down (resp. up) a macroscopic strain gradient produces a relaxation of stresses, which is detectable if the diffusion coefficient is high enough (VÖLKL [1972]).

One easily shows that the diffusion coefficient D_{B*} of the B defect is related to the relaxation time τ_R by (ALEFELD *et al.* [1970]):

$$D_{B*} = \frac{1}{\varphi \tau_R} \left(\frac{d}{\pi} \right)^2, \tag{61}$$

where d is the length of the diffusion zone and φ the thermodynamic factor (§ 1.2.2). The main interest of the Gorsky relaxation is to give access to D_{B*} without the need of any diffusion model. Note that here the length scale is d, the sample size, and not a, the atomic size [eqs. (59) or (60)]. We see in table 1 that this method is well suited for high diffusion coefficients.

2.2.1.6. Magnetic relaxation in ferromagnetic alloys. In ferromagnetic alloys the local interactions between momentum and local order give rise to relaxation phenomena similar to those observed under stress. Their origin is to be found in the *induced anisotropy energy*, the theory of which was built up by NÉEL [1951, 1952, 1954] and TANIGUCHI [1955]. We have an ordering energy U_i given by [see eqs. (53) and (54)]:

$$U_i = w \cos^2 \theta, \tag{62}$$

where θ is the angle between the local moment and the symmetry axis of the defect under consideration. The origin of w lies in the perturbation by the defect of exchange integrals between magnetic atoms and of spin-orbit coupling.

This anisotropy energy gives rise to three kinds of relaxations.

The first, analogous to the Snoek relaxation, is due to reorientation of interstitial impurities in bcc crystals during a change of field direction. The relationship between jump frequency, relaxation time and diffusion coefficient is the same as in the Snoek relaxation.

References: p. 466.

The second is the analogue of the Gorsky effect. In a domain wall the interaction between the magnetostrictive stresses and the strain field of interstitials can be minimized by diffusion through the wall. This diffusion gives rise to an after-effect. The relaxation time is a factor $(\delta/a)^2$ larger than the preceding one (as in the mechanical case), δ being the domain wall thickness (KRONMÜLLER [1978]).

The third can be called a *magnetic Zener effect* and is due to the ordering of ferromagnetic alloys in a magnetic field. The theory was built up by NÉEL [1954] in a quasi-chemical model and by VILLEMAIN [1970] with inclusion of second-nearest neighbour order. The link between relaxation time and diffusion is as difficult to establish as in the Zener effect. However, the sensitivity is extremely high and allows study of diffusion at exceedingly low defect concentrations (10^{-8}–10^{-10} vacancy fraction, CHAMBRON and CAPLAIN [1974]). (See also ch. 26, §5.3.3.3.)

2.2.1.7.   Kinetics of short-range ordering.   Any physical property sensitive to atomic order can be used to follow the kinetics of ordering and therefore to study atomic mobility: resistivity (RADELAAR [1966]), X ray-, electron- or neutron diffraction (PENISSON and BOURRET [1975]). Nevertheless we need to relate quantitatively the order parameter and the measured quantity. Further, the link between ordering kinetics and diffusion coefficients is as difficult to establish as in the Zener effect.

2.2.2.   Spectroscopic methods

2.2.2.1.   Nuclear magnetic resonance.   In a static magnetic field H_0 (say 10^3 Gauss) a nuclear spin of magnitude I takes a precession motion at the Larmor frequency ω_0. Simultaneously the degeneracy of the $2I + 1$ energy levels is raised. A macroscopic sample is an assembly of nuclear spins and will then display a magnetic moment along H_0, M_z, and a transverse part $M_\perp$, zero at equilibrium. If we apply a transverse radiofrequency magnetic field $H_\perp$ with a pulsation ω near ω_0, this field will induce transitions between the $2I + 1$ Zeeman levels of each spin. Experiments show, and theory confirms in many cases (ABRAGAM [1961]), that the time evolution of the total moment of the sample M is given by the *Bloch equation*:

$$\frac{\partial M}{\partial t} = \gamma M \wedge H - \frac{M_\perp}{T_2} - \frac{M_z - M_z^{eq}}{T_1} + \nabla[D \cdot \nabla(M - M^{eq})], \qquad (63)$$

where γ is the gyromagnetic ratio, M^{eq} the equilibrium value of the magnetic moment and D the diffusion coefficient of the nuclei. T_1 is the relaxation time of the longitudinal part M_z and corresponds to an energy transfer between lattice and spins system. T_2 is the relaxation time of the transverse part $M_\perp$. The values of T_1 and T_2 are fixed by various interactions between spins, either direct or indirect via electrons. On each nuclear site these interactions create a local field (approx. 1 Gauss) which fluctuates, due to atomic vibrations and jumps. It induces transitions between levels and then settles their lifetime. However, if the frequency of the atomic displacements becomes of the order of magnitude of the frequency of the precession motion due to this local field, the spins will be sensitive only to the time average of it. This average is zero and the lifetime is no longer limited by interactions: this is the so called *motional narrowing* of absorption lines, which explains part of the variation of T_1 and T_2 with temperature.

Equation (63) shows that two techniques can be used to determine diffusion coefficients. Firstly, the last term of eq. (63) gives a time evolution of $M_\perp$ when the sample is put in a field gradient G according to:

$$M_\perp(t) = M_0 \exp\left(-\frac{t}{T_2} - \frac{1}{3}D\gamma^2 G^2 \tau^2 t\right).$$

The measurements of $M_\perp$ versus time t then gives D without any further hypothesis (ABRAGAM [1961]).

We can also measure either the width of absorption lines in steady-state resonance (ω near ω_0), or the decay of M_z and $M_\perp$ parts with time after the perturbation by a "pulse" of $H_\perp$ field. In this last case, the decays fit the laws $M_z = M_0[1 - \exp(-t/T_1)]$ or $M_\perp = M_0 \exp(-2t/T_2)$. Now the BLOEMBERGEN *et al.* theory [1948] expresses T_1 and T_2 in terms of Fourier transforms of the time correlation function of dipolar interactions (the main interaction in many cases) due to nuclear motions. We then have to postulate a diffusion mechanism, to calculate correlation functions and to compare it with experimental T values in order to deduce a diffusion coefficient.

The original work of Bloembergen was done for diffusion in liquids and later extended to the case of random walk and defect mechanism in lattices (TORREY [1954]), including correlation effects (WOLF [1979]).

2.2.2.2. Mössbauer effect. Gamma rays can be emitted or absorbed by nuclei. The width Γ of the corresponding lines is very narrow, of the order of 10^{-9} eV. Owing to the recoil energy of the emitter, the emission line of free nuclei is shifted by a much larger amount. This shift then prevents the resonant absorption by other nuclei. On the other hand, if the emitter is embedded in a crystal, Mössbauer has shown that a part of the emissions occurs without recoil. In this case resonant absorption can occur. However, if one of the emitting or absorbing nuclei is moving, either by thermal vibration or diffusion jumps, the line is broadened and the broadening gives access to atomic mobility. More precisely, SINGWI and SJÖLANDER [1960a] have shown that the emission, or absorption, cross-section is given by:

$$\sigma(\omega) = \frac{\sigma_0 \Gamma}{4\hbar} \int_{r,t} \exp\left[i(Kr - \omega t) - \frac{\Gamma}{2\hbar}|t|\right] G_s(r,t)\,dr\,dt, \tag{64}$$

where $G_s(r,t)$ is the Van Hove autocorrelation function and K the wave vector of the γ photon of frequency $2\pi/\omega$. In a classical system G_s gives the probability of finding at (r,t) a particle located initially at $(0,0)$. Therefore $G_s(r,t)$ contains all information about diffusion processes. SINGWI and SJÖLANDER [1960a, b] have given the theory of diffusion broadening in the case of liquids and of random jumps on a lattice. In the last case the broadening is given by:

$$\Delta\Gamma = \frac{12\hbar}{b^2}D(1-\alpha),$$

References: p. 466.

where b is the jump distance and α a (generally small) function often neglected but (strongly) K-dependent. This dependence can give very valuable information about the anisotropy of diffusion jumps (FLINN [1980]). Nevertheless the constraints of: (i) high recoilless fraction (large detectable signal), and (ii) measurable $\Delta\Gamma/\Gamma$, say between 10^{-1} and 10^2, limit the available tracers to ^{57}Fe, ^{119}Sn, ^{151}Eu and ^{161}Dy (JANOT [1976]).

2.2.2.3. Quasi-elastic neutron scattering.

A monoenergetic neutron beam can be scattered by nuclei embedded in a solid without any energy transfer, that is, without phonon emission or creation. This is the exact parallel, in the case of neutrons, of the Mössbauer effect for γ photons. More precisely, VAN HOVE [1954] has shown that eq. (64) gives the incoherent scattering differential cross-section for scattering vector K and energy transfer ω. In this case Γ has to be taken as zero, and σ appears to be the (r,t) Fourier transform of G_s. Therefore atomic motions, as given by $G_s(r,t)$, induce a broadening of the elastic peak, the measurement of which versus ω gives access to atomic mobility.

Two experimental techniques can be used (SPRINGER [1972]). For the first, one uses small K values, corresponding to large r, where $G_s(r,t)$ is well represented by:

$$G_s(r,t) = (4\pi Dt)^{-3/2} \exp(-r^2/4Dt).$$

The elastic peak then has a Lorentzian shape with a FWHM of $2\hbar K^2 D$. The use of this method, at low K, is therefore limited by the energy resolution of spectrometers.

In the second method, one starts from a diffusion model which allows G_s to be calculated. One then fits the parameters of the model to scattering measurements at various K. If one works with fairly large K and small r, the method is very sensitive to the details of the jump mechanism.

Neutron scattering techniques, owing to an energy resolution of the spectrometers much more limited than in the case of Mössbauer spectroscopy ($\sim 10^{-7}$ with backscattering geometry, against $\sim 10^{-9}$ eV), are well suited for fast diffusion, like that of hydrogen in metals (GISSLER [1972]) or sodium self-diffusion (AIT SALEM *et al.* [1979]).

3. Self-diffusion in pure metals

The pure metals are undoubtedly the most studied as regards their point defects and diffusion properties. Traditionally, one distinguishes between *normal self-diffusion* which occurs in most metals, and the *anomalous self-diffusion* which takes place in about ten body-centered cubic metals. A detailed review on this subject can be found in PETERSON [1978].

3.1. Normal self-diffusion

According to LE CLAIRE [1976], normal self-diffusion complies with the three following empirical rules:

– the diffusion coefficient obeys the Arrhenius law: $D = D_0 \exp(-Q/kT)$;
– the D_0 values range from 5×10^{-6} to 5×10^{-4} m^2/s;
– the activation energy is related to the melting temperature by the expression:
$Q = 34T_M$, where T_M is the melting point of the metal (in Kelvin), Q is then expressed in calories per mole. This behaviour—the Van Liempt relation—is roughly followed by most metals (see fig. 8).

In fact one often observes a curvature in the Arrhenius plot; it is mainly restricted

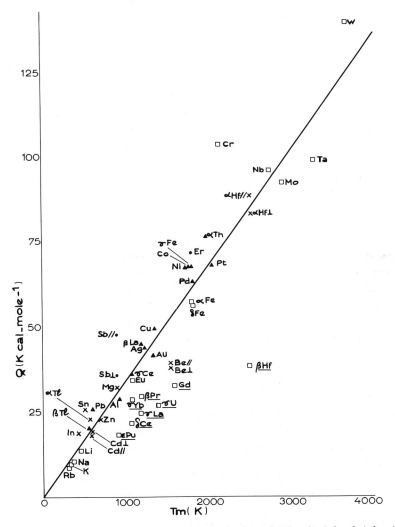

Fig. 8. Van Liempt relation for some metals. Experimental values of Q for: fcc (triangles), bcc (squares), and other structures (crosses). Anomalous bcc structures are underlined. The straight line represents the Van Liempt relation: $Q = 0.034T_M$ in kcal/mole.

to high temperatures but sometimes it is present over the whole temperature range (for instance in sodium). This curvature is always such that the actual D values at high temperature are larger than the values extrapolated from the low-temperature region. The D values in the noncurved regions of the Arrhenius plot are otherwise normal.

The vacancy character of the diffusion in these normal metals is now well established and accepted by everyone; in contrast, there are still some controversies about the curvature of the Arrhenius plots. In order to explain these abnormally high values of D_0 and Q in the curved region of the Arrhenius plots, three hypotheses can be retained among all the possibilities which have been discussed in §1.4.1:

– A vacancy mechanism occurs over the whole temperature range but because of a strong thermal expansion coefficient for the vacancy, D_0 and Q increase with temperature (GILDER and LAZARUS [1975]).

– Both vacancies and divacancies contribute to the diffusion, with an increasing participation of the latter at high temperatures (SEEGER and MEHRER [1970]).

– A vacancy mechanism occurs and the curvature is due to the dynamical correlation between successive jumps (vacancy double jumps) (DAFANO and JACUCCI [1977]).

Experimentally the following data are available: frequency factor D_0, activation energy Q, isotope effect E and activation volume ΔV. When the Arrhenius plot is curved, we notice that D_0 and Q increase with T whereas E decreases with T; for example, for self-diffusion in silver, E decreases from 0.72 to 0.58 when T increases from 673 to 954°C (zirconium is an exception: E increases with T; but this is an abnormal bcc metal, as we will see later). The variations of ΔV with P and T have not been well studied except for sodium. Any of the three assumptions can explain these experimental data; for example the decrease with temperature of the isotope effect is obvious for the mixed vacancy + divacancy mechanism since the correlation factor for the divacancy mechanism is smaller than for the vacancy mechanism. As a result, since the contribution of the divacancies to the diffusion increases with T the apparent correlation factor and then the isotope effect will decrease. But this variation of E with T can also be explained with the two other assumptions. Likewise the variation of D_0 and Q with T is compatible with all three hypotheses.

However, measurements of defect properties after quenching can only be understood if vacancies *and* divacancies are present (PETERSON [1978]); in addition, the analysis of tracer and NMR data on self-diffusion in sodium seems also to favour the mixed vacancy–divacancy mechanism (BRÜNGER et al. [1980]). Although these two statements are not very general *a consensus does exist in favour of the mixed vacancy–divacancy mechanism.* Thus, in general when the Arrhenius plots are curved the data are fitted by assuming a two-defect mechanism, in addition a possible dependence of enthalpies and entropies on temperature is sometimes taken into account (see for instance SEEGER and MEHRER [1970] or PETERSON [1978]).

At the present time there are ten "normal" metals with a curved Arrhenius plot: five fcc metals (Al, Ag, Au, Cu and Ni) and five bcc metals (Li, Na, Nb, Ta and V).

A plot which is not curved does not mean that only one mechanism occurs; the absence of curvature can be simply due to the fact that the temperature range under study is too small.

The isotope effect E is always smaller for the bcc than for the fcc metals; this may be due to a more important divacancy contribution to the diffusion or to smaller ΔK. For some bcc metals the divacancy contribution to the diffusion seems to be very substantial; one explains in this way the high activation energies for chromium and tungsten.

In summary, most of the self-diffusion data in pure metals can be explained with the mixed vacancy–divacancy mechanism. Empirical rules ($5 \times 10^{-6} < D_0 < 5 \times 10^{-4}$ m^2/s, $Q = 34T_M$) are related to the monovacancy mechanism; too large values of D_0 and Q with respect to these empirical rules are interpreted as being due to divacancies.

3.2. Anomalous self-diffusion

Ten bcc metals do not satisfy the empirical rules of § 3.1: *they present abnormally low values of the frequency factor D_0 and of the activation energy Q*. These ten bcc metals are: β-Ti, β-Zr, β-Hf, γ-U, ϵ-Pu, γ-La, δ-Ce, β-Pr, γ-Yb and β-Gd. *All of them undergo at least one phase transformation before reaching the bcc structure*; for instance Ti and Zr are hexagonal at room temperature and they switch to the bcc structure at 882°C and 979°C, respectively.

β-Ti and β-Zr have been studied over a large temperature range; they show a strong curvature of the Arrhenius plot (much stronger than for "normal" metals).

The D_0 and Q values at high temperature are "normal" enough but at low temperature (near the temperature of transformation) these values are abnormally low. For the other anomalous bcc metals, the temperature range which has been studied is too narrow to display any curvature but the D_0 and Q values are also smaller than for normal metals. These low values of D_0 and Q entail high values for D (near the melting point, D for these anomalous bcc metals is one or two orders of magnitude larger than for "normal" metals).

Negative activation volumes have been found for δ-Ce and ϵ-Pu (possibly due to interstitial-type mechanism); the isotope effect E for β-Zr seems to increase with temperature (from 0.285 at 916°C to 0.411 at 1727°C), in contrast with the other data of isotope effects for self-diffusion.

Many explanations have been proposed in order to account for these low values of D_0 and Q: strong contribution of the short-circuits, presence of extrinsic vacancies due to the impurities, interstitial mechanisms, etc. All these assumptions have been ruled out by experiment. Since the common character of these ten metals is the existence of one or several phase transformations to reach the bcc structure, it seems reasonable to think that the observed anomalies are due to this transition. It is in this spirit that SANCHEZ and DE FONTAINE [1975] attempted to explain the self-diffusion of β-Ti, β-Hf and β-Zr. For these metals there are, near the temperature of the $\beta \rightarrow \alpha$ transition, embryos of ω phase (this phase is stable under pressure), the

References: p. 466.

structure of which is the same as the structure of a jumping atom in the saddle position in the bcc lattice. Thus, when the temperature approaches the transition temperature, there are more and more embryos of phase ω and so more and more atoms in an easy jumping position; the diffusion is then enhanced.

Although for the other anomalous bcc metals no similar indication is available, one can postulate a similar explanation.

3.3. Prediction of the self-diffusion coefficients

There are three possible ways to predict the diffusion coefficients:
- by theoretical calculation;
- by simulation of the jump;
- by empirical laws.

3.3.1. Theoretical calculation of D

The calculation of the enthalpies and entropies of formation and migration of the defect involved allows the determination of the diffusion coefficient. The techniques used in this type of calculation are beyond the scope of this review and we refer the reader to specialized treatises, for instance GERL and LANNOO [1978].

FLYNN [1968], using the dynamic theory of diffusion, has established a very useful expression for the vacancy jump frequency:

$$w = (3/5)^{1/2} \, \nu_D \exp\left(- \frac{C\Omega \, \delta^2}{kT} \right).$$

ν_D is the Debye frequency, C an average of the elastic constants of the material, Ω the atomic volume and δ is the fractional displacement towards the saddle point, beyond which the atomic jump necessarily goes to completion. δ has to be fitted; it is 0.3225 for fcc metals and 0.2588 for bcc metals. To obtain the diffusion coefficient, this jump frequency has to be multiplied by the atomic fraction of the vacancies.

3.3.2. Simulation of the jump

The technique used for simulation of the jump is molecular dynamics (see for example DOAN [1978]) which allows "experiments" to be performed in the computer. The principle is the following: one solves the motion equations for N atoms, the interactions of which are described by an appropriate potential. It is then possible, when a vacancy has been introduced among the N atoms, to record the number of jumps Γ of this vacancy. From the plot of log Γ versus $1/T$ one obtains the migration parameters of the vacancy. This technique gives no information about the formation constants of the defect. The possibility of a dynamic correlation between vacancy jumps at high temperatures has been displayed thanks to this method.

3.3.3. Empirical relations

Empirical relations are numerous, and we only present the most important:
- *The Zener formula* (ZENER [1951]). This has been established for interstitial

solutions and therefore deals only with migration. The idea is that the migration free enthalpy is due to the elastic work required to strain the lattice so that the interstitial can jump. The relation has been empirically extended to self-diffusion. This expression relates the entropy of diffusion ΔS to the activation energy Q via Young's modulus (or shear modulus):

$$\Delta S = \frac{\lambda \beta Q}{T_M},$$

where λ is a constant which depends on the lattice ($\lambda = 0.55$ for fcc and 1 for bcc); $\beta = -d(\mu/\mu_0)/d(T/T_M)$, where μ is Young's modulus (or shear modulus) and μ_0 the value of μ at 0 K; T_M is the melting temperature. The review by LAZARUS [1960] shows that there is a pretty good agreement between experimental and calculated values of ΔS.

– *The Varotsos formula* (VAROTSOS [1978]). This is based on the idea that the free enthalpy of diffusion has the form $\Delta G = CB\Omega$, where C is a constant which depends on the lattice, B is the bulk modulus and Ω the atomic volume. Thus for cubic materials:

$$D = a^2 \nu \exp\left(-\frac{CB\Omega}{kT}\right).$$

The agreement with experimental data seems fairly good.

– *Other empirical relations.* These include the *Van Liempt relation*: $Q = 32T_M$ (at present one prefers $Q = 34T_M$); the *Nachtrieb relation*: $Q = 16.5L_M$ (at present one prefers $Q = 15.2L_M$), L_M is the latent heat of melting; finally the *Keyes relation*: $\Delta V = 4\chi Q$, where ΔV is the activation volume and χ the compressibility.

4. Self- and solute diffusion in dilute alloys

The first part of this section deals with the substitutional alloys for which the vacancy mechanism is expected to be dominant.

The second part deals with those alloys which do not meet the requirements of a "normal" diffusion behaviour and in which the solute diffusivity is often much larger than the solvent diffusivity.

4.1. Vacancy diffusion in dilute A–B alloys

4.1.1. Standard models for bcc and fcc alloys

In the fcc lattice, the difference between the first and second neighbour distances is large enough to allow us to ignore the interaction between a solute atom and a vacancy beyond the nearest-neighbour distance. The same dissociative jump frequency w_3 is therefore attributed to the three possible dissociative jumps (fig. 9) which separate a vacancy from a neighbouring solute atom; w_4 is the frequency of the reverse jump. w_2 stands for the solute–vacancy exchange and w_1 for the vacancy

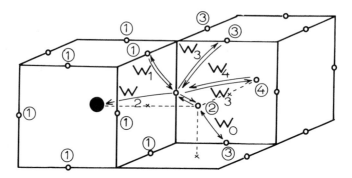

Fig. 9. Standard five-frequency model for solute diffusion in fcc lattices by a vacancy mechanism. The encircled figures denote more and more distant shells of neighbours around the solute atom (solid circle).

jump around the solute atom which does not break the solute–vacancy complex. w_0 is a jump not affected by the solute atom. Detailed balancing implies that:

$$w_4/w_3 = \exp(-E_B/kT)$$

where E_B is the binding energy of the vacancy–solute pair (E_B is negative for an attractive binding).

All the physical quantities which will be compared to experimental diffusion data in dilute alloys are functions of only three independent ratios of these five jump frequencies, namely w_2/w_1, w_3/w_1 and w_4/w_0.

In the bcc lattice, conversely, the second-neighbour distance is close to the first-neighbour distance and the solute–vacancy interaction energy is not negligible at the second-neighbour distance. Four distinct dissociative frequencies are defined for a vacancy escaping from the first-neighbour shell (w_3, w_3' and w_3'') and from the second-neighbour shell (w_5). The frequencies of the reverse jumps are w_4, w_4', w_4'' and w_6, respectively (fig. 10). The solute–vacancy exchange frequency is w_2. If we denote the interaction energies at the first- and second-neighbour distances by E_{B1} and E_{B2}, respectively, detailed balancing requires that:

$$w_4'/w_3' = w_4''/w_3'' = \exp(-E_{B1}/kT),$$
$$w_6/w_5 = \exp(-E_{B2}/kT),$$
$$w_6 w_4/w_5 w_3 = w_4'/w_3'.$$

The calculation of tracer diffusion coefficients has never been performed with the whole set of frequencies. Simplifying assumptions have always been made to reduce the large number of unknown parameters.

– *MODEL I* assumes that $w_4' = w_4'' = w_6 = w_0$. These equalities imply in turn $w_3' = w_3''$ and $w_3 w_5 = w_3' w_4$. All the physical quantities which will be compared to experimental data can be expressed as function of w_3/w_3' and w_2/w_3' only.

– *MODEL II* restricts the interaction to first neighbour distances and assumes that

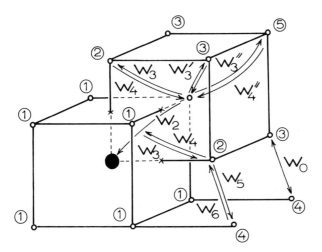

Fig. 10. Standard model for solute diffusion in bcc lattices by a vacancy mechanism.

$w_3 = w_3' = w_3''$ and $w_5 = w_6 = w_0$. These equalities imply $w_4 = w_4' = w_4''$. The physical quantities which are to be compared with the experimental data are function of w_2/w_3 and w_4/w_0 only.

4.1.2. Kinetic expressions of the phenomenological coefficients L_{AA}, L_{AB}, L_{BA} and L_{BB}

The purpose of the calculation is to express these coefficients as functions of the jump frequencies, the solute and vacancy concentrations, and the various interaction energies between the species. Two methods have been used so far.

4.1.2.1. Pair association method. In the pair association method, the stationary fluxes J_A, J_B and J_V are calculated in the presence of a constant electric field E, which biases the jump frequencies of the vacancy. The bias can take two distinct values, ϵ_A and ϵ_B, according to the chemical nature of the atom which exchanges with the vacancy. Hence:

$$w_2^\pm = w_2(1 \pm \epsilon_B), \qquad w_i^\pm = w_i(1 \pm \epsilon_A) \text{ for } i \neq 2,$$

where the superscript $\pm$ stands for a jump frequency in the direction of the electric field $(+)$ or in the reverse direction $(-)$. It can be shown that ϵ_A and ϵ_B are proportional to the thermodynamic forces $Z_A^* eE$ and $Z_B^* eE$, respectively, which act upon the species A and B. The final kinetic expressions of the fluxes are then compared with the phenomenological expressions in order to deduce the L_{ij}'s.

For a fcc lattice, the calculation has been carried out at first order in C_B and to an increasing degree of accuracy by including more and more distant shells from the solute (HOWARD and LIDIARD [1963], MANNING [1968], BOCQUET [1974]). For a bcc lattice the calculation has been recently published in the frame of the two approximations quoted above (SERRUYS and BRÉBEC [1982b]). For both structures, the common form of the results is the following:

$$L_{AA} = \frac{nD_A^*(0)}{f_0 kT}(1 + b_A C_B),$$

$$L_{AB} = L_{BA} = \frac{nC_B D_B^*(0)}{kT}G,$$

$$L_{BB} = \frac{nC_B D_B^*(0)}{kT},$$

where n is the number of lattice sites per unit volume; $D_A^*(0)$ and $D_B^*(0)$ are the solvent and solute tracer diffusion coefficients in pure A ($C_B = 0$); G is the *vacancy wind* term L_{AB}/L_{BB} which accounts for the coupling between J_A and J_B through the vacancy flux J_V. Tables 2 and 3 summarize the expressions of $D_A^*(0)$, $D_B^*(0)$, b_A and G for both structures.

A more accurate calculation of 7F can be performed, which includes more distant shells from the impurity atom and which can be plugged into the above expressions without introducing any inconsistency (MANNING [1964]).

4.1.2.2.   Linear response method. In the linear response method, a time-dependent electric field $E(t)$ is applied to the alloy and instantaneous values of the fluxes J_A, J_B and J_V are calculated. It is shown that the calculation of the L_{ij}'s reduces to the solution, by a Green's function method, of closely related random-walk problems in the unperturbed ($E = 0$) state of the system. All the possible trajectories of the vacancy around the tracer atom are taken into account and not only those contained

Table 2

Theoretical expressions of various quantities entering the phenomenological coefficients in a fcc lattice ($f_0 = 0.781$).

$$D_{A^*} = 2s^2 C_v w_0 f_0, \qquad D_{B^*}(0) = 2s^2 C_v \frac{w_4}{w_3} w_2 f_B;$$

$$u = w_2/w_1, \qquad v = w_3/w_1, \qquad w = w_4/w_0;$$

$$f_b = (2 + 7Fv)/(2 + 2u + 7Fv);$$

$$7F = 7 - \frac{20w^4 + 38w^3 + 2062w^2 + 3189w}{4w^4 + 90w^3 + 656w^2 + 1861w + 1711};$$

$$G = \frac{(3v - 2) + (7 - 7F)v(1/w - 1)}{1 + 3.5Fv};$$

$$b_A = -19 + w(4/v + 14) - \frac{14(1 - F)(1 - w)[3v - 2 + (1 + u + 3.5v)(1/w - 1)] + (w/v)(3v - 2)^2}{1 + u + 3.5Fv};$$

$$7F(\text{Manning}) = 7 - \frac{10w^4 + 180.5w^3 + 927w^2 + 1341w}{2w^4 + 40.2w^3 + 254w^2 + 597w + 436}.$$

C_v is the vacancy concentration in pure A.
s is the jump distance.

Table 3

Theoretical expressions of various quantities entering the phenomenological coefficients in a bcc lattice ($f_0 = 0.727$).

$$D_{A^*}(0) = \frac{4}{3}s^2 C_v w_0 f_0, \qquad D_{B^*}(0) = \frac{4}{3}s^2 C_v w_2 \frac{w_4'}{w_3'} f_B, \qquad f_B = \frac{7F\,w_3'}{2\,w_2 + 7F\,w_3'}$$

Quantity	Expression	
	Model I	Model II
u	w_3 / w_4'	w_4 / w_0
v	w_2 / w_3'	w_2 / w_3
$7F$	$\dfrac{1174u^2 + 3339u + 1657}{587u + 507}$	$\dfrac{96u^3 + 1324u^2 + 4510u + 3325}{32u^3 + 324u^2 + 810u + 475}$
A_1	$1174v(1-u) - 2348u^2 + 958u + 2030$	$8u^2 + 77u + 155$
A_2	$2v(587u + 507) + 1174u^2 + 3339u + 1657$	$32u^3 + 324u^2 + 810u + 475$
A_3		$\dfrac{(8u + 7 + 2v)A_2 - 32u(u+1)A_1}{4u(u+1)}$
G	$2\dfrac{-1174u^2 + 1201u + 1067}{1174u^2 + 3339u + 1657}$	$2\dfrac{(8u-7) - 32(u^2-1)A_1/A_2}{(8u+7) - 32u(u+1)A_1/A_2}$
b_A	$-7 + 6u + 2(u-1)A_1/A_2$ $+ \dfrac{2u-4}{587u + 53}\left[587(u-1) + (587u+507)\dfrac{A_1}{A_2}\right]$	$-13 + 12u + \dfrac{6u + 2v(u-1) - 7}{2u(u+1)A_3}$ $\times[(8u-7)A_2 - 32(u^2-1)A_1]$
$7F(M)$	$\dfrac{2u^2 + 5.1817u + 2.476}{u + 0.8106}$	$\dfrac{3u^3 + 33.43u^2 + 97.38u + 66.06}{u^3 + 8.68u^2 + 18.35u + 9.433}$

in few coordination shells, as was done in the pair association method.

This general formalism has been used for the fcc structure and has confirmed the results previously obtained by the pair association method (ALLNATT [1981]). Its true interest lies in its ability to deal with all nonstationary problems such as the relaxation phenomena (LIDIARD [1981]).

4.1.3. Experimentally accessible quantities

We restrict ourselves to the experiments which are commonly used to deduce the vacancy jump frequencies at the root of the models for bcc and fcc lattices.

The measurements performed on pure solvent A consist in determining:
- the solvent and solute tracer diffusivities $D_A^*(0)$ and $D_B^*(0)$;
- the isotope effect for solute diffusion, $f_B \Delta K_B$. The ΔK_B factor must be evaluated in some way to extract f_B. Several theories have tried to determine ΔK_B as a function of the ratio m_B/m_0 where m_B and m_0 are the masses of the solute and of the solvent

References: p. 466.

respectively (ACHAR [1970], FEIT [1972]): but they apparently do not fit with the experiments performed in lithium (MUNDY and McFALL [1973]).

The measurements of alloying effects are performed on dilute A–B alloys and comparison is made with the same quantity determined in pure A, in order to extract the slope of the linear resulting variation. These measurements usually determine:

– The *linear enhancement factor* b_1 for solvent tracer diffusion $D_A^*(C_B)$, defined by

$$D_A^*(C_B) = D_A^*(0)(1 + b_1 C_B).$$

b_1 is a function of the partial correlation factors of the solvent jumps in the vicinity of a solute atom: these factors have been numerically tabulated for the fcc lattice (HOWARD and MANNING [1967]) as well as for the bcc lattice (LE CLAIRE [1970b], JONES and LE CLAIRE [1972]). The solute diffusion coefficient D_B^* also varies linearly with the solute concentration, according to:

$$D_B^*(C_B) = D_B^*(0)(1 + B_1 C_B).$$

It is experimentally observed that b_1 and B_1 have the same sign and are roughly of equal magnitude whenever the diffusion mechanism is the same for A* and B* in the alloy (it would not be true in Pb-based alloys, §4.2.2!). This means physically that the preponderant effect of the solute is to increase (or decrease if b_1 is negative) the total vacancy concentration, which affects solvent and solute diffusivity roughly to the same extent. B_1 is a function of the solute jump frequencies in the vicinity of another solute atom (BOCQUET [1973]; LE CLAIRE [1978]).

– The linear enhancement factors b_M and b_T for the shift of inert markers and solvent tracer markers in an electric field. If we denote the rates of these shifts by V_M and V_T, b_M and b_T are defined according to:

$$V_M(C_B) = V_M(0)(1 + b_M C_B), \qquad V_A^*(C_B) = V_A^*(0)(1 + b_T C_B).$$

b_M and b_T have been calculated as functions of the vacancy jump frequencies (DOAN [1972]; BOCQUET [1973]; DOAN and BOCQUET [1975]; LIMOGE [1976a]) and are given by:

$$b_T = b_A + 1 + f_0 G \frac{Z_B^*}{Z_A^*} \frac{D_B^*(0)}{D_A^*(0)},$$

$$b_M = b_A + f_0 \frac{D_B^*(0)}{D_A^*(0)} \left[\frac{Z_B^*}{Z_A^*} (1 + G) + G \right].$$

– The vacancy wind term $G = L_{AB}/L_{BB}$ can be measured from the solute enrichment or depletion in the neighbourhood of a sink (ANTHONY [1971, 1975]) or by combining tracer diffusion experiments with Kirkendall shift measurements in differential couples A + A–B (HEUMANN [1979]; HOSHINO *et al.* [1981a]).

4.1.4. Determination of vacancy jump frequencies

Jump frequencies depend on the interatomic potential which should, in principle, be deduced from ab-initio calculations. Unfortunately an accurate knowledge of these potentials is far from being acquired and one usually proceeds differently. Jump frequencies are instead fitted to the experimental results.

As already mentioned, diffusion data yield only three jump frequency ratios for an fcc lattice and only two for a bcc lattice; thus only three independent measurements are required for fcc alloys and two for bcc alloys. Any additional result is highly desirable and is used to check the consistency of the experiments. If this consistency cannot be maintained in view of a new result, this may mean that one (or more) experimental results are not worthy of confidence or that the model does not correctly represent the experimental system.

All the dilute alloys of fcc structure, for which we know the jump frequency ratios, are displayed in table 4. Whenever the number of experiments is equal to three, one reference only is quoted. When the experimental data are redundant, several references are given. The error bars on the final values of these ratios are large: at least 50% for the best cases, up to an order of magnitude for the worst. We have to keep in mind that any ratio which departs too much from unity (say less than 10^{-2} or larger than 10^{2}) may be an indication that the weak perturbation assumption at the root of the model is violated in the alloy under consideration. A similar table of jump frequency ratios has recently been published (HERZIG *et al.* [1982]).

The search for these frequency ratios is not always straightforward, as can be seen from the following examples:
- Al–Cu: the value of the self-diffusion coefficient is still today highly controversial. At 858 K it is measured or evaluated to be 1.66×10^{-13} m^2/s (FRADIN and ROWLAND [1967]), 3.03×10^{-13} m^2/s (SEEGER *et al.* [1971]), 3.66×10^{-13} m^2/s (BEYELER et ADDA [1968]), 3.73×10^{-13} m^2/s (LUNDY and MURDOCK [1962]) and 4.51×10^{-13} m^2/s (PETERSON and ROTHMAN [1970]). Using Anthony's result, which establishes that no solute redistribution occurs in the neighbourhood of a vacancy sink, very different values of $G = L_{AB}/L_{BB}$ are deduced according to the value which is retained for the self-diffusion coefficient. It is easy to check that one obtains $G = -0.4; -0.01; +0.203; +0.226$, and $+0.43$, respectively. The jump frequency ratios which stem from such scattered values of G are highly different of course; in addition they do not fit with the measurement of inert marker shifts in dilute alloys (LIMOGE [1976a]).

Finally, according to SEEGER *et al.* [1971], 40% of the total diffusivity at 858 K is due to divacancies. This fact cannot be ignored any longer, and a revised version of the atomic model should be presented to take properly into account the contribution of the divacancies to diffusion and electromigration.
- Pb–Cd: self-diffusion in lead meets the usual requirements of normal diffusion. On the other hand, the solute diffusivity is roughly 20 times as large as the solvent diffusivity: this fact alone is not an indisputable proof that another mechanism is operating. MILLER [1969] pointed out that the linear enhancement factor b_1 exhibited a value which was not compatible with the ratio D^*_{Cd}/D^*_{Pb} if the vacancy mechanism were the only one to operate. This is the reason why he proposed a new mechanism with interstitial–vacancy pairs (§ 4.2.2).

References: p. 466.

Table 4
Jump frequency ratios for dilute fcc alloys.

Alloy	T (K)	D_B^*/D_A^*	f_B	b_1	b_T	G	Ref.	w_2/w_1	w_3/w_1	w_4/w_0
Ag–Cd	1060	3.8	0.41	4			c	2.6	0.3	0.85
	1133	3.28	0.71	9.2			b	0.49	0.07	0.52
	1153	3.18		6.5	−12		a	0.5	0.07	0.46
	1197	2.96	0.62	13.7			b	1.7	0.8	1.7
Ag–In	1064	5.7	0.35	17.5			c	4.7	0.7	1.9
Ag–Sn	1043	5.8	0.46	15.6			c	1.8	0.2	1.1
Ag–Zn	1010	4.1	0.52	12.6			d	1.53	0.27	1.15
	1153	3.9	0.57	12.7			d	1.54	0.39	1.30
	1153	3.9		12.7	6		a	1.20	0.26	1.12
Au–In	1075	8.6	0.26	71			e	212	45	5.5
	1175	7.5	0.26	49			e	40	7.3	4.2
Au–Sn	1059	16.4	0.16	130			e	NO SOLUTION		
				73			f	1.5	1.2	6.3
Au–Zn	1058	6.2	0.15	24			e	942	85	2.9
	1117	5.7	0.15	23			e	973	85	2.6
Cu–Au	1133	1.15	0.9	8.1			g		0.2	0.10.6
Cu–Cd	1076	10.2		35		−0.7	h	0.1	1	3
	1076	10.2	0.22	35			h	7.6	0.6	2.8
Cu–Co	1133	0.81	0.85	0			g	2	4.2	1.2
	1133	0.81	0.88	0			g	0.3	0.4	0.76
Cu–Fe	1293	1.1	0.8	−5			i	0.4	0.09	0.3
Cu–In	1005	13.3		42		−0.71	j	18	0.5	3
	1089	11.4		43		−0.57	j	11	1	4
	1089	12	0.07	43			e	33	0.8	3.2
Cu–Mn	1199	4.2	0.36	5			c	3.4	0.35	0.95
Cu–Ni	1273	0.36		−5		0.07	k	0.2	1	1
	1273	0.36		−5.3		0.12	l	0.27	0.42	0.53
Cu–Sb	1005	24.1		79		−1.2	j	15	0.40	5
Cu–Sn	1014	15.5		40		−1.06	j	13	0.2	2
	1014	17	0.15	40			e	7.5	0.14	1.7
	1089	13.6		48		−0.84	j	7	0.33	3
	1089	14.1	0.15	48			e	11	0.5	3.3
Cu–Zn	1168	3.56	0.47	7.3			m	2.5	0.5	1.2
	1168	3.3		8		−0.22	k	3	0.5	1
	1220	3.4	0.47	8.8			m	3.6	0.9	1.5

[a] DOAN and BOCQUET [1975]; [b] BHARATI and SINHA [1977]; [c] HERZIG *et al.* [1982]; [d] ROTHMAN and PETERSON [1967]; [e] HILGEDIECK [1981]; [f] REINHOLD *et al.* [1980]; [g] ECKSELER and HERZIG [1978]; [h] HOSHINO *et al.* [1981b]; [i] BOCQUET [1972]; [j] HOSHINO *et al.* [1982]; [k] HIRANO [1981]; [l] DAMKÖHLER and HEUMANN [1982]; [m] PETERSON and ROTHMAN [1971].

For bcc alloys, data are still scarce: we refer the reader to LE CLAIRE'S review [1978]. Let us notice that the jump frequency ratios which are mentioned therein for the Nb–Fe dilute alloy yield a value of the solute correlation factor which does not agree with the measured one (ABLITZER [1977]; ABLITZER and VIGNES [1978]). This has led the latter authors to abandon the assumption of a pure vacancy mechanism.

4.1.5. Determination of the solute–vacancy binding energy

The only relevant quantity for determining the binding energy E_B of the solute–vacancy complex is the ratio w_4/w_3, which cannot be deduced from the knowledge of w_2/w_1, w_3/w_1 and w_4/w_0.

In a recent paper, DIRKES and HEUMANN [1982] proposed a simple procedure for simulating the vacancy trajectory around the solute and to extract from this trajectory the desired quantity. It is true that the ratios w_2/w_1, w_3/w_1 and w_4/w_0 are sufficient to determine, at each step of a Monte Carlo simulation, the direction of the most probable next jump. But these authors used an incorrect definition of the vacancy concentration on a first neighbour site of the solute. This concentration is not related to the number of times that the vacancy was located on a first-neighbour site of the solute, but rather to the time the vacancy really spent on this site. This definition needs the knowledge of the mean residence time of the vacancy on each site (i.e., the inverse of the total escape frequency from this site). It is easily checked that the fraction of the total time which has been spent on a first-neighbour site involves one more independent frequency ratio, w_1/w_0 (BOCQUET [1983]).

Diffusion experiments are not sufficient to determine this binding energy. Experiments of another kind must be added: for instance a direct determination of the total vacancy concentration in a dilute alloy, as already done for Al–Ag and Al–Mg (BEAMAN *et al.* [1964]; BEAMAN and BALLUFFI [1965]).

4.2. A–B alloys with a high solute diffusivity

4.2.1. Purely interstitial solutes

Light elements like H, C, N, O are known to dissolve interstitially in many bcc and fcc metals. No theoretical criterion has yet been found to predict with confidence the localization of the interstitial atom in the host lattice. In many bcc metals, C, O and N are believed to be located on octahedral sites; but dual-occupancy models (octahedral + tetrahedral position) have been invoked to account for the upward curvature of their Arrhenius plot at high temperatures (FARRARO and McLELLAN [1979]). For the case of hydrogen, a simple empirical rule has been proposed (SOMENKOV and SHIL'STEIN [1979]): H dissolves in the tetrahedral position in all the host metals which have an atomic radius larger than 0.137 nm (Sc, Ti, Y, Zr, Nb, La, Hf, Ta, W) and in the octahedral position for the others (Cr, Mn, Ni, Pd). Vanadium is the link between the two groups and is believed to have a dual occupancy. In Fe, H is expected to be located in octahedral sites although no clear experimental proof has ever been given. The insertion into the host lattice is

References: p. 466.

accompanied by a (generally) large distortion of the surroundings, which can give rise to Snoek-type or Gorsky-type relaxations (§ 2.2).

The diffusivity of such interstitials in metals has been measured over orders of magnitude by complementary techniques (relaxation methods, tracers, out-gassing, etc.). The Arrhenius plot is straight or exhibits a small curvature at high temperatures. This curvature has been tentatively explained by different models (FARRARO and McLELLAN [1979]), either a single mechanism with a temperature-dependent activation energy or several mechanisms (or defects) acting in parallel.

For very light interstitials like hydrogen and its isotopes, or the positive muon μ^+, quantum effects play a significant role at low temperatures. Several regimes are expected to be observed in the following order with increasing temperature (STONEHAM [1979]; KEHR [1978]):

(i) *coherent tunneling*, the interstitial propagates through the lattice like a free electron;

(ii) *incoherent* (or *phonon-assisted) tunneling*, the ground state levels of an occupied and an unoccupied interstitial site have different energies; the tunneling process requires the assistance of phonons which help to equalize the levels of neighbouring sites;

(iii) *classical regime*, the jumping atom receives from the lattice the amount of energy which is required to overcome the potential barrier of the saddlepoint configuration;

(iv) *high-temperature regime*, the residence time on a site is comparable to the time of flight between two neighbouring sites.

The second and third regimes have been observed in many systems. Whether coherent tunneling can actually be observed in real systems or not is still controversial (STONEHAM [1979]; GRAF et al. [1980]).

Let us mention the reversed isotope effect which is observed in fcc metals at low temperatures: tritium is found to diffuse faster than deuterium, which diffuses faster than hydrogen. Several models have been proposed to account for this anomaly (TEICHLER [1979]; KAUR and PRAKASH [1982]). See also ch. 17, § 3.3.2.7 for the interaction of self-interstitials with solute atoms.

4.2.2. Complex diffusion mechanisms

The most widely studied case is the case of dilute Pb-based alloys.

In lead, several solute atoms (Cu, Ag, Au, Pd, Ni, Zr) diffuse from 10^3 to 10^6 times faster than the solvent tracer. Other elements (Na, Bi, Sn, Tl) diffuse roughly at the same rate. A third group (Cd, Hg) diffuses at rates between the two extremes. It is well established that these properties are in no way related to any short-circuit diffusion path and that they reflect a bulk property. We already mentioned in § 4.1.4 why a pure vacancy mechanism should be rejected for cadmium diffusion in lead.

The high value of the diffusivities led many investigators in the past to think in terms of an interstitial-like diffusion mechanism; it can be shown however, by particular examples, that a purely interstitial mechanism would not yield a value of the linear enhancement factor b_1 consistent with experiment. This is why many authors proposed more complex mechanisms involving interstitial–vacancy complexes, interstitial clusters etc. It can be said that, in the course of the last ten years, each new experiment has brought information which was in conflict with the preceding pictures and which required, as a consequence, the introduction of a new defect or of a new mechanism.

Today the consensus is roughly as follows:
– Very fast diffusers dissolve partly as substitutionals and partly as interstitials in lead. The total diffusivity is therefore the sum of both contributions; pairs made up of an interstitial solute and a host vacancy are expected to play a dominant role;
– multidefects (interstitial solute atoms sharing one substitutional lattice site) are necessary to account for the diversity of experimental results, especially for the signs and the order of magnitude of the linear enhancement coefficients b_1 and B_1 (WARBURTON [1975]; KUSUNOKI *et al.* [1981]);
– solute atoms which diffuse roughly as fast as the solvent dissolve presumably as substitutionals (except Sn: DECKER *et al.* [1977]);
– a general and detailed atomic model including all these defects is still lacking. A recent attempt is by VANFLEET [1980]. The reader is referred to an extensive review by WARBURTON and TURNBULL [1975].

Lead is not a unique case. Similar problems arise in other polyvalent metals like Sn, In or Tl (WARBURTON and TURNBULL [1975]; LE CLAIRE [1978]), in bcc metals like Nb (ABLITZER [1977]; SERRUYS and BRÉBEC [1982a]), and for rare-gas diffusion (He) in fcc metals like Au, Ni, Al (WILSON and BISSON [1973]; MELIUS and WILSON [1980]; SCHILLING [1981]).

5. *Diffusion in concentrated alloys*

We shall restrict outselves to binary alloys. The first two sections are devoted to the diffusion of A* and B* tracer atoms in homogeneous disordered and ordered alloys. The third section will deal with chemical diffusion, that is, diffusion in the presence of chemical gradients.

5.1. Diffusion of A* and B* tracers in homogeneous disordered alloys

5.1.1. Experimental results
Diffusion measurements in concentrated binary alloys are legion, but only few alloys have been investigated throughout the whole composition range: Ag–Au (MALLARD *et al.* [1963]), Au–Ni (KURTZ *et al.* [1955]; REYNOLDS *et al.* [1957]), Co–Ni (MILLION and KUČERA [1969, 1971]; HIRANO *et al.* [1962]; HÄSSNER and LANGE [1965]), Cr–Ni (ASKILL [1971]), Cu–Ni (MONMA *et al.* [1964]), Fe–Ni (CAPLAIN and CHAMBRON [1977]), Fe–Pd (FILLON and CALAIS [1977]), Ge–Si (McVAY and DUCHARME [1974]), Nb–Ti (GIBBS *et al.* [1963]; PONTAU and LAZARUS [1979]), Pb–Tl (RESING and NACHTRIEB [1961]). For Fe–Ni, the diffusion has been studied through a magnetic relaxation method which yields only apparent values for the formation and migration energies of the vacancy.

References: p. 466.

Two general trends can be outlined:
- The same kind of empirical correlations as for self-diffusion in pure metals are observed between the preexponential factors D_0 and the activation energy Q, or between Q and the melting temperature T_m of the alloy.
- The diffusion coefficients D_{A*}^{AB} and D_{B*}^{AB} for a given temperature and composition do not differ by more than one order of magnitude. When they do, it might be an indication that the diffusion mechanism for the two tracers is not the same (Ge–Si or Pb–Tl). Some cases still offer matter for controversy, like Ge–Si alloys (PIKE et al. [1974]). For brevity, D_{A*}^{AB} and D_{B*}^{AB} will be denoted by D_{A*} and D_{B*} in what follows.

5.1.2. Atomic models for diffusion in a disordered alloy

The first difficulty to overcome consists of choosing the right approximation, which will yield a tractable result. The extension of dilute alloy models leads to intractable results involving a growing number of unknown parameters (BOCQUET [1973]). * This is the reason why most models approximate the effect of the local surroundings on the height of the potential barrier by using a small number of pair interaction energies for the stable (E_{ij}) and the saddle-point (E_{ij}') configurations. Such models can be shown to connect consistently the thermodynamics (reflected in the E_{ij}'s) and the kinetic behaviour of the alloy (reflected in the E_{ij}''s) since the assumption of detailed balancing is fulfilled. The most recent model (RADELAAR [1970]) accounts fairly well for the observed kinetics of short-range ordering in Ag–Au alloys (RADELAAR [1968]) and Fe–Ni alloys (CAPLAIN and CHAMBRON [1977]).

The reader should keep in mind three main limitations of such models:
- They do not calculate D_{A*} and D_{B*} but only the activation energies for diffusion Q_{A*} and Q_{B*}. The preexponential factors D_{0A} and D_{0B} are not known and are arbitrarily assumed to remain constant. This is unjustifiable, but we still lack a model which would account for the variations of D_{0A} and D_{0B} throughout the whole composition range.
- They ignore correlation effects. Such effects can be calculated in rather simple cases only, like solute or solvent diffusion in pure metals. The dependence of the jump frequency on the local composition of the surroundings breaks the translational symmetry of the lattice and raises a mathematical difficulty which has never been solved. Such correlation effects can however be evaluated approximately in the frame of simplified models (see following section).
- These models use pair energies and assume implicitly that the energy of the alloy can be summed in this way, which is not always true (case of transition metals). Even if we decide a priori to describe the interactions between atoms through "effective" pair energies, nothing is known about their possible variations with the alloy concentration. Thus a more fundamental theory such as the electronic theory

---

* A simplified extension of the dilute alloy model to less dilute alloys (from 2 at% to 15 at%) has been worked out by HEHENKAMP [1981]; it seems to account fairly well for experimental data provided suitable binding energies of vacancy–solute clusters are fitted on diffusion experiments.

of alloys must be used to predict such variations on physically grounded arguments (DUCASTELLE [1978]).

Finally, these models do not yet have any predictive power: while pair energies in the stable position can be deduced from thermodynamic measurements, saddle-point pair energies conversely can be deduced from experiments involving diffusion jumps, that is, from the diffusion experiments themselves! Such models can only claim to reproduce the experimental values of D_{A*} and D_{B*} provided a suitable choice of pair energies is made.

5.1.3. Manning's random alloy model

In this over-simplified model, the alloy is assumed to be random and the vacancy exchanges at rate w_A with A atoms, and w_B with B atoms, whatever the composition of the local surroundings (fig. 11). Consistent expressions of D_{A*}, D_{B*} and of the vacancy diffusion coefficient D_V have been calculated (MANNING [1971]). The most important finding lies in the fact that the vacancy no longer follows a random walk; its successive jumps are correlated and a vacancy correlation factor f_V smaller than unity shows up in the final expressions:

$$D^*_{A(B)} = \lambda\, s^2\, C_V f_{A(B)} w_{A(B)}, \qquad D_V = \lambda\, s^2\, f_V \overline{w},$$

where $f_V = (C_A w_A f_A + C_B w_B f_B)/f_0$ and $f_0 = M_0/(M_0 + 2)$ is the correlation factor for self-diffusion, $\overline{w} = C_A w_A + C_B w_B$, and finally, $f_{A(B)} = M_0 f_V \overline{w}/(M_0 f_V \overline{w} + 2 w_{A(B)})$ for A (B).

It can be shown that these expressions are not the exact solution of the oversimplified model but only a mean-field approximation (BOCQUET [1981]). Monte Carlo simulations have been performed for random alloys, which take into account the detailed occupancy of the sites surrounding the vacancy. If $\langle R^2(n) \rangle$ is the mean-square displacement of the vacancy after n jumps, it is confirmed that the quantity $\langle R^2(n) \rangle / ns^2$ is indeed equal to f_V (BOCQUET [1973]; DE BRUIN *et al.* [1975]). The agreement is good even in the "percolative region" of the alloy (large value for $\Theta = w_A/w_B$ and low concentration of species A).

An attempt has been made recently to drop the assumption of randomness; further theoretical work is required to ground this preliminary result (STOLWIJK [1981]).

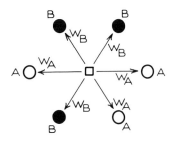

Fig. 11. Manning's random alloy model.

References: p. 466.

5.2.   Diffusion of A* and B* tracers in ordered binary alloys

We restrict ourselves to alloys of CsCl structure; the corresponding B2 symmetry is characterized by the existence of two interpenetrating simple cubic lattices, α and β. Each α-site is surrounded by eight first-neighbour β-sites and conversely. The non-equivalence of α and β sites demands a more detailed study of the possible point defects and of their most probable migration mechanisms.

5.2.1.   Point defects in ordered alloys of CsCl type

At 0 K a stoichiometric A–B alloy is perfectly ordered: the N_A atoms of species A occupy the α-sites; the N_B atoms occupy the β-sites. When the temperature is raised, several kinds of defect are expected to appear:

– *antistructure* or *substitutional defects*: A atoms can occupy β-sites and are denoted A_β, their number is $N_{A\beta}$, B atoms can occupy α-sites (B_α, $N_{B\alpha}$);

– vacancies: denoted by V_α on α-sites and V_β on β-sites. Depending on the values of the pair-interaction energies E_{ij}, the alloy will choose preferentially one type of defect or the other (or both). The existing alloys belong to two distinct groups:

(i) In the first group (AgCd, AgMg, AgZn, AuCd, AuZn, BeCu, BeNi, CuZn, NiZn) the defects are mainly antistructure defects on *both* sublattices (A_β *and* B_α). The departure from stoichiometry is compensated by A_β defects for A-rich alloys and B_α defects for B-rich alloys. The apparent formation energy E_F^V of thermal vacancies can be different on both sublattices.

(ii) In the second group (AlCo, AlFe, AlNi, AlPd, CoGa, GaNi, InPd), antistructure defects B_α are highly improbable because of too high a formation energy (α denotes the sublattice of the transition metal named A here). Thus only A_β is allowed to form. It is easy to show that the maintenance of stoichiometry requires the simultaneous creation of two V_α vacancies on the α-sublattice (hence the name, *triple defect*, often given to $A_\beta + 2V_\alpha$). The departure from stoichiometry is therefore compensated in two different ways: for an A-rich alloy the major defect is A_β; for a B-rich alloy, the major defect is V_α. This is why the departure from stoichiometry towards the B-rich side can induce very high vacancy concentrations on one sublattice (up to 10% in CoGa on the gallium-rich side). These vacancies are often called *constitutional vacancies*. Although they have been given a different name, it is essential to remember that their properties are in no way different from the properties of the so-called *thermal vacancies*. Indeed, their concentration is also given by a standard free-energy minimization. But in the present case, the existence of two sublattices and the values of the pair energies E_{ij} mean that the result of the calculation is highly sensitive to a small variation of the composition (especially around stoichiometry), contrarily to what is observed in a disordered alloy at the same concentration. Although the apparent formation energy of thermal vacancies can be very low (as low as 0.3 eV in NiGa: EDELIN [1979]) in such alloys, the principal control parameter of the system for imposing a given vacancy concentration is no longer the temperature but the composition. All the theoretical calculations performed so far (e.g. EDELIN [1979]) are based on a zeroth-order treatment

(BRAGG and WILLIAMS [1934]); although they are crude, they account fairly well for all the presently known experimental situations, provided reasonable values of the adjustable pair energies E_{ij} are chosen.

A first and simple explanation has been recently given to account for the fact that a particular alloy belongs to the first or to the second group (NEUMANN [1980]). Using a crude bond-breaking picture, this author shows that the number of substitutional defects is dominant whenever the mixing enthalpy ΔH_f is (algebraïcally) higher than -0.3 eV/atom; the number of triple defects is dominant otherwise. It is very gratifying to ascertain that this correlation is very well obeyed.

Experimentally, little is known up to now on the defect concentrations. Combining lattice parameter measurements with sample length measurements (Simmons and Balluffi's technique; ch. 17, §2.2.1.2) yields only the *total* vacancy concentration in the sample: it has been determined in several alloys (CoGa: VAN OMNEN and DE MIRANDA [1981]; AlFe: HO and DODD [1978], PARIS and LESBATS [1978]; GaNi: HO *et al.* [1977]).

Other experimental techniques are necessary in order to gain a sharper insight into the defect populations on each sublattice. First results have been obtained through positron annihilation in CuZn (CHABIK and ROZENFELD [1981]) or direct observation in a field ion microscope in AlFe (PARIS and LESBATS [1975]); but extracting meaningful values from the raw data demands a delicate analysis of positron trapping at vacancies for the first technique, and a careful analysis of image contrast for the second. Further experimental work is needed.

5.2.2. Experimental results

Most of the experiments measured the tracer diffusion coefficients D_{A^*} and D_{B^*} as a function of temperature and composition. A few determinations of migration energy also exist. Isotope effect experiments will be commented on below (§5.2.3).

Only a small number of ordered alloys has been well studied: AgMg (DOMIAN and AARONSON [1965]), AlNi (HANCOCK and McDONNELL [1971]), AuCd (GUPTA *et al.* [1967]), AuZn (GUPTA and LIEBERMAN [1971]), CoGa (BOSE *et al.* [1979], STOLWIJK *et al.* [1980]), CuZn (KUPER *et al.* [1956]), GaNi (DONALDSON and RAWLINGS [1976]).

Without entering into detail, the following trends can be outlined:
– At constant composition, the activation energy for diffusion is higher in the ordered than in the disordered phase. There is a break of the Arrhenius plot at the critical temperature T_c of ordering. In the ordered phase, the Arrhenius plot is always more or less curved (KUPER *et al.* [1956]).
– At constant temperature, the diffusion coefficients vary with composition and exhibit a minimum at stoichiometry (or in the close neighbourhood of stoichiometry). This minimum is very sharp for some alloys (V-shaped curve for AgMg or AlNi) and less pronounced for others: it is accompanied by a maximum of the activation energy and of the preexponential factor. The existence of this maximum is qualitatively understood: the formation and migration energies of the vacancy are both increasing functions of the long-range order parameter S which goes through a

References: p. 466.

maximum at stoichiometric (or nearly stoichiometric) composition.

– D_{A^*} and D_{B^*} differ by no more than a factor of two or three for the alloys in which the defects are predominantly of substitutional type (AgMg, AuCd, AuZn): this holds for all temperatures and compositions investigated. The difference between D_{A^*} and D_{B^*} is more pronounced for the alloys belonging to the second group.

The functional dependence of the migration and formation energies (E_M, E_F) of the vacancy on the long-range order parameter S has been investigated. A simple model yields a quadratic enhancement for both quantities and, therefore, for the total activation energy Q (GIRIFALCO [1964]):

$$E_M = E_M^0\left(1 + \alpha_M S^2\right), \qquad E_F = E_F^0\left(1 + \alpha_F S^2\right),$$

$$Q = Q_0\left(1 + \alpha_D S^2\right).$$

The experiments are not decisive, however:

– In AlFe alloys, the migration energy of the vacancies which have been retained by quenching varies roughly as S^2 (RIVIÈRE and GRILHÉ [1974]). But it is clear from the data that the results, within the error bars, can as well be accounted for by a linear law.

– In CuZn, the diffusion coefficients of Cu* and Zn* tracers (KUPER et al. [1956]) have been plotted logarithmically as a function of $(1 + \alpha_D S^2)/T$ (GIRIFALCO [1964]). The Arrhenius plot is a straight line only if the theoretical values of the long-range order parameter S_{BW} (BW stands for Bragg and Williams) are arbitrarily replaced by the experimental values S_{exp} which have been determined by X-ray measurements. It can be checked however that S_{exp} is not well accounted for by a Bragg–Williams approximation and that a more sophisticated treatment must be used (COWLEY [1950]). An interesting observation is that S_{Cowley}^2 is equal to S_{BW} at the same temperature: therefore the quadratic dependence of Q on S_{exp}^2 can also be interpreted as a linear dependence of Q on S_{BW}. Plugging experimental values of S into a theoretical model which does not account quantitatively for the experiments raises a delicate question of consistency.

5.2.3. Atomic models for diffusion in ordered alloys

Several atomic mechanisms have been proposed and are depicted in fig. 12:

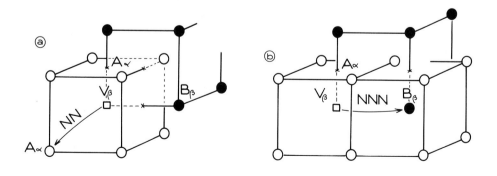

Diffusion in metals and alloys

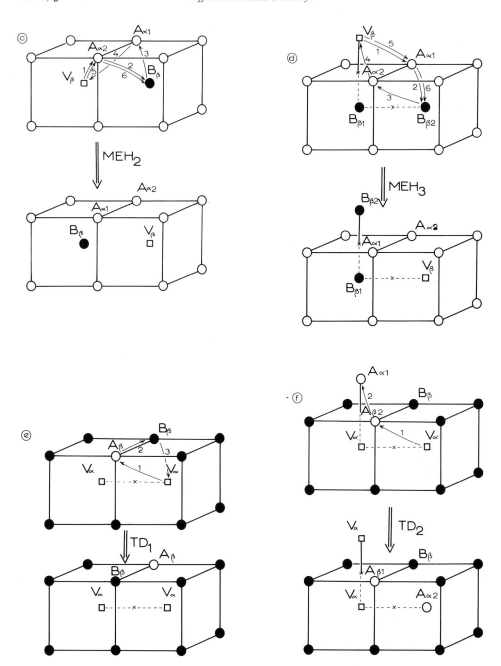

Fig. 12. Jump mechanisms for ordered alloys exhibiting a B2 symmetry. Left-hand page: (a) nearest-neighbour jump (NN); (b) next-nearest neighbour jump (NNN). This page: (c, d) six-jump cycles bringing an A atom to a 2nd or 3rd-neighbour distance; (e, f) possible jumps for a triple defect. (Solid circles denote B atoms; open circles: A atoms; squares: vacancies.)

– *Vacancy nearest-neighbour jump* (NN): this kind of jump exchanges species A and B on their sublattices and does not preserve the local order. The surroundings of the diffusing species must provide the supplement of energy required for disordering (fig. 12a).

– *Vacancy next-nearest-neighbour jump* (NNN): this jump preserves the local order since the species would remain on their sublattice. It is not unreasonable since it has been already invoked at higher temperatures in bcc pure metals (fig. 12b).

– *Mc Combie–Elcock–Huntington mechanism* (MEH): the diffusing atom and the vacancy are supposed to belong to the same sublattice and to be second-nearest neighbours (MEH$_2$, fig. 12c) or third-nearest neighbours (MEH$_3$, fig. 12d). They exchange places via a closed cycle made up with six NN vacancy jumps (McCOMBIE and ELCOCK [1958]; ELCOCK [1959]; HUNTINGTON *et al.* [1961]). The diffusion coefficients D_{A^*} and D_{B^*} are always close to one another (D_{A^*}/D_{B^*} ratio in the range 2/3–3/2). This cycle has been expected to occur with a significant probability with the argument that its net result does not alter the local order of the alloy. The correlation factor for this mechanism is also expected to be small. The few isotope measurements in ordered alloys have been interpreted with this picture in mind: a low value of $f\Delta K$ (as in FeCo) has been often taken as an indirect proof of the effectiveness of the MEH mechanism. This last conclusion must be considered with caution: Monte Carlo simulations (FROHBERG [1971]; ARNHOLD [1981]) have shown that the correlation factor is not small as proposed originally but rather large (roughly equal to 0.80); this holds under the assumption that the mechanism operates alone and that the vacancy migrates along its ring-shaped cycle with forward jumps only, thus ignoring the possible occurrence of backward jumps. If backward jumps are permitted, the same type of simulation work shows also that the number of six-jump cycles which go to completion is far too small to contribute significantly to matter transport in comparison with the contribution of NN jumps alone. Indeed, the occupancy of the lattice sites by A and B species in the ordered structure determines the height of the various potential barriers in such a way that the vacancy is led to perform an unusually large number of backward jumps: this tends correspondingly to decrease the tracer correlation factor down to a range of values which is comparable to the experimentally observed isotope effects.

– *Triple-defect jump* (TD): in ordered structures containing a high concentration of triple defects, the divacancy $2V_\alpha$ is often supposed to be strongly bound to an antistructure atom A_β. The migration of this complex (figs. 12e, f) involves NN vacancy jumps for species A and NNN vacancy jumps only for species B (since the latter cannot occupy an α-site). Such a mechanism has been proposed for CoGa (VAN OMNEN and DE MIRANDA [1981]).

The isotope-effect experiments for self- and solute diffusion are commonly believed to clarify the atomic mechanism of the migration in a decisive way. Similar experiments have been performed on a few alloys with the same underlying belief. But the results are still too sparse to allow the building of any coherent picture of migration in ordered alloys; e.g., in β-brass, no significant difference between the isotope effects in the ordered and disordered alloys has been found (PETERSON and

ROTHMAN [1971]). Even if the measured isotope effect can be set equal to $f\Delta K$, the ΔK factor has never been calculated in such complicated cases as concentrated and ordered alloys, but rather only for very simple systems like pure metals (BENNETT [1975]).

5.3. Chemical diffusion

When diffusion takes place in a region of the sample where the chemical gradients cannot be ignored, the diffusion coefficients of the various components are no longer constant, as in homogeneous alloys, but depend on space and time through the composition.

In what follows, we examine the case of chemical diffusion and the Kirkendall effect in binary alloys. The reader is referred to more extensive reviews for the case of multi-phase and multi-component systems (ADDA and PHILIBERT [1966]).

5.3.1. Chemical diffusion in binary systems and Kirkendall effect

5.3.1.1. Description and interpretation of a typical experiment.

The simplest diffusion experiment to carry out consists in clamping together two pieces of pure metals A and B, to anneal this couple long enough and to determine, at the end of the run, the concentration profile all along the sample. What is observed is a spreading of the initially step-like profile together with a shift of the initial welding interface (defined by inert markers such as oxide particles or tungsten wires) with respect to the ends of the couple which have not been affected by the diffusion (fig. 13). This shift results from the *Kirkendall effect* and finds its origin in the fact that the diffusivities D_A and D_B are not equal. Indeed, if D_A is larger than D_B species A penetrates into B at a faster rate than B into A: as a consequence, the B-rich part of the sample must increase its volume to accommodate the net positive inward flux of matter. This increase will be achieved at the expense of the A-rich part by shifting the interface towards A. This observation was reported for the first time by SMIGELKAS and KIRKENDALL [1947] on copper–zinc alloys: the zinc is the faster diffuser and the welding interface (called *Kirkendall plane*) shifts towards the

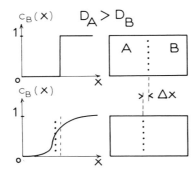

Fig. 13. Kirkendall effect experiment with a diffusion couple made of two pure metals A and B.

References: p. 466.

zinc-rich side of the couple. This experiment was a milestone in the history of solid-state diffusion: it definitely ruled out the assumption of a direct exchange $A \leftrightarrows B$ mechanism which was formely proposed and which would have implied equal diffusivities for both species.

It must be noted that a Kirkendall effect has also been observed in liquids: it is expected indeed to be very general, since the first convincing interpretation of the phenomenon is not based on any detailed mechanism for matter transport (DARKEN [1948]).

The simultaneous measurements of the displacement rate V of the Kirkendall plane and of the chemical diffusivity $\tilde{D}$ in that plane yield the intrinsic diffusion coefficients D_A and D_B for the composition of the Kirkendall plane. In order to know D_A and D_B at several concentrations, one should prepare the corresponding number of differential couples, which are made of two alloys with different compositions. In fact it can be shown that a single experiment is needed, provided that a complete set of inert markers has been inserted on both sides of the welding interface (CORNET and CALAIS [1972]).

In what follows we suppose that the observed effect is unidirectional, and that only one space coordinate x is needed, in conjunction with the time variable t, to describe the evolution of the system. The transformation $x/\sqrt{t} \to \lambda$ in Fick's second Law shows that the solution $C(x,t)$ can be expressed as a one-variable function $C(\lambda)$. We know from experiment that the Kirkendall plane has a constant concentration during the diffusion anneal, and accordingly that it is characterized by a constant value of λ. As a consequence, the Kirkendall shift Δx varies as $\sqrt{t}$; no exception to this simple law has ever been reported.

A similar behaviour has also been observed for any inert marker which is not located in the Kirkendall plane at $t = 0$; after a time lag, the duration of which depends on the distance from the Kirkendall plane, the inert marker starts moving with the same time law (LEVASSEUR and PHILIBERT [1967]; MONTY [1972]).

Up to now no atomic mechanism for matter transport has been mentioned; but if we know it, something more can be said about the Kirkendall plane.

We suppose in the following that the vacancy mechanism is operating. In all the experiments performed so far, the inert markers are invariably made of materials which have a high melting temperature. The formation and migration energies of the vacancy in such materials are significantly larger than in the surrounding matrix. As a consequence, the markers are impermeable to the vacancy flux. Under this condition, it can be shown that such a marker shifts along with the lattice planes (KRIVOGLAZ [1969]), whatever the type of its interface with the matrix (coherent or incoherent). Thus, the measurement of the Kirkendall shift is nothing but the measurement of the lattice plane shift.

The above formalism can be easily enlarged to account for the case in which the average atomic volume varies with the concentration of the alloy (BALLUFFI [1960]).

5.3.1.2. Vacancy wind effect – Manning's approximation. In the original formulation of the Kirkendall effect, the flux J_A of species A stems only from the chemical potential gradient $\nabla \mu_A$ of species A (DARKEN [1948]).

At infinite dilution, the solid solution becomes ideal ($\varphi = 1$) and the intrinsic diffusion coefficient D_A must tend towards the tracer diffusion coefficient D_{A^*}. Hence:

$$D_A = D_{A^*}\varphi, \qquad D_B = D_{B^*}\varphi.$$

These relationships are known as *Darken's equations*; we know however, from the thermodynamics of irreversible processes, that the off-diagonal term cannot be neglected. More general expressions can be established [see eqs. (6)]:

$$D_A = \frac{kT}{n}\left(\frac{L_{AA}}{C_A} - \frac{L_{AB}}{C_B}\right)\varphi, \qquad D_B = \frac{kT}{n}\left(\frac{L_{BB}}{C_B} - \frac{L_{BA}}{C_A}\right)\varphi.$$

There is no simple way to relate theoretically the L_{ij}'s to experimentally accessible quantities such as tracer (or intrinsic) diffusion coefficients. This has been done only in the particular case of a simplified random-alloy model (MANNING [1968]) for which $\varphi = 1$. The following expressions are then obtained:

$$L_{AA} = n\frac{C_A D_{A^*}}{kT}\left(1 + \frac{2\,C_A D_{A^*}}{M_0 D^*}\right),$$

$$L_{AB} = L_{BA} = 2n\frac{C_A C_B D_{A^*} D_{B^*}}{kT\,M_0\,D^*},$$

$$L_{BB} = \frac{nC_B D_{B^*}}{kT}\left(1 + \frac{2\,C_B D_{B^*}}{M_0 D^*}\right),$$

where n is the average number of sites per unit volume, $f_0 = M_0/(M_0 + 2)$ is the self-diffusion correlation factor for a vacancy mechanism, D_{A^*} and D_{B^*} are the tracer diffusion coefficients in the alloy and D^* is the average $C_A D_{A^*} + C_B D_{B^*}$. These expressions are arbitrarily assumed to hold even for a non-random alloy where the thermodynamic factor φ is not unity. Hence the final expressions for the intrinsic diffusivities are still given by eqs. (17) with:

$$r_A = 1 + 2\frac{C_A(D_{A^*} - D_{B^*})}{M_0 D^*},$$

$$r_B = 1 + 2\frac{C_B(D_{B^*} - D_{A^*})}{M_0 D^*}.$$

Hence:

$$\tilde{D} = (C_A D_{B^*} + C_B D_{A^*})\varphi\left[1 + 2\frac{C_A C_B(D_{A^*} - D_{B^*})^2}{M_0 D^*(C_A D_{B^*} + C_B D_{A^*})}\right].$$

The last term in the the brackets is called a *vacancy wind* term since it reflects the coupling between the transport of species A and B through the vacancy flux. We note that Manning's equations predict a chemical diffusion coefficient $\tilde{D}$ always larger than that given by Darken's equations. The match of both sets of equations with experimental results will be reviewed in the following section.

References: p. 466.

Two recent attempts have been made to drop the restrictive assumption of randomness (HEUMANN [1979]; DAYANANDA [1981]), but the resulting expressions have not yet been compared with data obtained on actual alloys with an appreciable amount of short-range order.

Before closing this section, a last remark should be made concerning the structure of Darken's or Manning's expressions: in both sets of equations the thermodynamic factor φ enters in a multiplicative way. In some cases the variations of φ with respect to concentration or temperature may outweigh the variations of other factors. This situation can be met accidentally as in Au–80 at% Ni (REYNOLDS et al. [1957]) but is also expected to happen in well defined situations: for any alloy which tends to unmix at low temperatures, φ goes through zero at the top of the coexistence curve at some critical temperature T_c. It is easy to show that the maximum of the coexistence curve is such that the second derivative of the molar free energy, d^2f/dC_B^2, vanishes. A short derivation yields:

$$\frac{d^2f}{dC_B^2} = \frac{kT}{C_A C_B}\left(1 + \frac{d \log \gamma_A}{d \log C_B}\right) = \frac{kT}{C_A C_B}\varphi,$$

where γ_A is the activity coefficient of species A.

A convincing illustration of a vanishing $\tilde{D}$ has been reported for Nb–34 at% H (VÖLKL and ALEFELD [1978]). At the critical temperature T_c, the Arrhenius plot of $\tilde{D}$ bends downwards and $\tilde{D}$ falls several orders of magnitude, whereas the Arrhenius plot of the hydrogen tracer diffusion exhibits a normal behaviour. This phenomenon is called *critical slowing down*; the top of the coexistence curve is the very point where the alloy hesitates between two conflicting forms of behaviour:
– high-temperature behaviour where all the concentration fluctuations flatten out ($\tilde{D} > 0$);
– low-temperature behaviour where the concentration fluctuations of large wavelengths are amplified ($\tilde{D} < 0$) in order to allow the system to decompose into two phases of different compositions (spinodal decomposition).

5.3.1.3. Experimental check of vacancy wind effect. Let us recall first that accurate measurements are difficult: in many cases the Kirkendall shift is of the same order of magnitude as the diameter of the inert markers; cavities are often observed on the side of the faster diffusing species, indicating a local vacancy supersaturation; the thermodynamic factor is not known better than within 5–10 percent (ELDRIDGE and KOMAREK [1964]). The departure of the actual experimental conditions from the theoretical assumptions (vacancies everywhere at thermal equilibrium, purely unidirectional fluxes, etc.) probably induce further errors of unknown magnitude.

Only a few systems have been explicitly studied to compare Manning's and Darken's formulations, namely: AgAu (MEYER [1969], DALLWITZ [1972], MONTY [1972]); AgCd (BUTRYMOWICZ and MANNING [1978], IORIO et al. [1973]); AlNi (SHANKAR and SEIGLE [1978]); AuCu (HEUMANN and ROTTWINKEL [1978]); CuZn (SCHMATZ et al. [1966]); TiVa (CARLSON [1976]). Without entering into great detail, two general trends can be extracted from these studies:

– In most cases, Manning's vacancy wind correction to Darken's expressions for D_A and D_B improves the agreement of the experimentally measured values of the Kirkendall shift Δx and of the ratio D_A/D_B with the corresponding calculated quantities. "Calculated" means that D_A and D_B are evaluated by plugging the experimental values of D_{A^*}, D_{B^*} and φ into Manning's or Darken's equations.

– However, whereas the ratio D_A/D_B is fairly well accounted for, the individual values of D_A and D_B are often larger than the calculated ones (by a factor of two as in the case of AuCu!) and the experimental Kirkendall shift has also a tendency to be larger than the theoretical one. (Except for AlNi, where $\tilde{D}_{meas.}$ is smaller than $\tilde{D}_{theor.}$ for both models.)

The reason for this discrepancy is not yet clearly understood. As pointed out by CARLSON [1978], Manning's correction to Darken's expressions holds only for a random alloy; this condition is never fulfilled in real systems. But it is difficult to acknowledge that dropping the assumption of randomness will correct Manning's expressions to such an extent that the large disagreement between the calculated and measured values of D_A and D_B will be cancelled out.

6. Electro- and thermomigration

At temperatures where diffusion is noticeable, atoms of a pure metal, or of an alloy, are caused to drift by a gradient of electric potential or of temperature. We saw (§4.1.2) that this phenomenon, also called the *Soret effect* in the case of thermal gradients, has been used to study phenomenological coefficients. It has also been used practically to purify some refractory metals. Last, but not least, it is a way to study the electronic structure of point defects (vacancies, impurity atoms) at high temperatures and its variation during jumps.

6.1. Thermodynamical aspects

In the case of a substitutional binary alloy, we have shown in § 1.2.2 that under a gradient of electric potential, $-E$, and/or temperature, ∇T, the equations of fluxes can be written as:

$$J_A = -D_A \nabla n_A + (L_{AA}Z_A^* + L_{AB}Z_B^*)eE - (L_{AA}\overline{Q}_A + L_{AB}\overline{Q}_B)\frac{\nabla T}{T},$$

$$J_B = -D_B \nabla n_B + (L_{BA}Z_A^* + L_{BB}Z_B^*)eE - (L_{BA}\overline{Q}_A + L_{BB}\overline{Q}_B)\frac{\nabla T}{T},$$

$$J_V = -J_A - J_B. \tag{65}$$

If we define J_e and J_q as the electron and the heat flux, respectively, we have the two definitions (DOAN [1971]):

$$z_A^* = \left(\frac{J_e}{J_A}\right)_{J_B=E=0} \quad \text{and} \quad Q_A^* = \left(\frac{J_q}{J_A}\right)_{J_B=\nabla T=0}. \tag{66}$$

References: p. 466.

The effective valence Z_A^* and the reduced heat of transport $\bar{Q}_A$ are then defined by:

$$Z_A^* = z_A - z_A^*, \quad \text{and} \quad \bar{Q}_A = Q_A^* - \Delta H_{FV} \tag{67}$$

and the equivalent relations for the B component.

The $\bar{Q}_A$ relation is due to the effect on vacancies of the temperature gradient. It is derived under the hypothesis of a local equilibrium concentration of vacancies. It therefore has no counterpart in the electric field case. Any deviation from this equilibrium (see §8) invalidates the comparison between microscopic evaluations of Q^* and experimental $\bar{Q}$.

In self-diffusion, B represents an isotope of A, so eqs. (65) give, in the case of electromigration:

$$J_{A^*} = -D_{A^*} \nabla n_{A^*} + Z_A^* \frac{eE}{kT} n_{A^*} \frac{D_{A^*}}{f_0},$$

where f_0 is the self-diffusion correlation factor. The thermomigration case is given by an analogous equation, $\bar{Q}_A$ and $-\nabla T/T$ replacing Z_A^* and E.

Such self-diffusion experiments then give access to the true values Z_A^* and $\bar{Q}_A$. For solute diffusion, one calculates easily (dropping the ∇n_{B^*} term):

$$J_B = n_B D_{B^*} \frac{eE}{kT} \left[Z_B^* + Z_A^* \frac{L_{AB}}{L_{BB}} \right] = Z_B^{**} n_B D_{B^*} \frac{eE}{kT}.$$

Measurements can then give access only to the *apparent* effective valence Z_B^{**} (or heat of transport Q_B^{**}). This value differs from the true one, Z_B^*, by the vacancy wind term $Z_A^* L_{AB}/L_{BB}$ (MANNING [1968]). The ratio L_{AB}/L_{BB} varies approximately from $+2$ to -2 and can then give a very large correction to Z_B^*, especially in polyvalent solvents. Equations (65) are written in the lattice frame, and so are defined the Z_B^{**} and Q_B^{**} values. But if the fluxes are, for some reason, measured in another reference frame, they give access to other values of coupling coefficients. For example in the laboratory frame, one obtains:

$$J_B = n_B D_{B^*} \frac{eE}{kT} \left(Z_B^{**} - \frac{D_{A^*}}{D_{B^*}} Z_A^{**} \right),$$

where the bracketed term defines the apparent effective valence in the fixed frame.

6.2. Microscopic analysis

Atoms in a metal under a gradient of potential or temperature are submitted to a force which has a double origin. On one hand, one finds a static part called *direct* in the electric case, or *intrinsic* in the thermal one. The direct force is due to the unscreened action of the electric field on the true ionic charge [eq. (67), term z_A] and the intrinsic contribution corresponds to the enthalpy transfer due to an atomic jump (WIRTZ [1943], BRINKMAN [1954], LE CLAIRE [1954]). In this approximation the heat of transport Q_A^* [eq. (67)] is nothing else than a part of the migration enthalpy

(HUNTINGTON [1968]). On the other hand electrons and phonons in metals are highly mobile carriers, either thermal or electrical. Therefore their scattering at atoms which are neighbours of a vacancy gives rise to a second contribution: the electron or phonon *breeze*.

In the case of electromigration, FIKS [1959] and HUNTINGTON and GRÖNE [1961] have given a model of this scattering part, treating electrons as semiclassical particles. BOSVIEUX and FRIEDEL [1962] have used the free-electron model in the Born approximation to give a quantum-mechanical expression of the z^* term. More recently, there have been a lot of very involved, but more rigorous treatments of this term (KUMAR and SORBELLO [1975], TURBAN *et al.* [1976], SCHAICH [1976], RIMBEY and SORBELLO [1980]). Apart from a controversy on the existence of a screening effect in z^*, which could exactly cancel the direct force (TURBAN *et al.* [1976]), all these treatments give essentially the same results, their main interest being to define more precisely the validity range of the preceding models. The main results are the following:

(i) The scattering part of the effective valence is given by:

$$z^* = -\frac{z_A}{2}\left[100\frac{\Delta\rho^{\text{saddle}} + \Delta\rho^{\text{stable}}}{\rho_0} - \mathcal{F}_0\right] \tag{68}$$

where $\Delta\rho^{\text{saddle}}$ and $\Delta\rho^{\text{stable}}$ are the residual resistivities (expressed in $\mu\Omega$cm per at%) of B or A atoms in saddle or stable position (their sum, $\Delta\rho^{\text{saddle}} + \Delta\rho^{\text{stable}}$, is denoted by $\Delta\rho_{\text{EM}}$ in table 7, below); ρ_0 is the matrix resistivity and $\mathcal{F}_0$ is a correction term due to the neighbouring vacancy, of course zero for an interstitial solute. We find that in normal metals, owing to the order of magnitude of $\Delta\rho$ and ρ_0, the (possible) direct term is completely negligible.

(ii) In polyvalent metals, or transition metals with a hole conductivity, we have two opposite contributions like eq. (68), one for electrons and one for holes, and a partial compensation between them. In that case, the effective valence is much lower, and difficult to calculate (FIKS [1973], HUNTINGTON and HO [1963], LIMOGE [1976b], GUPTA [1982]).

The situation is more troublesome in thermomigration. FIKS [1961], GERL [1967] and SORBELLO [1972] have calculated the phonon scattering contribution. The result, as given by Gerl, is a positive term, of the order of 100 kJ/mole (or lower after CROLET [1971]) and linear in temperature, contrary to SCHOTTKY's calculation [1965]. The electron term is more firmly established and according to GERL [1967]:

$$Q_{\text{el}}^* \propto z^*,$$

and so gives a negative contribution in normal metals. The final value $\overline{Q}$ is then the result of the compensation between four terms, and theoretical calculations are very questionable (DOAN *et al.* [1976]). Recently GILLAN [1977] proposed to go back to the thermodynamic definition, eq. (66), of Q^* to calculate it. This way has however not been much used till now to give quantitative results.

6.3. Experimental methods

In electro- or thermotransport, three techniques have been used. In the first, one measures the total atomic flux $J_A + J_B = -J_V$. This is done by measuring the displacement of inert markers with respect to the ends of the sample. This method can be used only for self-diffusion but is able to yield a good accuracy if vacancy elimination conditions are well controlled (GERL [1968]; LIMOGE [1976a]).

In the second method one establishes a steady state between external force, either E or ∇T, and the induced concentration gradient. Measurement of the concentration profile gives access to effective valence, or heat of transport, *in the laboratory frame* (fig. 14a). The accuracy is generally not very high and the method is restricted to solute diffusion.

In the third method one uses a thin deposit of tracer between two bulk samples of solvent. This deposit will spread (§1.2.5) as a Gaussian in electromigration and simultaneously displace (fig. 14b) due to the external force. This displacement with respect to the welding interface gives the coefficient Z^{**}, or Q^{**}. The accuracy is very high and the method is as suitable for self-diffusion as for solute diffusion (GILDER and LAZARUS [1966], DOAN [1971]), although its use in thermomigration needs some care (CROLET [1971]).

6.4. Experimental results and discussion

The reader can find an exhaustive review of electromigration experimental results in PRATT and SELLORS' monograph [1973]. For thermomigration he is referred to ORIANI's article [1969].

Let us first discuss thermomigration results.

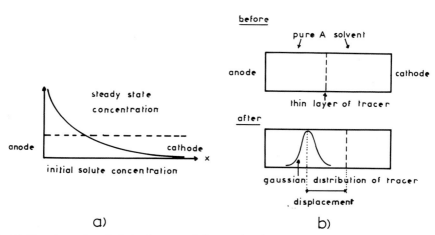

Fig. 14. Experimental methods in electro- and thermomigration. (a) Steady state method: initially, the sample has a homogeneous solute concentration; during current flow a steady-state gradient of concentration is established, the force due to the current flow being equilibrated by the force due to the gradient. (b) The tracer, initially deposited as a thin layer, is spread as a Gaussian in electromigration and also displaced as a whole with respect to the welding interface.

6.4.1. Thermomigration

In table 5, we display the heat of transport Q_B^* for interstitial solutes: in this case we naturally have no trouble with vacancy equilibrium! We note first that Q_B^* generally has the same sign for all solutes in a given solvent. There is also some correlation between Z_B^* and Q_B^*, but opposite to the one predicted by Gerl's model, pointing nevertheless to the role of *electron breeze* in both cases. In table 6, we display the heat of transport in self-diffusion in common metals. One sees im-

Table 5
Effective valences and heats of transport of interstitial impurities.

Solvent	Solute	Z_B^*	Q_B^* (kJ/mole)
Ti	H	~1 [c]	+21.7 [b]
	C	>0 [a]	–
	O	<0 [a]	–
V	H	1.5 [d]	1.4 [f]
	O	1 to 1.5 [e]	17 to 29 [e]
	N	–	17 to 29 [e]
Fe$_\alpha$	H	0.25 [a]	−33 to −23 [b]
	D	0.4 [a]	−33 to −23 [b]
	C	4.3 [a]	−71 to −100 [b]
	N	5.7 [a]	−75 [b]
Ni	H	0.5 [a]	−6.3 to −0.8 [b]
	D	0.7 [a]	−6.3 to −0.8 [b]
	C	–	–
Y	H	−0.3 to −0.9 [a]	–
	N	−0.9 to −2.8 [a]	–
	O	−1.2 to −2.6 [a]	–
Zr$_\beta$	C	>0 [a]	–
	N	–	>0 [b]
	O	<0 [a]	–
Nb	H	2.5 [d]	12 [f]
	C	0.6 [a]	54 [h]
	O	6.5 to −2 [a]	−67 [f]
Pd	H	>0 [a]	–
Ta	H	0.5 [d]	28.5 [g]
	O	0 to 2 [g]	−20 to −80 [g]
	N	–	−10 to −40 [g]

[a] PRATT and SELLORS [1973]; [b] ORIANI [1969]; [c] MARECHE *et al.*
[1979]; [d] ERCKMANN and WIPF [1976]; [e] MATHUNI *et al.* [1976]; [f]
PETERSON and SMITH [1982]; [g] MATHUNI *et al.* [1979]; [h] CARLSON
and SCHMIDT [1981].

References: p. 466.

Table 6

Thermomigration – effective heats of transport
in self-diffusion, after ORIANI [1969].

Metal	$\bar{Q}_A$ (kJ/mole) [a]
Na	-6.3
Al	-6.3 to $-8.4, +46$
Cu	$-22.6, 0, +16.7$
Ag	0
Au	$-27, 0$
Pb	$+8.8$
Zn	$-0.8, 0, +9.6$ to 14.6
Fe_α } Fe_γ	$< 0, 0, +38$ to 314
Co	$+221$ to $+1380$
Ni	< 0
Pt	$+38$ to $+56$
Ti	$< 0, +773$
Zr	-29 to -502

[a] For some elements there are several experimental values from different authors, separated by commas.

mediately the strong dispersion either for a given element or for similar elements. This underlines the experimental difficulties and also a possible departure from equilibrium of the vacancy distribution (§§ 1.2.2, 6.1 and 8.1). Transition metals display large $\bar{Q}_A$ values. This has been explained by HUNTINGTON [1966] as the result of additive contributions of electrons and holes, contributions which are opposite in electromigration, leading to small Z^*.

6.4.2. Electromigration

In table 5 are also given the Z_B^* values for interstitial solutes. As in thermomigration, we see that most such solutes migrate in the same direction in a given solvent. The hole contribution is clearly seen in transition metals with hole conductivity. In table 7 are displayed Z_B^* of various solutes in copper, silver and aluminium. We have also shown the residual resistivities $\Delta\rho_M$ given by classical measurements and $\Delta\rho_{EM}$ deduced from electromigration studies using relation (68) (LIMOGE [1976b]). Contrarily to thermomigration, we see that our predictive understanding of the electron breeze term is fairly good: the solute valence effect is for example well reproduced, especially in copper and silver. The case of aluminium is less satisfactory, probably owing to (i) a badly accounted-for vacancy wind effect and (ii) fairly strong band-structure effects in this polyvalent metal.

Table 7
Valence effect in solute electromigration in normal solvent
(after LIMOGE [1979b].

Solvent	Solute	Z_B^* (a)	$\Delta\rho_{EM}$ [b]$(\mu\Omega cm/at\%)$	$\Delta\rho_M$ [c]$(\mu\Omega cm/at\%)$
Copper	Cu	-8	0.98	0.33
(1300 K)	Ag	-6	0.62	0.35
	Cd	-9	1.14	1.31
	In	-16	2.36	3.95
	Sn	-30	5.13	8.3
	Sb	-40	6.64	10.9
Silver	Ag	-7.5	0.43	0.38
(1150 K)	Zn	-18.7	2.1	2.9
	Cd	-30	3.8	2.2
	In	-43.5	5.7	6.1
	Sn	-69	9.9	11.6
	Sb	-103	15	15
Aluminium	Al	-13.7	0.73	< 0.9
(900 K)	Cu	-6.2	0.26	1.5
	Ag	-17.3	1.01	2.1
	Cd	-16.9	1.02	1.5
	Au	-19.4	1.21	> 2.2
	Fe	-148	9.9	11.6

[a] Z_B^* is the true effective valence.
[b] The resistivity sum $\Delta\rho_{EM}$ is deduced from Z_B^* by eq. (68).
[c] $\Delta\rho_M$ is the resistivity sum as directly measured.

6.5. Electromigration in short-circuits

Migration under external forces, mainly an electric field, takes place also in diffusion short-circuits, such as surfaces and grain boundaries (GB) (ADAM [1971]). A first manifestation of this phenomenon is the *induced migration of GB* under an electric field. This result is now well established both at high temperatures, $T/T_m > 0.7$ (LORMAND [1970]) and at lower temperatures, $T/T_m \approx 0.3$ (HAESSNER *et al.* [1974]). The interpretation however is not clear, and in particular it is not obvious how to deduce the migration of an atomic configuration, such as a GB, from the sum of the forces exerted on the constituent atoms. A second manifestation, of great technological impact, is the large matter transport along short circuits in these samples which have a high ratio (surface + GB area)/(bulk). This is the case for the very thin evaporated aluminium stripes used as electrical connections in solid-state electronic devices. Owing to the high current density a rapid breaking intervenes, even at low temperatures (D'HEURLE [1971]). In gold, silver and copper films, BREITLING and HUMMEL [1972] have found migration towards the cathode in GB, i.e., $Z_{gb}^* > 0$, but BERENBAUM and ROSENBERG [1969] obtained a reverse result. These

References: p. 466.

contradictions are probably due to badly controlled experimental conditions (hot points, local thinning, etc.). Experiments done under better-controlled conditions, for solute diffusion in silver bicrystals (MARTIN [1972]) or in thin aluminium films (D'HEURLE and GANGULEE [1972]) do not show any striking difference from volume migration. Nevertheless, a theory of the GB electromigration force remains to be built. The addition of some solutes (copper, chromium, magnesium) that segregate to GB of aluminium can considerably slow down the aluminium migration, without any modification of the electromigration force. The breaking time is then enhanced by orders of magnitude (D'HEURLE and GANGULEE [1972]).

6.6. Electromigration as a purification process

The interested reader can find a recent review of this topic in PETERSON [1977]. The basis of this method is very simple: if a solute, i.e. an impurity, displays a non-zero effective valence Z_B^*, it will segregate to one end of a sample, of length l, under an electric field (see fig. 14a, above). There remains, then, a depleted, purified zone elsewhere. But as the time needed is proportional to $4l/Z_B^* D_B$, one easily sees that this method is especially efficient for interstitial solutes, or in the liquid state. In fact it has been used mainly for interstitial gaseous impurities in refractory metals.

7. Diffusion along short-circuits

Short-circuits consist of all the regions of the lattice which have lost their perfectly ordered structure: grain boundaries and interfaces, dislocations and surfaces. They have in common the following properties:
– The diffusivity is much higher than in the bulk and is detectable in a temperature range where bulk diffusion is negligible.
– The disordered regions interact chemically with the point defects, the diffusing species and with the components of the alloy: the concentrations in the short-circuits are different from that in the bulk.
– They can be modified by the diffusion process itself, which can lead to changes in the ledge and kink densities on a surface, diffusion-induced migration of a grain boundary, etc.
– Their detailed atomic structure is often unknown; when an approximate knowledge is available (as in the case of low-index surfaces), the structure always appears very complex.
– The properties of point defects at surfaces and grain boundaries (formation and migration energies, interaction with the substrate or with other defects) are not yet firmly established.

We recall first the phenomenological approach which has been fruitfully used to interpret grain-boundary diffusion experiments, as well as some recent progress in this area. We next treat the atomistic approach to grain-boundary diffusion and shall mention the use of molecular dynamics calculations. The case of surface diffusion will be treated separately.

7.1. Phenomenological approach

The basic idea of the continuous models consists of modeling the (one-) two-dimensional short-circuit as a (pipe) slab, along which the diffusion coefficient D' is much larger than that in the bulk D.

The diffusion equations are then written in both media with suitable matching conditions at the interfaces. For the grain boundary depicted in fig. 15, the two following equations are written:

$$\frac{\partial c}{\partial t} = D\nabla^2 c, \quad |x| > a$$

for the balance equation in the bulk; $2a$ is the thickness of the boundary, and

$$\frac{\partial c'}{\partial t} = D'\frac{\partial^2 c'}{\partial y^2} + \frac{D}{a}\frac{\partial c}{\partial x}\Big|_{a+\epsilon}, \quad |x| < a, \epsilon \to 0^+$$

for the balance equation in the grain boundary; the first term is the usual flux divergence term along the y direction; the second term accounts for the lateral exchanges between the slab and the bulk; the concentration inside the boundary is assumed independent of x.

The matching conditions at the interface $x = \pm a$ depend on the problem under consideration:
– for self-diffusion, $c' = c$,
– for solute diffusion $c' = kc$, where k is the grain-boundary segregation factor and under the assumption that c' remains much smaller than the solute concentration inside the boundary at saturation. For the case of a grain boundary in a concentrated alloy or the case of an interface in a two-phase system, the reader is referred to BERNARDINI and MARTIN [1976]. (See also ch. 13 concerning equilibrium grain-boundary segregation, especially §6.2.)

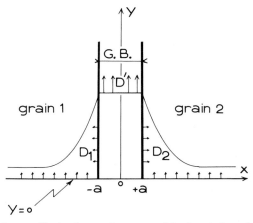

Fig. 15. Equiconcentration profile in the continuous model of grain-boundary diffusion. The slab thickness is $2a$; $y = 0$ is the plane of the tracer deposit.

References: p. 466.

The solution has been calculated only under simplifying assumptions pertaining to the geometry of the short-circuit or the type of the source:
– Only one isolated short-circuit is considered; it is assumed to be perpendicular to the surface where the source is deposited.
– Whenever the source is of finite thickness, its concentration is uniform along the plane $y = 0$; the surface diffusion coefficient of the deposited species is taken to be infinitely fast to prevent any depletion of the tracer in the area where the short-circuit emerges from the bulk.

7.1.1. Semi-infinite bicrystal

The problem of an infinite source (constant surface concentration) has been solved in an approximate way by FISHER [1951] and in exact form by WHIPPLE [1954]. The problem of the finite source has been solved by SUZUOKA [1961a, b, 1964].

The theoretical quantity which is used to analyze the experiments is not the concentration $C(x,t)$ but its integral $\overline{C}$ along a plane at depth y from the surface:

$$\overline{C}(y,t) = \int_{-\infty}^{-a} C(x,t)\, dx + \int_{-a}^{+a} C'(x,t)\, dx + \int_{a}^{\infty} C(x,t)\, dx.$$

It is ascertained that:
– The grain-boundary diffusion coefficient D' cannot be directly determined, because it shows up in all the expressions in the form $2akD'$. A separate measurement of k and an evaluation of $2a$ is needed to go further.
– The overall shape of the solution is practically independent of the initial condition (infinite source or thin layer) provided that the quantity $\beta = (D'/D)[ka/(Dt)^{1/2}]$ is large enough (in practice, larger than 5). In that case, log $\overline{C}$ varies as $y^{6/5}$ (LE CLAIRE [1963]). A more detailed discussion of the validity of the above solution can be found elsewhere (MARTIN and PERRAILLON [1979]).

7.1.2. Semi-infinite crystal with an isolated dislocation

A revised version of the calculation has been recently proposed (LE CLAIRE and RABINOVITCH [1981]). It is shown that log $\overline{C}$ varies linearly with y for distances which are large compared to the penetration depth into the bulk [$y > 4(Dt)^{1/2}$]:

$$\frac{\partial \log \overline{C}}{\partial y} = -A \Big/ \left(k\, a^2 \frac{D'}{D} - a^2 \right)^{1/2},$$

where A is a slowly varying function of the time and a is the radius of the pipe. The slope of the straight line is thus nearly independent of time in the case of diffusion along an isolated dislocation pipe: this is in contrast with the case where the dislocations are closely arranged into walls or boundaries and in which the slope varies as $t^{-1/4}$ (LE CLAIRE [1963]).

The diffusion coefficient D' along the dislocation cannot be determined since only the combination ka^2D' appears in the expression.

7.1.3. Short-circuit networks

In actual crystals, short-circuits are present in high concentration and their orientations with respect to the diffusion direction are more or less random. They make up some kind of connected network along which diffusion is much faster than in the bulk. Three diffusion regimes can be distinguished, according to the bulk penetration depth $(Dt)^{1/2}$ being smaller than, equal to or larger than a characteristic length l of the network: l is the average diameter of the grains in the case of a grain-boundary network and the average distance between two pinning points in the case of a dislocation network (HARRISON [1961]):

(i) When bulk diffusion is totally negligible and when the penetration depth along the network is larger than l, the concentration profile is expected to be similar to a bulk diffusion profile with D' instead of D. This is called *Harrison's C regime*.

(ii) When bulk diffusion is not negligible but $(Dt)^{1/2}$ remains much smaller than l, the short-circuits do not interact with each other: no significant amount of the diffusing species which has diffused through and out of a first short-circuit ever reaches another short-circuit. It can be shown that an approximate value of $2akD'$ (or ka^2D') can be deduced from plotting log $\bar{C}$ as a function of y (LEVINE and MacCALLUM [1960]): this is called *Harrison's B regime*.

(iii) Whenever the bulk diffusion depth is larger than l, the diffusion fields of neighbouring short-circuits overlap and none of the solutions quoted above can be used. This is *Harrison's A regime*. A simple expression of the effective diffusivity D_{eff} can be proposed, taking into account the fraction f of the lattice sites which belong to the short-circuits (HART [1957]):

$$D_{\text{eff}} = fD' + (1 - f)D.$$

Harrison's classification has been extended to the case where the grain boundaries are moving at rate V (CAHN and BALLUFFI [1979]); Harrison's A regime is encountered whenever $(Dt)^{1/2}$ *or* Vt is larger than l; Harrison's B regime is split into distinct regimes according to the velocity of the grain boundary; Harrison's C regime remains untouched.

Let us mention that a continuous approach has been recently proposed for Harrison's A regime (AIFANTIS [1979]; HILL [1979]). A diffusion field is associated with each family of high-diffusivity paths. The total solution results from the superposition of these diffusional fields, which are connected with each other and with the bulk through quasi-chemical reactions. Interesting new features have been predicted, in particular a non-Fickean character of the diffusion in simple cases.

7.1.4. Experimental results

The reader is referred to a recent compilation of experiments (MARTIN and PERRAILLON [1979]). It is observed that:

– For self-diffusion, the apparent activation energy in a grain boundary is roughly 0.4–0.6 times the activation energy for bulk diffusion.

– For solute diffusion, the apparent activation energy includes the interaction energy of the solute with the boundary.

References: p. 466.

– For diffusion along the interface separating two phases of different chemical compositions, the results are still too scarce and somewhat controversial. The first experiments in Ag–Fe (BONDY *et al.* [1971]; JOB *et al.* [1974]) or Ag–Cu (PÉRINET [1975]) showed unusually large activation energies; recent experiments in α/γ interfaces of stainless steels (JUVÉ-DUC *et al.* [1980]), however, exhibit activation energies which agree fairly well with the activation energy for diffusion along grain boundaries of the γ-phase.

7.2. New advances in grain-boundary diffusion

7.2.1. Impurity effects
This topic is treated in chapter 13, §5.2.

7.2.2. Diffusion-induced grain-boundary migration
The diffusion of two chemically different species along a grain boundary may under certain conditions induce a lateral displacement of this boundary, in a temperature range where the lattice diffusion is negligible. This lateral movement (perpendicular to the grain-boundary plane) is not necessarily uniform and as a consequence the boundary can be distorted. The swept area which is left in its wake has a different chemical composition from that of the bulk (fig. 16). The driving force of this evolution has its origin in the fact that the amount of energy which has been gained by changing the composition of the swept areas over-compensates the amount of energy that the alloy had to spend in order to increase the grain boundary surface. This phenomenon has been observed in several alloys during mixing or unmixing. The only mechanism which is consistent with the experiments performed so far is a Kirkendall effect along the grain boundary (BALLUFFI and CAHN [1981]; assuming a vacancy mechanism, they showed that the difference between the

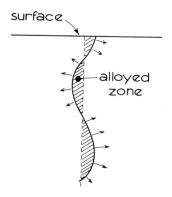

Fig. 16. Lateral displacement of a grain boundary due to a Kirkendall effect along the boundary. The hatched regions have a composition different from that of the surrounding matrix. The dashed line is the initial position of the boundary.

diffusivities of the two species produces a divergence of the vacancy flux inside the boundary. This divergence is accommodated by the climb of the grain-boundary dislocations, which provokes the observed lateral displacement. It is not difficult to show that this mechanism is self-sustaining, but little is known about the reasons why it starts.

7.3. Atomistic approach to diffusion in short-circuits

7.3.1. Atomic model for grain-boundary diffusion

The continuous approach has proved its efficiency for interpreting the experimental results which have been collected up to now. However, it raises several questions:
- What is the grain boundary thickness? How can it be defined in a precise way?
- What is a diffusion coefficient inside a grain-boundary?
- Is the assumption of local equilibrium between the bulk and the grain boundary justified?
- What does the solution look like for very short times, i.e., times smaller than a jump period in the bulk?

BENOIST and MARTIN [1975a, b]) were able to answer these questions with the following simple model. The grain boundary is modelled as a (100) plane of a simple cubic array, in which the atom jump frequency is Γ' and is supposed to be larger than the jump frequency Γ of the atom in the rest of the lattice. Γ_i and Γ_0 stand for the atom jump frequencies from the bulk into the grain-boundary and conversely. The starting transport equation is written as follows:

$$\frac{\partial C(r,t)}{\partial t} = \sum_{r'} \left[C(r',t) \Gamma_{r' \to r} - C(r,t) \Gamma_{r \to r'} \right],$$

where $C(r,t)$ stands for the tracer concentration on site r at time t; $\Gamma_{r' \to r}$ for the jump frequency for site r' to site r; $\sum_{r'}$ is extended to sites r' which are first neighbours of site r. The solution is calculated with a boundary condition corresponding to the instantaneous source of the continuous approach. The main results can be summarized as follows:
- In the limit of large bulk penetration (more precisely, a large number of jumps in the bulk, i.e. $\Gamma t \gg 1$), the solution is equivalent to Suzuoka's solution (see §7.1.1). The expression for the parameter β is:

$$\beta = \frac{D'}{D} \frac{ka}{(Dt)^{1/2}} = \frac{\Gamma'}{\Gamma} \frac{\Gamma_i}{\Gamma_0} \frac{1}{2(\Gamma t)^{1/2}}.$$

Since the bulk diffusion coefficient is Γb^2 (b is the lattice parameter), the comparison of the two solutions yields $D' = \Gamma' b^2$; the segregation factor k is equal to Γ_i / Γ_0 and the grain-boundary thickness is b.

In the case where the grain boundary is modelled as p parallel planes, it is found that its thickness is pb. It must be noticed that this thickness is not altered even if the bonds between the sites in the bulk and the sites in the boundary are stretched

References: p. 466.

perpendicularly to the boundary plane. The "thickness" of the grain-boundary is not related to the actual atomic relaxations at the grain boundary but only to the *number* of high-diffusivity paths which are available for the tracer.
– In the limit of small penetration depth in the bulk, the identification with the continuous solution is impossible. At very short times ($\Gamma t < 0.1$) the exact solution tends towards a Gaussian with $\Gamma' b^2$ as diffusion coefficient.

This model has been modified to account for more realistic grain-boundary structures. We refer the reader to the original papers (COSTE *et al.* [1976]). We must mention that such a sophisticated model does not take into account the correlation effects of tracer diffusion. The latter should be calculated in the same spirit as was done for dislocations (ROBINSON and PETERSON [1972]).

7.3.2. Molecular dynamics calculations of point-defect properties

Computer studies always suffer from the fact that they rest entirely on the knowledge of proper interatomic potentials. The latter have been calculated from first principles only in a very few cases. Semi-empirical and analytical potentials are often preferred (like Morse-type functions) as well as Lennard–Jones potentials which hold only for rare-gas lattices. But it is hoped (and assumed) that the order of magnitude for the studied properties will be accounted for and that the observed qualitative trends will not be too sensitive to the detailed shape of the potentials which are used throughout the simulations.

Molecular dynamics calculations have been performed very recently (BALLUFFI *et al.* [1981]; KWOK *et al.* [1981]; CICCOTTI *et al.* [1982]). The studied case is a tilt

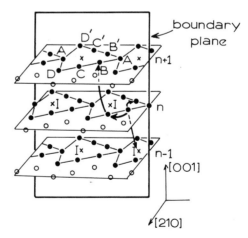

Fig. 17. Schematic picture of a typical tilt boundary simulated in a fcc lattice by molecular dynamics. Solid circles denote atoms belonging to the boundary. Open circles denote neighbouring atoms of the bulk. The scale of the drawing has been magnified along [001]. B and B′ denote sites of preferential occupancy for the vacancy; C is an intermediate unstable position during the course of a jump sequence ($B_n \to C_n \to B_{n+1}$) or ($B_{n-1} \to C_n \to B_{n+1}$). I is the interstitial location.

boundary; its structure is schematically pictured in fig. 17. The main relevant points are the following:

  – Above 0.5 T_m, the spontaneous formation of *Frenkel pairs* (interstitial atom + vacancy) is observed. The atom located on site B_n moves towards site I_{n-1} as indicated by the arrow. The mobilities of the two kinds of defect are very different: whereas the interstitial atom remains trapped in the low atomic density part of the boundary, the vacancy jumps rapidly along the boundary.

  – Self-diffusion is deduced to occur by a vacancy mechanism. The correlation factor, which is extracted from the simulation runs, is of the expected order of magnitude ($f_0 \approx 0.66$).

  – At higher temperatures, the relaxation of neighbours around the vacancy is more pronounced: the vacancy appears as rather delocalized.

  – A significant anisotropy is observed: the vacancy migrates more rapidly along the tilt axis than perpendicularly to it. But this anisotropy is more marked in Balluffi's results than in Ciccotti's: it is not yet known whether this difference stems from the difference in crystal structures (bcc against fcc structure), or from some as yet uncontrolled artefact of either calculation.

7.4. Surface diffusion

Although free surfaces can actually play the role of short-circuits for bulk diffusion (inner surfaces of cavities, surfaces along a crack), they have been mostly studied for their own sakes.

We shall not repeat hereafter the continuous approach which has been already used for interface or grain-boundary diffusion; grain 2 in fig. 15 has only to be replaced by vacuum and no exchange between the surface and the vacuum is allowed. As in the case of a grain boundary, the characteristic quantity which appears in equations is δD_S, where δ is the "thickness" of the surface layer and D_S the surface diffusion coefficient. We shall focus in the following on the atomistic point of view.

7.4.1. Atomic structure and point defects

A surface is essentially made up of terraces which are portions of low-index surfaces; these terraces are separated by ledges of atomic height, along which kinks are present (*TLK* model: fig. 18). Ledges and kinks have a double origin:

  – A geometrical one, to provide the misorientation of the actual surface with respect to the dense planes of the terraces (θ and α angles in fig. 18).

  – A thermally activated one for entropy purposes.

Such a description is thought to hold in a range of low temperatures where the formation free energy of ledges is large enough to keep their thermal density at a low level (in practice between 0 K and $0.5T_m$).

As predicted by BURTON *et al.* [1951] a dramatic change in the surface topology occurs at some transition temperature T_R, at which the formation free energy of the ledges vanishes (or becomes very small): as a consequence the surface becomes

References: p. 466.

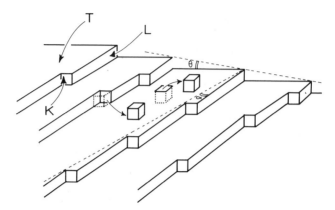

Fig. 18. Terrace–Ledge–Kink (TLK) model for low-index surfaces. The formation of adatoms (the extra atoms bulging out from the plane of a low-index surface) and advacancies (the anti-defects to adatoms) is represented.

delocalized (ch. 9, §4.2). This transition (called *roughness transition*) is due to a large number of steps of increasing height which make the edges of the terraces indistinguishable. This has been clearly illustrated by Monte Carlo simulations on (100) surfaces of a simple cubic lattice (LEAMY and GILMER [1974]; VAN DER EERDEN *et al.* [1978]) Figure 10 of ch. 9 shows examples of LEAMY and GILMER'S computations. T_R is roughly given by

$$T_R = 0.5\epsilon/k,$$

where ϵ is the strength of the first-neighbour bond. In what follows, we restrict ourselves to surfaces maintained well below T_R.

Point defects are also present, namely adatoms and advacancies (see fig. 18); they can be created pairwise at a site of a terrace or separately at a ledge or a kink. The latter case is energetically favoured with respect to the others and is thought to be dominant. Multi-defects can also form by clustering adatoms or advacancies.

Theoretical calculations of point-defect properties on low-index surfaces have so far been performed very crudely. Semi-empirical potentials, which are fitted to bulk properties, are used in such calculations (WYNBLATT and GJOSTEIN [1968]; PERRAILLON *et al.* [1972]; FLAHIVE and GRAHAM [1980]). Although these potentials are well known to be inadequate to represent surface properties, one hopes that qualitative conclusions can nevertheless be drawn, which do not depend too much on the choice of the potential:

– The formation and migration energies for adatoms and advacancies are found to be highly sensitive to surface orientation.

– The formation energies for both kinds of defect are comparable, except for the (100) surface of an fcc lattice, where the formation energy of the advacancy is significantly smaller than the corresponding energy for the adatom. Therefore, both defects are expected to contribute significantly to matter transport. They will be created in roughly equal amounts, either separately at kinks or pairwise at terrace sites.

– The migration energies have been mainly calculated for adatoms on fcc and bcc surfaces. The few calculations of vacancy migration energies have been performed on copper; they show that the advacancy is the slower-diffusing defect except for the (100) surface where the reverse is expected (PERRAILLON *et al.* [1972]).

For fcc lattices, the migration energies of adatoms increase roughly with increasing surface roughness: $E_m(111) < E_m(113) < E_m(331) < E_m(001) < E_m(210)$. The case of the (110) plane is special; when going from Ir to Pt, Rh, Au, Pd, Ag, Ni, Cu in that order, the $E_m(110)$ migration energy, which is larger than $E_m(113)$ for Ir, decreases continuously down to $E_m(111)$ for Cu.

For bcc lattices, the migration energies are roughly in the following order: $E_m(110) \sim E_m(211) \sim E_m(321) < E_m(310) < E_m(001) < E_m(111)$.

A further difficulty stems from the fact that diffusion is expected to be highly anisotropic on non-perfect surfaces: the migration energy along dense rows or in deep channels is usually smaller than the migration energy across these rows or channels. This may obscure the ordering of low-index surfaces with respect to their migrational properties. It should be mentioned that more sophisticated calculations of point defects at surfaces are underway, concerning the binding energy of an adatom to a ledge site (THOMPSON and HUNTINGTON [1982]) or the migration energies of an adatom on (100) and (110) surfaces of tungsten (DESJONQUÈRES and SPANJAARD [1982]). The calculated migration energies to date are in good agreement with the experimental data.

Diffusion is thought to take place through individual jumps only at very low temperature ($T < 0.15T_m$). At higher temperatures, several new mechanisms have been proposed: jumps to more distant neighbours, contribution of multidefects performing collective jumps, multiple jumps caused by a strong dynamic correlation, an exchange mechanism in which the adatom kicks a solvent atom out of the wall of a channel (BASSETT and WEBBER [1978], HALICIOGLU and POUND [1979]); and finally, at still higher temperatures, a delocalization of the adatom, which spends most of its time in flight rather than on equilibrium sites. All these mechanisms have been observed in molecular dynamics calculations on fcc Lennard–Jones crystals (TULLY *et al.* [1979]; DE LORENZI *et al.* [1982]).

The next step in the analysis is to deduce a macroscopic *surface diffusion coefficient* D_S as a function of the individual jump frequencies which have been measured or calculated. Following CHOI and SHEWMON [1962], one is intuitively led to write it as:

$$D_S = \frac{1}{4} \sum_{i=1}^{p} \Gamma_i d_i^2,$$

where p is the total number of jump types, Γ_i and d_i their frequency and length. However, this expression holds only under restrictive conditions:
– All the diffusion mechanisms must contribute independently to matter transport. At each step, the diffusing atom should be allowed to make a choice between all the

References: p. 466.

p available jump types which are at its disposal.

– All the sites of the surface should be equivalent. The defects should be in equilibrium everywhere and their concentrations should be uniform all over the surface, with no preferential occupancy or trapping sites. This requirement can only be met for close-packed perfect surfaces with no ledges or kinks, e.g., a (111) surface in the fcc lattice.

Real surfaces are not perfect: ledges and kinks are thought to trap the defects. Moreover the jump frequency for the motion along a ledge is different from the frequency for jumping over the ledge. If ledges and kinks could be uniformly distributed over the surface, the equivalence of the surface sites would be maintained and the same expression of D_S could still be used.

As a matter of fact, we know that the misorientation of a real surface from a perfect one is provided by one (or more) periodic array(s) of ledges and kinks. This periodicity (as opposed to uniformity) contradicts the assumption of equivalence between sites, and a new analysis has to be carried out. This has been done only for (310), (*h*10) and (*h*11) surfaces (h is any positive integer) of the fcc lattice (COUSTY *et al.* [1981]; COUSTY [1981]), thanks to the atomistic approach which has been already worked out for grain-boundary diffusion (BENOIST and MARTIN [1975a,b]): the method consists of defining a new unit supercell containing all the different types of sites and making up such a basic pattern that it can be used to generate the surface sites by translations in two directions. Effective jump frequencies across this cell, in the direction of the ledges and perpendicularly to them, can be determined by matching the solution of the discrete approach to Suzuoka's solution with the same boundary conditions. The exchanges of matter between the bulk and the surface are taken into account; but, in its present form, this model requires the knowledge of the atom jump frequencies out of (and into) all the different types of surface sites, which is far beyond the scarce experimental information which is available at present. No accurate check of the model can be done as yet.

7.4.2. Experimental results

7.4.2.1. Microscopic data.
The Field Ion Microscope (FIM) technique (ch. 10A, § 10.3.2) has provided an irreplaceable insight into the migration mechanisms and migration energies of adatoms deposited on low-index surfaces. Table 8 sums up and compares the theoretical values (FLAHIVE and GRAHAM [1980]) and the experimental ones which have been obtained on W (COWAN and TSONG [1975]; GRAHAM and EHRLICH [1974, 1975]), Ni (TUNG and GRAHAM [1980]), Rh (AYRAULT and EHRLICH [1974]) and Pt (BASSETT and WEBBER [1978]).

The calculated values are always significantly smaller than the experimental ones [except for W(111)]: the crudeness of the potentials would prevent any quantitative conclusion anyway. The ordering of surfaces predicted by theory is actually observed for Rh and Pt, but it fails grossly for Ni. The reason for this major discrepancy is not known.

In the FIM technique the diffusing atom is deposited from a vapour onto the surface at a temperature where no matter exchange between the bulk and the surface

Table 8
Migration energies of self-adatoms on various low-index planes (in eV).

| Surface | fcc metal | | | | | | Surface | bcc metal | |
| | Ni | | Rh | | Pt | | | W | |
	Exp.	Theor.	Exp.	Theor.	Exp.	Theor.		Exp.	Theor.
111	–	0.02	0.16	0.05		~ 0.05	110	0.90	0.46
113	0.31	0.21	0.54	0.44	0.53	0.50	211	0.85	0.28
110	0.23	0.02	0.60	0.48	0.84	0.58	321	0.82	0.13
331	0.45	0.15	0.64	0.62	0.84	0.63	111	1.80	2.92
001	–	–	0.88	0.70	–	–	–	–	–

is allowed: the adatom is therefore in high supersaturation and its formation energy cannot be measured with this technique.

We must remember however that such data, although very useful, cannot be used to deduce any absolute value of the surface diffusion coefficient D_S or any information about the diffusion anisotropy, for two reasons:

– The surface diffusion coefficient D_S incorporates the concentration of defects, which cannot be reached by the FIM technique. Only the formation energy of advacancies has been measured recently above room temperature by positron annihilation on copper and silver. The values which are reported are close to 1 eV within experimental uncertainty, that is, only 20% lower than the corresponding energy in the bulk (LYNN and WELCH [1980]).

– The surface diffusion coefficient D_S is usually measured at a range of much higher temperatures where other diffusion mechanisms may come into play.

For solute adatoms diffusing on surfaces we refer the reader to a recent review (EHRLICH and STOLT [1980]), and the modification of self-diffusion on surfaces to which impurities have segregated is treated in ch. 13, §5.2.

The anisotropy of the adatom jump frequency, which is theoretically predicted from the geometrical structure of the surface, is often observed. But it also depends on the chemical nature of the diffusing adatom: on the (110) surface of Pt, Au adatoms diffuse only along channels parallel to ⟨110⟩ whereas Pt and Ir adatoms diffuse two-dimensionally with no noticeable anisotropy (BASSETT and WEBBER [1978]).

7.4.2.2. Macroscopic data. Mass transfer experiments consist in measuring the rate at which a solid changes its shape (at constant volume) in order to minimize its surface free energy. Several techniques can be used: thermal grooving of a grain boundary (MULLINS and SHEWMON [1959]), blunting of a sharp tip (NICHOLS and MULLINS [1965a]), decaying of an isolated (or of a periodic array of) scratch(es) (KING and MULLINS [1962]; NICHOLS and MULLINS [1965b]). The possible contributions of bulk diffusion or the evaporation–condensation mechanism must be subtracted to deduce the part due to surface diffusion only. This technique does not yield the surface diffusion coefficient D_S but the product $\gamma_S D_S$ (where γ_S is the

References: p. 466.

surface tension) or, more precisely, some average of this product over the orientation of all the facets making up the macroscopic profile.

A second technique involves the use of a radioactive tracer and consists in measuring the concentration profile of the diffusing species: it has been used only recently for copper surface self-diffusion (COUSTY [1981]) and solute diffusion on surfaces of pure copper (GHALEB [1983]). This technique does not yield D_S but the product δD_S where δ is some "thickness" of the surface layer in the continuous approach. For both techniques two crucial points must be checked throughout the diffusion run:

− The absence of any impurity or any two-dimensional superstructure of impurities, both of which might significantly alter the diffusion rate (BONZEL [1976]). In the presence of various contaminants (Bi, S, Cl) the surface self-diffusivity can be increased by several orders of magnitude: diffusivities as high as 10^{-4} m^2/s have even been reported (RHEAD [1975]).

− The absence of any reconstruction of the surface: this point can only be checked for the radiotracer technique, because mass transfer experiments are performed on surfaces which evolve in time.

Three points must be noted: (i) The apparent activation energy for self-diffusion is significantly larger than the migration energy of adatoms which is measured with the FIM technique. The difference is attributed to the energy which is required to form the defects contributing to matter transport. This means physically that the density of defect sources and sinks (steps, kinks) is probably large enough to insure the equilibrium defect concentration throughout the experiment at such temperatures. (ii) The self-diffusion Arrhenius plot is often curved (RHEAD [1975]). If this curvature is not an artefact of the experimental techniques, several explanations can be proposed: contribution of several kinds of defects (advacancies and adatoms, clusters of adatoms, etc.), contribution of multiple jumps, formation of thermal kinks (NEUMAN and HIRSCHWALD [1972]), local melting of the surface (RHEAD [1975]). (iii) Whether the crystallographic structure of the surface induces a marked anisotropy of the surface diffusion coefficient or not is still a matter of controversy. At 0.6 T_m on (110) surfaces of pure nickel, the scratch-decaying technique shows a rather large anisotropy (roughly two orders of magnitude: BONZEL and LATTA [1978]), whereas the tracer technique for copper self-diffusion (COUSTY [1981]) or for silver diffusion on copper (ROULET [1973]) exhibits only a small difference between the coefficients along two perpendicular directions (at most a factor of 4).

8. Diffusion under non-equilibrium defect concentrations

Up to now we have discussed diffusion problems involving point defects in thermal equilibrium. In particular we focussed mainly on vacancies; but in some conditions, often of great technological importance, a high supersaturation of point defects, interstitials and vacancies, can be sustained in steady state. With respect to vacancy-related diffusion, an acceleration of kinetics is the main phenomenon to be observed. Interstitials however, have a high formation enthalpy, and therefore a zero equilibrium concentration. In that case, apart from an acceleration, new phenomena which are unknown at equilibrium can appear, as we shall see in §8.3.2.

If we create point defects in a material in excess of thermal equilibrium, a supersaturation will build up, which results from a competition between creation and elimination. The new diffusion coefficient will be given by

$$D_{acc} = k_v D_v C_v + k_i D_i C_i, \qquad (69)$$

where k_i and k_v are coefficients depending on mechanism and jump frequencies, D_i and D_v are the defect diffusion coefficients and C_i and C_v their *total* concentrations. The problem of enhanced diffusion is then to calculate the actual C_i and C_v according to the experimental conditions of creation and elimination.

Many situations are now well known in materials science where this situation prevails. Without claiming to be exhaustive, we mention the following cases: (i) If vacancy sinks are not very efficient in a sample submitted either to a quench or to a temperature gradient, we can observe a vacancy supersaturation. (ii) Such a supersaturation can also be created in an alloy by vacancy injection from the surface by a Kirkendall mechanism due to preferential depletion of one of the components by dissolution or oxidation (BURTON [1982]). (iii) Point defects are also created during plastic deformation. (iv) Under irradiation by energetic particles, a high level of supersaturation can be sustained.

In all these cases the point defect supersaturation is able to accelerate the diffusion and to induce through a coupling effect a segregation in alloys. Let us look first at the cases which involve vacancies only.

8.1.   Quenched-in vacancies

Vacancy sinks include free surfaces, dislocations and grain boundaries. Vacancies can also be lost for diffusion by agglomeration as dislocation loops, stacking fault tetrahedra or voids. In some cases (very low dislocation density, surface oxidation for example) these sinks become ineffective, and a volume supersaturation is created, which in turn enhances diffusion beyond the "thermal" value. A very important example of the role of quenched-in vacancies is given by the kinetics of age-hardening in alloys displaying precipitation-hardening. We know that GP zone formation is far too rapid to be accounted for by the thermal diffusion only: the role of quenched-in vacancies was stressed early (GUINIER [1959]) and later the importance of vacancy–solute complexes (GIRIFALCO and HERMAN [1965]) was recognized in the so-called "vacancy pump" model.

Another very interesting application is the enhancement after quench of the ordering kinetics in alloys. This phenomenon forms the basis of a method of studying defect properties in metals by relaxation measurements (§2.2: also ROBROCK [1981]). This could also be the case in some thermomigration experiments (MATLOCK and STARK [1971]). These authors have measured the heat of transport of aluminium and found $\overline{Q}$ values of 46 kJ/mole in a single crystal and -8.4 kJ/mole in a polycrystalline sample, pointing to the importance of the vacancy formation enthalpy in eq. (67). The same conclusion was drawn from measurements of solute diffusion in a temperature gradient in aluminium or silver (MCKEE and STARK [1975]), SHIH and STARK [1978]). In all these cases, grain boundaries are the only efficient vacancy sinks. The polycrystalline sample is then at equilibrium but not the single crystal. In this last case the hot end imposes its vacancy concentration on the cold one. Therefore the diffusion coefficient is fixed by (i) the hot-end vacancy concentration, (ii) the cold-end vacancy mobility. The same inefficiency of internal sinks forms the basis of ANTHONY's method [1971] which has been used to determine the coupling term L_{AB}/L_{BB}. In aluminium the elimination of quenched-in vacancies takes place on the surface, and the resulting defect flux drives a solute segregation in or out of the sample, the measurement of which gives access to the L_{AB}/L_{BB} term.

8.2. Cold-work-induced defects

It is now firmly established that during plastic deformation, point defects, probably mainly vacancies, are created by dislocation interactions (WINTENBERGER [1959], GONZALES *et al.* [1975a, b]). However, the high dislocation density in that case prevents a high supersaturation level (RUOFF and BALLUFFI [1963]). It is then clear that diffusion should be accelerated at low temperature, but also that any attempt to determine this enhancement by classical macroscopic methods (§2.1) is hopeless. Artefacts due to surface roughness induced by the slip bands (RUOFF [1967]) or pipe diffusion in dislocations will always screen the actual effect. However, this enhancement can be rendered visible by a local method sensitive to a small number of jumps, such as the Zener effect (NEUMANN *et al.* [1961]) or GP zone formation kinetics (KELLY and CHIOU [1958]).

8.3. Defects created by irradiation

8.3.1. Irradiation-enhanced diffusion

This topic has great importance, both through its technological consequences and through its use as a tool for studying point defects at high temperature. We mention the recent reviews by ADDA *et al.* [1975], SIZMANN [1978] and ROTHMAN [1981].

During an energetic irradiation, in the case of metals by electrons, ions or neutrons, vacancies and interstitials are created, either as isolated Frenkel pairs or as complex clusters, the so-called *cascades*. Avoiding technical refinements, the number of such defects is roughly given by $N_d = KT_D/2E_d$ (TORRENS and ROBINSON [1972]) where T_D is the elastic energy given to the lattice, E_d the displacement threshold energy, near 40 eV, and K an efficiency factor near 0.8. To calculate the resulting concentrations, two methods have been used. The first is the Monte Carlo simulation method (DORAN [1970], LANORE [1974]). We have no space to discuss it here and refer the reader to the previously quoted review articles. The other one was initially

References: p. 466.

proposed by LOMER [1954] and progressively refined since. The ingredients of Lomer's model are the following:
- Production rate G of spatially uncorrelated point defects;
- motion by random walk with coefficients D_i and D_v;
- annealing by mutual recombination at rate K_r, at fixed sinks uniformly distributed at rate K_i and K_v, or at surfaces;
- only pure metals are considered.

Defect concentrations are then solutions of the following equations:

$$\frac{\partial C_1}{\partial t} = G + D_v \nabla^2 C_v - K_r C_i C_v - K_v (C_v - C_v^o),$$

$$\frac{\partial C_i}{\partial t} = G + D_i \nabla^2 C_i - K_r C_i C_v - K_i C_i, \tag{70}$$

where C_v^o is the thermal vacancy concentration.

These equations have generally to be solved numerically. Nevertheless, far from the surface, after a very complex transient regime, the duration of which is of the order of $1/K$, with K the lower of K_v and K_i, one obtains a steady-state regime characterized by:
- $D_i C_i = D_v (C_v - C_v^o)$ with elimination at sinks;
- $C_i = C_v - C_v^o$ with mutual recombination only;
- $C_v \sim (G/D_v)^{1/2}$ at low temperatures, i.e., for dominant mutual recombination;
- $C_v \sim (G/D_v)L$ at high temperatures, i.e., for dominant sink elimination,

where L is the mean distance between sinks. At very high temperatures, $T/T_m \gtrsim 0.5$, the defect mobility is sufficient to prevent any noticeable defect supersaturation, and the enhancement is negligible. In table 9 are given the main characteristics of D_{acc} [see eq. (69)] in Lomer's model. To analyze the experiments we must keep in mind that in most cases they are done near the surface, a condition which is not included in the simple form above. A correction is then necessary (ERMERT *et al.* [1968]).

The enhancement being noticeable only at low temperatures, that is, at low mobility, D_{acc} will be lower than 10^{-20} m²/s and the experiments are very difficult. This fact can explain the fairly general discrepancy observed between the tracer

Table 9

Characteristics of D_{acc} in Lomer's model [eq. (69)]; after ADDA *et al.* [1975].

Regime	Activation energy of D_{acc}			Dose-rate dependence (G = dose rate)
	Term due to interstitials	Term due to vacancies	Total	
Recombination only	$\frac{1}{2}H_m^i$	$H_m^v - \frac{1}{2}H_m^i$	complex	$G^{1/2}$
Elimination on sinks	0	0	0	G
Elimination both by recombination and on sinks	$\frac{1}{2}H_m^v$	$\frac{1}{2}H_m^v$	$\frac{1}{2}H_m^v$	$G^{1/2}$

H_m^i and H_m^v are the migration enthalpy of, respectively, the interstitial and the vacancy.

References: p. 466.

experiments and the predictions of Lomer's model, the measured values being generally too high, either in self or solute diffusion (ADDA *et al.* [1975]). However, Lomer's model also rests on numerous crude approximations, for example, in the calculation of various rate terms K or in the k_i and k_v factors [eq. (69)]. To clarify the situation, new and well controlled self-diffusion experiments using modern sectioning techniques would be highly desirable. Relaxation methods, however, are well suited in this case, owing to their high sensitivity. The recent results of HALBWACHS and HILLAIRET [1978] and of HALBWACHS *et al.* [1978a, b] on Ag-Zn alloys by Zener relaxation displays a good agreement with the predictions of Lomer's model, if one supposes that, in these alloys, the vacancies are less mobile than the interstitials. This result was confirmed by electron-microscopic studies (REGNIER and HALBWACHS [1980]).

8.3.2. Irradiation-induced segregation and phase transformation

Irradiation-induced precipitation in *undersaturated* alloys is now a well established phenomenon in a large number of systems. We display in table 10 the characteristics of such precipitation in binary alloys. This effect has to be clearly distinguished from a simple radiation-enhanced precipitation in an oversaturated alloy.

At a given defect creation rate G, the precipitation of a non-equilibrium phase appears in a well defined temperature interval (see figs. 19 and 20). This result then defines a new variable which has to be added to the classical phase diagram: the

Table 10
Binary alloys where radiation-induced precipitation has been found.

Alloy	Projectile	Precipitate	Morphology
Ni–Be	Ni$^+$ ions	β-NiBe	at interstitial dislocation loops
Ni–Si	neutrons	γ'-Ni$_3$Si	at interstitial dislocation loops
	Ni$^+$ ions	γ'-Ni$_3$Si	at interstitial dislocation loops
	electrons	γ'-Ni$_3$Si	at interstitial dislocation loops
	H$^+$ ions	γ'-Ni$_3$Si	homogeneous, coherent, in regions of non-uniform defect production
Ni–Ge	electrons	γ'-Ni$_3$Ge	at cavities or dislocations lines
Al–Zn	neutrons	β-Zn	homogeneous precipitation
	electrons	GP zones + β-Zn	homogeneous precipitation
Al–Ag	electrons	$\{100\}$ silver-rich platelets	homogeneous precipitation
Pd–W	H$^+$, N$^+$ ions	bcc W	at dislocation loops
	electrons	Pd$_8$W	homogeneous
W–Re	neutrons	χ-WRe$_3$	homogeneous
Cu–Be	electrons	G.P. zones + γ	homogeneous
Mg–Cd	electrons	Mg$_3$Cd	?

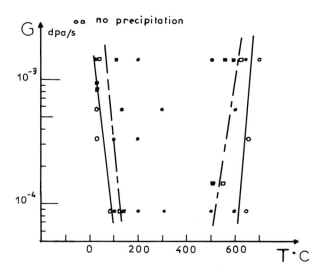

Fig. 19. "Phase diagram", in a flux–temperature section, for the system Ni–Si irradiated by 1 MeV electrons (after BARBU and MARTIN [1977]). Solid line: precipitation borderline for a concentration of 6 at% Si, dashed line idem for 2 at% Si.

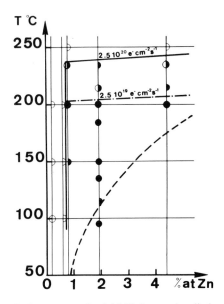

Fig. 20. Solvus lines in the Al–Zn system under 1 MeV electron irradiation (after CAUVIN and MARTIN [1981]). Open half-circles: no precipitation; solid half-circles: precipitation at low, or high, flux; dashed line: solvus line without irradiation.

References: p. 466.

defect creation rate (or irradiation flux), in addition to the temperature, pressure and composition (ADDA *et al.* [1975]).

Two ways have been explored to explain these results. The first one is a constraint-equilibrium one: the stored energy due to point defects could displace the free enthalpy curves, to such an extent that it renders stable under irradiation a phase which is normally unstable. Careful calculations of this effect have shown that the order of magnitude of the possible displacement is too low to explain the great majority of the results (BOCQUET and MARTIN [1979]). The second explanation is due to ANTHONY [1972]. Irradiation-created point defects are eliminated, partly by diffusion to sinks, and the resulting defect fluxes induce, through a coupling effect, local solute supersaturations beyond the solubility limit.

Many authors have developed this idea and extended it to the case of interstitials (OKAMOTO and WIEDERSICH [1974], JOHNSON and LAM [1976], BARBU [1978, 1980]). The most elaborate numerical solutions give a fairly good account of experimental results. In particular, the role of sinks, dislocation loops or surfaces is well understood. Nevertheless, the low-temperature borderline remains to be explained (BARBU [1978]). In all these models the solute supersaturation results from a balance between the interstitials, which always carry the solute down the gradient and the vacancies, which can act in both directions (BARBU [1980]). At high temperatures the precipitation disappears owing to the lowering of the defect supersaturation.

More recently a new kind of precipitation has been experimentally discovered: *homogeneous precipitation* (table 10). With a model in the same spirit, CAUVIN and MARTIN [1981] have been able to show that the recombination term in the defect balance equations can render a concentration fluctuation unstable without benefit of any sink. The driving force for segregation is also the flux-coupling mechanism between defects and solute. The observed results are well described by this model, once more with the exception of the low-temperature borderline (CAUVIN [1981]).

Irradiation-induced segregation and phase transformations are further discussed in ch. 17, §4.4.

References

ABLITZER, D., 1977, Phil. Mag. **36**, 391.

ABLITZER, D., and A. VIGNES, 1978, J. Nucl. Mater. **69–70**, 97.

* ABRAGAM, A., 1961, The principles of nuclear magnetism (University Press, Oxford).

ACHAR, B.N.N., 1970, Phys. Rev. **B2**, 3848.

ADAM, P., 1971, Z. Naturf. **26a**, 40.

* ADDA, Y., and J. PHILIBERT, 1966, La diffusion dans les solides (Presses Universitaires de France, Paris).

ADDA, Y., M. BEYELER and G. BRÉBEC, 1975, Thin Solid Films **25**, 107.

AIFANTIS, E.C., 1979, Acta Metall. **27**, 683.

AIT SALEM, M., T. SPRINGER, A. HEIDEMANN and B. ALEFELD, 1979, Phil. Mag. **A39**, 797.

ALEFELD, G., J. VÖLK and G. SCHAUMANN, 1970, Phys. Stat. Sol. **37**, 337.

ALLNATT, A.R., 1981, J. Phys. **C14**, 5453, 5467.

ANTHONY, T.R., 1971, Impurity Currents Generated by Vacancy Currents in metals, in: Proc. Conf.

Atomic transport in Solids and Liquids, Marstrand (1970), eds. A. Lodding and T. Lagerwall (Zeitschrift für Naturforschung, Tübingen) p. 138.

ANTHONY, T.R., 1972, Solute Segregation and Stresses Generated around Growing Voids in Metals, in: Conf-71060, Proc. Conf. Radiation-induced Voids in Metals, Albany (1971), eds. J.W. Corbett and L.C. Ianniello (USAEC, Oak Ridge) p. 630.

ANTHONY, T.R., 1975, Atom Currents Generated by Vacancy Winds, in: Diffusion in Solids, Recent Developments, eds. A.S. Nowick and J.J. Burton (Academic, New York) p. 353.

ARNHOLD, V., 1981, Inaugural dissertation, Münster.

ASKILL, J., 1971, Phys. Stat. Sol. **8**, 587.

AYRAULT, G., and G. EHRLICH, 1974, J. Chem. Phys. **60**, 281.

BAKKER, H., 1971, Phys. Stat. Sol. **44**, 369.

BALANZAT, M., and J. HILLAIRET, 1980, The Zener relaxation: A Convenient Tool to Study Vacancy Sources and Sinks in a Metal Lattice, in: Proc. Conf. Internal Friction and Ultrasonic Attenuation in Solids, Manchester (1980), ed. C.C. Smith (Pergamon Press, New York) p. 123.

BALLUFFI, R.W., 1960, Acta Metall. **8**, 871.

BALLUFFI, R.W., and J.W. CAHN, 1981, Acta Metall. **29**, 493.

BALLUFFI, R.W., T. KWOK, P.D. BRISTOWE, A. BROKMAN, P.S. HO and S. YIP, 1981, Scripta Metall. **15**, 951.

BARBU, A., 1978, Thèse, Univ. Nancy.

BARBU, A., 1980, Acta Metall. **28**, 499.

BARBU, A., and G. MARTIN, 1977, Scripta Metall. **11**, 771.

BARDEEN, J., and C. HERRING, 1951, Diffusion in Alloys and the Kirkendall Effect, in: Atom Movements, ed. J.H. Hollomon (ASM, Cleveland, OH) p. 87.

BASSETT, D.W., and P.R. WEBBER, 1978, Surf. Sci. **70**, 520.

BEAMAN, D.R., and R.W. BALLUFFI, 1965, Phys. Rev. **137**, 917.

BEAMAN, D.R., R.W. BALLUFFI and R.O. SIMMONS, 1964, Phys. Rev. **A134**, 532.

BENNETT, C.H., 1975, Exact Defect Calculations in Model Substances, in: Diffusion in Solids, Recent Developments, eds. A.S. Nowick and J.J. Burton (Academic, New York) p. 73.

BENOIST, P., and G. MARTIN, 1975a, Thin Solid Films **25**, 181.

BENOIST, P., and G. MARTIN, 1975b, J. Physique. Colloq. **C4**, 213.

BENOIST, P., J.L. BOCQUET and P. LAFORE, 1977, Acta Metall. **25**, 265.

BERENBAUM, L., and R. ROSENBERG, 1969, Thin Solid Films **4**, 187.

BERNARDINI, J., and G. MARTIN, 1976, Scripta Metall. **10**, 833.

BERRY, B.S., and J.L. OREHOTSKY, 1968, Acta Metall. **16**, 683.

BEYELER, M., and Y. ADDA, 1968, J. Physique **29**, 345.

BHARATI, S., and A.P.B. SINHA, 1977, Phys. Stat. Sol. (a) **44**, 391.

BLOEMBERGEN, N., E.M. PURCELL and R.V. POUND, 1948, Phys. Rev. **73**, 679.

BOCQUET, J.L., 1972, Acta Metall. **20**, 1347.

BOCQUET, J.L., 1973, Thèse, Univ. Paris-Sud.

BOCQUET, J.L., 1974, Acta Metall. **22**, 1.

BOCQUET, J.L., 1981, CEA (Saclay, France) Internal Report, R-5112.

BOCQUET, J.L., 1983, J. Phys. **F13**, L33.

BOCQUET, J.L., and G. MARTIN, 1979, J. Nucl. Mater. **83**, 186.

BONDY, A., P. REGNIER and V. LEVY, 1971, Scripta Metall. **5**, 345.

BONZEL, H.P., 1976, CRC Crit. Rev. Solid State Sci. **6**, 171.

BONZEL, H.P., and E.E. LATTA, 1978, Surf. Sci. **76**, 275.

BOSE, A., G. FROHBERG and H. WEVER, 1979, Phys. Stat. Sol. (a) **52**, 509.

BOSVIEUX, C., and J. FRIEDEL, 1962, J. Phys. Chem. Solids **23**, 12.

BRAGG, W.L., and E.J. WILLIAMS, 1934, Proc. Roy. Soc. **A145**, 699.

BRÉBEC, G., 1978, Diffusion Atomique, in: Defauts Ponctuels dans les Solides (Les Editions de Physique, Orsay) p. 181.

BREITLING, H.M., and R.F. HUMMEL, 1972, J. Phys. Chem. Solids **33**, 845.

BRINKMAN, J.A., 1954, Phys. Rev. **93**, 345.

Brünger, G., O. Kanert and D. Wolf, 1980, Solid State Commun. **33**, 569.

Burton, B., 1982, The Interaction of Oxidation with Creep Processes, in: Single Crystal Properties, vol. B1, ed. D.J. Fisher (Trans. Tech. S.A., Rockport) p. 1.

Burton, M.K., N. Cabrera and F.C. Frank, 1951, Phil. Trans. Roy. Soc. **A243**, 299.

Butrymowicz, D.B., and J.R. Manning, 1978, Metallurg. Trans. **9A**, 947.

Cahn, J.W., 1967, Trans. AIME **242**, 166.

Cahn, J.W., and R.W. Balluffi, 1979, Scripta Metall. **13**, 499.

Caplain, A., and W. Chambron, 1977, Acta Metall. **25**, 1001.

Carlson, O.N., and F.A. Schmidt, 1981, J. Less-Common Met. **79**, 97.

Carlson, P.T., 1976, Metallurg. Trans. **7A**, 199.

Carlson, P.T., 1978, Metallurg. Trans. **9A**, 1287.

* Carslaw, H.S., and J.C. Jaeger, 1959, Conduction of Heat in Solids (Clarendon Press, Oxford).

Cauvin, R., 1981, Thèse, Univ. Nancy.

Cauvin, R., and G. Martin, 1981, Phys. Rev. **B23**, 3332.

Chabik, St., and B. Rozenfeld, 1981, Appl. Phys. **25**, 143.

Chambron, W., and A. Caplain, 1974, Acta Metall. **22**, 357.

Choi, J.Y., and P.G. Shewmon, 1962, Trans. Met. Soc. AIME **224**, 589.

Chu, W.K., J.W. Mayer and M.A. Nicolet, 1978, Backscattering Spectrometry (Academic, New York).

Ciccotti, G., M. Guillope and V. Pontikis, 1982, Grain-Boundary Structure and Diffusion: a Molecular Dynamics Simulation, in: Proc. Conf. Diffusion in Metals and Alloys, Tihany (Hungary), ed. F.J. Kedves (Kossuth Univ., Debrecen, Hungary).

Compaan, K., and Y. Haven, 1956, Trans. Farad. Soc. **52**, 786.

Compaan, K., and Y. Haven, 1958, Trans. Farad. Soc. **54**, 1498.

Cook, H.E., and J.E. Hilliard, 1969, J. Appl. Phys. **40**, 2191.

Cornet, J.F., and D. Calais, 1972, J. Phys. Chem. Solids **33**, 1675.

Coste, V., P. Benoist and G. Martin, 1976, Calcul de la Fréquence Moyenne de Saut des Atomes le long de Joints de Grains à Structure Périodique, in: Proc. 19ème Colloque Métall., La Diffusion dans les Milieux Condensés, Théories et Applications, Saclay 1976 (INSTN, Saclay, France) p. 507.

Cousty, J., 1981. Thèse, Univ. Paris-Sud; Internal Report CEA-R-5143 (Saclay).

Cousty, J., R. Peix and B. Perraillon, 1981, Surf. Sci. **107**, 586.

Cowan, P., and T.T. Tsong, 1975, Phys. Lett. **53A**, 383.

Cowley, J.M., 1950, Phys. Rev. **77**, 669.

* Crank, J., 1956. The Mathematics of Diffusion (Clarendon Press, Oxford).

Crolet, J.L., 1971, Thèse, Univ. Paris-Sud.

Dafano, A., and G. Jacucci, 1977, Phys. Rev. Lett. **39**, 950.

Dallwitz, M.J., 1972, Acta Metall. **20**, 1229.

Damköhler, R., and Th. Heumann, 1982, Phys. Stat. Sol. (a) **73**, 117.

Darken, L.S., 1948, Trans. AIME **175**, 184.

Dayananda, M.A., 1981, Acta Metall. **29**, 1151.

De Bruin, H.J., G.E. Murch, A. Bakker and L.P. Van der Mey, 1975, Thin Solid Films **25**, 47.

Decker, D.L., J.D. Weiss and H.B. Vanfleet, 1977, Phys. Rev. **B16**, 2392.

* De Groot, S.R., and P. Mazur, 1969, Non-Equilibrium Thermodynamics (North-Holland, Amsterdam).

De Lorenzi, G., G. Jacucci and V. Pontikis, 1982, Surf. Sci. **166**, 391.

Desjonqueres, M.C., and D. Spanjaard, 1982, J. Phys. **C15**, 4007.

D'Heurle, F.M., 1971, Proc. IEEE **59**, 1409.

D'Heurle, F.M., and A. Gangulee, 1972, Solute effects on Grain Boundaries, Electromigration and Diffusion, in: The Nature and Behaviour of Grain Boundaries, ed. H. Hu (Plenum, New York).

Dirkes, H., and Th. Heumann, 1982, J. Phys. **F12**, L 67.

Doan, N.V., 1971, Thèse, Univ. Paris-Sud.

Doan, N.V., 1972, J. Phys. Chem. Solids **33**, 2161.

Doan, N.V., 1978, Dynamique Moléculaire, in: Defauts Ponctuels dans les Solides (Les Editions de Physique, Orsay) p. 285.

DOAN, N.V., and J.L. BOCQUET, 1975, Thin Solid Films **25**, 15.

DOAN, N.V., J.L. BOCQUET and Y. LIMOGE, 1976, Diffusion sous Champ Électrique et Gradient de Température, in: Proc. 19ème Colloque Métall., La Diffusion dans les Milieux Condensés, Théories et Applications, Saclay 1976 (INSTN, Saclay, France) p. 911.

DOMIAN, H.A., and H.I. AARONSON, 1965, Simultaneous Diffusion of Silver and Magnesium in Stoichiometric Monocrystalline β-AgMg, in: Diffusion in Body-Centered Cubic Metals (ASM, Cleveland, OH) p. 209.

DONALDSON, A.T., and R.D. RAWLINGS, 1976, Acta Metall. **24**, 285.

DORAN, D.G., 1970, Rad. Eff. **2**, 249.

DUCASTELLE, F., 1978, Electronic Structure and Equilibrium Properties of Metals and Alloys, in: Solid State Phase Transformations in Metals and Alloys, Aussois, 1978 (Les Editions de Physique, Orsay) p. 51.

ECKSELER, H., and C. HERZIG, 1978, Phys. Stat. Sol. (b) **85**, 185.

EDELIN, G., 1979, Acta Metall. **27**, 455.

* EHRLICH, G., and K. STOLT, 1980, Ann. Rev. Phys. Chem. **31**, 603.

EINSTEIN, A., 1905, Ann. Phys. **17**, 549.

ELCOCK, E.W., 1959, Proc. Roy. Soc. (London) **73A**, 250.

ELDRIDGE, J., and K.L. KOMAREK, 1964, Trans. AIME **230**, 226.

ENGELMANN, C., 1977. Analyse par Observation Directe des Réactions Nucléaires. Rétrodiffusion de Particles Chargées, in: Les techniques de l'Ingénieur, ed. C. Engelmann, p. 2561.

ERCKMANN, V. and H. WIPF, 1976, Phys. Rev. **37**, 341.

ERMERT, U., W. RUPP and R. SIZMANN, 1968, Thermal and Radiation-Enhanced Self-Diffusion in Gold Single Crystals at low Temperature, in: Proc. Int. Conf. Vacancies and interstitials in metals, Jülich 1968 (KFA Jülich) p. 30.

FARRARO, R., and R.B. MCLELLAN, 1979, Mat. Sci. Eng. **39**, 47.

FEIT, M.D., 1972, Phys. Rev. **B5**, 2145.

FIKS, V.B., 1959, Fiz. Tverd. Tela **1**, 16.

FIKS, V.B., 1961, Sov. Phys. Solid. State **3**, 724.

FIKS, V.B., 1973, Fiz. Metall. Metalloved. **36**, 253.

FILLON, J., and D. CALAIS, 1977, J. Phys. Chem. Solids **38**, 81.

FISHER, J.C., 1951, J. Appl. Phys. **22**, 74.

FLAHIVE, P.G., and W.R. GRAHAM, 1980, Surf. Sci. **91**, 449.

FLINN, P.A., 1980, Diffusion in Solids and Liquids, in: Application of Mössbauer Spectroscopy VII, ed. R.L. Cohen (Academic, New York) p. 393.

FLYNN, C.P., 1968, Phys. Rev. **171**, 682.

* FLYNN, C.P., 1972, Point Defects and Diffusion (Clarendon Press, Oxford) p. 306.

FRADIN, F.Y., and T.J. ROWLAND, 1967, Appl. Phys. Lett. **11**, 207.

FRANK, F.C., and D. TURNBULL, 1956, Phys. Rev. **104**, 617.

FROHBERG, G., 1971, Habilitationsschrift, Berlin, p. 132.

GERL, M., 1967, J. Phys. Chem. Solids **28**, 725.

GERL, M., 1968, Thèse, Orsay.

GERL, M., and M. LANNOO, 1978, Structure Electronique, in: Defauts Ponctuels dans Les Solides (Les Editions de Physique, Orsay) p. 29.

GHALEB, D., 1983, Thèse, Univ. Paris-Sud.

GIBBS, G.B., D. GRAHAM and D.H. TOMLIN, 1963, Phil. Mag. **8**, 1269.

GILDER, H.M., and D. LAZARUS, 1966, Phys. Rev. **145**, 507.

GILDER, M., and D. LAZARUS, 1975, Phys. Rev. **B11**, 4916.

GILLAN, M.J., 1977, J. Phys. **C10**, 1641.

GIRIFALCO, L.A., 1964, J. Phys. Chem. Solids **24**, 323.

GIRIFALCO, L.A., and H. HERMAN, 1965, Acta Metall. **13**, 583.

GISSLER, W., 1972, Ber. Bunsen Gesell. **76**, 770.

GONZALES, R., J. PIQUERAS and L.I. BRU, 1975a, Phys. Stat. Sol. **29**, 161.

GONZALES, R., J. PIQUERAS and L.I. BRU, 1975b, Mat. Sci. Eng. **20**, 95.

GORSKY, W.S., 1935, Z. Phys. der Sowjetunion **8**, 457.

GRAF, H., G. BALZER, E. RECKNAGEL, A. WEIDINGER and R.I. GRYNSZPAN, 1980, Phys. Rev. Lett. **44**, 1333.

GRAHAM, W.R., and G. EHRLICH, 1974, Surf. Sci. **45**, 530.

GRAHAM, W.R., and G. EHRLICH, 1975, Thin Solid Films **25**, 85.

GUINIER, A., 1959, Adv. Solid State Phys. **9**, 293.

GUPTA, D., 1975, Thin Solid Films **25**, 231.

GUPTA, D., and D.S. LIEBERMAN, 1971, Phys. Rev. **B4**, 1070.

GUPTA, D., D. LAZARUS and D.S. LIEBERMAN, 1967, Phys. Rev. **153**, 863.

GUPTA, R.P., 1982, Phys. Rev. **B25**, 5188.

HÄSSNER, A., and W. LANGE, 1965, Phys. Stat. Sol. **8**, 77.

HAESSNER, F., S. HOFMANN and H. SECKEL, 1974, Scripta Metall. **8**, 299.

HALBWACHS, M., and J. HILLAIRET, 1978, Phys. Rev. **B18**, 4927.

HALBWACHS, M., J. HILLAIRET and S.R. COST, 1978a, J. Nucl. Mater. **69–70**, 776.

HALBWACHS, M., J.T. STANLEY and J. HILLAIRET, 1978b, Phys. Rev. **B18**, 4938.

HALICIOGLU, T., and G.M. POUND, 1979, Thin Solid Films **57**, 241.

HANCOCK, G.F., and B.R. MCDONNELL, 1971, Phys. Stat. Sol. (a) **4**, 143.

HARRISON, L.G., 1961, Trans. Farad. Soc. **57**, 1191.

HART, E.W., 1957, Acta Metall. **5**, 597.

HEHENKAMP, T., 1981, Microchim. Acta Suppl. **9**, 15.

HERZIG, C., H.J. ROCKOSCH and R. HILGEDIECK, 1982, Isotope Effect Measurements for Impurity Diffusion in Copper, Silver and Gold, in: Proc. Conf. Diffusion in Metals and Alloys, Tihany (Hungary), ed. F.J. Kedves (Kossuth Univ., Debrecen, Hungary).

HEUMANN, Th., 1979, J. Phys. **F9**, 1997.

HEUMANN, Th., and Th. ROTTWINKEL, 1978, J. Nucl. Mater. **69–70**, 567.

HILGEDIECK, R., 1981, Inaugural dissertation, Münster.

HILL, J.M., 1979, Scripta Metall. **13**, 1027.

HIRANO, K., 1981, Jump Frequency Analysis on Impurity Diffusion in Cu Based on New Data, in: Proc. Yamada Conf. V. – Point Defects and Defect Interactions in Metals, Kyoto (Japan), eds. J.I. Takamura, M. Doyama and M. Kiritani (Univ. of Tokyo Press, 1982) p. 541.

HIRANO, K., R.P. AGARWALA, B.L. AVERBACH and M. COHEN, 1962, J. Appl. Phys. **33**, 3049.

HO, K., and R.A. DODD, 1978, Scripta Metall. **12**, 1055.

HO, K., M.A. QUADER, F. LIN and R.A. DODD, 1977, Scripta Metall. **11**, 1159.

HOSHINO, K., Y. IIJIMA and K. HIRANO, 1981a, Phil. Mag. **A44**, 961.

HOSHINO, K., Y. IIJIMA and K. HIRANO, 1981b, Isotope Effect and Diffusion of Cadmium in Copper, in: Proc. Yamada Conf. V – Point Defects and Defects Interactions in Metals, Kyoto (Japan), eds. J.I. Takamura, M. Doyama and M. Kiritani (Univ. of Tokyo Press, 1982) p. 562.

HOSHINO, K., Y. IIJIMA and K. HIRANO, 1982, Acta Metall. **30**, 265.

HOWARD, R.E., 1966, Phys. Rev. **144**, 650.

HOWARD, R.E., and A.B. LIDIARD, 1963, J. Phys. Soc. Jap. **18**, Suppl. II, 197.

* HOWARD, R.E., and A.B. LIDIARD, 1964, Rep. Prog. Phys. **27**, 161.

HOWARD, R.E., and J.R. MANNING, 1967, Phys. Rev. **154**, 561.

HUNTINGTON, H.B., 1966, Bull. Am. Phys. Soc. **11**, 265.

HUNTINGTON, H.B., 1968, J. Phys. Chem. Solids **29**, 1641.

HUNTINGTON, H.B., 1973, Electro- and thermomigration in metals, in: Diffusion, Proc. ASM Conf., Cleveland 1972 (ASM, Cleveland, OH).

HUNTINGTON, H.B., and A.R. GRÖNE, 1961, J. Phys. Chem. Solids **20**, 76.

HUNTINGTON, H.B., and S.C. HO, 1963, J. Phys. Soc. Jap. **18**, Suppl. II, 20.

HUNTINGTON, H.B., N.C. MILLER and V. NERSES, 1961, Acta Metall. **9**, 749.

IORIO, N.R., M.A. DAYANANDA and R.E. GRACE, 1973, Metallurg. Trans. **4**, 1339.

JANOT, C., 1976, J. Physique **37**, 253.

JOB, B., J. MATHIE and P. REGNIER, 1974, Acta Metall. **22**, 1197.

JOHNSON, R.A., and N.Q. LAM, 1976, Phys. Rev. **B13**, 4364.

JONES, M.J., and A.D. LE CLAIRE, 1972, Phil. Mag. **26**, 1191.

JUVÉ-DUC, D., D. TREHEUX and P. GUIRALDENQ, 1980, Mat. Sci. Eng. **42**, 281.

KAUR, R., and S. PRAKASH, 1982, J. Phys. **F12**, 1383.

KEHR, K.W., 1978, Theory of the Diffusion of Hydrogen in Metals, in: Hydrogen in Metals, eds. G. Alefeld and J. Völkl (Springer, Berlin) vol. 1, p. 197.

KELLY, A., and C. CHIOU, 1958, Acta Metall. **6**, 565.

KING, R.T., and W.W. MULLINS, 1962, Acta Metall. **10**, 601.

KRIVOGLAZ, M.A., 1969, Phys. Met. and Metallogr. **28**, 1.

KRONMÜLLER, H., 1978, Magnetic After-Effects, in: Hydrogen in Metals, eds. C. Alefeld and J. Völkl (Springer, Berlin) vol. 1, p. 289.

KUMAR, P., and R.S. SORBELLO, 1975, Thin Solid Films **25**, 25.

KUPER, A.B., D. LAZARUS, J.R. MANNING and C.T. TOMIZUKA, 1956, Phys. Rev. **104**, 1536.

KURTZ, A.D., B.L. AVERBACH and M. COHEN, 1955, Acta Metall. **3**, 442.

KUSUNOKI, K., K. TSUMURAYA and S. NISHIKAWA, 1981, Trans. Japan. Inst. Met. **22**, 501.

KWOK, J., P.S. HO, S. YIP, R.W. BALLUFFI, P.D. BRISTOWE and A. BROKMAN, 1981, Phys. Rev. Lett. **47**, 1148.

LAM, N.Q., N.V. DOAN, L. DAGENS and Y. ADDA, 1981, J. Phys. **F11**, 2231.

LANORE, J.M., 1974, Rad. Eff. **22**, 153.

LAZARUS, D., 1960, Solid State Phys. **10**, 71.

LEAMY, H.J., and G.H. GILMER, 1974, J. Cryst. Growth 24/25, 499.

LE CLAIRE, A.D., 1951, Phil. Mag. **42**, 673.

LE CLAIRE, A.D., 1954, Phys. Rev. **93**, 344.

LE CLAIRE, A.D., 1958, Phil. Mag. **3**, 921.

LE CLAIRE, A.D., 1963, Brit. J. Appl. Phys. **14**, 351.

LE CLAIRE, A.D., 1966, Phil. Mag. **14**, 1271.

LE CLAIRE, A.D., 1970a, Correlation Effects in Diffusion in Solids, in: Physical Chemistry, an Advanced Treatise, eds. H. Eyring, D. Henderson and W. Jost (Academic, New York) vol. 10, ch. 5.

LE CLAIRE, A.D., 1970b, Phil. Mag. **21**, 819.

LE CLAIRE, A.D., 1976, Le Point Actuel sur la Théorie de la Diffusion, Anomalies de Diffusion, in: Proc. 19ème Colloque Métall., La Diffusion dans les Milieux Condensés, Théories et Applications, Saclay, 1976 (INSTN, Saclay, France).

LE CLAIRE, A.D., 1978, J. Nucl. Mater. **69–70**, 70.

LE CLAIRE, A.D., and A.B. LIDIARD, 1956, Phil. Mag. **1**, 518.

LE CLAIRE, A.D., and W.M. LOMER, 1954, Acta Metall. **2**, 731.

LE CLAIRE, A.D., and A. RABINOVITCH, 1981, J. Phys. **C14**, 3863.

LEVASSEUR, J., and J. PHILIBERT, 1967, C.R. Acad. Sci. Paris **264**, Sér. C, 277.

LEVINE, H.S., and C.J. MacCALLUM, 1960, J. Appl. Phys. **31**, 595.

LIDIARD, A.B., 1981, The Kinetics of Atomic Transport in Crystals. Report AERE-TP 909, Harwell.

LIMOGE, Y., 1976a, Thèse, Univ. Paris-Sud.

LIMOGE, Y., 1976b, Electromigration dans l'Aluminium, in: Proc. 19ème Colloque de Métall., La Diffusion dans les Milieux Condensés, Théories et Applications, Saclay, 1976 (INSTN, Saclay, France) p. 971.

LOMER, W.M., 1954, AERE Report T/R 1540.

LORMAND, G., 1970, Thèse, Lyon.

LUNDY, T.S., and J.F. MURDOCK, 1962, J. Appl. Phys. **33**, 1671.

LYNN, K.G., and D.O. WELCH, 1980, Phys. Rev. **B22**, 99.

MALLARD, W.C., A.B. GARDNER, R.F. BASS and L.M. SLIFKIN, 1963, Phys. Rev. **129**, 617.

MANNING, J.R., 1964, Phys. Rev. **136**, A 1758.

* MANNING, J.R., 1968, Diffusion Kinetics for Atoms in Crystals (Van Nostrand, Princeton).

MANNING, J.R., 1971, Phys. Rev. **B4**, 111.

MARECHE, J.F., J.C. RAT and H. HEROLD, 1979, Z. Phys. Chem. Neue Folge **115**, 137.

MARTIN, G., 1972, Phys. Stat. Sol. **14**, 183.

MARTIN, G., and P. BENOIST, 1977, Scripta Metall. **11**, 503.

MARTIN, G., and B. PERRAILLON, 1979, Measurements of Grain Boundaries Diffusion, in: Grain Boundary Structure and Kinetics, ASM Materials Science Seminar 1979 (ASM, Metals Park, OH) p. 239.

MATANO, C., 1933, Jap. J. Phys. **8**, 109.

MATHUNI, J., O.N. CARLSON, E. FROMM and R. KIRCHHEIM, 1976, Metallurg. Trans. **7A**, 977.

MATHUNI, J., R. KIRCHHEIM and E. FROMM, 1979, Acta Metall. **27**, 1665.

MATLOCK, J.H., and J.P. STARK, 1971, Acta Metall. **19**, 923.

MC COMBIE, C.W., and E.W. ELCOCK, 1958, Phys. Rev. **B2**, 1451.

MCKEE, R.A., and J.P. STARK, 1975, Acta Metall. **23**, 1145.

MC VAY, G.L., and A.R. DUCHARME, 1974, Phys. Rev. **B9**, 627.

MELIUS, C.F., and W.D. WILSON, 1980, Rad. Eff. **53**, 111.

MEYER, R.O., 1969, Phys. Rev. **181**, 1086.

MILLER, J.W., 1969, Phys. Rev. **181**, 1095.

MILLION, B., and J. KUČERA, 1969, Acta Metall. **17**, 339.

MILLION, B., and J. KUČERA, 1971, Czech. J. Phys. **B21**, 161.

MONMA, K., H. SUTO and H. OIKAWA, 1964, J. Japan. Inst. Met. **128**, 188.

MONTY, C., 1972, Thèse, Univ. Paris-Sud.

MULLEN, J.G., 1961, Phys. Rev. **124**, 1723.

MULLINS, W.W., and P.G. SHEWMON, 1959, Acta Metall. **7**, 163.

MUNDY, J.N., and W.D. MCFALL, 1973, Phys. Rev. **B7**, 4363.

* MÜNSTER, A., 1966, Thermodynamique des Processus Irréversibles (Presses Universitaires de France, Paris).

NACHTRIEB, N.H., and G.S. HANDLER, 1954, Acta Metall. **2**, 797.

NÉEL, L., 1951, J. Phys. Rad. **12**, 339.

NÉEL, L., 1952, J. Phys. Rad. **13**, 249.

NÉEL, L., 1954, J. Phys. Rad. **14**, 225.

NEUMAN, G. and W. HIRSCHWALD, 1972, Z. Phys. Chem. Neue Folge **Bd.8**, 515.

NEUMANN, C.H., D. LAZARUS and D.B. FITCHEN, 1961, J. Phys. Chem. Solids **20**, 170.

NEUMANN, J.P., 1980, Acta Metall. **28**, 1165.

NICHOLS, F.A., and W.W. MULLINS, 1965a, J. Appl. Phys. **36**, 1826.

NICHOLS, F.A., and W.W. MULLINS, 1965b, Trans. AIME **233**, 1840.

NOWICK, A.S., 1952, Phys. Rev. **88**, 925.

* NOWICK, A.S. and B.S. BERRY, 1972, Anelastic Relaxation in Crystalline Solids (Academic, New York).

OKAMOTO, P.R., and H. WIEDERSICH, 1974, J. Nucl. Mater. **53**, 336.

ORIANI, R.A., 1969, J. Phys. Chem. Solids **30**, 339.

PARIS, D., and P. LESBATS, 1975, Scripta Metall. **9**, 1373.

PARIS, D., and P. LESBATS, 1978, J. Nucl. Mater. **69–70**, 628.

PÉRINET, F., 1975, Rapport CEA-4657, Saclay.

PENISSON, J.M., and A. BOURRET, 1975, Mise en Ordre de l'Alliage Fe–Ni, in: Proc. 4th Int. Conf. on High-Voltage Electron Microscopy, Toulouse (1975), eds. B. Jouffrey and P. Favard (Sté Française de Microscopie Electronique, Paris) p. 205.

PERRAILLON, B., I.M. TORRENS and V. LEVY, 1972, Scripta Metall. **6**, 611.

PETERSON, D.T., 1977, Electromigration as a Purification Process, in: Electro- and Thermotransport in Alloys, eds. R.E. Hummel and H.B. Huntington (AIME, New York) p. 54.

PETERSON, D.T., and M.F. SMITH, 1982, Metallurg. Trans. **13A**, 821.

PETERSON, N.L., 1975, Isotope Effects in Diffusion, in: Diffusion in Solids, Recent Developments, eds. A.S. Nowick and J.J. Burton (Academic, London) p. 115.

PETERSON, N.L., 1978, J. Nucl. Mater. **69–70**, 3: Proc. Int. Conf. on the Properties of Atomic Defects in Metals, Argonne (1976), eds. N.L. Peterson and R.W. Siegel.

PETERSON, N.L., and S.J. ROTHMAN, 1970, Phys. Rev. **B1**, 3264.

PETERSON, N.L., and S.J. ROTHMAN, 1971, Diffusion and Correlation Effects in Copper–Zinc Alloys, in: Proc. Conf. Atomic Transport in Solids and Liquids, Marstrand (1970), eds. A. Looding and T. Lagerwall (Zeitschrift für Naturforschung, Tübingen) p. 248.

PHILIBERT, J., 1976, Techniques Actuelles de l'Etude de la Diffusion en Volume, in: Proc. 19ème Colloque de Métall., La Diffusion dans les Milieux Condensés, Théories et Applications, Saclay, 1976 (INSTN, Saclay, France) p. 255.

PIKE, G.E., W.J. CAMP, C.H. SEAGER and G.L. McVAY, 1974, Phys. Rev. **B10**, 4909.

PONTAU, A.E., and D. LAZARUS, 1979, Phys. Rev. **B19**, 4027.

* PRATT, J.N., and R.G.R. SELLORS, 1973, Electrotransport in Metals and Alloys, in: Diffusion and Defect Monograph Series, ed. F.H. Wöhlbier (Trans. Tech. Publications, Aedermannsdorf, Switzerland).

* PRIGOGINE, I., 1947, Etude Thermodynamique des Phénomènes Irréversibles (Desoer, Liège).

RADELAAR, S., 1966, J. Phys. Chem. Solids **27**, 1375.

RADELAAR, S., 1968, Phys. Stat. Sol. **27**, K63.

RADELAAR, S., 1970, J. Phys. Chem. Solids **31**, 219.

REGNIER, P., and M. HALBWACHS, 1980, Electron Microsc. **4**, 204.

REINHOLD, U., A. NEIDHARDT, G. KRAUTHEIM and A. ZEHE, 1980, Phys. Stat. Sol (a) **61**, K13.

RESING, H.A., and N.H. NACHTRIEB, 1961, J. Phys. Chem. Solids **21**, 40.

REYNOLDS, J.E., B.L. AVERBACH and M. COHEN, 1957, Acta Metall. **5**, 29.

RHEAD, G.E., 1975, Surf. Sci. **47**, 207.

RIMBEY, P.R., and R.S. SORBELLO, 1980, Phys. Rev. **B21**, 2150.

RIVIÈRE, J.P., and J. GRILHÉ, 1974, Phys. Stat. Sol. (a) **25**, 429.

ROBINSON, J.T., and N.L. PETERSON, 1972, Surf. Sci. **31**, 586.

ROBROCK, K.H., 1981, Mechanical Relaxation Studies of Point Defects in Metals, in: Internal Friction and Ultrasonic Attenuation in Solids, Lausanne (1981), J. Physique **C5**, 709.

ROSENBLUM, M.P., F. SPAEPEN and D. TURNBULL, 1980, Appl. Phys. Lett. **37**, 184.

ROTHMAN, S.J., 1981, Effects of Irradiation on Diffusion in Metals and Alloys, in: Phase transformations and Solute Redistribution in Alloys during Irradiation, ed. F.V. Nolfi Jr. (Applied Science Publishers, Barking, UK).

ROTHMAN, S.J., and N.L. PETERSON, 1967, Phys. Rev. **154**, 552.

ROULET, C., 1973, Surf. Sci. **36**, 295.

RUOFF, A.L., 1967, J. Appl. Phys. **38**, 3999.

RUOFF, A.L., and R.W. BALLUFFI, 1963, J. Appl. Phys. **34**, 2862.

SANCHEZ, J.M., and D. DE FONTAINE, 1975, Phys. Rev. Lett. **35**, 227.

SCHAICH, W.L., 1976, Phys. Rev. **B13**, 3350.

SCHILLING, W., 1978, J. Nucl. Mater. **69–70**, 465.

SCHILLING, W., 1981, Helium as Point Defect in Metals, in: Proc. Yamada Conf. V: Point Defects and Defect Interactions in Metals, Kyoto (Japan, 1981), to be published.

SCHMALZRIED, H., 1974, Solid State Reactions (Academic, New York) ch. 7.

SCHMATZ, D.J., H.A. DOMIAN and H.I. AARONSON, 1966, J. Appl. Phys. **37**, 1741.

SCHOTTKY, G., 1965, Phys. Stat. Sol. **8**, 357.

SEEGER, A., 1976, The Interpretation of Radiation Damage in Metals, in: Proc. Conf. Fundamental Aspects of Radiation Damage in Metals, Gatlinburg, USA (1975), eds. M.T. Robinson and F.W. Young Jr. (ERDA Report CONF-751006, Oak Ridge) vol. 1, p. 493.

SEEGER, A., and H. MEHRER, 1970, Analysis of Self-Diffusion and Equilibrium Measurements, in: Vacancies and Interstitials in Metals, eds. A. Seeger, D. Schumacher, W. Schilling and J. Diehl (North-Holland, Amsterdam) p. 1.

SEEGER, A., D. WOLF and H. MEHRER, 1971, Phys. Stat. Sol. (b) **48**, 481.

SERRUYS, Y., and G. BRÉBEC, 1982a, Phil. Mag. **A45**, 563.

SERRUYS, Y., and G. BRÉBEC, 1982b, Phil. Mag. **A46**, 661.

SHANKAR, S., and L.L. SEIGLE, 1978, Metallurg. Trans. **9A**, 1467.

SHIH, S., and J.P. STARK, 1978, Phys. Rev. **B18**, 711.

SINGWI, K.S., and A. SJÖLANDER, 1960a, Phys. Rev. **120**, 1093.

SINGWI, K.S., and A. SJÖLANDER, 1960b, Phys. Rev. **119**, 863.

SIZMANN, R., 1978, J. Nucl. Mater. **69–70**, 386.

SMIGELKAS, A.D., and E.O. KIRKENDALL, 1947, Trans. AIME **171**, 130.

SNOEK, J.L., 1939, Physica **6**, 591.

SOMENKOV, V.A., and S.S. SHIL'STEIN, 1979, Prog. Mater. Sci. 24, 267.

SORBELLO, R.S., 1972, Phys. Rev. **B6**, 4757.

SORBELLO, R.S., 1975, Comm. Solid State Phys. **6**, 117.

* SPRINGER, T., 1972, Quasi-elastic Neutron Scattering for the Investigation of Diffusive Motion in Solids and Liquids (Springer, Berlin).

STOLWIJK, N.A., 1981, Phys. Stat. Sol. (b) **105**, 223.

STOLWIJK, N.A., M. VAN GEND and H. BAKKER, 1980, Phil. Mag. **A42**, 783.

STONEHAM, A.M., 1979, Hyperfine Interactions **6**, 211.

SUZUOKA, T., 1961a, Trans. Japan Inst. Met. **2**, 25.

SUZUOKA, T., 1961b, Trans. Japan. Inst. Met. **2**, 176.

SUZUOKA, T., 1964, J. Phys. Soc. Jap. **18**, 839.

TANIGUCHI, S., 1955, Sci. Rep. Res. Inst. Tohoku Univ. **A7**, 269.

TEICHLER, H., 1979, Hyperfine Interactions **6**, 251.

THOMPSON, M.D., and H.B. HUNTINGTON, 1982, Surf. Sci. **116**, 522.

TORRENS, I.M., and M.T. ROBINSON, 1972, Computer Simulation of Atomic Displacement Cascades in Metals, in: Proc. Conf. Radiation-Induced Voids in Metals, Albany (1971), eds. J.W. Corbett and L.C. Ianello (USAEC, Oak Ridge) p. 739.

TORREY, H.C., 1954, Phys. Rev. **96**, 690.

TULLY, J.C., G.H. GILMER and M. SHUGARD, 1979, J. Chem. Phys. **71**, 1630.

TUNG, R.T., and W.R. GRAHAM, 1980, Surf. Sci. **97**, 73.

TURBAN, L., P. NOZIERES and M. GERL, 1976, J. Physique **37**, 159.

VAN DER EERDEN, J.P., P. BENNEMA and T.A. CHEREPANOVA, 1978, Prog. Cryst. Growth Charact. **1**, 219.

VANFLEET, H.B., 1980, Phys. Rev. **B21**, 4340.

VAN HOVE, L., 1954, Phys. Rev. **95**, 249.

VAN OMNEN, A.H., and J. DE MIRANDA, 1981, Phil. Mag. **A43**, 387.

VAROTSOS, P.A., 1978, J. Phys. **F8**, 1373.

VILLEMAIN, P., 1970, 3rd Cycle Thesis, Grenoble University.

VÖLKL, J., 1972, Ber. Bunsen Gesell. **76**, 797.

* VÖLKL, J. and G. ALEFELD, 1978, Diffusion of Hydrogen in Metals, in: Hydrogen in Metals, eds. G. Alefeld and J. Völkl (Springer, Berlin) vol. 1, p. 321.

WARBURTON, W.K., 1975, Phys. Rev. **B11**, 4945.

WARBURTON, W.K., and D. TURNBULL, 1975, Fast Diffusion in Metals, in: Diffusion in Solids – Recent Developments, eds. A.S. Nowick and J.J. Burton (Academic, New York) p. 171.

WELCH, D.O., and A.D. LE CLAIRE, 1967, Phil. Mag. **16**, 981.

WHIPPLE, R.T.P., 1954, Phil. Mag. **45**, 1225.

WILSON, W.D., and C.L. BISSON, 1973, Rad. Eff. **19**, 53.

WINTENBERGER, M., 1959, Acta Metall. **7**, 549.

WIRTZ, K., 1943, Z. Phys. **44**, 231.

WOLF, D., 1979, Spin Temperature and Nuclear Spin Relaxation in Matter (Clarendon Press, Oxford).

WOLF, D., 1980, J. Phys. Chem. Solids **41**, 1053.

WYNBLATT, P., and N.A. GJOSTEIN, 1968, Surf. Sci. **12**, 109.

ZENER, C., 1943, Trans. AIME **152**, 122.

ZENER, C., 1947, Phys. Rev. **71**, 34.

ZENER, C., 1951, J. Appl. Phys. **22**, 372.

Further reading

The references in the preceding list marked with an asterisk can also be used for general reading.

Diffusion data

All numerical results concerning diffusion are gathered in: Diffusion and Defect Data (DDD), eds. F.H. Wohlbier and D.J. Fisher (Trans. Tech. Publications, Aedermannsdorf, Switzerland), a review which appears three times a year.

General references

"Diffusion in Solids – Recent Developments", 1975, eds. A.S. Nowick and J.J. Burton, (Academic, New York).
Stark, J.P., 1976, Solid-State Diffusion (Wiley, New York).
Proc. Int. Conf. on Atomic Defects in Metals, Argonne (1976), eds. N.L. Peterson and R.W. Siegel, J. Nucl. Mater. 69–70 (1978).
Proc. Int. Conf. on Diffusion in Metals and Alloys, Tihany (Hungary), 1982, ed. F.J. Kedves (Kossuth University, Debrecen, Hungary), To be published.

Molecular Dynamics simulation and diffusion in liquids

Kushick, J., and B.J. Berne, 1977, Molecular Dynamics methods: Continuous Potentials, in: Statistical Mechanics, part B, modern Theoretical Chemistry 6, ed. B.J. Berne (Plenum, New York).
Hansen, J.P., and I.R. McDonald, 1976, Theory of Simple Liquids (Academic, London).

Diffusion under stresses and stress gradients

Larché, F.C., and J.W. Cahn, 1982, Acta Metall. **30**, 1835, and references therein.

Diffusion in thin films

Balluffi, R.W. and J.M. Blakely, 1975, Thin Solid Films **25**, 363.
Martin, G., and B. Perraillon, 1976, Diffusion dans les milieux limités, in: Proc. 19ème Colloque de Métall., La Diffusion dans les Milieux Condensés, Théories et Applications, Saclay 1976 (INSTN, Saclay, France) p. 367.

Precipitation under irradiation

Phase Stability under Irradiation, Proc. of the Fall Meeting of AIME, Pittsburgh (1980), eds. J.R. Holland, L.K. Mansur and D.I. Potter (The Metallurgical Society of AIME, Warrendale, 1981).
Phase transformations and Solute Redistribution in Alloys during Irradiation, ed. F.V. Nolfi, Jr. (Applied Science Publishers, Barking, UK).

CHAPTER 9

SOLIDIFICATION

H. BILONI

Laboratorio de Entrenamiento Multidisciplinario
para la Investigacion Tecnologica (LEMIT – CIC)
1900 La Plata, Argentina

R.W. Cahn and P. Haasen, eds.
Physical Metallurgy; third, revised and enlarged edition
© *Elsevier Science Publishers BV, 1983*

1.   Introduction

In this chapter we intend to give a general view of the formation of the solid from its melt. The phase transformation is generally driven by the extraction of heat from the melt and the first part of this chapter deals with heat flow during controlled solidification used to obtain single crystals, as well as with the more conventional metal–mould system. Then, the fundamentals of the freezing process are treated under the headings: (i) Nucleation; (ii) interface kinetics; (iii) solute distribution for a plane solid–liquid (S–L) interface; (iv) solid–liquid interface morphologies; (v) polyphase solidification. Following this, fluid flow and associated phenomena are discussed. The last portion of the chapter deals with the application of solidification principles to conventional and continuous casting, welding, manipulation of the structure on the basis of the fundamental concepts treated, and new processes developed as a consequence of the application of those concepts.

2.   Heat flow in solidification

In this section we present some of the concepts connected with heat flow in order to understand the fundamentals of the freezing process.

2.1.   Controlled solidification

Much of the understanding of solidification laws comes from unidirectional solidification experiments based on the simple principle that the extraction of latent heat must be achieved without allowing the melt to supercool sufficiently to permit nucleation of new crystals. In practice, this requires a heat sink that removes heat from the crystal and a heat source that supplies heat to the melt. The extensive use of this technique by CHALMERS and his school (CHALMERS [1971]) produced the basis of modern understanding in solidification. The basic heat flow objectives are to obtain a thermal gradient across the interface and to move it in such a way that the interface moves at a controlled rate. For a planar S–L interface, the heat balance is given by:

$$K_s G_s - K_1 G_1 = d_s L V, \tag{1}$$

where K_s is the thermal conductivity of the solid metal, K_1 the thermal conductivity of the liquid, G_s the temperature gradient in the solid at the S–L interface, G_1 the temperature gradient in the liquid, V the growth velocity, d_s the density of the solid metal and L the heat of fusion. If undercooled melts are not considered, the predicted maximum growth velocity occurs when $G_1 = 0$:

$$V_{max} = \frac{K_s G_s}{d_s L}. \tag{2}$$

For growth rates corresponding to single crystal growth (10^{-2}–10^{-4} cm/s) the thermal gradient in the solid can be described by the expression:

$$G_s = \left(\frac{2h}{rK_s}\right)^{1/2}(T_e - T_0) \tag{3}$$

where h is the heat transfer coefficient for heat loss to surroundings, r the radius of the crystal, T_e the equilibrium melting temperature of the metal and T_0 the ambient temperature.

2.2. Heat transfer in the metal–mould system

When hot metal is poured into a cold mould, the liquid superheat, specific heat and heat of fusion of the solidifying metal pass through different thermal resistances corresponding to the liquid, the solidifying metal, the metal–mould interface and the mould itself. On the other hand, in different parts of the metal–mould system the heat transfer occurs by conduction, Newtonian transfer, convection or radiation. Formal treatment of this problem presents considerable complexity, resulting in differential equations subject to nonlinear boundary conditions. Additional complexities appear for more complicated geometries, for the variation of the properties of the metal–mould system with temperature and for the behaviour of unstable S–L interfaces as is commonly found for alloys. Figure 1 shows schematically the thermal conditions for a simple geometry and a solidifying pure metal presenting a plane S–L interface.

It is important to know the solidification rate as well as the thermal profile in the metal–mould system. Considerable effort has been devoted to treating the problem analytically in order to develop reliable predictions for use in casting design. The mathematical approaches to this goal can be divided into exact analytical, approximate analytical and non-analytical solutions or methods. The exact analytical methods can be generalized but the principal restriction from a physical point of view is the need to assume a perfect thermal contact at the metal–mould interface. The approximate analytical solutions involve the imposition of a mathematical expression to derive a solution for the thickness, X, as a function of time, t. A finite value of the *heat-transfer coefficient at the metal–mould interface*, h_i, is considered, but in general these methods are limited to the case of perfectly chilled moulds. The non-analytical methods can be divided into graphic, numerical, analogical and digital. Each individual case has to be specified separately without any generalization (RUDDLE [1957]; JONES [1969]; CLYNE and GARCIA [1980]).

When the melt enters into contact with the mould walls at zero time, the mould surface is at ambient temperature and the liquid is at the melting point plus the superheat imposed on the melt. The thermal contact is not perfect and fig. 2a indicates the complex nature of the contact between metal and mould that influences the *thermal interfacial resistance*, R_i, and as a consequence the value of $h_i = 1/R_i$. When the mould surface is covered by a coating a *global interface thermal resistance*, R_{ig}, can be considered. R_{ig} takes into account the two interface thermal resistances (metal–coating and coating–mould, plus the thermal resistance of the coating

References: p. 573.

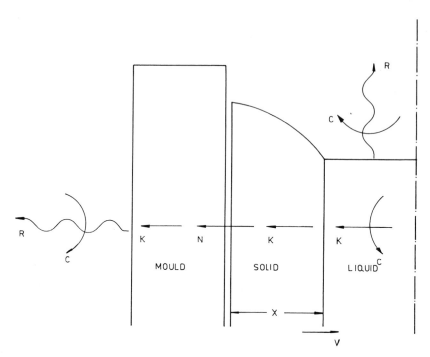

Fig. 1. Thermal conditions for a simple geometry of a solidifying pure metal. In the figure, K corresponds to heat transfer by conduction, N to Newtonian heat transfer, C to convectional heat transfer and R to heat transfer by radiation.

(BILONI [1977]). One must also keep in mind the air gap developed between the mould surface and the solidifying metal for $t > 0$ as a consequence of the liquid–solid transformation. As a consequence, the physical nature of the thermal contact can change from point to point and its efficiency depends on the characteristics of the system: wetting capacity of the melt, existence of oxides, grease, etc. upon the mould surface, mould surface microgeometry, etc. As a consequence, h_i can be considered an average macroscopic parameter (PRATES and BILONI [1972]). On this basis, fig. 2b corresponds to a Newtonian equivalent model wherein the heat flux across the interface is proportional to the temperature drop across the interface and the heat flow is given by

$$\dot{q} = h_i (T_{i,s} - T_{i,m}),$$ (4)

where $h_i = K_i/e$, e being the equivalent thickness of the metal–mould interface and K_i its thermal conductivity. An important point to keep in mind is that any measure of h_i corresponds to the *average value* represented by the equivalent model of fig. 2b but local values could be considerably different, as fig. 2a shows.

   If the thermal resistance of the liquid is not taken into account, the superposition of the thermal resistance of the solidified *metal* (R_s), the thermal resistance of the

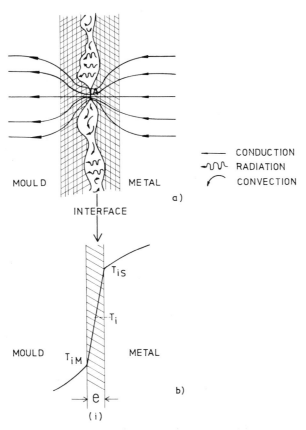

— CONDUCTION
RADIATION
CONVECTION

MOULD   METAL

a)

INTERFACE

MOULD   METAL

(i)   b)

Fig. 2. Nature of the thermal contact between the metal and the mould and equivalent Newtonian model of the metal–mould interface. (a) The complex nature of the contact and different types of heat transfer occurring at the interface are shown schematically. In point A a local good contact assures a higher heat conduction. As a consequence R_i will be lower and h_i higher than in the rest of the metal–mould interface. (b) The equivalent Newtonian model is based on an average value of R_i and h_i.

mould (R_m) and R_i will influence the solidification rate, as well as the structures and substructures obtained. Taking into account that at the beginning of the solidification process the only finite value is R_i, in those processes where the thickness of the solidifying sample is small, heat flow is controlled to significant extent by R_i. Permanent mould-casting, die-casting, splat-cooling and powder manufacturing processes can be included. Several authors have attempted to determine h_i in different processes and conditions. Although in fact some time variation $[h_i = f(t)]$ exists (JONES [1969]), in general h_i is considered constant. HILLS [1965] gives a summary of the h_i values measured or calculated by different authors in continuous casting mould. PRATES and BILONI [1972] used a fluidity test in order to determine h_i through an expression that takes into account the geometrical characteristics of the

References: p. 573.

test, the physical constants of the metal, the mean velocity of the liquid into the channel and the variation of the fluidity length with the liquid superheat. MEHRABIAN [1982] reported the measurement of h_i in splat-cooling (chapter 28, § 1.2), pressurized aluminium casting against a steel mould and liquid die-casting against a steel mould. This author estimates that an upper limit exists for practically achievable heat transfer rates between liquid and substrates of about $h_i = 10^5-10^6$ J/m²K s. Table 1 gives the order of magnitude of h_i for different conditions of a metal in contact with a mould.

Concerning the solidification rate in unidirectional solidification, PIRES et al. [1974] proposed a model where R_s, R_m and R_i have a cumulative effect upon the solidification time, when liquid superheat is neglected. The approximate analytical solution obtained has the form:

$$t_s(X) = AX^2 + BX,$$
(5)

where:

$$A = \frac{1}{4Q^2 a_s},$$
(6)

$$B = \frac{Ld_s}{h_i(T_e - T_0)}.$$
(7)

Here, a_s is the thermal diffusivity of the solid metal, d_s is the density of the solid, and the meaning of Q is explained below.

Equation (5) describes two effects superimposed: (i) The time necessary to solidify a metal of specified thickness when $R_i = 0$, that is, when the thermal contact between the metal and mould is perfect. This situation is described by the *Lyubov analytical solution*, a particular case of the more general analytical solution due to Schwarz that considers the liquid superheat, neglected in this case (RUDDLE [1957]). (ii) The time necessary to solidify a metal of specified thickness when $R_s = R_m = 0$ and $R_i \neq 0$, that is, the second term considers the effect of the Newtonian thermal resistance at the metal–mould interface. In eq. (6), Q is the solidification constant

Table 1

Order of magnitude of heat-transfer coefficient, h_i, for different processes.

Process	h_i (J/m²K s)
Massive mould, polished	4×10^3
Massive mould, coated	7.5×10^2
Cooled mould, polished	5×10^3
Cooled mould, coated	10^3
Pressure-cast	$3 \times 10^3 - 3 \times 10^4$
Die-cast	5×10^4
Drop-smash	$10^4 - 10^5$
Splat-cooling	$10^5 - 10^6$

corresponding to the Lyubov solution and is obtained by trial and error from the expression

$$Q \exp(Q^2)[M + \operatorname{erf} Q] - \frac{1}{\sqrt{\pi} \, L^+}, \tag{8}$$

where M is the mould constant * and L^+ the dimensionless latent heat **.

PIRES *et al.* [1974] successfully checked eq. (5) for the particular case of refrigerated moulds in undirectional solidification of Sn, Pb, Zn and Al. In that case $M = 0$, corresponding to a more simplified form of the general Schwarz equation. As a result the Lyubov solution becomes the *Stefan solution* (RUDDLE [1957]), and Q is obtained from expression (8) for $M = 0$. Later, GARCIA and PRATES [1978] formulated the same mathematical model and extended the experiments to massive moulds, using the Lyubov solution of eq. (5) (GARCIA *et al.* [1979]). In several papers the method is named "Virtual Adjunct Method" (VAM). These authors calculated the h_i value from the experimental curves $X = f(t)$ through eq. (7), where the constant B can be determined experimentally. The values obtained compare quite well with those obtained by the fluidity test and those quoted in table 1.

3. Nucleation

In a solidification process, *nucleation* can be defined as the formation of a small crystal within its own melt, able to grow. Traditionally this subject has been treated under two headlines: *homogeneous* and *heterogeneous nucleation.*

3.1. Theory of homogeneous nucleation

The establishment of a S–L interface is not very easy from a thermodynamic point of view. Although below T_e the solid phase has the lower free energy, a small particle is not necessarily a stable phase as a consequence of the free energy associated to the S–L interface. The change in free energy corresponding to the liquid–solid transition must, then, include not only the specific free energy of the two phases but also the free energy of the interface. From a kinetic point of view it is possible to arrive at the same result on the basis that the atoms at the surface of a very small crystal have a higher energy than the surface atoms of a larger crystal. Therefore, the equilibrium temperature at which atoms arrive and leave at the same rate is lower for a very small crystal than for a larger one. As a consequence, a solid particle will be in equilibrium with the liquid when its radius of curvature has a particular value, known as the *critical radius.* Taking into account that at higher supercooling there is more free energy to compensate the surface free energy, the

---

* $M = (K_s C_s d_s / K_m C_m d_m)^{1/2}$; subscripts s and m refer to solid metal and mould, respectively; C is specific heat.
** $L^+ = L / C_s (T_e - T_0)$.

References: p. 573.

critical radius will decrease with increasing supercooling.

On the other hand, at any temperature there will be within the melt a statistical distribution of atom clusters of different size having the characteristics of the solid phase. At any temperature there is a maximum size of such *embryos* that is likely to exist. This size increases with the temperature decrease. Homogeneous nucleation occurs when the supercooling is such that there are some embryos with a radius larger than the critical radius (HOLLOMON and TURNBULL [1953]). According to CHALMERS [1964], the process can be described in the following steps:

3.1.1. Calculation of the critical radius

The variation of the free energy, ΔG, takes into account the variation of the volume free energy and the surface free energy. For an embryo of spherical shape of radius r:

$$\Delta G = -\tfrac{4}{3}\pi r^3 \frac{L\Delta T}{T_e} + 4\pi r^2 \gamma_{sl}, \tag{9}$$

where γ_{sl} is the solid–liquid interfacial free energy and ΔT is the supercooling.

In fig. 3 are plotted the expressions for the volume term, the surface term and ΔG. The *critical radius*, r^*, is defined for the condition $\partial \Delta G/\partial r = 0$:

$$r^* = \frac{2\gamma_{sl}T_e}{L\Delta T}. \tag{10}$$

3.1.2. Nucleation rate

It is assumed that the number of embryos of n_i atoms is given by the following

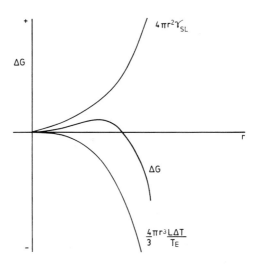

Fig. 3. Change of free energy due to the formation of a spherical crystal.

expression

$$n_{\mathrm{i}} = n \exp\left(-\frac{\Delta G}{kT}\right),$$ (11)

where n is the total number of atoms per volume unit, k is the Boltzmann constant, and ΔG the variation of energy given by eq. (9). For the critical radius:

$$n_{\mathrm{i}}^* = n \exp\left(-\frac{\Delta G^*}{kT}\right).$$ (12)

Considering eqs. (9) and (10):

$$\Delta G^* = \frac{16}{3}\pi\frac{\gamma_{\mathrm{sl}}^3 T_{\mathrm{e}}^2}{L^2 \Delta T}.$$ (13)

If it is now assumed that each critical nucleus grows into a crystal and is thereby removed from the distribution of cluster sizes, the subsequent rate of formation is determined by the rate at which smaller embryos reach critical size. The following expression is obtained for the *nucleation rate*, I:

$$I = n_{\mathrm{s}}^* \varepsilon \nu_{\mathrm{L}} n \exp\left(-\frac{\Delta G_{\mathrm{d}}^* + \Delta G^*}{kT}\right),$$ (14)

where n_{s}^* is the number of atoms of liquid in contact with the surface of the critical nucleus (~ 100), ε is the probability of a given atomic jump direction ($\sim 1/6$); ν_{L} is the atomic vibrational frequency ($\sim 10^{13}$), and ΔG_{d}^* is the free energy of activation for diffusion in the melt ($\Delta G_{\mathrm{d}}^* \sim kT$).

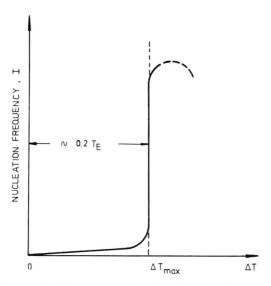

Fig. 4. Variation of the nucleation frequency as a function of the liquid supercooling for homogeneous nucleation (after PRATES and DAVIES [1978]).

References: p. 573.

TILLER [1970] analyzed several contributions to the total free energy of formation of embryos neglected in the simple theory reflected by eq. (14).

3.1.3. Nucleation temperature

Plotting eq. (14) as $I = f(\Delta T)$, the increase of I is very fast at a critical undercooling corresponding to about $0.2T_e$(fig. 4). It is so sensitive to the term within the exponential, that changes in the preexponential of eq. (14) of some orders of magnitude do not appreciably affect the calculated undercooling for sensible nucleation. The theory then permits, through eqs. (13) and (14), the average values of the interfacial free energy γ_{sl} to be determined.

3.2. Theory of heterogeneous nucleation

Most metals solidify with much smaller supercooling than the maximum $\Delta T \approx 0.2$ predicted by the theory of homogeneous nucleation. This is due to the presence of solid particles or the walls of the container than catalyze the nucleation by reducing the volume of the critical-sized nucleus, as sketched in fig. 5, where homogeneous and heterogeneous nucleation are compared for a flat catalytic surface and isotropic γ_{sl}. At a supercooling ΔT the critical radius of curvature is given by eq. (10). For the simplest case, a solid catalytic substrate with a plane surface, equilibrium exists when

$$\gamma_{cl} - \gamma_{cs} = \gamma_{sl} \cos \theta, \tag{15}$$

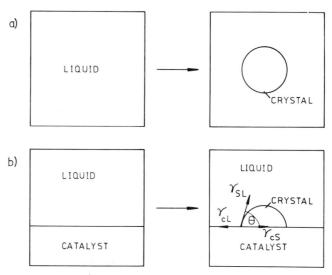

Fig. 5. Schematic comparison of (a) homogeneous and (b) heterogeneous nucleation of a crystal in a supercooled liquid with a flat catalytic surface and an isotropic crystal–liquid surface energy (after CANTOR [1983a]).

where γ_{cl} is the catalytic–liquid interfacial free energy and γ_{cs} the catalytic–crystal (solid) interfacial free energy.

In this model the thermodynamic barrier to nucleation ΔG^* is given by:

$$\Delta G^* = \frac{16}{3}\pi\frac{\gamma_{sl}^3 T_e^2}{L^2\Delta T^2}f(\theta),\tag{16}$$

where:

$$f(\theta) = \frac{(2+\cos\theta)(1-\cos\theta)^2}{4}.\tag{17}$$

In eq. (16), compared with homogeneous nucleation, the free energy barrier is reduced by a factor depending on the contact angle. Any value of θ between 0° and 180° corresponds to a stable angle. When $\theta = 0$, $\Delta G^* \approx 0$ and the growing solid "wets" the surface. As a result, the solidification can begin immediately when the liquid reaches the freezing point. From the classical heterogeneous nucleation point of view, a good nucleant corresponds to the existence of a small contact angle between the nucleating particle and the growing solid. According to eq. (15) this implies that γ_{cs} must be lower than γ_{cl}. However, the values of γ_{cs} and γ_{cl} are not known, and as a consequence, the potential catalytic effectiveness of a nucleant cannot be predicted. TILLER [1970] pointed out that there is no clear insight what determines θ and how it varies with: (i) lattice disregistry between surface and the stable phase; (ii) topography of the catalytic substrate surface; (iii) chemical nature of the catalytic substrate and (iv) adsorbed films on the catalytic substrate surface. This remains true today.

3.3. Comparison between experiments and nucleation theory

3.3.1. Homogeneous nucleation

Experiments on nucleation from the melt present as a principal problem the difficulty of removing unknown impurity particles which act as heterogeneous nuclei. Starting with the pioneering work done by TURNBULL and CECH [1950], several techniques have been used. Recently, PEREPEZKO and ANDERSON [1980] summarized the principal supercooling methods for slow cooling rates used in the field, shown in fig. 6. Figure 6a corresponds to the dispersion of a high purity melt into a large number of small drops within a suitable medium. For metals that melt below 500°C, organic carrier fluids are used. For systems with high melting temperatures, molten salts and glasses are convenient. In both cases, independence and separation are maintained by the use of thin and inert coatings which are considered non-catalytic to nucleation. As a consequence, only a small fraction of the drops may contain potent nucleants and the maximum supercooling for homogeneous nucleation can be achieved. Figure 6b corresponds to the substrate method where a small sample of liquid is placed on an inert substrate in an inert or reducing atmosphere. The onset of solidification is determined by visual observation of the

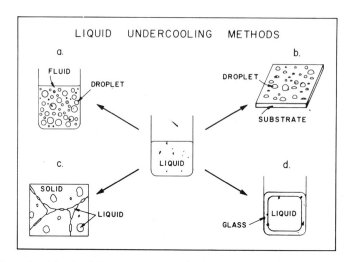

LIQUID   UNDERCOOLING   METHODS

Fig. 6. Sample configuration in different liquid supercooling methods (after PEREPEZKO and ANDERSON [1980]).

change in surface reflectivity of a metal droplet of about 50–100 μm in diameter. WANG and SMITH [1950] developed an entrained technique consisting of chill-cast alloys which contained a small amount of interdendritic eutectic in the as-cast structure. On annealing at temperatures between the solidus and the liquidus of the alloy, droplets are formed within the solid matrix grains. Thermal analysis is used to detect the supercooling of the droplets, fig. 6c. Figure 6d corresponds to the encased melt method where bulk samples are used (WALKER [1961]; KATTAMIS and FLEM-INGS [1966]). The melt is encased by a glass or slag layer and it is believed that the supercooling is promoted by isolating the liquid from possible catalytic sites on container walls as well as by a possible "deactivation" of nucleating centres distributed within the melt. Each of the supercooling methods described allows for an assessment of the maximum supercooling temperature obtained by direct meth-ods. With rapid cooling procedures, temperature measurement is difficult to accom-plish with accuracy (PEREPEZKO and LEBEAU [1981]).

The results of the application of techniques of droplet dispersion for many materials have been summarized by TURNBULL [1956]: (i) $\Delta T_{\max}$ for most liquids is more than $0.15 T_{\mathrm{e}}$, (ii) $\Delta T_{\max}/T_{\mathrm{e}} \approx 0.18$ for fcc and bcc metals. (iii) The molar interfacial energy, γ_{g}, can be calculated through the following expression:

$$\gamma_{\mathrm{g}} = Z^{1/3} v_{\mathrm{g}}^{2/3} \gamma_{\mathrm{sl}}, \tag{18}$$

where Z is Avogadro's number and v_{g} is the molar volume. (iv) The ratio of γ_{g} to the *molar heat of fusion, L,* is of the order of 0.5 for metals and 0.3 for semimetals. Recently, PEREPEZKO *et al.* [1979], using the droplet emulsion technique, obtained supercoolings almost twice as large as those indicated by earlier work and by

Turnbull's theory. As a result, these authors suggest that the experiments connected with nucleation on a substrate represent the onset of heterogeneous nucleation. Moreover, this implies that the values of γ_{sl} calculated from those supercoolings understimate the actual values. More recently, TURNBULL [1981] reanalyzed his results obtained on the kinetics of nucleation of mercury dispersions and those obtained by PEREPEZKO and RASMUSSEN [1978]. Together with a critical discussion for the prefactors of eq. (14) for different droplet surfactants, Turnbull speculated about the possible mechanisms that could change the maximum supercooling obtained in different experiments in relation to the theoretical value, advancing the following possibilities: (i) Continuous solid coatings, whether glassy or crystalline, on small droplets could, owing to different thermal contraction, develop sufficient stress to displace the thermodynamic equilibrium temperature; (ii) supercooling might also be increased substantially by a partitioning with further dispersion of the discrete droplets by excess surfactant; (iii) in relation to impurity effects, if $\partial T/\partial x_i \gtrsim 0$, where x_i is the impurity concentration, the limited supercooling may be substantially changed, even by several degrees, by impurities in amounts too small to affect T_e appreciably.

3.3.2. Heterogeneous nucleation

Heterogeneous nucleation is intellectually attractive, but most of the results do not seem to follow the predictions (CHADWICK [1973]). More recently, CANTOR and DOHERTY [1979] analyzed the different types of experiments in order to investigate the catalytic effect of the nucleants. This effect has been investigated by inserting nucleating particles or a single nucleation surface into the liquid, by observing liquid droplets on an inert of nucleating substrate, and by studying the effect on nucleation of a primary solid phase in alloy droplets of an inert substrate. In most cases the validity of the experiments can be questioned as a result of the possible existence of extraneous impurities influencing the nucleation effect. The most reliable results are those presented by SOUTHIN and CHADWICK [1978] and BOSWELL and CHADWICK [1980], who used an entrained technique of the type of fig. 6c. This technique eliminates problems of contamination because both the liquid droplets and the catalytic nucleating surfaces are formed internally during the heat treatment. Although nucleation at small supercoolings was found only in those couples where crystal structure and bonding were similar, these factors were considered to be insufficient in themselves for efficacious heterogeneous nucleation. On the other hand, the experimental results obtained were compared with the homogeneous nucleation data given by Turnbull for pure metals, which, as was stated before, are at present under discussion. In addition, whereas in pure metals the driving force is, to a very good approximation, directly proportional to the supercooling in the liquid, in alloys it is a function of both temperature and composition. As a consequence, nucleation to a constant or to a variable composition must both be taken as possibilities. Thus, at present the first steps in the comprehension of the heterogeneous nucleation phenomena have been taken through the establishment of reliable experimental techniques, but the understanding of the process is still poor.

References: p. 573.

4. Interface kinetics

The nature of the S–L interface is expected to have a decisive influence on the kinetics and morphology of crystal growth, but still the discussion continues on the character of the interface as well as the value of the driving force necessary to move the interface forward. For solidification, the parameter which determines the driving force is the *kinetic supercooling* ΔT_k of the melt in the region of the interface.

Essentially, the interface can advance by two processes: (i) *Non-uniform or lateral growth* where the interface advances by lateral motion of steps that are *a* interplanar distances in height, where $a \geqslant 1$. A molecule can attach itself to the solid at the edge of a step and as a result the surfaces only grow by the passage of the steps. (ii) *Uniform or continuous growth*. In this case the surface advances without needing steps, that is, growth can equally well proceed from any point.

4.1. Growth mechanisms

Three basic growth mechanisms are thought to occur and the growth laws for all of them may be written as a relationship between the solidification rate, V, and the departure from equilibrium, ΔT_k, required to drive the process.

4.1.1. Two-dimensional nucleation

In order to create the necessary surface steps for lateral growth, surface clusters must be nucleated upon a surface initially *singular,* that is, atomically smooth. The classical theory of two-dimensional nucleation was developed by VOLMER and MANDER [1931] and the growth law has the form:

$$V \propto \exp\left(\frac{-\alpha_2^2 \gamma_a^2 T_e}{4\alpha_1 Lk\Delta T_k} \right), \tag{19}$$

where α_1 and α_2 are shape factors, k is the Boltzmann constant and γ_a is the interfacial free energy per atom. According to expression (19), at large supercooling the nucleation rate will be so high that the growth is better described by the *continuous mechanism.*

4.1.2. Growth by screw dislocations

If one or more screw dislocations emerge at the S–L interface it is not necessary to form new layers in order to assure the lateral growth. The step generated by each dislocation moves one plane each time it sweeps around the dislocation (FRANK [1949]). It was shown by HILLIG and TURNBULL [1956] that the distance between neighbouring turns of the spiral is inversely proportional to ΔT_k, and therefore the total length of step is directly proportional to ΔT_k. The rate of growth, therefore, will be

$$V \propto \Delta T_k^2, \tag{20}$$

because the rate of growth per unit length of step should also be proportional to ΔT_k (CHALMERS [1964]).

4.1.3. Uniform or continuous growth

TURNBULL [1949] described kinetics for *continuous growth* of a rough solid surface through the classical rate theory. In order to cross the interface from liquid to solid a molecule must acquire an activation free energy. Taking into account the frequency of liquid–solid transitions and the frequency in the reverse direction, an expression is obtained that predicts that, as the supercooling increases, V will first increase linearly, then go through a maximum and finally decrease. For the small supercoolings usually considered in metals, the kinetic law has the form

$$V \propto \Delta T_k. \tag{21}$$

Figure 7 shows the predicted variation of growth according to the three classical laws described.

There is still another mechanism in crystal growth, connected with the existence of steps at the S–L interface: the *reentrant angle* resulting from the emergence of twin planes at the S–L interface. However, a quantitative growth law relating V to ΔT_k for this mechanism has still not been formulated (FLEMINGS [1974]).

4.2. Nature of the solid–liquid interface

As was pointed out above, knowledge of the nature of the S–L interface would allow prediction of the kinetics of crystal growth and under which circumstances the laws sketched in fig. 7 will operate. JACKSON [1958] presented a nearest-neighbour bond model and assumed that the extra molecules are randomly arranged on the crystal surface, initially plane. He obtained an expression for the change in free energy on adding molecules to a fraction N_A/N of N possible sites of the surface at

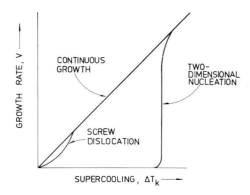

Fig. 7. Growth rate versus interface supercooling according to the three classical laws of crystal growth.

References: p. 573.

the equilibrium temperature:

$$\frac{\Delta G}{NkT_e} = \alpha N_A \left(\frac{N - N_A}{N^2} \right) - \ln\left(\frac{N}{N - N_A} \right) - \frac{N_A}{N} \ln\left(\frac{N - N_A}{N_A} \right), \tag{22}$$

where

$$\alpha = \left(\frac{L}{kT_e} \right). \tag{23}$$

α is a factor depending on the crystallography of the interface. This theory has been successfully used to classify and categorize growth morphologies (JACKSON [1971]). Equation (22) may be represented for different values of α (fig. 8). When $\alpha < 2$, the interface is *rough* from the atomistic point of view and solidification occurs by *continuous growth*. In these circumstances, from a macroscopic point of view the S–L interface is, in general, *non-faceted*. When $\alpha > 2$, the interface is atomistically *smooth* and solidification occurs by *layer or lateral growth*. This results in the formation of crystal faces and the macroscopic shape of the interface will in these circumstances be *faceted*. In principle the theory allows for a transition to occur between lateral growth and continuous growth. The effect of increasing the supercooling is to swing the right-hand side of each curve down to an amount roughly proportional to ΔT_k

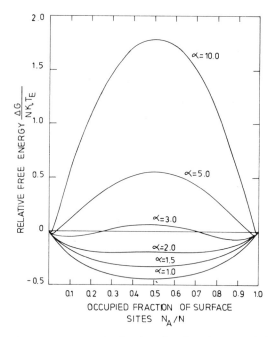

Fig. 8. Relative surface free energy versus the fraction of surface sites occupied; α is dependent on the crystal face, the type of crystal considered as well as the phase from which the crystal grows (after JACKSON [1958]).

and to α. In this way, faces with α just a little greater than 2 may become rough at some value of supercooling (JACKSON et al. [1967]).

In the concept of the *diffuse interface* the transition from solid to liquid takes place over a number of atomic layers, and the thermodynamic properties of the layers of atoms within the transition zone vary continuously from those of the liquid to those of the solid (CAHN [1960]), (CAHN et al. [1964]). This theory gives a qualitative understanding of the interface kinetics but the quantitative understanding of the interface attachment kinetics is still limited to a coarse-level parametric description (TILLER [1971]). According to the theory, at rest or at sufficiently low growth rates the interface will assume an equilibrium configuration and when it is displaced by an integral number of lattice planes it will have the same equilibrium configuration. The free energy of the interface may be drawn schematically as a sinusoid. If the applied driving force for growth is less than the free energy change between maxima the interface can only advance by a lateral mechanism, in which the mean position of the interface over each terrace differs from the next only by an integral number of monolayers. If the driving force is sufficiently high there is no longer a potential barrier and continuous growth occurs.

Figures 9a, b, displaying the two common methods of representing the kinetic data, show the theoretically predicted growth rate curve as a function of ΔT_k for interfaces with emergent dislocations (TILLER [1971]). For $0 < |\Delta T_k| < |\Delta T_k^*|$, classical lateral growth must occur; for $|\Delta T_k^*| < |\Delta T_k| < |\pi\Delta T_k^*|$, a gradual transition from the classical lateral growth to uniform (continuous) growth occurs. For $|\pi\Delta T_k^*| < |\Delta T_k|$, uniform growth occurs. The *critical value of the supercooling*, ΔT_k^*, is defined by:

$$\Delta T_k^* = \frac{g_{max}\gamma_0 T_e}{a_0 L}, \tag{24}$$

where a_0 is the intermolecular distance, γ_0 is the surface free energy of the minimum free energy configuration and g_{max} is a "diffuseness parameter"; $g_{max} \approx 1$ for sharp interfaces and rapidly becomes very much less as the interface becomes diffuse. Cahn has not given a method of calculating g_{max} and the theory can only be used to give an empirical value for g_{max}. Moreover, a conclusive experiment showing the transition predicted by the theory has not yet been performed (JACKSON et al. [1967], WOODRUFF [1973]). Meanwhile, though there is no conclusive evidence of a transition from lateral to continuous growth, more experimental evidence exists for the existence of two-dimensional nucleation type of behaviour (WOODRUFF [1973], FLEMINGS [1974]).

More recently, JACKSON [1974] discussed new advances in the understanding of crystal growth from the melt through the use of statistical treatments and computer simulation. An important fact is that the ratio L/kT_e presented in eq. (23) is important in all the statistical multilevel models of interface structure developed by TEMKIN [1964, 1969] and LEAMY and JACKSON [1971]. A common feature of all these models is that the thickness of the interface increases with decreasing L/kT_e. For these models, the equilibrium interface configuration depends on the entropy of transformation or, equivalently, on its reciprocal, the reduced surface temperature

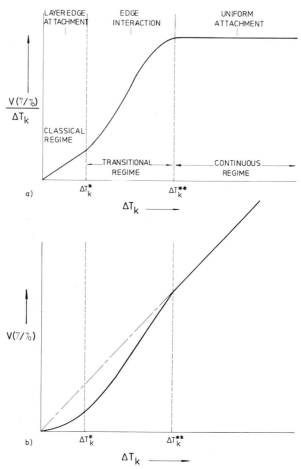

Fig. 9. Theoretically predicted growth rate curve as a function of supercooling, ΔT_k, for interfaces with emergent dislocations. The growth rate (ordinates) is adjusted for the temperature dependence of the melt viscosity, and differs for curves (a) and (b) by the factor ΔT_k; $\Delta T_k^{**} = \pi \Delta T_k^{*}$. (After TILLER [1971].)

kT/E where E is the bond energy. For a small entropy of transformation (high kT/E), the interface is so rough that there is not a periodic variation of its energy with position through the lattice. Thus, the interface is free to move according to the continuous growth law. For a large entropy of transformation (low kT/E), steps can exist on the surface and the growth rate depends on the rate of formation and motion of such steps. Figure 10 contains computer simulations of a surface at several values of kT/E (LEAMY and GILMER [1974]). The structure of surfaces is further discussed in ch. 8, § 7.4.1.

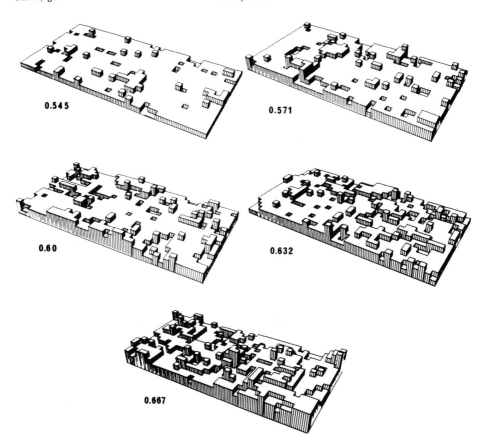

Fig. 10. Perspective drawings of representative surface configurations at various values of kT/E (after LEAMY and GILMER [1974]).

5. *Redistribution of solute for a plane interface*

Controlled plane-front solidification of alloys has been used extensively in order to manipulate the solute distribution. Considering a binary dilute alloy bar, there are two basic procedures of freezing. One is to melt all of it and then freeze it from one end. This procedure is called *normal freezing*. The other is to melt a portion of the solid and move this molten portion through the remainder of the solid so that melting and freezing are performed progressively; this method is called *zone melting* (PFANN [1957, 1978]). The type of solute distribution that one wishes to incorporate into a crystal will determine the freezing conditions to be used in its preparation. This section will present a short summary of the knowledge extensively reviewed, among other authors, by TILLER [1963], CHALMERS [1964] and FLEMINGS [1974].

References: p. 573.

5.1. The partition coefficient

The salient feature of the solid–liquid equilibrium relationship is conveniently described by the *equilibrium partition coefficient*

$$k_0 = \frac{C_s}{C_l}. \tag{25}$$

Figure 11 shows the two possibilities for k_0. For simplicity in general we discuss the most common case where $k_0 < 1$; k_0 is a characteristic of each system; however, during solidification this value is rarely achieved and an *effective distribution coefficient, k,* is considered.

5.2. Normal freezing

For constant conditions during controlled solidification, four types of solute distribution can occur during normal freezing as a result of the freezing conditions, (fig. 12). They are:

5.2.1. Equilibrium freezing
The S–L interface advances so slowly that diffusion in both phases maintains equilibrium at all times. These conditions are never obtained in practice (fig. 12a).

5.2.2. Non-mixing freezing
The freezing is rapid enough that only liquid diffusion controls the solute distribution at the interface. Solid diffusion and convection are considered negligible. Figure 12b corresponds to the solute distribution along the bar. Three distinct regions can be considered: an initial transient, a steady-state region and a terminal transient. Figure 13 shows the distribution of solute in liquid and solid during solidification along the bar until the steady state is obtained.

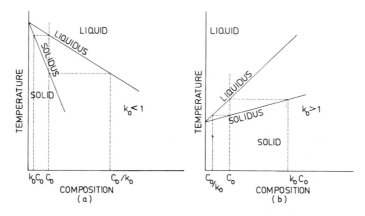

Fig. 11. Solidus–liquidus relationships for dilute binary alloys.

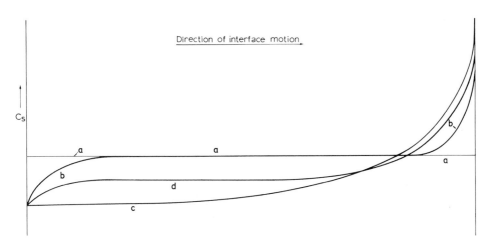

Fig. 12. Solute distribution after uniaxial solidification: (a) complete diffusion in solid and liquid; (b) mixing by diffusion in liquid only; (c) complete mixing in liquid; (d) partial mixing in liquid, including convection.

Expressions for distribution of solute in the solid in both transients as well as in the liquid in front of the interface have been developed. When the steady state condition has been reached the solute distribution in the liquid in front of the interface has the form:

$$C_1 = C_0 \left[1 + \frac{1 - k_0}{k_0} \exp\left(-\frac{V}{D_1} z \right) \right], \tag{26}$$

where D_1 is the solute diffusion coefficient in the liquid and z the distance from the interface. In eq. (26) the effective thickness of the solute rich layer is given by the *characteristic distance*, D_1/V. The solute distribution in the initial transient has a characteristic distance $D_1/k_0 V$. As a consequence its length depends on the k_0 value. Taking into account that the final transient corresponds to the solute build-up in front of the interface during the steady-state condition, its length will be of the order of D_1/V.

5.2.3. Complete mixing process

The characteristics of the freezing allow for a complete solute mixing in the liquid but with negligible diffusion in the solid. The solute distribution along the bar (fig. 12c) is given by the expression:

$$C_s = k_0 C_0 (1 - f_s)^{k_0 - 1}, \tag{27}$$

where f_s is the solidified fraction of the bar. This is the classical *Scheil* [1942] *equation*.

References: p. 573.

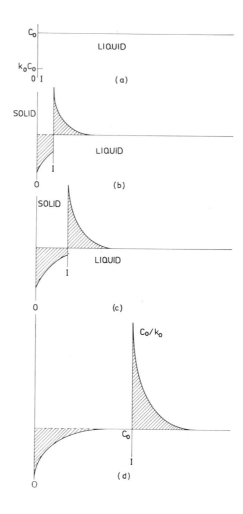

Fig. 13. Distribution of solute during initial transient until steady-state condition is obtained (after CHALMERS [1964]).

5.2.4.   Convection effects, partial-mixing freezing

Liquid metal flow in crystal growth, resulting from free convection due to solute or thermal gradients in the liquid, has been reviewed by different authors: HURLE [1972], CARRUTHERS [1976], PIMPUTKAR and OSTRACH [1981]. The interval between the extreme cases, non-mixing freezing and complete-mixing freezing, was bridged by BURTON et al. [1953]. A diffusion boundary layer d_f is assumed, outside which liquid composition is maintained uniform by convection and inside which mass transport is only by diffusion. A general expression of the effective distribution coefficient k is then obtained:

$$k = \frac{k_0}{k_0 + (1 - k_0) \exp\left[\left(-\frac{Vd_f}{D_1}\right)\frac{d_s}{d_1}\right]}. \tag{28}$$

In general d_s/d_1, the ratio of densities of solid and liquid, is considered to be nearly one. According to the freezing conditions, k varies between 1 and k_0. For partial-mixing freezing conditions the solute distribution (fig. 12d) is given by:

$$C_s = kC_0(1 - f_s)^{k-1}. \tag{29}$$

The solute distribution is affected by the fluid flow through the parameter Vd_f/D_1 in eq. (28) that defines the k value.

5.3. Zone-melting

The most important variables in the zone-melting process are: (i) Zone length; (ii) charge length; (iii) distribution of solute in the charge; (iv) vapour pressure; (v) moving conditions and (vi) zone travel rate. The manipulation of these variables could produce a large variety of impurity distributions in the solid charge. The most important variant of the method is *zone-refining*, of fundamental importance in modern transistor technology as well as in the production of high purity metals, for both basic and technological uses. Figure 14 is a schematic view of a multipass zone refining device, a more efficient system than the single-pass system originally developed. A general equation that expresses solute C_s as a function of distance x for any number n of zone passes through a charge of specified length has not been derived, but a basic differential equation from which computed solutions are obtained, including cases of a concentration-dependent value of k and a variable zone length l_z, is given by:

$$\left(\frac{l_z}{k}\right)dC_n(x) = \left[C_{n-1}(x + l_z) - C_n(x)\right]dx. \tag{30}$$

This expression relates the change in solute concentration in the just-forming solid at x in the nth pass to the difference between the fluxes of solute entering and leaving the zone. PFANN [1978] published different computed distributions and even in the

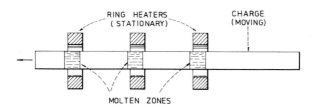

Fig. 14. Schematic of zone-refining, showing three molten zones travelling along an ingot (after PFANN [1957]).

References: p. 573.

case of a charge of 10 zone length long for a non-favorable value of k (0.5), the ultimate *relative* purity (compared with the initial state) after many zone passes is 10^{-4}, a very significant purity.

Another variant of zone-melting is the controlled addition of a desired impurity to a crystal in order to obtain a uniform concentration of a soluble impurity along the bar. This goal, impossible by conventional methods, is obtained through the *zone-levelling* operation. Several variants of the method are discussed by PFANN [1957, 1978]. One of the most widely used is the distribution of an impurity having a very small solubility in the solid. The solute is placed only in the first zone length of the starting charge, the remainder being pure solid solvent. As the zone travels, it leaves behind a small but very uniform concentration of the desired impurity. For $k_0 = 0.01$ the concentration falls only 10% in ten zone lengths, but even this decrease can be prevented by reducing the volume of the zone as it travels, in order to maintain the concentration of the zone constant. This method has been extremely effective for preparing segregation-free ingots of Ge and Si.

Temperature-gradient zone-melting (TGZM) is an ingenious method based on a solution–diffusion–freezing action. If for an alloy system AB, a thin layer of solute B is placed between blocks of solvent A in a temperature gradient, in such a way that the temperature of the layer is above the lowest melting temperature of the system and the hottest temperature in the solid is below the melting point of A, the layer will dissolve some A, become molten and expand its length in the direction of increasing temperature. The effect of the process is the migration of the molten zone through the block in the direction of increasing temperature, leaving behind it a trail of solid A saturated with B according to the A–B diagram. The factors influencing the process are length, composition, trail rate and shape of the zone (PFANN [1957, 1978]).

6. Solid–liquid interface morphologies

Most of the processes connected with solidification involve the existence of an unstable or irregular S–L interface at a microscopic level. As a consequence, different kinds of morphologies determine the microstructure of the growing phase, affecting the mechanical properties of the material.

6.1. Interface stability theory

The morphological stability theory is a detailed kinetic study of the growth or decay of a perturbation according to the laws of heat flow and diffusion. Excellent reviews are available in the literature (SEKERKA [1973]), (CHERNOV [1974]), (DELVES [1974]), (LANGER [1980]). According to SEKERKA [1973] the theory makes use of the following steps: (i) obtain an analytical solution of the unperturbed problem; (ii) imagine that there occurs an arbitrary infinitesimal perturbation in the shape of the interface; (iii) obtain, via classical perturbation theory, an approximate solution for the case of the perturbed interface; (iv) examine the solution for the perturbed case to see if the perturbation will grow or decay with time. As a consequence a stability criterion can be established, i.e., the growth conditions for a stable or unstable interface; (v) for growth conditions where the interface is unstable, deduce the manner in which the interface will change with time.

We consider the interface stability theory as very important in connection with solidification processes, mainly free dendritic growth and segregation substructures arising from unidirectional solidification of alloys. These two cases will be treated in some detail.

6.2. Free dendritic growth

Free *dendritic* growth arises when a crystal nucleus grows in a supercooled melt. The word dendritic means "treelike" and the kinetic advantage of the dendrite is its ability to lose easily, by enhanced diffusion in three directions from its leading tip, the rejected solute (when alloys are considered) and latent heat. This is called the "point effect of diffusion". DOHERTY [1980] presents a comprehensive description of the basic characteristics of the dendritic structure, that is: (i) the main stem with the dendrite tip of curvature; (ii) the secondary arms, tertiary and higher-order arms; (iii) preferred growth directions, according to the crystallography of the metal or alloy considered. At present, the theory is quite consistent with experimental results for pure metals presenting a rough interface, that is, non-faceted materials. Thus we shall give this case special attention. The analysis of free dendritic growth requires the coupling of three independent processes: (i) the instability of a growing spherical nucleus; (ii) the propagation of the dendritic main stem and (iii) the non-steady-state solution of dendrite branches.

6.2.1. The instability of a growing spherical nucleus
In this case, treated by MULLINS and SEKERKA [1963], a sphere of radius R is perturbed by some spherical harmonic $Y_{l,m}(\theta, \phi)$ having an infinitesimally small amplitude δ, to give a S–L interface defined by:

$$r = R + \delta Y_{l,m}(\theta, \phi), \tag{31}$$

where r is the radius of the perturbed sphere and δ is the amplitude of a particular harmonic perturbation. The unperturbed sphere grows into a liquid of temperature T_∞ with a growth rate

$$\dot{R} = K_1 \frac{\Delta T}{RL}, \tag{32}$$

where the supercooling $\Delta T = T_E - T_\infty - 2T_E\Gamma/R$ includes the capillarity effect. $\Gamma = \gamma_{sl}/L$ is a capillarity constant and γ_{sl} is the S–L interface surface free energy per unit area, assumed isotropic.

In evaluating the instability there are two conditions which may be considered important:

References: p. 573.

(i) $\dot{\delta}/\delta > 0$, where:

$$\frac{\dot{\delta}}{\delta} = \left[(l' - 1) \frac{K_1}{R^2 L} \right] \left(\Delta T - \frac{T_e \Gamma}{R} \left[(l' + 1)(l' + 2) + l'(l' + 2) \frac{K_s}{K_1} \right] \right). \tag{33}$$

Instability of this form occurs whenever the harmonic $l' \geqslant 2$ and

$$\Delta T > \left(\frac{T_e \Gamma}{R} \left[(l' + 1)(l' + 2) + l'(l' + 2) \frac{K_s}{k_1} \right] \right). \tag{34}$$

Taking into account the fact that R grows with time, the instability of the form $\dot{\delta}/\delta > 0$ may not be apparent and a *relative instability criterion* may be adopted:

(ii) $\dot{\delta}/\delta > \dot{R}/R$. This is satisfied whenever:

$$(l' - 2)\Delta T > (l' - 1) \left(\frac{T_e \Gamma}{R} \right) \left[(l' + 1)(l' + 2) + l'(l' + 2) \frac{K_s}{K_1} \right] \tag{35}$$

and $l' \geqslant 3$. Taking into account the critical nucleation radius at the supercooling considered, $R^* = 2T_e \Gamma / (T_e - T_\infty)$, from eq. (34) we obtain for $l' = 2$ the *absolute instability criterion* $R = R(7 + 4K_s/K_1) = 11R$ (for the simplified condition $K_s = K_1$). The *relative instability* is obtained from eq. (35) for $l' = 3$ and $R = R(21 + 15K_s/K_1) = 36R$ for the same simplified condition.

CORIELL and PARKER [1967] extended the stability theory for the growing sphere to include the effect of growth kinetics. Under similar supercooling conditions metals should have a much smaller critical radius than nonmetals and the general picture of the process corresponds to a nucleus initially spherical becoming distorted as it grows. For nonmetals the growth kinetics appear to stabilize the shape, but in the case of metals the deformation is relevant at sizes only few times the critical radius for growth under a given supercooling. On the other hand, CAHN [1967] postulated that anisotropy of the interfacial free energy will cause the distorted nucleus to reflect this when it goes unstable. He concluded that one of the main effects of anisotropy will be to impose on the shape initial perturbations reflecting the anisotropy. HUANG and GLICKSMAN [1981b] measured in succinonitrile droplets a 1% anisotropy in the S–L interfacial energy for the ⟨100⟩ directions. Experiments by the same authors show the transition from predendritic to dendritic morphology associated with protuberances in those crystallographic directions (GLICKSMAN [1981]). The same type of evidence was obtained by CHAN *et al.* [1976, 1978] for growth of NH_4 dendrites, and by KISS and BILONI [1968] in very dilute Al–Cu alloys, using special metallographic techniques and tridimensional models developed from metallographic cross-sections.

6.2.2. Propagation of the dendrite main stem

For many years scientists attempted to explain dendritic growth rates in pure materials by means of steady-state models. In these models the dendrite is replaced by a branchless, semi-infinite body which translates uniformly along its length, and the steady-state motion is assumed to be governed by heat flow consistent with appropriate thermodynamic boundary conditions at the moving interface.

Taking into account the fact that experimental observations show that, for a fixed supercooling, the dendrite grows at a constant rate and its form does not change during growth, many attempts have been made in order to calculate the radius of curvature of the dendrite tip, ρ, and the dendrite velocity V as a function of the *melt supercooling*. For a pure material with melting point T_e, which is supercooled to a temperature T_∞, a dimensionless supercooling $\Delta\theta$ is defined as $\Delta\theta = (T_e - T_\infty)c_p/L$, c_p being the thermal specific heat of the liquid phase. As a dendrite grows, the total supercooling $\Delta\theta$ is divided between three processes: $\Delta\theta_T$ in dissipating latent heat of fusion, $\Delta\theta_c$ a term reflecting the capillarity effect and $\Delta\theta_k$ the kinetic process of attachment at the S–L interface:

$$\Delta\theta = \Delta\theta_T + \Delta\theta_c + \Delta\theta_k. \tag{36}$$

As pointed out by HUANG and GLICKSMAN [1981a], the fully time-dependent dendritic growth corresponds to a steady-state heat diffusion problem around a smooth, shape-preserving interface. In order to solve the steady state dendritic heat transfer problem, two boundary conditions are considered at the surface of the dendrite: (i) the temperature at each point of the S–L interface equals the *local* equilibrium temperature, influenced by the capillarity effect; (ii) the latent heat released at the interface during solidification is constantly conducted away through the adjoining solid and liquid phases. In order to solve the problem under these two boundary conditions, the shape of the dendrite must be *assumed* in most of the models. GLICKSMAN *et al.* [1976] give a summary of the different models of dendrite growth delineating their differences as well as their similarities. In this sense, table 2, based on the paper by GLICKSMAN *et al.* [1976], summarizes for each theory: (i) the dendrite shape assumed; (ii) in which part of the dendrite the capillarity effect through the Gibbs–Thompson condition is considered; (iii) in which part of the dendrite the heat flux condition during growth is considered; (iv) in which part of the dendrite, if any, the molecular attachment kinetics related to $\Delta\theta_k$ is considered; (v) special characteristics of the model, under the heading "comments". At the same time, these authors performed very reliable experiments on 99.999% pure succinonitrile, assuring free growth conditions as well as the attainment of thermal diffusion conditions. Among the theories appearing in table 2, three have the form:

$$V = \beta G (\Delta\theta)^{b_1}, \tag{37}$$

able to be treated experimentally: (i) Trivedi's theory, an advanced form of Temkin's original model; (ii) the modified version of Ivantsov's original model and (iii) Nash and Glicksman's more exact treatment where both capillarity and flux conditions were applied rigorously to every point of the dendrite surface; as a result the dendrite shape is not constrained to a geometry assumed a priori. β and b_1 are numerical constants, specific for each theory, G is a lumped parameter, $a_1\Delta S_f L/c_p\gamma_{sl}$, where a_1 and c_p are the thermal diffusivity and specific heat of the liquid phase, respectively, ΔS_f the entropy of fusion and L the enthalpy of fusion. Although Trivedi's and Nash and Glicksman's theories predicted the correct power law,

References: p. 573.

Table 2
Steady-state theories of dendritic growth [a].

Theory	Dendrite shape	Gibbs–Thomson boundary condition	Thermal flux balance	Molecular attachment boundary condition	Comment
BOLLING–TILLER [1961]	paraboloid of revolution	tip only	tip only	tip only	
FISHER [1950]	cylinder with hemispherical cap	cap only	approximated by macroscopic theory	none	$V \propto \Delta T^2$
GLICKSMAN–SCHAEFER [1967, 1968]	paraboloid of revolution	tip only	tip only	tip only	"modified Ivantsov"
HOLTZMANN [1970a, b]	paraboloid of revolution	all points	tip only	all points	
HORVAY–CAHN [1961]	elliptical paraboloids	none	all points	none	isothermal theory
IVANTSOV [1947]	paraboloid of revolution	none	all points	none	isothermal theory
NASH–GLICKSMAN [1974]	unconstrained body of revolution	all points	all points	none	non-linear theory
SEKERKA *et al.* [1967]	paraboloid of revolution	tip only	all points	none	"modified Ivantsov"
TARSHIS–KOTLER [1968]	paraboloid of revolution	all points	tip only	all points	
TEMKIN [1960]	paraboloid of revolution	all points	tip only	all points	
TRIVEDI [1970]	paraboloid of revolution	all points	tip only	all points	"modified Temkin"

[a] From GLICKSMAN *et al.* [1976].

$b_1 = 2.65$, none of the theories predicted the correct growth velocity, that is, the coefficient β.

As was stated above, the theories have been formulated in order to predict V as a function of ρ for a given $\Delta\theta$. As the dendrite grows, the total dimensionless supercooling, from eq. (36) is given by:

$$\Delta\theta = P_e'(\exp P_e') E_1(P_e') + \Delta\theta_c + \Delta\theta_k, \tag{38}$$

where $E_1(P_e')$ is the exponential function $\int_{P_e'}^{\infty}(e^{-u}/u)\,du$, P_e' is the *Peclet number* at the dendrite tip, defined by the relationship $P_e' = (V\rho/2a_1)$. The term $\Delta\theta_c$ reflecting the influence of the capillarity is also itself a function of V and of ρ, which in turn is a function of V (HUANG and GLICKSMAN [1981a]). $\Delta\theta_c$ and $\Delta\theta_k$ can be taken into account or not according to the different models, see table 2.

In order to obtain unique relationship for V versus $\Delta\theta$, a conventional but arbitrary criterion is to assume that the dendrite will adopt the radius ρ_{opt} that gives the *maximum velocity, V_{max}*. In other words, the theory predicts a growth velocity which, at fixed supercooling, passes through or approaches a maximum as a function of the tip radius; this maximum velocity locates the actual operating point of the dendrite (with $\rho = \rho_{opt}$). Often the above theoretical approach is referred to in the literature as the *maximum-velocity theory*. If the value of the tip radius adopted by the dendrite is not ρ_{opt}, the value of V will be smaller than V_{max}. The reliable experiments performed by GLICKSMAN et al. [1976] indicate that real dendrites grow with appreciable lower velocities than is predicted by the maximum-velocity theory. As a consequence, it is now generally accepted that the failure of the theory in predicting the relation between V and $\Delta\theta$ is related to the use of the maximum velocity concept.

At present there exists a general agreement that for a given supercooling a dendrite does not assume a radius that gives maximum growth rate. Rather it assumes a velocity which allows it to grow with the largest *stable* radius of curvature. HUANG and GLICKSMAN [1981a] performed systematic measurements of dendrite tip radius and growth velocity in succinonitrile, discussing at the same time the several stability models existing in the literature. The most rigorous of the theories corresponds to LANGER and MÜLLER-KRUMBHAAR [1978] (LM-K) where rigorous mathematics and extensive numerical computation were used in order to study the interface behaviour of the whole dendrite. These authors showed that the steady-state growth of a dendrite depends upon: (i) satisfying the heat-transfer diffusion field surrounding the dendrite; (ii) maintaining a *marginally stable* interface at the dendrite tip. This marginally stable criterion can be expressed mathematically as $V\rho^2 = Cte$, through an expression where the stability constant is

$$\sigma^* = \frac{2a_1 d_0}{V\rho^2}, \tag{39}$$

where d_0 is a capillarity factor defined as $T_e\gamma_{sl}c_p/L^2$. Equation (39) implies that the dendrite grows in such a way that at this particular value of σ *all* the unstable modes at the dendrite tip vanish. In the treatment of (LM-K), tipsplitting exists for $\sigma < \sigma^*$

References: p. 573.

and sidebranch formation for $\sigma > \sigma^*$. σ^* is a constant estimated by (LM-K) to be 0.025 ± 0.007 in the limit of small P'_e. The $\pm 30\%$ uncertainty reflects the uncertainty in the numerical procedures used to solve the equations. HUANG and GLICKSMAN [1981a], on the basis of prior work by DOHERTY *et al.* [1978], developed a simplified analysis in which the tip region of a dendrite is approximated as a portion of a sphere freezing at the same rate. In this case the marginal stability criterion obtained is

$$\sigma^* = \frac{2a_1 d_0}{V\rho^2} = \frac{2}{(m+1)(2m+1)}, \qquad (40)$$

where m is the order of spherical harmonics. It is considered that the lowest-order spherical harmonic which can perturb the tip of a dendrite growing in a $\langle 100 \rangle$ direction and also satisfy the cubic requirement for a four-fold rotation axis has $m = 6$. As a consequence, eq. (40) becomes:

$$\sigma^* = \frac{2a_1 d_0}{V\rho^2} = 0.0192, \qquad (41)$$

lying within the $\pm 30\%$ uncertainty of the (LM-K) theory.

The expressions for V versus $\Delta\theta$ and ρ versus $\Delta\theta$ obtained by HUANG and GLICKSMAN [1981a] are:

$$V = 2\sigma^* G P'^2_e (\Delta\theta), \qquad (42)$$

$$\rho = \frac{a_1}{G\sigma^*} P'^{-1}_e (\Delta\theta). \qquad (43)$$

Figure 15 corresponds to the comparison of the dendrite-tip operating state as-measured (solid circle) with theoretical predictions. Open circles indicate the maximum growth velocities predicted by two non-isothermal models. The dashed lines locate the operating state predicted by the simplified spherical stability criterion developed by HUANG and GLICKSMAN [1981a], which agrees with the experimental results. The experimental point lies at a portion remote from the maxima and in a region in which the various theories tend to converge. On the other hand, the experimental results obtained by HUANG and GLICKSMAN [1981a] show that the stability criterion applied to the Temkin and Ivantsov models agrees quite well with experiments for $V = f(\Delta T)$ and $\rho = f(\Delta T)$ except at small supercoolings due to convection effects.

In very recent work, TRIVEDI [1982] considered the theory of dendritic and Widmanstätten plate growth and a first-order perturbation analysis is developed assuming that the tip region can be approximated by a cylindrical shape. As a result he is able to treat the stability of a moving cylindrical interface instead of the approximate spherical model proposed by HUANG and GLICKSMAN [1981a]. In connection with free dendritic growth of pure materials, the only case treated in this section, Trivedi found through his theoretical analysis that: (i) the convective term due to the motion is found to lower significantly the growth rate of dendrites when the Peclet number is greater than 0.1 (the upper limit discussed above in connection

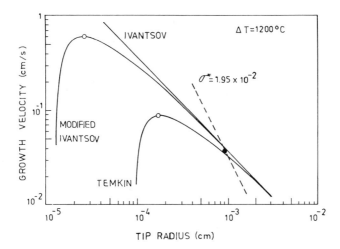

Fig. 15. Comparison between theoretical predictions and experiments concerning the dendrite-tip operating state for succinonitrile. The open circles correspond to the maximum growth velocities predicted by the Temkin and modified Ivantsov models. The dashed line corresponds to the stability criterion, which agrees with the experimental point (solid circle). (After HUANG and GLICKSMAN [1981a].)

with the succinonitrile experiments); (ii) the stability criterion $V\rho^2 = Cte$ no longer holds true when the Peclet number exceeds 0.1, and increases with P'_e or the supercooling. For $P'_e < 0.1$ his calculations are in close agreement with HUANG and GLICKSMAN's [1981a] results.

6.2.3. The non-steady-state solution of dendrite branches

Recently, HUANG and GLICKSMAN [1981b] published a quite complete study of dendrite sidebranching structure in succinonitrile. The results cover: (i) origin of the sidebranch perturbations; (ii) the mechanism of the sidebranch evolution; (iii) the sidebranch competitive growth during solidification; and (iv) the kinetics of isothermal and dynamic sidebranch coarsening during solidification.

6.2.3.1. Sidebranch formation. It is suggested that the slight anisotropy in S–L interface energy of about 1% in succinonitrile plays an important role in the branching mechanism in connection with the S–L interface instability as was discussed in § 6.2.1. The tip region, initially a body of revolution, bulges in four longitudinal $\langle 100 \rangle$ planes and then perturbs into branch-sheets. The secondary arm spacing close to the dendritic tip is proportional to the tip radius ρ. In succinonitrile, HUANG and GLICKSMAN [1981b] found that the secondary arm spacing near the tip of a dendrite is slightly greater than 2ρ, independent of the supercooling. This circumstance arises because the sidebranches form by amplification of the periodic disturbances which emanate from the advancing dendrite tip. Thus, the steady motion of the marginably stable tip produces interfacial disturbances which eventually develop into sidebranches. Figure 16 shows how from the smooth tip of an

References: p. 573.

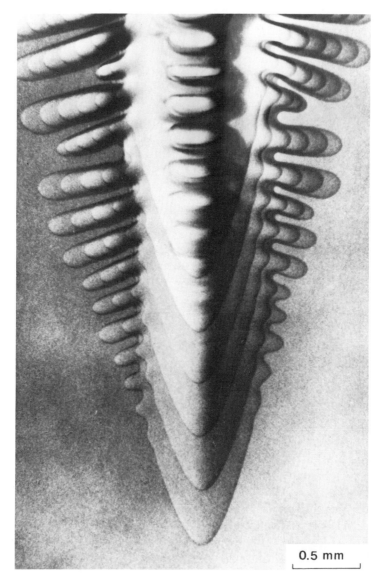

Fig. 16. Superimposition of time-lapse photographs corresponding to the growth of a succinonitrile dendrite. The sidebranch evolution on the ⟨100⟩ branching sheets is noticeable. (After HUANG and GLICKSMAN [1981b].)

advancing dendrite, periodic bumps spread and rapidly develop into branches (GLICKSMAN [1982]). The same figure shows how the growth trajectories of the oscillatory instabilities point about 20° forward from the ⟨100⟩ direction orthogonal to the growth axis. It is considered that the direction of the branch growth is determined by the propagation velocity of the wave, but at present the conditions are considered too complicated to be treated in detail.

In connection with the origin of the sidebranch perturbations, prior theories (KOTLER and TILLER [1968]) have as a basis a dendrite considered as an optimized solution (V_{max}, ρ_{opt}) and the time dependent model of the sidebranch evolution considered a perturbation source necessary in order to initiate the branching instabilities. In opposition, the stability theory suggests that a sidebranch perturbation arises as a direct result of the intrinsic instability existing at all regions of the dendrite other than at the tip. In other words, sidebranches evolve because of the morphological instability associated with the dendrite surfaces in the neighborhood of the tip. HUANG and GLICKSMAN [1981b] concluded that dendrite's axial steady-state tip growth and the sidebranch non-steady-state evolution are relatively independent and do not interfere with each other in any significant extent.

6.2.3.2. The scaling laws. The same authors also show that the normalized dendrite tip radius versus supercooling presents a relationship $\rho/\lambda_s = 1.2$ over a wide range of supercooling, λ_s being the *planar perturbation wavelength*. At the same time, the normalized secondary branch spacing versus supercooling is about three times this value. Taking into account that the tip radius and branch spacing are two characteristic dimensions of a dendrite, the general morphology of a dendrite can be scaled to λ_s. λ_s being inversely proportional to ΔT, it follows that the general morphology of a dendrite can be scaled to supercooling. Also, the dendrite growth kinetics can be scaled to supercooling, in this case to $\Delta T^{2.7}$ as predicted by the theory and in agreement with experimental results, particularly in the dimensionless supercooling range 5×10^{-2}–3×10^{-3}, where the *thermal diffusion* of latent heat is the growth-limiting transport process. Similarly, the sidebranch growth velocity, that is, the perturbation amplification rate, is also scaled to $\Delta T^{2.7}$.

6.2.3.3. Sidebranch coarsening. Extensive information was obtained by HUANG and GLICKSMAN [1981b] and their results can be summarized as follows:

(i) Using the concept of "active sidebranches", the branch spacing measured increases according to a power law relationship with increasing time or distance away from the dendrite. A branch is judged "active" when it is equal or longer than the next "active" branch closer to the dendrite tip. Since the first 8–10 branching bumps are always active (fig. 16) the definition is easily applied from the tip backwards. At some distance from the dendrite tip, certain sidebranches experience slower growth than the others (fig. 16) and competitive sidebranch growth develops. As a result of this process, a *dynamic coarsening* of the branch spacing occurs during solidification.

(ii) It was found that the sidebranches begin to coarsen dynamically for times longer than an "incubation time" defined by:

$$\tau = 8\frac{\lambda_{tip}}{V},\tag{44}$$

where λ_{tip} is the minimum dendrite arm spacing near the tip. Equation (44)

References: p. 573.

represents the time required for a steady-state dendrite to develop about eir'
sidebranches (that always are "active"). As a result, an *incubation length* can ь
easily obtained from eq. (44), representing the length of dendrite near the tip region,
within which the branches are controlled only by the perturbation wave and where
dynamic branch coarsening is not expected. On the other hand, a relationship
between incubation length and dendrite growth velocity can be established and the
growth velocity can be related to the heat extraction rate. The experimental results
show that even at high heat extraction rates dendrite sidebranches still undergo
dynamic coarsening, unless the dendrite length is smaller than the incubation length.

(iii) Concerning *isothermal coarsening,* although different types of branch coarsening processes were observed, the capillarity-driven coarsening effect is the sole
mechanism responsible for coarsening during isothermal heat-treatment.

As a result of the above concepts, a complete description of the coarsening
process during solidification consists of two mechanisms: 1) through a competitive
side-branch growth mechanism only a selected number of branches is allowed to
grow actively; 2) a nearly isothermal environment exists for the short, inactive
branches trapped between active branches that eventually are eliminated through
isothermal coarsening. The first mechanism appears as the principal one in order to
explain the changes in branch spacings during solidification, the second being an
additional process helping to stabilize the branch spacings set up by the branch
competition mechanism.

In summary, it is quite apparent that the use of model systems such as pure
succinonitrile gives considerable information about free dendritic growth. The
scaling laws involving material parameters (latent heat, specific heat, entropy,
surface energy, etc.) as well as processing parameters such as supercooling, cooling
rate, casting speed, etc., allow the possibility to extend the results to systems of
practical interest such as pure aluminum (GLICKSMAN [1982]).

6.3. Unidirectional solidification of alloys

Interface instability during unidirectional solidification of dilute alloys for different S–L interface velocities is important from the technological point of view, as a
result of the different degrees of microsegregation associated with, and the possibility of extrapolation to industrial alloys. SEKERKA [1973] and WOODRUFF [1973]
gave a detailed mathematical explanation of the conditions of instability for a dilute
binary alloy having temperature and solute profiles for $k_0 < 1$, as a function of the
distance z from the S–L interface for constrained growth at velocity V (fig. 17). This
linear-dependent stability analysis was carried out by MULLINS and SEKERKA [1963,
1964] and SEKERKA [1967]. More recently, MEHRABIAN [1982] published a comprehensive survey of the application of the morphological stability theory for different
S–L interface velocities.

The perturbation at the S–L interface growing in the z direction is given by

$$z = \delta \exp\left(\sigma_1 t + i w_x x + i w_y y\right), \tag{45}$$

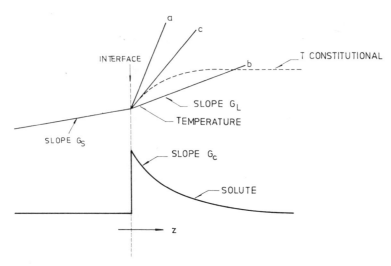

Fig. 17. Temperature and solute profile for $k_0 < 1$ as a function of distance z measured from the S-L interface when constrained growth at a velocity V occurs for a dilute binary alloy. The concept of constitutional supercooling is included.

where δ is the perturbation amplitude at $t = 0$ and w_x and w_y are spatial frequencies. The interface is stable if the real part of σ_1 is negative for all perturbations. The value of σ_1 is determined by solving the steady-state heat flow and diffusion equations with appropriate boundary conditions. For the stability–instability demarcation ($\sigma_1 = 0$), the equation simplifies to a criterion which identifies three factors contributing to the overall stability of the interface: the solute field, the capillarity forces and the thermal field:

$$m_1 G_c \underbrace{\frac{w^* - \dfrac{V}{D_1}}{w^* - (1 - k_0)\dfrac{V}{D_1}}}_{\text{Solute field}} - \underbrace{\frac{T_e \gamma_{sl} w^2}{L d_s}}_{\substack{\text{Capillarity} \\ \text{force}}} + \underbrace{\frac{K_s G_s + K_1 G_1}{2 \overline{K}}}_{\text{Thermal field}} \gtrless 0. \qquad (46)$$

G_s is the unperturbed gradient temperature in the solid, $\overline{K} = (K_s + K_1)/2$, d_s is the solid density and:

$$w^* = \frac{V}{2 D_1} + \left[\left(\frac{V}{2 D_1} \right)^2 + w^2 \right]^{1/2}, \qquad w^2 = w_x^2 + w_y^2; \qquad (46a)$$

$$G_c = \frac{- V C_\infty (k_0 - 1)}{D_1 k_0}. \qquad (46b)$$

The sign of inequality (46) determines whether the interface is stable or unstable. The first term represents the effect of solute diffusion and, being positive, is always

References: p. 573.

destabilizing. The second term, involving capillarity, has a stabilizing influence for all wavelengths, though its effect is most favourable at short wavelengths. This is the sort of stabilizing effect to be expected from surface tension. The last term is stabilizing for positive temperature gradients; if the temperature gradients are negative, the term is destabilizing. If pure material is considered, this is the only destabilizing term, because then the solute field does not exist. Different conditions may be considered:

(i) If the interface grows at slow velocities, $w^* \approx w \gg V/D_1$, the capillarity forces are small and the solute diffusion is complete, that is, the solute diffusion is efficient in displacing solute across the interface; inequality (46) as *instability criterion* becomes:

$$m_1 G_c \geqslant \frac{K_s G_s + K_1 G_1}{2 \overline{K}}. \tag{47}$$

If, in addition, eq. (47) is coupled with eq. (1), and $VLd_s \ll 2K_1 G_1$, inequality (46) as *stability criterion* becomes:

$$(K_1/\overline{K})G_1 > m_1 G_c, \tag{48}$$

which reduces to the *constitutional supercooling criterion* (to be examined in more detail in § 6.3.1) for $K_s \approx K_1$.

(ii) Returning to inequality (46), the stability condition can be written:

$$\frac{1}{m_1 G_c} \frac{K_s G_s + K_1 G_1}{2 \overline{K}} - \frac{T_e \gamma_{sl} w^2}{Ld_s m_1 G_c} + \frac{\left(w^* - \dfrac{V}{D_1} \right)}{\left(w^* - (1 - k_0) \dfrac{V}{D_1} \right)} \gtrless 0. \tag{49}$$

Now we denote the last term of inequality (49) by $F(w)$, and the sum of the last two terms by $G(w)$.

Figure 18 shows the form of the last two terms of inequality (49), as well as the two basically different possible forms of $G(w)$ sum, that is, $G_1(w)$ and $G_2(w)$. For small w:

$$F(w) = \left(\frac{D_1^2}{V^2 k_0} \right) w^2. \tag{50}$$

If the constant $D_1^2/V^2 k_0$ is less than the constant in the capillarity term, $G(w)$ becomes $G_2(w)$ (fig. 18); this corresponds to the condition $G(w)_{max} = 0$. This is the *absolute stability criterion*:

$$m_1 G_c \left(\frac{D_1^2}{V^2 k_0} \right) w^2 - \frac{T_e \gamma_{sl} w^2}{Ld_s} < 0, \tag{51}$$

or: $$A_0 = \frac{k_0 T_e \gamma_{sl}}{m_1 G_c L d_s} \left(\frac{V}{D_1} \right)^2 > 1. \tag{52}$$

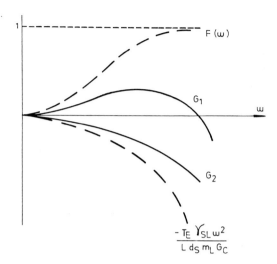

Fig. 18. General form of the two components of the function $G(w)$ and two possible forms of the sum.

On the other hand, the general condition for stability is given by curve $G_1(w)$, with a maximum for some w greater than zero. This general condition for stability can be rewritten (SEKERKA [1973]):

$$\frac{G_1}{V} + \frac{L}{2K_1} < \frac{(-m_1 C_\infty)}{D_1} \cdot \frac{(1-k_0)}{k_0} \cdot \frac{K_s + K_1}{2K_1} \cdot \xi, \tag{53}$$

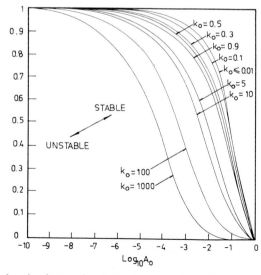

Fig. 19. Stability function ξ versus log A_0 for different values of k_0 (after SEKERKA [1973]).

References: p. 573.

where C_∞ is the liquid composition far from the S–L interface; in general $C_\infty \approx C_0$. The function $\xi(A_0, k_0)$ is displayed graphically in fig. 19.

(iii) According to MEHRABIAN [1982], the *absolute criterion* is a good approximation for high interface velocities. Figure 20, due to CORIELL and SEKERKA [1980], describes the critical concentration of Cu above which interface instability occurs as a function of the interface velocity V in directional solidification of Al–Cu alloys for a temperature gradient in the liquid of 2.0×10^4 K/m. The absolute stability criterion corresponds to the right side of fig. 20. Figure 21, due to MEHRABIAN [1982], maps out the calculated G_L and V combinations that lead to homogeneous plane solidification as a function of the percentage Cu in Al–Cu alloys. It is quite

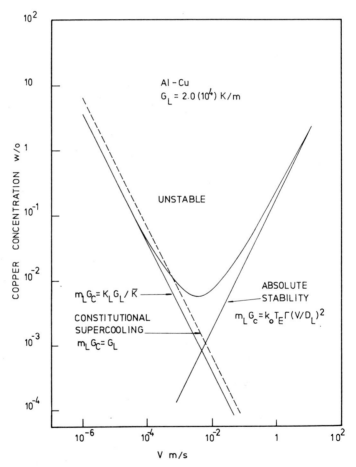

Fig. 20. Interface stability as a function of the interface velocity V and Cu concentration for Al–Cu alloys unidirectionally solidified under a gradient in the liquid of 2.0×10^4 K/m. The curve corresponds to morphological stability theory. Lines correspond to constitutional supercooling, modified constitutional supercooling and absolute stability. (After CORIELL and SEKERKA [1980].)

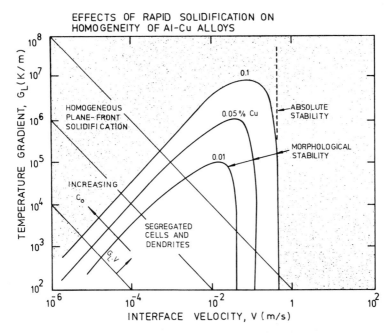

EFFECTS OF RAPID SOLIDIFICATION ON
HOMOGENEITY OF Al–Cu ALLOYS

Fig. 21. Different conditions of plane front growth versus cellular and dendrite growth, determined by different values of G_1 and V in Al–Cu alloys. The lines separating the two regimes correspond to the locus of morphological stability. (After MEHRABIAN [1982].)

evident that at high interface velocities the region of morphological stability is independent of the temperature gradient and the absolute stability criterion controls the S–L interface stability in that region.

In summary, the stability theory predicts that for the case of unidirectional solidification of alloys the constitutional supercooling criterion is a good approximation to the onset of instability, but short-wavelength perturbations at high interface velocities are stabilized owing to capillarity forces. If the thermal field is stabilizing, the interface velocity for absolute stability is a function of the solute content and is independent of the temperature gradient in the liquid (fig. 21).

6.3.1. Relationship to constitutional supercooling

For most processes at low interface velocities, common in industrial practice, the classical theory of *Constitutional Supercooling* (CS) (TILLER *et al.* [1953]) is an important tool in order to predict the S–L interface instabilities arising during controlled growth conditions. The theory makes use of thermodynamic concepts in order to determine if the liquid ahead of a moving interface is supercooled with respect to its composition. The theory considers the solute distribution in front of the interface given by eq. (26) and the corresponding liquidus temperature given by

References: p. 573.

the expression

$$T_1 = T_e - m_1 C_\infty \left[1 + \frac{1 - k_0}{k_0} \exp\left(-\frac{V}{D_1} z \right) \right]. \tag{54}$$

The temperature in the liquid ahead of the unperturbed interface is

$$T = T_e + \frac{m_1 C_\infty}{k_0} + G_1 z. \tag{55}$$

Figure 17, above, considers three possible values of the actual temperature. For case (b), the actual temperature is less than the equilibrium (constitutional) temperature T_1 for a range of values of z and the liquid is said to be *constitutionally supercooled*; as a consequence the S–L interface is unstable. Case (a), where the actual temperature exceeds the equilibrium temperature, corresponds to a stable S–L interface. Case (c) is a limit between conditions (a) and (b). It can easily be demonstrated that the interface will be unstable for

$$\frac{G_1}{V} < -m_1 C_\infty \frac{(1 - k_0)}{D_1 k_0}. \tag{56}$$

Inequality (53) becomes identical to inequality (56) when $L/2K_1 \to 0$, $(K_s + K_1)/2K_1 \to 1$ and $\xi \to 1$.

The decrease of the parameter G_1/VC resulting from inequality (56) controls the evolution of the S–L interface from plane to dendritic. Even when the evolution of the instability is continuous it is possible to recognize discrete stages of the substructure, studied by many authors by means of various techniques reported by BILONI et al. [1966] and BILONI [1968]: optical observations after liquid decanting, radioactive tracers and anodic oxidation giving interference colours, the last method being one of the most powerful even when extremely dilute alloys such as 99.993% and 99.9993% purity Al were studied (BILONI et al. [1965a]). In addition, a quenching technique is often used in order to detect the morphology of the S–L interface through suitable metallography, as used among others by AUDERO and BILONI [1972]. All the techniques are based on the fact that the interface instabilities have as a consequence a redistribution of solute that can reveal the origin and development of the S–L interface instabilities. With increasing CS the following discrete stages may be defined: (i) planar S–L interface; (ii) nodes or depressions at the interface; (iii) elongated or bidimensional cells; (iv) regular of hexagonal cells; (v) distorted or branched cells; (vi) dendritic cells or arrayed dendrites.

6.3.1.1. Cell formation. Many authors determined experimentally that the CS criterion responds reasonably well to the transition from plane to unstable interfaces (CHALMERS [1964]), (FLEMINGS [1974]). BILONI et al. [1966], through critical experiments with Sn–Pb ($k_0 < 1$) and Sn–Sb ($k_0 > 1$) alloys, were the first to establish that depressions at the S–L interface rather than projections are the first sign of interface instability. Current knowledge of the origin of the instability and its evolution can be summarized as follows:

(i) The first sign of instability is segregation associated with depressions at the interface: grain boundaries, striation boundaries and isolated depressions or *nodes*. These nodes are ordered in tetragonal Sn base alloys (BILONI *et al.* [1966]) and fcc Pb–Sn alloys (MORRIS and WINEGARD [1969]). However, in Zn–Cd hexagonal close-packed alloys the first array of nodes is disordered (AUDERO and BILONI [1973]). Alloy crystallography as well as crystal orientation have a large influence on the morphology of the interface formed after the breakdown of the planar interface.

(ii) The grooves associated with grain boundaries and striation boundaries act as built-in distortions of the plane front, and interface breakdowns begin here, spreading outward to other portions of the crystal (SCHAEFER and GLICKSMAN [1970]). The same effect occurs adjacent to the container surface (SATO and OHIRA [1977]).

(iii) Although, as was mentioned, under normal conditions of the formation of the cell substructure perturbation theory can be considered as only a refinement of the simple CS theory, perturbation theory agrees quite well with some experimental results (MORRIS and WINEGARD [1966]), (SHIBATA *et al.* [1978]) and qualitatively with others (SATO and OHIRA [1977]). The preferential growth of interfacial waves at interfacial defects (threading dislocations) which may be distributed at random (BILONI *et al.* [1966]) is an alternative model but without critical experimental evidence.

(iv) The evolution from nodes or depressions at the interface until a regular or hexagonal substructure is obtained as the CS varies in front of the interface, operates through a node mechanism that changes slightly depending on the alloy crystallography (MORRIS and WINEGARD [1969]), (BILONI *et al.* [1965b]), (BILONI *et al.* [1967]), (AUDERO and BILONI [1973]). Figure 22 corresponds to the evolution from planar interface to cellular interface at the decanted interface and behind it after suitable metallographic preparation.

(v) A significant characteristic of the substructure evolution is its reversibility as a function of the values of the parameter G_1/VC_∞ (MORRIS and WINEGARD [1969]).

6.3.1.2. Cellular–dendritic transition. Although prior work on unidirectional solidification of dilute alloys followed by observations at the decanted interface established a criterion of transition from hexagonal to "dendritic" cells depending on the parameter $G_1/V^{1/2}$ and based on the appearance of the first signs of branches at the cells (CHALMERS [1964]), current knowledge indicates that the evolution between the discrete stages (iv) and (vi) defined at the end of § 6.3.1 can be considered continuous and dependent on the crystallography under study. In this sense, in Sn–Pb alloys (bc tetragonal) an increase in CS after cellular growth relates directly to an increase in the number of nodes in the hexagonal cell walls. These nodes serve as the origin for lines of segregation extending within the body of a cell and can thus be assumed to represent the earliest form of branching. In stage (vi) defined in § 6.3.1, each dendrite corresponds to a cooperative evolution of several cells contained in a "supercell" that corresponds to a *longitudinal striation* (BILONI and BOLLING [1963], BILONI *et al.* [1967]). The striation substructure consists of low-angle grain boundaries, with a misorientation between 1° and 5°, emerging at the S–L interface, which in presence of solute are a preferential place for segregation. TILLER [1970] treated in extenso the mechanism associated with the origin of

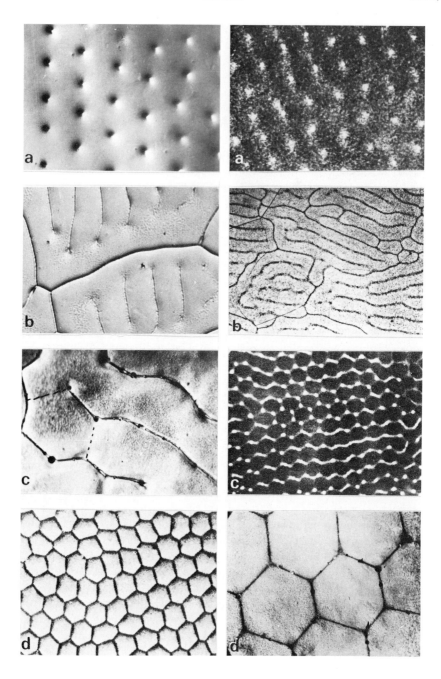

Fig. 22. Evolution of the segregation substructure as a function of constitutional supercooling at the decanted interface (left) and behind it after suitable metallographic treatment (right). The amount of CS increases from (a) to (d). Various magnifications. (After BILONI [1970].)

dislocations during crystal growth as well as the dislocation distribution in arrays, such as the above-mentioned striations.

AUDERO and BILONI [1972] for close-packed hexagonal alloys and MORRIS and WINEGARD [1969] and KATTAMIS and FLEMINGS [1965] in the case of cubic alloys determined the characteristics of the cellular–dendritic transition. In hexagonal alloys, dendrite arms form at cell-wall nodes, and cells become distorted. It is quite evident that in the case of cubic alloys each cell protrudes as a dendrite. CHALMERS [1964] proposed the name of *cellular dendrites* for this type of substructure, where each cell protrudes with the characteristics of a dendrite forming a square, instead of hexagonal, array growing in the characteristic dendritic direction. Figure 23 shows the cellular dendritic morphology in a cubic alloy. Most of the experimental results involving quantitative measurements of the segregation associated with dendrites growing under a continuing constraint such as a temperature gradient has been performed in cubic alloys, mainly the Al–Cu system or steels. Although CHALMERS' terminology appears appropriate, we shall adopt also and alternatively the more general denomination of *arrayed dendritic growth* proposed by BOLLING and FAIN-STEIN-PEDRAZA [1974] for a steady unidirectional growth of dendrites from a liquid under a constant positive temperature gradient.

6.3.1.3. Arrayed dendritic growth. Considerable theoretical and experimental work has been done in order to understand the characteristics of the arrayed dendritic growth. BRODY and FLEMINGS [1966] presented an approximate model predicting that the supercooling ΔT at the dendrite is given by (fig. 24):

$$\Delta T = \frac{G_1}{V} D_1. \tag{57}$$

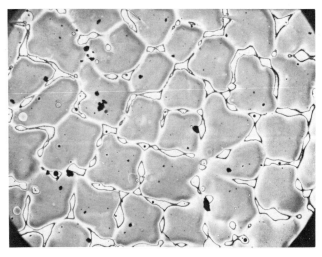

Fig. 23. A polished and etched section of a Pb–Sn crystal, revealing cellular dendritic growth in the typical array corresponding to fcc alloys (after BILONI *et al.* [1967]).

References: p. 573.

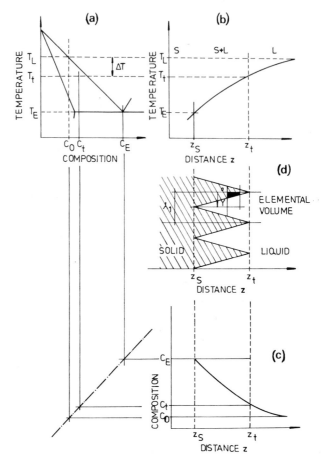

Fig. 24. Conceptual model of cellular dendritic freezing, showing: (a) portion of the phase diagram; (b) schematic temperature distribution in the melt; (c) distribution of solute within the liquid of the mushy zone; (d) representation of platelike, unbranched dendrites showing the position of a characteristic elemental volume. (After BRODY and FLEMINGS [1966].)

This analysis neglected the variation of the tip radius, but for many year has been a very useful tool to understand many microsegregation problems (FLEMINGS [1974]). BURDEN and HUNT [1974a] developed a model to explain the variation of the tip temperature as a function of the growth conditions in unidirectional solidification (that is, V and G_1) measured experimentally by the same authors (BURDEN and HUNT [1974b]. The model predicts that supercooling can be considered to occur as a result of the build-up of average solute concentration ahead of the growth front, depending mainly on the imposed temperature gradient, together with an additional term necessary to satisfy mass balance at the interface. The treatment uses as theoretical device an optimization principle in order to determine the dendrite tip dimension; the results agreed quite well with experiments. Through this model the composition of the dendrite tip, C_t, can be calculated:

$$C_t = C_\infty(1 - a) + bC_\infty, \tag{58}$$

where:

$$a = \frac{G_1 D_1}{m_1 V C_\infty}; \tag{58a}$$

$$b = \left(\frac{-2\psi V(1 - k_0)}{m_1 D_1 C_\infty}\right)^{1/2}. \tag{58b}$$

The supercooling in front of the interface is given by:

$$\Delta T = \frac{G_1 D_1}{V} + 2^{3/2}\left(\frac{-m_1(1 - k_0)C_\infty\psi}{D_1}\right)^{1/2} V^{1/2}; \tag{59}$$

$$\psi = \frac{\gamma_{sl}}{\Delta S_f}. \tag{59a}$$

TRIVEDI [1980] considers the relative importance of solute diffusion, thermal diffusion and capillarity effects defining three characteristic lengths:

Diffusion length: $l_s = \dfrac{2D_1}{V}$; \hfill (60)

Thermal diffusion length: $l_t = k_0\dfrac{\Delta T_0}{G}$; \hfill (61)

Capillarity length: $l_c = \dfrac{\gamma_{sl}}{\Delta S_f k_0 \Delta T_0}$; \hfill (62)

and the dimensionless parameters

$$\mathcal{Q} = \frac{l_c}{l_s} = \frac{\gamma_{sl}V}{2\Delta S_f k_0 \Delta T_0 D_1}; \tag{63}$$

$$\mathcal{G} = \frac{l_s}{l_t} = \frac{2GD_1}{Vk_0\Delta T_0}, \tag{64}$$

where G is an "effective temperature gradient" and ΔT_0 is the difference between the liquidus and the solidus temperature of the alloy under consideration. The solution of heat, mass transfer equations along with the appropriate dendrite stability criteria shows that dendrite characteristics such as composition, temperature and radius of curvature of the dendrite are determined by the dimensionless parameters $\mathcal{Q}$ and $\mathcal{G}$. Noting that $\mathcal{Q}$ becomes predominant at large V, whereas $\mathcal{G}$ becomes predominant at small V, at large V the dendrite characteristics are independent of temperature gradient whereas at low velocities $\mathcal{G}$ controls dendrite characteristics. More recently, KURZ and FISHER [1981], through a simple form of the stability criterion together with the consideration of a hemispherical dendrite cap, obtained simple expressions for radius tip temperature, Peclet number $P'_e = V\rho/2a_1$, tip concentration and temperature as well as primary dendrite spacing as a function of V and G_1. Also, in this model, G_1 is predominant at low S–L interface velocities and V at high solidification rate. For both models the agreement with BURDEN and HUNT's [1974b] experiments on Al–2% Cu are reasonable.

6.3.1.4. Dendrite spacing. Many theoretical and experimental studies have been performed on *primary dendrite spacing*, λ_1. Most authors agree that the expression

$$\lambda_1 = A_1 G_1^{-m'} V^{-n'} \tag{65}$$

reflects the relationship existing between the primary dendrite spacing and the cooling rate $(G_1 V)$. In eq. (65), A_1, m' and n' are constants and a discrepancy exists, especially as to the value of n'. Recently, HUNT [1979] derived an expression,

$$\lambda_1 = A_1 G_1^{-0.5} V^{-0.25}, \tag{66}$$

that coincides closely with the expression derived by KURZ and FISHER [1981] for high values of V, where arrayed dendritic morphology arises. However, upon review many authors considered that eq. (65) reflects the real value of λ_1 with values of m' and n' near -0.5 (FLEMINGS [1974]; OKAMOTO *et al.* [1975]; OKAMOTO and KISHITAKE [1975]; YOUNG and KIRWOOD [1975]). On the other hand, in steels a broad discrepancy exists as to the values of m' and n', although many of the experimental studies have not been performed under controlled solidification conditions. JACOBI and SCHWERDTFEGER [1976], controlling G_1 and V separately, obtained values of $m' = -0.25$ and $n' = -0.72$. More recently, FLEMINGS [1982] presented an expression that for high values of the heat mould transfer coefficient (h_i) becomes:

$$\lambda_1 = A_1 (G_1 V)^{-3/8}. \tag{67}$$

Furthermore, theoretical attempts to quantitatively explain the available data in the literature have been unsuccessful (KLAREN *et al.* [1980]), and a very recent paper by MASON *et al.* [1982] cast doubts on the validity of eq. (65) which implies that the effects of composition, G_1 and V on λ_1 are independent of each other. Their experimental results show that, although the effect of composition is somewhat smaller for the dendritic structure, the effects of G_1 and V are strongly coupled. As a result, these authors considered that eq. (65) must be used with caution.

The validity of eq. (65) as well as the true values of m' and n' are quite important in order to obtain, in rapid solidification processes, the value of V through eq. (65) when λ_1 is measured. In this sense, MASON *et al.* [1983] found that at high velocity a relationship $\lambda_1 = A_1 G_1^{-m}$ for constant composition and velocity exists. However, even then the value of the exponent is found to depend on velocity.

Regarding *secondary dendrite branch spacing*, λ_2, there exists a general agreement in the sense that the arm spacing becomes finer with increasing cooling rate. The most complete and careful investigation on the effect of solute is that by HOWARTH and MONDOLFO [1962], which showed that in Al–Cu alloys λ_2 decreased with increasing solute. Regarding the relationship between λ_2 and $(G_1 V)$, the most widely accepted expression is:

$$\lambda_2 = B_1 (G_1 V)^{-n'}, \tag{68}$$

where B_1 is a constant and $n' \approx 1/3$. On the other hand it is necessary to consider that the final secondary dendrite spacing in a fully solidified casting is usually much coarser than the one formed initially, as a result of coarsening effects during solidification (KATTAMIS *et al.* [1967]). Little is known about what controls the constant B_1, but it appears that it becomes smaller as the temperature interval between liquidus and solidus (ΔT_0) increases (DOHERTY [1984]).

6.3.1.5. Microsegregation in cellular and arrayed dendritic structures. In order to develop a theory able to predict microsegregation in cellular and arrayed dendritic growth, BRODY and FLEMINGS [1966] were the first to provide an approximate model, neglecting tip undercooling. The more recent studies treated in § 6.3.1.3 permit a more realistic treatment of solute redistribution overall at high solidification rate. SOLARI and BILONI [1980] considered the model presented by BRODY and FLEMINGS [1966] (fig. 24), but with an extra assumption: there exists an undercooling in front of the interface as a consequence of a build-up of solute and the effect of curvature of the S–L interface. The general expression for the local distribution of solute is:

$$C_s = k_0 C_0 \left[\frac{a-b}{k_0 - 1} + \left(1 - \frac{(a-b)k_0}{(k_0 - 1)} \right) \left(1 - \frac{f_s}{1 + \alpha_\theta k_0} \right)^{k_0 - 1} \right]; \qquad (69)$$

$$\alpha_\theta = \frac{D_s}{l_0^2} t_f = \frac{4 D_s t_f}{\lambda_1^2}, \qquad (69a)$$

with:

t_f = local solidification time;
$l_0 = \lambda_1/2$ = half of the cellular spacing;
D_s = solid diffusion coefficient;
f_s = solidified fraction.

The dimensionless parameter a is given by expression (58a) and takes into account the build-up of the solute in front of the interface. b is given by eq. (58b) and takes into account the effect of curvature of the interface. α_θ allows for diffusion in the solid. In general, for $k_0 < 1$, $a < 0$ and b always > 0.

Figure 24 shows the conceptual model of arrayed dendritic freezing with the representation of the platelike cellular dendrites and the position of the elemental volume to be considered. At present this model is the only one existing in the literature that is able to predict cellular and arrayed dendritic microsegregation.

For cellular (arrayed) dendritic solidification, a can be taken as zero (low G_1), and if α_θ is neglected (SOLARI and BILONI [1980]):

$$C_s = k_0 C_0 \left[\frac{-b}{1 - k_0} + \left(1 + \frac{bk_0}{k_0 - 1} \right)(1 - f_s)^{k_0 - 1} \right]. \qquad (70)$$

6.3.1.6. Diffusion during solidification. The parameter that determines the extent of homogenization during freezing is α_θ [eq. (69a)]. Recently, KURZ and CLYNE [1981] analyzed critically the homogenization model proposed by BRODY and FLEMINGS [1966]; the latter is essentially correct for $\alpha_\theta < 0.1$ (that is, with limited

References: p. 573.

solid diffusion during the solidification process) but presents problems when α_θ becomes higher, as has been demonstrated by FLEMINGS et al. [1970] using numerical treatment. Large values of α_θ lead to computed solute distributions which are physically impossible in that the temperature at which solidification is complete lies above the equilibrium solidus, that is, the last solid to form is less than the nominal composition C_0 of the alloy. Essentially, the model proposed by KURZ and CLYNE [1981] involves the following steps:

(i) Rather than assuming linear growth of the volume element considered in the microsegregation model proposed by BRODY and FLEMINGS [1966], the alternative parabolic growth law proposed by the same authors is adopted. As a consequence, the following expression is calculated:

$$C_s = k_0 C_0 \left[1 - (1 - 2\alpha_\theta k_0) f_s \right]^{(k_0 - 1)/(1 - 2\alpha_\theta k_0)}. \tag{71}$$

(ii) A function $\Omega(\alpha_\theta)$ is defined having the form

$$\Omega(\alpha_\theta) = \alpha_\theta \left[1 - \exp\left(-\frac{1}{\alpha_\theta} \right) - \frac{1}{2} \exp\left(-\frac{1}{2\alpha_\theta} \right) \right]. \tag{72}$$

(iii) The sequence of operations required in the modified model is first to establish α_θ from eq. (69a), then to evaluate $\Omega(\alpha_\theta)$ through eq. (72) and finally to predict the solidification behaviour by replacing α_θ with $\Omega(\alpha_\theta)$ in eq. (71). The result is a description of the solidification process that behaves correctly over the whole range of the values of the parameter α_θ. It appears that, when limited solid diffusion is considered during ingot solidification ($\alpha_\theta < 0.1$), BRODY and FLEMING'S [1966] equation,

$$C_s = k_0 C_0 \left(1 - \frac{f_s}{1 + \alpha_\theta k_0} \right)^{k_0 - 1}, \tag{73}$$

can quite satisfactorily be used to replace the more exact Kurz and Fisher solution. However, when very rapid diffusion occurs as in the case of interstitials, as the C in steels, the proposed modified analysis proposed by KURZ and FISHER [1981] leads to a more realistic description of the behaviour in mushy-freezing alloys.

6.3.1.7. Experimental results in microsegregation. Very recently, PALACIO et al. [1982], in careful experiments performed on Al–2% Cu alloys, determined the Cu concentration in cellular and cellular-dendritic tips in unidirectional solidification experiments. This is equivalent to measuring the composition at the axes of the cellular dendrites, or arrayed dendrites, sketched in fig. 24. Figure 25 shows the composition of the cellular and cellular dendrite centres for different theories when Al–2% Cu alloy is considered for different values of G_1 and V. Superimposed are the experimental points obtained by PALACIO et al. [1982]. The square points correspond to experiments where V and G_1 were measured. The circles denote those points where G_1 was measured but V was obtained from measuring λ_1 through eq. (65). The results obtained vary according to the value of the coefficients m' and n' adopted. Two possibilities are considered: 1) $m' = n' = -0.5$ and 2) $m' = -0.5$, $n' = -0.25$.

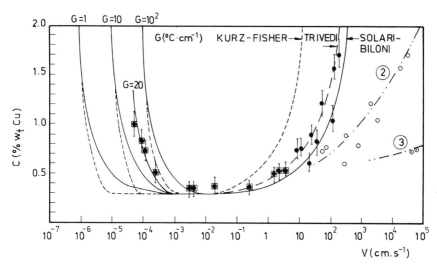

Fig. 25. Composition versus V and G_1 for different models considering arrayed dendritic growth for the case of Al–2% Cu alloy. The figure shows the experimental points obtained by PALACIO *et al.* [1982]. Squares correspond to measurements of both V and G_1. Solid circles correspond to the measurement of V through eq. (65), assuming $m' = n' = -0.5$. Open circles correspond to $m' = -0.5$ and $n' = -0.25$, according to HUNT [1979] (curve 2), or KURZ and FISHER [1981] (curve 3), see table 3.

Table 3 gives three possible results according to the values of A_1, m' and n' assumed by PALACIO *et al.* [1982], HUNT [1979] and KURZ and FISHER [1981]. Figure 25 shows that at low and intermediate values of V all the models of cellular dendritic growth predict the dendrite composition quite well. At higher velocities, when $m' = n' = -0.5$ is assumed, the prediction by TRIVEDI [1980] is excellent, followed by eq. (69). When $m' = -0.5$ and $n' = -0.25$ is assumed, the experimental results obtained are inconsistent with all the theoretical models.

Regarding the experiments on redistribution of solute during undirectional solidification within a cellular or arrayed dendritic substructure as is usually obtained in columnar growth during conventional casting, the model developed by BRODY and FLEMINGS [1966] and its extension by SOLARI and BILONI [1980] postulates a continuous increase of solute from centre to periphery of the dendrites as a result of the complete mixing of the liquid. At low values of V and G_1 such as corresponding to columnar growth in castings, the constants a and b and α_θ in eq. (69) can be taken zero, and eq. (69) then reduces to the Scheil equation (27). That the Scheil equation well describes the solute distribution in the columnar zone of ingots has been proved, among other authors, by KATTAMIS and FLEMINGS [1965] for low alloy steels and WEINBERG and TEGHTSOONIAN [1972] for Cu-base alloys. CALVO and BILONI [1971], combining anodic oxidation techniques with electron microprobe measurements, obtained a clear map of the solute segregation together with quantitative

Table 3

Results obtained by PALACIO et al. [1982], comparing the theoretical treatment of SOLARI and BILONI [1980] with experimental results.

no.	Sample		Tip composition		Growth velocity		
	λ_1 (cm)	G_1 (°C/cm)	theory (wt% Cu)	experiment (wt% Cu)	P–S–B [a] (cm/s)	H [b] (cm/s)	K–F [c] (cm/s)
1	–	20	0.68	0.80 ± 0.08	8×10^{-5}		
2	–	30	1.35	1.12 ± 0.12	5×10^{-5}		
3	–	30	0.77	0.73 ± 0.08	1×10^{-4}		
4	–	20	0.44	0.49 ± 0.07	2×10^{-4}		
5	–	10	0.29	0.33 ± 0.05	2.5×10^{-3}		
6	–	10	0.29	0.34 ± 0.05	4.2×10^{-3}		
7	2×10^{-2}	30	0.29	0.41 ± 0.05	1.3×10^{-2}		
8	1×10^{-2}	30	0.32	0.34 ± 0.05	1.3×10^{-1}		
9	4×10^{-3}	10	0.40	0.50 ± 0.03	1.5×10^{0}		
10	3.5×10^{-3}	7.5	0.41	0.52 ± 0.03	2×10^{0}		
11	3.3×10^{-3}	7	0.44	0.56 ± 0.03	3×10^{0}		
12	2.2×10^{-3}	5	0.54	0.75 ± 0.09	7.6×10^{0}	4.9×10^{1}	4×10^{4}
13	2×10^{-3}	5	0.57	0.76 ± 0.09	9.2×10^{0}	7.2×10^{1}	5.9×10^{4}
14	1.5×10^{-3}	4	0.70	0.81 ± 0.09	2.0×10^{1}	3.5×10^{2}	2.9×10^{5}
15	1.0×10^{-3}	4	0.92	1.19 ± 0.11	4.6×10^{1}	1.8×10^{3}	1.5×10^{6}
16	1.0×10^{-3}	10	0.71	0.70 ± 0.10	2×10^{1}	2.8×10^{2}	2.3×10^{5}
17	8.0×10^{-4}	2	1.40	1.50 ± 0.11	1.4×10^{2}	1.7×10^{4}	1.4×10^{7}
18	8.0×10^{-4}	10	0.79	0.85 ± 0.11	3×10^{1}	6.9×10^{2}	5.72×10^{5}
19	7.0×10^{-4}	2	1.59	1.70 ± 0.11	1.9×10^{2}	3.0×10^{4}	2.4×10^{7}
20	6.0×10^{-4}	9	1.12	1.10 ± 0.11	8.0×10^{1}	2.7×10^{3}	2.2×10^{6}

[a] With $\lambda_1 = A_1 V^{-0.5} G_1^{-0.5}$, $A_1 = 1.35 \times 10^{-2}$ $\therefore V = (1.35 \times 10^{-2}/\lambda_1 G_1^{0.5})^2$; PALACIO et al. [1982].

[b] With $\lambda_1 = 2.83(k_0 \Delta T_0 D_1 \Gamma)^{0.25} V^{-0.25} G_1^{-0.5}$ $\therefore V = (1.30 \times 10^{-2}/\lambda_1 G_1^{0.5})^4$; HUNT [1979].

[c] With $\lambda_1 = 4.3(\Delta T_0 D_1 \Gamma/k_0)^{0.25} V^{-0.25} G_1^{-0.5}$ $\therefore V = (6.90 \times 10^{-2}/\lambda_1 G_1^{0.5})^4$; KURZ and FISHER [1981].

measurements of the Cu concentration in Al–1% Cu alloys, that are in agreement with the above mentioned authors.

Very recently, FLEMINGS [1981] presented a comprehensive review on segregation and structures in rapidly solidified cast metals connected with current research at MIT. In a related paper, MASUR and FLEMINGS [1982], using the STEM, which relates X-ray intensity to composition, measured the composition of very fine dendritic cells of Al–4.5% Cu solidified at very high cooling rate (2×10^5 K/s) and $V = 0.6$ m/s. According to SOLARI and BILONI [1980], under these conditions eq. (70) would apply. Figure 26 shows: (i) The experimental results obtained by MASUR and FLEMINGS [1982], (ii) the variation of C_s as a function of f_s according to the predictions of eq. (70). It is quite evident that the segregation profile is consistently described by this equation in close agreement with the experimental results.

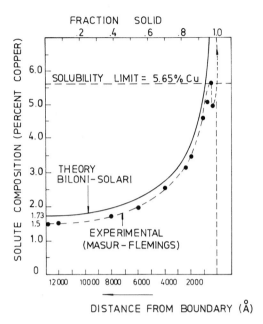

Fig. 26. Comparison between experiments performed by MASUR and FLEMINGS [1981] on composition of cellular dendrites from centre to periphery in Al–4.5% ribbon grown at 0.6 m/s, and theoretical composition given by eq. (70) due to SOLARI and BILONI [1980].

7.   *Polyphase solidification*

7.1.   Peritectic solidification

In a peritectic system the solidification starts by the primary precipitation of a phase α_P. Below the peritectic temperature, a new solid β_P phase will form with a strong tendency to grow along the α_P–L interface and, thus, to isolate the primary phase from contact with the liquid. The reason for this tendency is that the phase diagram (fig. 27) predicts the reaction:

$$\alpha_P + L \rightarrow \beta_P. \tag{74}$$

Thus, it may seem natural that β_P should grow where both the parent phases are present. However, the β_P phase may also grow by primary precipitation into the liquid, in particular if the temperature is gradually decreasing. As a consequence, there may be a competition between the two modes of growth (HILLERT [1979]). KERR *et al.* [1974] distinguish between a *peritectic reaction* and a *peritectic transformation.* The former requires that all three phases be in contact with each other so that the liquid (L) and primary solid phase (α_P) can react directly to form the second solid phase (β_P). In a peritectic *transformation,* the liquid (L) and α_P phase are not necessarily in contact and the β_P phase may be produced by long-range

References: p. 573.

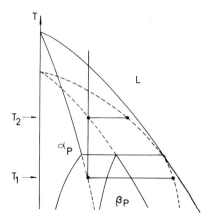

Fig. 27. Peritectic phase diagram. The temperatures for stationary planar growth of the α_p phase, T_1, and of the β_p phase, T_2, are indicated at the corresponding alloy composition. (After HILLERT [1979].)

diffusion. The reaction is a specific case of the transformation, and thus the distribution or connectivity of the L, α_p and β_p phases determine whether the reaction can take place. According to HILLERT [1979] and FREDRIKSSON and NYLENT [1982] in most peritectic situations, first the primary precipitated phase, α_P, will partially dissolve by diffusion of solute through the liquid from the β_p–L boundary to the L–α_p boundary (fig. 28a). Then the β_p layer increases in thickness

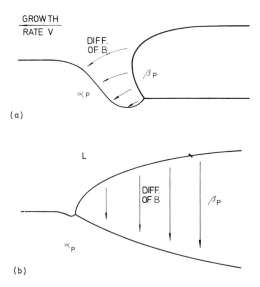

Fig. 28. Peritectic reaction and peritectic transformation. (a) In the peritectic *reaction* a second solid phase, β_p, grows along the surface of the primary phase α_p. (b) In the peritectic *transformation,* diffusion of B atoms through the already formed second phase β_p occurs. (After HILLERT [1979].)

during the subsequent cooling after its formation by peritectic reaction; this is achieved through the subsequent peritectic transformation (fig. 28b).

7.1.1. Aligned peritectic growth

By the application of a temperature gradient it is possible in peritectic alloys to obtain unidirectional solidification. Theoretically, with a large enough temperature gradient a planar solidification front may be developed and when applied to peritectic alloys of composition that fall within the $(\alpha_p + \beta_p)$ field the result may be an aligned $(\alpha_p + \beta_p)$ two-phase structure. From experimental results, although a rod-like aligned $(\alpha_p + \beta_p)$ structure has been obtained (BOETTINGER [1974]; BRODY and DAVID [1979]), the formation of a planar solidification front with a coupled growth of the two solid phases has not been observed. Instead, alternating bands of α_p and β_p were obtained (BOETTINGER [1974]; OSTROWSKI and LANGER [1979]; TITCHENER and SPITTLE [1975]). Through thermodynamic arguments HILLERT [1979] has explained these results. In fig. 27 an alloy of the indicated composition can solidify to pure α_p at a temperature T_1. If the temperature gradient is successively increased, the temperature of the solidification front will decrease continuously and the dendritic morphology will change to cellular and finally it will become planar at T_1. However, the extrapolated phase boundary for the $(\beta_p + L)$ equilibrium indicates that, in absence of α_p, it should be possible to make the same alloy solidify to pure β_p with a planar solidification front at T_2, which is higher than T_1. If the β_p phase is nucleated at T_2 it may thus form a complete layer ahead and out of contact with the planar α_p front which is at T_1. The β_p phase in contact with the liquid is however not stable with respect to α_p at the temperature T_2 because it is above the peritectic temperature. As a consequence, if α_p is now nucleated it may grow along the β_p–L interface and again form a planar α_p front. In this way, alternating α_p and β_p bands can form.

7.2. Eutectic solidification

Eutectic solidification is the formation of two or more solid phases simultaneously from the liquid. The eutectic alloys are very important in the casting industry owing to their peculiar characteristics: (i) low melting point compared with those of the pure components, simplifying melting and casting operations: (ii) excellent flow properties and better feeding behaviour, comparable to pure metals as a result of a smoother S–L interface than in proeutectic alloys where dendrite formation obstructs the partially solidified channels; (iii) a zero freezing range which reduces casting defects such as segregation and shrinkage porosity; (iv) the possibility of forming "in-situ" composites in order to obtain materials possessing not only great strength but also great thermal stability. Among the most common eutectic or near-eutectic alloys of industrial importance are the cast irons, the Al–Si alloys, wear-resistant welding alloys and solders. Eutectic solidification can be described through the following stages, at least in lamellar eutectics: the eutectic liquid is supercooled and one of the solid phases nucleates, causing solute enrichment in the surrounding liquid and sympathetic nucleation of the second solid phase. Repeated sympathetic nucleation and/or overgrowth of one solid phase by the other produces a growth centre for an individual eutectic grain. Solidification then proceeds primarily by edgewise growth at the ends of the solid-phase particles. The most probable mechanism for lamellar growth has been described by TILLER [1958] through the sequence heterogeneous nucleation – overlap and edgewise growth of both phases. This type of growth is often described as a *coupled growth process*. As solidification continues, spatial and crystallographic rotation of the solid together with competitive overgrowth of adjacent eutectic grains lead to a stable solidification front, with the surviving eutectic grains having, as far as possible, maximized the solidification rate, minimized the $\alpha_E - \beta_E$ interfacial energy and oriented the $\alpha_E - \beta_E$ interfaces in the heat flow direction for efficient edgewise growth (CANTOR [1983b]). The ability of one solid phase in the eutectic to stimulate nucleation of the other varies widely for different α_E and β_E phases and, in general, knowledge about the nucleation process in eutectic solidification is rather poor (MONDOLFO [1965]). Thus, this section will treat mainly theory and experiments concerning steady state directional solidification, a method which has furnished, as in the case of dilute alloys, a large number of reliable results. By treating stationary states, a clearer insight can be obtained into the growth behaviour of eutectic alloys. This, in turn, should lead to a better qualitative understanding the real cast structures (KURZ and FISHER [1979]).

The formation and properties of composite materials based on unidirectionally solidified eutectics are treated in ch. 29.

7.2.1. Eutectic classification

When a eutectic liquid solidifies, the resulting material generally consists of a finely dispersed two-phase microstructure but the exact arrangement of the two phases can vary widely, depending on the solidification conditions and the particular eutectic alloy being solidified. As a result, though there have been many attempts to provide a simple classification of the wide range of eutectic microstructures, none has been entirely successful (CHADWICK [1963]). Although no definitive method of classifying eutectic morphologies has yet been developed, at present the more rational approach is to classify eutectics according to the solidification behaviour of their component phases (HUNT and JACKSON [1966]). A correlation is made between eutectic morphologies (faceted or non-faceted) and the entropies of fusion of the α_E and β_E phases, concepts both discussed in § 4.2. The results correlate reasonably well, though not perfectly, with eutectic microstructures. The classification refers to: class I: non-faceted–non-faceted eutectics (nf–nf); class II: non-faceted–faceted eutectics (nf–f); class III: faceted–faceted eutectics (f–f). Not very much is known about the solidification of class III eutectics but extensive research has been done on eutectics of class I and class II.

7.2.2. Class I: Non-faceted–non-faceted eutectics

Eutectic mixtures of two non-faceting phases tend to form regular microstructures consisting of either alternate lamellae of α_E and β_E or rods of α_E embedded in β_E. *Lamellar* or *rod-like eutectics* usually contain faults in the arrangement of the two phases, consisting of kinks, branches and terminations of the lamellae or rods. A three-dimensional analysis of the structure shows that, because of the faults of the microstructure, both phases are always continuous over large regions considered as eutectic grains. An *eutectic grain* can be described approximately as two inter-penetrating single crystals of the two component phases having almost constant crystallographic orientation.

As CANTOR [1983b] points out, in this type of eutectic solidification, described as a *coupled growth process,* the two phases, α_E and β_E, solidify side by side with an approximately planar and isothermal S–L interface, supercooled ΔT below the equilibrium temperature. During solidification, the A-rich phase rejects B atoms into the liquid and the B-rich phase rejects A atoms. At a solidification rate V the growth process is controlled by a balance between: (i) the rate of lateral diffusion ahead of the S–L interface, which is faster when there is a small *interlamellar* or *interrod spacing*, λ_E, and (ii) the energy of the α_E–β_E interface which is smaller for large λ_E; this energy exerts its influence at the α_E–β_E–L triple point by producing a curvature in the S–L interface.

A number of approximate theories of lamellar growth have been proposed (ZENER [1946]; TILLER [1958]; HILLERT [1957]; JACKSON and HUNT [1966]). The basis of all these treatments is illustrated in fig. 29. The supercooling ΔT at the S–L interface is given by

$$\Delta T = \Delta T_D + \Delta T_c + \Delta T_k, \tag{75}$$

where ΔT_D is the supercooling due to the variation in composition from the eutectic composition. The expected variation of this term is shown in fig. 29b. ΔT_c is the supercooling due to capillarity and ΔT_k is the interface kinetic supercooling. In the case of eutectic class I, ΔT_k can be neglected when compared with ΔT_D. The second approximation in the treatment is to consider that the total supercooling, ΔT, given by eq. (75) is constant across the interface. Thus across the interface, any variation in T_D must be balanced by a variation in ΔT_c, giving $\Delta T = \Delta T_D + \Delta T_c = $ const. at each point of the interface. ΔT_D has a minimum value near the α_E–β_E–L groove, and the radius of curvature should, therefore, be smallest in these regions. This leads to an interface shape similar to that shown in fig. 29c. JACKSON and HUNT [1966] have shown that the predicted interface shape agrees very well with the interface shape observed in the transparent hexachloroethane–carbon bromide model system. The solution of the steady-state diffusion equation for the S–L interface leads to a solution of the type

$$\Delta T = K_1 \lambda_E V + K_2 / \lambda_E, \tag{76}$$

where K_1 and K_2 are constants. Equation (76) is shown schematically for a fixed growth rate in fig. 30, where ΔT is high for large lamellar spacings where diffusion is difficult, and for small spacings where curvature effects are important. The values of λ_E and ΔT are not fixed uniquely by V. Then some further condition is required.

References: p. 573.

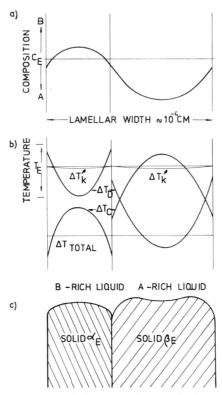

Fig. 29. (a) Profile of B over an α_E–β_E interface. (b) Contributions of the supercooling due to composition (ΔT_D), curvature (ΔT_c) and interface kinetics (ΔT_k) to the total amount of supercooling (ΔT) existing at the S–L interface. (c) Shape of the lamellar S–L liquid interface. (HUNT and JACKSON [1966].)

The simplest possibility is that growth is preferred at the minimum ΔT for a given V or, equivalently, maximum V for a given ΔT. This theoretical criterion, often called the *extremum condition*, is analogous to the *maximum growth rate criterion* discussed in § 6 where dendritic growth was analyzed. Equation (76) becomes:

$$\lambda_E^2 V = K_2/K_1,\tag{77}$$

or: $$\Delta T^2/V = K_3,\tag{78}$$

K_3 being a constant. These equations have been experimentally verified in many class I eutectics, and according to TASSA and HUNT [1976] the extremum condition responds quite well to experimental verification.

    Concerning lamellar stability, spacings smaller than that at the extremum condition are inherently unstable and thus the extremum spacing is expected to be the minimum observed (JACKSON and HUNT [1966]). SUNDQUIST [1968] refers to the spacing of maximum velocity as the *lower catastrophic limit* (LCL). Spacings somewhat larger than the extremum are stable but when they become very much larger,

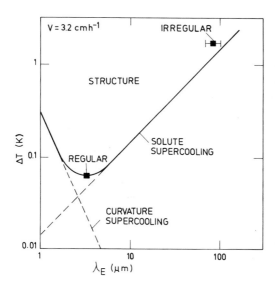

Fig. 30. Supercooling, ΔT, as a function of lamellar spacing, λ_E, for a given growth rate. The curve was calculated by fitting minimum to measured values of supercooling and spacing for a regular camphor–naphthalene eutectic. The irregular growing eutectic that occurs at the same composition shows higher values of ΔT and λ_E, but it lies practically on the theoretical curve due to JACKSON and HUNT [1966]. (After KURZ and FISHER [1979].)

by a factor of two or more, the interface curvature cannot maintain an isothermal interface and a *pocket* develops in one phase and drops progressively back from the interface until growth of the other phase ultimately occurs in it. As a consequence, the local spacing is abruptly reduced by a factor of two (HUNT and JACKSON [1966]; FLEMINGS [1974]. This is named the *upper catastrophic limit* (UCL) by SUNDQUIST [1968].

A theoretical justification of the extremum condition in terms of a balance between the forces acting on the moving interface has been presented by SHINGU [1979].

7.2.2.1.   Rod growth and lamellar–rod transition. There is considerable interest in establishing the factors that govern which of the two morphologies, lamellar or rod-like, will occur. There are some rules but also a number of effects which cannot be explained. A further complication is that many eutectics undergo a transition between the two morphologies when the solidification conditions are changed. Experimentally, it is found that eutectics in which one phase has a very low volume fraction tend to grow in a rod-like manner. This can be explained on the basis that a rod-like structure has lower total surface energy than a lamellar structure when the volume fraction of one of the phases is less than about 30%. Lamellar-to-rod transitions can occur with increasing solidification rate, decreasing temperature gradient or variation in the solidification direction. However, the same variations in other alloy systems have the opposite result, that is, a transition from rod to lamellar eutectics. On the other hand, CHADWICK [1963] proposed that the transition from lamellae to rods can occur as a result of constitutional supercooling due to a third element acting as an impurity in addition to the A and B elements of the eutectic. The same author explains that constitutional supercooling caused by an impurity can result in a cellular type structure. The mechanism is essentially similar to the cellular breakthrough in single-phase solidification treated in § 6; for a critical value of G_1/V the planar S–L interface can become unstable and the solidification front becomes corrugated. In view of the fact that the eutectic lamellae try to remain normal to the S–L interface the product is a characteristic arrangement of lamellae and or rods in *eutectic colonies*. Regarding the instability criterion between a plane front and an unstable one leading to a cellular type structure, BERTORELLO and BILONI [1969] propose that this corresponds to the inception of morphological changes in the structure, related to interface depressions, when a minimum of constitutional supercooling exists: these include grain boundaries and node-like junctions as reported by GRUZLESKI and WINEGARD [1968] but also fault terminations at the S–L interface.

7.2.3.   Class II: Non-faceted–faceted eutectics

When (nf–f) eutectics are compared with (nf–nf) eutectics it is quite clear that the degree of regularity is much lower and also the spacings are much larger. As a consequence, some authors have termed (nf–f) eutectics *irregular*. Taking into account the fact that eutectics of technological importance such as Al–Si and Fe–C belong to class II, in the last decade a substantial effort has been mounted in order to establish a theory able to predict the formation of (nf–f) eutectics as well as their structural characteristics. FISHER and KURZ [1977], and KURZ and FISHER [1979, 1980] have presented reviews of the knowledge in the field together with first approximations to a formal description of the (nf–f) eutectic growth, as well as their principal characteristics when unidirectional solidification is used. These characteristics can be summarized as follows:

(i) A large interfacial spacing together with a wide dispersion of local spacing is observed. In a plot of $\lambda_E V^2$ against volume fraction of the phase considered faceted, according to the classification mentioned in § 7.2.1, together with volume-fraction dependence of eutectic spacings for (nf–nf) eutectics according to JACKSON and HUNT's [1966] predictions, it can be clearly seen that typical (nf–f) eutectics have anomalously large spacings when compared to (nf–nf) and to theoretical predictions.

(ii) The supercoolings of (nf–f) eutectics are high when compared to those of (nf–nf) eutectics and higher than those predicted by JACKSON and HUNT [1966]. Earlier investigations introduced a kinetic term in order to explain this effect, but it was shown by STEEN and HELLAWELL [1975] that the kinetic supercooling of Si in Al–Si eutectic is too low to explain the measured supercoolings.

Studies performed on the model system camphor–naphthalene permitted important results to be obtained, as a consequence of the fact that the system exhibits two distinct eutectic growth forms: one regular and the other irregular. When ΔT and spacing λ_E are plotted as a function of growth rate both values fall on the theoretical curve for regular eutectic growth but, in the case of the irregular eutectic form, both values are much larger and, as a consequence, the coarseness of the structure has a direct effect on the supercooling of the growing eutectics. This means that if eq. (76) is considered to hold for both regular and irregular structures, a coarse spacing will lead to higher supercooling (TOLOUI and HELLAWELL [1976]). Figure 30 shows that the theoretical relationship corresponds satisfactorily with the experiments. This agreement is explained by KURZ and FISHER [1979] in terms of the fact that the faceted phase of the (nf–f) eutectic form presents anisotropic growth kinetics and, as a consequence, presents difficulty of branching in comparison with the non-faceted phase. The result is the impossibility of reaching the optimum spacing given by the minimum supercooling in fig. 30. In summary, the large spacings and supercoolings can be explained by *non-optimum* growth with occurs because the (nf–f) eutectic cannot change easily, whereas a (nf–nf) eutectic always grows with that spacing which gives the maximum growth rate or interface tempera-ture. Then, the anisotropic growth kinetics of the faceted phase leads to what might be termed *branching-limited growth*. As a consequence, the (nf–f) eutectic can only change its morphology via catastrophic changes and, in order for this to occur, the spacing must increase to the upper catastrophic limit (UCL) (fig. 31). The observed spacing will be between the two limits defined in fig. 31 (LCL and UCL).

(iii) The supercooling and the spacing for a given growth rate decrease as the temperature gradient at the S–L interface is increased, and experimentally it is observed that the increase of the gradient has as a consequence a flatter interface. It is suggested that the gradient increase tends to prevent the formation of depressions in the non-faceted phase. As a result, the solute concentration at the nf-phase–melt

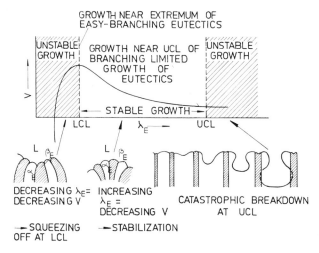

Fig. 31. Growth criteria for eutectic structures. The extremum condition is related to the lower catastrophic limit (LCL), the breakdown of the structure to the upper catastrophic limit (UCL). Depressions in the low volume fraction is the type of instability that permits branching. This is the proposed criterion determining the spacing of class II eutectics. (After KURZ and FISHER [1979].)

References: p. 573.

interface increases. This should cause the nf phase to branch at a smaller separation and thus is equivalent to a lowering of the UCL in fig. 31.

7.2.4. Crystallography

Eutectic crystallography is not as simple as was long supposed and now it seems to be clear that it is determined by a complex balance of many competitive effects, such as the presence or absence of epitaxial nucleation, anisotropy of the $\alpha_E-\beta_E$ interfacial energy, anisotropic kinetics of the α_E-L and β_E-L interfaces and the ability for changing crystallographic orientations during solidification. CANTOR [1983] presents a comprehensive study on the crystallography of, and interfaces in eutectic alloys, concluding that the above-mentioned balance is different for each eutectic. As a consequence it is necessary to take care in order to avoid rash generalizations. In this rather difficult field the use of electron microscope techniques, able to study fine details of dislocations and edges at eutectic interfaces, seems to be the most powerful way to produce an improvement of the general understanding of the crystallographic relationships between the phases growing cooperatively during eutectic solidification.

7.2.5. Eutectic range

Usually, a *hypoeutectic* or a *hypereutectic* alloy solidifies by dendritic growth of the primary phase between the liquidus and eutectic temperatures, followed by eutectic solidification of the remaining interdendritic liquid. However, there is a *range* of composition and supercooling where it is possible to freeze liquids to solids having entirely eutectic microstructures and growing with a stable planar interface. This range of conditions is known as the *coupled zone*. Pioneering investigations in this field were those of TAMMANN and BOTSCHWAR [1926] and KOFLER [1950] in organic systems, which established that at low or zero temperature gradients the extent of the eutectic range increases with growth velocity. Later on, MOLLARD and FLEMINGS [1967] showed that the widening of the coupled zones was not restricted to high growth rates but, with a positive temperature gradient, could also be obtained at low growth rates with a high G_l/V ratio. Apart from those mentioned, milestones in the development of the knowledge of the coupled zone are the investigations by HUNT and JACKSON [1967], JACKSON [1968], BURDEN and HUNT [1974c], TASSA and HUNT [1976] and FISHER and KURZ [1979].

Taking into account the fact that the description of the transition from pure eutectic to eutectic plus dendrites has not yet been successfully solved by the use of perturbation analysis (JORDAN and HUNT [1971]; HURLE and JAKEMAN [1971]), at present the problem of calculating the coupled zone can only be solved for a simpler approach consisting of four steps (KURZ and FISHER [1979]): (i) Consider all the growth forms possible in the fully stationary state, i.e., α_E, β_E crystals and eutectic. (ii) Analyze the growth kinetics of these forms. (iii) Determine the interface temperatures of the growth forms as a function of V, and possibly of G_l. (iv) Apply the *competitive growth criterion*, e.g., that the morphology having the highest interface temperature for a given growth rate, or the highest growth rate for a given

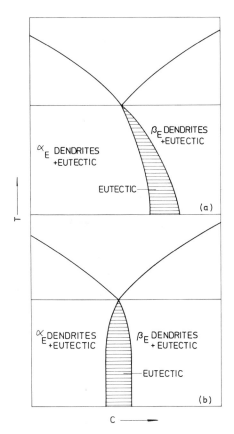

Fig. 32. Two types of coupled zone: (a) a skewed zone corresponding to (nf–f) eutectics such as Al–Si and Fe–C; b) symmetrical zone corresponding to (nf–nf) eutectics such as Pb–Sn (after KURZ and FISHER [1979]).

supercooling will be the one observed. The range of temperatures as a function of composition, within which the eutectic fulfills this condition, that is, the coupled zone, is then usually plotted on the phase diagram (fig. 32). KURZ and FISHER [1979], on the basis of the methodology outlined above, present a quite complete state of the knowledge in the field, concerning both (nf–nf) and (nf–f) eutectics, as well as comparisons between current theory and experimental results, when steady-state growth is involved. As these authors have remarked, an important problem which remains to be solved is the description of morphological transitions in eutectic systems during non-stationary and equiaxed growth.

7.3. Monotectic solidification

In systems containing a liquid miscibility gap there occurs a phase reaction liquid $L_1 \rightleftarrows$ solid S_1 + liquid L_2. Formally this reaction is the same as a eutectic reaction

References: p. 573.

except that on cooling, one of the product phases is a liquid which solidifies at a lower temperature; in the terminal eutectic reaction $L_2 \to S_1 + S_2$, the L_2 phase is always the minor product phase (fig. 33). Such a reaction is termed *monotectic* and systems containing this type of reaction are potentially important from an industrial point of view in connection with bearing alloys, free-machining alloys and micro-filters (GRUGEL and HELLAWELL [1981]).

Although earlier work exists on controlled solidification of monotectic alloys (FLEMINGS [1974]), recent work, both theoretical and experimental (CAHN [1979]; GRUGEL and HELLAWELL [1981]), has clarified the formation mechanism of the structure observed during directional solidification: (i) When a wide temperature interval between the monotectic horizontal and the upper consolute or critical temperature exists, the fibrous or composite structure obtained consists essentially of closely packed tubes of uniform diameter. In this case the three phases establish an equilibrium surface–energy balance $\gamma_{s_1 l_2} \gtrless \gamma_{s_1 l_1} + \gamma_{l_1 l_2}$, where $\gamma_{s_1 l_2}$ is the interfacial energy between S_1 and L_2, $\gamma_{s_1 l_1}$ the interfacial energy between S_1 and L_1 and $\gamma_{l_1 l_2}$ the interfacial energy between L_1 and L_2. (ii) When the temperature interval is small, the minor phase L_2 tends to coalesce into globules, which may be tenuously inter-connected. In this case L_1 preferentially wets S_1, to the exclusion of L_2. (iii) A transition from one to the other type of behaviour can be affected by ternary alloy additions, altering the height of the miscibility gap and hence the values of surface energies.

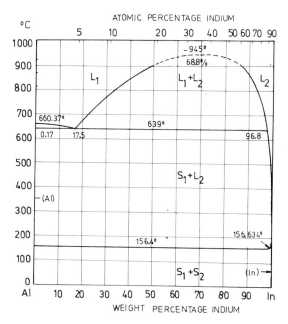

Fig. 33. Al–In monotectic-type diagram.

8. *Fluid flow and casting structure*

The ability of a molten metal or alloy to flow has two important implications: the first is that it can be poured from the container in which it was melted into the mould in which it is to solidify; the second is that the relative motion of different parts of the liquid can occur while it is solidifying. Both aspects are quite important in connection with the casting structure in the broad sense defined by CHALMERS [1964]: size, shape, orientation and perfection of the crystals; distribution in the metal of the chemical elements, that is, macro- and micro-segregation and inclusions; external and internal topology of the metal: porosity, soundness and surface shape and finish.

8.1. Fluidity

FLEMINGS [1974] reviewed the state of the art and the contributions of his school to the study of this property. For the metallurgist, fluidity is an empirical measure of a processing characteristic measured through one of several types of tests where the hot metal is caused to flow in a long channel of small cross-section and the length of the metal flow before it is stopped by solidification is the measure of fluidity. More recently, MORALES *et al.* [1977] and AGUILAR RIVAS and BILONI [1980a, b] made additional contributions to the study of fluidity in Al–Cu alloys. Linear fluidity tests plotting the fluidity length versus the time at which the test is done, $L_f = f(t)$, with different metallostatic pressures and superheats combined with "graphs of flow" (FELIU *et al.* [1962]; FELIU and SIGUIN [1963]) and different metal–mould heat transfer coefficients (h_i) were used. In addition, the use of careful metallographic analysis of the fluidity samples gave information about the vein closing mechanism. A rationalization of the variables acting on the fluidity property is now possible: (i) The $L_f = f(t)$ graphs have two stages; (ii) for a given fluidity test, in general the first stage represents a high percentage of the fluidity length but depends on variables independent of the true capacity of flow of the metal or alloy: superheat, the h_i value and the metallostatic pressure; (iii) the second stage, in general percentually low, reflects the intrinsic ability of the metal or alloy to flow. For a given metal or alloy its value will depend on the h_i value. In summary, the metal entering the channel flows until all the superheat is eliminated in a first stage. After that the liquid flows on the basis of its latent heat of fusion.

8.2. Convection in the bulk liquid

During the last 15 years the effect of fluid flow upon casting structure has been increasingly examined by scientists. In normal or "natural" conditions, convections from three sources can exist: 1) convection introduced by the momentum of pouring; 2) thermal convection during solidification, and 3) *constitutional convection* arising from the fact that once solidification has started in an alloy, solute elements, having a different density, begin to sink or rise. COLE [1971] treated in detail all the types of convection mentioned as well as the different geometries under which they appear. WEINBERG [1975] reviewed the contributions made with his associates using radioactive tracer techniques in rectangular moulds and horizontal rods, two of the most common geometries used in research and practice in solidification processes. The radioactive tracer technique used proved to be very sensitive and overcame the handicap of other experiments performed with transparent model liquids having a much lower conductivity than liquid metals. In the case of a square enclosure, measurements of radial flow velocities for a range of temperature differences and ambient temperatures were compared to relevant solutions of the Navier–Stokes equations and found to be in agreement. The solutions were also applied to materials of lower termal conductivity, including water. The flow pattern was markedly different and high discrepancy was observed in the flow velocity as a function of distance from the vertical wall. These results are a clear indication that a water model cannot be used to simulate fluid flow resulting from thermal gradients in casting. The investigations performed in long rods established the flow velocity as a function of the average temperature gradient along the rod; moreover, the pattern of fluid flow found helped to explain some results observed in the onset of instability of the S–L interface in unidirectional solidification – for example, the substructure segregation (nodes, bidimensional cells, etc.) formed in a wide irregular band about the periphery of the crystals in a previously unaccountable way, as reported by WEINBERG [1975] and COLE [1971].

The important variables influencing severity of thermal convection are contained in the *Grashof number* N_{Gr} and the *Prandtl number* N_{Pr}:

$$N_{Gr} = \frac{gL_0^3 \beta_1 \delta T}{\nu 2}, \tag{79}$$

$$N_{Pr} = \frac{c_p \eta}{K_1}, \tag{80}$$

where g is the acceleration due to gravity, L_0 is a characteristic length of the system, β_1 is the volumetric coefficient of thermal expansion of the liquid, δT is the temperature difference, ν is the kinematic viscosity, c_p is the specific heat, η the viscosity and K_1 the thermal conductivity of the liquid.

8.2.1. Fluid flow manipulation

Natural convection can be enhanced or reduced during the solidification process. The effects on the resultant structures are important as a result of two combined effects: change in the heat transfer and change in the shear forces on the S–L interface by the fluid flow. COLE [1971] gives a detailed review of the different methods used. The factors leading to a reduction in heat transfer include: a) decrease in buoyancy forces in convection with the orientation of the S–L interface with respect to the gravity vector; b) the application of a magnetic field to a convective fluid that impresses a body force on the fluid to reduce the convective motion of the fluid elements; c) rotation of the convecting fluid, giving a similar effect to the application of a magnetic field; here the additional force is a Coriolis force which deflects particles of fluid in a direction normal to the axis of rotation and normal to the direction of the particle motion.

On the other hand, increases in heat transfer can be accomplished by increasing relative fluid motion, especially in the neighbourhood of the S–L interface. Rotation or oscillation of the crucible, a rotating magnetic field or electric–magnetic field interactions can be used. Regarding the effects of vibration induced by different methods, CAMPBELL [1981] has recently published a detailed review of the state of the art.

8.3. Crystal multiplication

JACKSON *et al.* [1966] and O'HARA and TILLER [1967] postulated that a multiplication mechanism is responsible for the separation of crystals from the dendrites growing in a thermal or constitutionally supercooled liquid. In the case of alloys the interaction of natural or forced convection with the dendritic substructure can be rationalized. In effect, when secondary branches form, they must grow through the solute-rich layer existing around the primary stalk. However, the initial growth is slow, since the secondary branch is influenced by this layer and the latent heat field of the primary stalk. When it passes through the layer the secondary branch enters the bulk liquid of lower solute concentration and can grow more rapidly. The consequence is a thin neck of the secondary branch having a lower point of fusion. Then, any slight increase in the local temperature or a shear force due to local fluid flow can detach portions of the dendrites. These crystals may be able to survive in other portions of the liquid and, if the thermal and constitutional conditions are appropriate, can subsequently grow.

8.4. Ingot structure

The classical representation of the ingot macrostructure shows three distinct zones: the chill zone, a peripherial region of small equiaxed grains, the columnar zone and a central equiaxed zone. Extensive research has been done in order to know the origin and development of the three zones.

8.4.1. Chill zone

BOWER and FLEMINGS [1967], BILONI and MORANDO [1968] and PRATES and BILONI [1972] were able to simulate the thermal conditions existing at the chill zone. The formation of this structure involves complex interactions of liquid metal flow, metal–mould heat transfer, nucleation catalysis and dendritic growth. Chill-zone grains depend both on independent nucleation events or a "copious nucleation mechanism" (CHALMERS [1964]) and on crystal multiplication induced by melt turbulence during pouring. BILONI [1980] rationalizes the origin and development of the chill zone through the analysis of the segregation substructure:

(i) The value of the heat transfer coefficient at the metal–mould interface appears

References: p. 573.

to control the number of nuclei formed in contact with the mould surface. These nuclei can be recognized through the metallographic detection of predendritic regions (BILONI and CHALMERS [1965]).

(ii) Mould wall materials and coatings have a decisive influence on the structure and substructure of the ingot surface. The value of the metal–mould heat transfer coefficient is decisive in which mechanism is responsible for the origin of the chill zone and the segregation substructure permits a decision as to which mechanism operates. Figures 34a–c exemplify these concepts.

(iii) Above a critical rugosity, the surface microprofile controls the density of predendritic nuclei and a one-to-one relationship arises between them and the asperities of the surface. The existence of predendrites (fig. 34b) is a proof of local high heat transfer at the asperities, taking into account the segregation profile of the predendrites having the nominal composition of the alloy at the centre (BILONI and CHALMERS [1965]). MORALES *et al.* [1979] determined that the distribution of asperities through a given microprofile at the mould walls can be decisive in the

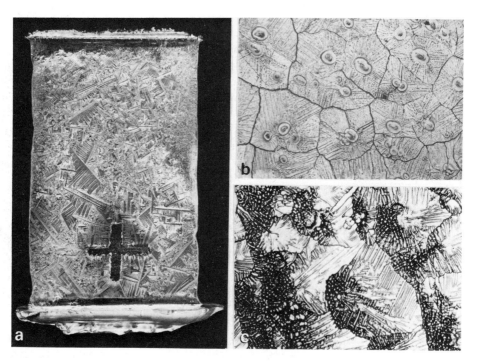

Fig. 34. (a) Chill plate of Al–1% Cu cast in a copper mould coated with lamp black, except the cross which appears with different reflectivity; ×1.3. (b) Substructure corresponding to the uncoated region of fig. 34a. Each grain has a predendritic region as origin; ×120. (c) Substructure corresponding to the finer grains of the duplex structure of fig. 34a, grown in contact with the lamp-black coating. Notice the "cells", probably produced by a multiplication mechanism, as origin of the dendrites; ×120. (After BILONI [1980].)

structure and quality of the casting surface, as well as the size of the columnar crystals, something to take into account when a given shape and size of the casting grains is desired (ROSS and MONDOLFO [1980]).

8.4.2. Columnar zone

The origin of the columnar zone has been analyzed by WALTON and CHALMERS [1959]. These authors described the competitive mechanism through which the favourably oriented crystals eliminate those less favourably oriented and a texture arises. In the case of fcc alloys, a preferred ⟨100⟩ orientation is characteristic of the structure. From a structural point of view, in essence most of the concepts concerning the evolution of the S–L interface as a function of constitutional supercooling existing in front of the interface can be applied, as well as those connected with the redistribution of solute during the solidification. One difference is connected with the grain geometry. In general, when unidirectional solidification is performed in crystal growth the growth direction is upwards and convection is a minimum. In conventional ingots the macroscopic shape of the S–L interface governs the orientation of the dendrites. When natural convection acts, the columnar growth is non-radial because convection sweeps past the S–L interface. On diminishing convection through magnetic fields or the Coriolis effect, the interface becomes vertical and columnar grains grow radially (COLE [1971]). When columnar growth occurs in the presence of high solute concentration and low temperature gradient, a substructure other than cellular–dendritic can appear. In this case, the solidification front is composed by dendrite groups rather than individual dendrites. These are the so-called *superdendrites* where the normal coupling between primary dendrites becomes unstable, certain dendrites grow ahead of their neighbours and large interdendritic spacings result (COLE and BOLLING [1968]; FAINSTEIN-PEDRAZA and BOLLING [1975]).

In aluminum-base alloys and under particular conditions a characteristic structure appears. It is composed of laminar grains growing from a common origin and as a consequence "colonies" are formed with a conic shape. This structure has different names in the literature but most commonly is called *feather crystals.* Generally, it appears with continuous or semicontinuous casting and in welding processes. Occasionally it is observed in conventional casting. With respect to alloy composition, Ti seems to be necessary, and the conditions favouring the formation of the structure are: (i) High thermal gradients; (ii) critical solute content of the alloy; (iii) critical range of solidification rate; (iv) controlled agitation of the liquid in front of the S–L interface. How the structure is nucleated is not clear but the most widely accepted mechanism corresponds to the existence of stacking faults on the octahedral planes. Regarding the feather (or twinned) crystal growth, one of its principal characteristics is that in competition with columnar grains it tends to eliminate them. This is a sign of a better efficiency in the redistribution of solute during solidification and also a sign that the dendrite tips grow at a higher temperature. The mode of atomic deposition at the S–L interface is under discussion, as in general all aspects of the origin and development of this structure, which really offers an open field of research (BILONI [1980]).

References: p. 573.

8.4.3. Equiaxed zone

The segregation substructure of each equiaxed grain shows a central region that has different names in the literature and can have different morphologies, ranging from non-dendritic to dendritic; and that has grown freely in the bulk liquid until the columnar region reaches the equiaxed grains. We prefer the generic name of *initial region* rather than others existing in the literature. During free growth of the equiaxed grains into the bulk liquid the heat evolution is from the solid to the liquid. When the columnar region touches the initial regions, the heat extraction changes and a cellular or cellular–dendritic substructure is developed (fig. 35) (BILONI [1968]). The freely growing crystal could have as origin a nucleation event or a fragmentary part of a crystal of the chill or columnar zone.

Essentially four theories exist about the origin of the equiaxed zone: (i) nucleation after the columnar zone has been formed, as a result of constitutional supercooling existing in the remaining liquid (WINEGARD and CHALMERS [1954]); (ii) all the crystals, equiaxed as well as columnar, originate during the initial chilling of the liquid in contact with the mould. This is the *Big-Bang* theory (CHALMERS [1963]). The considerations outlined above about the chill zone indicate that, in this theory, the origin of the grains could be either the copious nucleation or the multiplication mechanism; (iii) a remelting phenomenon occurring at the tip of the columnar crystals is responsible for the formation of the equiaxed zone (JACKSON *et al.* [1966]; O'HARA and TILLER [1967]); (iv) SOUTHIN [1967] proposed essentially the same mechanism but the crystals to be fragmented are those nucleated at the top of the

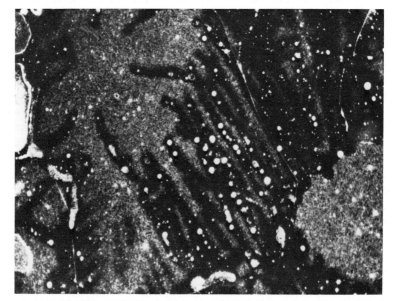

Fig. 35. Segregation substructure of an equiaxed grain in Al–1% Cu ingot after anodic oxidation. Notice the "initial" region followed by a cellular dendrite substructure. ×150. (After BILONI and CHALMERS [1965].)

ingot as a result of the radiation occurring in that region. Many experiments have been done in order to decide which of the theories identifies the nucleation mechanism responsible for the equiaxed zone. Probably more than one mechanism will operate, according to the type of experiment performed and the nature of the S–L interface.

Another variable to take into account is the size of the ingot, in connection with the problem of scaling up conclusions from the laboratory scale to the industrial scale (CHALMERS [1964]). MORANDO *et al.* [1970], in their experiments with 50 cm³, 500 cm³ and 5000 cm³ ingots, suggest that conclusions drawn from the 5000 cm³ ingots series performed with application of hot top (in order to eliminate the Southin mechanism) and manipulation of magnetic fields in order to isolate the other mechanisms, can be extrapolated to foundry practice. This work seems to prove that when natural convection is present, the Big-Bang mechanism is the most important and always operates. This seems to be in agreement with the difficulty of transporting remelted dendrite arms to the bulk liquid from the intricate network formed by the cellular–dendritic substructure forming the columnar grains in those experiments. However, if superdendrites develop, possibly the operation of the multiplication mechanism would be easier.

Regarding the mechanisms responsible for the transition between the columnar and the equiaxed zone, several theories exist (SOUTHIN [1967]; BILONI and CHALMERS [1968]; BURDEN and HUNT [1975]; DOHERTY *et al.* [1977]; FREDRIKSSON and HILLERT [1972]). However, all of them postulate the blockage of the columnar grains by the free crystals floating in the bulk liquid (giving rise to the substructure observed in fig. 35) through different mechanisms involving either mechanical blockage, thermal fields or solute fields effects. One of the necessary conditions, however, for the existence of the equiaxed region is the existence of natural convection.

8.5. Interdendritic fluid flow and macrosegregation

Work on macrosegregation has shown that flow of solute-rich interdendritic liquid, and in some cases mass flow of liquid plus solid in the mushy zone of a casting, is responsible for almost all types of *macrosegregation* observed. Several influences can generate such motion in a solidifying system; the most obvious is simple thermal convection in the bulk liquid. However, there also exists the density variation produced by local differences in solute content, giving rise to constitutional or "thermosolutal" convection. Superimposed on these mechanisms are the feeding mechanisms produced by liquid and solidification shrinkage and by solid contraction in the freezing zone. In some cases gas release provides added pressure for the displacement of residual liquid. The studies have been based on theoretical analysis, transparent analogues and experimental metallic systems. Many authors have contributed to the knowledge in this important and rather difficult field, which has been reviewed by BEELEY [1979], FREDRIKSSON and NILSSON [1978], WEINBERG [1975] and FLEMINGS [1974, 1976].

References: p. 573.

A general solution for macrosegregation considering fluid flow in three dimensions for a binary alloy with a constant partition ratio was first published by FLEMINGS and NEREO [1967] and used to predict solute distribution for inverse segregation in Al–Cu alloys. Subsequently the model was refined and extended at MIT and was applied by MEHRABIAN et al. [1970] to predict macrosegregation caused by a combination of solidification contraction and solute convection. The fluid dynamics of a volume element, where the forces acting are solid contraction, liquid contraction and gravity, is considered. The liquid is of variable density and the solid–liquid region is treated as a porous medium of variable porosity. The principal simplifying assumptions of the model are: (i) for the purpose of calculating flow velocities it is assumed that the fraction of liquid varies with position in the mushy zone only as a function of temperature and is calculated by assuming steady-state unidirectional heat and fluid flow; (ii) planar isotherms are assumed, so that for a constant liquidus slope, the liquid composition varies linearly with position in one direction; (iii) the density of the liquid varies linearly with composition; (iv) the density of the solid is constant. The model can be used to predict, for a given temperature distribution, different conditions existing in the mushy zone:

1) The solute redistribution within the unit element is given by:

$$\frac{\partial f_1}{\partial C_1} = -\frac{(1-\beta_2)}{(1-k_0)}\left[1 + \frac{v\,\nabla T}{\Delta\varepsilon}\right]\frac{f_1}{C_1}, \tag{81}$$

where:

f_1 = volume fraction of liquid,
C_1 = composition of the liquid,
$\beta_2 = (d_s - d_1)/d_s$ = solidification shrinkage,
d_s = density of the solid, d_1 = density of the liquid,
k_0 = partition ratio,
v = velocity vector of interdendritic liquid,
∇T = local temperature gradient,
$\Delta\varepsilon$ = local cooling rate.

Equation (81) permits to calculate the distribution of the volume fraction of liquid within the mushy zone.

2) The effect of gravity as a body force on the convective liquid within the mushy zone is introduced by using D'Arcy's Law, which is:

$$v = -\frac{K_p}{\eta f_1}(\nabla P + d_1 g), \tag{82}$$

where:

K_p = specific permeability,
η = viscosity of the interdendritic liquid,
∇P = pressure gradient,
g = acceleration due to gravity.

The permeability K_p depends on pore size and geometry. In the case of the mushy zone it has been proposed that

$$K_p = \lambda_C f_1^2 \tag{83}$$

where λ_C is a constant depending on dendrite arm spacing. Equation (82) predicts the velocity of interdendritic liquid flow within the mushy zone.

3) The combination of the equations describing the interdendritic fluid flow with the "local redistribution equation", (81):

$$\nabla \cdot \left(\frac{K_p d_1}{\eta} \nabla P + \frac{K_p d_1^2}{\eta} \boldsymbol{g} \right)$$

$$= - (d_1 - d_s) \frac{(1 - \beta_2)}{(1 - k_0)} \left[1 - \frac{K_p}{\Delta \varepsilon f_1} (\boldsymbol{P} + d_1 \boldsymbol{g}) \cdot \nabla T \right] \frac{f_1}{C_1} \frac{\Delta \varepsilon}{m_1} + f_1 \frac{d(d_1)}{dC_1} \frac{\Delta \varepsilon}{m_1}. \tag{84}$$

This equation can be solved along with appropriate boundary conditions to give the pressure within the mushy zone of a solidifying ingot.

4) Macrosegregation in an ingot is given in terms of the local average composition of solid after solidification is complete, $\bar{C}_s$:

$$\bar{C}_s = \frac{d_s k_0 \int_0^{1 - f_E} C_1 \, df_s + C_E f_E \, df_E}{d_s (1 - f_E) d_{sE} f_E}, \tag{85}$$

where f_E is the volume fraction of the eutectic, d_{sE} is the eutectic density and C_E is the eutectic composition.

8.5.1. Macrosegregation in industrial ingots

Figure 36 corresponds to a sketch of macrosegregation in a large steel ingot, showing the major types of macrosegregation commonly present. Most of them are a result of interactions between heat flow, fluid flow and mass transfer, and the modelling of these phenomena outlined above permits one to begin to understand their origins and eventual control (FLEMINGS [1976]). When the interdendritic flow velocity v just equals the flow required to feed local shrinkage, *no macrosegregation* exists:

$$\boldsymbol{n} \cdot \boldsymbol{v} = - \frac{\beta_2}{1 - \beta_2} \boldsymbol{n} \cdot \boldsymbol{V}, \tag{86}$$

where $\boldsymbol{n}$ is the unit vector perpendicular to a given isotherm within the liquid–solid zone and V is the S–L interface velocity vector. On the other hand, when

$$\boldsymbol{n} \cdot \boldsymbol{v} > - \frac{\beta_2}{1 - \beta_2} \boldsymbol{n} \cdot \boldsymbol{V} \tag{87}$$

negative macrosegregation arises and when

$$\boldsymbol{n} \cdot \boldsymbol{v} < - \frac{\beta_2}{1 - \beta_2} \boldsymbol{n} \cdot \boldsymbol{V} \tag{88}$$

References: p. 573.

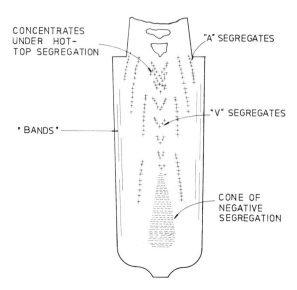

Fig. 36. Different types of macrosegregation in an industrial ingot (after FLEMINGS [1974]).

positive segregation exists. Most of the flow occurring during solidification sketched in fig. 36 proceeds from hot to cooler regions; then according to eqs. (87) and (88) the segregation ranges from negative to zero to slightly positive. However in the lower portion of the ingot of fig. 37a and upper portion of fig. 37b, the flow is inwards. Here the segregation is strongly positive:

$$\boldsymbol{n}\cdot\boldsymbol{v} > \boldsymbol{n}\cdot\boldsymbol{V}, \tag{89}$$

that is, if the interdendritic flow velocity in the growth direction exceeds the rate of movement of the isotherms, the flowing liquid melts channels in the interdendritic regions. As these channels form, flow in them becomes still greater, resulting in still more melting and formation of localized "pencil-like" segregates named *A segregates* in large ingots and *freckles* in other foundry processes.

Banding, or abrupt variations in composition which are seen on etched macrosections, results either from effect of bulk liquid flow in interdendritic flow or from sudden changes in heat transfer rate. *V segregates*, that is, a positive segregation, occur during the last part of the ingot solidification when the fraction of solid in the central equiaxed zone increases to somewhere in the range of 0.2–0.4. The solid network formed is not yet sufficiently strong to resist the metallostatic head and the metal continues to feed solidification shrinkage, but now the movement takes place along preferred shear planes, and fissures termed "internal hot tears" open up and are filled with solute-rich liquid.

The most plausible mechanism of formation of the *negative cone* at the bottom of ingots, which is relatively poor in solute and rich in inclusions, is the settling of crystallites toward the bottom of the ingots. On the way down these crystals

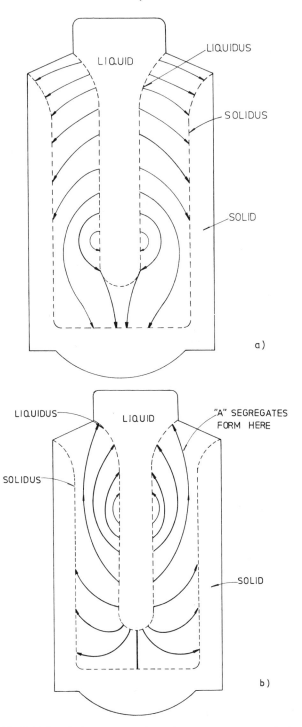

Fig. 37. Interdendritic fluid flow in ingots presenting columnar structure: (a) liquid density increases during solidification; b) liquid density decreases during solidification. (After FLEMINGS [1976].)

References: p. 573.

probably sweep inclusions or agglomerates of inclusions along. The *severe positive segregation just under the hot top* probably occurs during the final stages of solidification when the ingot feeding takes place only by interdendritic fluid flow.

8.6. Movement of liquid plus solid

When metals or alloys solidify in usual castings and ingots, a dendritic structure forms that develops cohesion when the alloy is as little as 20% solid. Thereafter strength develops rapidly. When the casting is deformed during solidification, deformation takes place preferentially along grain boundaries. Grains slide and roll over one another with small welds forming and breaking. Occasional bending of dendrite arms in the neighbourhood of the region of deformation is also seen. As deformation proceeds, open fissures may form ("hot tears") or the regions of deformations may be continuously fed by liquid. In this latter case segregated regions, sometimes called "filled hot tears" result, the same type of V segregates as described above (FLEMINGS and MEHRABIAN [1973]). Taking as a basis this theoretical and experimental background, SPENCER *et al.* [1972] showed that for several alloys, including Pb–15% Sn, vigorous agitation during solidification can prevent significant strength from developing until the fraction of solid is well above 0.4. The vigorous agitation results in fine, nearly spherical grains. At fractions of solid below about 0.4 this liquid–solid mixture behaves as do many types of slurries at the

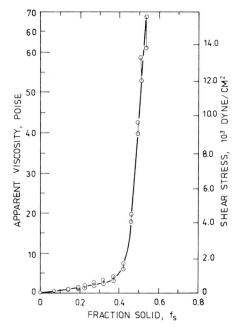

Fig. 38. Apparent viscosity of a vigorously agitated Pb–15% Sn alloy (after SPENCER *et al.* [1972]).

equivalent volume fraction of solid. Figure 38 shows the viscosity of the agitated alloy as a function of fraction of solid. The same figure shows the equivalent shear stress to cause steady flow which is several orders of magnitude lower than required when the liquid is not agitated (FLEMINGS [1974]). This is the basis of new processes to be discussed in § 11.

8.7. Porosity and inclusions

Porosity and inclusions are related with the quality of the casting in the broad sense, that is, soundness and mechanical properties.

8.7.1. Porosity

CAMPBELL [1968] reviewed the mechanism of pore formation in long-freezing alloys and considered, in agreement with other authors, that the initiation of pores can occur in two ways: either by a nucleation mechanism in which pores are created in the interior of the liquid–solid mass or by one of several non-nucleating mechanisms in which pores are created from the outside of the casting, principally during the feeding of the casting. The tendency for shrinkage porosity can be reduced by proper gating, and to this purpose even computers can be brought into play. From a solidification point of view it is important to consider those pores created during the process, when the remaining liquid at the center of the casting is more or less completely isolated by the surrounding solidified metal. The driving force for the creation can be either gas or solidification shrinkage or both. Evolution of gases during solidification and failure to feed solidification shrinkage are closely related phenomena that lead to porosity in cast alloys. This porosity may be localized into macroscopic cavities or be dispersed between dendrite arms and in grain boundaries as microporosity. Formation of porosity may be considered with reference to the models of cellular dendritic growth assumed when micro- and macrosegregation was treated (BRODY [1974]).

During solidification the gas will be rejected from the solid to the liquid, becoming concentrated in the liquid in the mushy zone. As the concentration of gas builds up in the liquid, its *equilibrium partial pressure*, P_g, builds up too:

$$P_g = \frac{P_g'}{\left(f_1(1 - k_0') + k_0'\right)^2},$$
(90)

where P_g' is the partial pressure of gas above the melt, and k_0' is the partition ratio for the gas.

If the effect of the solidification shrinkage is neglected, a bubble would be expected to form when the partial pressure of the gas equals the local metallostatic pressure, that is the pressure over the melt plus the depth of the melt plus enough extra pressure to overcome surface forces, i.e.:

$$P_g = P_z + \frac{2}{r_p} \gamma_{lv},$$
(91)

References: p. 573.

where P_Z is the metallostatic pressure at a depth Z below the surface, r_p is the radius of the pore and γ_{1v} is the liquid–vapour surface energy. If, however, metal shrinkage is taken into account, pores will form at lower pressures. Fluid flows in the channel between dendrites to feed the solidification shrinkage and the metallostatic head at the dendrite tips, P_Z, is the driving force for the flow. The pressure continuously decreases within the channel because of frictional dissipation of energy. When the pressure in the liquid becomes less than the partial pressure of the dissolved gas, P_g, minus the pressure to overcome surface energy, $2\gamma_{1v}/r_p$, a pore will form. The size of the pore depends on the volume fraction of shrinkage, liquid viscosity, rate of advance of dendrite tips and size of the mushy zone (BRODY [1974]).

8.7.2. Inclusions

At present it is very clear that inclusions exert an important influence on fracture behaviour of commercial materials. As a result, this portion of the field of solidification is receiving much greater attention. One source of inclusions is an inevitable feature of the production route and may be characterized as *primary inclusions* (FLEMINGS [1974]). One aim of good melting practice is to remove physically as many of the inclusions that form as possible. In the steel industry a significant reduction in inclusion content is obtained by the inclusion floating upward and adhering to or dissolving in the slag at the melt surface. In the case of aluminum and its alloys, the primary inclusions may be characterized as: (i) exogenous inclusions; (ii) fluxes and salts suspended in the melt as the result of a prior metal-treatment process; (iii) oxides of the melt which are both suspended on top of the melt and entrapped within it by turbulence. In the aluminum industry, filtering has become a common practice, and the development of better filters, in terms of characteristics such as porosity, length of bed and filter area as well as certain process variables such as melt flow rate is improving (ROSS and MONDOLFO [1980]; APELIAN [1982]).

The morphology of primary inclusions in cast metals varies depending on interface kinetics, relative surface energies, collision and inclusion viscosity. Another effect to take into account is the capture, or not, of the inclusion during solid growth. The capture of inclusions is determined not only by the solidification process itself but also by the whole complex of surface phenomena. Many experimental studies indicate that the particles may be repulsed for a long time by the growing crystals if the growth rate does not exceed a critical velocity, varying for different melts and for different particle materials in the melt (CHERNOV and TEMKIN [1976]).

Secondary inclusions are those which form during or after solidification of the major phase. Although in industrial practice the commercial alloys suppose the existence of multicomponent systems, a first approach to the understanding of the formation of secondary inclusions has been achieved through the considerations of ternary diagrams involving the most important impurity elements under consideration (FLEMINGS [1974]). Then, the solidification reactions occurring during the process, together with the value of the partition ratio of the solid solutions involved, play an important role in the type, size and distribution of inclusions in the final structure. Important ternary systems to be considered in steel are Fe–O–Si, Fe–O–S and Fe–Mn–S, from which the formation of silica, oxides and sulphide results. As an example of research in this field, FREDRIKSSON and HILLERT [1972], through carefully controlled solidification, were able to determine the formation of four types of MnS inclusions formed by different reactions.

9. *Continuous casting*

The continuous casting of ferrous and nonferrous metals has been investigated extensively over the last 25 years, reflecting the major position this casting technique has now assumed in industry. Figure 39 shows schematically the principles of the method, in general common to ferrous and nonferrous metals. Liquid metal is poured into the top of a water-cooled mould and the casting is withdrawn continuously by mechanical means. Usually, especially in the steel industry, a reciprocative motion is superimposed to prevent sticking. The most important characteristic of this process is that a steady state is maintained. TAYLOR [1975] and WEINBERG [1979] for steels, and EMLEY [1976] and BAKER and SUBRAMIAN [1980] for aluminum and its alloys, have presented excellent up-to-date reviews on the research and technology involved in this field.

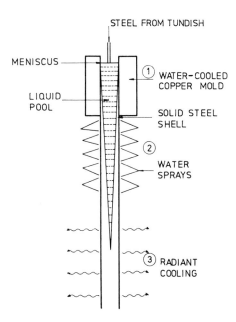

Fig. 39. Schematic representation of the three zones of heat removal in continuous casting of steel (after WEINBERG [1975]).

References: p. 573.

9.1. Continuous casting of steel

Solidification occurs initially at the mould walls and meniscus, forming a thin shell which progressively thickens to approximately 1.3–1.5 cm when it leaves the mould. The prediction of the shell formation is fundamental in order to prevent breakout during the operation. A series of models has been developed, based on an analysis of the heat balance in the system, and comparisons between measured and calculated thickness have been made using a variety of experimental techniques. These include measuring the residual shell when breakouts occur, radioactive tracer additions to the liquid pool and sulphur addition, among other methods. Recently, CLYNE *et al.* [1980] have provided an outline of the different approaches that can be used to model solidification during the continuous casting of steel by means of unidimensional heat flow analysis, while finite difference methods have also been used (LAIT *et al.* [1974].

The cast structure of continuously cast steels, as with static casting, consists of both columnar and equiaxed grains. The lower the pouring temperature, the higher the fraction of equiaxed grains, as in conventional castings. Regarding microsegregation, the models already discussed can be applied to the continuously cast grains but the macrosegregation associated with the fluid flow during the solidification process is still not clear in continuous casting (WEINBERG [1979]).

9.2. Continuous casting of aluminum and its alloys

In aluminum alloys there are three factors which influence departure of the ingot shell from the mould: (i) shrinkage at the ingot shell itself; (ii) thermal strain within the ingot shell; (iii) shrinkage in the block section below the mould and the associated mechanical strains in the shell. All of these are connected with the primary and secondary water-cooling systems and can affect the ingot structure, principally at the surface of the ingot. The air gap developed when the shell departs from the mould can give rise to defects of various types; during the process, the thin shell that forms in the mould is in unstable contact with the mould face. Where gap formation occurs, there is increased resistance to heat transfer and consequently reheating of the skin. Reheating results in gross segregation and exudations, retards the solidification in the subsurface zones and leads to variations in the cell size of the outer surfaces of ingots. Zones of coarse dendritic cells may extend to 2–3 cm below the surface. Associated with the coarse cells are large particles of intermetallic constituents, which may be exposed by the surface machining that is usually necessary, prior to fabrication (BOWER *et al.* [1971]).

Several methods have been proposed in order to reduce the surface defects but the most successful are those that reduce the heat extraction at the mould through the control of the microgeometry of the mould surface, for example by machining vertical grooves in the face of the mould in such a way that, owing to the surface tension of the molten aluminum, it does not fill the grooves. More recently, attempts to achieve mouldless casting have been made in order to improve the metal surface quality. Under this approach, electromagnetic casting was developed in the Soviet

Union by GETSELEV [1971]. In this system the molten metal is supported by an electromagnetic field until it enters the direct quench. No subsurface zones are formed, since the cooling is continuous and uninterrupted.

10. *Fusion welding structures*

In most metallurgical processes the scientific approach to process improvement is to obtain correlations between operational variables, metallurgical structures and mechanical properties. However, for many years in fusion welding technology only correlations between operational variables and mechanical properties were considered. Only in the last twenty years has the scientific approach begun to be applied as a consequence of needs in, among others, nuclear, space and off-shore technology, where quality assurance is mandatory.

The fusion weld structure is a result of complex transformations and interactions starting with metal–gas and metal–flux reactions in the liquid state followed by the formation of the *primary structure* by solidification. Pioneering work by SAVAGE and his school initiated the correlation between operational variables and primary structures (SAVAGE *et al.* [1965]). More recently, DAVIES and GARLAND [1975] presented a comprehensive review of solidification structures of fusion welds interpreting the macro- and microstructures formed during different fusion welding processes in terms of basic solidification principles.

An *actual structure* (known as *secondary structure* when phase transformations are involved, as in the case of steels) is obtained as a consequence of phase transformations occurring during the process and controlled by thermal distribution around the weld pool and subsequent cooling too to room temperature (SAVAGE *et al.* [1976]). (The secondary structure is not further discussed here.) The final structure is composed subject to different phases, physical and chemical heterogeneities, all influenced by the constraints imposed by the weld geometry. As in all metal structures, analysis can be done at three levels: (i) the macroscopic scale, characterizing the shape, size distribution and orientations of the grains; this is the *macrostructure*; (ii) the microscopic scale concerned with macro- and microsegregation, inclusions, porosity, etc.; (iii) the crystallographic and atomic scale, mostly concerned with crystal lattice defects. The application of special metallographic techniques able to differentiate between primary and secondary structures permits the basic principles of the L–S transformation treated in the preceding sections to be correlated with the origin and development of the structures at the macro- and microscopic levels, the principal aim of this section.

A crude analysis of a weld indicates that a line seems to separate the fusion region from the *heat-affected zone* (HAZ). However, careful metallographic analysis reveals the following zones schematically shown in fig. 40: (i) a mixed molten zone, or "composite region"; (ii) an unmixed molten zone; (iii) a partially melted zone and (iv) a true HAZ (SAVAGE and SZEKERES [1967]).

References: p. 573.

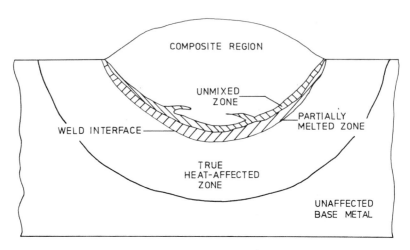

Fig. 40. Schematic representation of the different zones of a weld (after SAVAGE and SZEKERES [1967]).

10.1. Mixed molten zone

The formation of this zone is directly related with the mechanisms involved in the L–S transformation and the basic principles were discussed in preceding sections.

10.1.1. Nucleation and epitaxial growth

Heterogeneous nucleation theory affirms that a good wetting of the substrate by the melt improves nucleation. In the specific case of fusion-welding processes, the wetting is perfect becuase the substrate is provided by the partial melting of the base-metal grains. The solidification starts from there. The growing crystals have the same crystallographic orientation as the partially melted grains and for this reason the process is known as *nucleation and epitaxial growth* (SAVAGE et al. [1968a]). During growth a preferred orientation arises, corresponding to the cellular–dendritic substructure developed during solidification; a selection of grains occurs and a growth texture arises. The type of macrostructure will be discussed later on but the tendency is to develop a columnar structure.

10.1.2. Weld pool geometry

The weld-pool geometry is a function of the weld speed and the balance between the heat input and the cooling conditions. These conditions establish a dynamic equilibrium between the heat extraction capacity of the system in two directions: one perpendicular and another parallel to the welding direction. If the welding speed is low the pool will be elliptical and for higher welding speeds a tear-drop pool shape arises. The geometry of the weld pool places certain requirements on local solidification rates at different points along the pool interface if the shape of the pool is to remain constant. If crystal growth is considered isotropic and takes place along the direction of the maximum thermal gradient then the *local solidification rate*, R_w, at any position at the pool boundary should be given by:

$$R_w = V_w \cos \theta_1, \tag{92}$$

where V_w is the welding speed and θ_1 is represented in fig. 41a. However, taking into account the anisotropy of crystal growth, that is, the existence of preferential crystallographic directions during growth, the local solidification rate must be corrected according to the following expression (NAKAGAWA *et al.* [1970]):

$$R_w = \frac{R_n}{\cos(\theta_1' - \theta_1)} = \frac{V_w \cos \theta_1}{\cos(\theta_1' - \theta_1)}, \tag{93}$$

where R_n is the growth rate in a direction normal to the isotherm and θ_1' is the angle between the welding direction and the direction of favoured growth (fig. 41b). Thus, in welding the solidification rate is greatest on the weld centre-line where $\theta_1 = 0°$. At this point the temperature gradients are shallowest because of the distance from the welding heat source. This is the contrary to the situation in castings, where maximum solidification rates are normally associated with maximum gradients and vice versa (DAVIES and GARLAND [1975]).

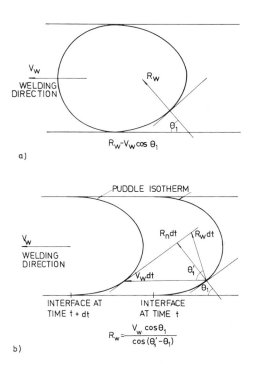

Fig. 41. (a) Solidification rates at different positions of the weld pool if isotropic growth is assumed (after DAVIES and GARLAND [1975]). (b) Relationship between welding speed and actual growth rate (after NAKAGAWA *et al.* [1970]).

References: p. 573.

10.1.3.   Solidification structures and substructures in the mixed molten zone

As was pointed out above, the liquid pool shape determines the columnar growth direction as well as the solidification rate and the thermal gradient into the liquid. Columnar grain segregation substructures are determined by the S–L interface morphology, related to G_l/V and constitutional supercooling as analyzed in § 6. At the beginning of epitaxial growth, G_l/V is high and the interface tends to be plane; quite rapidly the S–L interface becomes unstable and in practice reaches the condition of cellular dendritic growth. As a result, most of the concepts discussed in § 6.2 for unidirectional solidification of alloys and in § 8 for columnar growth in conventional castings can be applied to the columnar growth in welding: micro- and macrosegregation, banding, inclusions, etc. In addition, the geometry of the weld-pool influences the dendritic spacing (DAVIES and GARLAND [1975]).

10.2.   Welding macrostructure

Different classifications of welding macrostructures appear in the literature. While some authors refer to the primary structure, others consider also the sec-

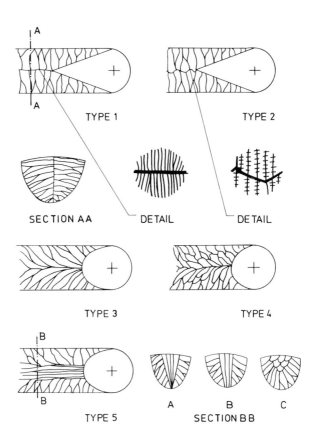

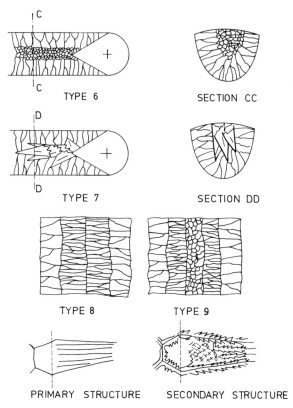

Fig. 42. Schematic representation of the nine types of macrostructures possible in fusion welding processes (after PEREZ *et al.* [1981]).

ondary structure (SAVAGE *et al.* [1968b]; PATON [1959]; GANAHA and KERR [1978]; BÄCKERUD and EDVARSSON [1976]; NAKAGAWA *et al.* [1972]; KATO *et al.* [1972]). Recently PEREZ *et al.* [1981] rationalized the origin and development of the different fusion welding structures on the basis of their own experiments and critical comparisons with former classifications: figure 42 shows schematically nine types of macrostructures observed in different fusion welding processes. All show a columnar zone which may occupy the entire weld (types 1–4) or be accompanied by grains growing along the welding direction (type 5), by equiaxed grains (type 6), by feathery crystals as discussed in § 8.4.2 (type 7), or by mixed coarse and fine grains (types 8, 9); these last are characteristic of electroslag welding (PATON [1959]).

10.3. Structure of unmixed molten zone

This zone has been characterized by SAVAGE and SZEKERES [1967] and appears generally in welds made with filler metal additions. It is a thin zone composed of

References: p. 573.

base metal which melted and resolidified without mixing with the filler metal during the passage of the weld puddle. Although the weld puddle is quite turbulent, a stagnant layer of liquid metal exists at the extremities of the puddle. The detection of this zone can be achieved with proper metallographic etching as used by SAVAGE and SZEKERES [1967] in HY-80 steel weldments. This unmixed region does not have properties similar to the major portion of the weld metal and can be the location of initiation sites of microcracking as well as corrosion susceptibility in stainless steel.

10.4. Structure of partially melted zone

During the welding process the base metal near the fusion line is submitted to a thermal cycle and, as a consequence, inclusions of low melting point as well as any segregated zones can be melted. From a solidification point of view this phenomenon is very important because these regions resolidify and the contraction during the subsequent cooling may be a source of microcracks.

10.5. Heat-affected zone

The metal near the weld is submitted to a heterogeneous thermal cycle, generating different solid phase transformations as a function of temperature and time. The final result is a mixture of structures characterized by different grain sizes. Near the fusion line the grain size is in general large as a result of rapid growth at temperatures near the melting point of the metal.

11.   Structure manipulation and new processes

The concepts discussed in the previous sections are the basis used by metallurgists in order to manipulate the structure. The aim of this manipulation is to obtain better physical and mechanical properties as well as to develop new processes. A summary of some studies and developments will be presented in this last section of the chapter.

11.1.   Structure manipulation

In § 8 final structures obtained under "natural conditions" existing during the solidification process were described. These *natural conditions* can be defined as the fluid flow obtained by conventional operational conditions, natural convection during solidification as well as heterogeneous nucleation operating, in general, under unknown conditions. In that section, as well as in §§ 6 and 7, were mentioned some methods in order to minimize convection. However, in most cases the aim was the isolation of the basic mechanisms promoting the final structure and substructures – i.e., better understanding. If, on the other hand, fluid flow, thermal conditions and chemical conditions are changed appropriately, it should be possible to control the structure and as a result to obtain different, and better, properties.

11.1.1. Single-crystal growth from the melt

In § 2.1 we treated the thermal conditions in order to grow single crystals under controlled solidification. The production of single crystals by solidification is useful both to study the laws governing solidification in pure metals and alloys and also to provide single crystals for scientific studies, especially of mechanical properties (chs. 19–22) and for technological devices as, for example, in the electronic industry. Thus we consider single crystal production as an important example of structure manipulation.

CHALMERS [1964] presents in the Appendix of his book an excellent review of the different methods available for single crystal preparation; more recently THORNTON [1968] considered techniques for the growth of *alloy* single crystals in detail. In general, the same methods can be used for the growth of *bicrystals* if grain-boundary properties are to be studied. Four main methods are used: (i) In the *Bridgman method* the mould containing the melt is lowered through the furnace and the solidification begins either at a point of the bottom or on a seed located in an extension of the bottom of the boat. A variant of this method is the so called *soft mould method* (NOGGLE [1953]) in which a shaped ingot is embedded in dry alumina powder, melted and then frozen slowly from one end. This method produces, in general, crystals with lower density of defects as a result of a much lower incidence of stresses arising from differential thermal contraction of the mould and the crystal. (ii) The *Chalmers method* is a variation of the Bridgman method and a horizontal boat is used. Many studies related to the study of solidification phenomena have been performed with this method, which permits the decantation of the remaining liquid when solid and liquid coexist. However, as was discussed in § 8, problems can arise as a result of convection during growth. (iii) The *Czochralski method,* also known as *crystal pulling,* consists of a melt contained in a crucible and a seed crystal that is dipped into it from above and then slowly rotated and withdrawn. The purpose of the rotation is to maintain symmetry of the crystal and decrease the solute-enriched layer at the S–L interface. (iv) In the *floating-zone method,* zone-melting principles are used and, as in the preceding method, no mould is used. Essentially the molten zone is held in place by surface tension forces, sometimes aided by a magnetic field.

In growing alloy crystals the control of constitutional supercooling through the value of the parameter $G_l V / C_0$ as discussed in § 6 is important in order to maintain a stable plane interface and thus avoid microsegregation. To achieve this, steep thermal gradients and a low growth rate must be used. For alloy phases formed by a peritectic reaction, THORNTON [1966] developed a special method involving two stages of solidification. During the first stage, a few dendrites form along the rod unidirectionally grown. During the second stage, the dendritic structure is converted into a single crystal structure and the coring microsegregation removed by a homogenization process.

11.1.2. Influence of gravity on macro- and microstructure

In experiments under natural conditions, that is, under the influence of the gravity vector on earth, this variable is responsible for: (i) convection phenomena through differences in density associated with differences in temperature or concentration, which leads, as has already been seen, to different forms of micro- and macrosegregation; (ii) sedimentation mechanisms in polyphase media involving at least one fluid phase; they are brought about by density differences, but Brownian motion caused by molecular level fluctuations comes into play, giving rise to vertical concentration gradients; (iii) segregation phenomena within a single fluid phase; (iv) buoyancy; (v) hydrostatic pressure (MALMEJAC [1981]; FREDRIKSSON [1980]). As a consequence, the elimination of gravity would have a marked influence on macro- and microstructures resulting from solidification processes. This line of research has been encouraged as a result of the space programs organized by NASA, ESA and the Soviet Union. However, in order to understand properly the effect of the absence of the g vector, a proper knowledge of its influence on earth is necessary (GLICKSMAN [1981]). Although the effect of convection upon resultant structures was discussed for some cases in § 6, when dendritic growth was treated the effect of this variable was only mentioned in passing. GLICKSMAN and HUANG [1979, 1981] analyzed the interplay between the removal of the latent heat, produced in the S–L interface by diffusion and/or convective flow as a function of the supercooling, and the g vector orientation; in succinonitrile at low supercooling, convection is dominant, and the morphology of the dendrites is strongly affected by the g vector orientation. At this point it is important to point out that in the studies reported in § 6 on succinonitrile all the morphological analysis of dendrites correspond to the case were the dendritic growth was parallel to the g vector. In this case symmetric growth occurs.

11.1.3. Microgravity

The common denominator of the research in this area is the reduction of: (i) sedimentation and buoyancy; (ii) gravity-driven convection and (iii) hydrostatic pressure. In order to obtain a microgravitational environment for various periods, from seconds to practically unlimited time, different methods are used: satellites, orbiting space stations, rockets, aircraft, drop towers. The wide variety of experiments and disciplines involved in microgravity research opens a new field where elementary properties and mechanisms, as modified by the near null value of gravity may be studied. They can be summarized as follows (MALMEJAC [1981]):

(i) Distribution of the constituents in the initial fluid phase.

(ii) Phenomena of mass and heat transfer in the absence of thermoconvection; in this area the drastic reduction of thermoconvection implies the increased influence of other mechanisms in general masked on earth, namely: a) mass fluxes resulting from surface tension gradients or *Marangoni convection;* b) fluid movement as a result of expansion associated with phase changes or of the presence of electric, magnetic or thermoacoustic fields; c) mechanism of solute redistribution through diffusion; d) damping of temperature fluctuations in the fluid phase; e) effect of absence of gravity on phase interfaces or the meniscus, etc.

(iii) Possible modifications of the S–L interfacial energy affecting nucleation phenomena.

(iv) Phase transition phenomena in the vicinity of critical points.

(v) Properties related to free surfaces or to interfaces: adhesion, cohesion, distribution of the heterogeneous phases or modifications of interface morphologies.

(vi) Kinetics of transient phenomena in the vicinity of critical points.

(vii) Formation mechanisms of twin crystals, cellular substructures, etc.

(viii) Techniques for forming or preparing materials without crucibles, direct formation of whiskers, thin films without substrates, production of hollow spheres with extremely thin walls, zone melting across a very wide diameter, techniques of brazing or welding by electron bombardment, etc.

Microgravity research efforts have been improved significantly in the last ten years and especially in the solidification field, they offer a promising approach to manipulate the structure. In the specific field of casting structure, one of the most interesting results of microgravitational solidification to date is the definitive conclusion that convection is necessary in order to obtain a columnar-to-equiaxed transition. In effect, in a low-gravity environment under any operational conditions, only completely columnar structures are obtained because all grain multiplication mechanisms are supressed; the thermal conditions change in such a way as to cause the liquid to cool more slowly. This results in a steeper temperature gradient in the liquid ahead of the S–L interface and grains produced through the Big-Bang mechanism (§ 8.4.3) are melted (PAPAZIAN and KATTAMIS [1980]).

11.1.4. Grain refinement

The methods which may be used to obtain fine-grained materials as a consequence of solidification processes can be classified into thermal, constitutional and energy-induced (BOLLING [1971]). Each of them can operate principally through two mechanisms: nucleation or crystal multiplication.

11.1.4.1. Thermal methods. From a thermal point of view we are concerned principally with two possibilities:

(i) *Chill effect:* when molten metals contact the cold walls of the mould, or *chills,* all the melt superheat is removed from the molten metal and the liquid becomes locally supercooled. The number of nucleation centres increases while the size of the centres decreases and nucleation takes place catastrophically everywhere in the liquid. Techniques such as splat-cooling (ch. 28), slab- and die-casting and the application of chills utilize this approach, with varying efficiencies according to melt size. Recent work by MORALES *et al.* [1979] indicates that wall microgeometry of the mould as influenced by machining, polishing and coating has a profound influence on the grain structure of the casting. When the liquid enters into contact with surface asperities, there is a high rate of heat extraction on the lamellar film of the liquid in contact with the asperities and as a consequence predendritic nuclei will form. A suitable microprofile designed on the surface can promote a specific distribution of predendritic nuclei. Along this line of reasoning, fig. 43 shows quite dramatically how the coating microprofile can influence the columnar grain size, starting from the predendritic nuclei promoted by the microprofile of the mould wall (MORALES *et al.* [1979]). Taking into account the concepts discussed in § 8 concern-

References: p. 573.

Fig. 43. Longitudinal section of an ingot poured from the bottom, after macroetch. The different grain size has as origin mould walls with different microgeometries. The small columnar grains start at the asperities of an alumina mould coating presenting a controlled microgeometry; the very large grain started from a wall coated with a very smooth film of lamp black. (After MORALES *et al.* [1979].)

ing the formation of the ingot structure where two basic concepts were recognized – *copious nucleation* and *crystal multiplication* – we can, then, affirm that a rough surface, a very cold mould or a mould that can absorb large amounts of heat, a low pouring temperature, convection currents that stir the melt, all favour a fine-grained zone. In castings made in a metal mould poured with little superheat, the outer fine-grained columnar zone may extend far enough toward the center to meet the fine-grained zone freezing in from the other size and the whole casting may be fine-grained. On the contrary, in sand or plaster castings where the mould has very low heat transfer and heat absorption, the freezing, even at the start, is very slow and the fine-grained zone is very thin, if not totally absent, except at the mould surface where a controlled microprofile can promote, even at low average heat-transfer, predendritic nuclei as a consequence of high local heat transfer on the asperities (ROSS and MONDOLFO [1980]).

(ii) *Supercooling methods:* pioneering work by WALKER [1961] stimulated structural studies on supercooled melts. If a bath of molten metal is supercooled below its equilibrium temperature and then nucleated, dendritic growth will occur very rapidly from the point of nucleation, at rates increasing with increasing supercooling. Little change in grain size of about 0.1–0.2 cm is observed until a critical supercooling of about 175 K is obtained in pure nickel (WALKER [1961]) and about 160 K in iron-base alloys (KATTAMIS and FLEMINGS [1967]). At these points a sharp order-of-magnitude decrease in grain size is observed and grains between 0.02 and 0.01 cm are obtained. Basically, three theories have been advanced to explain this sharp transition: a) Cavitation occurs at the S–L interface at a particular supercooling and as a consequence the high pressure differences associated with this cavitation can change the equilibrium freezing temperature according to the Clausius–Clapeyron equation (HORVAY [1965]). b) A multiplication mechanism operates as a result of a high instability of dendrites, formed at large supercooling as a consequence of recalescence, together with fluid motion able to remelt and detach dendrite arms (GLICKSMAN [1965]). c) A recrystallization mechanism is induced by forces operating after the observed transition (POWELL and HOGAN [1969]).

On the basis of theoretical calculations connected with cavitation effects and with the catastrophic disintegration observed by GLICKSMAN and SCHAEFER [1968] in dendrites growing at high velocities, the two first mechanisms are thought to be the most probable in order to explain the sharp transition in grain size (CAMPBELL [1981]).

A variant of the supercooling method is the so called *denucleation,* a concept introduced by MARCANTONIO and MONDOLFO [1974] working with aluminum alloys. If the nucleants that act at low supercooling can be removed (by centrifuging during freezing, among other methods) a denucleated melt regardless of its size can be supercooled to a temperature well below its freezing point where it can be made to freeze rapidly on a chosen nucleant. These authors were able to reduce considerably the grain size of pure aluminum by this method. Also in Al–Mn alloys denucleation produces refinement of the grain structure in continuously cast billets and retention in solution of a higher percentage of Mn.

11.1.4.2. Constitutional methods. In order to refine the grain structure through changes in the alloy constitution or composition, the most important approach is the enhancement of heterogeneous nucleation centres using the so-called *inoculants.* Then the grain-refining action is based on heterogeneous nucleation theory and as a result the general characteristics of a good refiner can be stated: low surface energy between substrate and melt; low interfacial energy between solid and substrate and as a consequence low disregistry and high chemical affinity. In addition, settling of the inoculants must be prevented through a minimization of density differences between inoculants and melt; the precipitation of some high-temperature compound which remains stable at the temperature of solidification assuring a *clean* and *reactive* surface is also thought desirable. On this rather simple basis the principal problem is still to know, or to measure, the wetting angle θ, between the nucleated solid and the added catalytic substrate. Also there remains the problem of evaluating factors such as surface area and surface character of the nucleant which the present theory does not consider in detail.

In the area of inoculation a typical example is the addition of Ti and B to aluminum. These elements quickly react with the aluminum and apparently suitable complexes are formed by a peritectic reaction. However, this mechanism is not the only one that has been postulated, and GLASSON and EMLEY [1968] discussed in detail the different possible mechanisms that are still under discussion (ROSS and MONDOLFO [1980]; PEREPEZKO and LEBEAU [1982]). Despite this uncertainty about details of nucleation mechanisms, improvements have been made in the theory in order to predict the final grain size as a function of the dispersion and density of nucleant particles, at least in the case of grain refinement of aluminum alloys (MAXWELL and HELLAWELL [1975]; HELLAWELL [1979]).

References: p. 573.

In the model considered by these authors, the ability of a substrate to act as a surface for heterogeneous nucleation is defined by the *wetting angle, θ*, without entering into the details of the nucleation mechanism at the substrate surface level, and comparison is made between the final grain density (N_v^G) and the initial substrate density (N_v^P) for each set of freezing conditions. Other variables to take into account are the substrate particle radius (R_0) and the values of thermal and solute supercooling existing during the process of nucleation and growth.

As the melt cools below the freezing point, two processes take place concurrently. Solid nucleates on the available substrate surfaces at a rate which rises exponentially with the supercooling and, when the temperature has fallen below a certain limit, nucleated particles start to grow and evolve latent heat. The cooling rate decreases as nucleation and growth accelerate until the temperature reaches a minimum and recalescence occurs. Negligible nucleation and growth occur during the first part of the cooling curve. However, the nucleation rate rises rapidly to a maximum at a temperature just before the minimum. Afterwards the number of nucleation events decreases quickly as the available particles are exhausted and particularly as recalescence begins. Consequently, nucleation is almost complete just beyond the minimum temperature; after that there is only growth. The grain density varies according to the nucleation rate and reaches the final level by the time recalescence begins. However, the growing particles are still relatively far apart and the volume fraction of solid (V_f) is still small when nucleation has already finished (FURRER [1984]). MAXWELL and HELLAWELL [1975] computed the form of cooling curves for a variety of freezing conditions, obtaining important results. Figure 44 shows the concepts discussed above for specific conditions. In order to discuss the factors influencing the nucleation process, comparison is made between the final grain density and the initial substrate density. For each set of freezing conditions a critical particle density exists, above which an increase in the particle density produces negligible further grain refinement. When this limit is high, with the necessary amount of particles present, the as-cast grain size will be as fine as is possible for the particular casting conditions, and the following factors are relevant: (i) considering that efficient heterogeneous nucleation occurs only for $θ < 10°$, a decrease of $θ$ by approximately 3° increases the final grain density by an order of magnitude; (ii) a similar increase in the final grain density is obtained by a variation of the local cooling rate by a factor of five within the range typical for semicontinuous casting (0.1–2.5 K/s); (iii) probably the most important information obtained is the influence of *solute supercooling* as it varies from system to system. In effect, the grain-refining activity of a good potential catalyst is precluded if the growth temperature is not significantly depressed below the freezing point of the alloy. This depression can be considered inversely proportional to a parameter X_1 equal to $1/C_0 m_1(1 - k_0)$, a measure of solute rejection in any system. In order to facilitate comparison, fig. 45 relates to contact angle $θ = 4°$ and cooling rate $P = 0.5$ K/s, for the systems Al–Ti, Al–Zr and Al–Cr. The figure shows that the dramatic variation in the grain-refining action is strongly dependent on the solute supercooling (which varies inversely as X_1); the figure also confirms that the critical inoculant particle density beyond which

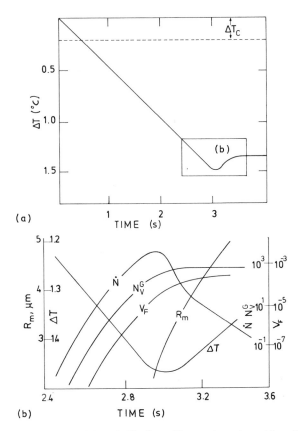

Fig. 44. (a) Cooling curve computed for Al–Ti alloys. The number of particles of Al_3T_i is $10^3/mm^3$; $R_0 = 1$ μm; the initial cooling rate is 0.5 K/s and $\theta = 7°$. (b) Details corresponding to the indicated area in fig. 44a. The computed quantities are: $\dot{N}$ = frequency of nucleation events (per mm^3 s); N_v^G = final grain density (per mm^3); V_F = volume fraction of solid metal, and R_m = mean radius of solid metal spheres. (After HELLAWELL [1979].)

further grain refinement is not achieved, increases as X_1 decreases.

11.1.4.3. Energy-induced methods. A large variety of methods exists in order to refine the grain structure through energy-induced methods having as purpose either an increased nucleation through cavitation or enhancement by crystal multiplication, principally through breaking off of dendrite arms. Methods such as ultrasonic, mechanical vibration, bubbling agitation, rotating magnetic fields, magnetic–electric interaction and mould oscillation have been used by many investigators. COLE and BOLLING [1969] and CAMPBELL [1981] present comprehensive reviews in the field. Although cavitation is responsible for grain refinement in some experimental conditions, today it is generally accepted that the best, and cheapest, method of grain refinement using energy-induced methods is to *promote crystal multiplication during*

References: p. 573.

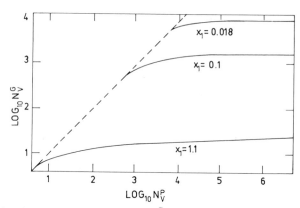

Fig. 45. Computed variation of final grain density, N_v^G, with initial substrate (inoculant) density, N_v^P, for three inoculants in aluminum, with $\theta = 4°$, cooling rate 0.5 K/s and different values of the parameter $X_1 = 1/(C_0 m_1(1 - k_0))$, where m_1 is the slope of the liquidus curve: Al–Ti ($X_1 = 0.018$); Al–Zr ($X_1 = 0.1$); Al–Cr ($X_1 = 1.1$). (After HELLAWELL [1979]).

the solidification process. The multiplication mechanism acts, principally, through forced convection currents promoted in the melt disrupting the incipient dendritic structure.

11.1.5. Modification

Among the most important foundry alloys are those based on the iron–graphite and Al–Si systems. The properties of these metal–nonmetal eutectic alloys are dominated by the morphologies with which the nonmetallic phases solidify. The *modification* of the structure of these alloys and its effect on the mechanical properties is a clear example of the manipulation of the structure on the basis of the application of basic principles. In both systems, the modification of the structure can be accomplished either by rapid cooling or by controlled addition of specific elements. The advantage of the use of additions is that it is essentialy independent of the casting section thickness. Thus we shall refer mostly to modification by additives.

11.1.5.1. Aluminum–silicon alloys. Many studies have been carried out in order to find the mechanism of modification in Al–Si alloys and comprehensive reviews exist in the literature (CHADWICK [1963]; SMITH [1968]; HELLAWELL [1970]). From a structural point of view the modification of Al–Si consists of a morphological change of the silicon phase, both in primary silicon crystals (when hypereutectic alloys are considered) and in the eutectic mixture. In ordinary or unmodified Al–Si alloys, the silicon crystals are plate-like and those present in the eutectic appear as coarse needles randomly oriented. The addition of small amounts of alkaline or alkaline earth metals drastically changes the appearance of primary and eutectic crystals, greatly refining the eutectic structure. The current state of knowledge about the modification process holds that it is a phenomenon involving nucleation and growth. From a nucleation point of view it is considered that in the non-modified alloys the silicon is nucleated by the AlP compound (P being an impurity) at little or no supercooling. Thus, even in hypoeutectic alloys, the silicon crystallizes first in the form of faceted crystals with random orientation. The addition of Na or similar metals transforms the AlP compound into another compound, Na_3P in the case of Na addition, which does not nucleate silicon. Thus, the silicon is denucleated and freezes at the same time as the aluminum as a coupled eutectic. The supercooling, which for the non-modified alloys is from 0 to 4 K, for the modified alloys ranges from 8 to 15–20 K. The accelerated crystallization due to this supercooling contributes to the refining of the structure (CROSSLEY and MONDOLFO [1966]; ROSS and MONDOLFO [1980]). In addition, a consensus exists in the sense that additives such as Na have a restrictive effect on silicon crystal growth, both proeutectic or eutectic. Several authors studied the growth of silicon crystals with increasing amount of Na in the melt (FREDRIKSSON *et al.* [1973]; STEEN and HELLAWELL [1975]; KOBAYASHI *et al.* [1976]). In general, the morphological change of proeutectic Si crystals is extrapolated to the change in morphology occurring in the eutectic where smaller and rounded silicon crystals are formed. The most probable type of growth for the unmodified plate-like crystals is twinned growth and the reason for this type of growth is the slow attachment kinetics on {111}. The impurities which can cause modification probably are not absorbed uniformly in the faceted phase but accumulate at the S–L front. The adsorption or accumulation increases the kinetic supercooling on planes other than {111} of silicon, resulting in a more isotropic and uniformly restricted growth (see especially KOBAYASHI and HOGAN [1979]).

11.1.5.2. Cast iron. It is known that cast iron, belonging to the family of high Fe–C alloys, can behave and undergo transformations according to either the stable iron–graphite system or the so-called "metastable" $Fe–Fe_3C$ system. As a consequence, the eutectic may be austenite–graphite or austenite–cementite (ledeburite). Apart from this important circumstance, the complex chemical composition of the material – the commercial alloys containing additions such as carbon, silicon, sulphur, manganese and phosphorus and usually trace elements such as lead, tin, antimony and bismuth as well as gaseous elements such as hydrogen, nitrogen and oxygen – has important and powerful effects on the structure of cast iron (MOR-ROGH [1968a]). Although both forms of cast iron (white and grey) have technological importance, the most interesting from a structural point of view is the stable diagram iron–graphite, and the different morphologies that the graphite can achieve. These different morphologies will influence the properties. Several forms of graphite precipitation from the melt are known and semantic problems seem to exist in the literature. In many papers names such as flake, undercooled, fibrous, coral, vermicular, cylindrite, spherulitic, and nodular graphite appear. As a consequence some confusion arises among scientists and foundrymen. However, recent work intends to rationalize the origin and development of different forms of graphite in connection with nucleation and growth mechanisms (DOUBLE and HELLAWELL [1975]). In this section the present status of knowledge in the area will be discussed briefly.

MORROGH [1968a, b] has published excellent reviews on nucleation and growth of graphite presenting different morphologies and it is known that formation of

References: p. 573.

iron–graphite eutectic is favoured by elements such as Si and Al, because the temperature range over which that eutectic can freeze before supercooling into the region of carbidic eutectic solidification increases substantially when these elements are present. At the same time, if *inoculation techniques* are used the promotion of the grey (i.e. graphitic) solidification is also promoted. Several theories exist about the mechanism involved in inoculation and most of them are connected with impurities existing in the melt or in the inoculant that promotes heterogeneous nucleation of the graphite. FeSi being the most powerful and common inoculant used in industrial practice, the nucleation mechanism must be connected with the addition of these particles. Very recently, WANG and FREDRIKSSON [1981] carefully studied the dissolution of particles of FeSi by quenching of the melt during different stages of the process. On the basis of the experimental observations a theory of an inhomogeneous distribution of C and Si in the melt was formulated. The theory assumes that this inhomogeneous distribution gives rise to a locally high supersaturation of graphite, and as a consequence homogeneous nucleation is promoted. The theory, still based on a simple diffusion model that does not consider the effect of convection, seems to be promising in order to explain experimental observations such as the effect of holding time, superheat temperature, degree of stirring of the melt, proportion of white iron in the charge and type of furnace used, as well as the action of graphite-promoting elements (Al, Ni, Cu, Co, P) and antigraphiting elements (Mg, Fe, V, Cr, Mo, W). Concerning the action of these elements, those that lower the binding force between Fe and C atoms favour the existence of localized high carbon activity areas and enhance the effects of inoculation. On the contrary, the promoters of carbides tend to destroy the localized supersaturated areas reducing the inoculation effects.

It is generally accepted that cast iron inoculated with FeSi presents the graphite phase of the eutectic with a flake morphology and eutectic *grains* or *colonies* form during solidification; within each of the grains graphite forms and grows. MINKOFF [1977] gives a detailed description of graphite growth with different morphologies.

While the eutectic growth involving flakes is a coupled growth of the type discussed in § 7 for unidirectional solidification of (nf–f) eutectics and the growing graphite skeleton is always in contact with the eutectic liquid, in *spherulitic* or *nodular cast iron* the situation is completely different and it is generally agreed that the nodular graphite is nucleated in the liquid phase and starts to grow in it but at some later stage the nodule becomes enveloped by an austenite shell and the subsequent growth occurs by diffusion of carbon through the shell (MORROGH [1968b]; WETTERFALL *et al.* [1972]). This form of growth is a consequence of *modification* by addition to the melt of reactive impurities such as Mg, Ce or rare-earth metals. During growth initially the impurity goes to $(10\bar{1}0)$ steps of the advancing graphite (0001) surface and stops crystal growth. For small reactive impurity concentrations, separated holes form on the flake surface. For increasing impurity content the crystal surface is proportionally blocked in growth. At this stage the normal flake growth is impeded by the impurity. From these observations the action of reactive impurities is interpreted as an impediment to flake growth, allowing other forms to develop. In order for the new forms to occur temperatures must decrease as a condition for the growth steps to traverse the decreasing spacing of absorbed impurity atoms (MINKOFF [1977]). It is quite possible that all the other forms of graphite named above are intermediate forms between these two extremes, flakes and nodular graphite, conditioned by cooling rate and impurity concentration (DOUBLE and HELLAWELL [1975]).

11.2. New processes

The application of the basic principles discussed in § 11.1 permits not only the manipulation of structure, and as a consequence, properties, in conventional processes but also allows new processes to be developed. In a recent paper FLEMINGS [1980] delineates the ways in which fundamental ideas are built into a useful understanding of practical solidification processes. Through a process of *analysis* and *synthesis* new processes can be developed. In this intellectual process the analysis corresponds to the intelligent manipulation of the knowledge obtained during fundamental research where "blocks" of understanding are developed. The *synthesis* can be qualitative, as in many of the cases treated in § 11.1, but increasingly, processes become more costly and complex. As a consequence mathematical modelling plays a more and more important role, aided by increasingly powerful computers and sophisticated methods of experimental modelling to test the mathematical model. Thus, modelling is frequently a part of *synthesis*. Some examples will be given.

11.2.1. Electroslag refining process
Electroslag-refining (ESR) consists of a secondary remelting of metals and alloys having as aim a better material from structural and soundness points of view. Current is carried via a consumable electrode to a slag bath where it generates an ohmic resistance. As the current flows from the tip of the electrode through the pool of slag, the slag will reach a temperature ranging from 300–400 K above the melting point and will cause the electrode to melt. Drops of the molten metal pass through the slag into the metal pool underneath, where the metal solidifies in a water-cooled mould. Details of the electroslag process from a solidification point of view have been reviewed by FREDRIKSSON and JARLEBORG [1971]. Two of the most important factors that determine the quality of an ESR ingot are the structure and the homogeneity. Since profit increases with the diameter of the ingot, modelling is necessary in order to obtain optimum conditions. Taking as a basis the knowledge of macrosegregation as a result of fluid flow, discussed in § 8, as well as the laws of fluid dynamics which can be used to control fluid flow, it is possible to minimize macrosegregation through ingot rotation, altering the interdendritic flow behaviour. Moderate rotational speeds during solidification eliminate defects and minimize surface-to-center macrosegregation (POIRIER *et al.* [1976]).

11.2.2. Rheocasting and thixocasting
In § 8.6 it was mentioned that vigorous agitation during solidification has as a consequence a change in the structure, due to dendrite fragments breaking off. This,

References: p. 573.

together with the fluid-like behaviour of liquid–solid mixtures even with about 0.4 fraction of solid, is the underlying principle of *rheocasting* (from the Greek root "rheo", to flow). The alloy is allowed to freeze slowly and at the same time is subjected to strong shear forces that break off the dendrite fragments. If the alloy is poured when the viscosity is still low, it can be made to fill the mould, in spite of the fact that a substantial portion of it is already frozen (SPENCER *et al.* [1972]). Each dendrite fragment becomes a separate crystal and a very fine grain size can be achieved without the disadvantages inherent in the use of grain-refining additions. The process also affects other casting features as a result of the fact that the alloy is already partly frozen when cast. Thus, shrinkage is reduced and economy in risers and gating may be substantial. Pouring temperature can also be much lower and as a consequence the amount of heat to be removed is lower and thermal stresses are reduced. Through this method all kinds of casting can be made but also the method can be used in order to precast slugs to be used in a subsequent casting process. When ready to cast, the slugs are heated rapidly to the partially molten state, dropped in the die-casting machine and forced under pressure into the mould. This method is named *thixocasting* (FLEMINGS [1976], FLEMINGS [1979]). By this method the metal treatment can be done at a separate location and time, and the slugs stored for die-casting when convenient. One of the important advantages of thixocasting is the dramatic improvement in die life (ROSS and MONDOLFO [1980]).

Diverse applications of rheocasting principles have appeared in recent years. Thus, MATSUMIYA and FLEMINGS [1981] extended the application of the solidified rheocast slurry to strip-casting. Through the method of analysis–synthesis, using mathematical modelling, rheocast material is cast onto a moving belt which then travels horizontally in a space between the belt and a rotating drum. The semisolid metal simultaneously flows and flattens under the wheel and solidifies. The process parameters, including segregation, shape, crack formation and surface quality of the sheet were studied and optimized experimentally. Through mathematical modelling of heat flow during solidification and deformation behaviour, good agreement between calculation and experiments was observed for: solidification time, roll separation forces as well as shape of the strip as it passes through the deformation zone.

Another application of rheocasting principles is the development and production of metal-matrix composites containing nonmetallic particles, taking advantage of the rheological behaviour and structure of the partially solidified and agitated matrix. Important results have been obtained in composites of 2014, 2024 and 201 aluminum alloys containing particulate additions of Al_2O_3 and SiC. This composite fabrication is based on work by SATO and MEHRABIAN [1976]; the particulate or fibrous nonmetals are added and retained by the partially solid alloy slurry regardless of wetting. The high viscosity of the slurry and the presence of a high volume fraction of primary solid in the alloy slurry prevents the nonmetallic particles from floating, settling or agglomerating. With increasing mixing times, after addition, interaction between the particles and the alloy matrix promotes bonding. The composites are subsequently reheated above their liquidus temperature in a second induction furnace and forged into shape with hydraulic presses. This process is very promising in order to obtain wear-resistant alloys.

11.2.3. Fractional melting

LUX and FLEMINGS [1979a, b] have developed a new method for purifying metals, consisting essentially in heating them within the liquid–solid region while simultaneously pressing them against a filter to remove the interdendritic liquid. A mathematical model of the process shows it to be capable of achieving comparable purification to that obtained in multipass zone-refining and orders of magnitude better than obtainable by isothermal fractional solidification. The final structures of the refined solid obtained in experiments with Sn–Pb alloys are fine-grained and completely devoid of second phases. This process seems to be very promising in scrap recycling as well as upgrading of high-purity alloys.

11.2.4. Rapid-solidification processes

In the last few years, increasing importance has been attained by the so-called *rapid-solidification processes* that commonly result in progressive departures from the microstructures produced by conventional casting, generally in the direction of increased refinement and chemical homogeneity. Among these, *atomization* and *surface melting by laser devices* are becoming more and more important. These methods are further treated in ch. 28. As a consequence, we mention them here only as very promising processes able to obtain controlled structures with minimum segregation, maximum cleanliness and good forming characteristics when powders are obtained by atomization methods, as well as controlled surface structure with special properties of resistance to wear or corrosion when surface melting is used.

References

AGUILAR RIVAS, R.A., and H. BILONI, 1980a, Z. Metallk. **71**, 264.
AGUILAR RIVAS, R.A., and H. BILONI, 1980b, Z. Metallk. **71**, 309.
APELIAN, D., 1982, in: Aluminum Transformation Technology and Applications 1981, eds. C.A. Pampillo, H. Biloni, L. Mondolfo and F. Sacchi (ASM, Metals Park, OH) p. 423.
AUDERO, M.A., and H. BILONI, 1972, J. Cryst. Growth **12**, 297.
AUDERO, M.A., and H. BILONI, 1973, J. Cryst. Growth **18**, 257.
BÄCKERUD, L., and T. EDVARSSON, 1976, Scand. J. Metall. **5**, 262.
BAKER, C., and V. SUBRAMIAN, 1980, in: Aluminum Transformation Technology and Applications 1979, eds. C.A. Pampillo, H. Biloni and D.E. Embury (ASM, Metals Park, OH) p. 335.
BEELEY, D.R., 1979, in: Solidification and Casting of Metals (The Metals Society, London) p. 319.
BERTORELLO, H.R., and H. BILONI, 1969, Trans. Met. Soc. AIME, **245**, 1375.
*BILONI, H., 1968, in: The Solidification of Metals (Iron & Steel Inst. London, publication no. 110) p. 74.
BILONI, H., 1970, Metallurgia ABM (Ass. Brasileira de Metais) **26**, 803.
BILONI, H., 1977, Ciencia Interamericana **18** (3–4), 3.
BILONI, H., 1980, in: Aluminum Transformation Technology and Applications 1979, eds. C.A. Pampillo, H. Biloni and D.E. Embury (ASM, Metals Park, OH) p. 1.
BILONI, H., and G.F. BOLLING, 1963, Trans. Met. Soc. AIME **227**, 1351.

BILONI, H., and B. CHALMERS, 1965, Trans. Met. Soc. AIME **233**, 373.

BILONI, H., and B. CHALMERS, 1968, J. Mater. Sci. **3**, 139.

BILONI, H., and R. MORANDO, 1968, Trans. Met. Soc. AIME **242**, 1121.

BILONI, H., G.F. BOLLING and H.A. DOMIAN, 1965a, Trans. Met. Soc. AIME **233**, 1926.

BILONI, H., G.F. BOLLING and G.S. COLE, 1965b, Trans. Met. Soc. AIME **233**, 251.

BILONI, H., G.F. BOLLING and G.S. COLE, 1966, Trans. Met. Soc. AIME **236**, 930.

BILONI, H., R. DI BELLA and G.F. BOLLING, 1967, Trans. Met. Soc. AIME **239**, 2012.

BOETTINGER, W.J., 1974, Metallurg. Trans. **5**, 2023.

*BOLLING, G.F., 1971, in: Solidification (ASM, Metals Park, OH) p. 341.

BOLLING, G.F., and D. FAINSTEIN-PEDRAZA, 1974, Acta Metall. **22**, 1033.

BOLLING, G.F., and W.A. TILLER, 1961, J. Appl. Phys. **32**, 2587.

BOSWELL, P.G., and G.A. CHADWICK, 1980, Acta Metall. **28**, 209.

BOWER, T.F., and M.C. FLEMINGS, 1967, Trans. Met. Soc. AIME **239**, 1629.

BOWER, T.F., H.D. BRODY and M.C. FLEMINGS, 1966, Trans. Met. Soc. AIME **236**, 624.

BOWER, T.F., D.A. GRANGER and J. KEVERIAN, 1971, in: Solidification (ASM, Metals Park, OH) p. 385.

*BRODY, H.D., 1974, in: Solidification Technology, eds. J.J. Burke, M.C. Flemings and A.E. Qorum (Brook Hill Publ., Chestnut Hills, MA) p. 53.

*BRODY, H.D., and S.A. DAVID, 1979, in: Solidification and Casting of Metals (The Metals Society, London) p. 144.

BRODY, H.D., and M.C. FLEMINGS, 1966, Trans. Met. Soc. AIME **236**, 615.

BURDEN, M.H., and J.D. HUNT, 1974a, J. Cryst. Growth **22**, 99.

BURDEN, M.H., and J.D. HUNT, 1974b, J. Cryst. Growth **22**, 109.

BURDEN, M.H., and J.D. HUNT, 1974c, J. Cryst. Growth **22**, 328.

BURDEN, M.H., and J.D. HUNT, 1975, Metallurg. Trans. **6A**, 240.

BURTON, J.A., R.C. PRIM and W.P. SLICHTER, 1953, J. Chem. Phys. **21**, 1987.

CAHN, J.W., 1960, Acta Metall. **8**, 554.

CAHN, J.W., W.B. HILLIG and G.W. SEARS, 1964, Acta Metall. **12**, 1421.

CAHN, J.W., 1967, in: Crystal Growth, ed. H.S. Peiser (Pergamon Press, Oxford) p. 681.

CAHN, J.W., 1979, Metallurg. Trans. **10A**, 119.

CALVO, C., and H. BILONI, 1971, Z. Metallk. **62**, 664.

CAMPBELL, J., 1968, The British Foundryman, April, p. 147.

CAMPBELL, J., 1981, Int. Met. Rev. **26**, 71.

CANTOR, B., 1983, Eutectics, in: Phase Boundaries, eds. G.A. Chadwick and D.R. Smith (Academic, London) in press.

CANTOR, B., 1984, Nucleation from the Melt, in: Encyclopedia of Materials Science and Engineering, ed. M.B. Bever (Pergamon Press, Oxford) in press.

CANTOR, B., and R.D. DOHERTY, 1979, Acta Metall. **27**, 33.

CARRUTHERS, J.R., 1976, Thermal Convection Instabilities Relevant to Crystal Growth from Liquids, in: Preparation and Properties of Solid State Materials, vol. 2 (Marcel Dekker, New York).

CHADWICK, G.A., 1963, Prog. Mater. Sci. **12**, 2.

CHADWICK, G.A., 1973, Proc. Int. Symposium Chem. Met. of Iron and Steel, p. 207.

CHALMERS, B., 1963, J. Austr. Inst. Metals, **8**, 255.

CHALMERS, B., 1964, Principles of Solidification (Wiley, New York).

CHALMERS, B., 1971, in: Solidification (American Society for Metals, ASM, Metals Park, OH) p. 295.

CHAN, S.K., H.H. KEIMER and M. KALHWEIT, 1976, J. Cryst. Growth, **32**, 303.

CHAN, S.K., H.H. KEIMER and M. KALHWEIT, 1978, J. Cryst. Growth, **43**, 229.

CHERNOV, A.A., 1974, J. Cryst. Growth **24/25**, 11.

CHERNOV, A.A., and D.E. TEMKIN, 1976, in: Crystal Growth and Materials, eds. E. Kaldis and H.J. Scheel (North-Holland, Amsterdam) p. 3.

CLYNE, T.W., and A. GARCIA, 1980, J. Heat and Mass Transfer **23**, 773.

CLYNE, T.W., A. GARCIA, P. ACKERMANN and W. KURZ, 1980, The use of empirical analytical and numerical models to describe solidification of steel during continuous casting, conf. on Modelling of Casting and Welding Processes, Rindge, NH, USA, 3–8 Aug. (private communication).

*COLE, G.S., 1971, in: Solidification (ASM, Metals Park, OH) p. 201.

COLE, G.S., and G.F. BOLLING, 1968, Trans. Met. Soc. AIME **242**, 153.

COLE, G.S., and G.F. BOLLING, 1969, Proc. 16th Sagamore Army Materials Research Conf., quoted by G.F. Bolling, 1971.

CORIELL, S.R., and R.L. PARKER, 1967, in: Crystal Growth, ed. H.S. Peiser (Pergamon Press, Oxford) p. 703.

CORIELL, R.S., and R.F. SEKERKA, 1980, Rapid Solidification, Processing and Technologies II (Claitor's Publish. Div., Baton Rouge) p. 35.

CROSSLEY, P.A., and L.F. MONDOLFO, 1966, Modern Casting **49**, 89.

DAVIS, G.J., and J.G. GARLAND, 1975, Int. Met. Rev. **20**, 83.

DELVES, R.T., 1974, Crystal Growth I (Pergamon Press, Oxford) p. 40.

*DOHERTY, R.D., 1980, in: Crystal Growth, 2nd Ed., ed. B.R. Pamplin (Pergamon Press, Oxford) p. 485.

DOHERTY, R.D., 1984, Dendritic Solidification, in: Encyclopedia of Materials Science and Engineering, ed. M.B. Bever (Pergamon Press, Oxford) in press.

DOHERTY, R.D., P.D. COOPER, M.H. BRADBURY and F.J. HONEY, 1977, Metallurg. Trans. **8A**, 397.

DOHERTY, R.D., B. CANTOR and S. FAIRS, 1978, Metallurg. Trans. **9A**, 621.

DOUBLE, D.D., and A. HELLAWELL, 1975, in: The Metallurgy of Cast Iron, eds. B. Lux, I. Minkoff and F. Mollard (Georgi Publ. Co., St. Saphorin, Switzerland) p. 503.

EMLEY, E.F., 1976, Int. Met. Rev. **21**, 75.

FAINSTEIN-PEDRAZA, D., and G.F. BOLLING, 1975, J. Cryst. Growth **28**, 311.

FELIU, S., and D. SIGUIN, 1963, Trans. Amer. Foundry Soc. **71**, 145.

FELIU, S., L. LUIS, D. SIGUIN and J. ALVAREZ, 1962, Trans. Amer. Foundry Soc. **70**, 838.

FISHER, J.C., 1950, quoted by B. Chalmers, 1964, p. 105.

FISHER, D.J., and W. KURZ, 1977, Proc. Conf. on Quality Control of Engineering Alloys and the Role of Metals Science, Delft, eds. H. Nieswaag and J.W. Schut, p. 59.

FISHER, D.J., and W. KURZ, 1979, in: Solidification and Casting of Metals (The Metals Society, London) p. 57.

*FLEMINGS, M.C., 1974, Solidification Processing (McGraw-Hill, New York).

FLEMINGS, M.C., 1976, Scand. J. Metall. **5**, 1.

*FLEMINGS, M.C., 1979, in: Solidification and Casting of Metals (The Metals Society, London) p. 479.

FLEMINGS, M.C., 1980, Proc. Warwick Conf., to be published.

*FLEMINGS, M.C., 1981, Segregation and Structure in Rapidly Solidified Cast Metals, Metallurgical Treatises, eds. J.K. Tien and J.F. Elliot (Met. Soc. AIME, Warrendale) p. 291.

*FLEMINGS, M.C., and R. MEHRABIAN, 1971, in: Solidification (ASM, Metals Park, OH) p. 311.

FLEMINGS, M.C., and NEREO, 1967, Trans. Met. Soc. AIME **239**, 1449.

FLEMINGS, M.C., D.R. POIRIER, R.V. BARONE and H.D. BRODY, 1970, J. Iron Steel Inst. **208**, 371.

FRANK, F.C., 1949, Disc. Farad. Soc. **5**, 48.

FREDRIKSSON, H., 1980, Proc. Vth ESA–PAC Symp. on European Rocket and Balloon Programmes and Related Research, Bournemouth (UK) 14–18 April, 1980 (ESA SP-152) p. 497.

FREDRIKSSON, H., and M. HILLERT, 1972, Scand. J. Metall. **2**, 125.

FREDRIKSSON, H., and O. JARLEBORG, 1971, J. Metals **23**, Sept., 32.

FREDRIKSSON, H., and S.O. NILSSON, 1978, Metallurg. Trans. **9B**, 111.

FREDRIKSSON, H., and T. NYLENT, 1982, Met. Sci. **16**, 283.

FREDRIKSSON, H., M. HILLERT and N. LANGE, 1973, J. Inst. Metals, **101**, 285.

FURRER, P., 1984, Control of Grain Size, in: Encyclopedia of Materials Science and Engineering, ed. M.B. Bever (Pergamon Press, Oxford) in press.

GANAHA, T., and H.W. KERR, 1978, Met. Techn. **5**, 62.

GARCIA, A., and M. PRATES, 1978, Metallurg. Trans. **9B**, 449.

GARCIA, A., T.W. CLYNE and M. PRATES, 1979, Metallurg. Trans. **10B**, 85.

GETSELEV, Z.N., 1971, J. Metals, **23**, 38.

GLASSON, E.L., and E.F. EMLEY, 1968, in: The Solidification of Metals (Iron & Steel Inst., London, publication no. 110) p. 1.

GLICKSMAN, M.E., 1965, Acta Metall. **13**, 1281.

GLICKSMAN, M.E., 1981, private communication.

GLICKSMAN, M.E., 1982, in: Aluminum Transformation Technology and Applications 1981, eds. C.A. Pampillo, H. Biloni, L. Mondolfo and F. Sacchi (ASM, Metals Park, OH) p. 347.

GLICKSMAN, M.E., and S.C. HUANG, 1979, Proc. 3rd European Symp. on Materials Science in Space (ESM-SP-142) p. 309.

GLICKSMAN, M.E., and S.C. HUANG, 1981, Adv. Space Res. Vol. I, 25.

GLICKSMAN, M.E., and R.J. SCHAEFER, 1967, J. Cryst. Growth **1**, 297.

GLICKSMAN, M.E., and R.J. SCHAEFER, 1968, J. Cryst. Growth **2**, 239.

GLICKSMAN, M.E., R.J. SCHAEFER and J.D. AYERS, 1976, Metallurg. Trans. **7A**, 1747.

GRUGEL, R.N., and A. HELLAWELL, 1981, Metallurg. Trans. **12A**, 669.

GRUZLESKI, J.E., and W.C. WINEGARD, 1968, Trans. Met. Soc. AIME **242** 1785.

HELLAWELL, A., 1970, Prog. Mater. Sci. **15**, 3.

HELLAWELL, A., 1975, in: The Metallurgy of Cast Iron, eds. B. Lux, I. Minkoff and F. Mollard (Georgi Publ. Co., St. Saphorin, Switzerland) p. 526.

*HELLAWELL, A., 1979, in: Solidification and Casting of Metals (The Metals Society, London) p. 161.

HILLERT, M., 1957, Jernkontorets Ann. **141**, 757.

*HILLERT, M., 1979, in: Solidification and Casting of Metals (The Metals Society, London) p. 81.

HILLIG, W.B., and D. TURNBULL, 1965, J. Chem. Phys. **24**, 219.

HILLS, A.W.D., 1965, J. Iron and Steel Inst. **203**, 18.

HOLLOMON, J.H., and D. TURNBULL, 1953, Prog. Met. Phys., vol. 4 (Interscience, New York) p. 333.

HOLTZMANN, E.G., 1970a, J. Appl. Phys. **41**, 1460.

HOLTZAMNN, E.G., 1970b, J. Appl. Phys. **41**, 1469.

HORVAY, G., 1965, J. Heat and Mass Transfer **8**, 195.

HORVAY, G., and J.W. CAHN, 1961, Acta Metall. **9**, 965.

HORWARTH, J.A., and L.F. MONDOLFO, 1962, Acta Metall. **10**, 1037.

HUANG, S.C., and M.E. GLICKSMAN, 1981a, Acta Metall. **29**, 701.

HUANG, S.C., and M.E. GLICKSMAN, 1981b, Acta Metall. **29**, 717.

*HUNT, J.D., 1979, in: Solidification and Casting of Metals (The Metals Society, London) p. 1.

HUNT, J.D., and K.A. JACKSON, 1966, Trans. Met. Soc. AIME **236**, 843.

HUNT, J.D., and K.A. JACKSON, 1967, Trans. Met. Soc. AIME **239**, 864.

HURLE, D.T.J., 1972, J. Cryst. Growth **13/14**, 39.

HURLE, D.T.J., and E. JAKEMAN, 1968, J. Cryst. Growth **3/4**, 574.

IVANTSOV, G.P., 1947, Dokl. Akad. Nauk SSSR **58**, 567.

JACKSON, K.A., 1958, in: Liquid Metals and Solidification (ASM, Metals Park, OH) p. 174.

JACKSON, K.A., 1968, Trans. Met. Soc. AIME **242**, 1275.

JACKSON, K.A., 1971, in: Solidification (ASM, Metals Park, OH) p. 121.

JACKSON, K.A., 1974, J. Cryst. Growth **24/25**, 130.

JACKSON, K.A., and J.D. HUNT, 1966, Trans. Met. Soc. AIME **236**, 1129.

JACKSON, K.A., J.D. HUNT, D.R. UHLMANN and T.P. STEWARD, 1966, Trans. Met. Soc. AIME **236**, 149.

JACKSON, K.A., D.R. UHLMANN and J.D. HUNT, 1967, J. Cryst. Growth **1**, 1.

JACOBI, H., and K. SCHWERDTFEGER, 1976, Metallurg. Trans. **7A**, 811.

JONES, H., 1969, J. Inst. Metals **97**, 38.

JORDAN, R.M., and J.D. HUNT, 1971, J. Cryst. Growth **11**, 141.

KATO, H., F. MATSUDA and T. SENDA, 1972, Trans. Japan Weld. Soc. **3**, 69.

KATTAMIS, T.Z., and M.C. FLEMINGS, 1965, Trans. Met. Soc. AIME **233**, 992.

KATTAMIS, T.Z., and M.C. FLEMINGS, 1966, Trans. Met. Soc. AIME **236**, 1523.

KATTAMIS, T.Z., and M.C. FLEMINGS, 1967, Modern Casting **52**, 97.

KATTAMIS, T.Z., J. COUGHLIN and M.C. FLEMINGS, 1967, Trans. Met. Soc. AIME **239**, 1504.

KERR, H.W., J. CISSE and G.F. BOLLING, 1974, Acta Metall. **22**, 677.

KISS, F.J., and H. BILONI, ref. 31 in H. BILONI, 1968.

KLAREN, C.M., J.D. VERHOEVEN, and R. TRIVEDI, 1980, Metallurg. Trans. **11A**, 1853.

KOBAYASHI, K., and L.M. HOGAN, 1979, Phil. Mag. **A40**, 399.

KOBAYASHI, K., P.H. SHINGU and R. OZAKI, 1976, J. Mater. Sci. **11**, 399.

KOFLER, A., 1950, Z. Metallk. **41**, 221.

KOTLER, G.R., and W.A. TILLER, 1968, J. Cryst. Growth **2**, 287.

KURZ, W., and T.W. CLYNE, 1981, Metallurg. Trans. **12A**, 965.

KURZ, W., and D.J. FISHER, 1979, Int. Met. Rev. **24**, 177.

KURZ, W., and D.J. FISHER, 1980, Acta Metall. **28**, 777.

KURZ, W., and D.J. FISHER, 1981, Acta Metall. **29**, 11.

LAIT, J.E., J.K. BRIMACOMBE and F. WEINBERG, 1974, Ironmaking and Steelmaking **2**, 90.

*LANGER, J.S., 1980, Rev. Mod. Phys. **53**, 1.

LANGER, J.S., and H. MÜLLER-KRUMBHAAR, 1978, Acta Metall. **26**, 1681.

LEAMY, H.J., and G.H. GILMER, 1974, J. Cryst. Growth **24/25**, 499.

LEAMY, H.J., and K.A. JACKSON, 1971, J. Appl. Phys. **42**, 2121.

LUX, A.L., and M.C. FLEMINGS, 1979a, Metallurg. Trans. **10B**, 71.

LUX, A.L., and M.C. FLEMINGS, 1979b, Metallurg. Trans. **10B**, 79.

MALMEJAC, Y., 1981, private communication.

MARCANTONIO, J.A., and L.F. MONDOLFO, 1974, Metallurg. Trans. **5**, 1325.

MASON, J.T., J.D. VERHOEVEN and R. TRIVEDI, 1983, J. Cryst. Growth, in press.

MASUR, L.J., and M.C. FLEMINGS, 1982, Proc. 4th Conf. on Rapidly Quenched Metals, Sendai, Japan, 1981 (Japan Inst. of Metals, Sendai) p. 1557.

MATSUMIYA, T., and M.C. FLEMINGS, 1981, Metallurg. Trans. **12B**, 17.

MAXWELL, I., and A. HELLAWELL, 1975, Acta Metall. **23**, 901.

MEHRABIAN, R., N. KEANE, and M.C. FLEMINGS, 1970, Metallurg. Trans. **1**, 1209.

MEHRABIAN, R., 1982, Int. Met. Rev. **27**, 185.

MINKOFF, I., 1968, in: The Solidification of Metals (Iron & Steel Inst., London, publication no. 110) p. 251.

MINKOFF, I., 1977, Proc. Conf. on Quality Control of Engineering Alloys and the Rôle of Metals Science, Delft, eds. H. Nieswaag and J.W. Schut, p. 79.

MOLLARD, F., and M.C. FLEMINGS, 1967, Trans. Met. Soc. AIME **239**, 1534.

MONDOLFO, L.F., 1965, J. Austr. Inst. Metals **10**, 169.

MORALES, A., J.J. FISSOLO, and H. BILONI, 1977, Z. Metallk. **68**, 180.

*MORALES, A., M.E. GLICKSMAN, and H. BILONI, 1979, in: Solidification and Casting of Metals (The Metals Society, London) p. 484.

MORANDO, R., H. BILONI, G.S. COLE and G.F. BOLLING, 1970, Metallurg. Trans. **1**, 1407.

MORRIS, L.R., and W.C. WINEGARD, 1969, J. Cryst. Growth **6**, 61.

MORROGH, H., 1968a, J. Iron and Steel Inst. **206**, 1.

*MORROGH, H., 1968b, in: The Solidification of Metals (Iron & Steel Inst., London, publication no. 110) p. 238.

MULLINS, W.W., and R.F. SEKERKA, 1963, J. Appl. Phys. **34**, 323.

MULLINS, W.W., and R.F. SEKERKA, 1964, J. Appl. Phys. **35**, 444.

NAKAGAWA, H., H. KATO, F. MATSUDA and T. SENDA, 1970, J. Japan. Weld. Soc., **39**, 94.

NAKAGAWA, H., H. KATO, F. MATSUDA and T. SENDA, 1972, Trans. Japan. Weld. Soc. **3**, 54.

NASH, G.E., and M.E. GLICKSMAN, 1974, Acta Metall. **22**, 1283.

NOGGLE, T.S., 1953, Rev. Sci. Instr. **24**, 184.

O'HARA, and W.A. TILLER, 1967, Trans. Met. Soc. AIME, **239**, 497.

OKAMOTO, T., and K. KISHITAKE, 1975, J. Cryst. Growth **29**, 137.

OKAMOTO, T., K. KISHITAKE and I. BESSHO, 1975, J. Cryst. Growth, **29**, 131.

OSTROWSKI, A., and E.W. LANGER, 1979, in: Solidification and Casting of Metals (The Metals Society, London) p. 139.

PALACIO, H., M. SOLARI and H. BILONI, 1982, unpublished.

PAPAZIAN, J.M., and T.Z. KATTAMIS, 1980, Metallurg. Trans. **11A**, 483.

PATON, B., 1959, Electroslag Welding (Foreign Language Publishing House, Moscow).

*PEREPEZKO, J.H., and I.E. ANDERSON, 1980: Synthesis and Properties of Metastable phases, eds. E.S. Machlin and T.S. Rowland (Trans. Met. Soc. AIME, Warrendale, Pa.) p. 31.

*PEREPEZKO, J.H., and S.E. LEBEAU, 1982, in: Aluminum Transformation Technology and Applications 1981, eds. C.A. Pampillo, H. Biloni, L. Mondolfo and F. Sacchi (ASM, Metals Park, OH) p. 309.

PEREPEZKO, J.H., and D.H. RASMUSSEN, 1978, Metallurg. Trans. **9A**, 1490.

*PEREPEZKO, J.H., D.H. RASMUSSEN, I.E. ANDERSON and C.R. LOPER, 1979, in: Solidification of Castings and Alloys (The Metals Society, London) p. 169.

PEREZ, T., M. SOLARI and H. BILONI, 1981, Int. Inst. Weld. DOC 11-541-81.

PFANN, W.G., 1957, Zone Melting, 1st Ed. (Wiley, New York).

*PFANN, W.G., 1978, Zone Melting, 2nd Ed. (Kruger, New York).

PIMPUTKAR, M., and S. OSTRACH, 1981, J. Cryst. Growth **55**, 614.

PIRES, O.S., M. PRATES and H. BILONI, 1974, Z. Metallk. **65**, 143.

POIRIER, D.R., R. MEHRABIAN, M.C. FLEMINGS and J.H. KLEIN, 1976, Proc. 23th Sagamore Army Materials Research Conf. on Non-Destructive Evaluation of Materials, Raqueth Lake, NY, unpublished.

POWELL, G.L.F., and L.M. HOGAN, 1969, Trans. Met. Soc. AIME **245**, 407.

PRATES, M., and H. BILONI, 1972, Metallurg. Trans. **3**, 1501.

PRATES, M., and G.J. DAVIES, 1978, Solidifiçao e fundiçao de metais e suas ligas (Ed. Univ. San Pablo) p. 18.

ROSS, A.B.De, and L.F. MONDOLFO, 1980, in: Aluminum Transformation Technology and Applications 1979, eds. C.A. Pampillo, H. Biloni and D.E. Embury (ASM, Metals Park, OH) p. 81.

*RUDDLE, R.W., 1957, The Solidification of Castings (The Institute of Metals, London).

SATO, A., and R. MEHRABIAN, 1976, Metallurg. Trans. **7B**, 443.

SATO, T., and G. OHIRA, 1977, J. Cryst. Growth **44**, 78.

SAVAGE, W.F., and E.S. SZEKERES, 1967, Welding J. **46**, 94–s.

SAVAGE, W.F., C.D. LUNDIN and A.H. ARONSON, 1965, Welding J. **44**, 175–s.

SAVAGE, W.F., C.D. LUNDIN and T.F. CHASE, 1968a, Welding J, **47**, 522–s.

SAVAGE, W.F., C.D. LUNDIN and R.J. HRUBEC, 1968b, Welding J. **47**, 420–s.

SAVAGE, W.F., E.F. NIPPES and J.S. ERICKSON, 1976, Welding J. **55**, 213–s.

SCHAEFER, R.J., and M.E. GLICKSMAN, 1970, Metallurg. Trans. 1, 1973.

SCHEIL, E., 1942, Z. Metallk. **34**, 70.

*SEKERKA, R.F., 1967, Crystal Growth (Pergamon Press, Oxford) p. 691.

SEKERKA, R.F., 1973, Crystal Growth: an Introduction, ed. P. Hartman (North-Holland, Amsterdam) p. 403.

SEKERKA, R.F., R.G. SEIDENSTICKER, D.R. HAMILTON and J.D. HARRISON, 1967, quoted by Glicksman *et al.*, 1976.

SHIBATKA, K., T. SATO and G. OHIRA, 1978, J. Cryst. Growth **44**, 419.

SHINGU, P.H., 1979, J. Appl. Phys. **50**, 5473.

SMITH, R.W., 1968, in: The Solidification of Metals (Iron & Steel Inst., London, publication no. 110) p. 224.

SOLARI, M., and H. BILONI, 1980, J. Cryst. Growth **49**, 451.

SOUTHIN, R.T., 1967, Trans. Met. Soc. AIME **236**, 220.

SOUTHIN, R.T., and G.A. CHADWICK, 1978, Acta Metall. **26**, 223.

SPENCER, D., R. MEHRABIAN and M.C. FLEMINGS, 1972, Metallurg. Trans. **3**, 1925.

STEEN, H.A.H., and A. HELLAWELL, 1975, Acta Metall. **23**, 529.

SUNDQUIST, B.E., 1968, Acta Metall. **16**, 1413.

TAMMANN, G., and A.A. BOTSCHWAR, 1926, Z. Anorg. Chem. **157**, 27.

TARSHIS, L.A., and G.R. KOTLER, 1968, J. Cryst. Growth **2**, 222.

TASSA, M., and J.D. HUNT, 1976, J. Cryst. Growth **34**, 38.

TAYLOR, C.R., 1975, Metallurg. Trans. **6B**, 359.

TEMKIN, D.E., 1960, Doklad. Akad. Nauk SSSR **132**, 1307.

*TEMKIN, D.E., 1964, Crystallization Processes (Transl. by Consultants Bureau, New York, 1966) p. 15.

TEMKIN, D.E., 1969, Sov. Phys. Crystallogr. **14**, 344.

THORNTON, P.H., 1966, Trans. Met. Soc. AIME **236**, 592.

THORNTON, P.H., 1968, in: Techniques of Metals Research, ed. R.F. Bunshah (Interscience, New York) vol. 1, part 2, p. 1069.

TILLER, W.A., 1958, in: Liquid Metals and Solidification (ASM, Metals Park, OH) p. 276.

*TILLER, W.A., 1963, Principles of Solidification, in: Art and Science of Crystal Growing, ed. J.J. Gilman (Wiley, New York) p. 276.

TILLER, W.A., 1970, Solidification, in: Physical Metallurgy, 2nd Ed., ed. R.W. Cahn (North-Holland, Amsterdam) p. 403.

*TILLER, W.A., 1971, in: Solidification (ASM, Metals Park, OH) p. 59.

TILLER, W.A., K.A. JACKSON, J.W. RUTTER and B. CHALMERS, 1953, Acta Metall. **1**, 453.

TITCHENER, A.P., and J.A. SPITTLE, 1975, Acta Metall. **23**, 497.

TOLOUI, B., and A. HELLAWELL, 1976, Acta Metall. **24**, 565.

TRIVEDI, R., 1970, Acta Metall. **18**, 287.

TRIVEDI, R., 1980, J. Cryst. Growth **49**, 219.

TRIVEDI, R. 1982, private communication.

TURNBULL, D., 1949, in: Thermodynamics in Metallurgy (ASM, Metals Park, OH) p. 282.

*TURNBULL, D., 1956, Solid State Physics, vol. 3 (Academic, New York) p. 225.

*TURNBULL, D., 1981, Progress in Materials Science, Chalmers Anniversary Volume, eds. J.W. Christian, P. Haasen and T.B. Massalski (Pergamon Press, Oxford) p. 269.

TURNBULL, D., and R.E. CECH, 1950, J. Appl. Phys. **21**, 804.

VOLMER, M.I., and M. MANDER, 1931, Z. Phys. Chem. A154, 97.

WALKER, J.L., 1961, in: Physical Chemistry of Process Metallurgy, ed. G.R. St. Pierre (Interscience, New York) p. 845.

WALTON, D., and B. CHALMERS, 1959, Trans. Met. Soc. AIME **215**, 447.

WANG, C.H., and H. FREDRIKSSON, 1981, 48th Int. Foundry Congress, Varna, Bulgaria, private communication.

WANG, G.C., and C.S. SMITH, 1950, Trans. Met. Soc. AIME **188**, 136.

WEINBERG, F., and E. TEGHTSOONIAN, 1972, Metallurg. Trans. **3**, 93.

WEINBERG, F., 1975, Metallurg. Trans. **6A**, 1971.

WEINBERG, F., 1979, in: Solidification and Casting of Metals (The Metals Society, London) p. 235.

WETTERFALL, S.E., H. FREDRIKSSON and M. HILLERT, 1972, J. Iron and Steel Inst. **210**, 323.

WINEGARD, W., and B. CHALMERS, 1954, Trans. Quart. ASM **46**, 1214.

*WOODRUFF, D.P., 1973, The Solid–Liquid Interface (Cambridge Univ. Press, London).

YOUNG, K.P., and D.H. KIRKWOOD, 1975, Metallurg. Trans. **6A**, 197.

ZENER, C., 1946, Trans. Met. Soc. AIME **167**, 550.

Further reading

The publications marked with an asterisk in the above list of references may be consulted.

CHAPTER 10A

QUALITATIVE AND QUANTITATIVE SURFACE MICROSCOPY

H.E. EXNER

Max-Planck-Institut für Metallforschung
Institut für Werkstoffwissenschaften
7000 Stuttgart 1, FRG

R.W. Cahn and P. Haasen, eds.
Physical Metallurgy; third, revised and enlarged edition
© *Elsevier Science Publishers BV, 1983*

Introduction to chapters 10A and 10B

In technical materials, the microstructure develops during processing. Apart from rare cases where microstructural features persist unchanged in nature and geometry from the raw material to the final product (e.g., hard nonmetallic refractory particles), each individual processing step influences the amount, the composition and the geometric appearance of the constituents and of defects in a material. This is due to the fact that microstructures usually are far from the ideal thermodynamic and geometric equilibrium predicted by thermodynamic (or rather thermostatic) considerations (see ch. 6 on metallurgical thermodynamics and ch. 7 on phase diagrams). The usual route – casting, plastic forming, heat-treating – leads to microstructures vastly different from those obtained after powder-metallurgical production, for example. Vice versa, the mechanics of the individual processing techniques can be best studied by monitoring the microstructural changes as a function of processing conditions (compare, for example, ch. 9 on solidification; ch. 10b, §2; chs. 14 and 15 on diffusive and nondiffusive phase transformation, respectively, or ch. 25 on recrystallization). Knowledge of the details of the formation of microstructures is essential in order to understand the relationships between processing parameters and the behaviour of materials in practical application. Since the most important technological properties are strongly influenced by the microstructure (see, for example, ch. 22 on the mechanical properties of multiphase alloys) this understanding is important for the development of metallic (as well as nonmetallic) materials.

Several definitions of the term *microstructure* have been given in the literature (see, for example PETZOW and HORNBOGEN [1970], HORNBOGEN [1981], HOUGARDY [1981], or SCHATT [1981]). For the purpose of this book, the following seems appropriate: The microstructure of crystalline materials is defined by the type, the structure and the number of phases, by the number, the geometric appearance (size, shape etc.) and the topological arrangement of the individual phase regions and their interfaces, and by the type, structure and geometry of lattice defects (which are in most cases not part of the thermodynamic equilibrium structure). The experimental study of microstructure is termed *metallography*.

Metallography dates back to the 17th century when English, French and German scientists first studied metallic objects by means of simple optical devices (see, for example, SMITH [1960], TENSI [1968] or PUSCH [1979]). The birth of modern metallography took place 200 years later and is dated to 1863 when H.C. Sorby developed an incident-light microscope, or to 1865 when he first observed and described some microstructural elements of technical iron. Today, a large arsenal of devices and techniques for microstructural investigations has become available. Figure 1 shows the historical development of the resolving power of surface microscopy.

This first part of chapter 10, chapter 10A, deals with the techniques of microscopy and metallography as means for microstructural investigation. It focuses on

qualitative and quantitative methods of optical and scanning-electron surface microscopy with short reviews of the other imaging and compositional analyzing
techniques. A special chapter (chapter 11) is devoted to transmission electron
microscopy, including analytical TEM. In the second part of *this* chapter, chapter
10B, the different types of lattice defects involved in the formation of microstructure
("elements of microstructure") and the genesis of microstructures will be discussed.

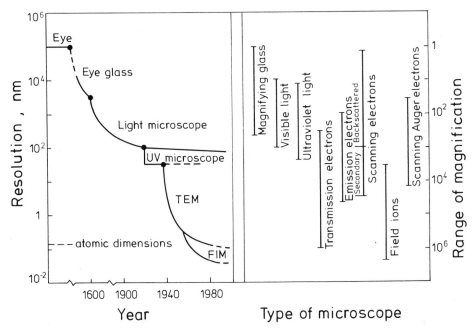

Fig. 1. Development of surface microscopy and useful range of magnification for some important types of
microscopes (after PETZOW and HORNBOGEN [1970]).

1. Optical microscopy

Metallic materials are usually opaque; therefore investigations of plane cross-sections by incident light prevail in metallography. However, the transparency of some
metals and silicon to infrared light in thin sections has been effectively exploited.
Optically, the individual components of a metallic alloy differ in their amplitude and
phase characteristics. While amplitude objects become visible owing to differences in
light absorption and thus appear in different grey shades or even colours, phase
objects only differ in the refractive indices which cannot be recognized without
additional provision. The preparation of cross-sections, the enhancement of contrast
by etching and other methods, as well as the microscopic set-up must be carefully

References: p. 638.

Table 1
Steps of metallographic sample preparation (after PETZOW and EXNER [1968]).

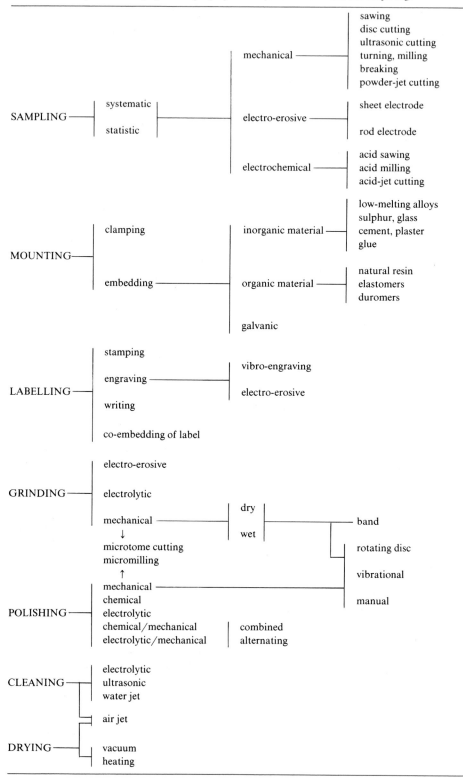

optimized for the material under investigation and adjusted to the purpose of the investigation in order to get maximum information from a microscopic study.

1.1. Metallographic specimen preparation

The essential steps and techniques of metallographic sample preparation are shown in table 1. This large variety of methods has been described in a systematic way in handbooks, e.g. by SCHUMANN [1980], PETZOW and EXNER [1968] and SAMUELS [1971]; details are discussed in a multitude of papers in a variety of journals (see *Further reading* at the end of this chapter). The technical details will not be discussed here; rather, a few basic aspects are reviewed.

1.1.1. Sampling

The location from which a specimen is taken depends on whether the investigation is aimed (1) to give data for a specific area (systematic sampling), e.g. if the origin of a failure is clearly visible, (2) to characterize a larger piece (e.g. a laboratory sample) or (3) to characterize the quality of a large amount of material (as in quality control). In the last two cases the statistical fluctuations due to unavoidable inhomogeneities must be considered, and usually more than one specimen is necessary to get a reliable result (statistical sampling). Since usually nothing is known as to the degree of homogeneity, statistical parameters (usually taking the arithmetic mean and the relative standard error, see, e.g., PETZOW and EXNER [1968]) should be determined from samples which are taken either at arbitrary or at specially defined locations. Furthermore, damaging the specimen during cutting it from a larger piece gives rise to erroneous results: Electro-erosive cutting ("spark-machining"), for example, changes the composition near the cut faces to an appreciable depth: e.g., 0.9 and 0.3 wt% carbon (stemming from the electrolyte) and 0.8 and 0.2 wt% copper (from the electrode) were found in pure iron at 50 and 150 μm depth, respectively, below the electro-eroded surface. Careful work (slow and interrupted cutting) reduces the depth of influence to 10 μm. Mechanical cutting (usually by water-cooled wheels) does not change the composition but introduces stresses to a depth of 100 μm and more (WAVER [1973], WELLNER [1980] and KIESSLER *et al.* [1982]). In spite of the disadvantages of these commonly used techniques, others, like chemical cutting by a fast-moving endless wire wetted by an aggressive liquid, available commercially as "acid saws", are only used for special purposes (for single crystals, semiconductors, brittle intermetallics, etc.) because of the long cutting times needed (hours, instead of the minutes needed for mechanical cutting).

1.1.2. Mounting

Embedding or clamping are relatively uncritical operations. Some resins reach a temperature up to 150°C during curing, which may lead to annealing effects in the

References: p. 638.

specimen; others are cold-setting. Edge-rounding during preparation of a section can be avoided by galvanic deposition of copper or nickel on top of a thin surface layer which is to be examined. Smearing and edge-rounding of open porosity during polishing can be avoided by infiltration of a low-viscosity resin under vacuum or by a well-wetting melt (solder for metals, glass for ceramics).

1.1.3. Grinding

The surface of a cut cross-section usually shows a high degree of irregularity which is removed in successive steps of grinding with emery paper (paper covered with SiC particles closely graded from coarse to fine between 80 and 20 μm, see fig. 2). Heating can be limited to a tolerable degree using water-cooling, but deformation of the surface is unavoidable (SAMUELS [1971], PETZOW and EXNER [1968], WAVER [1973] and KIESSLER *et al.* [1978]). It was found empirically (LIHL and MEYER [1960]) that the deformation depth X_D is a square function of scratch depth X_s ($X_D = aX_s - bX_s^2$, where a and b are material constants). Figure 2 shows the depth of scratches, the deformation depth and the total depth influenced in grinding of steel. In an oblique taper section, the deformed layer becomes visible after etching (fig. 3).

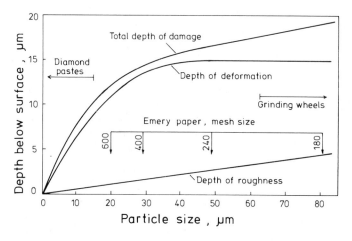

Fig. 2. Depth of roughness, depth of deformation and total depth of damage as a function of particle size of the grinding and polishing medium (after PETZOW and EXNER [1968]).

1.1.4. Polishing

In order to prepare a surface free of artefacts, the damaged layer is removed by polishing. While it is relatively easy to obtain scratch-free surfaces, preparation of an ideally undisturbed surface is difficult if not impossible by *mechanical polishing*. As shown repeatedly (most recently by TURLEY and SAMUELS [1981] for copper) mechanically polished surfaces show all the signs of plastic deformation (shear-bands, recrystallization, subgrains, etc.) even after prolonged polishing with fine grades ($< 1 \mu$m). The depth of the remaining disturbance is small ($< 1 \mu$m) and is tolerable for most purposes. *Chemical* and *electrolytic polishing* techniques do not cause deformation (PETZOW and EXNER [1968]). Another technique leaving little surface damage is ion-milling or ion-polishing (LEHTINEN and MELANDER [1980]), i.e., sputtering of the surface resulting from the impact of energetic argon ions (used more frequently for preparation of TEM foils). Removal of the layer damaged during grinding by polishing is time-consuming. If sample preparation is not carefully controlled, deformation from the coarse grinding steps may resist and may influence not only the microscopic appearance (BÜHLER and HOUGARDY [1979], SAMUELS [1971] and POKORNY [1980]) but also X-ray measurements (line broadening, blurring of reflections) or mechanical tests like indentation hardness and toughness (BERNST [1965] and EXNER [1969a]). Figure 4 shows the influence of various polishing methods on reflectivity, which is sensitive to surface damage.

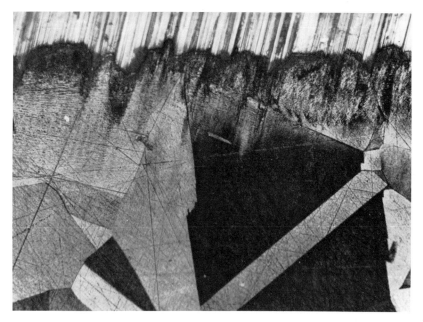

Fig. 3. Deformed layer in brass (CuZn 30) after cutting by a new diamond wheel. Oblique section (5° to surface). Etched. 200×. (From KIESSLER *et al.* [1982].)

Investigations under polarized light suffer from surface strain as well. *Thermal polishing*, i.e., annealing in vacuo after mechanical polishing, was shown to produce

References: p. 638.

smooth strain-free surfaces by uniform evaporation (IRANI and CAHN [1971]).

Disc-polishing using emulsions of carefully graded loose diamond or alumina powders on cloth is the usual way of mechanical polishing. For hard materials, a drill-like set-up using a wooden stick with diamond paste has advantages. Material removal is adequate and most materials can be polished this way. Microcutting by diamond blades has been used as a one-step, time- and labour-saving preparation mode for soft materials. Such *ultramicrotoming* (for references see PETZOW and EXNER [1968] and KLOCKENKÄMPER *et al.* [1979]) has been shown to produce very large localized deformation (BÜCKLE [1964]); nevertheless, if the cutting parameters are optimized, a surprisingly perfect surface quality of microcut metals can be achieved (PETZOW and KNOSP [1973] and PETZOW and EXNER [1975]). More recently, a micromilling process has been developed by which cross-sections and serial sections of medium-hard metals and alloys can be prepared (KIESSLER and ELSSNER [1980] and PETZOW and EXNER [1975]).

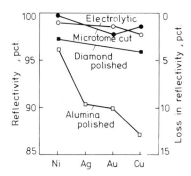

Fig. 4. Reflectivity (in percent of cleavage surface) of metal surfaces polished by different techniques (after PETZOW and KNOSP [1973]).

There is a nearly infinite number of recipes for chemical and electrochemical polishing. References and reviews are found in all metallographic standard texts, e.g., TEGART [1956], PETZOW and EXNER [1968], BIGGS [1970] and SHIGOLEV [1974]. Theoretical approaches are available (e.g. WAGNER [1954] and TOUSEK [1981], for reviews and early references see PETZOW and EXNER [1968] and BIGGS [1970]); however, they do not allow deduction of optimized polishing procedures for a given material. For electrolytic polishing, the form of the current density–voltage curve suggests which potentials should be used to avoid etching effects. (Usually a plateau is observed where polishing occurs.) It has been shown recently that these curves should be measured under practical conditions and not in special cells (RÖSCHEN-BLECK and WOLTER [1979]). In spite of the limited exact theoretical knowledge on the mechanisms of mechanical, chemical and electrolytic processes, preparation of metallographic cross-sections is not a limiting factor for microstructural investigations since the state of the art allows the investigator to deal with even the most difficult materials.

1.1.5. Replica techniques

Surface studies by transmission electron microscopy are possible by pressing a foil of a suitable substance tightly to the surface or to form a replicating foil by casting an organic replica. This technique was used extensively prior to the development of scanning electron microscopy for high-resolution surface studies. Sample preparation is well developed (see, for example, GOODHEW [1973]). Replicas can also be studied by optical microscopy, scanning electron microscopy (§ 2) and soft X-ray microscopy (§ 3.3.1). For remote sampling (e.g. for large engineering components which must not be destroyed, for temperatures up to 120°C or for radioactive materials), replica techniques using movable preparation equipment are frequently the best if not the only way for microscopic inspection (see, for example, PELLOUX [1970], WENDLER and NEUBAUER [1979] and BIRNER and LÖHBERG [1980]). Replication techniques have also been applied more recently in optical and SEM fractography, e.g. for the study of stress-corrosion cracking (CONOR [1972]) and fatigue crack initiation (BROWN and SMITH [1982]). Serial sectioning of plastic replicas is much easier than that of the sample itself, and was proposed for three-dimensional reconstruction of fracture surfaces (BAUER and HALLER [1981]).

1.2. Etching and other contrasting techniques

The human observer is capable of distinguishing between different phases and lattice defects if these show a grey or colour contrast in microscopic viewing. Polished surfaces rarely provide sufficient contrast owing to the fairly similar reflectivity of metallic phases, and contrast enhancement is usually necessary. A number of metallographic techniques are available to reveal the microstructure.

1.2.1. Chemical and electrolytic etching

When a polished surface is attacked by an etching medium, different phases and different lattice orientations usually show differing rates of dissolution. Crystal imperfections and grain boundaries are locations of increased dissolution potential. These differences in chemical and electrolytic attack are the basis for the most frequently used metallographic techniques for optical contrast enhancement. In the monographs by BECKERT and KLEMM [1976] and by PETZOW [1976,1978] known recipes for technical metals and alloys are reviewed. Theoretical understanding of material removal (see, for example, ENGEL [1958], SCHAARWÄCHTER [1968], BIGGS [1970], HERBSLEB and SCHWAAB [1978]), though well established in corrosion science, is rarely used for finding the optimum etching conditions for a new material. Usually these are established empirically, aided by educated guesses. Local changes in reflectivity and shadows produced by the rough topography of the specimen surface give rise to grey contrast when viewed in the microscope. Thus, grain-boundary grooves and facets, height differences between grains of different orientation and between phases, or etch pits at points where dislocations penetrate the cross-section, are typical contrast features created by attack-etching.

1.2.2. Thermal etching

The thermodynamic instability of a polished surface will lead to effects similar to those mentioned in § 1.2.1 when material transport is activated by heating. The basic mechanism is surface diffusion (rather than selective evaporation), and the kinetics of thermal grain-boundary grooving and facetting are well understood (see, for example, MULLINS [1961]). Thermal etching is advantageously used for chemically stable materials such as ceramics (compare fig. 7c below).

1.2.3. Ion-etching

The basis of the well known but infrequently used technique of ion-etching, reviewed recently by WECHSUNG [1977] and POHL and BURCHARD [1980], is cathodic atomization (sputtering) by bombardment of the surface with chemically neutral (e.g. argon) or reactive (e.g. oxygen) ions. The physics of sputtering has been surveyed by ÖCHSNER [1975] and recently by PIVIN [1983]. The rate of material removal depends on the atomic weights of the material and the ions (the highest rates being observed when these are approximately equal), on the energy and density of the ions hitting the surface, and on the atomic bonding in the material. By adjusting the sputtering parameters (voltage, gas pressure), selective material removal can be made to produce a clear topography and clean surfaces. Ion-etching is advantageously used for composite materials and if surface-sensitive analytical methods are to be applied.

1.2.4. Staining (tinting)

A large number of so-called etching techniques do not produce a surface relief by dissolving the surface but produce a surface layer by a chemical reaction (JEGLITSCH [1968]). These layers vary in thickness as a function of composition and orientation of the microstructural components. They are transparent and rather than having a specific colour themselves, produce interference colours varying with thickness, d. Light waves reflected at the surface and at the layer–substrate interface interact, causing extinction of a specific wavelength λ_e according to the equation (for normal incidence)

$$\lambda_e = \frac{2n}{m} d, \tag{1}$$

where m determines the order of interference ($m = 1, 3, 5 \cdots$ corresponds to $0, 1, 2, \cdots$ order) and n is the refractive index of the deposited layer; for a more detailed discussion see § 1.2.5.

Reaction layers of which the thickness varies with composition of the substrate can be deposited by chemical attack, by electrolytic processes, e.g. by potentiostatic oxidation (anodizing), or by oxidation when heating a metallic specimen in air (thermal tinting). Tinting techniques have been extensively discussed in the literature (see, for example, JEGLITSCH [1968], GRÜTZNER and SCHÜLLER [1969], BERAHA [1970], YANKOVITH [1970], BERAHA and SPIGHLER [1977], HERBSLEB and SCHWAAB [1978], GAHM and JEGLITSCH [1981], GAHM *et al.* [1982], WECK and LEISTNER [1982] and many others). In its early days, the colour contrast obtained after depositing interference layers in the presence of oxygen (reactive sputtering) was also attributed to varying thickness (ONDRACEK and SPIELER [1973]); in fact it depends on an other optical principle, as discussed in detail in the next section.

1.2.5. Interference-layer contrast

A plane-parallel layer of a non-absorbing or weakly absorbing substance acts like an optical reflection–interference filter which, by multiple reflection at the metal–layer and layer–air interfaces, causes contrast enhancement between neighbouring phase regions, provided these differ in their optical constants. The optical principles of these effects have been reviewed by PEPPERHOFF and ETTWIG [1970], ZOGG *et al.* [1977], BÜHLER and HOUGARDY [1979,1980], BÜHLER [1981], and a large number of applications in metallographic practice have been published (for references see BÜHLER and HOUGARDY [1979,1980], EXNER and ROTH [1980], GAHM and JEGLITSCH [1981], GRÄF [1981] and WU *et al.* [1982]). The important factor in interference-layer colour contrasting is the phase shift of the light-wave reflected at the layer–metal interface. In normal bright-field microscopy, differences of this phase angle are much too small for metallic phases to be detectable. The transparent or semitransparent layers enhance these differences dramatically, revealing a pronounced colour contrast if two conditions are fulfilled:

(i) The *phase condition* relates thickness of the layer d, the optical properties of the metallic phase (phase shift of the reflected wave through the angle δ) and of the layer (refractive index n), and the order of interference (defined by m as above) to the wavelength λ_{min} for which interference causes maximum reduction in intensity:

$$\lambda_{min} = 4\pi nd/[\pi(m-1)+\delta]. \tag{2}$$

Usually, the first-order interference ($m = 1$) yields the best results.

(ii) The *amplitude condition* describes the relative intensity R_{min} of the reflected light with wavelength λ_{min}. For non-absorbing layers,

$$R_{min} = \frac{\text{intensity of reflected wave}}{\text{intensity of incident wave}} = \left(\frac{q-q_m}{1-q\cdot q_m}\right)^2, \tag{3}$$

with

$$q = (n-1)/(n+1), \qquad q_m = \sqrt{(n_m-n)^2 + k_m^2/(n_m+n)^2 + k_m^2}.$$

n_m and k_m are the refractive index and the absorption coefficient of the metallic phase, respectively. Much effort is being undertaken at present (BÜHLER and HOUGARDY [1979], BÜHLER and KOSSEL [1981]), to determine n_m and k_m values for phases occurring in metallic materials in order to be able to calculate the required n, λ_{min} and d values for maximum contrast between phases present in a material. The contrast is defined by $K = (R_1 - R_2)/R_1$, where R_1 and R_2 ($R_1 > R_2$) are the relative reflectivities of two phases, and reaches a maximum if $R_2 = 0$, i.e, when interference causes complete extinction of the colour under consideration in one of the two phases ($K = 1$). If, then, a filter for the corresponding wavelength λ is used, this phase appears black. If white light is used, maximum colour contrast will be obtained.

Plane-parallel interference layers can be deposited by evaporation or by sputtering. In order to fulfill the amplitude-condition $R_{min} = 0$, a non-absorbing layer must have a high refractive index if the substrate has a high reflectivity (as do all metallic phases). ZnS, ZnSe, TiO_2 and ZnTe ($n = 2.4-3.5$) are used for evaporation. *Absorbing* layers can be deposited by reactive sputtering. This technique, first described by BARTZ [1973], uses a low gas pressure ($\sim 10^{-6}$ bar, usually oxygen) in the sputtering chamber. A commercially available device has proved very useful in practical application (BÜHLER and HOUGARDY [1979], EXNER and ROTH [1980]) and, at least in principle, allows layers to be produced with widely varying optical properties. A disadvantage is the fact that calculating the optimum contrast conditions becomes somewhat more difficult than for non-absorbing layers (ZOGG *et al.* [1977]). The reason that interference contrasting is described here more fully than other methods is that this technique is as yet not widely familiar, has excellent reproducibility and versatility and will presumably substitute many of the classical contrasting techniques. The extreme sensitivity of the human eye for colour hues and the possibility of using filters makes colour-contrasting highly attractive. In addition, quantitative evaluation with respect to phase composition and exact phase identification (see, for example, ZOGG *et al.* [1977]) are possible. Care must be taken in the latter cases in photographic reproduction which may change the original colours appreciably (CROUSE *et al.* [1977] and EXNER *et al.* [1980]).

1.3. Principles of light microscopy and optical contrast enhancement

The highly developed state of the mechanical and optical design of microscopes used in metallographic work makes it impossible to come near to an adequate description in the context of a book on physical metallurgy. A large number of monographs are available which treat the basic as well as the practical aspects of optical microscopy and photography comprehensively (e.g., PAYNE [1957], ÖTTEL [1959], MALIES [1959], FREUND [1960,1969], KINGLAKE [1965], BIGGS [1970], LOVELAND [1970], PHILLIPS [1971], GALOPIN and HENRY [1972], MODIN and MODIN [1973], BEYER [1974], ROST [1981] among others). Accordingly, the optical fundamentals (e.g. wave optics, properties of lenses and correction for aberrations) or the various components of the optical microscope (illumination systems and light sources, objectives and eyepieces, polarizers, interferometric attachments, phase contrast equipment, stages etc.) need not be discussed in detail here. Important features are the resolution limit, depth of focus, and the different ways to enhance contrast by optical manipulations.

1.3.1. Resolution and depth of focus

Figure 5 shows the *limiting resolution* (minimum distance d between two points (in μm) and maximum number of lines per unit length $1/d$ (in lines per mm), seen as separate features) and the *depth of focus* as a function of the objective's numerical aperture $n \sin \alpha$ (where n is the refractive index of the medium between the objective's front lens, e.g. 1 for air, 1.25 for cedar oil, and α is half the opening angle of the objective; thus, $n\sin \alpha$ is a quantitative measure for the amount of light reaching the objective). The resolution limit is, in theory, $d = 0.6\ \lambda/n\sin \alpha$, where λ is the wavelength used. For green light ($\lambda = 500$ nm) using an immersion oil between specimen and high-power objective (resulting in a numerical aperture $n \sin \alpha = 1.25$), we get $d = 0.24\ \mu$m. In practice, however, the resolution limit is close to 1 μm even if the illumination system as well as all the lenses and apertures are optimally adjusted. Magnifications between 500 and 1000 times the numerical aperture, i.e., up to 1000 $\times$, are useful while higher magnifications yield no additional information and therefore are called *empty magnification*. The depth of focus is inversely proportional to the square of the numerical aperture and is extremely limited at high magnifications (approx. 0.1 μm).

1.3.2. Bright-field illumination

By far the majority of microstructural investigations by optical microscopy are carried out with vertical illumination, usually called *bright field*, and most optical micrographs of metallic materials are taken this way. The contrast is a result of locally varying light intensity due to one of the pretreatments of the specimen section discussed above. The human eye can differentiate between two grey levels if the contrast K is approximately 0.2, i.e., five grey levels between black and white are easily distinguishable. Photomultipliers and television cameras are more sensitive,

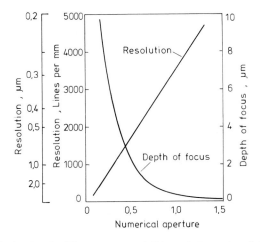

Fig. 5. Theoretical resolution (resolved lines per mm and distance between two distinguishable points) and depth of focus as a function of the objective's numerical aperture (theoretical for green light).

References: p. 638.

and more than a hundred grey levels can be registered. If higher contrast is needed, one of the special techniques described in the next four sections (sometimes improperly called "optical etching") can be useful.

1.3.3. Oblique illumination, dark field and stop contrast

If the direction of the incident light is changed from vertical to oblique, the contrast can be reversed with a gain in contrast which, for suitable specimen surfaces, is often striking. This can be achieved by simply moving the condenser aperture slightly off the optical axis, which produces a shadow-like contrast. While such *oblique illumination* is only applicable for low magnifications (long-working-distance objectives), a very useful alternative is *dark-field illumination*: The light from the light source does not pass through the objective but is reflected to the surface by a ring-shaped mirror or lens around the objective so that only stray (diffusely reflected) light reaches the objective. Rough surfaces, fissures, pores, grain boundaries and other surface irregularities are revealed, appearing bright on a dark background. This technique also lends itself for checking the quality of polish since scratches clearly show as bright lines. *Opaque-stop microscopy* produces images similar to dark field. Instead of changing the illumination, a ring stop is placed between the light source and the condenser lens. By moving the stop, different areas may be illuminated. Tilt angles with respect to flat portions of the specimen surface have been measured, for example during studying tilt and twist boundaries (BIGGS [1970]). This is possible to a high degree of accuracy (depending on magnification, of the order of 1′ to 60′ of arc). For qualitative inspection, opaque-stop microscopy provides a sensitive type of dark-field contrast at no loss in resolution.

1.3.4. Polarized-light microscopy

Plane-polarized light (produced by placing a polarizer in front of the condenser lens) vibrates in one plane only. When reflected from an optically isotropic surface, the direction of polarization does not change and will be transmitted by an analyzer placed behind the eyepiece and set parallel to the polarizer. If the analyzer is rotated, the transmitted light intensity is reduced and ideally drops to zero at crossed position of polarizer and analyzer. If the plane-polarized beam is reflected by an optically anisotropic surface it is sub-divided into two components vibrating at right angles to each other. The intensities of the components vary as a function of crystallographic orientation and its relation to the plane of polarization. Therefore, the amount of light transmitted by the analyzer is a function of the orientation of a crystal which causes changes in brightness (*degree of extinction*) when the specimen stage is rotated or, for a polycrystalline material, for the various crystals when viewed with crossed polars. Furthermore, some optically anisotropic substances (e.g. nonmetallic inclusions such as cuprous oxide) show distinctly different tints in white polarized light due to an optical effect called *reflection pleochroism*, owing to a variation of reflectivity with wavelength or degree of extinction. The tint and its change when rotating the analyzer or the stage are characteristic for such materials.

Polarized light is particularly useful in metallography for differentiating between optically isotropic and anisotropic components of the structure and for revealing the grain structure and twins in anisotropic metals and alloys, such as Zn, Mg, Ti and V. Though the polished surface must be wholly strain-free, some metals which are hard or impossible to etch can be effectively examined (IRANI and CAHN [1971]). Even the cubic crystals can become optically active if etch pits or grooves are produced by etching (for references see PHILLIPS [1971]) or by coating with an anisotropic film e.g., by anodizing or by other epitaxially grown films. Comprehensive reviews on the use of polarized reflected light as an aid in metallography (and mineralogy) are available (CONN and BRADSHAW [1952], HARTSHORNE and STUART [1952], MOTT [1952], PHILLIPS [1971], GALOPIN and HENRY [1972], MODIN and MODIN [1973], among others). The quantitative use of polarized light has been restricted mainly to transmitted light in the fields of petrography and biology, though various measurements are possible in reflection on metals as well. A special application is the imaging of magnetic domains in metal crystals making use of the Kerr effect, reviewed by BOWMAN and BOOTH [1971]. The contrast which results from a rotation of polarization direction by only 1' to 20' of arc can be improved by interference layers (see § 1.2.5).

1.3.5. Phase contrast and interference contrast

Before some of the modern sample preparation techniques (e.g. interference-layer deposition or reproducible electrolytic etching) were fully developed, optical techniques transforming phase-angle or height differences into grey or colour contrast gained some interest in metallography (GABLER and MITSCHE [1952], JEGLITSCH and MITSCHE [1967], BEYER [1974] and MODIN and MODIN [1973]). Though they were developed more than 30 years ago, now available with some higher-priced metal microscopes, and described in detail in numerous publications (e.g. ÖTTEL [1959], JEGLITSCH and MITSCHE [1967] and BEYER [1974]) their applications in studying metallic microstructures have remained few.

Phase contrast (used extensively for transmitted-light studies in biology, see, for example, YAMAMOTO and TAIRA [1983]) transforms the invisibly small phase-angle shift caused by a small difference in height (or in optical properties) of an object and its surrounding into an amplitude- (light-intensity) difference visible to the human eye. This is effected by retarding (positive phase contrast) or accelerating (negative phase contrast) a portion of the directly reflected wave by half a wavelength by inserting a phase platelet. Interference of this modified reflected wave from the phase object with the unmodified wave yields a grey contrast, i.e. the image of the phase object, in the field of view. Extremely small height differences (1–5 nm) become visible whereas in bright field a step height of approximately 100 nm is necessary for detection.

Interference contrast uses polarized light and a prism arrangement which splits the polarized light into two beams of equal intensity, the directions of which diverge by a small angle. These two beams hit the surface at slightly different positions and, after reflection, interfere with each other after passing a crossed polarizer. Several technical arrangements are possible; those used in practice are the differential

References: p. 638.

interference contrast due to Nomarksi (generally known as *Nomarski contrast*) and Michelson interference (CONN and BRADSHAW [1952], JEGLITSCH and MITSCHE [1967], PHILLIPS [1971], ROSENBERGER [1977]). If height differences exist at a specimen surface, the different levels appear in different colour hues which can be changed by shifting the prism. JEGLITSCH and MITSCHE [1967] have demonstrated applications of interference contrast with steel and cast iron as examples; other applications covering a multitude of materials are interesting as well (BENESOVSKY and IHRENBERGER [1965], SPIESS [1965], BEYER [1974] and ROSENBERGER [1977]).

1.3.6. Filters
By the appropriate choice of illumination wavelengths the contrast between differently coloured constituents may be enhanced. Alternatively to coloured glass, a movable-wedge interference filter allows monochromatic light of any wavelength to be selected. The contrast obtained is especially suitable for photography (where green light is usually used) and for automatic image-analyzing equipment with a television camera as the detector.

1.4. Special optical devices and accessories

1.4.1. Stereomicroscopy
Optical stereomicroscopes (see, for example, WATTS [1982]) are useful for rough surfaces up to $100 \times$ magnification. A recent version allows vertical as well as $45°$ side viewing without tilting the object. Today, the larger depth of focus and wide range of magnification available with scanning electron microscopy has nearly completely replaced optical stereomicroscopy for studies of rough surfaces. Optical stereomicroscopes have kept their place in the metallographic laboratory for quick inspection and quality control purposes.

1.4.2. High-temperature microscopy
Heating stages for high-temperature optical microscopy need a long-working-distance objective (e.g. a reflecting objective) that will offer the necessary oxidation protection. They are also on the way to obsolescence since stages for scanning or photo-emission electron microscopy (§§ 2 and 3.4.1) are now available and used much more often than optical hot stages. Reviews of earlier work which often resulted in important new information on the transformation behaviour of metallic alloys, on melting and on other kinetic processes have been published by REINACHER [1965], LOZINSKIJ [1961], MITSCHE *et al.* [1964,1969], MODIN and MODIN [1973] and KULMBURG *et al.* [1974]. Besides the technical problems which now seem under better control (MUGGLI and MC CRONE [1977], HOEKSTRA and BRUIS [1979]), the question remains unsettled whether processes observed on the polished surface take place in the bulk qualitatively or quantitatively in the same way.

1.4.3. Television cameras
First attached to the optical microscope for demonstration purposes, television

Surface microscopy

cameras, as was soon realized by an English company, could be adapted for quantitative analyses of microstructural images by adding a voltage threshold and a few electronic components. This started a rapid development of *quantitative television microscopes*. The modern versions are now the most powerful automatic devices for image analysis, details of which will be discussed below (§4.1).

1.4.4. Microphotometry and ellipsometry

Only twenty years ago, microscope *photometers* were introduced in metallography after having been used for some time in ore microscopy. Several highly sensitive commercial instruments are now available which use photomultipliers to register the intensity of reflected light (usually compared to a standard). Identification of small microstructural components (e.g. nonmetallic inclusions), detection of surface damage, orientation and concentration analysis, and sensitive detection of phase boundaries in quantitative image analysis were prominent early applications (MITSCHE and SCHEIDL [1964] and PETZOW and KNOSP [1973]). Measurement of optical constants, e.g., for contrast calculations in interference-layer contrasting, have become an important domain of photometry (KNOSP [1969], BÜHLER and HOUGARDY [1979], AYDIN and BÜHLER [1981] and AYDIN et al. [1983]). Another sensitive reflection technique is *ellipsometry* (see, for example, VISSCHER [1973] and AZZAM and BASHARA [1977]) which uses the phase shift of linearly polarized light for unambiguous determination of optical constants and for following the growth kinetics of thin surface films down to atomic dimensions.

1.4.5. Interferometry

One of the most useful techniques for measuring the height of surface steps and other topographic features with high resolution (routinely 10–100 nm in reflection) is interferometry (KELLER [1977]). For *double-beam interferometry*, the same set-up as for interference contrast is used. The prism arrangement is set in such a way that interference of the two beams after reflection at an oblique plane surface causes a linear sinusoidal fluctuation of brightness which to the human eye appears as a series of parallel black stripes. If the surface is not plane, the stripes are distorted or set off (at steps). The width of the stripes can be reduced by a more difficult *multiple-beam interference* arrangement (TOLANSKI [1960]), and their distance from each other, corresponding to half the wavelength in height, can be suitably chosen by adjusting the prisms. (For interference contrast as described in §1.3.5 infinite stripe distance, i.e., only one brightness minimum, is used for illumination.) A large variety of microinterferometers are available (see, for example PHILLIPS [1971], MODIN and MODIN [1973], BEYER [1974], KOLOMYJCOV [1976] and KELLER [1977]). By measuring stripe distances and set-offs, height differences are determined. Also, angles of surface tilt can be measured with high accuracy. Among the applications in metallography have been studies of crystal growth kinetics (e.g. NANEV [1981]), of grain-boundary grooving (MYKURA [1955]) and of surface films and surface roughness (for references see BEYER [1974]).

References: p. 638.

1.4.6. Microhardness

Through a mechanical test, indentation hardness measurements using low loads (5–500 mN) are carried out microscopically. Micrometer eyepieces or, more often, specially designed arrangements which keep the image and the scale sharp simultaneously are used. Detailed specifications for microhardness testing are found in literature (MOTT [1956], BÜCKLE [1965], SEMLITSCH and BERGMANN [1969], GAHM [1969], DENGEL [1973], MORNHEIM [1977], among others). Microhardness indentations are often used as markers for measuring distances and for accessing surface deformations induced subsequent to the indentations.

2. Scanning electron microscopy

One of the most versatile instruments for microstructural investigations is the *scanning electron microscope* (SEM). Compared to the optical microscope it not only expands the resolution range by at least one order of magnitude (useful magnifications beyond $10^4 \times$) and the depth of field by two orders of magnitude (ranging from 1 μm at $10^4 \times$ to 2 mm at $10 \times$) but also offers a series of possibilities for image formation which are more or less easy to interpret and reveal a clear picture of plane cross-sections as well as three-dimensional surfaces such as, for example, fracture surfaces, deep-etched surfaces, or corroded surfaces of porous materials.

2.1. Basic features of SEM

Excellent monographs on the physical fundamentals, the various techniques, the instrumental details and the application of scanning electron microscopy are available (e.g. SEILER [1968], THORNTON [1968], HEYWOOD [1971], HEARLE et al. [1972], OATLEY [1972], WELLS [1974], GOLDSTEIN and YAKOWITZ [1977] and REIMER and PFEFFERKORN [1977]). The principle of the scanning electron microscope is rather simple: The electron beam, emitted usually from a heated tungsten cathode or from a LaB_6 cathode, is focussed by magnetic lenses to a small diameter ($\sim$ 10 nm). Future development will see field-emission cathodes as routine components which will allow further reduction of the probe diameter. The accelerating voltage usually ranges between 1–50 kV; the current through the surface is only approx. 10 pA.

The beam scans the field of view very much in the same way as in a cathode-ray tube. The magnification is increased by reducing the current in the deflection coils; the normal range is 1–50 000 $\times$. The SEM image is written on a high-quality screen (cathode-ray tube) with an image resolution typically of 0.1 mm which, at 10 000 times magnification, corresponds to 10 nm resolution on the specimen. The brightness of each picture point is determined by the detector signal which is of the order of a few pA and must be amplified by direct electron multiplication or by conventional amplifiers. Noisy background due to high amplification is the major cause for unclear images. The dramatic improvement of image quality and resolution during the two decades of commercial development is due to improvement of all components of the microscope (more sensitive detectors, more powerful cathodes and more precise scanning devices) and to noise reduction in all electronic devices.

Figure 6 shows the interaction between the primary electron beam and the sample: Various kinds of radiation are emitted which, when collected in a suitable detector, can be used for image formation. Table 2 gives some data important for imaging metallic microstructures. By far the most popular techniques are the *secondary electron mode* (SE) revealing surface topography and, in advantageous situations, also atomic-number and crystal-orientation contrast with high resolution and information from a small depth below the surface, and the *backscattered electron mode* (BE) which gives topographic as well as pronounced materials contrast from a much larger depth and width and therefore reduced resolution. Figure 7a shows a typical SE image, fig. 7b a typical BE image of polished metal surfaces. Detector electronics can be adjusted so as to respond to either SE or BE electrons with their quite different energy distributions.

Back-scattered electrons (BE) are produced by single large-angle as well as by multiple small-angle elastic scattering events. In the 10–20 kV range of incident beam voltage, approximately 50% of each type leave the surface with a wide spectrum of energies. As the atomic number of the material hit by the incident beam decreases, a smaller number of electrons are back-scattered and more energy is lost. In materials with high atomic number, a large number of electrons is back-scattered by atoms close to the surface, with little change in energy. Thus, yield, energy spectrum and depth of escape of back-scattered electrons are directly related to the atomic number of the material (fig. 8, see also §2.3.2).

Low-energy *secondary electrons* (SE) are formed by interaction of the primary

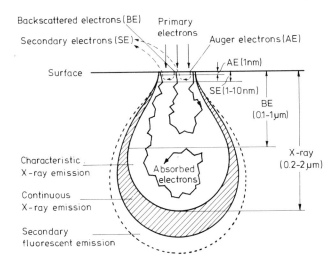

Fig. 6. Types of electron-beam-excited electrons and radiation (schematic) and depth of information in the scanning electron microscopes (SEM and SAM).

References: p. 638.

Table 2

Physical effects producing radiation, detector types and detected signals used for imaging and analyzing metal surfaces in the scanning electron microscope.

Detected signal	Type of detector	Information	Basis effects	Minimum resolution	Maximum depth of information	Remarks
Secondary electrons (SE)	Scintillator photomultiplier with Faraday cage	Surface topography, material contrast, crystal orientation contrast	SE yield depends strongly on surface tilt and weakly on atomic number and crystal orientation	5–20 nm	1–2 nm	Background due to SE excited by BE reduces resolution and enlarges depth of information. Material contrast can be suppressed by superimposing the inverted BE signal
Back-scattered electrons (BE)	Solid state or scintillator photomultiplier	Material composition, topography, crystal orientation	BE yield depends on atomic number, increasing for heavier elements	0.1–1 μm	0.1–1. μm depending on primary electron energy (acceleration voltage)	Topological contrast can be suppressed by a ring-shaped detector. Higher resolution can be obtained by using an energy filter
Specimen current (absorbed or target current)	No external detector necessary	Complementary contrast to BE	BE yield results in corresponding electrical current	0.1–1 μm	As with BE	Conventional amplification difficult and noisy. Used in early development of SEM, may revive with better amplifiers
X-rays	Semiconductor detector	Element distribution	Emission of characteristic radiation by electron bombardment	~1 μm	>1 μm	Element analysis by spectrometers, X-ray intensity images with point density corresponding to element concentration
Cathodo-luminescence	photomultiplier with mirror	Detection of nonmetallic and semiconducting phases	Emission of photons by electron bombardment	0.5–10 μm		Applicable to metallic materials in rare cases only

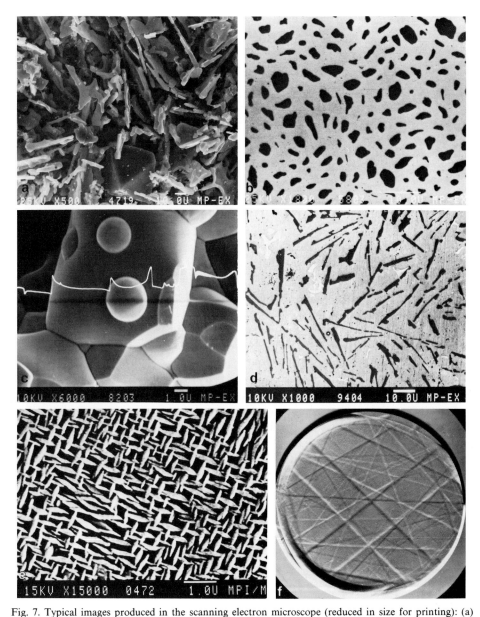

Fig. 7. Typical images produced in the scanning electron microscope (reduced in size for printing): (a) Topographic contrast by secondary electrons, aluminium–12 wt% silicon (aluminium matrix deep-etched). 300×. (From Paul and Mürrle [1981].) (b) Atomic-number (material) contrast by backscattered electrons, silver-matrix/nickel-fibre composite. 1080×. (From Mürrle *et al.* [1980].) (c) Topographic contrast by secondary electrons, alumina–10 wt% zirconium oxide ceramic, thermally etched. The black line is a contamination trace of the line scan which produces the intensity profile shown by the white line (*y*-modulation). 3600×. (From Bauer and Haller [1981].) (d) Secondary electron image revealing material roughness contrast. (The rough aluminium matrix appears brighter than the smoother silicon particles, due to polishing scratches.) Aluminium–12 wt% silicon alloy. 600×. (e) High-resolution backscattered electron image of partially stabilized zirconium oxide. (The martensitically transformed platelets are normal to the surface). 9000×. (f) Electron channelling pattern of tungsten grains in a tungsten–10 wt% nickel heavy metal. (From Takajo [1982].)

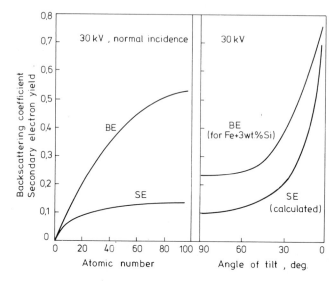

Fig. 8. Backscattering coefficient and secondary electron yield as a function of atomic number of the material hit by the electron beam (normal incidence), and as a function of inclination of surface with respect to the incident beam (schematic, after GOLDSTEIN and YAKOWITZ [1977]).

electrons with loosely bound atomic electrons. The energy distribution of secondary electrons depends on the primary energy of incident electrons, the number of outer-shell electrons, the atomic radius and, most pronouncedly, on the surface barrier of the material. The energy of SE electrons which occurs with maximum frequency is an order of magnitude lower than that of the incident electrons, and at 50 eV the frequency of SE electrons approaches zero. The probability that low-energy secondary electrons will escape from the surface decreases exponentially with the depth of their generation. More than half of the total yield is emitted within a depth of about 0.5 nm. Obviously, high-energy back-scattered electrons excite SE electrons as well, contributing to the noise and decreasing lateral resolution. The yield is not strongly dependent on atomic number (for Au it is higher only by a factor of two than for C, see fig. 8). The main factor for secondary electron yield is the angle between incident beam and sample surface. Since the envelope of the excited volume (see fig. 6) moves closer to the surface when the beam hits the surface at a small angle, SE yield increases. Thus, variations of surface inclination cause pronounced changes of SE yield (fig. 8). This fact is used for obtaining information on surface topography (§2.3.1).

A series of techniques are available to modify the signals in order to obtain better or additional information, as, for example, *black-level suppression* (i.e. differential amplification which distributes the contrast over the full range of the cathode-ray tube or the photographic film) or *nonlinear amplification* (contrast enhancement by preferential contrast expansion at either end of the gray scale, improving the visibility of features in otherwise dark holes). In *Y-modulation*, the CRT (cathode-ray tube) beam is deflected proportionately to the detector signal (fig. 7c) allowing detection of low contrast not apparent to the eye in the intensity-modulated image. If one of these signal transformations is used, its limitations and deficiencies must be considered in interpreting the image, otherwise artefacts may provide erroneous information. Some practical aspects of the more frequently used techniques for investigation in the materials laboratory have recently been reviewed by HILLMER [1979b].

2.2. Specimen preparation

The major advantage of scanning electron microscopy is that in many cases little effort is necessary for specimen preparation. Practical experience has been reviewed recently by NEWBURY and YAKOWITZ [1977a], and by HILLMER [1979a]. Clean, deformation-free cross-sections and clean fracture surfaces of metallic materials can be investigated directly. Non-conducting materials must be coated by a thin metal layer (10–100 nm, usually gold applied by sputtering or carbon and metals applied by high-vacuum evaporation) to avoid charging effects. Oxides caused by long-time exposure to the atmosphere or by high-temperature reaction can be removed electrolytically (YUZAWICH and HUGHES [1978]) or by hydrogen reduction (MADESKI [1980]). Cross-sections are prepared in exactly the same way as for light microscopy but care must be taken in cleaning since residual polishing liquids or etchants trapped in pores or cracks cause contamination of the surface when putting the sample into the vacuum chamber. Organic mounting resins and any other hydrocarbons (grease etc.) must be removed in order to keep contamination by carbon and cracking products as small as possible. The shape of microstructural features in multiphase alloys can advantageously be studied after deep etching to remove some of the matrix metal (see, for example, McCALL [1973], FREMUNT *et al.* [1980], MADESKI [1980], HUN-DE and JING-YUN [1980], or PAUL and MÜRRLE [1981]). Figure 7a shows an aluminium–silicon alloy with part of the aluminium matrix removed by etching. The octahedral shape of the primary silicon crystal and the complicated arrangement of the eutectic silicon lamellae would not show up as clearly in a plane cross-section.

Etching is not necessary when *material (atomic-number) contrast* is utilized for image formation: Differences of atomic number show up as differences in brightness, the phase containing lighter elements appearing darker. Unavoidable height differences of hard and soft phases after mechanical polishing result in additional and usually unwanted topographic effects. However, differences in surface roughness after polishing have been shown recently (BAUER and PAUL [1983]) to produce pronounced contrast between hard and soft phases if contamination is avoided (fig. 7d). Weak contrast mechanisms, as for example magnetic or electron channelling contrast, are impossible to detect in the presence of a deformed layer or of topographic features. Therefore, deformation-free and plane cross-sections must be

References: p. 638.

prepared by careful polishing when studying microstructures by means of these contrast mechanisms.

2.3. Typical forms of contrast

2.3.1. Topographic contrast

The most pronounced contrast effects result from the dependence of secondary electron (SE) yield, back-scattering coefficient and detector collection efficiency on the angle between the surface element and the primary electron beam (see §2.1) or the detector position, respectively. The resulting contrast (see fig. 7a) is analogous to an optical image where the light comes from the detector and the observation direction is that of the incident electron beam (NEWBURY [1977] and REIMER and PFEFFERKORN [1977]). The stereoscopic effect is enhanced by shadows in regions which are hidden from the detector and by enhanced emission at edges. These latter effects are disadvantageous when deep holes and cracks or transparent edges are present.

The high spatial resolution (both transversal and in depth) obtained with secondary electrons excited by the incident beam is disturbed by secondary electrons excited by the back-scattered electrons coming from deeper in the specimen; thus the clear topographic image can be obscured by atomic-number contrast and the resolution is reduced pronouncedly if special measures are not taken. There are several ways to reduce these effects (BLASCHKE [1979]). In addition to these compromises used in commercial instruments, superposition on the SE signal of the inverted BE signal seems to reduce interference from deep specimen layers almost completely (VOLBERT [1981] and PFEFFERKORN and BLASCHKE [1982]).

2.3.2. Material (atomic number) contrast

As discussed in §2.1, the yield of back-scattered electrons as well as that of secondary electrons is a function of the atomic number Z (fig. 8). Material contrast is useful for qualitative identification of phases and is especially suitable for quantitative evaluation of microstructural geometry by stereological techniques (see §4). However, the atomic number contrast is usually obscured by topology contrast (fig. 8) and, for secondary electrons, is sufficiently strong only in favourable cases, i.e., for ideally flat surfaces. For backscattered electrons, the topographic contrast can be greatly reduced even if the surface is rough by using ring-shaped detectors. Edge effects may still be a problem, and ideally flat polishing is necessary for difficult specimens in which the phases have similar compositions or consist of elements which are near neighbours in the periodic table. A difference of average atomic number, $\Delta Z < 1$ (i.e., even mixtures of nearest neighbours in the periodic table) is sufficient for slight material contrast, at least in the lower range of atomic numbers where the contrast is more pronounced (see fig. 8). Figure 7b shows an example of strong BE material contrast.

The limitation for many problems in physical metallurgy is the lack in resolution

Table 3

Information depth obtained with secondary and backscattered electrons for a few elements as a function of acceleration voltage of the primary electron beam, and with secondary electrons (according to SEILER [1968] and REIMER and PFEFFERKORN [1977]).

Element	Atomic number	Density (Mg/m^3)	Information depth (nm)					
			back-scattered electrons					secondary electrons
			5 keV	10 keV	20 keV	30 keV	50 keV	
C	6	2.3	330	970	2800	5300	11600	10
Al	13	2.7	120	360	1050	1950	4290	1.2
Cu	29	8.9	40	110	320	590	1300	0.5
Ag	47	10.5	30	90	270	500	1100	~1.0
Au	79	19.3	20	50	150	270	600	1.8

due to the large "depth of information" (see fig. 6) which, for highly dispersed phases, results in blurred edges and detection of features not intersected by the cross-section but close below it. If phase interfaces are normal to the cross-section, excellent resolution is obtained (fig. 7e).

By reducing the energy of the primary beam, these effects can be reduced. Table 3 shows the depth of information as a function of primary voltage. Even at low voltages, the depth of information from metal surfaces is at least one order of magnitude larger for backscattered electrons than for secondary electrons. Material contrast is reduced at lower voltages and additional contrast-enhancement techniques by surface treatment have been worked out for individual cases.

2.3.3. Electron channelling pattern, selected area channelling pattern contrast and Kossel patterns

Electron channelling patterns (ECP) arise because of the fact that the primary electrons penetrate into the crystal to a depth which depends on the atomic packing density along different crystallographic directions. If the electrons follow the channels between rows of atoms, their re-escaping probability becomes low. A large number of Bragg conditions are satisfied with quite small angular variations. By rocking the primary electron beam about a point in the sample, diffraction lines from a small area (< 10 μm) are obtained. These *selected-area electron channelling patterns* (SACP) are similar to Kikuchi patterns obtained in transmission electron microscopy (ch. 11, §3.2) and are therefore often called pseudo-Kikuchi patterns. Information on the crystal orientation and crystal perfection, grain boundaries, twins and other crystallographic features is obtained from minute regions of a surface layer less than 50 nm thick. An example is shown in fig. 7f. Extensive discussions of electron channelling contrast show its usefulness for materials investigations (MCCALL [1973], NEWBURY and YAKOWITZ [1977b] and PAYNE [1982]). In the investigation of fracture surfaces, bend contours were observed by ECP (DAVIDSON [1974]). The study of orientation relationships of twins and of local textures are

References: p. 638.

prominent examples of successful application for SACP. Though more often used in transmission or with higher primary energy in the electron microprobe analyzer, *Kossel patterns* (named after the explorer of this effect) are another efficient means to analyze the structure of small volumes in the order of μm^3 in the scanning electron microscope. Kossel lines arise by interference of X-rays excited by the focussed electron beam at the surrounding lattice planes. On the film, lines with bright–dark fine structure are obtained which are easily interpreted and give useful information on orientation, lattice parameter and lattice deformation after distortion (BRÜMMER and NIEBER [1975] and DINGLEY *et al.* [1982]). An interesting study of orientation relationships of new grains formed by recrystallization of aluminium, using the transmission Kossel technique in a modified electron microprobe analyzer (§ 3.5.2) by DOHERTY and CAHN [1972] is discussed in ch. 25, § 3.3.

2.3.4. Magnetic contrast

Magnetic fields of ferromagnetic crystals can affect the interaction of the primary beam or the resulting emission. *Type-I magnetic contrast* uses the deflection of the highly directional electrons by the leakage field and may amount up to 20% for materials with strong fields such as cobalt. The resolution with which the boundaries of magnetic domains can be picked up is only of the order of several μm owing to the diffuse nature of leakage fields. *Type-II magnetic contrast* arises from the deflection of primary electrons by the Lorentz force inside the crystal. Magnetic domains appear in light–dark contrast due to differences in backscattering coefficient, with a strong tilt-dependence, and can be enhanced by filtering using high-energy BE only, with a resolution in the order of 100 nm. (For details and applications of magnetic contrast see NEWBURY and YAKOWITZ [1977b], REIMER and PFEFFER-KORN [1977], or ELSBROCK and BALK [1982].)

2.3.5. Voltage contrast and electron-beam-induced current

Secondary electrons are sensitive to surface potentials and electric field gradients; a negative bias of a few volts activates emission while a positive field will impede emission. *EBIC* (*electron-beam-induced current*) depends on creation of excess electron–hole pairs by the electron beam and gives useful information on diffusion length and lifetime of minority carriers in semiconductor devices.

2.4. Accessory equipment

The large specimen chambers of most commercial instruments allow special stages to be mounted by which various experiments can be carried out to yield additional information on the nature of metallic microstructures and their development.

2.4.1. Stereomicroscopy

Simple tilting stages or goniometer stages allow stereopair micrographs to be taken which give an excellent three-dimensional impression of rough surfaces when viewed in a stereoscope by the "anaglyphe" method using a red and a green filter for the two images or viewing with polarized light. The tilt angle and the viewing distance determine the subjective impression of depth. Quantitative evaluation of the parallax yields accurate data on the $x-y-z$ coordinates which then can be combined to construct height profiles or height maps (e.g. BLASCHKE and WALTINGER [1971], BOYDE [1973], ARZT and FISCHMEISTER [1979], BAUER and EXNER [1981] and

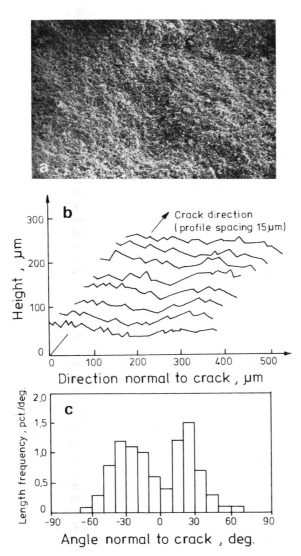

Fig. 9. Fracture-surface analysis by instrumented stereoscopy: (a) scanning electron micrograph evaluated by stereometry; (b) line profiles; (c) distribution of profile line length as a function of tilt angle of surface profiles perpendicular to crack direction. (After BAUER *et al.* [1982].)

References: p. 638.

BEATON and FILSHIE [1983]) and can be used to obtain characteristic parameters (roughness indices, distribution of tilt angles for surface elements etc.) for fracture surfaces and other rough surfaces. Figure 9 shows the profile map of a ceramic fracture surface together with the tilt-angle distribution.

2.4.2. Dynamic and non-ambient-temperature SEM

Large depth of focus and the possibility of rapidly changing the magnification in combination with mechanical or low- and high-temperature stages are prerequisites for continuous observation of specimens subject to applied stress, magnetic or electric fields, chemical reaction, and various effects due to cooling or heating. A multitude of phenomena in physical metallurgy have been studied, including deformation of superplastic lead–tin eutectic and the effect of stress and magnetic field on the configuration of magnetic domains in an iron–silicon alloy (NEWBURY and YAKOWITZ [1977b]), solid-state sintering (FULRATH [1972]), or liquid-phase sintering (RIEGGER *et al.* [1980]). Videorecording is an ideal way to register events of interest, and special devices have been developed to record fast processes such as cracking or martensitic transformation with much higher resolution than is possible with optical microscopy.

3. *Special techniques of surface microscopy and analysis*

In addition to light microscopy and transmission and scanning electron microscopy used routinely in all fields of materials research, development and control, microstructures can be investigated by several more exotic image techniques. While some of these, such as photoemission or field-ion microscopy, are of high interest for various advanced studies of material surfaces, others are still in the stage of experimentation, have been substituted by other techniques or are more useful in other fields of application like biology or mineralogy.

Instruments capable of analyzing the chemical nature and the electronic state of surface atoms have been developed at a rapid rate in the last few years, utilizing all kinds of interaction with incident photons, electrons and ions. Table 4 (p. 610) shows a summary of these techniques in a classification with respect to exciting and emitted species. The information obtained stems nearly exclusively from regions close to the surface and thus is decisively distinct from that furnished by bulk chemistry. If the lateral resolution is sufficiently good, the signals can also be used for surface imaging.

A full account of all available techniques cannot be given in this context but short surveys of those being used to some extent in the investigations of metal surfaces in physical metallurgy will be given in this section. Additional information on methods for chemical analysis of surfaces can be obtained from compilations by KANE and LARABEE [1974], CZANDERNA [1975], IBACH [1977], MCINTYRE [1978], BRÜMMER *et al.* [1980] and HOFMANN [1979,1980a,b].

3.1. Acoustic and thermal wave imaging

The acoustic microscope is a rather new development (LEMONS and QUATE [1974], KOCH [1979], QUATE [1979] and ASH [1980]). A piezoelectric crystal is attached to the sample, which emits acoustic signals and, after reflection at the surface, transforms them back to an electrical signal. This signal writes the image on a cathode ray tube. Oblique and stereo viewing are possible. The wavelength is similar to that of visible light (520 nm at 3 GHz), the resolution seems to be comparable or somewhat inferior. The information furnished by the acoustic microscope is different from that furnished by optical microscopes and by scanning electron microscopes in that it reveals sub-surface defects like grain boundaries. The most recent development is the scanning acoustic microscopy (WICKRAMASINGHE [1983]). To what extent these techniques are useful in physical metallurgy has yet to be demonstrated.

Macroscopic and microscopic features on the surface or close to it can be imaged using the dependence of the photoacoustic effect on local variations of the thermal properties of a material (density, specific heat and conductivity). This new technique, recently described in detail by ROSENCWAIG [1982], not only offers sensitive detection of minor as well as more substantial disruptions of the lattice structure (as, for example, foreign atoms in concentrations below 10^{-3}, vacancies, compositional changes, mechanical defects) but also a means for nondestructive depth profiling.

In a *thermal-wave microscope*, an electron beam (or a laser beam) is focussed and scanned across the surface of a sample. Periodic surface heating results as the beam intensity is modulated in the range of 10 Hz–10 MHz. Thus, thermal waves are produced which interact with features. Reflected and scattered waves are detected by monitoring local surface temperature by means of a gas microphone (*scanning photoacoustic microscopy, SPAM*), by measuring the deflection of a laser beam traversing through a liquid or gas layer adjacent to the heated surface (*optical beam deflection*) or by detecting the infrared radiation emitted from the sample surface. The spatial resolution is determined by the spot size of the incident beam, the thermal wavelength, and thermal conductivity ranging for metals from a few μm at high modulation frequency (1 MHz) to a few mm at 100 Hz. For thermal insulators, resolution is approximately one order of magnitude better. Since the depth of penetration into the material is proportional to the wavelength, the bulk of a sample can be reached at low frequencies, and thermoacoustic signals can be detected by ultrasonic transducers attached to the sample. This technique allows three-dimensional information to be obtained simply by changing the frequency and has been termed *thermoacoustic probe*. Usually, thermal-wave imaging systems are attached to scanning electron microscopes using excitation by the electron beam.

Application of both the thermal-wave microscope and the thermoacoustic probe have been mostly restricted to the investigation of microelectronic components where most of the features of interest lie within 10 μm of the surface (ROSENCWAIG [1982]). However, owing to the fact that the thermal waves are more sensitive to local variations in lattice structure than photons (optical or X-ray) and have a better resolution than acoustic and X-ray imaging, there are numerous potential applica-

References: p. 638.

Table 4

Classification of techniques for surface analysis and imaging with respect to incident and emitted species
(after WEHNER [1975], SHEMENSKI [1977], HOFMANN [1979] and BRÜMMER *et al.* [1980]).

Emitted species	Incident species			Electric field excitation
	Photons	Electrons	Ions	
Photons (radiation)	Optical microscopy, §1 Acoustic microscopy, §3.1 Fluorescence microscopy, §3.3.2 Laser thermal-wave microscopy, §3.1 Laser optical emission spectroscopy (LOES) X-ray diffraction (XRD), ch. 12 X-ray fluorescence spectroscopy (XFR), §3.3.2 X-ray topography, §3.3.1 High-resolution X-ray spectroscopy (EXAFS) Infrared absorption spectroscopy (IRS)	X-ray mapping, §3.5.1 Electron-beam induced X-ray spectroscopy (EPMA, WDS, EDS), §3.5.2 Cathodoluminescence (CD), §3.5.2 Thermal-wave microscopy and thermal probe, §3.1 Appearance-potential spectroscopy (APS)	Particle-induced X-ray emission (IIX, PIXE), §3.5.4 Surface analysis by neutral species and ion impact radiation (SCANIIR) Glow discharge optical spectroscopy (GDOS)	
Electrons	Photo-electron emission microscopy (PEEM), §3.4.1 Photo-electron spectroscopy for chemical analysis (ESCA, XPS, UPS), §3.4.2 X-ray-induced Auger electron spectroscopy (XAES)	Scanning electron microscopy (SEM), §2 Auger electron spectroscopy (AES), §3.6.1 Scanning Auger electron microscopy (SAM), §3.6.1 Low-energy electron diffraction (LEED), §3.6.2 Reflected high-energy electron diffraction (RHEED), §3.6.2	Ion-induced electron emission (IIEE) Ion-neutralization spectroscopy (IWS) Ion-induced Auger spectroscopy (IAES)	Field-electron microscopy (FEM), §3.2.1

Table 4 (continued)

Emitted species	Incident species			Electric field excitation
	Photons	Electrons	Ions	
Ions	Laser-microprobe spectroscopy (LAMMA)	Electron-stimulated ion desorption (ESID)	Ion-scattering spectroscopy (ISS), §3.7.1	Field-ion microscopy (FIM), §3.2.2
	Photo desorption		Rutherford back-scattering (RBS), §3.7.1	Field-desorption microscopy (FDS), §3.2.2
			Secondary-ion mass spectroscopy (SIMS, IMMA), §3.7.2	Atom probe (APFIM), §3.2.2

tions for other materials, e.g., for detection of phases and grains in alloys or composites without special contrasting or in-situ investigations during dynamic studies.

3.2. Field-electron and field-ion emission

Very high gradients of electric fields at the surface of a metal cause emission of electrons and ions. This is the basis of field-electron and field-ion microscopy.

3.2.1. Field-electron microscopy

Field-electron microscopes (FEM) are non-commercially made laboratory equipment in which an etched single-crystal tip is heated in high vacuum. The emitted electrons are accelerated by an anode and produce an image on a fluorescent screen. The intensity of electrons emitted (field emission current) depends on the voltage and the work of emission; the lattice structure and local geometric structure of surfaces can be studied with high resolution down to a few nanometers (MÜLLER [1936], EDELMANN [1980]).

The crystallographic structure of clean surfaces and (if by chance a grain boundary was located in the tip) the structure and the movement of grain boundaries as well as changes of the tip geometry and allotropic transformations of the tip material during heating have been studied; by measuring the energy distribution of the field electrons the electronic structure of the single-crystal tip was investigated (for references see EDELMANN [1980]). Absorption of gas from the vacuum chamber or of evaporated substances (metals or oxides) changes the image drastically, which has been used for studying the sites of adsorption, the migration of adsorbed species along grain boundaries and the formation of compounds.

References: p. 638.

3.2.2. Field-ion emission and field-ion desorption microscopy and the atom probe

Compared with field-electron microscopy, much higher resolutions, down to atomic dimensions (< 0.15 nm), are achieved in *field-ion microscopy* (FIM) (HREN and RANGANATHAN [1968], MUELLER and TSONG [1969], EDELMANN [1980] and WAGNER [1982]). Noble-gas atoms (usually helium) are ionized at the cooled surface of a pointed metal tip. The ions are accelerated by a high voltage and hit a channel-plate converter which produces and multiplies secondary electrons which are emitted radially to a fluorescent screen. In this way, a high-resolution image of the tip is obtained showing individual atoms and their arrangement (fig. 10). Terrace steps ionize most strongly and, therefore, appear bright. Lattice defects cut by the tip surface, such as dislocations, stacking faults, grain boundaries and antiphase boundaries in ordered structures, are revealed. Vacancies and interstitials can be

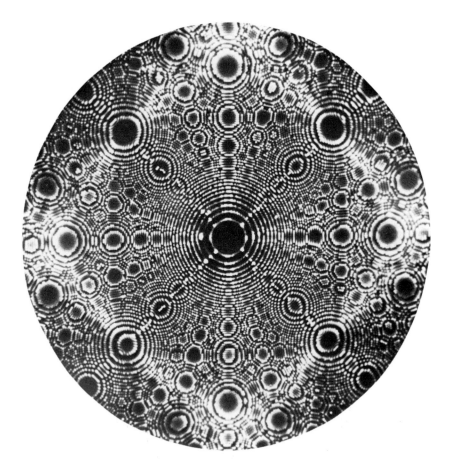

Fig. 10. Field-ion micrograph (reduced in size for printing) of a single-crystal platinum tip, (100)-oriented with facets of low-index planes. Magnification approx. 35×10^6. (From DOERR and OWNBY [1975].)

observed and their movement studied by taking photographs after certain time intervals. Moiré simulation was shown to provide a simple and direct means of visualizing the physical interpretation of field-ion micrographs (DOERR and OWNBY [1975]). Caution must be exercised in the interpretation of these images because the strong electric field may cause distortion effects in the surface layer of the tip.

If the field-ion microscope is combined with a *time-of-flight* (TOF) *mass spectrometer*, the chemical nature of atoms pulled off the tip surface by a very large high voltage impulse can be identified. The atom passes a hole in the screen and hits a detector, and from TOF the specific mass is calculated. By positioning the tip with respect to the aperture hole it is possible to focus each individual atom (FIM atomprobe). The same physical principle allows to analyze the chemical composition of the entire tip in the *field desorption microscope* (FDS). The image is formed by the desorbed atoms by activating the screen with a pulsed potential. Successive layers of the tip can be analyzed in this way (field evaporation). Using this technique, the morphology, crystallography and chemistry of special alloys and particles in statu nascendi have recently been analyzed by WAGNER and BRENNER [1978].

Furthermore, in-situ studies of radiation damage, adsorption and desorption, nucleation and all the other investigations mentioned above for field-electron microscopy (§ 3.1.1) can be carried out by field-ion microscopy and the atom probe (for recent reviews see EDELMANN [1980] and WAGNER [1980,1982]). However, FIM, FDM and the atom probe will presumably not be used in routine applications owing to the high effort involved in preparing suitable tips, especially if statistically significant results on variable features are needed, requiring a large number of tips owing to the extremely small volume (10^{-21} m^3) investigated.

3.3. Photon-induced radiation

As shown in table 4, a variety of kinds of radiation can be produced by photons hitting the surface. X-ray diffraction is used most widely in the study of metals and a separate chapter (ch. 12) is devoted to some aspects of this major technique and its applications. Here, a short account is given of two other methods capable of producing surface images.

3.3.1. X-ray microscopy and X-ray topography

Soft X-ray microscopy was developed early (see review by COSSLETT and NIXON [1960]) but was then overshadowed by the rapid growth of electron microscopy. More recently, with synchrotron radiation available, high-resolution scanning X-ray microscopy has proved to possess positive features (high contrast especially) in materials investigations (FEDER *et al.* [1977], ASH [1980] and DUKE [1981]).

For studying defects in the surface of single crystals, *X-ray topography* is a useful technique (TANNER [1977] and HÖCHE and BRÜMMER [1980]). The penetration depth of 5 μm and a lateral resolution of > 1 μm restricts application to relatively perfect crystals (defect density $< 10^5$/cm^2) but owing to its high selectivity for different types of defects and their location (subgrain boundaries, stacking faults, structure of ferromagnetic domains, dislocations) X-ray topography has become a standard technique for monitoring crystal quality, especially in the semiconductor industry. Imaging uses a Bragg reflection, the intensity of which varies with local variations of orientation, lattice parameter and structural factor. A classical study is the investigation of the internal magnetic structure of nontransparent ferromagnetic crystals (BOWMAN and BOOTH [1971]). It is not possible to magnify the image directly, owing to the lack of X-ray lenses. High-resolution film and photographic magnification has been widely used, typical exposure times ranging from 10 min to 2 h with a 1 kW X-ray source. More recently, digital image storage and accumulation have become available, providing better resolution and higher speed. Very recently, a study of the dynamic behaviour of dislocations in silicon under stress by transmission X-ray topography has been published (CHANG et al. [1982]) which demonstrates the efficiency of digital intensity accumulation.

3.3.2. Fluorescence microscopy and spectroscopy

If a fluorescing substance is irradiated by photons (X-rays or light of short wavelength, usually ultraviolet), some of the energy is re-emitted as light of longer wavelength which is typical for the substance. This effect is called *fluorescence* and is used in mineralogy for identification purposes and, after suitable staining with fluorescent substances, in biology (ROST [1981] and AXELROD et al. [1983]). Very few phases in metallic alloys are fluorescent, therefore this technique is rarely used. Extremely small amounts of fluorescent nonmetallic phases can be detected in this way.

For chemical analysis, *X-ray fluorescence* has been widely used in the last three decades and has become a standard technique in materials science and technology (BERTIN [1970] and FÖRSTERLING [1980]). The average composition of large areas (approximately 10 cm^2) and relatively thick surface layers (about 100 μm) is obtained by analyzing the X-ray spectra excited by a high-intensity X-ray beam which has a wide wavelength-distribution in order to assess all elements in a wide range of atomic numbers (9–92). Concentrations from some ppm to 100% can be evaluated with a relative accuracy up to 0.2%.

3.4. Photo-electron emission

Electrons excited by photons are used for high-resolution imaging and for chemical analysis of surface and thin films.

3.4.1. Photo-electron emission microscopy

Microscopes using electrons excited by ultraviolet light were developed in the late fifties and made commercially available at the end of the sixties (for reviews see WEGMANN [1972], SCHWARZER [1981]). In these photo-electron emission microscopes (PEEM), a high-intensity beam of ultraviolet light is focussed by means of quartz lenses and mirrors on a small area of a surface (area in the order of 0.2 mm^2, energy density several W/cm^2) which activates emission of relatively slow electrons. A high voltage is applied between the sample and a pierced anode facing the sample surface. These electrons, after passing the axial aperture of the anode and the magnetic lenses of a three-stage electron microscope, produce a highly magnified image on a fluorescent screen or a photographic film. Heating the sample up to temperatures of beginning thermionic emission allows in-situ high-temperature studies. Contrary to scanning electron microscopy, the light-beam cannot be focussed to a sufficiently small size, and integral image generation is used which has the advantage of small exposure times, varying with material and magnification from a tenth to a hundred seconds. The sample surface is cleaned by ion bombardment, but contamination is sometimes a problem in spite of the high vacuum in the chamber (typically 10^{-10} bar).

The intensity distribution of photo-electron emission is essentially determined by the variation of electron emission with material and orientation (material and orientation contrast), with the orientation of a surface element with respect to the optical axis (relief or topographical contrast) and with distortions of the magnetic field in the vicinity of tips and edges. The topographical contrast is stronger than in SEM images but the stereoscopic impression is usually less pronounced since the surface of the sample is always normal to the axis of projection and cannot be tilted. Material contrast is usually very clear in unetched plane surfaces if the work-functions of different phases in a material are sufficiently different, which is usually the case. Orientation contrast is only pronounced in cubic metals but not in non-cubic metals and alloys, in oxides or in carbides. Thus, material- and orientation contrast can be easily separated in most practical cases.

The only major draw-back of the commercial instrument termed *Metioscope* is its very high price. This restricts widespread application. However, those instruments applied for studies in materials research have provided much interesting information in all kinds of high-quality metallographic work (for references see WEGMANN [1972] and SCHWARZER [1981]). Owing to the very small depth of information (10 nm), the high lateral resolution (< 10 nm), the excellent phase separation and the possibility for in-situ heating, photo electron microscopy is excellently capable for quantitative kinetic studies of changes in microstructural geometry (DANNÖHL *et al.* [1971], WEGMANN [1972] and MIDDLETON and EDMONDS [1977]). For example, a recent study (TAYLOR and POLLARD [1982]) has revealed the bonding sequence (grain-boundary movement and annihilation) during diffusion-bonding of steel under load at temperatures up to 1000°C.

3.4.2. Photo-electron spectroscopy

The kinetic energy of photo-electrons leaving the surface can be analyzed by a spectrometer. From the electron energy spectrum, the chemical composition is obtained by calculating the binding energy of the emitted electrons. This technique is usually called ESCA (for *electron spectroscopy for chemical analysis*); more precisely, XPS (for *X-ray-induced photo-electron spectroscopy*, see also ch. 13, §3.2) and UPS (*ultraviolet-light-excited photoelectron spectroscopy*) are differentiated. Recent reviews of these techniques are available (for example CARLSON [1975], BRUN-DLE and BAKER [1977], BERG [1980] and HOFMANN [1980a]. The depth of information is of the order of 1 nm. By means of model calculations and standards, the chemical shift of X-ray-induced photo-electrons can be used to identify the valence state of metal atoms. Ultraviolet light has a lower excitation energy; UPS therefore yields information on the structure of valence bands. Owing to its higher surface sensitivity compared to XPS, UPS is used for analyzing adsorbed layers. Depth-profiling, yielding three-dimensional distribution of chemical composition is possible by nondestructive techniques (by varying the take-off angle with respect to the surface), or destructively, by successively removing layers by chemical or mechanical peeling or, most conveniently combined in the vacuum chamber, *ion-etching* (*sputtering*) with an inherent depth resolution down to monoatomic layers (HOFMANN [1980a,1981]). The lateral resolution is limited at about 1 mm, the detection limit is better than 0.1 at%. Typical applications of ESCA are the exact characterization of oxide layers formed on metal surfaces (allowing not only to specify composition of the oxidation products but also the electronic state of the metal atoms in the oxides), and, as reviewed by BRINEN [1974], investigations of catalytic reactions (chemical changes of the catalyst as well as of adsorbed species).

3.5. Electron-beam- and ion-induced radiation

As discussed earlier (§2) X-rays are excited when an electron beam hits a surface (see fig. 6 and table 2). In the scanning electron microscope, these signals can be used for obtaining qualitative information on the composition and imaging of the element distribution (*X-ray mapping*) and for semi-quantitative and, with dedicated instruments, for quantitative analysis of chemical composition of microstructural features (*energy-dispersive* and *wavelength-dispersive X-ray spectroscopy*).

3.5.1. X-ray mapping

In X-ray mapping, the X-ray emission is picked up by a suitable detector (see below) and an energy window is set which selects X-ray quanta typical for a specific element. The beam of the cathode-ray tube receives an intensity pulse whenever an X-ray quantum of this energy reaches the detector. Phase regions with high concentration of this element appear bright while others appear dark. If this is done for several elements consecutively, X-ray maps of the element distribution are obtained. Owing to the large depth of X-ray emission (see fig. 6) and the large back-ground noise due to bremsstrahlung, the resolution of X-ray maps is limited to a few μm.

3.5.2. Energy- and wavelength-dispersive X-ray spectroscopy

Quantitative analysis of the chemical composition of individual microstructural features became possible when instruments for analyzing the intensity distribution of X-ray impulses as a function of their energy became available. While the first successful *electron-beam microanalyser* (EPMA) built by CASTAING in 1949 (see GOLDSTEIN *et al.* [1977]) had a static beam, all modern instruments utilize a scanning beam dating back to Cosslett and Duncumb [1956] (deflected in the same way as described in §2.3 for the scanning electron microscope). The fact that secondary-electron images can be obtained in the microprobe and that X-ray detectors can easily be added to the scanning electron microscope has now led to the realization that the SEM and the scanning EPMA are in reality one and the same instrument (Goldstein *et al.* [1977]). In commercial versions, emphasis has usually been laid on only one of the two applications – imaging or chemical analysis – and on keeping the price low and the operation convenient, and so, dedicated instruments still are more wide-spread than combined SEM–EPMA which have left the development stage only recently.

The emitted spectrum of X-rays consists of the continuous radiation (bremsstrahlung) and the characteristic radiation (line spectrum). For detailed information on the physical principles see, for example, Dyson [1973], Reed [1975], or Reimer and Pfefferkorn [1977]. The line spectrum can be analyzed in two ways: (i) by wavelength-dispersive spectrometers, nearly exclusively used in the electron micro-probe, and (ii) by energy-dispersive spectrometers, usually attached to both EPMA and SEM.

In *wavelength-dispersive X-ray spectroscopy* (WDS) a monochromator crystal reflects an X-ray beam corresponding to some characteristic line of the element to be analyzed to a gas proportional counter. Since the intensity of X-ray emission is, to a first approximation, proportional to the amount of this element present at the spot where the sample surface is hit by the electron beam, the number of X-ray quanta is a measure of composition. Electron probe microanalyzers are usually equipped with several monochromator crystals, which allows more than one element to be analyzed at a time. The spectral resolution of wavelength dispersive spectrometers is better than 10 eV, and elements down to carbon can be analyzed in some instruments. The intensity readings are further processed in a computer for background correction and also correction to the estimated concentration of one element in the presence of X-ray fluorescence from other elements.

The *energy-dispersive method* (EDS) uses a lithium-drifted silicon solid-state detector which transfers the impulses of the full spectrum to a multi-channel analyzer. The information is displayed on a screen (overall X-ray spectrum or parts of it), or further processed (stored, corrected, subtracted from another spectrum or plotted) in conjunction with a computer. Fast qualitative (and semi-quantitative) information on the composition is thus available. Correction programs for quantitative analysis are not fully satisfactory; errors of 10–100% are usual. In contrast to wavelength-dispersive analysis which needs ideally flat surfaces, this technique can also be used for etched or fracture surfaces. For rough surfaces, shading effects must be considered since X-rays reach the detector along a straight path. The spectral resolution of energy-dispersive analysis is of the order of 150 eV and thus 10–20 times less than that of WDS. Elements with a difference larger than three between atomic numbers can be separated in favourable cases. Elements with higher atomic numbers (> 30) are easily separated by their significant lines while analysis of elements with atomic numbers between 12 and 30 often suffers from background

References: p. 638.

and superpositions. The material of the window in front of the detector (beryllium or plastic) prevents the analysis of elements below atomic number 11 (Na). Some recent windowless counters allow analysis of lighter elements.

Point-information or, with a slow scanning beam, line-profiles of the local composition are obtained. The depth of information depends on the specific density (atomic number) of the elements contained in the sample and the energy of the primary beam, and ranges between 1–10 μm with approximately the same lateral resolution. Higher resolution is obtained with thin foils or in favourable cases when the interfaces between adjacent regions of varying composition are perpendicular to the surface.

With the convenience provided by microcomputers, both electron probe micro-analyzers and energy-dispersive facilities attached to scanning electron microscopes have become highly efficient routine instruments. Applications of electron-beam-in-duced X-ray analysis in materials science and technology are countless. Recent reviews are available (YAKOWITZ and GOLDSTEIN [1977], REIMER and PFEFFERKORN [1977] and HILLMER [1979b], see also books cited in *Further reading*.

3.5.3. Cathodoluminescence

In addition to the above-mentioned effects an incident beam used for surface microscopy can also create electron–hole pairs. During recombination of these pairs, some materials emit long-wave radiation known as *cathodoluminescence* (CL) which can be exploited in the scanning electron microscope using suitable accessories (PFEFFERKORN and BLASCHKE [1974]). Biological and mineralogical application is frequent (see REIMER and PFEFFERKORN [1977] and GOLDSTEIN and YAKOWITZ [1977]). Only a few examples have been reported with metallic materials where radiation is caused by surface plasmon effects (BÖRSCH *et al.* [1961], SIEBER [1982] and RICHARDS and TRIGG [1982]).

3.5.4. Ion- and proton-induced X-ray emission

Similarly as in X-ray fluorescence and electron-beam-induced X-ray spectroscopy, X-rays activated by charged particles (ions, mostly protons) can be registered and analyzed with respect to intensity as a function of energy. *Particle- (or ion-) induced X-ray emission* (PIXE or IIX) was first introduced in nuclear physics where ion-ac-celerating facilities were available; now this method has spread since small accelera-tors are not much more expensive than other instruments described in this section. Fast chemical analysis of all elements with atomic numbers higher than 14 can be achieved with very high sensitivity (routinely 10^{-12} g, with sharply focused particles 10^{-18} g). The main fields of application have been in air pollution and in biology; however, several interesting studies including the detection of impurity traces in oxide layers, implantation and oxidation mechanisms of steel have been reported (for recent reviews see HOHMUTH and RUDOLPH [1980], JOHANSSON [1982]).

3.6. Electron–electron interaction

As discussed in detail in § 2, electron-beam-induced secondary electrons and backscattered electrons are most successfully used for surface imaging in the scanning electron microscope. Several other effects based on electron–electron interactions (table 4) provide additional information. With the availability of commercial instruments, these techniques (especially Auger electron spectroscopy) seem to have developed into major methods in materials research, capable of solving problems, especially those involving light elements, hitherto not treatable owing to lack of lateral or depth resolution. Combinations with other high-power instruments, e.g. the photoelectron emission microscope (BETGE *et al.* [1982]) or ion spectroscopy (see, for example, BRÜMMER *et al.* [1980]), will expand the power of surface microscopy (though at a very high price inherent in ultra-high vacuum devices) much further.

3.6.1. Auger-electron microscopy and spectroscopy

Emission of so-called *Auger electrons* (see also ch. 13, § 3.2) takes place when an electron hole in a lower shell (K, L or M) created by an incident electron beam is filled by an electron from a higher shell or the valence band, which transfers its excess energy to another electron; this last electron is emitted. The kinetic energy of the emitted electrons depends exclusively on the energy levels of the electron levels and this is typical for the element involved. In *Auger-electron spectroscopy* (AES), an electron detector and an electron spectrometer are used to register the number of electrons $N(E)$ as a function of energy E and the differentiated signal $dN(E)/dE$ is plotted and analyzed. With the aid of suitable corrections and calibration standards it is possible to obtain quantitative results (uncertainty ± 1–10 at%) for all elements but hydrogen and helium. Since the mean free path of the low-energy Auger electrons (20–2200 eV) is short, the information depth does not exceed 1–2 nm, i.e., it is three orders of magnitude smaller than that of X-ray analysis and thus is a real surface-analysis method. Information to lower depth into the bulk is obtained by consecutively sputtering off layers by argon (sputtering rate approximately 10 nm/min), and depth profiles can be plotted. Preferential sputtering and mixing effects due to sputtering have been observed which reduce resolution. The spectral resolution is better for the low-atomic-number elements; detection of 0.1–1 at% is possible, which may drop to 10 at% for heavy metals or if peaks are superimposed.

Sample preparation is not critical as long as clean surfaces are produced by sputtering inside the ultra-high vacuum chamber. Fracturing the sample in the specimen chamber is advantageous for analyzing precipitates or segregation at grain boundaries. An example of the application of AES in the analysis of segregation is shown in ch. 13, § 3.2 (figs. 10–12 of that chapter). Early applications of AES reviewed by FERRANTE *et al.* [1973] were restricted by the limited lateral resolution (several μm to mm). With modern instruments, lateral resolution has improved to much below 1 μm (down to 50 nm in favourable cases). By scanning the electron beam, successive points and line profiles can be analyzed, and an image can be formed by activating a CRT modulated by the signal intensity of the Auger electrons

References: p. 638.

in the same way as in X-ray mapping. *Scanning Auger microscopy* (SAM) has become an extremely valuable addition to surface microscopy owing to its high sensitivity for chemical composition, good lateral and extremely high depth resolution. The present state, progress and prospects of AES and SAM were recently reviewed by VENABLES and FATHERS [1982] (see also ASH [1980]) and the large variety of problems to which these techniques have been applied (including studies of contamination, inhomogeneity, diffusion, profile analysis of thin layers, segregation in grain boundaries and oxide layers and many other topics of scientific and technological work) is shown by recent compilations (KLAUA and ÖRTEL [1980], ASH [1980], HILLMER [1982] and PFEFFERKORN [1982]). An interesting study by GORETZKI *et al.* [1982] shows the distribution of impurities in steel and their role in formation of micropores and in embrittlement during welding, with fracture carried out in the instrument to avoid contamination. Other recent studies of segregation by MÖLLER *et al.* [1982] and DUDEK *et al.* [1982] show further attractive aspects of Auger analysis in materials research. Many examples will be found in ch. 13.

3.6.2. Low- and high-energy electron diffraction

Electron diffraction methods investigate the stray-angle distribution of a monochromatic electron-beam scattered back from surface atoms. *Low-energy electron diffraction* (LEED) uses primary energies between 10 and 500 eV (corresponding to wavelengths of 0.4–0.05 nm) and yields information on the structure and the electronic bonding states of surface atoms. *Reflection high-energy electron diffraction* (RHEED) can be applied similarly to X-ray diffraction; the high stray cross-section (10^6 times higher than that of X-rays) gives a higher sensitivity, the much more pronounced inelastic scattering limits depth of information and makes this method more sensitive to contamination and deformation of the surface. Recent reviews (for example BRÜCKNER [1980] and KLÖBER and SCHNEIDER [1980]) do not give a sufficiently clear picture of how useful these techniques have been in the past in the field of physical metallurgy, and RHEED is at present perhaps unduly neglected. Electron diffraction is advantageously used in combination with other techniques of surface analysis (especially with ion scattering and Auger-electron spectroscopy) adding information which cannot be obtained otherwise.

3.7. Ion spectroscopy

In addition to emission by high electric fields (see atom probe, §3.1.2) ions can leave the surface owing to excitation by photons, electrons, or ions (see table 4), or by scattering. The extremely high sensitivity of ion detectors can be used for analyzing the chemical composition of surfaces down to minute traces (for recent reviews see MCINTYRE [1978], BRÜMMER *et al.* [1980] and HOFMANN [1980a]).

3.7.1. Ion-scattering spectroscopy

In *ion-scattering spectroscopy* (ISS), also called *ion-reflection spectroscopy* and *Rutherford back-scattering* (RBS), the energy loss of noble gas ions (helium, neon, or argon) scattered elastically from a surface is analyzed. Ions with energies of the order of 0.1–10 keV which interact with the first layer of surface atoms are reflected, while those penetrating to deeper layers have a very low probability of re-escaping. The spectrum is analyzed with respect to the ratio of energy and charge of the ions and yields qualitative and semi-quantitative information on the chemical nature and the arrangement of surface atoms. Stray effects (inelastic or multiple scattering) reduce sensitivity in that the peaks become broader. At present, quantitative analysis is only possible by calibration (as with most other methods using ions) due to the unknown quantities of stray cross-sections and ion neutralization. ISS is in competition with AES, and it seems that it is superseded at present in metallurgical applications. Reviews on ISS and its uses have been published by CABONARA [1973], HOFMANN [1980a], and PECH [1980]. Its value for segregation studies is discussed in ch. 13, §3.2. Combination with other techniques of surface spectroscopy (AES, SIMS, especially with LEED, §3.6.2), is feasible in one instrument, increasing the information power of the individual methods in a pronounced way.

3.7.2. Secondary-ion mass spectroscopy

When a beam of energetic ions (usually argon, oxygen or nitrogen with 1–20 kV) is accelerated and focussed and impinges on a surface, it erodes the atoms at the sample surface which simultaneously become ionized positively or negatively and can be collected and analyzed in a mass spectrometer. *Secondary-ion mass spectroscopy (SIMS)* and its subcategories, *ion-microprobe mass analysis (IMMA)* and *statistical and dynamic secondary-ion mass spectroscopy (SSIMS and DSIMS)*, rate among the most powerful analytical instruments, revealing qualitative data on chemical traces in surfaces with a sensitivity of better than 1 ppm or 10^{-15} g. The maximum spatial resolution is approximately 1 μm. Some limiting factors have recently been reviewed by HEILAND [1982] and HOFMANN [1980a]. Depth resolution down to one monolayer makes possible depth profiling by continuous sputtering erosion. SIMS and IMMA have been utilized to a large extent in the fields of mineralogy and semiconductor technology but a number of applications in physical metallurgy have been reported as well (for references see BERKEY [1973], SHEMENSKI [1977], COLBY [1977], DÜSTERHÖFT [1980], HOFMANN [1980a], and CAHN et al. [1980]).

4.   Quantitative interpretation of microstructural geometry

Quantitative methods for characterizing the geometry of microstructures are an important means for understanding the relationship between production parameters and behaviour of technical materials in application as well as for providing the experimental basis for theoretical studies of microstructural genesis and its effect on mechanical and physical properties. The important elements of *quantitative microstructural analysis* (also termed *quantitative metallography*) are *image analysis*, i.e. the quantification of features visible in metallographic cross-sections or transmission

References: p. 638.

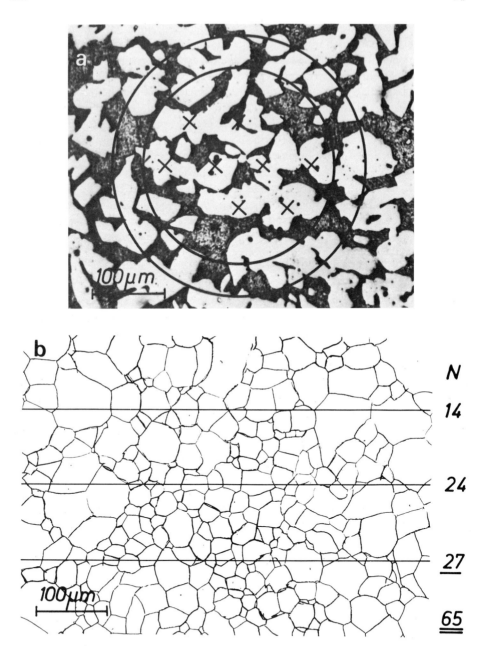

images; *stereology*, i.e. estimation of three-dimensional geometry from two-dimensional image data; and the *interpretation* of the three-dimensional parameters. After a short introduction to general techniques of image analysis and stereology, this

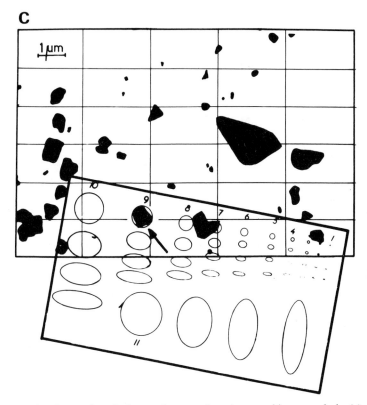

Fig. 11. Typical grid-, line- and graticule-counting procedures in manual image analysis: (a) point-counting for volume fraction analysis (circles can be used for interface density measurement, see text); (b) line-counting for determination of mean linear grain size of a single-phase material (numbers on the right margin show number of grain boundaries intersected); (c) graticule-counting for size distribution measurements (area of circles and ellipses of varying aspect ratio increase by a factor of two in each higher class).

section focusses on the application of quantitative analysis of microstructures to problems in materials science.

4.1. Image analysis

Simple comparison of microstructure with standard test charts is extensively used in quality control of materials (for example, ASTM standards for determination of grain size or of slag inclusions). The accuracy of these comparison methods is rather limited compared with counting techniques (EXNER [1969b] and EXNER and HOUGARDY [1983]). These semi-quantitative methods should not be used for research work and will not be discussed any further here.

When scanning an image for collecting data, counting with point and line grids, measurements along straight lines, or area measurements can be used. Each of these strategies has its merits, according to the purpose of the investigation (parameters to be determined) and available instrumentation (manual, semi-automatic or fully automatic.

The manual acquisition of image data is carried out directly at the microscope, using inserts in the ocular or ground plates with arrays of points or lines, or with micrographs and suitable grids or rulers (GAHM [1971], EXNER and HOUGARDY [1983]). Figure 11a shows a typical point grid superimposed over the microstructure of a two-phase material. The number of points falling within the black phase and the number of intersections between the outer circle and the perimeter lines of the black phase are counted (yielding, as discussed below, estimates for volume fraction of the black phase and its area of interface with the white phase). Figure 11b shows linear analysis of the grain size in a single-phase material. A number of fields must be evaluated in this way in order to get statistically significant numbers. Simple electronic counters and step stages are useful means to speed up these counting procedures. More complex data (size distribution and elongation of planar features) can be determined by simple graticules, an example of which is shown in fig. 11c. Manual methods for microstructural analysis have recently been reviewed by EXNER and HOUGARDY [1983].

The first step towards automation was realized in lineal scanners which were popular during the sixties and seventies (EXNER [1972a] and GAHM [1975]). More recently, semi-automatic instruments have been provided with digitizers as input device to a calculator or computer (see, for example, HILLJE and REDMANN [1976], EXNER [1978a] and EXNER and HOUGARDY [1983]). Digitizers are tablets by which the exact coordinates of points touched with a special pencil are registered at a high rate (up to 10^4 per second) with high precision (0.1 mm). The operator indicates the intersections of the scanning line with the perimeter or outlines the perimeters of the microstructural features using his ability to differentiate between features of different kind (composition, structure) on the basis of grey or colour shading and of shape. Thus, the operator keeps steady track of what is measured and is able to exclude artefacts by simple judgement. Modern instruments compute all relevant microstructural parameters from these data. Disadvantages are the high time-expenditure and concentration required, in addition to some danger of introducing human bias.

Fully automatic instruments are available with a wide efficiency range (FISCH-MEISTER [1981] and EXNER and HOUGARDY [1983]). Most of them use television-type scanning modules with electronic phase detection. Simple low-price instruments allow determination of a limited number of parameters for high-contrast situations, while modular high-price instruments with fast hardware or, more recently, flexible software modules and full grey-level image-storage with up to 1024×1024 picture-point lateral resolution and 256 steps of grey-level resolution combine high speed, versatility and convenience for any type of automatic image data acquisition. Scaling, shading correction, scanning-table steering and focussing are all carried out automatically, and all kinds of image manipulation (filtering, edge contrast enhancement, halo correction, the techniques outlined in §4.3 below, etc.) can be implemented if required. Figure 12a shows the grey-level histogram and fig. 12b demonstrates the effect of a special filter (pseudoplast filter) on the appearance of a light micrograph of a three-phase alloy. Phase discrimination (either by dedicated hard-

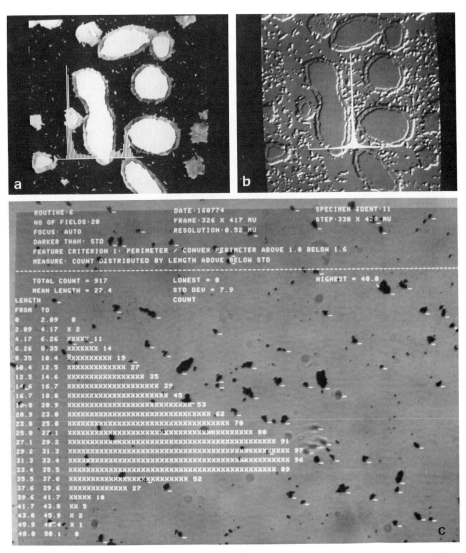

Fig. 12. Typical procedures of television-equipped fully automatic image analyzers: (a) Microscopic image of a three-phase copper–cadmium alloy with superimposed grey-level distribution (Kontron IBAS II); (b) Pseudoplast filter producing a plastic appearance by showing gradient variation only (Kontron IBAS); (c) Size-distribution analysis of nonmetallic inclusions in a dirty steel, with superimposed counting flags indicating proper detection and area distribution histogram (Cambridge Instruments QUANTIMET 720).

References: p. 638.

ware modules or by software algorithms), parameter selection and evaluation, statistical treatments and many other routines can be activated by push-button commands or by a simple computer program designed individually for any specific problem. As an example, fig. 12c shows the appearance of a microstructural evaluation on the monitor or screen of a modern atomatic image analyzer. "Interactive" devices – usually a light-pen to be used on the display monitor – allow the operator to use his judgment for excluding artefacts or adding missing details (e.g. parts of a grain-boundary network).

In principle, any image-forming instrument can be used as input device; only light microscopes and, more recently, scanning electron microscopes have been used in on-line configurations while transmission electron micrographs and other printed images have been evaluated only occasionally. An interesting modification is the combination of image analysis and energy-dispersive X-ray analysis (§3.1.1) for determining geometric parameters and composition of individual particles simultaneously (EKELUND and HERTZMANN [1981]).

Instrumentation for image analysis has developed rapidly over the past two decades (for historical and recent reviews see FISCHMEISTER [1965], GAHM [1971], EXNER [1972a], HOUGARDY [1976], FISCHMEISTER [1981] and EXNER and HOUGARDY [1983]) and is still advancing at a rapid rate. In this context, the dramatic developments in digital image processing must be mentioned, which not only are useful for quantitative image analysis but also for contrast enhancement, image restoration, or qualitative image description (GONZALEZ and WINTZ [1977]).

4.2. Planar characteristics and stereology

Image analysis yields a number of geometric characteristics describing the geometry of planar images of cross-sections or thin-film projections, the most important of which are listed in table 5. They usually can be qualitatively interpreted in terms of the three-dimensional microstructures from which they originate. Quantitative three-dimensional characteristics are obtained by a body of mathematical methods based on integral geometry and statistics which is called *stereology*. There is an enormous number of original papers and formulae spread over the scientific literature of fields as far apart as mathematics, geology, materials science and biology. Useful monographs and standard textbooks (DE HOFF and RHINES [1968], UNDERWOOD [1970], SALTYKOV [1974], WEIBEL [1979,1980] and EXNER and HOUGARDY [1983]) review the literature and should be consulted whenever a quantitative evaluation of spatial microstructures is attempted, in order to avoid misinterpretations and redundant derivations. A few of the more important aspects of microstructural geometry (table 5), their experimental evaluation from surface images and some applications in physical metallurgy are discussed in the following sections.

4.2.1. Volume-fraction analysis

Simple plausibility proofs as well as sophisticated mathematical treatments show that, for a homogeneously dispersed phase, area fraction, lineal fraction and point

Table 5

Some important geometric characteristics of planar images and three-dimensional microstructural features [a].

Planar characteristic [b]	Example	Corresponding three-dimensional characteristic [c]	Microstructural example
Area fraction, A_A	Particle intersects	* Volume fraction, V_V	Amounts of phases in multiphase material
Line density, L_A	Intersect perimeters	* Surface density, S_V	Grain-boundary or phase-interface area
Point density, P_A	Triple points in intersected grain-boundary network	* Line density, L_V	Length of dislocation lines or grain-boundary triple lines
Number density, N_A	Number of intersected particles	Numerical density, N_V	Number of particles
Distribution by area $f(a)$	Intersect area distribution	Distribution by number and linear size $f(l)$	Number of spherical particles as a function of diameter
Distribution by length $f(l)$	Chord length distribution	Distribution by volume $f(v)$	Number of grains as a function of volume
Mean size	Mean intersect area or mean linear intercept	* Mean linear size $\bar{L}$ Mean volume, V	Mean linear grain size Mean particle volume
Distances	Nearest-neighbour distance	* Mean linear distance $\bar{D}$	Surface-to-surface distance of particles in one direction
		Nearest-neighbour distance	Distance of particles in dispersion-hardened materials
Shape characteristics	Area/perimeter ratio, length/width ratio	Shape parameters	Shape changes of particles or pores in processing
Planar curvature	Local and mean curvature	* Mean curvature	Curvature of pore–solid interfaces
Arrangement in plane	Random, regular, clustered	Arrangement in space	Clustering of carbides in high-speed steel
		Connectivity	Number of closed loops in the pore space of a sintered material
		* Contiguity	Amount of surface shared with other grains of the same phase in a multiphase material

[a] Three-dimensional parameters marked with an asterisk can be calculated from data obtained with planar images without any assumptions but randomness of sampling. All other three-dimensional characteristics are restricted to model geometries, to known shapes or known size distribution or both, or can only be assessed by three-dimensional measurements (stereometry, serial sectioning or chemical disintegration).

[b] Subscript A indicates that quantity is per unit area.

[c] Subscript V indicates that quantity is per unit volume.

References: p. 638.

fraction are statistically unbiased estimates for the volume fraction, i.e., in standard nomenclature (UNDERWOOD [1970], WEIBEL [1980] and EXNER and HOUGARDY [1983]):

$$V_V = A_A = L_L = P_P. \tag{4}$$

The experimental error of this estimate decreases with an increasing number of points counted or lines and areas measured and, at a 5% level of error probability, for point-counting using a wide-spaced regular point grid, is approximately (HILLIARD [1976]):

$$\pm \Delta V = 2 \left(P_P (1 - P_P) / P \right)^{1/2}, \tag{5}$$

where P is the total number of points of the test grid. A more stringent evaluation of errors includes the variation of area fractions between different test fields (NICHOLSON [1978]).

Volume fraction has been the parameter most frequently used in quality control of materials and has found many useful applications in materials research. It is obviously closely related to composition and exerts a decisive effect on the properties of multiphase materials. In equilibrium phase diagrams, the lever rule allows phase boundaries to be determined to a high accuracy with a minimum number of samples. For example, LINDÉN [1972] has redetermined the two-phase region in the copper–aluminium system, and ALDINGER [1969] has shown excellent agreement of results obtained by classical and by image-analyzing methods in the four-phase region of the Ag–Cu–Cd–Zn diagram. Modern phase-diagram studies employ computer calculations to a high degree which are facilitated if accurate quantitative data are available.

A typical field for volume-fraction analysis is the determination of nonmetallic inclusions, of carbides, and of the time–temperature dependence of phase transformations in steels. Figure 13 shows a typical isothermal time–temperature–transformation (TTT) diagram for a chrome–molybdenum steel which makes it possible to read not only the nature of phases obtained after a certain holding time at constant temperature but also the fraction of austenite transformed (LAFOND and MOLIEXE [1975]). Studies of transformation kinetics of discontinuous precipitation or recrystallization are further examples. A very interesting aspect of volume-fraction analysis is the possibility of determining local composition, which is straightforward if the equilibrium compositions of the individual phases present in the microstructure are known. Thus, segregation and inhomogeneity phenomena and other systematic compositional variations (e.g. the carbon distribution in the surface of a hardened steel part, as described by FISCHMEISTER [1972]) can be quantitatively determined, sometimes with as good or better accuracy than by microchemical methods.

4.2.2. Surface density

Dispersity of a microstructural component (isolated particles as well as complex-shaped continuous or semi-continuous phases) can best be quantitatively described

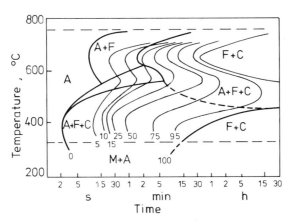

Fig. 13. Isothermal time–temperature transformation diagram for a chromium–molybdenum steel. (A = austenite, F = ferrite, C = carbide, M = martensite). The heavy lines give start and end of a reaction, the numbers at the thin curves give the volume fraction of austenite transformed. (After LAFOND and MOLIEXE [1975].)

with a single number by measuring the density of its interface area per unit volume. Stereology (SALTYKOV [1974], UNDERWOOD [1970] and WEIBEL [1980]) tells us that:

$$S_V = 2P_L, \tag{6}$$

where S_V is the interface area per unit volume of the material (surface density) and P_L is the number of intersections (per unit length) between a scanning line and the intersections of a plane cross-section with the interface as seen in a metallographic image. If we relate the interface of a microstructural component (phase α) to the volume of this particular component, we get the specific surface of the α-phase:

$$S_V^\alpha = S_V/V_V = 4N_\alpha/L_\alpha = 2P_L/P_P, \tag{7}$$

where L_α is the length of the line inside the α-phase ($L_\alpha = LV_V$, L is the total length of the scanning line) and N_α is the number of α-regions transversed by the scanning line. Of course, the density of grain-boundary area can be determined in the same way.

An analysis of statistical errors shows (HILLIARD [1976]) that the standard error, ΔS_V, is approximately

$$\Delta S_V = kS_V/\sqrt{P}, \tag{8}$$

where P is the total number of intersections and k is approximately 1.2 for contiguous grains and 4 for randomly dispersed particles. The range $S_V \pm \Delta S_V$ corresponds to 5% error probability (95% significance level).

Prominent examples of application of surface-density measurements are found in powder metallurgy, where the pore–solid interface provides the driving force for sintering processes (ch. 30, § 1.1), in the study of coarsening processes (grain growth

References: p. 638.

and particle growth, ch. 25, §4.1) and in finding correlations between microstructure and properties. Figure 14 shows two simple examples of the latter, where linear relationships between the hardness of bronze and its grain-boundary density

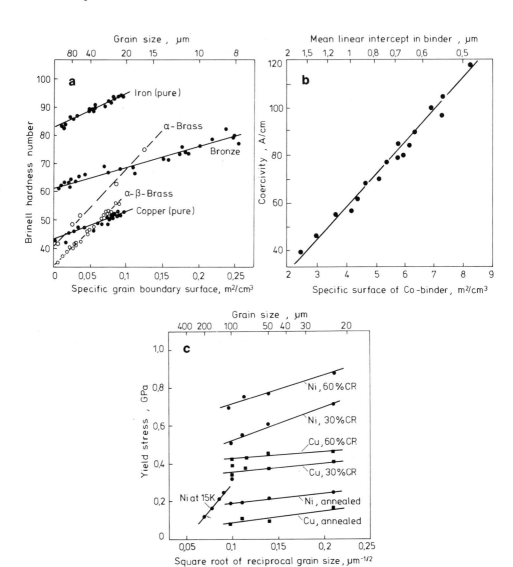

Fig. 14. Simple relationships between properties and microstructural geometry: (a) hardness of some metals as a function of grain-boundary density (data from SALTYKOV [1974] and RHINES [1976]); (b) coercive force of the cobalt phase in tungsten carbide–cobalt hardmetals as a function of interface density (after FISCHMEISTER and EXNER [1966]); (c) Yield strength of some metals as a function of square root of mean linear grain size, CR = cold reduction in percent (data from WANG and MURR [1980] and RAZA [1982]).

(SALTYKOV [1974], RHINES [1976] and ONDRACEK [1978]) and between the coercive
force and the interface per unit volume of magnetic cobalt phase in WC–Co hard
alloys used in cutting and wear applications (FISCHMEISTER and EXNER [1966]) are
observed.

The concept of surface density is less popular for characterizing microstructural
geometry in physical metallurgy than might have been expected considering its
versatility combined with extreme ease of evaluation. While for the separate determination of number and size of particles simplifying assumptions about shape are
necessary (see below), the only requirement for obtaining significant numbers for S_V
is statistical sampling, while shape effects have no influence. Surface densities can
also be used for describing the contiguity, i.e. the degree to which grains of a phase
are connected in space (GURLAND [1958], EXNER and FISCHMEISTER [1966]) or the
degree of preferred orientation (SALTYKOV [1974]). In modelling microstructure–
property relationships or processes of microstructural genesis during casting, heat-
treatment, deformation, etc., surface densities are most useful quantities for averaging the complex geometric appearance of phases in most technical materials.

4.2.3. Size and distance

In contrast to volume fraction and surface density or specific surface, three-dimensional size and separation (distance) are not related to two-dimensional data in a
simple manner. Only if the shape of an object is known can its size be defined by a
single parameter. The assessment of nearest-neighbour distances requires knowledge
of the spatial arrangement of objects, which is often not available from planar
images. Thus, models are needed to estimate size and distance and their distribution.

The most useful model relates to specific surface and surface density. The size and
distance can be described by the average linear distances between the surface points
inside (mean linear size) and outside (mean linear distance) the volume covered by a
phase α. For multiphase materials we get the *mean linear intercept* (*mean linear
particle size* for a dispersed phase):

$$\bar{L}_\alpha = L_\alpha/N_\alpha = 4\frac{V_V}{S_V}, \tag{9}$$

and the *mean linear distance* between the surface elements of phase α:

$$D_\alpha = (L - L_\alpha)/N_\alpha = 4\frac{1 - V_V}{S_V}. \tag{10}$$

For space-filling grains ($V_V = 1$), the *mean linear grain size* (mean linear grain
intercept, Heyn's grain size) is:

$$\bar{L} = 1/N_L = 2S_V. \tag{11}$$

This concept makes it possible to characterize size and distance independently of
shape, arrangement, or size distribution. *Mean intersect area* (Jeffries' grain size) is
an indirect measure related to the length of grain edges per unit volume (FISCHMEIS-
TER and ARZT [1981]) but has no concise meaning for isolated particles, if shape is

not uniform (and simple). There are numerous other measures of these quantities *, all relying on model geometries (for references and derivations see DE HOFF and RHINES [1968], THOMPSON [1972], UNDERWOOD [1970] and WEIBEL [1980]). The assumptions made are usually clearly stated in the original papers but often neglected by users of the final results, which may lead to erroneous conclusions.

Measures of distance other than that defined in eq. (10) rely on a specific geometric shape. For example, nearest-neighbour distances in three dimensions can be calculated from two-dimensional counts if the shape and size of all particles is identical and if the volume fraction is not too high (see, for example, BANSAL and ARDELL [1972]) or if parallel platelets are considered (ROOSZ et al. [1980] and TÖRRÖNEN [1980]). However, if the nearest-neighbour distances of irregularly shaped and distributed particles is to be estimated, no reliable methods are available. (See also ch. 29, fig. 4.)

The same problem arises when three-dimensional *size distributions* are calculated from distributions of linear intercepts or from intercept areas. Only if the shape is extremely simple (sphere, cube, ellipsoid) are concise unfolding procedures available **. Special reviews (EXNER [1972b], SIMPSON and STANDISH [1977], FISCHMEISTER and ARZT [1981] and CRUZ-ORIVE [1978]) rather than standard text books should be consulted for useful conversion procedures. For establishing three-dimensional grain and particle size distributions, chemical methods (e.g., attack of aluminium by liquid gallium) are used to separate isolated grains or particles and to evaluate them microscopically or by weighing. It is interesting to note that logarithmic normal size distributions have been observed in most cases (see, for example, EXNER [1972b] and RHINES and PATTERSON [1982]).

There are a large number of problems in materials research where size, distance and size-distribution are relevant. One of the best-known relationships between microstructural geometry and properties is the Hall–Petch relationship predicting a linear dependence of yield stress of polycrystalline materials on the square root of reciprocal grain size (ch. 19, §8). It has been shown recently that size distribution has a significant influence on this relationship (KÜHLMEYER [1978]) since deformation starts at the largest rather than the average grain (ESSMANN et al. [1968]). Experimental results confirm the simple form of the equation (fig. 14c) owing to the fact that the shape of grain-size distributions in most annealed single-phase materials

---

* A measure of size frequently used is $\bar{R} = 3\bar{L}/4$, derived by simply relating the radius of a sphere to its mean linear intercept. It is obvious that the result obtained does not give much more useful information than does $\bar{L}$ or S_V: $\bar{R}$ is the radius of equally-sized spheres with the same specific surface and volume fraction (but not average volume or number) as the (irregular) particles or grains. For space-filling polyhedra, similar size measures can be derived (THOMPSON [1972]) which, however, are similarly restricted in describing the geometry of real grain structures.

** Recently, KING [1982] has derived a method for assessing three-dimensional size distributions (cumulative particle mesh size distributions) for irregular particles from planar data, i.e. area distribution of sections or projections, or from linear intercept distributions. No a priori assumptions on regular geometric shape, convexity, congruency or particular functional form of the size distribution are made. However, a shape-dependent constant must be known or determined experimentally for a uniformly sized sample.

is fairly similar. However, this is not always the case: the width of grain-size distributions in recrystallized metals depends strongly on deformation prior to annealing, even at long annealing times (OKAZAKI and CONRAD [1972] and RHINES and PATTERSON [1982]). It is interesting to note that prestraining changes the parameters but not the general form of the Hall–Petch relationship (WANG and MURR [1980], see fig. 14c).

Other useful equations involving mean size and distance are derived for simplified geometries, often taking a model in which grains or particles are assumed to be spheres of uniform size. For instance, the Zener relationship for dispersed particles limiting the grain size (ch. 25, § 3.7),

$$\bar{L} = k\bar{L}_\alpha / V_V \tag{12}$$

(where $\bar{L}$ is the equilibrium grain size in a material with particles of mean linear size $\bar{L}_\alpha$ and volume fraction V_V), is usually derived in this way (PORTER and EASTERLING [1981]). k is a constant derived theoretically for randomly dispersed single-size spheres ($k = 4/3$). Slightly deviating numbers for k are obtained experimentally, owing to the fact that the effect of particles (or pores) on grain-boundary mobility depends on shape, location and size distribution.

Equations describing the kinetics of grain growth and particle growth by Ostwald ripening or coalescence, the dependence of dendrite arm spacing and lamellar spacing on freezing rate, and several other processes determining the size of microstructural features have been derived on the basis of simplified model geometries some of which are discussed in more detail in other chapters (e.g. ch. 10B, § 2). Experimental proofs given on the basis of quantitative microscopy will be statistically significant and free of systematic errors only if the geometric details of the theoretical models are compatible with the real microstructure. As an example, fig.

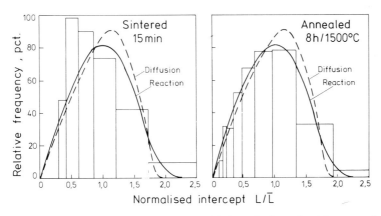

Fig. 15. Size distribution of spherical VC particles in a nickel matrix sintered and heat-treated at 1500°C (liquid matrix). Histograms: experimental results; solid curves: theoretical prediction (after EXNER [1973]). (a) Sintered 1 h, mean linear intercept $\bar{L} = 17,5$ μm; (b) annealed 8 h, mean linear intercept $\bar{L} = 45.5$ μm.

References: p. 638.

15 shows the comparison of size distributions of vanadium carbide particles of spherical shape with predictions made by the Wagner–Lifshitz theory for Ostwald ripening (ch. 10B, §3.2.2). Perfect agreement for reaction-controlled growth is obtained for long annealing times while significant deviations exist for the as-sintered (i.e. briefly annealed) state (EXNER [1973]). This comparison is made on the basis of linear intercepts (EXNER and LUKAS [1971]) rather than of sphere diameters, since unfolding of the experimental data generally increases the experimental scatter pronouncedly (NICHOLSON [1978]).

4.2.4. Shape, shape-related and other complex parameters

The most difficult problem in quantification of microstructural geometry is shape. Though numerous attempts have been made to find parameters for "average" shape in three dimensions, a general solution is not available, and some proposed parameters (see, for example UNDERWOOD [1970,1976,1980], FISCHMEISTER [1974], MEDALIA [1980] and EXNER and HOUGARDY [1983]) are very limited, while others are of not much use at all since they either cannot be assessed experimentally or are size-sensitive. There are two ways out: one is to use planar shape descriptors for sections or projections as a "fingerprint" for three-dimensional shape, the other is serial sectioning in order to get the three-dimensional reconstructions or to isolate individual grains and particles chemically (RHINES and PATTERSON [1982] and DE HOFF [1982]).

Description by morphological coefficients (Fourier or Walsh, see MELOY [1980]) is one way to quantify planar geometry concisely, but results in parameters quite abstract from human perception.

Classical shape parameters to describe various aspects such as elongation, bulkiness, waviness, or symmetry can be defined on the basis of combining metric properties like area, perimeter, Ferret's diameter, moments of inertia, etc. (BEDDOW et al. [1980], SCHWARZ [1980] and EXNER and HOUGARDY [1983]). Applications of planar shape descriptors to problems in physical metallurgy have remained scarce, but now – with the availability of shape parameters in most automatic instruments – they can be used for descriptive purposes or for establishing empirical correlations for shape-sensitive properties of materials. As an example, a close correlation between fracture strength of eutectic aluminium–silicon alloys and shape of the silicon precipitates has been demonstrated recently (PAUL et al. [1982]).

Serial sectioning has been used to evaluate topological parameters, mainly in connection with studying the grain shape in metals (RHINES et al. [1974] and RHINES and PATTERSON [1982]) and the development of microstructure during sintering (DE HOFF et al. [1972] and AIGELTINGER and EXNER [1972]). In this way, the *number of separate parts* (or, in other words, the number of pores or particles) per unit volume can be assessed. Stereological equations relating numbers per unit area or unit length to numbers in three dimensions are usually not reliable since they depend on information concerning shape- and size-distribution. Another useful topological parameter is *connectivity* (or genus) which describes the number of connections (channels) between nodes (larger regions). Figure 16 shows the results of a study of

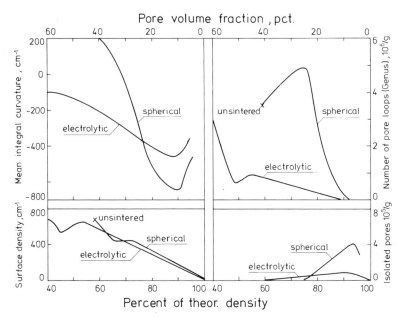

Fig. 16. Changes of metric and topological properties of pore space in sintered copper powder as a function of porosity varied by sintering at 1000°C. The spherical and the electrolytic (dendrite-shaped) powders show different pore structures at comparable porosity. The right part of the figure clearly shows the formation of new contacts (increasing genus) at the early sintering stage and the closure of pore channels (sharply decreasing genus) and formation of isolated pores and their disappearance by shrinking in the later stages. These topological changes are also reflected by the metric properties shown in the left part of the figure: Surface density and integral mean curvature decrease due to smoothening of the pore–solid interface but increase for a short period when the channels start to close and at the very late stages when isolated pores shrink. (After AIGELTINGER and EXNER [1972].)

sintered copper on which the geometric properties of the pore space have been followed up as a function of porosity, i.e. pore volume fraction (AIGELTINGER and EXNER [1972]). If chemical disintegration for isolating microstructural features is not feasible, serial sectioning, though extremely time-consuming even with automatic sample preparation, automatic instrumentation and computer processing, may be the ultimate answer to geometric analysis of irregularly shaped microstructural features in three dimensions (DE HOFF [1982]).

Another important aspect closely related to both shape and size is *curvature*. Variations of local curvature provide the driving forces for shape changes and coarsening of microstructural features (e.g. fibers, pore systems, precipitations, etc.) but are difficult to quantify. Integral mean curvature, on the other hand, can be measured quickly and unambiguously from cross-sections (DE HOFF [1980]) and is a sensitive parameter for monitoring the path of microstructural changes during annealing (DE HOFF and ISAWARAN [1982]).

Finally, there remains the problem of characterizing the *arrangement* of microscopic features. Again, three-dimensional characterization must rely on simplifying assumptions or on serial sectioning. The classification (random, regular, clustered) and quantitative description of planar arrangement of features defined by a characteristic point (e.g. centre of gravity) on the basis of nearest-neighbour distance distributions is possible (SCHWARZ and EXNER [1983]); other statistical procedures are known from other fields, e.g. from pattern recognition or cluster analysis. Up to the present, application of arrangement parameters to materials is near to non-existent. A very interesting exception is a study on the arrangement of carbides in high-speed steels, which has shown the feasibility of simple statistical concepts and the value of *arrangement analysis* (WERLEFORS *et al.* [1979]).

4.3. Mathematical morphology

In addition to these classical geometric parameters, a special methodology based on "structuring elements", termed *mathematical morphology* has been developed, largely in France, into a consistent and practically useful framework for image analysis. A full theoretical account of this field, including all pertinent references, has been published by SERRA [1982]. There is no space here to describe these difficult concepts in detail. Attempts to give a comprehensible treatment of image analysis and of image manipulation based on mathematical morphology can be found in the literature (NAWRATH and SERRA [1979], FISCHMEISTER [1981] and EXNER and HOUGARDY [1983]). Some procedures which have been proven useful in practical work are outlined in the following.

The microstructure or, rather, its binary image is treated as a set of points which can be transformed by various operations in order to extract characteristic parameters of this set, which then are used to describe the geometry of the microstructure. The effects of the most useful operations, erosion and dilatation, are demonstrated in fig. 17. *Erosion* is achieved by moving the structuring element from picture-point to picture-point and removing all those points which do not fulfill a specified criterion, e.g. that all neighbour points are inside the dispersed features shown in fig. 17a, which, in other words, means removing all points at the edge of the features. By this operation, the two small features 1 and 2 and the bridge connecting two parts of the large particle are eliminated. The area of the large feature has obviously become smaller as shown by the dashed line in fig. 17a. By *dilatation*, i.e. by adding all those matrix points which have at least one neighbouring point inside the features, the original size is very closely reconstructed but the two small features are still gone as is the bridge between the two large features (fig. 17b). Therefore, this combined operation is called *opening*. Similarly, if dilatation is carried out first, followed by erosion (figs. 17c and 17d) the result is reversed and a bridge is formed by this combined operation called *closing*.

It is obvious that this manipulation very effectively allows the elimination of small features or contacts arising from detection noise in automatic instruments or to separate relevant information from the image. Another operation for segmenting connected features is the *grassfire transformation* (NAWRATH and SERRA [1979])

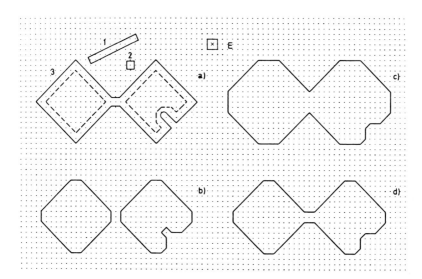

Fig. 17. Two-dimensional image transformations by operations of mathematical morphology (EXNER and HOUGARDY [1983]). E is the element of 5 picture-points (with the reference point in the center) by which the following operations are carried out: (a) Original features and eroded outline (dashed) of feature 3; (b) dilated outline of eroded fig. 17a; (c) dilated outline of fig. 17b; (d) eroded outline of fig. 17c. Combined operations are called opening (a and b) and closing (c and d).

allowing identification and counting of separate particles and grain corners by alternating or repeated erosions and dilatations. The concepts of *covariograms* and *star function* (SERRA [1982]) are useful for spacing and size measurements. Most information obtainable in this way should be strictly considered as fingerprint-type information on microstructural geometry (FISCHMEISTER [1981]) owing to the lack of quantitative relationship with three-dimensional characteristics of the microstructure and to uncontrolled effects of image distortion. The stereological aspects of mathematical morphology have been discussed recently by SERRA [1982]. In general, however, this alternative concept should be very useful in all those cases when relative changes of microstructures need to be quantified, while in cases where physical modelling of microstructural changes is attempted, stereological parameters should be preferred.

4.4. Further aspects

Generally, more than one single geometric aspect is of relevance in characterizing the microstructural geometry of multiphase materials, and a combination of parameters will be needed to give a full description. Such combinations have been proposed for studying the evolution of microstructure (for example, during sintering, see fig. 16 and ch. 30) or for empirical correlations with mechanical properties (for example,

References: p. 638.

those of cast and annealed aluminium alloys (PAUL et al. [1982]), of cemented
carbides (EXNER and GURLAND [1970]) or of sintered steel (EXNER and POHL [1978]).
In addition to these and other examples cited here, successful applications of
quantitative characterization of microstructural geometry have been reported in the
literature; some of these have been reviewed recently, for example by FISCHMEISTER
[1972], HOUGARDY [1975], LAFOND and MOLIEXE [1975], RHINES [1976], MATHY
[1977], EXNER [1978b], ONDRACEK [1978,1982], and EXNER and HOUGARDY [1983].
Quite often, however, data are published not so much to aid the solution of a
materials problem but rather to demonstrate the feasibility of a new technique or a
new instrument. Considering the high standard of methodology now achieved, it
seems timely to utilize quantitative analysis of microstructure more directly as a clue
for understanding the behaviour of materials during processing and in application.

References

AIGELTINGER, E., and H.E. EXNER, 1972, Z. Werkstofftechn. (J. Mater. Tech.) 3, 425.
ALDINGER, F., 1969, Metallography 2, 363.
ARZT, E., and H.F. FISCHMEISTER, 1979, Pract. Metallogr. 16, 547.
ASH, E.A., ed., 1980, Scanned Image Microscopy (Academic, London).
AXELROD, D., N.L. THOMPSON and T.P. BURGHARDT, 1983, J. Microsc. 129, 19.
AYDIN, I., and H.E. BÜHLER, 1981, in: Metallographie – Techniken der Gefügebeschreibung bei metal-
    lischen and keramischen Werkstoffen, Pract. Metallogr. Special Issue 12, eds. H.E. Bühler, K. Dieser
    and W.U. Kopp (Dr. Riederer Verlag, Stuttgart) p. 35.
AYDIN, I., H.E. BÜHLER, G. ELSSNER and I. STAPF, 1983, Pract. Metallogr. 20, 105.
AZZAM, R.M.A., and N.M. BASHARA, 1977, Ellipsometry and Polarized Light (North-Holland, Amster-
    dam).
BANSAL, R.P., and A.J. ARDELL, 1972, Metallography 5, 97.
BARTZ, G., 1973, Pract. Metallogr. 10, 311.
BAUER, B., and H.E. EXNER, 1981, Stereolog. Jugosl. 3, Suppl. 1, 255.
BAUER, B., and A. HALLER, 1981, Pract. Metallogr. 18, 327.
BAUER, B., and J. PAUL, 1983, Pract. Metallogr. 20, 213.
BAUER, B., M. FRIPAN and V. SMOLEJ, 1982, in: Fracture and the Role of Interfaces, vol. 2, Fatigue, eds.
    K.L. Maurer and F.E. Matzer (Engineering Materials Advisory Services, Warley) p. 591.
BEATON, C., and B. FILSHIE, 1983, Pract. Metallogr. 20, 31.
BECKERT, M., and H. KLEMM, 1976, Metallographisches Ätzen (Deutscher Verlag für Grundstoffindustrie,
    Leipzig).
BEDDOW, J.K., M.D. NASTA and G.C. PHILIP, 1980, in: Testing and Characterization of Fine Particles,
    eds. J.K. Beddow and T. Meloy (Heyden, London) p. 44.
BENESOVSKY, F., and A. IHRENBERGER, 1965, Pract. Metallogr. 2, 31.
BERAHA, E., 1970, Pract. Metallogr. 7, 131 and 242.
BERAHA, E., and B. SPIGHLER, 1977, Color Metallography (ASM, Metals Park, OH).
BERG, U., 1980, in: Handbuch Festkörperanalyse mit Elektronen, Ionen und Röntgenstrahlen, eds. O.
    Brümmer, J. Heydenreich, K.H. Krebs and H.G. Schneider (Vieweg, Braunschweig) p. 315.
BERKEY, E., 1973, in: Microstructural Analysis, Tools and Techniques, eds. J.L. McCall and W.M.
    Mueller (Plenum, New York) p. 287.
BERNST, R., 1965, Pract. Metallogr. 2, 162.
BERTIN, E.P., 1970, Principles and Practise of X-Ray Spectrometric Analysis (Heyden, London, and
    Plenum, New York).

BETGE, H., G. GERTH and D. MATERN, 1982, in: Electron Microscopy 1982, vol. 1 (Deutsche Gesellschaft für Elektronenmikroskopie, Frankfurt) p. 69.

BEYER, H., 1974, Theorie und Praxis der Interferenzmikroskopie (Akademische Verlagsgesellschaft Geest und Portig, Leipzig).

BIGGS, W.D., 1970, in: Physical Metallurgy, 2nd Ed., ed. R.W. Cahn (North-Holland, Amsterdam) p. 655.

BIRNER, E., and R. LÖHBERG, 1980, Pract. Metallogr. **17**, 14.

BLASCHKE, R., 1979, Beiträge elektronenmikroskopische Direktabbildung von Oberflächen, vol. 12/1 (Verlag R.A. Remy, Münster) p. 359.

BLASCHKE, R., and H. WALTINGER, 1971, Beiträge elektronenmikroskopische Direktabbildung von Oberflächen, vol. 4/2 (Verlag R.A. Remy, Münster) p. 425.

BÖRSCH, H., C. RADELOFF and G. SAUERBREY, 1961, Z. Physik 464.

BOWMAN, M.J., and A.D. BOOTH, 1971, Metallography **4**, 103.

BOYDE, A., 1973, J. Microsc. **98**, 452.

BRINEN, J.S., 1974, J. Electron Spectrosc. **5**, 377.

BROWN, R., and G.C. SMITH, 1982, Metallography **15**, 269.

BRÜCKNER, J., 1980, in: Handbuch Festkörperanalyse mit Elektronen, Ionen und Röntgenstrahlen, eds. O. Brümmer, J. Heydenreich, K.H. Krebs and H.G. Schneider (Vieweg, Braunschweig) p. 165.

BRÜMMER, O., and J. NIEBER, 1975, Microchim. Acta, Suppl. **6**, 345.

BRÜMMER, O., J. HEYDENREICH, K.H. KREBS and H.G. SCHNEIDER, eds., 1980, Handbuch Festkörperanalyse mit Elektronen, Ionen und Röntgenstrahlen (Vieweg, Braunschweig).

BRUNDLE, C.R., and A.D. BAKER, 1977, Electron Spectroscopy: Theory, Techniques and Application (Academic, London).

BÜCKLE, H., 1964, Berg- und Hüttenmänn. Monatsh. **109**, 72.

BÜCKLE, H., 1965, Mikrohärteprüfung und ihre Anwendung (Verlag Berlin Union, Stuttgart).

BÜHLER, H.E., 1981, in: Microstructural Science, vol. 9, eds. G. Petzow, R. Paris, E.D. Albrecht and J.L. McCall (Elsevier North-Holland, New York) p. 19.

BÜHLER, H.E., and H.P. HOUGARDY, 1979, Atlas der Interferenzschichten-Metallographie (Deutsche Gesellschaft für Metallkunde, Oberursel).

BÜHLER, H.E., and H.P. HOUGARDY, 1980, Atlas of Interference-Layer Metallography (Deutsche Gesellschaft für Metallkunde, Oberursel, and The Metals Society, London).

BÜHLER, H.E., and D. KOSSEL, 1981, Pract. Metallogr. **18**, 385.

CABONARA, R.S., 1973, in: Microstructural Analysis, Tools and Techniques, eds. J.L. McCall and W.M. Mueller (Plenum, New York) p. 315.

CAHN, R.W., J.E. EVETTS, J. PATTERSON, R.E. SOMEKH and C.K. JACKSON, 1980, J. Mater. Sci. **15**, 702.

CARLSON, T.A., 1975, Photoelectron and Auger Spectroscopy (Plenum, New York).

CHANG, S.L., H.J. QUEISSER, H. BAUMGART, W. HAGEN and W. HARTMANN, 1982, Phil. Mag. **46**, 1009.

COLBY, J.W., 1977, in: Practical Scanning Electron Microscopy, eds. J.I. Goldstein and H. Yakowitz (Plenum Press, New York, London) ch. 14, p. 529.

CONN, G.K.T., and F.J. BRADSHAW, 1952, Polarized Light in Metallography (Butterworths, London).

CONOR, P.C., 1972, Metallography **5**, 301.

COSSLETT, V.E., and P. DUNCUMB, 1956, Nature **177**, 1172.

COSSLETT, V.E., and W.C. NIXON, 1960, X-Ray Microscopy (Cambridge University Press).

CROUSE, R.S., R.J. GRAY and B.C. LESLIE, 1977, in: Interpretive Techniques in Microstructural Analysis, eds. J.L. McCall and P.M. French (Plenum, New York) p. 43.

CRUZ-ORIVE, L.M., 1978, J. Microsc. **112**, 153.

CZANDERNA, A.W., ed., 1975, Methods of Surface Analysis (Elsevier, Amsterdam).

DANNÖHL, H.D., R. GRABER and L. WEGMANN, 1971, Microstructures **2**, 15.

DAVIDSON, D.L., 1974, in: SEM 1974, Proc. 7th Annual SEM Symp. (IIT Research Institute, Chicago) p. 927.

DE HOFF, R.T., 1980, Mikroskopie **37**, 32.

DE HOFF, R.T., 1982, paper presented at Stereology 82, Symp. Int. Soc. for Stereology, Sheffield.

DE HOFF, R.T., and C.V. ISAWARAN, 1982, Metallurg. Trans. **13A**, 1389.

DE HOFF, R.T., and F.N. RHINES, 1968, Quantitative Microscopy (McGraw-Hill, New York).

DE HOFF, R.T., E. AIGELTINGER and K.R. CRAIG, 1972, J. Microsc. **95**, 69.

DENGEL, D., 1973, Z. Werkstofftechn. (J. Mater. Techn.) **4**, 292.

DINGLEY, D.J., C. HARPER and S. LONG, 1982, in: Electron Microscopy and Analysis 1981, Conf. Series **61**, ed. M.J. Goringe (The Institute of Physics, Bristol and London) p. 63.

DOERR, R.M., and P.D. OWNBY, 1975, Pract. Metallogr. **12**, 78.

DOHERTY, R.D., and R.W. CAHN, 1972, J. Less-Common Met. **28**, 279.

DUDEK, H.J., R. BORATH and H.J. IGELMUND, 1982, Beiträge elektronenmikroskopische Direktabbildung von Oberflächen, vol. 15 (Verlag R.A. Remy, Münster) p. 49 and 61.

DÜSTERHÖFT, H., 1980, in: Handbuch Festkörperanalyse mit Elektronen, Ionen und Röntgenstrahlen, eds. O. Brümmer, J. Heydenreich, K.H. Krebs and H.G. Schneider (Vieweg, Braunschweig) p. 315.

DUKE, P.J., 1981, Proc. Roy. Microsc. Soc. **16**, 186.

DYSON, N.A., 1973, X-Rays in Atomic and Nuclear Physics (Longman Group, London).

EDELMANN, C., 1980, in: Handbuch Festkörperanalyse mit Elektronen, Ionen und Röntgenstrahlen, eds. O. Brümmer, J. Heydenreich, K.H. Krebs and H.G. Schneider (Vieweg, Braunschweig) p. 263.

EKELUND, S., and S. HERTZMANN, 1981, in: Computers in Materials Technology, ed. T. Ericson (Pergamon Press, Oxford) p. 153.

ELSBROCK, J.B., and L.J. BALK, 1982, Beiträge elektronenmikroskopische Direktabbildung von Oberflächen, vol. 15 (Verlag R.A. Remy, Münster) p. 17.

ENGEL, H.J., 1958, Arch. Eisenhüttenw. **29**, 73.

ESSMANN, U., M. RAPP and M. WILKENS, 1968, Acta Metall. **16**, 1275.

EXNER, H.E., 1969a, Trans. Met. Soc. AIME **245**, 677.

EXNER, H.E., 1969b, Pract. Metallogr. **6**, 639.

EXNER, H.E., 1972a, in: Stereology and Quantitative Metallography, ASTM Spec. Tech. Publ. **504** (Amer. Soc. Testing Materials, Philadelphia).

EXNER, H.E., 1972b, Int. Metallurg. Rev. **17**, 111.

EXNER, H.E., 1973, Z. Metallk. **64**, 273.

EXNER, H.E., 1978a, Pract. Metallogr. **15**, 15.

EXNER, H.E., 1978b, in: Quantitative Metallography (Associazione Italiana di Metallurgia, Milano) p. 313.

EXNER, H.E., and H.F. FISCHMEISTER, 1966, Arch. Eisenhüttenw. **37**, 417.

EXNER, H.E., and J. GURLAND, 1970, Powder Metallurg. **13**, 13.

EXNER, H.E., and H.P. HOUGARDY, 1983, Quantitative Analysis of Microstructures (Deutsche Gesellschaft für Metallkunde, Oberursel) in press.

EXNER, H.E., and H.L. LUKAS, 1971, Metallography **4**, 325.

EXNER, H.E., and D. POHL, 1978, Powder Metallurg. Int. **10**. 193.

EXNER, H.E., AND J. ROTH, 1980, Pract. Metallogr. **17**, 365.

EXNER, H.E., H. BACK and J. ROTH, 1980, Pract. Metallogr. **17**, 344.

FEDER, R., E. SPILLER, J. TOPALIAN, A.N. BRÖRS, W. GUDAT, B.J. PANESSA, Z.A. ZADUNAISKY and J. SEDAT, 1977, Science **197**, 259.

FERRANTE, J., D.H. BUCKLEY, S.V. PEPPER and W.A. BRAINARD, 1973, in: Microstructural Analysis, Tools and Techniques, eds. J.L. McCall and W.M. Mueller (Plenum, New York, London) p. 241.

FISCHMEISTER, H., 1965, Pract. Metallogr. **2**, 257.

FISCHMEISTER, H., 1972, J. Microsc. **95**, 25.

FISCHMEISTER, H.F., 1974, Z. Metallk. **65**, 558.

FISCHMEISTER, H., 1981, in: Computers in Materials Technology, ed. T. Ericson (Pergamon Press. Oxford) p. 109.

FISCHMEISTER, H.F., and E. ARZT, 1981, in: Gefüge der Metalle (Deutsche Gesellschaft für Metallkunde, Oberursel) p. 177.

FISCHMEISTER, H., and H.E. EXNER, 1966, Arch. Eisenhüttenw. **37**, 499.

FÖRSTERLING, G., 1980, in: Handbuch Festkörperanalyse mit Elektronen, Ionen und Röntgenstrahlen, eds. O. Brümmer, J. Heydenreich, K.H. Krebs and H.G. Schneider (Vieweg, Braunschweig) p. 81.

FREMUNT, P., J. SVEJCAR and J. VARHANICEK, 1980, Pract. Metallogr. **17**, 497.

FREUND, H., ed., 1960, Handbuch der Mikroskopie in der Technik (Umschau Verlag, Frankfurt) vol. 1, Die optischen Grundlagen, die Instrumente und Nebenapparate für die Mikroskopie in der Technik, part 2, Allgemeines Instrumentarium der Auflichtmikroskopie.

FREUND, H., ed., 1969, Handbuch der Mikroskopie in der Technik (Umschau Verlag, Frankfurt) vol. 3, Mikroskopie der metallischen Werkstoffe, part 2, Qualitative und quantitative Untersuchungsverfahren in der Metallkunde.

FULRATH, R.M., 1972, in: SEM 1972, Proc. 5th Annual SEM Symp. (IIT Research Institute, Chicago) p. 17.

GABLER, F., and R. MITSCHE, 1952, Arch. Eisenhüttenw. **23**, 145.

GAHM, J., 1969, Zeiss-Mitteilungen **5**, 40.

GAHM, J., 1971, Zeiss-Mitteilungen **5**, 249.

GAHM, J., 1975, in: Quantitative Gefügeanalyse in Medizin, Biologie und Materialentwicklung, Pract. Metallogr., Special Issue **5**, ed. H.E. Exner (Dr. Riederer Verlag, Stuttgart) p. 29.

GAHM, H., and F. JEGLITSCH, 1981, in: Microstructural Science, vol. 9, eds. G. Petzow, R. Paris, E.D. Albrecht and J.L. McCall (Elsevier North-Holland, New York) p. 65.

GAHM, H., F. JEGLITSCH and H. HÖRL, 1982, Pract. Metallogr. **19**, 369.

GALOPIN, R., and N.F.M. HENRY, 1972, Microscopic Study of Opaque Minerals (Heffer, Cambridge,).

GOLDSTEIN, J.I., and H. YAKOWITZ, eds., 1977, Practical Scanning Electron Microscopy (Plenum, New York).

GOLDSTEIN, J.I., H. YAKOWITZ and D.E. NEWBURY, 1977, in: Practical Scanning Electron Microscopy, eds. J.I. Goldstein and H. Yakowitz (Plenum, New York) p.1.

GONZALES, R.C., and P. WINTZ, 1977, Digital Image Processing (Addison–Wesley, Reading, MA).

GOODHEW, P.J., 1973, Specimen Preparation in Materials Science (North-Holland, Amsterdam, and American Elsevier, New York).

GORETZKI, H., S. STURLESE and V. FRANZONI, 1982, Beiträge elektronenmikroskopische Direktabbildung von Oberflächen, vol. 15 (Verlag R.A. Remy, Münster) p. 73.

GRÄF, I., 1981, in: Microstructural Science, vol. 9, eds. G. Petzow, R. Paris, E.D. Albrecht and J.L. McCall (Elsevier North-Holland, New York) p. 45.

GRÜTZNER, G., and H.J. SCHÜLLER, 1969, Pract. Metallogr. **6**, 346.

GURLAND, J., 1958, Trans. AIME **212**, 452.

HARTSHORNE, N.H., and A. STUART, 1952, Crystals and the Polarising Microscope (Edward Arnold, London).

HEARLE, J.W.S., J.T. SPARROW and P.M. CROSS, 1972, The Use of Scanning Electron Microscopy (Pergamon Press, Oxford).

HEILAND, W., 1982, Beiträge elektronenmikroskopische Direktabbildung von Oberflächen, vol. 15 (Verlag R.A. Remy, Münster) p. 33.

HERBSLEB, G., and P. SCHWAAB, 1978, Pract. Metallogr. **15**, 213.

HEYWOOD, V.H., ed., 1971, Scanning Electron Microscopy – Systematic and Evolutionary Applications (Academic, London).

HILLIARD, J.E., 1976, in: Fourth International Congress for Stereology, NBL Spec. Techn. Publ. **413**, eds. E.E. Underwood, R. De Wit and G.A. Moore (National Bureau of Standards, Gaithersburg) p. 59.

HILLJE, G., and G. REDMANN, 1976, Pract. Metallogr. **12**, 629.

HILLMER, T., 1979a, Pract. Metallogr. **16**, 476.

HILLMER, T., 1979b, Pract. Metallogr. **16**, 521.

HILLMER, T., 1982, Pract. Metallogr. **19**, 509.

HÖCHE, H.R., and O. BRÜMMER, 1980, in: Handbuch Festkörperanalyse mit Elektronen, Ionen und Röntgenstrahlen, eds. O. Brümmer, J. Heydenreich, K.H. Krebs and H.G. Schneider (Vieweg, Braunschweig) p. 57.

HOEKSTRA, S., and W.H.J. BRUIS, 1979, Pract. Metallogr. **16**, 583.

HOFMANN, S., 1979, Tantala **26**, 665.

HOFMANN, S., 1980a, in: Analytiker-Taschenbuch, eds. H. Kienitz, R. Bock, W. Fresenius, W. Huber and G. Tölg (Springer) p. 287.

HOFMANN, S., 1980b, Surf. Interf. Anal. **2**, 148.

HOFMANN, S., 1981, Analusis **9**, 181.

HOHMUTH, K., and W. RUDOLPH, 1980, in: Handbuch Festkörperanalyse mit Elektronen, Ionen und Röntgenstrahlen, eds. O. Brümmer, J. Heydenreich, K.H. Krebs and H.G. Schneider (Vieweg, Braunschweig) p. 149.

HORNBOGEN, E., 1981, Z. Metallk. **72**, 739.

HOUGARDY, H.P., 1975, Research Film **8**, 444.

HOUGARDY, H.P., 1976, in: 4th Int. Congr. for Stereology, NBL Spec. Techn. Publ. **431**, eds. E.E. Underwood, R. De Wit and G.A. Moore (National Bureau of Standards, Gaithersburg) p. 141.

HOUGARDY, H.P., 1981, in: Metallographie – Techniken der Gefügebeschreibung bei metallischen und keramischen Werkstoffen, Pract. Metallogr. Special Issue **12**, eds. H.E. Bühler, K. Dieser and W.U. Kopp (Dr. Riederer Verlag, Stuttgart) p. 9.

HREN, J.H., and S. RANGANATHAN, 1968, Field Ion Microscopy (Plenum, New York).

HUN-DE, Z., and W. JING-YUN, 1980, Pract. Metallogr. **17**, 608.

IBACH, H., ed., 1977, Electron Spectroscopy for Surface Analysis (Springer, Berlin).

IRANI, R.S., and R.W. CAHN, 1971, Metallography **4**, 91.

JEGLITSCH, F., 1968, in: Handbuch der Mikroskopie in der Technik, vol. 3, ed. H. Freund (Umschau Verlag, Frankfurt) part 1, p. 187 and 247.

JEGLITSCH, F., and R. MITSCHE, 1967, Radex Rundschau, 587.

JOHANSSON, S.A.E., 1982, Phys. Blätter **38**, 359.

KANE, P.F., and G.B. LARABEE, eds., 1974, Characterization of Solid Surfaces (Plenum, New York).

KELLER, H.E., 1977, in: Interpretive Techniques for Microstructural Analysis, eds. J.L. McCall and P.M. French (Plenum, New York) p. 105.

KIESSLER, G., and G. ELSSNER, 1980, in: Metallographie, Anschliff- und Dünnschlifftechnik an Metallen, Keramiken und Kunststoffen, Pract. Metallogr. Special Issue **11**, eds. H.E. Bühler and W.U. Kopp (Dr. Riederer Verlag, Stuttgart) p. 21.

KIESSLER, G., L. GESSNER and G. ELSSNER, 1978, in: Metallographie und Keramographie, Pract. Metallogr., Special Issue **9**, eds. W.U. Kopp and H.E. Bühler (Dr. Riederer Verlag, Stuttgart) p. 113.

KIESSLER, G., H. RAPP and G. ELSSNER, 1982, in: Metallographie, Pract. Metallogr., Special Issue **13**, eds. H.E. Bühler, K. Dieser and W.U. Kopp (Dr. Riederer Verlag, Stuttgart) p. 9.

KING, R.P., 1982, Powder Technol. **32**, 87.

KINGLAKE, R., ed., 1965, Applied Optics and Optical Engineering (Academic, New York).

KLAUA, H., and G. ÖRTEL, 1980, in: Handbuch Festkörperanalyse mit Elektronen, Ionen und Röntgenstrahlen, eds. O. Brümmer, J. Heydenreich, K.H. Krebs and H.G. Schneider (Vieweg, Braunschweig) p. 295.

KLOCKENKÄMPER, R., A. BEYER and M. MONES, 1979, Pract. Metallogr. **16**, 53.

KLÖBER, J., and H.A. SCHNEIDER, 1980, in: Handbuch Festkörperanalyse mit Elektronen, Ionen und Röntgenstrahlen, eds. O. Brümmer, J. Heydenreich, K.H. Krebs and H.G. Schneider (Vieweg, Braunschweig) p. 185.

KNOSP, H., 1969, Z. Metallk. **60**, 526.

KOCH, R., 1979, Pract. Metallogr. **16**, 11.

KOLOMYJCOV, J.V., 1976, Interferometry (Masinostroenie, Leningrad). In Russian.

KÜHLMEYER, M., 1978, Einfluss der statistischen Korngrössenverteilung auf die Streckgrenze von Stahl (Verlag Stahleisen, Düsseldorf).

KULMBURG, A., F. KORNTHEUER and P. SCHIMMEL, 1974, Pract. Metallogr. **11**, 183.

LAFOND, C., and F. MOLIEXE, 1975, in: Quantitative Gefügeanalyse in Medizin, Biologie und Materialentwicklung, Pract. Metallogr., Special Issue **5**, ed. H.E. Exner (Dr. Riederer Verlag, Stuttgart) p. 200.

LEHTINEN, B., and A. MELANDER, 1980, Metallography **13**, 283.

LEMONS, R.A., and C.F. QUATE, 1974, Appl. Phys. Lett. **24**, 163.

LIHL, F., and H. MEYER, 1960, Z. Metallk. **51**, 186.

LINDÉN, G., 1972, Pract. Metallogr. **9**, 3.

LOVELAND, R.P., 1970, Photomicrography – A Comprehensive Treatise (Wiley, New York).

LOZINSKIJ, M.G., 1961, High-Temperature Microscopy (Pergamon Press, Oxford).

MADESKI, A., 1980, Pract. Metallogr. **17**, 598.

MALIES, H.M., 1959, Applied Microscopy and Photo-Micrography (Fountain Press, London).

MATHY, H., 1977, Microsc. Acta, Suppl. **3**, 3.

MCCALL, J., 1973, in: Microstructural Analysis – Tools and Techniques, eds. J.L. McCall and W.M. Mueller (Plenum, New York) p. 93.

MCINTYRE, N.S., ed., 1978, Quantitative Surface Analysis of Materials, ASTM Spec. Tech. Publ. **634** (Amer. Soc. Testing Mater., Philadelphia).

MEDALIA, A.I., 1980, in: Testing and Characterization of Fine Particles, eds. J.K. Beddow and T. Meloy (Heyden, London) p. 66.

MELOY, T.P., 1980, in: Testing and Characterization of Fine Particles, eds. J.K. Beddow and T. Meloy (Heyden, London) p. 1.

MIDDLETON, C.J., and D.V. EDMONDS, 1977, Metallography **10**, 55.

MITSCHE, R., and H. SCHEIDL, 1964, Berg- und Hüttenmänn. Monatsh. **109**, 82.

MITSCHE, R., F. JEGLITSCH and F. GABLER, 1964, Berg- und Hüttenmänn. Monatsh. **109**, 110.

MITSCHE, R., F. GABLER and F. JEGLITSCH, 1969, in: Handbuch der Mikroskopie in der Technik, vol. 3, ed. H. Freund (Umschau Verlag, Frankfurt) part 2, p. 269.

MODIN, H., and S. MODIN, 1973, Metallurgical Microscopy (Butterworths, London).

MÖLLER, R. H. VIEFHAUS, E. EHRHARD and H.J. GRABKE, 1982, Beiträge elektronenmikroskopische Direktabbildungen von Oberflächen, vol. 15 (Verlag R.A. Remy, Münster), p. 79.

MORNHEIM, A.F., 1977, in: Interpretive Techniques for Microstructural Analysis, eds. J.L. McCall and P.M. French (Plenum, New York) p. 117.

MOTT, B.W., 1952, Polarized Light in Metallography (Butterworths, London).

MOTT, B.W., 1956, Micro-Indentation Hardness Testing (Butterworths, London).

MÜLLER, E.W., 1936, Z. Phys. **102**, 734.

MUELLER, E.W., and T.T. TSONG, 1969, Field Ion Microscopy (American Elsevier, New York).

MÜRRLE, U., H.E. EXNER and D. STÖCKEL, 1980, Metall **34**, 617.

MUGGLI, R.Z., and W.C. MC CRONE, 1977, in: Interpretative Techniques for Microstructural Analysis, eds. J.L. McCall and P.M. French (Plenum, New York) p. 127.

MULLINS, W.W., 1961, Phil. Mag. **6**, 1313.

MYKURA, H., 1955, Acta Metall. **3**, 436.

NANEV, C., 1981, Jenaer Rundschau **5**, 219.

NAWRATH, R., and J. SERRA, 1979, Microsc. Acta **82**, 101.

NEWBURY, D.E., 1977, in: Practical Scanning Electron Microscopy, eds. J.I. Goldstein and H. Yakowitz (Plenum, New York) ch. 4, p. 95.

NEWBURY, D.E., and H. YAKOWITZ, 1977a, in: Practical Scanning Electron Microscopy, eds. J.I. Goldstein and H. Yakowitz (Plenum, New York) ch. 6, p. 211.

NEWBURY, D.E., and H. YAKOWITZ, 1977b, in: Practical Scanning Electron Microscopy, eds. J.I. Goldstein and H. Yakowitz (Plenum, New York) ch. 5, p. 149.

NICHOLSON, W.L., 1978, J. Microsc. **113**, 223.

OATLEY, C.W., 1972, The Scanning Electron Microscope (Cambridge University Press).

ÖCHSNER, H., 1975, Appl. Phys. **8**, 185.

ÖTTEL, W.O., 1959, Grundlagen der Metallmikroskopie (Akademische Verlagsgesellschaft Geest und Portig, Leipzig).

OKAZAKI, K., and H. CONRAD, 1972, Trans. Japan. Inst. Metals **13**, 198.

ONDRACEK, G., 1978, in: Quantitative Analysis of Microstructures in Materials Science, Biology and Medicine, Pract. Metallogr. Special Issue **8**, ed. J.L. Chermant (Dr. Riederer Verlag, Stuttgart) p. 103.

ONDRACEK, G., 1982, Acta Stereol. **1**, 5.

ONDRACEK, G., and K. SPIELER, 1973, Pract. Metallogr. **10**, 324.

PAUL, J., and U. MÜRRLE, 1981, Pract. Metallogr. **18**, 418.

PAUL, J., H.E. EXNER and D. MÜLLER-SCHWELLING, 1982, Z. Metallk. **73**, 50.

PAYNE, B.O., 1957, Microscope Design and Construction, 2nd Ed. (Cooke, Troughton and Simms, York, UK).

PAYNE, S.M., 1982, in: Electron Microscopy and Analysis 1981, Conf. Series **61**, ed. M.J. Goringe (The Institute of Physics, Bristol, London) p. 287.

PECH, P., 1980, in: Handbuch Festkörperanalyse mit Elektronen, Ionen und Röntgenstrahlen, eds. O. Brümmer, J. Heydenreich, K.H. Krebs and H.G. Schneider (Vieweg, Braunschweig) p. 345.

PELLOUX, R.M., 1970, in: Applications of Modern Metallography Techniques, ASTM Spec. Techn. Publ. **480** (Amer. Soc. Testing Mater., Philadelphia) p. 127.

PEPPERHOFF, W., and H.H. ETTWIG, 1970, Interferenzschichten-Mikroskopie (Dr. Steinkopf Verlag, Darmstadt).

PETZOW, G., 1976, Metallographisches Ätzen, Materialkundlich-Technische Reihe, vol. 1 (Gebr. Bornträger, Berlin).

PETZOW, G., 1978, Metallographic Etching (ASM, Metals Park, OH).

PETZOW, G., and H.E. EXNER, 1968, in: Handbuch der Mikroskopie in der Technik, vol. 3, ed. H. Freund (Umschau Verlag, Frankfurt) part 1, p. 37.

PETZOW, G., and H.E. EXNER, 1975, in: Microstructural Science, eds. P.M. French, R.J. Gray and J.L. McCall (American Elsevier, New York) vol. 3, p. 291.

PETZOW, G., and E. HORNBOGEN, 1970, Z. Metallk. **61**, 81.

PETZOW, G., and H. KNOSP, 1973, Metallography **6**, 249.

PFEFFERKORN, G., ed., 1982, Beiträge elektronenmikroskopische Direktabbildung von Oberflächen (Verlag R.A. Remy, Münster).

PFEFFERKORN, G., and R. BLASCHKE, 1974, in: SEM 1974, Proc. 4th Annual SEM Symp. (IIT Research Institute, Chicago) p. 143.

PFEFFERKORN, G., and R. BLASCHKE, 1982, Beiträge elektronenmikroskopische Direktabbildung von Oberflächen, vol. 15 (Verlag R.A. Remy, Münster). p. 1.

PHILLIPS, V.A., 1971, Modern Metallographic Techniques and their Applications (Wiley–Interscience, New York).

PIVIN, J.C., 1983, J. Mater. Sci. **18**, 1267.

POHL, M., and W.G. BURCHARD, 1980, in: Metallographie, Anschliff- und Dünnschlifftechnik, Pract. Metallogr., Special Issue **11**, eds. H.E. Bühler and W.U. Kopp (Dr. Riederer Verlag, Stuttgart) p. 42.

POKORNY, A., 1980, Pract. Metallogr. **17**, 23.

PORTER, D.A., and K.E. EASTERLING, 1981, Phase Transformations in Metals and Alloys (Van Nostrand–Reinhold, Wokingham, New York).

PUSCH, R., 1979, Pract. Metallogr. **16**, 26 and 79.

QUATE, C.F., 1979, Scientific American, Spektrum der Wissenschaft **24**.

RAZA, S.M., 1982, Scripta Metall. **16**, 1325.

REED, S.J.B., 1975, Electron Microprobe Analysis (Cambridge University Press).

REIMER, L., and G. PFEFFERKORN, 1977, Rasterelektronenmikroskopie (Springer, Berlin).

REINACHER, G., 1965, Pract. Metallogr. **2**, 45.

RHINES, F.N., 1976, in: 4th Int. Congr. for Stereology, NBL Spec. Techn. Publ. **431**, eds. E.E. Underwood, R. De Wit and G.A. Moore (National Bureau of Standards, Gaithersburg) p. 233.

RHINES, F.N., and B.R. PATTERSON, 1982, Metallurg. Trans. **13A**, 985.

RHINES, F.N., K.R. CRAIG and R.T. DE HOFF, 1974, Metallurg, Trans. **5**, 413.

RICHARDS, B.P., and A.D. TRIGG, 1982, in: Electron Microscopy and Analysis 1981, Conf. Series **61**, ed. M.J. Goringe (The Institute of Physics, Bristol, London) p. 227.

RIEGGER, H., J.A. PASK and H.E. EXNER, 1980, in: Sintering Processes, ed. G.C. Kuczynski (Plenum, New York) p. 219.

RÖSCHENBLECK, B., and K. WOLTER, 1979, in: Fortschritte in der Metallographie, Pract. Metallogr., Special Issue **10**, eds. F. Jeglitsch and G. Petzow (Dr. Riederer Verlag, Stuttgart) p. 95.

ROOSZ, A., Z. GACZI and M.K. BAAN, 1980, Metallography **13**, 299.

ROSENBERGER, H.E., 1977, in: Interpretative Techniques for Microstructural Analysis, eds. J.L.McCall and P.M. French (Plenum, New York) p. 79.

ROSENCWAIG, A., 1982, Science **218**, 223.

ROST, F.W.D., 1981, Proc. Roy. Microsc. Soc. **16**, 44.

SALTYKOV, S.A., 1974, Stereometrische Metallographie (Deutscher Verlag für Grunstoffindustrie, Leipzig).

SAMUELS, L.E., 1971, Metallographic Polishing by Mechanical Methods (Pitman, Melbourne, London).

SCHAARWÄCHTER, W., 1968, in: Handbuch der Mikroskopie in der Technik, vol. 3, ed. H. Freund (Umschau Verlag, Frankfurt) part 1, p. 291.

SCHATT, W., 1981, Einführung in die Werkstoffwissenschaft (Deutscher Verlag für Grundstoffindustrie, Leipzig).

SCHUMANN, H., 1980, Metallographie (Deutscher Verlag für Grunstoffindustrie, Leipzig).

SCHWARZ, H., 1980, Mikroskopie **37**, Suppl., p. 64.

SCHWARZ, H., and H.E. EXNER, 1983, J. Microsc. **129**, 155.

SCHWARZER, R.A., 1981, Microsc. Acta **84**, 51.

SEILER, H., 1968, Abbildung von Oberflächen mit Elektronen, Ionen und Röntgenstrahlen, Hochschultaschenbücher **428/428a** (Bibliographisches Institut, Mannheim).

SEMLITSCH, M., and B. BERGMANN, 1969, in: Handbuch der Mikroskopie in der Technik, vol. 3, ed. H. Freund (Umschau Verlag, Frankfurt) part 2, p. 347.

SERRA, J., 1982, Image Analysis and Mathematical Morphology (Academic, London).

SHEMENSKI, R.M., 1977, in: Metallography as a Quality Control Tool, eds. J.L. McCall and P.M. French (Plenum, New York) p. 109.

SHIGOLEV, P.V., 1974, Electrolytic and Chemical Polishing of Metals (Freund, Tel Aviv).

SIEBER, B., 1982, in: Electron Microscopy and Analysis 1981, Conf. Series **61**, ed. M.J. Goringe (The Institute of Physics, Bristol, London) p. 223.

SIMPSON, I.D., and N. STANDISH, 1977, Metallography **10**, 149 and 443.

SMITH, C.S., 1960, A History of Metallography (University of Chicago Press).

SPIESS, H.J., 1965, Freiberger Forschh. **B111**, 87.

TAKAJO, S., 1982, Teilchenwachstum durch Koaleszenz während des Flüssigphasensinterns von Fe–Cu und Cu–Ag, Ph. D. thesis (University of Stuttgart).

TANNER, B., 1977, X-Ray Diffraction Topography (Pergamon Press, Oxford).

TAYLOR, D.S., and G. POLLARD, 1982, Metallography **15**, 225.

TEGART, W.J. McG., 1956, Electrolytic and Chemical Polishing of Metals (Pergamon Press, London).

TENSI, H.M., 1968, in: Handbuch der Mikroskopie in der Technik, vol. 3, ed. H. Freund (Umschau Verlag, Frankfurt) part 2, p. 1.

THOMPSON, A.W., 1972, Metallography **5**, 366.

THORNTON, P.R., 1968, Scanning Electron Microscopy: Applications to Materials and Device Science (Chapman and Hall, London).

TÖRRÖNEN, K., 1980, Metallography **13**, 329.

TOLANSKI, S., 1960, Surface Microtopography (Longmans, Green and Co., London).

TOUSEK, J., 1981, Pract. Metallogr. **18**, 471.

TURLEY, D.M., and L.E. SAMUELS, 1981, Metallography **14**, 275.

UNDERWOOD, E.E., 1970, Quantitative Stereology (Addison–Wesley, Reading, MA).

UNDERWOOD, E.E., 1976, in: 4th Int. Conf. for Stereology, NBL Spec. Techn. Publ. **431**, eds. E.E. Underwood, R. De Wit and G.A. Moore (National Bureau of Standards, Gaithersburg) p. 91.

UNDERWOOD, E.E., 1980, in: Testing and Characterization of Fine Particles, eds. J.K. Bedow and T. Meloy (Heyden, London) p. 77.

VENABLES, J.A., and D.J. FATHERS, 1982, in: Electron Microscopy 1982, Vol. 1 (Deutsche Gesellschaft für Elektronenmikroskopie, Frankfurt) p. 18.

VISSCHER, W., 1973, Z. Werkstofftechn. (J. Mater. Techn.) **4**, 320.

VOLBERT, B., 1981, Beiträge elektronenmikroskopische Direktabbildung von Oberflächen, vol. 14 (Verlag R.A. Remy, Münster).

WAGNER, C., 1954, J. Electrochem. Soc. **101**, 225.

WAGNER, R., 1980, Phys. Blätter **36**, 65.

WAGNER, R., 1982, Field-Ion Microscopy, Springer Series Crystals, vol. 6 (Springer, Berlin).

WAGNER, R., and S.S. BRENNER, 1978, Acta Metall. **26**, 197.

WANG, S., and L.E. MURR, 1980, Metallography **13**, 203.

WATTS, J.T., 1982, Proc. Roy. Microsc. Soc. (London) **17**, 192.

WAVER, G., 1973, Z. Werkstofftechn. (J. Mater. Techn.) **4**, 298.

WECHSUNG, R., 1977, Vacuum-Techn. **26**, 227.

WECK, E., and E. LEISTNER, 1982, Metallographic Instruction for Colour Etching by Immersion (Deutscher Verlag für Schweisstechnik, Düsseldorf).

WEGMANN, L., 1972, J. Microsc. **96**, 1.

WEHNER, G.K., 1975, in: Methods of Surface Analysis, ed. A.W. Czanderna (Elsevier Scientific, Amsterdam) p. 5.

WEIBEL, E.R., 1979, Stereological Methods, vol. 1, Practical Methods for Biological Morphometry (Academic, London).

WEIBEL, E.R., 1980, Stereological Methods, vol. 2, Theoretical Foundations (Academic, London).

WELLNER, P., 1980, Pract. Metallogr. **17**, 525.

WELLS, O.C., 1974, Scanning Electron Microscopy (McGraw–Hill, New York).

WENDLER, B., and B. NEUBAUER, 1979, Pract. Metallogr. **16**, 3.

WERLEFORS, T., C. ESKILLSON and S. EKELUND, 1979, Scand. J. Metallurgy **8**, 221.

WICKRAMASINGHE, H.K., 1983, J. Microsc. **129**, 63.

WU, W.T., I. AYDIN and H.E. BÜHLER, 1982, Pract. Metallogr. **19**, 347.

YAKOWITZ, H., and J.I. GOLDSTEIN, 1977, in: Practical Scanning Electron Microscopy, eds. J.I. Goldstein and H. Yakowitz (Plenum, New York) p. 401.

YAMAMOTO, K., and A. TAIRA, 1983, J. Microsc. **129**, 49.

YANKOVITH, H., 1970, in: Application of Modern Metallographic Techniques, ASTM Spec. Techn. Publ. **480** (Amer. Soc. Testing Mater., Philadelphia) p. 49.

YUZAWICH, P.M., and C.W. HUGHES, 1978, Pract. Metallogr. **17**, 607.

ZOGG, H., S. WEBER and H. WARLIMONT, 1977, Pract. Metallogr. **14**, 553.

Further reading

Journals

The following journals are specifically devoted to aspects of metallographic sample preparation and microscopic investigation of materials:

Practical Metallography, bilingual English/German (Dr. Riederer Verlag, Stuttgart).

Metallography (Elsevier Science Publishing Co., New York).

Journal of Microscopy (Royal Microscopical Society, London).

Ultramicroscopy (North-Holland Publishing Co., Amsterdam).

Microscopica Acta (Springer-Verlag, Berlin).

Mikroskopie (Verlag Georg Fromme & Co., Vienna, Munich).

Acta Stereologica (John Wiley and Sons, London).

Most of the standard journals in the field of physical metallurgy and materials science report frequently on metallographic techniques, surface microscopy, surface analysis, and stereology, with emphasis on the application of these techniques.

Books

Ash, E.A., ed., Scanned Image Microscopy (Academic Press, London, 1980).

Beyer, H., Theorie und Praxis der Interferenzmikroskopie (Akademische Verlagsgesellschaft Geest und Portig, Leipzig, 1974).

Brümmer, O., J. Heydenreich, K.H. Krebs and H.G. Schneider, Handbuch der Festkörperanalyse mit Röntgenstrahlen (Vieweg, Braunschweig, 1980).

Bühler, H.E., and H.P. Hougardy, Atlas of Interference-Layer Metallography (Deutsche Gesellschaft für Metallkunde, Oberursel, and The Metals Society, London, 1980).

Czanderna, A.W., ed., Methods of Surface Analysis (Elsevier Scientific, Amsterdam, 1975).

Exner, H.E., and H.P. Hougardy, Quantitative Analysis of Microstructures (Deutsche Gesellschaft für Metallkunde, Oberursel, 1983).

Freund, H., ed., Handbuch der Mikroskopie in der Technik, 8 Volumes (Umschau Verlag, Frankfurt).

Galopin, R., and N.F.M. Henry, Microscopic Study of Opaque Materials (W. Heffer and Sons, Cambridge, 1972).

Goldstein, J.I., and H. Yakowitz, eds., Practical Scanning Electron Microscopy (Plenum, New York, 1977).

Goodhew, P.J., Specimen Preparation in Materials Science (North-Holland, Amsterdam, and American Elsevier, New York, 1973).

Hearle, J.W.S., J.T. Sparrow and P.M. Cross, The Use of Scanning Electron Microscopy (Pergamon Press, Oxford, 1972).

Loveland, R.P., Photomicrography – A Comprehensive Treatise (Wiley, New York, 1970).

Modin, H., and S. Modin, Metallurgical Microscopy (Butterworths, London, 1973).

Mueller, E.W. and T.T. Tsong, Field Ion Microscopy (American Elsevier, New York, 1969).

Mulvey, T., and R.K. Webster, Modern Physical Techniques in Materials Technology (Oxford University Press, 1974).

Pendry, J.B., Low-Energy Electron Diffraction (Academic, New York, 1974).

Pepperhoff, W., and H.H. Ettwig, Interferenzschichtenmikroskopie (Dr. Steinkopf Verlag, Darmstadt, 1970).

Petzow, G., Metallographic Etching (ASM, Metals Park, OH, 1978).

Phillips, V.A., Modern Metallographic Techniques and their Applications (Wiley, New York, 1971).

Reimer, L. and G. Pfefferkorn, Rasterelektronenmikroskopie (Springer, Berlin, 1977).

Saltykov, S.A., Stereometrische Metallographie (Deutscher Verlag für Grundstoffindustrie, Leipzig, 1974).

Samuels, L.E., Metallographic Polishing by Mechanical Methods (Pitman, Melbourne, London, 1971).

Schatt, W., Einführung in die Werkstoffwissenschaft (Deutscher Verlag für Grundstoffindustrie, Leipzig, 1981).

Schumann, H., Metallographie (Deutscher Verlag für Grundstoffindustrie, Leipzig, 1980).

Thornton, P.R., Scanning Electron Microscopy, Applications to Materials and Device Science (Chapman and Hall, London, 1968).

Underwood, E.E., Quantitative Stereology (Addison–Wesley, Reading, MA, 1970).

Weibel, E.R., Stereological Methods, vol. 2, Theoretical Foundations (Academic, London, 1980).

Wells, O.C., Scanning Electron Microscopy (Mc Graw–Hill, New York, 1974).

CHAPTER 10B

MICROSTRUCTURE

H. GLEITER

Fachbereich Werkstoffphysik und Werkstofftechnologie
Universität des Saarlandes
6600 Saarbrücken, FRG

R.W. Cahn and P. Haasen, eds.
Physical Metallurgy; third, revised and enlarged edition
© *Elsevier Science Publishers BV, 1983*

1. Definition and outline

The *microstructure* of crystalline materials is defined by the type, structure, number, shape and topological arrangement of phases and/or lattice defects which are in most cases not part of the thermodynamic equilibrium structure.

In the first part of this chapter, the different types of lattice defects involved in the formation of microstructure (*elements of microstructure*) will be discussed. As far as the arrangement, shape and crystal structure of phases are concerned, we refer to chs. 5, 9, 14–16, and 28. The second part of this chapter will be devoted to the present understanding of the *development* of microstructures.

2. Elements of microstructure

2.1. Point defects, dislocations and stacking faults

Point defects, point-defect clusters, dislocations and stacking faults are important elements of the microstructure of most materials. The atomistic structure and properties of these defects are discussed in chs. 17 and 18.

2.2. High-angle grain boundaries

2.2.1. Equilibrium structure
Control of the grain size is one of the most widely used means of influencing the properties of materials. Consequently, intense efforts have been directed in recent years toward a better understanding of grain boundaries. The progress achieved is documented in several comprehensive reviews (BALLUFFI [1980], AUST [1981] and GLEITER [1982]). Two groups of grain-boundary models may be distinguished: *dislocation* or *disclination models* and *atomic-matching models*. This classification is not rigorous. In fact, several models of hybrid character have been proposed.

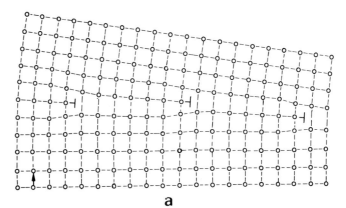

a

2.2.1.1. Dislocation and disclination models. The idea of modelling a high-angle grain boundary in terms of an array of closely spaced dislocations (fig. 1b, READ and SHOCKLEY [1950]) is an extension of the well established structure of small-angle

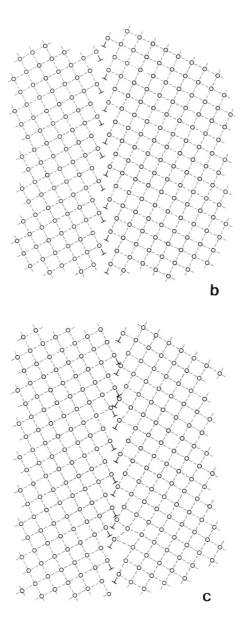

Fig. 1. Dislocation models of symmetrical tilt boundaries in a simple cubic structure: (a) low-angle boundary; (b) 53° (high-angle) boundary; (c) 60° boundary.

References: p. 708.

boundaries (fig. 1a). If the dislocations are uniformly spaced in the plane of the boundary, a low-energy interface is assumed to be formed as the strain fields of the dislocations extend into the lattices of both crystals over a distance comparable with the spacing of the dislocation array (St. Venant's principle), which is a relative minimum for periodic arrays. A uniform dislocation spacing can only result if the dislocation spacing is equal to an integral number of lattice planes terminating at the boundary. For all other tilt angles (e.g. 60° tilt) the boundary may be described as a boundary with a uniform dislocation spacing (e.g. a 53° tilt boundary, fig. 1b) and a superimposed small-angle tilt boundary that accounts for the deviation from the tilt angle required for uniformly spaced dislocations (e.g., the deviation of $7° = 60° - 53°$; fig. 1c). The idea of describing a boundary which deviates from a low-energy structure in terms of the superposition of a low-energy boundary and a small-angle boundary has been increasingly used in association with dislocation models as well as with boundary models that are not based on the dislocation concept.

The work of Read and Shockley, which is generally considered as a major achievement of the theory of interfacial structures, suffers from two inherent limitations. First, the singular behaviour of the elastic strain fields near the dislocation centres was dealt with by removing the singularity mathematically with an inner "cut-off" radius. The second deficiency is the linear superposition of the strain fields of the individual dislocations, which results in complete neglect of the interactions among the dislocations in the array.

In order to ameliorate these deficiencies, the cores of dislocations in grain boundaries were modelled either by a hollow-core dislocation description (LI [1961]), a nonlinear approach (GLEITER [1977]) or by picturing the material in the core region as a second phase (MASAMURA and GLICKSMAN [1974]). All three approximations indicate that core–core interaction effects become dominant if the dislocation spacing approaches the core diameter. The cores then spread in the boundary plane and merge above a critical dislocation density, forming a slab of core material (*delocalized dislocations*). As a consequence, grain-boundary dislocation models starting from the (implicit or explicit) assumption that boundary dislocations and lattice dislocations are structurally alike, may have to be regarded with caution.

In order to avoid the inherent difficulties associated with any dislocation description of an interface, *disclination models* have been suggested (SHIH and LI [1975]). The major advantage of this description is to replace the (frequently unknown) Burgers vector of boundary dislocations by a (known) rotation vector along the common axis of the two crystals. An attempt to improve the modelling of the elastic distortions was made by portraying grain boundaries in terms of an array of voids and/or asymmetric cracks on whose surfaces are distributed *surface dislocations* (MARCINKOWSKI and JAGANNADHAM [1978]). These surface dislocations are the boundary dislocations required to render the void-surfaces stress-free. The boundary shown in fig. 2a contains no elastic energy and consists of large voids which, in turn, correspond to a high surface energy. The total amount of free surface energy can be reduced at the expense of lattice strain by a partial coalescence of the two faces (fig. 2b). In order to make the surface of the voids stress-free, an array of surface-disloca-

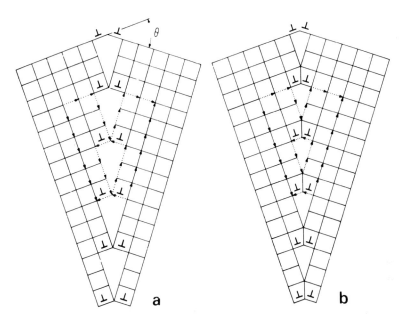

Fig. 2. Unrelaxed tilt-type symmetric 36,9° grain boundary (a) and a partially coalesced modification of this boundary (b) (after MARCINKOWSKI and JAGANNADHAM [1976]).

tion dipoles has to be distributed on them. The energy of the boundary can now be computed by determining the equilibrium configuration of the surface dislocations on the grain surfaces as well as those required to screen their stress field. The calculations indicate that a minimum-energy configuration of the boundary is obtained if the boundary dislocations are spread in the plane of the interface, supporting the idea that dislocations in grain boundaries may be delocalized. Hence, models of boundaries using lattice-type dislocations have to be regarded with caution. According to the computer simulations of grain-boundary structures (cf. § 2.2.1.3), rigid-body relaxations may in many cases be the most important mode of reducing the energy of a boundary: thus it appears that dislocation models may be improved by incorporating rigid-body relaxation effects.

The development of the crystallographic approach to interface structure was pioneered by BOLLMANN (1970) in the form of the *O-lattice theory*. The goal of this theory is to provide a mathematical method for calculating the crystallographic structure, the arrangement and the permissible Burgers vectors of dislocations in grain boundaries. The O-lattice approach starts from the assumption that all interfaces are ordered. The approach is geometric in nature and embodies the concepts of shear transformations and of the coincidence-site lattice. Following the early ideas of the dislocation model (fig. 1), boundaries between two crystals are

References: p. 708.

assumed to have a low-energy structure for certain orientation relationships. This low-energy structure is visualized as consisting of finely spaced arrays of dislocations (*primary dislocations*). Any deviation from these low-energy orientation relationships is accommodated by a network of dislocations, called *secondary dislocations.* For example, in terms of the boundary shown in fig. 1, the primary dislocations are the equally spaced dislocations of the low-energy structure shown in fig. 1b. The secondary dislocations are the extra dislocations (fig. 1c) required to account for the deviation of 7° from the low-energy structure. In order to develop a formalism that permits the computation of these dislocations for any interface, we consider two interpenetrating crystal lattices of different orientations, but not necessarily of the same type of lattice structure. As any relative translational position of the two crystal lattices is permitted, in the general case no coincidence between atomic sites of the two lattices exists. (The existence of such sites would require a specification of the translational position.) Nevertheless, the concept of "matching" (cf. §2.2.1.3 on coincidence models) between both crystals can still be maintained if we define as a point of best "match" a coincidence of points in crystallographically equivalent positions in the two lattices. All points with the same coordinates relative to the respective crystal lattice not only are lattice sites but also include the entire continuous space of the crystal, i.e., any point between the lattice sites, e.g. the centre of the unit cell although not occupied by an atom. These points of coincidence are called the *O points*. The O points can form a point lattice within the interpenetrating lattices or a lattice consisting of parallel lines (O-line lattice) or of parallel planes (O-plane lattice). If we have two lattices 1 and 2, the point-to-point correlation between them may be written as

$$x^{(2)} = A x^{(1)},$$ (1)

where $x^{(2)}$ and $x^{(1)}$ are the vectors (expressed in the coordinates of lattices 1 and 2, respectively) characterizing the same point in space. A is the transformation matrix between the two lattices. Obviously, a point in lattice 2 with the coordinates $x^{(2)}$ coincides with an equivalent point of lattice 1 if the difference between $x^{(2)}$ and $x^{(1)}$ is zero or a translation vector b of lattice (1):

$$x^{(2)} - x^{(1)} = b.$$ (2)

Expressing $x^{(1)}$ in $x^{(2)}$ by means of eq. (1) yields

$$(I - A^{-1}) x^{(2)} = b$$ (3)

where I is the unity matrix. All the vectors $x^{(2)}$ defined by eq. (3) are the O points according to the above definition. If we characterize the O point by a vector $x^{(O)}$ the entire lattice of O points (*O-lattice*) is given by eq. (3):

$$(I - A^{-1}) x^{(O)} = b.$$ (4)

The O-lattice vectors $x^{(O)}$ are obtained explicitly by inverting eqs. (4). Provided the determinant $|I - A^{-1}| \neq 0$, we find

$$x^{(O)} = (I - A^{-1})^{-1} b.$$ (5)

Equation (4) is a generalization of Frank's formula (FRANK [1950]). Wigner–Seitz-type cells can be then be constructed around the O-lattice points and the regions of worst match are given by the cell walls separating neighbouring points of the O lattice. The intersection of a grain boundary with an O-lattice cell wall between two O elements is a dislocation (*primary dislocation*) and the connecting vector between the two corresponding b vectors is its Burgers vector.

Many of the details of the O-lattice structure cannot be worked out in detail unless more is known of the nature of the low-energy structure. This question will be discussed in §2.2.1.2. and is related to the choice of A. The transformation A can be chosen in an infinite number of ways and each choice leads to a different O lattice. In fact, dislocation structures have been observed, for example in $\langle 110 \rangle$ twist boundaries in gold, which corresponded to different choices of A. A plausible choice of A is the one that maximizes the volume of the O lattice. This choice minimizes the dislocation content which is further decreased if the boundary plane passes through as many O elements as possible. An example of an O-lattice computation worked out in detail may be found in the review by SMITH and POND [1976]. If the orientation relationship between the two crystals is slightly changed (i.e. the transformation matrix is changed from A to A'), the periodicity of the O-lattice pattern is lost. If A generates a boundary of low energy, it may be energetically more favourable to conserve the O lattice corresponding to A and to correct for the deviation by creating a dislocation network (*secondary dislocations*). The Burgers vectors of these secondary dislocations can be computed by using the same approach as discussed above if it is assumed that the secondary dislocations are perfect dislocations with respect to the periodic structure of the low-energy boundary, i.e. the boundary corresponding to A. By analogy to the O-lattice construction, the ensemble of possible Burgers vectors of perfect secondary boundary dislocations defines a new lattice, which is called the *DSC lattice*. It is so named because the *d*isplacement of one crystal with respect to the other by a DSC vector causes a *s*hift of the periodic boundary pattern which is *c*omplete. If the actual transformation relating two lattices (1) and (2) is A' and the transformation A produces a nearby low-energy boundary, the residue $AA' = B$ is accommodated by secondary dislocations with DSC Burgers vectors. The basic equation then becomes:

$$(I - B^{-1})x^{(O2)} = d^{(SC)},$$

where d^{SC} is the lattice vector of the DSC lattice [(corresponding to b in eq. (4)] and $x^{(O2)}$ is the O lattice between the O lattices formed by the low-energy orientation relationship A and the actual (nearby) orientation relationship A'.

As the theory is purely geometric in nature, it cannot provide information about the actual structure of the primary and/or secondary dislocations. The general condition for forming a localized (primary or secondary) dislocation is that the energy reduction due to the relaxation around the O elements is equal to or larger than the energy required to form the dislocation strain field. Otherwise the misfit remains delocalized and the dislocation modelling is of limited physical significance. The question to what extent all grain boundaries can be represented by low-energy structures and superimposed (localized) dislocation networks has recently been reviewed by GOODHEW [1980] who pointed out that relatively few examples exist as yet in which the predicted dislocation structures have been revealed. This discrepancy may be due to the delocalization of the misfit dislocations in many boundaries. The importance of this effect was emphasized by observations on the misfit dislocation structure of $\alpha-\beta$ brass interfaces (KLUGE-WEISS and GLEITER [1979]). If the $\langle 110 \rangle$ planes of β-brass are approximately parallel to the $\langle 111 \rangle$ planes of α-brass, a dislocation network is formed which can be explained satisfactorily in terms of the crystallographic theory. However, if the crystals are slightly rotated out of this orientation relationship, the dislocation network becomes invisible due to delocalization of the dislocations. Hence, a non-localization of the misfit in the cell walls may exist, even if the dislocation spacing is large in comparison with the lattice- or boundary periodicity. Effects of this type have occasionally led to some confusion. In a purely geometrical sense, the misfit dislocations are always present as they are geometrically necessary. However, their physical significance depends on the existence of a long-range strain field which is only present if they are localized.

This problem is closely related to the *plane-matching* model of grain boundaries. In several cases, electron micrographs of high-angle grain boundaries exhibited periodic arrays of dislocation, although no high-density coincidence-orientation relationship (§ 2.2.1.3) was nearby. The observed spacing and orientation of the lines agreed however with the idea of families of lattice planes which impinge on the boundary from the adjoining grains in such a manner that their traces in the boundary are slightly mismatched (fig. 3). These observations prompted PUMPHREY [1972] to propose that matching of certain sets of lattice planes is a significant parameter for the structure of interfaces. Recently, evidence for the existence of a plane-matching structure in phase boundaries has been presented by means of high-resolution electron microscopy (GRONSKI and THOMAS [1977]).

2.2.1.2. Atomic-matching models – island models.   Originally, the idea of modelling the structure of a grain boundary in terms of regions (islands) of good and poor atomic fit was proposed by MOTT [1948] without specifying the characteristics of atomic structure of good or poor fit. The most quantitative form of the model was developed by GIFKINS [1967]. Gifkins' model pictures a grain boundary as consisting of islands of good fit, separated by channels of relaxed vacancies. The islands of good fit are identified with the microfacets that have been observed by field ion microscopy. The channels of relaxed vacancies (§ 2.2.2.1) may reside in the ledges which surround the protrusions. The dimensions of the facets are estimated to be in the range of 5–50 atomic diameters.

2.2.1.3. Atomic-matching models – coincidence models.   The first attempt to correlate predictively the crystallographic parameters of a boundary (e.g, the lattice structure of the crystals forming the interface, the orientation relationship between the two crystals, the boundary inclination, etc.) with the actual atomic arrangement in the interface was made by KRONBERG and WILSON [1949] who applied the concept of *lattice coincidence* – which was developed independently by several crystallographers – to grain boundaries. An example of a coincidence lattice is

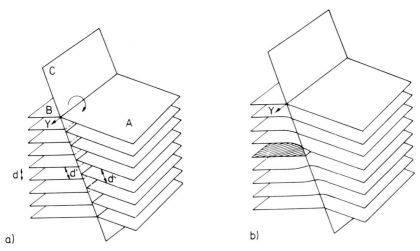

Fig. 3. Schematic representation of a plane-matching structure in a boundary for two stacks of planes (A and B) slightly rotated about the Y axis (a). d′ and d″ define the projected spacings of the two stacks on the boundary plane (C). As d′ ≠ d″, a mismatch of the terminating planes results. After relaxations have been allowed, an array of edge dislocations is seen to be generated (b) with lines along the Y direction, permitting the matching of the two stacks of lattice planes at the boundary. (After RALPH *et al.* [1977]).

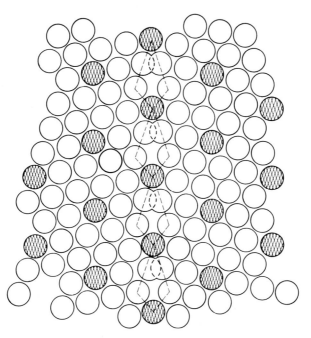

Fig. 4. Lattice-coincidence model of a 18° tilt-type grain boundary between two hexagonal arrays of atoms. The atoms at coincidence sites are indicated by cross-hatching. The "surfaces" of the two crystals are marked by dashed lines.

References: p. 708.

shown in fig. 4. The atoms indicated by hatched circles occupy sites at which the two lattices would coincide (lattice coincidence) if they were extended to the other side of the boundary. Obviously, the density and arrangement of the coincidence-site lattice depends on the orientation relationship between the crystals. Orientation relationships resulting in a large number of coincidence sites were called *coincidence-orientation relationships* and the corresponding boundaries are termed *coincidence boundaries*. About two decades later, the coincidence concept was extended to non-coincidence boundaries by combining it with the dislocation model (§ 2.2.1.1; BRANDON *et al.* [1964]). Boundaries between crystals deviating from an ideal coincidence-orientation relationship were proposed to consist of areas with an array of coincidence atoms in the plane of the boundary (boundary coincidence) separated by (misfit) dislocations. The significance of boundary inclination was incorporated in the model by suggesting that the boundary follows the planes containing a high density of coincidence sites in order to minimize the misfit, as the boundary consists in these regions of atomic groups with little strain. Boundaries constrained to lie at an angle to the most densely packed coincidence-plane were visualized to take a step structure. In recent years, the coincidence concept has been extended further (BISHOP and CHALMERS [1968]) to interfaces (*near-coincidence boundaries*) between crystals of which the superposition of the lattice forms commensurate two-dimensional atomic nets in the interface. Thus, atomic matching occurs only for a specific grain-boundary plane. Again, deviations from these conditions are taken up by dislocation networks. In the further development of the atomistic models of grain boundaries, attention was focused essentially on two problems: (i) the characterization of the structures of boundaries of low energy and (ii) the development of the general crystallographic theory of grain boundaries. These two problems led to two separate lines of development. The general crystallographic theory that finally emerged was discussed in the preceding section. Let us now consider the ideas put forward to improve the understanding of the characteristics features of low-energy boundary structures.

The concept of atoms occupying coincidence sites (in terms of boundary or lattice coincidences) had to be abandoned after it was recognized from computer simulations of the atomic structure of grain boundaries (WEINS *et al.* [1971]) that two crystals forming a coincidence boundary relax by a shear-type displacement (rigid-body shear) from the position required for the existence of coincidence-site atoms at the boundary (figs. 5a and b). This conclusion was confirmed in subsequent years by numerous more sophisticated computer simulations as well as by experimental observations.

The physical reason for the rigid-body relaxation may be seen from figs. 4 and 5. Figure 4 shows the boundary structure predicted by the lattice-coincidence model. Both closely and widely spaced pairs of atoms exist, resulting in a high-energy structure. The energy of the boundary may be lowered by translating the two crystals (without rotation) so that the "hills" on the "surface" of one crystal coincide with the "valleys" on the "surface" of the other crystal (fig. 5a) followed by the relaxation of individual atoms into minimum-energy positions (fig. 5b). The existence of rigid-body relaxations led CHALMERS and GLEITER [1971] to propose

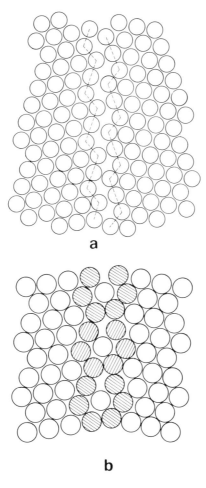

a

b

Fig. 5. Structure of the boundary shown in fig. 4 after a "rigid-body relaxation" of the two hexagonal arrays of atoms in order to remove large interatomic repulsion or attraction forces (a) and subsequent relaxation of individual atoms into positions of minimum energy (b). The interaction potential assumed between the atoms corresponds to gold.

that the boundary periodicity rather than the existence of boundary coincidence per se is the physical meaningful parameter. In fact, the existence of small structural units with an atomic packing density comparable to that in a perfect lattice was hypothesized to result in low-energy boundaries (fig. 5b). By extending the concept of BISHOP and CHALMERS [1968] the following structural model of grain boundaries was proposed (CHALMERS and GLEITER [1971]): boundaries of low energy consist of only one type of (relaxed) structural units, whereas the structure of high-energy boundaries may be derived from a simple rule of mixing of the low-energy structural units of nearest low-energy boundaries (GLEITER [1971]). This boundary model has

References: p. 708.

recently been confirmed by detailed computer simulations of boundaries (SUTTON and VITEK [1983]). Furthermore, this description in terms of mixtures of relaxed structural units corresponds directly to one in terms of boundary dislocations, as described in §2.2.1.1. At present the structural unit model seems to be the most generally accepted description of grain-boundary structure (cf. ch. 11, §8.2).

2.2.1.4. Atomic-matching models – polyhedral unit models. The concept of describing the atomic arrangements in grain boundaries in terms of densely packed atomic groups (e.g. the groups existing in amorphous structures) led to the development of the *polyhedral unit models*. Apparently, the idea of comparing the atomic arrangements in a grain boundary with the atomic arrangements existing in amorphous structures was first proposed by POTAPOV et al. [1971]. They analyzed the three-dimensional atomic structure of grain boundaries in tungsten by means of field-ion microscopy. Boundaries were found to consist of periodically arranged rings formed by five atoms with a central atom between the rings (fig. 6). On the basis of these observations it was concluded that a grain boundary may be represented in terms of the atomic configurations existing in amorphous metals. Some years later, a similar structural concept was worked out in details by several other authors (ASHBY et al. [1978] and POND et al. [1978]). For example, fig. 7 shows the interpretation of the structure of a 36.9° [100] tilt boundary between fcc crystals in terms of the polyhedral unit model.

The comparison between grain-boundary structures and structural elements of amorphous materials is not without problems as the atoms in a boundary cannot relax to the same extent as in a glass. In an interface, the boundary conditions are given by the periodic structure of the two crystals on both sides, whereas an atomic group in a glass has no such periodic boundary conditions for its relaxation. This

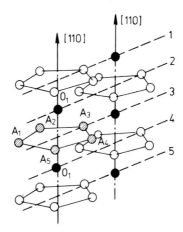

Fig. 6. Schematic diagram of the arrangement of the atoms in a 40° ⟨110⟩ tilt boundary in tungsten, derived from a sequence of field ion microscopy images. The position of the ⟨110⟩ common tilt axis in the two grains is indicated. Numbers 1–5 indicate subsequent layers of the boundary. Letters A_1–A_5 label one of the polyhedral rings proposed by POTAPOV et al. [1971].

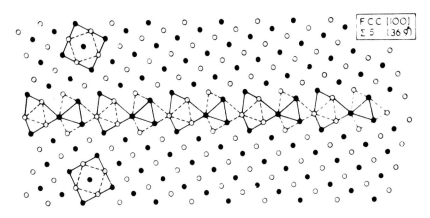

Fig. 7. Structure of a 36.9° ⟨100⟩ tilt boundary between fcc crystals, in terms of polyhedral units. The boundary is composed of stacks of capped trigonal prisms.

difference is borne out by several experiments. For example, positron annihilation measurements (CHEN and CHANG [1974]) and Mössbauer studies (OZAWA and ISHIDA [1977]) suggest that the atomic packing in grain boundaries is more "open" than in a glassy structure. A severe shortcoming of all existing boundary models is the neglect of electronic effects. In fact, studies (HERRMANN *et al.* [1976]) of low-energy boundaries in metals with the same lattice structure but different electronic structure suggest a division of all low-energy boundaries into two groups: "electron-sensitive" and "electron-insensitive" boundaries. Physically, this different behaviour was interpreted in terms of the different atomic arrangements in the boundaries. If the atomic arrangement is similar to the lattice structure (e.g., in a twin boundary), the boundary energy is low irrespective of the contribution of the conduction electrons to the boundary energy. However, for boundaries with complex atomic structures, the electronic contribution to the boundary energy is crucial so that any electronic variation (e.g. a variation of the Fermi energy) affects the boundary behaviour. In fact, free-electron calculations showed that the positive charge deficit associated with a grain boundary may be the dominant part of the boundary energy (SEEGER and SCHOTTKY [1959]).

Furthermore, it should be pointed out that the considerations so far discussed have neglected the effect of temperature, pressure etc. on the boundary structure. Studies of grain-boundary migration, sliding and boundary energy measurements as a function of temperature and pressure suggest the existence of *structural phase transformations* in grain boundaries, similar to the well-known phase transformations of free surfaces.

Two types of phase transformations have been hypothesized: transitions between two types of ordered boundary structures of different symmetry (for a review cf. GLEITER [1980]) and transformations of the order–disorder type (KIKUCHI and CAHN [1980]).

The discussion so far has primarily concentrated on grain boundaries in metals.

References: p. 708.

In recent years, evidence has been presented (e.g. SUN and BALLUFFI [1979] and FÖLL and AST [1981]) suggesting that similar structural principles may also hold for grain boundaries between crystals with ionic, van der Waals or covalent bonding.

Relatively little is known of the correlation between the atomic structure of grain boundaries and the segregation of solute atoms. Measurements of solute-induced grain-boundary embrittlement (ROY *et al.* [1982]) suggest that the distribution of solute atoms at or in the vicinity of a grain boundary, and the interfacial solute concentration depend on the boundary structure. At low-energy boundaries (boundaries of good atomic matching) the solute enhancement was a minimum. In boundaries deviating from structures of good matching, the solute concentration increased. These additional solute atoms were present in the form of groups of solute atoms in the vicinity of the intrinsic boundary dislocations required by the deviation from the low energy structure. (See also ch. 13, especially §4.2.4).

2.2.2. Non-equilibrium structures

During deformation, quenching etc. the structure of boundaries may deviate from the equilibrium structure discussed above. Two structural defects in grain boundaries have so far been studied. They will be discussed in the next two sections.

2.2.2.1. Point defects.   In boundaries of good atomic fit the structure of vacancies (for a review, cf. GLEITER [1981]) may be described as an empty site surrounded by a displacement field that extends primarily into the lattices of the adjoining crystals (localized vacancy, fig. 8a). A second type of vacancy structure is found in boundaries of relatively poor atomic matching (fig. 8b). In this case, the core of the vacancy is associated with large atomic displacements that tend to spread out the free volume associated with the defect in the plane of the boundary (delocalized vacancy). The existence of two different vacancy structures in grain boundaries may be understood in terms of the interatomic forces. If an atom is removed from a boundary with poor atomic matching, the interatomic forces in the vicinity of this atom are no longer in equilibrium and the atoms in this region start to relax, which in turn triggers further atomic displacements in neighbouring parts of the boundary, etc. Such an avalanche of atomic relaxations is not triggered in the boundary of good atomic fit as it would destroy the structure of good fit, which requires a large energy.

2.2.2.2. Dislocations.   The structure of dislocations that are not part of the equilibrium boundary structure (extrinsic boundary dislocations) is believed to be of significance for recrystallization, high-temperature deformation and the annealing of irradiation defects. For example, an *extrinsic dislocation* results if a slip dislocation of the lattice enters a grain boundary during plastic deformation. This extrinsic dislocation may then be superimposed onto an *intrinsic dislocation structure* which has already existed in the (equilibrated) boundary (§2.2.1) before the extrinsic dislocation entered the interface. The following models for the structure of extrinsic dislocations in grain boundaries have been put forward.

The *dissociation model* (BOLLMANN [1970]) describes the extrinsic boundary dislocations in all types of grain boundaries in terms of DSC dislocations. A lattice

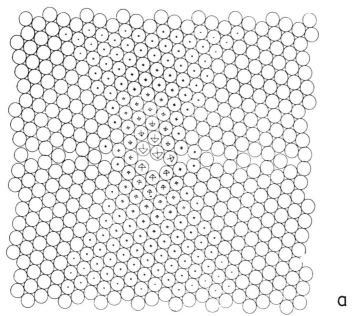

Fig. 8a. Computed atomic structure of a vacancy in the boundary shown in fig. 5b. The arrows indicate the atomic displacements (relative to the vacancy-free boundary) associated with the vacancy. The largest and smallest arrows correspond to displacements of 25.5% and 0.64% of the interatomic spacing, respectively.

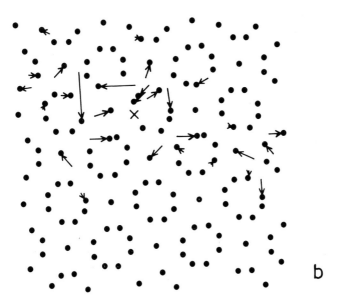

Fig. 8b. Displacement field around a vacancy in a 36.9° ⟨001⟩ twist boundary in bcc tungsten. The plane of the figure coincides with the plane of the boundary. Only atoms lying in the boundary plane are shown. The crystals (above and below the boundary) are not shown. The arrows represent the atomic relaxations due to introduction of the vacancy at the position indicated by the cross. The arrows are three times as long as the actual atomic relaxations. (After BRISTOWE *et al.* [1980].)

References: p. 708.

dislocation entering a boundary and forming an extrinsic dislocation is envisaged as dissociating into boundary dislocations, the Burgers vectors of which are given by the primitive DSC lattice vectors. The major energy source for driving the dissociation reaction is believed to be the reduction in the elastic energy associated with the long-range strain field of the dislocations.

The dislocation *core delocalization model* (GLEITER [1977]) proposes that the structure of an extrinsic dislocation depends on the boundary structure. In boundaries with well-defined boundary dislocations, the incorporation of an extrinsic dislocation is assumed to occur by a dislocation reaction of the type described in the previous section. However, for high-energy boundaries the reaction is proposed to occur by the *spreading* of the dislocation cores in the plane of the boundary (figs. 9a, b). The physical reason for the spreading of the core of the extrinsic boundary dislocations seems to be the reduction in the long-range strain field energy of the

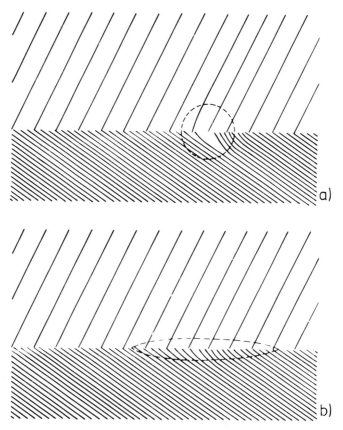

Fig. 9a, b. Schematic diagrams showing the structure of localized (a) and delocalized (b) boundary dislocations. Dashed lines indicate approximate size of the dislocation cores. For simplicity, only one set of lattice planes of the two adjoining crystals forming the boundary is shown.

extrinsic boundary dislocation. If an extrinsic dislocation is introduced into a boundary of high energy, the delocalization of the core influences the boundary energy insignificantly as the original boundary structure was already of high energy. The energy density in the core of a high-energy boundary is of the order of the latent heat of fusion. This energy density is an upper limit, and, hence, the introduction of an additional dislocation into such a high-energy structure cannot increase the energy significantly further. However, the increase in the size of the dislocation core reduces the energy stored in the long-range strain field of the dislocation, without increasing the boundary energy significantly. Therefore, the total energy of the system (consisting of the sum of the dislocation energy plus the energy of the boundary before the dislocation was introduced) is reduced if the core of the dislocation is widely spread in the plane of the boundary.

The basic idea of the *strain sharing model* (HORTON *et al.* [1974]) is as follows. An extra dislocation entering a boundary will repel neighbouring structural dislocations, and if they can move to some extent, they will change their initial spacing q to give a region over which the spacing changes from q to $q/2 + \delta x$, where δx is the movement of the structural dislocations on either side of the extra dislocation (figs. 9c, d). The group of displaced dislocations, including the original extra dislocation, now represents the extrinsic dislocation. If the relaxation, or accommodation, of the

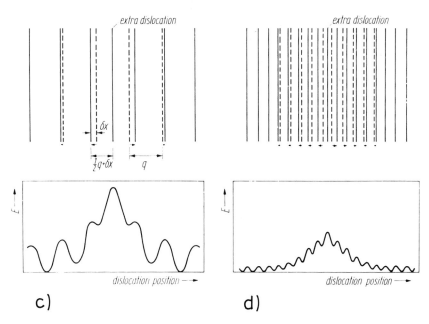

Fig. 9c, d. Schematic illustration of the spreading of the elastic strain field E of an extra dislocation (marked) when added to a network of parallel boundary dislocations with the same Burgers vector. Solid lines indicate position of added dislocation and final dislocation positions; dashed lines indicate original positions. In (d) the density of structural dislocations is greater than in (c). (From HORTON *et al.* [1974].)

References: p. 708.

structural array is extensive, the strain field of the extrinsic dislocation will be effectively spread out over a large area and the original extra dislocation line added will tend to lose its identity.

2.3. Small-angle boundaries

Small-angle boundaries are interfaces between crystals that differ in orientation by only a few degrees. It is now well established (AMELINCKX [1964]) that boundaries of this type consist of periodic, two-dimensional networks of dislocations separated by (elastically strained) regions in which the crystal lattice is defect-free (fig. 1a). As was discussed in §2.2, the physical reason for the formation of small-angle boundaries is the cancellation of the long-range strain fields of the individual dislocations. The general crystallographic correlation between the orientation relationship and the dislocation arrangement in a small-angle boundary is given by the formalism of Frank (FRANK [1950]) or the more elaborate scheme of the O-lattice theory (§2.2.1.1). However, the actual dislocation structures may be quite complex, in particular, effects resulting from dissociation processes and structural changes in the dislocation core. Effects of this type seem to be a general feature of small-angle boundaries in materials with low stacking-fault energies (BOURRET and DESSAULT [1979]). The formation of a small-angle boundary from a random array of dislocations may be understood in terms of the strain-field interaction. The stresses at the end of a dislocation wall segment P (fig. 10) attract the surrounding edge dislocations which then become incorporated and result in wall growth. Similar arguments apply to the incorporation of individual dislocations in the lattice, adjacent to a sub-boundary,

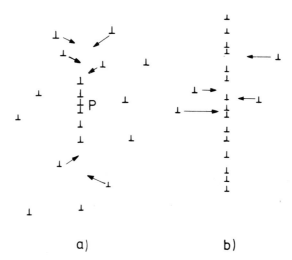

Fig. 10. Formation of a small-angle boundary from a random array of dislocations. The dislocation wall segment P (a) attracts dislocations from the surrounding lattice, and incorporates them, growing into a boundary (b).

called *dislocation knitting* (MIEKK-OJA and LINDROOS [1972]). Three mechanisms for the migration and for structural changes of dislocation walls have been proposed: Conservative motion of small-angle boundaries, if the slip planes of all dislocations (LI *et al.* [1953]) are parallel; in the two other cases, the migration process involves dislocation glide and climb. Two types of climb mechanisms have been reported: The dislocations of neighbouring small-angle boundaries may join up to a single dislocation wall by a climb-and-glide motion along the boundary (HU [1963]; fig. 11). The second climb mechanism involves the simultaneous movement of the individual boundary dislocations by vacancy emission and absorption (AMELINCKX and DEKEYSER [1959], GLEITER [1969]).

Small-angle boundaries may be formed by cold-working, recovery, polygonization fatigue or creep (see chs. 19, 20, 24, 25). The topological arrangement of the boundaries and their dislocation content depends on the following parameters: strain, strain rate, strain amplitude, temperature, stress, time, stacking-fault energy, solute content and dispersion of second phase particles. The interplay between these parameters and the resulting dislocation arrangement has been discussed by McQUEEN [1977].

2.3.1. Glissile dislocation walls

In addition to dislocation walls between crystals differing slightly in orientation (small-angle boundaries), two other types of dislocation walls are important for the

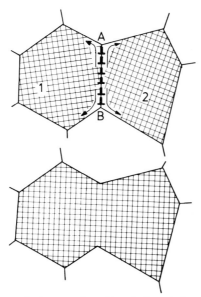

Fig. 11. Migration and structural changes of small-angle boundaries. The dislocations forming the boundary AB are incorporated into the boundaries surrounding the grains 1 and 2 by dislocation rearrangement along the interfaces as indicated. This dislocation rearrangement results in a rotation of 1 and 2 so that both crystals acquire identical orientations ('subgrain rotation').

References: p. 708.

microstructure of materials: (i) dislocation walls separating a deformation twin from the untwinned matrix and (ii) dislocation walls between martensitic phases and the surrounding parent phases. Both types of interface consist of dislocations. They are, however, different in structure from small-angle boundaries (cf. ch. 15, §2.4).

2.4. Structure of interphase boundaries

The energy of an interphase boundary evidently depends on many parameters, e.g. interfacial misfit, the type of atomic bonding between and within the phases, the size and shape of the crystals, etc. Many models, introduced to analyze interphase boundaries, take into account only one or a few of these parameters and have accordingly only limited predictive power. In fact, any comparison between models of interphase boundaries and experimental results implies that an equilibrated boundary structure has been achieved. It should perhaps be made clear that there are relatively few experimental observations on any type of interphase boundaries which definitely represent equilibrium. As long as processes associated with interphase boundary migration or with coherency loss are in action, the kinetic controls on the nature of the interface outweigh the thermodynamic ones, and any agreement between experiment and theory may be fortuitous.

Most of the models for interphase boundaries have been constructed by analogy with grain boundaries. Hence, for the conceptual background, we refer back to the section on grain boundaries.

2.4.1. Coincidence models

Coincidence modeling assumes good interfacial registry to be equivalent to low interfacial energy. Although this model takes into account only one of the governing parameters, it was successfully applied to interfaces between crystals of the same type of bonding. In terms of this model, the understanding of the structure of interphase boundaries reduces to the understanding of the misfit dislocations. Several approaches to this problem have been proposed, all of which make use of the O-lattice formalism. As was pointed out in §2.2.1.1 on O-lattice theory, three sets of misfit dislocations normally exist in an interface. However, for the three boundary planes lying parallel to pairs of the O-lattice unit vectors, only two arrays are produced. It was, therefore, suggested (BOLLMANN and NIESSEN [1968]) that one of these three interfaces would be energetically most favourable. Several purely geometric parameters were suggested for searching out energetically favourable interfaces (ECOB and RALPH [1981]). A critical comparison between the boundary energy and these parameters indicates (KNOWLES *et al.* [1982]) that one must be cautious in using such geometric parameters as a measure for relative interfacial energies.

A different approach to the problem was taken by OLSON and COHEN [1979]. They started from the concept of *coherency*, defining a coherent interface as one for which corresponding lattice planes and lattice directions are continuous across the interface. A discrete dislocation description of an interphase boundary deviating from coherency was developed by applying the Bilby–Frank equation to determine the dislocation content of the interface. The results obtained suggested that *coherency dislocations* and *anti-coherency dislocations* exist in the (equilibrium) structure of an interphase boundary. The coherency dislocations accomplish the lattice strain required to maintain continuity of the lattices of two phases at the interface (figs. 12a–c) although the (relaxed) lattice plane spacings are different. Coherency may be reduced by the introduction of anticoherency dislocations which accomplish a lattice-invariant deformation and decrease strain energy by cancelling a portion of the stress field of the coherency dislocations (fig. 12d). In a series of papers, Aaronson and co-workers (cf. RIGSBEE and AARONSON [1979]) studied, theoretically and experimentally, interphase boundaries which are expected to be partially coherent. The boundaries were defined as $\{111\}_{fcc}\|\{110\}_{bcc}$ and a rotation about an axis normal to these planes. Interfaces of this type were found to contain regions of good atomic matching for a wide range of lattice parameter ratios. An increase of the coherency resulted if the interface was allowed to switch atom matching layers by structural ledges (ch. 14, §2.2.3). Although the structural ledges cause a deviation of the apparent habit plane from the $\{111\}_{fcc}$, the conjugate habit planes along which the lattices actually matched remained $\{111\}_{fcc}\|\{110\}_{bcc}$. A network of misfit dislocations was found to be midway between coherent regions on the broad faces of the structural ledges. They converted the remaining "non-coherent" regions, which lie between the coherent regions, to conventional partial coherency with essentially all

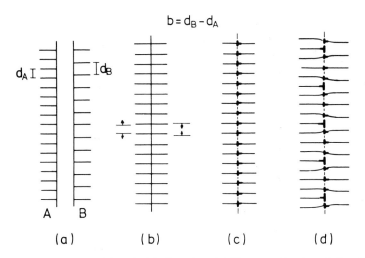

Fig. 12. Interphase boundary with uniaxial distortion. (a) Two crystals, A and B, with different interplanar spacings, d_A and d_B. (b) Position of planes across the interface if the lattices A and B form a fully coherent interface. (c) Dislocations required to achieve full coherency between A and B (fig. 12b). The sets of lattice planes of A and B, with different (relaxed) spacings, become equally spaced by introduction of the virtual dislocations shown (coherency dislocations). (d) Semicoherent boundary with anticoherency dislocations superimposed on coherency dislocations of (c). (From OLSON and COHEN [1979].)

References: p. 708.

of the misfit concentrated about the core of the misfit dislocations. Burgers vector analyses showed that those interfaces having the most coherency also have the misfit dislocations with the smallest Burgers vector, and, hence, the lowest interfacial energy. In every such instance, the misfit dislocation Burgers vector is a bulk-lattice type which lies in the atomic conjugate habit planes of the interface.

The most significant difference between the above model and the model of ECOB and RALPH [1981] is that the former model maximizes interfacial coherency (O-point density) before relaxation into a dislocation structure. The two descriptions become identical only if the dislocation structure has no physical significance (i.e., for disordered boundaries, ECOB and RALPH [1981]).

A large body of experimental observations comparing the actual atomic structure of interphase boundaries with the prediction of atomic matching is available in the literature. These observations are based on epitaxial-growth studies and investigations of precipitation processes and of the solidification of multiphase alloys. From the (relatively few) cases where the interphase boundaries studied were equilibrated, the following trend seems to emerge. Interphase boundaries between crystals of the same type of bonding exhibit misfit dislocation structures and energies that are consistent with the concept of atomic matching. In the case of phase boundaries between crystals of different types of bonding, controversial observations have been reported. For example, in the cases of interphase boundaries between Cu and Cu_2O, Si and Pd_2Si, Co and Cr_2N, and Fe and $M_{23}C_6$, the experimental observations are well accounted for by the idea of atomic matching. However, in other systems, for example in boundaries between Fe and Fe_2Nb (COCKS and BORLUND [1975]), the observed orientation relationships did not give the best conceivable atomic matching. Similar arguments seem to apply to the cube–cube orientation relationships observed for the precipitation of NaCl-type carbides in austenitic steel. For all but ZrC, the same orientation relationship is found despite the variety of lattice mismatch. Perhaps the most striking examples are observations on low-energy interfaces between Ag and NaCl and polymer and ionic crystals. In the case of Ag–NaCl, the low-energy orientations were measured by rotating small silver spheres sintered onto the (100) surface of a NaCl crystal into the orientations of lowest energy. The lattice mismatch in the boundaries of minimum energy was about 30%, whereas boundaries of good atomic matching were not found to have low energies (ERB et al. [1982]). All low-energy orientations observed exhibited high lattice symmetry (e.g. a cube–cube relationship) suggesting that long-range interactions may be significant. A similar result was reported in a systematic study for boundaries between polymer crystals and different ionic crystals (KONTSKY et al. [1966]). Although the lattice constants of the ionic crystals varied between 0.4 and 0.7 nm, the orientation relationship of lowest energy remained identical, suggesting lattice matching to be of minor importance.

2.4.2. Frank–Van der Merwe model

The essential feature of the Frank–Van der Merwe model (VAN DER MERWE [1973]) is that it allows the bonding between the atoms of the two crystals to be different in strength and type. By analogy to the Peierls–Nabarro model for interatomic forces in a dislocation, the bonding across the interphase boundary is represented by a periodic potential acting between the atoms adjoining the interface. The energy of the long-range strain field of interfacial defects is computed from elasticity theory. The approach has been criticized on the grounds that the interaction between the crystal halves is localized to the two atomic planes adjoining the interface and that the continuous assumption may break down when the dislocation spacing is only a few lattice constants.

In an alternative but equivalent approach, the interphase boundary structure is derived by considering the forces on threading dislocations in two-phase systems (JESSER and MATTHEWS [1968]).

2.4.3. Computer simulation

This method is based on the self-evident notion that the structure attained at a crystalline interface is governed by the principle that atomic adjustments will occur until the (free) energy of the system is a minimum. The method accepts given representations for atomic interaction potentials and minimizes the total energy by varying the atomic positions, subject to certain constraints, such as specifying the relative orientation of the two crystals at large distances from the interface. So far, two computational methods have been applied to interphase boundaries. FLETCHER and LODGE [1975] developed a variational method by using the Fourier transform of the interaction potential, and carried out the calculations in reciprocal space. This accounts for important simplifications as compared to the interaction-force method of DARLING and FIELD [1973]. In the last decade, the computation of the structure of grain-boundary structures has led to the development of sophisticated computational methods (§ 2.2.1.3). In principle, these methods may also be applied to phase boundaries. Apparently, this has not yet been done. The major difficulty of computer simulation methods is the representation of interatomic interactions in the vicinity of any interface. Electron screening effects as well as compositional variations have to be taken into account. At the moment, little hope exists that these difficulties can be solved in the near future. Band-structure calculations suggest that electron screening effects and compositional variations may be the dominant factors.

2.4.4. Ball-and-wire model

The assumption that low energy and high density of coincidence sites is equivalent implicitly assumes, inter alia, that the bonding across the interface is isotropic. It is accordingly not applicable to crystals, such as certain semiconductors, with highly directional covalent bonding. The ball-and-wire model, first introduced by HORNSTRA [1958], to simulate core structures of dislocations in the diamond structure, is particularly suited for representation of interface structure in such systems, the qualitative correspondence between wires and directional bonds being evident. Clearly this model, like the coincidence-lattice model, is one of geometrical matching. The model was subsequently employed in the analysis of planar defect structures in semiconducting compounds. HOLT [1974] has demonstrated its applica-

References: p. 708.

tion to epitaxial heterojunctions in the (111) planes of one sphalerite structure on another or on a diamond crystal structure. The mismatch at the interface revolves into an hexagonal network of edge-type misfit dislocations in which a dislocation line is characterized by a row of 'dangling' bonds rather than the edge of a terminating atomic plane.

The various interfacial models of this type differ according to the nature of the interatomic forces. Evidence for metallic, ionic or covalent interaction forces at interphase boundaries comes from laser–Raman spectroscopy, X-ray photoelectron spectroscopy, electron tunneling spectroscopy and secondary ion mass spectroscopy, showing for example covalent Si–O–Si-type bonds at the interface between glass and polysiloxane and similarly covalent Fe–O–Si- and Cr–O–Si bonds between metal oxides and polysiloxane. Other organic molecules were found to form interphase boundaries of purely ionic character with metal oxides. If the interfacial bonding by metallic, ionic or covalent forces is weak, forces of van der Waals type have been shown to control the adhesion between phases of different structure (OROWAN [1970]).

2.4.5. Electron effects

Bearing in mind that the electronic contribution to the surface tension of transition metals is of the order of the experimentally observed total values (CYROT-LACKMANN [1968]), one may expect that the electronic contribution to the energy of interphase boundaries may also be the dominant term. A rigorous solution of the problem seems beyond present computational capabilities. However, a few attempts have been made assuming the interface to be planar, sharp and atomically smooth.

The simplest approach is to characterize two metals by two different work functions and two Fermi energies. Once they are put together, a dipole layer is created at the interface, which produces an electrostatic potential. By solving this problem in a linearized Thomas–Fermi approximation, and by means of a tight-binding approach, the interfacial energy between various transition metals was found to range between 1 eV and 0.1 eV for interfaces between Cr, Mo and W and transition metals of different transition series (ALLAN et al. [1974]). Although the approximations used are crude, their significance lies in the fact that these energies are comparable with the measured free energies of interphase boundaries, suggesting that electronic effects are generally not negligible.

One way to check the theoretical models experimentally is to measure the charge density at the interface. From measurement of the tensile strength of metal–dielectric joints, a charge density of about 10^{19} electrons/cm^3 was deduced (SKINNER et al. [1953]). However, this result has been questioned on several grounds. In order to enter the conduction band of the dielectric material, the electrons have to acquire an extra energy of 2–4 eV, which seems unlikely. Furthermore, the tensile strength should depend on the height of the potential barrier at the metal–dielectric material and should be independent of time. This was not observed. It was, therefore, suggested that van der Waals forces are dominant. On the other hand, the existence of double layers was demonstrated for Zr-coated Au spheres on CdS crystals. In this system, the energy of the interphase boundary changed as the intensity of illumination was varied (KRUPP and SCHNABEL [1973]). Different illumination intensities change the electronic properties of the photoconducting CdS and, hence, the double layer, leaving other forces, e.g. van der Waals forces, unaffected.

Owing to their great significance in modern technology, the electronic structure and properties of interphase boundaries between metals and semiconductors have been studied theoretically and experimentally in detail. A review of the present state of understanding has been published recently (MCCALDIN and McGILL [1980]).

2.4.6. The effect of temperature on the interfacial energy and width

The compositional profile of the interface between two coexisting phases A and B is a function of temperature. At low temperatures (where entropy effects are negligible), the compositional profile will be narrow in order to minimize the number of "wrong" (A, B) neighbours. If the temperature increases, configurational entropy tends to mix A and B in the interface region and, thus, widens the concentration profile. The earliest theoretical treatment of this problem was due to BECKER [1938], employing a broken-bond model under the assumption that both phases are homogeneous up to their common interface. The major objection to this model is that the width of the interface is not an independent variable, once the temperature and pressure of a system are specified. The discrete lattice approach was subsequently improved by HILLERT [1961] and MEIJERING [1966]. Both authors used statistical thermodynamics to obtain a set of difference equations (one for each lattice plane) from which the concentration profile may be calculated by minimizing the free energy of the system. Though correct, this approach requires tedious numerical solutions. Several years earlier, CAHN and HILLIARD [1958] developed a continuum description. They obtained the interfacial energy to be proportional to $(T_c - T)^{1/2}$. The concentration profile was found to be sigmoidal in shape, and it has a width that increases with temperature and diverges at the critical temperature T_c. In order to analyze anisotropy effects, discrete lattice models are more suitable as they reflect the geometric arrangement of the atoms in the interface.

Recently, LEE and AARONSON [1980] employed a nearest-neighbour broken-bond model to develop relationships for the concentration profile and the interfacial energy. The crystallography of the problem was incorporated by including the nearest-neighbour distribution in the interface. On this basis, the *anisotropy* of the energy (σ) of interphase boundaries was calculated. The ratio of the maximum/minimum values decreased from 1.3 at 0 K to less than 1.006 at $0.75T_c$. This result supports the conclusion of earlier computations that σ is isotropic at high temperatures (KIKUCHI and CAHN [1962]). A quasi-chemical approach to the problem of calculating σ was suggested by MIEDEMA and DEN BROEDER [1979]. The interfacial energy between two solids is split in a chemical and a geometrical contribution. The chemical term is the heat of solution of an isolated B atom in a matrix of A atoms. This part of the energy is taken from experimental measurements. The geometrical term accounts for the lattice distorsion in the vicinity of the interface and is, therefore, approximated by the energy of a high-angle grain

References: p. 708.

boundary. Although rather crude, the merit of this approach is to provide a means of estimating the cohesion energy between dissimilar metals. On the basis of this approach it is predicted that any two metals can be bonded, provided the initial surfaces are clean, even if the two metals do not alloy in the solid state. Tables listing the results of measurements on interphase boundary energies have been published by MURR [1975] and GUST et al. [1978].

2.4.7. Wide boundaries (transition region boundaries)

According to the arguments discussed in the preceding section, interphase boundaries are expected to be narrow (a few interatomic spacings wide) at temperatures far below T_c. Nevertheless, in some alloys wide boundaries were reported. Two types of wide boundaries may be distinguished: kinetically induced wide boundaries and boundaries for which the wide structure seems to represent the equilibrium. Wide interfaces ($\leqslant 0.2$ μm width) between α- and β-Ti were recognized as early as 1966 and seem to belong to the first category. In slowly cooled specimens ($\sim$ 100°C/h), the interface layer is a monolithic crystal with a fcc structure. The only phase consistent with the diffraction pattern would be TiH_2. However, as the amount of hydrogen required to form such a phase is several orders of magnitude more than the typical hydrogen content of the alloys, this possibility was discounted. The same applies to the possibility of modeling the observed transition region as a highly dislocated area. It was, therefore, suggested (RHODES and PATON [1979]) that the interface phase between α- and β-Ti is formed during the $\alpha \rightarrow \beta$ transformation as a result of sluggish diffusion of β-Ti stabilizers. The width of the phase is a function of the cooling rate from solution temperature, with a slower cooling rate prompting a broader interface. A kinetically induced interphase boundary phase was also observed in Ge–Al alloys (KÖSTER [1979]) during crystallization from the amorphous state. Crystallization from the amorphous state involves interphase boundary diffusion which can be enhanced by several orders of magnitude if a 10 nm thick layer of Al is formed at the interface. The remarkably high migration rate of the boundary between a parent phase and a massive phase prompted PEREPEZKO and MASSALSKI [1978] to suggest a widening of the transformation front to about 15–30 lattice constants in the migrating state. The experimentally observed correlation between the atomic structure of grain boundaries in Cu–Ag solid solutions and their ability to act as a nucleation site for a discontinuous reaction front may be understood if the migrating interfaces are assumed to have larger free volumes (and, hence, larger widths) than the stationary counterparts (WIRTH and GLEITER [1981]).

Wide interphase boundaries in the *equilibrated state* have been reported in a few cases. The temperature dependence of the ultimate strength of ice–metal (Cu, Al, Fe) interfaces suggests the existence of a liquid-like layer at the interphase boundary in a temperature range from about -30°C to 0°C, depending on the temperature, the orientation of the ice crystals and the nature of the metal (MANTOVANI and VALERI [1978]). Striking examples of wide interphase boundaries were directly reported in the system α/β quartz (fig. 13). At 573°C, quartz undergoes a phase transition from the α to the β phase. The interphase boundary between the two modifications

Fig. 13. Electron micrograph of the transition region between α and β quartz. The transition region consists of numerous Dauphiné twin domains. The arrows mark positions of defects in the transition region. (From VAN LANDUYT *et al.* [1981].)

consists of an array of Dauphiné twins, the mesh size of which becomes finer and finer until unresolvable in the β-phase (VAN LANDUYT *et al.* [1981]). A similar wide interphase boundary has been observed between the para-electric (cubic) and the ferroelectric (tetragonal) phase of $BaTiO_2$. In this case, the boundary may be described as a wide region in which the tetragonality of the crystal lattice increases continuously (MALIS and GLEITER [1979]). The existence of amorphous intercrystalline phases at interphase boundaries (and also grain boundaries) has been revealed by several authors in recent years by high-resolution electron microscopy (e.g. KRIVANEK *et al.* [1979]). Usually, such amorphous intergranular phases are believed to be induced by impurity enhancement. However, owing to the geometric constraints of the surrounding crystals, these phases cannot crystallize. Any crystallization would give rise to volume changes and, hence, strain energy which opposes the transformation and stabilizes the wide boundaries, even without an enhanced impurity content. In addition, theoretical arguments have been put forward showing that an intermediate layer between two covalent or ionic crystals may have a lower energy than a dense dislocation wall. Numerical results indicate two-dimensional analogues to Bernal's dense random packing polyhedra (ch. 28, § 3.1) to be specifically favoured, resulting in a glassy-type transition structure, the width of which may be several interatomic spacings (GUBANOV [1979]).

References: p. 708.

2.5. Interfaces between crystalline and amorphous phases

Interfaces between crystalline and non-crystalline phases play an important role in partially crystallized glasses and in partially molten materials. Most of our knowledge on the structure of crystalline–amorphous interfaces is limited to monatomic substances. For a recent review, we refer to the work by BONISSENT and MUTAFTSHIEV [1981].

Concerning the structure of crystalline–amorphous interfaces, three groups of models may be distinguished: lattice models, amorphous models and models deduced by means of simulation methods. In the case of *lattice models,* the glass (melt) is assumed to be an isomorphous continuation of the crystal. This idea was, apparently, first suggested by STRANSKI and KRASTANOV [1938], assuming the disordered region to be represented by a lattice of slightly larger interatomic spacings than those of the crystal. This approximation explains thermal expansion and the experimentally observed non-wettability of close-packed planes of the crystal by the melt owing to the impossibility of epitaxy between the ordered and the disordered state. This concept has recently been extended in the framework of the mean-field approximation (VAN LEEUWEN et al. [1974]). The results obtained suggest that the roughness of the interface increases with temperature and depends on the difference between the interatomic interaction energies of the crystalline and the non-crystalline state. The latter parameter also seems to control the mode of the migration of the interface, as follows. If the difference of interaction energies is large or if the undercooling is small, a ledge-type mechanism is favoured, otherwise the migration involves incorporation of isolated atoms (cf. ch. 14, § 2.2.4). This transition is physically closely related to adsorption processes. In terms of this analogy, the transition represents the change-over from first-order condensation on an atomically flat surface to a higher-order condensation on a kinked surface. The main deficiency of the lattice models is that configurational entropy calculations are difficult and the results obtained so far seem to be questionable.

The *amorphous models* try to improve on the lattice models by assuming the structure of the glass (melt) to be practically unchanged up to the surface of the crystal. The first approach of this kind goes back to TURNBULL [1964]. He represented the crystal–amorphous interface by a (mathematically) planar surface. For compatibility reasons (overlap of atoms), all atoms of the amorphous structure sectioned by this planar surface had to be removed. The resulting average density of the surface layer of the amorphous phase is, therefore, only half the bulk density. At low temperatures (glassy state) the interatomic repulsion between the atoms of the crystal and the glass prevents the reintegration of the "sectional atoms", resulting in an energy of the crystal–glass interface that is larger than half the heat of fusion (Stefan's rule). Following the same ideas, EWING [1971] attempted to refine the model by a more sophisticated estimate of the entropy of the crystal–amorphous interface. The two most critical assumptions in Ewing's work are that the entropy required to accommodate the amorphous solid to the crystal can be neglected and that the density distribution in a direction perpendicular to the interface is the radial

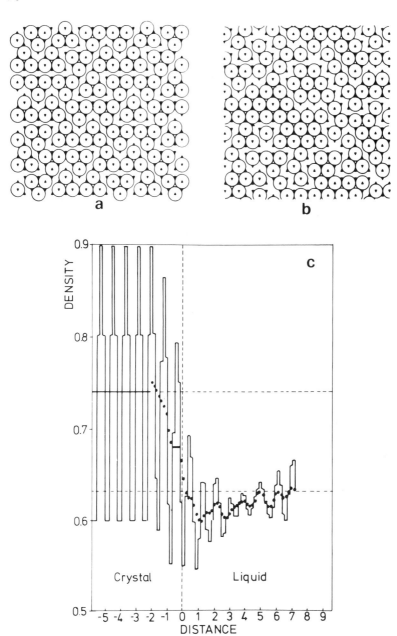

Fig. 14a, b. The possible structures for the "first" liquid layer in contact with a close-packed crystal surface: (a) from the model excluding octahedral configuration (after SPAEPEN [1975]); (b) according to the computer-built model (BONISSENT and MUTAFTSHIEV [1981]); (c) according to Monto-Carlo computations, density versus distance normal to the interface built on the (111) face of a fcc crystal (distance expressed in numbers of interatomic distances, a, density calculated in slices of $0.2a$; points indicate average density over five slices; after BONISSENT *et al.* [1979]).

References: p. 708.

pair distribution function of the glass. In order to improve on this point, FLETCHER [1975] calculated the density function perpendicular to the interface from the probability of atomic configurations having in the first layer the symmetry of the crystal surface. The "thickness" of the crystal–amorphous interface is found to be about 20 Å.

A further attempt along similar lines of thought was made by SPAEPEN [1975]. On the basis of results deduced from hard-sphere models of bulk liquids, the absence of octahedral holes was postulated in the interface region. One can then construct a disordered non-dense layer. As may be seen from fig. 14a, the interfacial region consists of different types of atomic clusters. In the *simulation models*, crystalline–amorphous interfaces are constructed for an ensemble of spheres following the Bernal procedure, with the boundary condition of a solid surface on one side. In practice, hard-sphere experiments as well as computer-generated random packing structures and Monte Carlo simulations have been employed. For details we refer to the review by BONISSENT and MUTAFTSHIEV [1981]. The results obtained (figs. 14a–c) indicate that the first liquid layer consists of two-dimensional epitaxial clusters separated by channels of misfit (figs. 14a, b and figs. 15a–c). These clusters disappear rapidly in the subsequent layers. The density deficit (fig. 14c) in the second and third layer is induced by the order and compactness of the crystal free surface which prohibits a continuous structural transition.

A few experimental studies have been performed on crystal–melt interfaces. They may be divided into growth-kinetic studies (reviewed by WOODRUFF [1973]) and

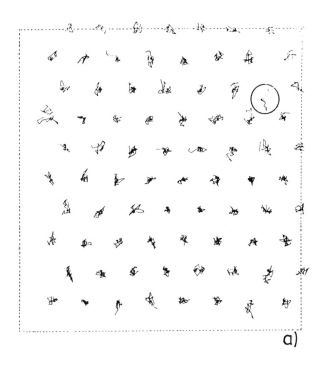

a)

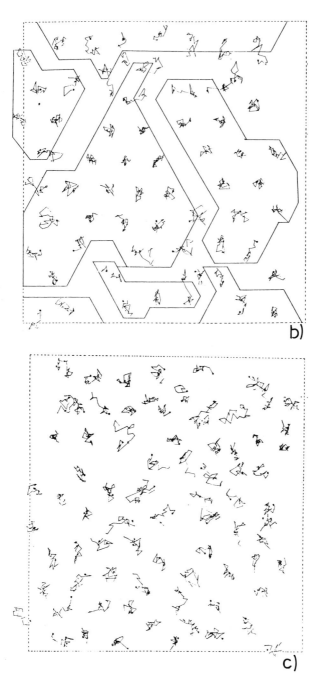

Fig. 15. Sectional views, parallel to and at different distances from the interface, of a model during a Monte-Carlo simulation: (a) top ⟨111⟩-lattice plane; (b) first liquid layer (solid lines indicate two-dimensional epitaxial clusters, see text), (c) liquid layer at a distance of four atomic diameters from the interface. (From BONISSENT *et al.* [1979].)

static measurements (reviewed by BONISSENT and MUTAFTSHIEV [1981]). The results of the kinetic experiments are more difficult to interpret as they depend on parameters, such as the free energies of crystal edges in the growth front etc. The observations by means of static experiments (e.g., contact angles) seem to suggest for metals almost spherical, Herring plots with a few small cusps (see also ch. 9, §4.2).

Clearly, boundaries between ordered and disordered phases are not limited to systems exhibiting atomic order. Similar boundaries exist in solids showing spin ordering (e.g., ferromagnetic materials, ch. 26), polarization ordering (e.g. ferroelectricity) and electron ordering (e.g. type-II superconduction or Wigner crystals). The boundaries in solids with spin ordering and in superconductors are discussed in chs. 25 and 27. Systems exhibiting polarization ordering are beyond the scope of this book at this effect is limited to nonmetals.

2.6. Antiphase boundaries

In a lattice with imperfect long-range order, superlattice regions (*domains*) may exist in which the arrangement of the atoms is out-of-step (out of phase) by a displacement $\vec{R}$ with respect to the arrangement in the adjacent domain (e.g., fig. 16a). The regions of contact between such domains are *antiphase boundaries*. For a review we refer to the paper by VAN TENDELOO and AMELINCKX [1975]. The two most important processes of generating antiphase boundaries are the passage of (partial) dislocations through an ordered structure and the growing together of different nuclei of order. Depending on the displacement between the two adjacent domains, two types of antiphase boundaries are distinguished: conservative (fig. 16a, horizontal section) and non-conservative (fig. 16a, vertical section) boundaries. In the first (second) case, the vector $(\vec{R})$ characterizing the relative displacement between two domains, is parallel (non-parallel) to the domain boundary. As $\vec{R}$ is constant along any boundary, a conservative boundary may become non-conservative on changing its orientation (fig. 16a).

If the repulsive forces between atoms of the same type on both sides of an antiphase boundary are large (e.g., between the atoms represented by large circles in fig. 16) the boundary can lower its energy by dissociating into two *partial domain boundaries* (fig. 16b). This process may be described as the movement of two dislocation dipoles, one along each boundary. An example of the splitting of an antiphase boundary is shown in fig. 16c. Clearly, if a non-conservative boundary contains a non-stoichiometric proportion of constituent atoms, its presence causes a variation in the composition of the crystal. On the other hand, a deviation from stoichiometry may be taken up by such boundaries. Experimental evidence for this correlation between non-stoichiometry and the antiphase boundary structure comes from observations on the arrangement and mobility of antiphase boundaries in alloys of varying composition. In ordered alloys with an $L1_2$ structure, domain boundaries prefer (100) planes in the stoichiometric case and non-cubic planes for all other compositions, as would be expected. By analogy with the impurity-drag effect for grain boundaries, a non-stoichiometric concentration of solute atoms was

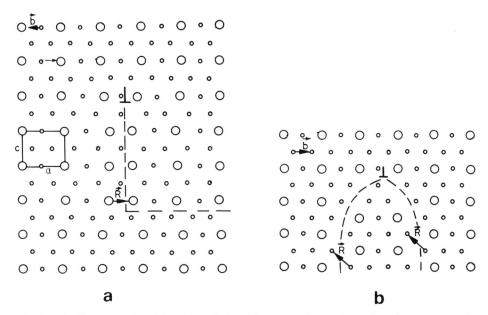

Fig. 16a, b. Structure of antiphase boundaries: (a) conservative (horizontal) and non-conservative (vertical) section of an antiphase boundary; (b) dissociation of the vertical section of the boundary shown in (a).

found to result in drag forces on migrating antiphase boundaries (§ 3.2.1). In ordered phases exhibiting non-centrosymmetric lattices, a type of boundary between ordered domains may be formed that does not exist in centrosymmetric crystals. This boundary is called *inversion boundary* (VAN TENDELOO and AMELINCKX [1979]). Inversion boundaries are boundaries between domains of which the structures are related by an inversion operation. Boundaries of this type play a role, for example, in ferroelectric materials.

In the vicinity of an antiphase boundary, a certain amount of disorder exists at finite temperatures, due to entropy effects. With increasing temperature, the width of the boundary (i.e. the region where the order parameter differs from unity) will increase by displacing more and more atoms from the lattice sites they would occupy in the case of perfect order. This effect is commonly called the thermally induced "widening" of the antiphase boundary.

A one-dimensional model of the effect based on the Bragg–Williams approxima- tion (BROWN [1959]) indicates that the boundary width is of the order of the interatomic distance except very close to the critical temperature, where it diverges. In a more sophisticated way, the variation of the boundary free energy with temperature was computed for AB-alloys with a bcc structure by means of the cluster variation method (KIKUCHI [1972]). At high temperatures, the boundary energy was found to become independent of the boundary position relative to the lattice planes. However, at low temperatures, boundaries centred between two rows

References: p. 708.

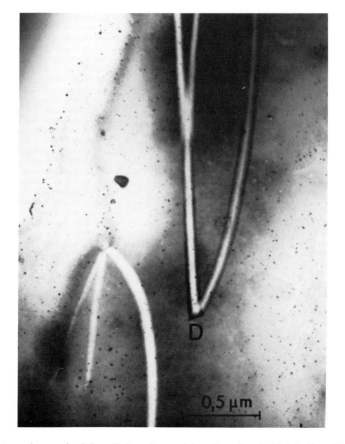

Fig. 16c. Electron micrograph of the splitting of an antiphase boundary in Ni$_3$Mo (from VAN TENDELOO and AMELINCKX [1975]).

of atoms had a lower energy than boundaries coinciding with atomic planes. This result suggests that second-order phase transformation occurs in antiphase boundaries between the "atomic centre boundary", stable at high temperatures, and the low-temperature structure centred between the atomic planes.

3. Development of microstructure

3.1. Basic aspects

The microstructure of a crystalline material may result from structural phase transformations and/or interaction processes between structural defects. In fact, a general and reciprocal relationship exists between microstructures and defect inter-actions. Any microstructure may be interpreted as the result of the interaction between structural defects and/or phase transformations. On the other hand, it should be possible to synthesize new microstructures (and, hence, materials with new properties) by utilizing this relationship, e.g., by means of more complex defect interactions (possibly combined with phase transformations). The thermomechanical treatment of materials represents an example of this kind. Microstructures generated by structural phase transformations only are discussed in chs. 9, 14, 15, 16 and 28. Microstructures resulting from the interaction between some specific types of lattice defects are treated in chs. 21, 22, 24, 26 and 27. In this chapter, attention will be focused on those microstructures that are not the result of phase transformations. Despite the complexity of all conceivable processes for the development of micro-structures, a guideline for a systematic understanding of the genesis of microstruc-tures may be provided by considering some relatively simple and well studied types of interaction processes involving only one or two types of structural defects. This "model approach" will be used here.

3.2. Microstructural changes motivated by interfacial-energy reduction

Three classes of microstructural changes driven by interfacial energy may be distinguished:

1. Microstructural changes in single-phase materials (without applied potential fields).

2. Microstructural changes in polyphase materials (without applied potential fields) when the materials have: (a) a dispersion-type structure; (b) a duplex (or a network) structure.

3. Microstructural changes due to the effects of applied potential fields (e.g. temperature-or electric field gradients).

An excellent review of these classes is by MARTIN and DOHERTY [1976].

3.2.1. Microstructural changes in single-phase materials, motivated by interfacial energy: domain and grain growth

Internal interfaces in solids – such as grain boundaries or domain boundaries in ordered systems (atomic order, spin order, polarization order, etc.) – are associated with a positive excess energy resulting in grain or domain growth. Local atomic arrangements at or near moving interfaces can differ significantly from arrange-ments at or near stationary interfaces, giving rise, for example, to drag effects (solute- or defect drag), structural changes of the interfaces due to defect production, etc. A complete theory of interfacial motion would have to account not only for these effects, but also for the topological changes of the array of interconnected interfaces during domain and grain growth. So far no such theory is at hand. However, models treating various aspects of the problem separately have been put forward. The problems of the growth of grains or magnetic domains are treated in chs. 25 and 26, respectively. As many growth theories make no distinction between grain and domain growth, we refer to ch. 25 for all theories that apply to both processes. This section will be limited to theories of domain growth only.

Two approaches to describe the motion of a domain wall have been proposed.

References: p. 708.

The earlier, widely used phenomenological approach states that the wall mobility is proportional to the thermodynamic driving force, the proportionality constant being a positive quantity called the mobility. The driving force in this approach is the product of the mean of the local principal curvatures of the interface and the excess free energy per unit area (σ). This approach leads to a growth law of the type $\langle D \rangle^2 \propto \sigma t$, where $\langle D \rangle$ is the average diameter of the domains in a polydomain structure and t is the time. This result has been experimentally confirmed for several ordered alloys (e.g. ARDELL et al. [1979] and ROGERS et al. [1975]) and can account for the broad distribution of domain sizes frequently observed experimentally.

Several physical justifications for this approach have been offered. By analogy with grain growth (BECK [1954]), the driving force for domain growth was assumed to be proportional to the domain boundary energy. More recently, HILLERT [1965] used a modification of the Ostwald ripening theory, confirming the $\langle D \rangle^2 \propto \sigma t$ law. This result also holds true if the theory is adapted to the specific geometries of domain wall arrangements (SAUTHOFF [1973]). Some of the foundations of Hillert's analysis were reexamined by LOUAT [1974], who pointed out that in grain growth, as opposed to Ostwald ripening, "grain collisions" occur in which faces are gained or lost. In order to allow for these factors, domain growth was considered as a particular case of a random walk process.

The approach of ALLEN and CAHN [1979] models the motion of an interface by solving a diffusion equation that has been modified to account for the thermodynamics of non-uniform systems (LANGER and SEKERKA [1975]). Domain walls (cf. § 2.6) have a width in which there are compositional and order-parameter variations, i.e., a crystal containing a domain wall is a non-uniform system. The order-parameter variation is the basis of a diffusion potential whose gradient results in an atomic flux. This description leads to a time-independent Ginsburg–Landau equation for changes in the order parameter and hence for the wall motion. In the limit of large radii (r) of wall curvature, the propagation velocity (V) of the wall is found to be proportional to r, but independent of the excess energy (σ) of the wall. This does not imply that the energy dissipation during domain growth is independent of σ. In fact, the energy dissipation may be shown to be proportional to σ.

Experimental tests were carried out in which σ was varied by two orders of magnitude. Domain-coarsening kinetics and σ were found to scale differently with temperature as was predicted theoretically. On the basis of the results discussed so far, we are led to conclude that cases exist where V is proportional to σ, and there are clearly other cases where V is independent or even nonlinearly dependent on σ (e.g. TURNBULL [1951] and LI [1969]). No general criterion seems apparent at present for relating V to σ and boundary curvature for different experimental conditions.

3.2.2. Microstructural changes in polyphase materials with a dispersion structure, motivated by interfacial energy: Ostwald ripening

If interfacial energy is the only driving force for an instability and if the rate of development of the instability is governed only by mass transport processes, the

linear dimension, d, of any microstructural feature can be shown (HERRING [1950])
to scale with time by the expression:

$$d^n = d_0^n + \alpha G t, \tag{1}$$

where d_0 is the value of d at time $t = 0$, G is the parameter of the appropriate mass
transport process and α is a dimensionless parameter which depends on the
geometry. The scaling exponent, n, takes the values: $n = 1$ for viscous flow, $n = 2$ for
interfacial control, $n = 3$ for volume diffusion in all phases, $n = 4$ for interfacial
diffusion and $n = 5$ for pipe diffusion. The growth laws discussed in the following
paragraphs for specific processes extend eq. (1) by giving explicit expressions for α
and G. Normally, microstructural changes in multiphase alloys involve changes of
shape, size and/or position simultaneously. For convenience, these three aspects are
discussed separately.

An array of inclusions or dislocation loops or pores of equilibrium shape, but
different sizes, interact because the concentration of solute atoms (or the concentration of vacancies, or the vapour pressure in a gaseous system) in the vicinity of small
(large) particles is higher (lower) than the average supersaturation. The solute,
therefore, flows from the smaller to the larger particles. Hence, smaller particles
shrink and larger particles grow by "devouring" the smaller ones, a process known
as *Ostwald ripening*. For reviews of various aspects of the problem, we refer to the
articles by JAIN and HUGHES [1978], KAHLWEIT [1975] and HENDERSON *et al.* [1978].
The phenomenon of Ostwald ripening was analyzed first for the solid state by
GREENWOOD [1956], and then independently and simultaneously by WAGNER [1961]
and by LIFSHITZ and SLYOZOV [1961], assuming the common case of spherical
precipitates growing by volume diffusion. Analogous expressions have been developed for other types of coarsening. The corresponding constants (α, G, n) of eq. (1)
are summarized in table 1. In the case of coarsening of spheres by volume diffusion,
which is the most commonly observed case ($r^3 \propto t$), a steady-state distribution of
sizes is predicted to be approached irrespective of the initial size distribution, with a
maximum particle size of $1.5 \bar{r}$, where $\bar{r}$ is the mean particle radius (figs. 17a, b).

A critical assumption in the Lifshitz–Slyozov–Wagner (LSW) theory is that the
diffusion fields around each particle are spherically symmetrical. This is strictly valid
for zero volume fraction of precipitates when the concentration gradients around
adjacent particles do not interfere. If the LSW theory is extended (ARDELL [1972]) to
account for finite volume fractions, the basic form of eq. (1) is retained but the
proportionality constant α is increased and the particle size distribution is broadened. The LSW analysis cannot persist to very large times, because ultimately the
system should ripen into one large particle. In fact, it was shown (KAHLWEIT [1975]
that the coarsening rate of the largest particles initially increases rather rapidly, then
passes through a maximum and slowly approaches zero for long periods of time. The
value of the coarsening rate predicted by the LSW theory is reached shortly before
reaching the maximum rate. The significance of coherency strains for Ostwald
ripening effects is still a matter of controversy and will be discussed in the next
sub-section on stability against coarsening. In the LSW treatment, solute transport is

References: p. 708.

Table 1

Ostwald ripening rates.

Rate-controlling process	Shape of particles	Expressions for constants [a]			Reference
		n	α	G	
Volume diffusion	Spheres	3	8/9	$D\sigma_b C_\alpha V_m / RT$	WAGNER [1961] LIFSHITZ and SLYOZOV [1961]
	Plates	3	$3A'(1 + A'/A'_{eq})$	$Df\sigma_b V_m / 2\,pRT$	DOHERTY [1982]
Grain-boundary diffusion	Spheres	4	9/32	$D_b\sigma C_\alpha V_m\delta / ABRT$	ARDELL [1972] KIRCHNER [1971]
Dislocation-pipe diffusion	Spheres	5	$(1{,}03)^5(3/4)^4 5/6\pi$	$D_d\sigma_b C_\alpha V_m qN\eta / RT$	ARDELL [1972]
Interface-limited growth		2	64/81	$\sigma_b\beta C_\alpha V_m / RT$	DOHERTY [1982]

[a] The symbols used are given below with their meaning or an expression

A	parameter, $A = 2/3 - \sigma_b/\sigma + (\sigma_b/\sigma)^2/24$.
B	parameter, $B = \frac{1}{2}\ln 1/f$.
A', A'_{eq}	average and equilibrium aspect ratios of precipitate, respectively.
C_α, C_β	precipitate and matrix concentrations, respectively.
D, D_b, D_d	general, boundary, and dislocation-pipe diffusion constants, resp.
f	function given by $f = C(1 - C_\alpha)/(C_\beta - C_\alpha)^2$.
N	number of dislocations intersecting one particle.
p	parameter tending to π for large precipitates.
q	diffusional cross-section of a dislocation.
R	gas constant.
T	temperature.
V_m	molar volume.
β	proportionality constant including the interface mobility.
δ	boundary thickness.
η	geometrical parameter.
σ (σ_b)	energy of grain boundary or interphase boundary.

assumed to be the rate-controlling process. Hence, modifications are required if other processes play a role, for example, ternary additions, solvent transport effects or dissociation of solute and/or solvent molecules. The latter case has been discussed by WAGNER [1961]. The effect of solvent transport may be accounted for (ORIANI [1964]) by modifying the diffusion parameter D in the LSW equations, leaving the main result (growth law, size distribution) unaltered. The modification of D becomes important, however, if we use growth-law observations to derive σ, D etc. The same applies to the effect of ternary additions on the ripening rate. Ternary additions alter the rate constants of coarsening by a factor $\frac{1}{3}(1 - K)^{-2}c_0^{-1}$, leaving the scaling law unchanged (BJORKLUND *et al.* [1972]). c_0 is the ternary alloy content and K is the distribution coefficient. Ostwald ripening of semi-coherent plate-shaped precipitates (Widmanstätten plates) represents yet another case for which the LSW

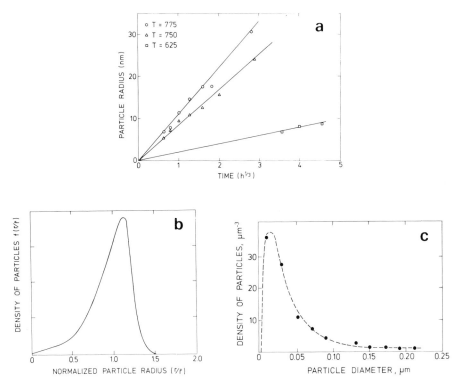

Fig. 17. (a) Plot of the particle radius against (time)$^{1/3}$ for a nickel–aluminium alloy annealed at three different temperatures (from ARDELL *et al.* [1966]). (b, c) Size distribution developed during Ostwald ripening: (b) theoretical prediction according to the Lifshitz–Slyozov–Wagner theory; (c) experimental observation on silica particles in copper annealed at 1173 K for 27 h. (From BHATTACHARYA and RUSSELL [1976].)

treatment cannot be applied without modifications. Ostwald ripening of Widmanstätten plates results in large aspect ratios, as the lengthening of these plates is diffusion-limited whereas the thickening is mobility-controlled by the good-fit (semi-coherent) interface (AARONSON *et al.* [1970] and FERRANTE and DOHERTY [1979]).

The experimental confirmations of the theoretical predictions on Ostwald ripening are still fragmentary (for a review see JAIN and HUGHES [1978]). Although numerous experiments confirming the scaling laws given in table 1 have been reported (for a review of the earlier data we refer to MARTIN and DOHERTY [1976]), the relatively small range of particle sizes that can be obtained experimentally is not sufficiently precise to allow unambiguous identification of the scaling exponent. In most cases, the observed size distributions are wider than those predicted by the theory (figs. 17b and 17c). Frequently, also a few large particles are found which are not a part of the main system of particles. Furthermore, a tail on the large-size side of the size distribution is observed, in contradiction to the LSW theory.

The available experimental evidence on the effect of volume fraction on coarsening is conflicting. Studies on Cu–Co alloys showed clear dependence on volume fraction, whereas other work (Ni_3Al in Ni, NbC in Fe, Cu in α-Fe) failed to detect any effect. Recent experimental work has evidenced the possibility of contact between growing precipitates. The theoretical discussion of this effect is based on independent growth of adjacent precipitates, the centre-to-centre distance between the particles remaining fixed (DAVIS et al. [1980a]). It is, however, difficult to see how the solute atoms are led into the narrowing gap between adjacent particles. An alternative hypothesis is that the particles will actually attract each other and move together in order to reduce the elastic strain energy. As similar effects have been seen in alloys with small lattice misfit (Ni–Cr–Al), this hypothesis seems not to provide a convincing explanation. In a number of alloys (e.g. carbides in steels, UAl_2 in α-U, θ in Al–Cu alloys) evidence has been presented suggesting substructure-enhanced diffusion, i.e., power laws during coarsening ($r^n \propto t$) where n is greater than 3. In none of these studies were attempts made to fit the results to one of the theoretically predicted relationships $r^n \propto t$ and no work seems to have been published which attempted to check if the details of the substructure-enhanced diffusion theories are correct. The general conclusion, though, is that the theories described seem successful in accounting qualitatively for the effect of lattice defects on coarsening.

3.2.2.1. Stability against coarsening. The general condition for Ostwald ripening to proceed is the decrease of the free energy. In the case of precipitates surrounded by an elastic strain field, the total energy (E) of an array of precipitates consists of the volume energy, the interfacial energy of the precipitates and the elastic energy of the strain fields. If the precipitate volume is constant, E depends only on the elastic energy and the interfacial energy. In the special case of two precipitates in a solid (volumes V_1 and V_2), the surface energy (S) and elastic energy (T) scale as ($V_1^{2/3} + V_2^{2/3}$) and ($V_1 + V_2$) + V_1V_2f/a^3, respectively, where a is the separation of the two precipitates and f is a function that is unity for distant precipitates. If $T \gg S$, the total energy (for $V_1 + V_2 =$ const.) has a minimum if $V_1 = V_2$. In other words, the strain energy stabilizes the two particles of the same size against coarsening into one large particle. Basically, the same arguments hold for infinite arrays of particles as was apparently first recognized by KHATCHATURYAN and SHATALOV [1969]. The general conditions for stability of precipitate arrays against coarsening were recently worked out by PERKOVIC et al. [1979]. Stability was found to be promoted by low interfacial energies, large elastic misfits and large volume fractions of precipitates. The phenomenon of elastic stabilization may be significant for the design of high-temperature alloys. In fact, the growth rates observed experimentally for θ' precipitates in Al–Cu alloys (BOYD and NICHOLSON [1971]) seem to support this view. AUBAUER [1972] has attempted to account for certain fine dispersions being stable against coarsening in terms of the diffuseness of the interface between a precipitate and the surrounding matrix, as described by CAHN and HILLIARD [1958]. If one assumes that the diffuse rim surrounding a precipitate is independent of precipitate size, it can readily be seen that the fraction of material that is in the precipitate and not in the rim will increase as the size increases. The bulk of the precipitate has a different structure and therefore a different atomic volume from the matrix while in the interface rim zone it is assumed that the structure changes steadily towards the matrix. Consequently, the precipitate and the rim zone are associated with an elastic distortion. The energy associated with this distortion increases as the particle grows, whereas the energy associated with the diffuse interfaces decreases as the total surface area is reduced during coarsening. If the surface energy is sufficiently small and if there is a finite rim thickness and appreciable strain energy, a minimum exists in the total energy, stabilizing the corresponding particle size. This conclusion was questioned because of the treatment of the strain energy used (De Fontaine [1973]) and because the precipitates, even if stabilized against growth, should be unstable against a change in shape, for example towards a disk (Morral and Louat [1974]). On the other hand, the Aubauer model seems to account successfully for several reported cases (Gaudig and Warlimont [1969], Warlimont and Thomas [1970]) where very fine dispersions of coherent ordered particles were seen to resist coarsening. For further details concerning stable arrays of precipitates, we refer to §3.5.1.1.

3.2.2.2. Technological applications of coarsening theory. In all types of coarsening, the rate of the process is proportional to the interfacial energy (σ) driving the process and the solubility C_α of the solute atoms. Furthermore for all, except the relatively rare interface-controlled situation, the coarsening rate also scales with the diffusion coefficient (D). Hence, alloys for high-temperature application, where low coarsening rates are desirable, may be obtained if σ, C_α or D are small. This expectation is borne out by various classes of high-temperature materials.

Nickel-based superalloys containing coherent ordered γ' precipitates (Ni_3Al structure) in a disordered γ-matrix (Ni–Al solid solution) have exceptionally *low interfacial energies* of the order of 10^{-2} J/m^2. As this energy increases with increasing lattice misfit between the γ and the γ' phases, alloys of zero misfit are expected to show maximum lifetime in creep experiments. This expectation is borne out by the observations. In fact, owing to the different solubility of most elements in the γ and γ' phase, the γ/γ' misfit can be tailored to zero by the addition of solute elements to equalize the lattice constants of both phases (e.g., Cr).

Low solubility can easily be achieved by using precipitate phases with high energies of formation and with a type of chemical bonding that differs from the surrounding matrix. The most well-known examples are low-solubility oxide-dispersed phases, e.g. Al_2O_3 in Al. Except for very special cases, such phases cannot be precipitated from a supersaturated solid solution. Therefore, other techniques, such as powder metallurgy, internal oxidation or implantation are commonly applied. If the atomic radius of the solute atoms differs strongly from the atomic size of the matrix material, the two metals normally show negligible solubility in the solid state. Alloys of this type (e.g. W–Na, Al–Fe) have also been used to obtain coarsening-resisting materials.

Low diffusion coefficients have been applied in several ferrous alloys to resist coarsening. For example, the addition of a third component which segregates

References: p. 708.

preferentially to the carbide phase (e.g. Cr, Mo, W) can slow down the coarsening of carbides considerably as it requires diffusion of both carbon and the third element and the latter, being substitutional, diffuses much more slowly than the carbon.

3.2.3. Microstructural changes in polyphase materials with a duplex structure, motivated by interfacial energy

A *duplex structure* (SMITH [1954]) is an oriented crystallographic unit consisting of two phases with a definite orientation relationship to each other. Technologically and scientifically, the most important group of duplex structures are rod- or plate-shaped duplex structures, such as directionally solidified eutectics (for a review cf. LIVINGSTON [1971]). As the growth of large lamellae at the expense of smaller ones is not associated with a decrease in the surface-to-volume ratio, lamellar structures are expected to coarsen (in the absence of substructural effects) only by motion of lamellar terminations.

Two mechanisms have been put forward for this process. CLINE [1971] and GRAHAM and KRAFT [1966] proposed the curvature at the lamellar termination (fault) to be associated with a flux of A atoms from the α phase to the β phase (fig. 18). The second mechanism of lamellar coarsening involves the diffusion of solute atoms from the finely spaced (λ_1) lamellae along a migrating boundary to the widely spaced (λ_2) lamellae on the other side of the interface (fig. 19). The theoretical analysis of the process (LIVINGSTON and CAHN [1974]) relates the boundary migration rate (V) to the spacing λ_2 of the widely spaced lamellae. The coarsening rate increases with increasing temperature and decreasing spacing of the lamellae as both effects reduce the diffusion times required. As short-circuit diffusion along grain boundaries becomes dominant at lower temperatures, coarsening by boundary migration is expected to become more prominent than coarsening by fault migration with decreasing temperatures as was observed experimentally. In comparison to coarsening by fault recession (fig. 18), coarsening by boundary migration becomes more important at finer spacings of the lamellae. *Rod-shaped microstructures* are unstable with respect to shape and dimensional changes as they may decrease the surface-to-volume ratio by these processes. As was pointed out by CLINE [1971] and ARDELL [1972], the processes involved in dimensional changes are identical to Ostwald ripening (§ 3.2.2). In alloys produced by eutectic growth, the microstructure may be initially stabilized by the very uniform rod diameter. The time required for the steady state distribution of rod diameters to be built up during coarsening may be longer than for normal precipitate coarsening where a whole spectrum of particle sizes is present at the very beginning. In the present paragraph, attention will be focused on shape changes due to the coarsening of rod-shaped microstructures. The growth of a shape perturbation on a cylinder was already analyzed a century ago by LORD RAYLEIGH [1878]. However, it is only relatively recently that quantitative models for the spheroidization of cylindrical precipitates have been put forward (CLINE [1971], HO and WEATHERLY [1975], NICHOLS [1976]). The theoretical treatments indicate (fig. 20) that a long fibre (length *l*) of radius *d* (with *l/d* > 7.2) is eventually replaced by a string of spheres (*Rayleigh instability*) where the sphere

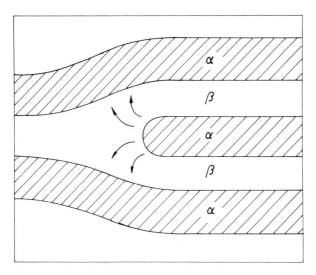

Fig. 18. Schematic of mass flux in the vicinity of a lamellar termination (fault). The curvature at the termination is proposed to induce mass flow of A atoms (from the α-phase) to the β matrix, leading to a recession of the termination with a corresponding increase in the thickness of the adjacent lamellae. (From CLINE [1971].)

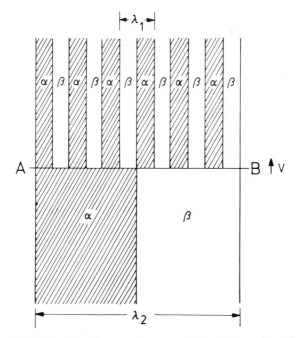

Fig. 19. Idealized model of discontinuous coarsening process. The grain boundary AB moves at a velocity V, consuming fine lamellae with spacing λ_1 and generating coarse lamellae with spacing λ_2. (From LIVINGSTON and CAHN [1974].)

References: p. 708.

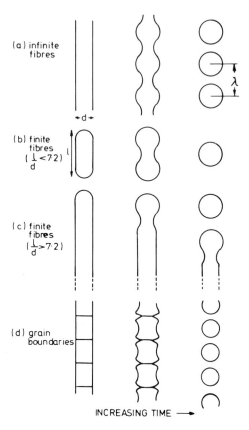

Fig. 20. Schematic representation of different modes of spheroidization of cylindrical inclusions (from McLean [1978]).

radii and spacing, λ, depend on the active kinetic processes. When the aspect ratio (l/d) is less than 7.2, shape relaxation to a single sphere is predicted. For infinite fibres, Rayleigh instabilities are predicted to dominate, whereas in the case of fibres with finite length, drop detachment at the end of the fibres (fig. 20c) should be the faster process. Experimental observation for metallic (W–Na, Al–Pb, fig. 21) and nonmetallic systems ($NaNO_3$–H_2O, Ni–Al_2O_3) seem to support the view that progressive spheroidization from the ends of the fibres dominates. Yet another mechanism of spheroidization, which applies to both fibrous and lamellar inclusions, exists when grain boundaries in either phase intersect phase boundaries between the fibres and the matrix. At the points of intersection, grooves develop and progressively deepen with time to establish a local equilibrium configuration. Eventually, the grooves cause a division of one phase and result in spheroidization (fig. 20d). This process seems to be a serious limitation to many directionally solidified eutectic materials for high-temperature operation. In addition to the instabilities mentioned

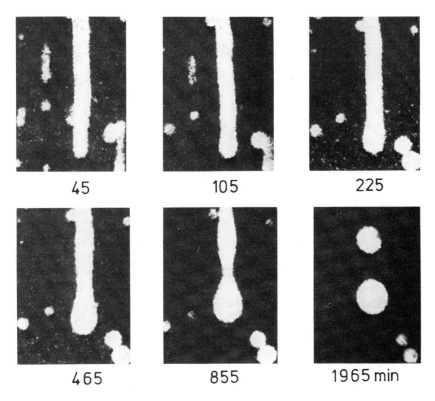

45   105   225

465   855   1965 min

Fig. 21. Series of microradiographs showing the change in shape of Pb inclusions in Al as a function of annealing time at 620°C (from MCLEAN [1973]).

so far, rod phases may also coarsen by *fault migration*. *Faults* are points of a rod at which additional rods form by branching or at which a rod terminates. The termination of a rod is expected to shrink backward for the same reasons as apply to the shrinkage of a terminating lamella (cf. fig. 18). Because of the negative radius of curvature at the rod–matrix interface at a branching point, the branches are expected to fill in, i.e., to migrate in the growth direction, as was observed. Theories of the kinetics of fault migration have been presented by CLINE [1971] and by WEATHERLY and NAKAGAWA [1971].

Instabilities were reported at the periphery of spherical cavities growing under stress along interfaces. If the stress was sufficiently large (WINGROVE and TAPLIN [1969]), finger-shaped instabilities were seen to develop. The critical parameter for the development of these instabilities instead of spherical growth seems to be the ratio of the diffusion coefficients at the cavity surface and a boundary supplying the vacancies (BEERÉ [1978]). Instabilities cannot develop if this ratio is large (typically > 100). For materials with slower surface diffusion, cavities above a critical size

References: p. 708.

become unstable. The critical size depends on the applied stress and the cavity spacing.

3.2.4. Coarsening by Brownian motion

The spontaneous random motion of gas-filled cavities, leading to a coarsening process by cavity coalescence when two cavities meet, has been deduced both by direct observation, and indirectly. The first observations were apparently made on UO$_2$ plates irradiated with neutrons to produce fission fragments (krypton, xenon) which precipitated in the form of gas-filled cavities (GULDEN [1969]). These cavities were seen in the electron microscope to show Brownian motion, the rate of which was controlled by volume diffusion in the host crystal for cavities above 3.7 nm diameter. Similar observations were made for helium-filled cavities in gold and copper, krypton in platinum and xenon in aluminium (cf. GEGUZIN and KRIVOGLAZ [1973]) and helium bubbles in vanadium (TYLER and GOODHEW [1980]).

3.2.5. Microstructural changes motivated by interfacial energy in the presence of external potential fields

The presence of a field of varying potential (e.g. due to a stress- or a temperature gradient, or due to electric or gravitational fields) modifies the driving forces for diffusion and, thus, may result in microstructural changes.

3.2.5.1. Temperature gradients.

The theory of diffusional migration was first developed for volume diffusion in a temperature gradient. In the subsequent decade this work was extended by several authors to surface-diffusion controlled processes and other fields, such as electric, magnetic, stress or gravitational field gradients. For a review of this development, we refer to the book by GEGUZIN and KRIVOGLAZ [1973].

The dominant physical reason for an inclusion to migrate in a temperature gradient is the temperature-dependence of the solubility. For example, let us consider a liquid inclusion in a solid. We assume that at the "front" side of the inclusion (where the temperature is highest), the liquid in contact with the solid has a lower solute content than at the (colder) "rear" surface. The different solute content results in a concentration gradient and, hence, in a flux of solute atoms from the rear to the "front" surface, which causes the "front" surface to melt and the "rear" surface to freeze. In addition to the atom flux resulting from this process, causing the inclusion to migrate *up* the temperature gradient, there is also a drag exerted on the atoms by a directional flux of phonons (phonon wind) which results from the temperature gradient. Similarly, in metals with aspherical Fermi surfaces, the diffusing atoms are dragged by an electron wind which appears under these circumstances in a temperature gradient. In the most simple case of a spherical inclusion in a temperature gradient, the velocity (v) of the inclusion of size R is found to depend linearly on the temperature gradient (grad T). The velocity v is proportional to (grad T) $\cdot R^n$, with $n = 0$, 1, -1 if the rate-controlling process is diffusion through the matrix, the particle–matrix boundary or the particle, respectively. As all parts of the inclusion move with the same velocity, there is no shape change during migration.

All of these results assume the matrix–particle interface to act as ideal sink and source for vacancies. If this is not so, the velocity is smaller or the inclusion is not mobile at all. The first experimental investigations on the motion of inclusions in a temperature gradient were apparently carried out on the motion of aqueous solution droplets in sodium nitrate (LEMMLEIN [1952]), although the motion of brine inclusions in a temperature gradient was already invoked by WHITMAN [1926] to explain the fact that Polar ice becomes purer at its cold upper surface. In the last decade, the motion of gaseous and liquid droplets in a temperature gradient has been studied in a variety of metallic and nonmetallic systems (e.g. He in Cu, Kr in UO_2, W in Cu, water in $NaNO_2$, water in KCL, water in NaCl, Li in LiF, NH_4Cl bubbles in NH_4Cl, gas-filled bubbles in KBr, NaCl, KCl, Pb in Al; for a review see GEGUZIN and KRIVOGLAZ [1973]). The observed migration velocities as well as the correlation between the velocity and the inclusion size was in all cases well accounted for by the theoretical prediction.

Above a certain temperature gradient, the migrating droplets (e.g. voids or gas bubbles in nuclear fuel elements, metal droplets in semiconductors or water droplets in ionic crystals) start to break down by the growth of protrusions from the rear corner releasing a thin trailing liquid veil. The physical reason for the breakdown is the difference between the thermal gradient at the edges and in the center of the droplets, resulting in different migration rates of the two regions. An additional factor comes in when the inclusion contains *two phases,* such as liquid and vapour. The additional factor is the change of the interfacial free energy with temperature, and it may cause the inclusion to migrate *down* the temperature gradient (ANTHONY and CLINE [1972]). Consider a spherical gas-filled inclusion in potassium chloride subjected to a temperature gradient. The wall of this gas-filled inclusion is assumed to be covered by a liquid film of brine. In addition to the normal diffusive flux from the hot to the cold surface, there is a flow of liquid in the liquid film caused by the fall in the liquid–vapour interfacial energy as the temperature falls. The interfacial-energy-induced flow in the liquid film is the essential step in the movement of the inclusion, as it carries potassium chloride that will be deposited at the hot side of the inclusion so that the inclusion moves to the cold end of the crystal. An analysis based on this model successfully predicted the observed velocities of two-phase inclusions in potassium chloride.

Probably the technologically most important observations are those of thermal migration of nuclear fuels through protective coatings in the temperature gradients associated with nuclear reactors (McLEAN [1982]). In recent years, thermal migration effects led to some concern over the microstructural stability of high-temperature alloys; in particular, in situ composite materials, exposed to high-temperature gradients, in turbine blades. Investigations on the thermal stability of eutectic composites (Ni-, Al-, Pb-base alloys) provide evidence for thermal instabilities under the conditions used in modern aircraft engines (HOUGHTON and JONES [1978]). The other problem of considerable practical relevance is the effect of temperature

References: p. 708.

gradients on Ostwald ripening. The available evidence is controversial, indicating – often for the same system – that thermal gradients may increase, not affect or decrease the rate of Ostwald ripening (e.g., DAVIS et al. [1980b], and JONES and MAY [1975]). This controversy may be due to different rate-controlling processes in the various experiments. Ostwald ripening is enhanced if adjacent migrating particles collide and join up (JONES and MAY [1975]) or because the back and front of an inclusion migrate with different velocities owing to the different temperatures at those sites (MCLEAN [1978]). However, temperature gradients can also decrease Ostwald ripening owing to the generation of a shape instability, as was discussed previously (veil formation).

3.2.5.2. Temperature cycling. This may affect the microstructure of alloys by three effects (MCLEAN [1982]):

  (i) a variation of the solubility of the phases;
  (ii) a differential thermal expansion leading to local strain gradients;
  (iii) capillary terms arising from the Gibbs–Thompson effect.

In the most alloys, the first effect seems to dominate and may result in accelerated Ostwald ripening or morphological changes, as was observed in composites that were remarkably stable under isothermal conditions (COOPER and BILLINGHAM [1980]).

3.2.5.3. Magnetic fields. The energy of a magnetic phase is altered by the presence of a magnetic field, and hence the microstructure of alloys that are magnetic will be changed by the application of a magnetic field. This subject has been extensively reviewed by CULLITY [1972]. Magnetic fields may affect both the atomic order in stable solid solutions and the precipitation from supersaturated solid solutions. In stable solid solutions, magnetic fields generate *directional order* (ch. 26, §5.3.3.3) by altering the proportion of like pairs that are aligned in the field direction. Such an alignment causes no change from the random situation in terms of the total fractions of like and unlike nearest-neighbour pairs.

During precipitation from solid solutions, magnetic fields favour the formation of those precipitates that are aligned with respect to the external field. The best known example is the preferred formation of magnetic rods aligned parallel to the magnetic field in Alnico alloys. A preferred orientation of precipitates may also be achieved during coarsening in the presence of a magnetic field. For example, if Fe_8N precipitates coarsened in a magnetic field, a complete orientation of the disc-shaped particles normal to the field direction was achieved (NEUHÄUSER and PITSCH [1971]). Owing to the smaller demagnetization factor, the spins of the precipitates parallel to the magnetic field (H) become aligned so that a single domain structure is formed. This domain structure increases the energy of the Fe_8N/Fe interphase boundary. Hence, precipitates oriented normal to H have the lowest free energy and, thus, grow at the expense of the other precipitates.

In materials of anisotropic magnetic susceptibility, external magnetic fields induce phase or grain-boundary migration. The observations so far available on this effect, are limited to grain-boundary migration experiments in diamagnetic bismuth (MULLINS [1956]).

3.2.5.4. Stress fields. By analogy with magnetic fields, external stresses can modify the atomic order in stable solid solutions and the precipitate morphology in two-phase alloys. Directional atomic order has been induced in Fe–Al alloys by stress-annealing (BIRKENBEIL and CAHN [1962]).

In two-phase materials external stresses may result in the alignment of precipitates and/or in shape changes. Several examples for the first effect have been reported: Fe_8N in FeN, Au in Fe–Mo–Au, θ and θ' in Al–Cu, $ZrH_{1.5}$ in Zr–H, Ti-hydride in Ti–H, γ' in Ni–Al alloys (MIGAZAKI *et al.* [1979]). Apparently, only a few observations of stress-induced shape changes have been published (MIGAZAKI *et al.* [1979], TIEN and COPLEY [1971]). Owing to the elastic anisotropy of the matrix and the precipitate, the free energy of a precipitate depends on the precipitate orientation and shape. The theoretical treatments of both effects (GEGUZIN and KRIVOGLAZ [1973], SAUTHOFF [1976] and WERT [1976]) seem to be consistent with the experimental observations. Similar effects have been observed in alloys undergoing an order–disorder or a martensitic transformation. When a CuAu single crystal is ordered, it becomes subdivided into many domains, the tetragonal (*c*) axes of which are parallel to any of the three original cubic axes. In the bulk material and without an external stress field, the three possible *c*-directions are randomly distributed among the domains. The application of a compressive stress during ordering imposes a bias on the distribution of the *c*-axes such that the cube axis nearest to the compression axis becomes the preferred direction for the *c*-axes of ordered domains (HIRABAYASHI [1954] and ARUNACHALAM and CAHN [1970]).

The microstructure of materials undergoing martensitic transformations (cf. ch. 15) depends on external stress fields. The following two factors contributing to this effect are most important (DELAEY and WARLIMONT [1975]): (i) The orientation variant on whose macroscopic shear system the maximal resolved applied shear stress is acting will grow preferentially. (ii) Near certain symmetric orientations, individual plates and self-accommodating groups will compete. Essentially, the same arguments apply to the microstructure of materials undergoing mechanical twinning. Effects of this type play an important role for shape-memory effects.

Gas bubbles situated at interfaces represent a special case of microstructural changes caused by stress fields. Owing to the compressibility of gas bubbles, the binding energy between a bubble and the interface depends on external stresses. Compression stresses lead to a decrease of the binding energy and, hence, may result in microstructural changes resulting from break-away effects of the boundaries from the bubbles (GREENWOOD *et al.* [1975]).

3.2.5.5. Electric fields. In bulk metals, strong electric fields may induce complex interactions between thermomigration and electromigration due to Joule heating. In thin films, efficient heat removal ensures reasonable isothermal conditions. Under these conditions, two effects resulting from the presence of electric fields were observed: (i) enhanced grain-boundary migration (LORMAND *et al.* [1974] and HAESSNER *et al.* [1974]) and (ii) the growth of grain-boundary grooves which can eventually penetrate the film so that nucleation and growth of voids by grain-boundary diffusion occurs (HO and KIRKWOOD [1974]). The theoretical understanding of the processes involved is still poorly developed. In fact, the driving force exerted by a dc current on grain boundaries in gold was found to be several orders of magnitude larger than the theoretically estimated value (HAESSNER *et al.* [1974]). A similar result was also found from the motion of rod-shaped tungsten inclusions in Cu and from the displacement of deep scratches on the surface of Ag owing to the passage of a current along wire-shaped samples.

3.3. Deformation

All forms of plastic deformation may result in important changes of the micro-structure of materials with respect to the distribution and density of defects as well as with regard to the morphology, volume fraction and sometimes also structure of second phases. They are discussed in chs. 14–25.

3.4. Multiphase microstructures generated by migrating lattice defects

3.4.1. Moving grain boundaries

If grain boundaries are forced (e.g., during recrystallization or grain growth) to sweep through a precipitate dispersion or a duplex structure, the following micro-structures may result (DOHERTY [1982], HORNBOGEN and KÖSTER [1982]):

(i) The boundary bypasses the precipitates which, therefore, retain their initial orientation and become incoherent (fig. 22a). Owing to the Gibbs–Thompson effect, the solubility of the precipitates rises so that the smaller precipitates may dissolve, as was observed, for example, in the case of NbC in γ-Fe.

(ii) The coherent precipitates or the components of a duplex structure dissolve after contact with the moving grain boundary, so that a supersaturated solid solution is obtained. From this supersaturated solid solution, the solvent may precipitate either continuously (fig. 22b) or discontinuously (fig. 22c). Both cases have been observed experimentally. The dissolution as well as the precipitation processes seem to occur far more rapidly than anticipated, suggesting strongly enhanced diffusion in the migrating interfaces and in the lattice behind due to vacancy supersaturation (SMIDODA *et al.* [1978], GOTTSCHALK *et al.* [1980]).

(iii) The grain boundaries can pass through the coherent precipitates and, thereby, preserve the preexisting microstructure (fig. 22d). This process seems rare as it requires the formation of new precipitates to match the rate of boundary migration.

(iv) The grain boundary is held by the coherent precipitates which then coarsen. This process occurs if the driving force for boundary migration is not sufficient to initiate one of the above processes.

(v) The moving grain boundary drags the precipitates (SMITH [1948]), as was reported for a variety of alloy systems containing gaseous particles as well as solid inclusions, for example, for He in Cu, He in U, air in camphor, carbides in various metal transition alloys, GeO_2 in Cu, B_2O_3 in Cu, SiO_2 in Cu, Ag in W, Ag in Sn, Al_2O_3 in Ni, Al_2O_3 in Ag. The experimental results have been reviewed by GEGUZIN and KRIVOGLAZ [1973] and GLEITER and CHALMERS [1972]. *Particle drag* results

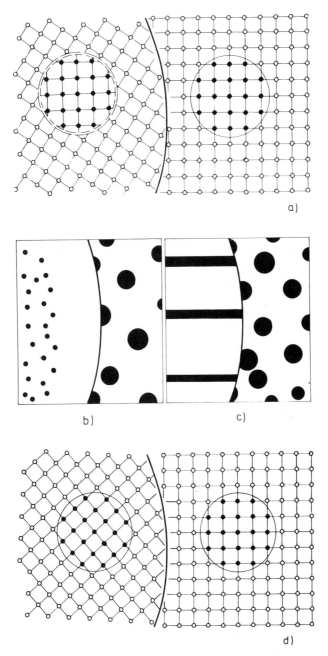

Fig. 22. Microstructural changes induced by a grain boundary migrating through a two-phase alloy containing dispersed precipitates: (a) transformation of coherent precipitates into incoherent ones as the boundary bypasses the precipitates; (b, c) dissolution of the precipitates, resulting a supersaturated solid solution, followed by continuous (b) and discontinuous (c) precipitation; (d) grain boundary passing through the precipitates without affecting the shape and size. The solid (open) circles in figs. 22a and 22d indicate solute (solvent) atoms.

References: p. 708.

from the directive movement of atoms from one ("front") side of the inclusion to the other ("rear") side. Hence, diffusional migration may occur by diffusion of atoms around or through the inclusion and diffusion of atoms along the particle–matrix interface. The kinetics of the particle drag may be controlled by the rate of one of these diffusion processes or by interfacial reaction at the boundary between the inclusion and the matrix. Examples of all cases mentioned have been reported and may be found in one of the reviews mentioned. Once particle drag starts, the boundary collects practically all particles in the volume which is swept. Particles collected in the boundary usually coarsen rapidly. Therefore, particle drag may result in the following changes of the properties of the boundary: (i) boundary brittleness and/or corrosivity due to a high density of undeformable particles, the electrochemical properties of which differ from the surrounding matrix; (ii) different mechanical chemical properties in the particle-free zone and in the rest of the

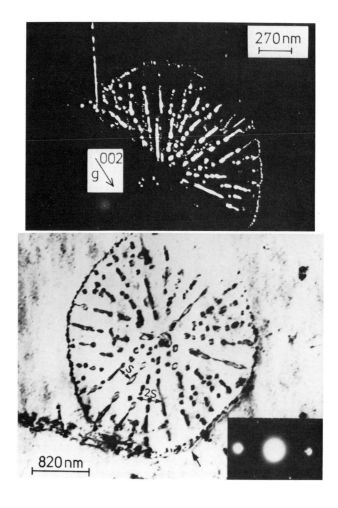

a)

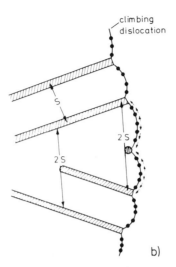

Fig. 23. (a) Bright-field and dark-field electron micrographs of colonies of silver precipitates in a Cu–5 wt% Ag alloy. The colonies formed behind the dislocation loops surrounding them. The loops expanded during colony growth. Two types of precipitates may be noticed. A chain of small precipitates along the dislocation loop, and large precipitates arranged radially in a spoke-like fashion. (b) Schematic model for colony formation by a two-step process involving the nucleation of a chain of small precipitates along the climbing dislocation followed by coarsening into large precipitates with a spacing S. (After WIRTH and GLEITER [1981a, b].)

material. At high driving forces (e.g., during recrystallization) particle drag seems negligible as it is possible for the mobile boundary to migrate past the inclusions.

3.4.2. Moving dislocations

The formation of colonies of precipitates in the vicinity of dislocations has been observed in a number of alloy systems, e.g., in iron, nickel, copper, aluminium and semiconductor materials.

In the initial model of this process (SILCOCK and TUNSTALL [1964]) and in the subsequent modification by NES [1974], a dislocation was proposed to climb so that precipitates can nucleate repeatedly in the moving stress field of the dislocation. During climb the dislocation emits vacancies. The incorporation of these emitted vacancies in the lattice of the precipitates is believed to reduce the precipitate–matrix mismatch energy, if the precipitating phase has a larger atomic volume than the surrounding matrix. In the opposite case, a vacancy flux from the precipitate to the dislocation was also invoked (GUYOT and WINTENBERGER [1974]).

More recently, the experimentally observed coupling between dislocation climb and precipitate formation was re-interpreted by two other models. Dislocations were proposed to climb owing to the annihilation of quenched-in vacancies, while the precipitates form simultaneously by heterogeneous nucleation in the stress field of the moving dislocation. A recent study by transmission electron microscopy (WIRTH and GLEITER [1981a,b]) led to the conclusion that coherency strain relaxation by

References: p. 708.

incorporation of vacancies in the precipitates may be only one of the processes involved. In fact, colony formation was found to occur (fig. 23a) by the climb of a prismatic dislocation loop which emits vacancies and, thus, generates a region of enhanced diffusivity. The excess solute atoms of this region of enhanced diffusivity migrate rapidly to the climbing dislocation and precipitate in the form of a chain of small particles (fig. 23b). Owing to their large surface-to-volume ratio, these fine particles rapidly coarsen by Ostwald ripening to form rows (colonies) of coarse precipitates behind the climbing dislocation loop. The spacing of the rows of coarse precipitates is controlled by the balance between the interfacial energy and the diffusion path. Under steady-state conditions, such systems are known to approach a constant precipitate spacing. Hence, if the dislocation loop expands during growth, a constant precipitate spacing can only be maintained by increasing the number of precipitates as the loop radius increases. This condition results in a spoke-like precipitate arrangement, as was observed (fig. 23).

3.5. Periodic microstructures

Two types of periodic microstructures are observed:
1. Periodic structures due to long-range interaction forces:
   a) precipitate lattices;
   b) void lattices;
   c) dislocation-loop lattices;
   d) dislocation lattices *;
   e) point-defect lattices, flux-line ** and magnetic-bubble lattices;
2. Periodic structures due to short-range interaction forces.

3.5.1. Periodic structures due to long-range interaction forces
3.5.1.1. Precipitate lattices. Several studies by means of X-ray diffraction and electron microscopy have revealed the existence of periodically arranged precipitates (fig. 24a) in alloys of Cu–Ni–Co, Cu–Ni–Fe, nickel-base alloys containing γ' (Ni_3X) precipitates, Cu–Ti, Au–Pt, Au–Ni, Co–Fe, Co–Nb, Co–Ti, Al–Zn, Fe–Bi, Fe–Be, as well as in Alnico–Ticonel alloys. The models first proposed (ARDELL *et al.* [1966] and KHATCHATURYAN [1969]) to account for the formation of periodic precipitate arrays were based on (long-range) elastic interaction forces between the precipitates, due to coherency strain between the precipitates and the surrounding matrix. Both the precipitates and the matrix were assumed to be elastically isotropic. JOHNSON and LEE [1979] refined these approaches by including the strain fields induced by neighbouring inclusions and by considering second-order terms. Elastically strained particles of arbitrary shape but identical moduli in an anisotropic medium were also shown (KHATCHATURYAN [1969], JOHNSON and LEE [1979] and

---

*For sub-boundaries see §2.3.
** Investigations of type-II superconductors are discussed in ch. 27.

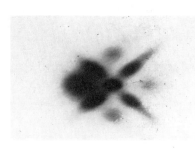

Fig. 24a. Dark-field electron micrograph and small-angle X-ray diffraction pattern of the precipitate lattice formed in an Fe–Be alloy (19.5 at% Be) after a 2 h anneal at 400°C. The specimen orientation is (100). (From TIAPKIN *et al.* [1976].)

MORI *et al.* [1978]) to form periodic arrays. The arrays correspond to one of the 14 Bravais lattices.

In the particular case of spherical inclusions in a cubic matrix with a negative anisotropy parameter, a simple cubic lattice of precipitates was found to form the minimum-energy arrangement which is stable with respect to externally induced fluctuations. Precipitates positioned along $\langle 100 \rangle$ directions of the matrix turned out to exhibit attractive interaction forces with a maximum value at 2–3 precipitate radii. This result may provide an explanation for the frequently observed alignment of precipitates along $\langle 100 \rangle$ directions. For $\langle 110 \rangle$ and $\langle 111 \rangle$ alignments, the interaction forces depend on the anisotropy factor of the matrix. $\langle 111 \rangle$ alignment in Mo is found to result in attractive forces, whereas the precipitates in the same arrangement in Cu and Ni repel. By applying these results to inclusions associated with a dipole-type strain field embedded in an iron lattice, a precipitate lattice with bcc structure was found to be stable. This arrangement corresponds approximately to the arrangement of N atoms in $Fe_{16}N_2$. So far, the discussion of precipitate lattices has been limited to systems in which the precipitation process occurs by nucleation and growth. In systems decomposing by a spinodal process, periodic arrangements of precipitates result from the time-dependent growth of concentration fluctuations. The processes involved and the factors governing the periodicity are discussed in ch. 14.

   3.5.1.2. Void lattices. EVANS' [1971] report on the creation of a stable bcc array (superlattice) of voids (ch. 17, §4.2) in irradiated Mo stimulated numerous studies on void lattices in other systems. Void lattices have been seen in Ni, Al, stainless steel, Mg, Mo, Mo–Ti, Nb, V, W and NbO, BaF_2, SrF_2, CaF_2 (fig. 24b). The models proposed for the ordering of voids are summarized in the papers by CHADDERTON *et al.* [1976], MARTIN [1977] and KRISHAN [1982]. EVANS [1983] has recently developed a novel model involving two-dimensional diffusion of interstitials on (110) planes in Mo.

   3.5.1.3. Dislocation-loop lattices. The first observation on the formation of dislocation loop lattices has apparently been made in neutron-irradiated copper. In

References: p. 708.

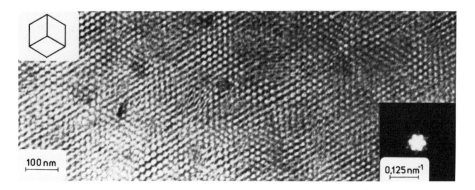

Fig. 24b. Void lattice in $\langle 111 \rangle$ fluorite. The diffraction pattern shows superlattice reflections around the transmitted beam. The structure of the void lattice is indicated in the diagram. (From CHADDERTON *et al.* [1976].)

subsequent years, periodic arrays of dislocation loops have been detected in Al, Ni, U, BeO, Ti, Mg and Zr. In the case of Ni and Al, ordered clusters of loops were observed. Stereomicroscopy revealed that the clusters consisted of about six loops forming a fcc superlattice (STIEGLER and FARRELL [1974]). As the lattice regions between the clusters were found to be elastically strained, elastic interaction forces were proposed to be the dominant factor for the formation of the loop lattice.

3.5.1.4. Point-defect lattices. By analogy with the formation of void lattices, point defects may be expected to form ordered arrangements. This idea is indeed confirmed by recent studies on vacancy and interstitial lattices in certain alloys (cf. HIRAGA [1973] and JUNG and TRENZINGER [1974]). In alloy forming vacancy lattices, e.g., vanadium carbides of the V_6C_5 type, a variation in the alloy concentration between V_6C_5 and V_8C_7 did not result in an expansion (or contraction) of the spacing of the carbon vacancies, but rather caused the formation of a one-dimensional long-period superlattice structure consisting of enantiomorphic domains of the superstructure V_6C_5. For obvious reasons, the linear dimension of the enantiomorphic domains depends on the vacancy (carbon) content and increases with the increase in carbon vacancies. In all vacancy lattices observed, elastic interaction forces are believed to be the most important parameter. In pure metals, vacancy or interstitial lattices have not yet been revealed experimentally. However, calculations based on the vacancy–vacancy interaction potential showed that vacancy lattices may exist with a simple cubic structure aligned parallel to the identical axis of the host lattice (CHANG [1976]). The vacancy lattice constant was found to be about three times the lattice constant of the atomic lattice in the case of K and Na.

3.5.2. Periodic structures due to short-range interactions

Ordered alloys, mostly of fcc structure in the disordered state, exhibit in the ordered state a regular three-dimensional array of antiphase boundary (APB) structures. Ordered structures of this type, which are called "long-period antiphase boundary structures", are treated in ch. 4, § 10.2.

3.6.   Microstructure in the vicinity of point defect sources and/or sinks

3.6.1.   Enhanced precipitation and precipitate-free zones

The significance of point-defect sources/sinks for the precipitation of solute atoms from supersaturated solid solutions was first demonstrated by BARNES *et al.* [1958] for the *enhanced precipitation* of helium atoms in the vicinity of point-defect sources. Helium atoms were injected into metals (spectroscopically pure Cu and Be) by bombardment with alpha particles. On subsequent heating, the He atoms have a tendency to precipitate within the metal in the form of gas bubbles and, to acquire the extra space necessary for this, they capture vacancies. Thus a blanket of bubbles forms in the vicinity of a vacancy source. For low He contents and large grain sizes, grain boundaries as well as dislocations are the most important vacancy sources. For small grains, grain boundaries are the dominant suppliers. These results were confirmed later for a variety of other metals. *Precipitate-free zones* of second-phase particles adjacent to grain boundaries in age-hardened alloys were originally attributed to the localized depletion of solute arising from preferential precipitation at the grain boundaries. However, it was soon recognized that local depletion of vacancies might be the more important factor, as a critical concentration of vacancies may be required for precipitate nucleation. In fact, this idea was discussed in terms of the thermodynamics of solute clustering (LORIMER and NICHOLSON [1969]) and in terms of the precipitation kinetics (PASHLEY *et al.* [1967]). Evidence for the local depletion of vacancies by annihilation at the boundaries was obtained from electron microprobe measurements and energy-analyzing electron microscopy for Al–Ag and Al–Zn–Mg alloys. The results of both investigations showed no solute depletion in the vicinity of the boundaries. In this simplified picture no coupling between vacancy flow and solid distribution is assumed. However, if a binding energy exists between solute atoms and vacancies, the vacancy flow from or to vacancy sources/sinks is necessarily coupled with a solute flow and, thus, produces a solute gradient in the vicinity of vacancy sources/sinks, such as grain boundaries, dislocations, pores, or free surfaces (JOHNSON and LAM [1976] and ANTHONY [1970]).

The solute segregation generated by vacancy flow involves two processes: the dragging of solute atoms by the moving vacancies and the reverse atom flow which is a consequence of vacancy flow. The first process dominates if the binding energy (E) between a vacancy and a solute atom is much greater than the thermal energy (kT). Under these circumstances, a solute atom is dragged to (from) the vacancy sink (source) so that solute enrichment (depletion) of the sink (source) regions will result. As a consequence, an enhanced density of precipitates forms in the vicinity of the sink. The opposite type of solute distribution may result in the second case ($E \ll kT$). For $E \ll kT$, solute atoms may be pumped in or out of the sink region depending on the relative diffusivity of solute and solvent atoms. When a vacancy flows into an enclosed sink region, an atom as a consequence must simultaneously flow out of this region. If the solute and solvent atoms in this region have identical mobilities, the ratio of solute to solvent atoms will remain the same as the original

References: p. 708.

ratio. However, if the mobility of the solute atoms is greater than of the solvent atoms, proportionately more solute than solvent atoms will be moved out of the enclosed region by intruding vacancies, producing a solute-depleted sink zone. The solute depletion of the sink region will not continue indefinitely but will stop when the solute flow generated by the vacancy flux is balanced by the opposing solute flow produced by the solute gradient.

Two special *solute pumping* processes were proposed for *hydrogen* in stress gradients. The first mechanism (Gorsky effect, for a review see VÖLKL [1972]) arises because hydrogen dissolved in a metal expands the crystal lattice of the host material. Hence, if a crystal contains a gradient in dilatation, the hydrogen concentration is enhanced in the dilatated region, e.g. in the vicinity of crack tips. The second effect (TILLER and SCHRIEFFER [1974]) is due to the redistribution of the free electrons in strain fields. Owing to this redistribution, dilatational centres (into which electrons flow) become cathodic. Hence, H^+ ions will migrate into the cathodic (dilatational) regions. Estimates for conditions typical for crack tips led to H^+ enhancements of up to ten orders of magnitude.

3.6.2. Irradiation-induced precipitation

In irradiated materials, a high supersaturation of vacancies and/or interstitials may be present. It follows from the previous section that the condensation of these point defects at suitable sinks (e.g. grain boundaries) may induce solute segregation in the vicinity of the sink. If this segregation is sufficiently strong, a local transgression of a phase boundary and, hence, irradiation-induced precipitation processes may be obtained, as has been reported for many alloy systems. For comprehensive reviews on this subject, we refer to conference proceedings (BLEIBERG and BENNET [1977] and POIRIER and DUPOUY [1979]), ch. 8 (§ 8.3.2) and ch. 17 (§ 4.4).

3.6.3. Point-defect condensation

The significance of point-defect sources/sinks for the development of microstructures resulting from point-defect condensation was discovered by etch-pit studies. Etch pits were observed to form on electropolished surfaces of Al crystals during cooling from elevated temperatures. The formation of the pits was attributed to the condensation of vacancies at the surface. In polycrystalline specimens, pits were not observed in the vicinity of high-angle grain boundaries, suggesting that the vacancies in the pit-free region had been drained by the boundaries. In regions far away from the free surface, supersaturated point defects may condense in the form of dislocation loops, stacking-fault tetrahedra and/or voids which may be observed by transmission electron microscopy. The condensation process leads to a non-uniform microstructure in polycrystalline specimens in the sense that *denuded zones* exist near grain boundaries. As the condensation occurs by a nucleation and growth process, a certain supersaturation of point defects is required. Hence, the observation of denuded zones suggests a lower point-defect supersaturation in the vicinity of grain boundaries than in the perfect lattice, owing to the annihilation of point defects at the boundaries. With the exception of coherent twins and small-angle boundaries, the results suggest that high-angle grain boundaries are ideal vacancy sinks so that the width of the denuded zones is diffusion-controlled (for a review see GLEITER [1981]).

3.7. Microstructure due to lattice defects formed by migrating grain boundaries

In recent years, it has become apparent that the microstructure of crystals growing by solid-state processes depends on the mode of crystal growth. The defect structures resulting from solid-state phase transformations and solid–liquid (glass) transformations, are discussed in chs. 9, 14–16, 25 and 28. In the present section, attention will be focussed on the microstructures developed due to the generation of vacancies, dislocations and twins by migrating grain boundaries. For a recent review of this field, we refer to the article by GLEITER [1981].

Creation of vacancies. The creation of vacancies by migrating boundaries has been studied by means of the diffusion coefficient, the density, the electric resistivity and the morphology of the precipitates formed in the crystal region behind migrating boundaries (GORLIK et al. [1972] and GOTTSCHALK et al. [1980]). The observations reported suggest that behind a migrating grain boundary a high supersaturation of vacancies may exist. The high vacancy supersaturation observed was explained in terms of "growth accidents" occurring during grain-boundary migration (GLEITER [1979]). A growth accident involves a jump of an atom of the growing crystal into the migrating boundary so that a vacant site is left behind in the lattice of the growing crystal. The excess vacancies retained in the lattice alter the properties of this crystal and exert a drag force on the migrating boundary ('vacancy drag', GLEITER [1979]) which may dominate impurity drag under certain conditions (ESTRIN and LÜCKE [1982]) (cf. also ch. 25, § 3.4.3).

Creation of dislocations. Indirect observations of dislocations created by migrating boundaries come from recrystallized materials. However, because of the high dislocation density ahead of the recrystallization front, the interpretation of these results is not unambiguous. A distinction between dislocations generated by the migrating interface and dislocations due to other processes is possible if the boundary migrates into a dislocation-free crystal or a crystal with low dislocation density. Studies of this type have been carried out in Cu, InP, InAs and Si (GLEITER et al. [1980]). The results obtained support the idea of dislocation generation by migrating boundaries. The generation process may be envisaged by growth accidents as well as the stress-induced dislocation emission (GASTALDI and JOURDAN [1979], GLEITER et al. [1980]).

Creation of two-dimensional lattice defects. The most prominent lattice defects generated during boundary migration (e.g. during grain growth) are *coherent twin boundaries* (cf. ch. 25, § 4.2). In order to explain the formation of twin boundaries during boundary migration, several models have been proposed. According to the *dissociation models* twins are formed by dissociating a grain boundary (A) into a twin boundary (T) and a new grain boundary (B). The *stimulation model* proposes that a twin boundary is created if a growing recrystallized grain meets a dislocation-bearing

References: p. 708.

fragment which lies accurately in a twinned orientation to it. Since the fragment has discharged its dislocations, it is now stress-free and able to grow at the expense of the surrounding deformed matrix. The *coalescence model* proposes twin boundaries to be formed if the orientation relationship between the impinging grains corresponds exactly to a twin orientation. The *growth-accident hypothesis* of twin-boundary formation follows the concept that twins are formed and terminated by errors of the stacking of the $\langle 111 \rangle$ planes which happen in a random way. Studies by optical microscopy, thermo-ionic and photoemission microscopy, transmission electron microscopy, X-ray topography, grain-boundary migration experiments in bicrystals and polycrystals have been reported (for a review see GLEITER [1981]). The results of these studies are inconsistent with the dissociation, the stimulation and the coalescence hypotheses. The observations so far available seem consistent only with the growth-accident hypothesis. In fact, in situ observations of twin formation in Al by X-ray topography agree with the evolution, shape and growth direction predicted by the growth-accident theory (GASTALDI and JOURDAN [1979]).

References

AARONSON, H.I., C. LAIRD and K.R. KINSMAN, 1970, Phase Transformations (ASM, Metals Park, OHio) p. 313.

ADDA, Y., B. BRÉBEC, N. DOAN and M. GEOL, 1966, Proc. Int. Symp. on Thermodynamics (IAEA, Vienna) vol. 2, p. 255.

ALLAN, G., M. LANNOO and L. DOBRZYNSKI, 1974, Phil. Mag. **30**, 33.

ALLEN, S.M., and J.W. CAHN, 1979, Acta Metall. **27**, 1085.

AMELINCKX, S., 1964, Solid State Physics, vol. 6, eds. F. Seitz and D. Turnbull (Academic, New York) p. 1.

AMELINCKX, S., and W. DEKEYSER, 1959, Solid State Phys., 325.

ANTHONY, T.R., 1970, Acta Metall. **18**, 307.

ANTHONY, T.R., and H.E. CLINE, 1972, Acta Metall. **20**, 247.

ANTHONY, T.R., and H.E. CLINE, 1973, Acta Metall. **21**, 117.

ARDELL, A., 1972, Acta Metall. **20**, 601.

ARDELL, A., R.B. NICHOLSON and J.D. ESHELBY, 1966, Acta Metall. **14**, 1295.

ARDELL, A., N. MARDESICH and C. WASNER, 1979, Acta Metall. **27**, 1261.

ARUNACHALAM, V.S., and R.W. CAHN, 1970, in: Proc. 3rd Bolton Landing Conf., eds. B. Kear, C. Sims, and N.S. Stoloff (Claitor's Publ. Div., Baton Rouge, LA) p. 215.

ASHBY, M.F., F. SPAEPEN and S. WILLIAMS, 1978, Acta Metall. **26**, 1647.

AUBAUER, H.P., 1972, Acta Metall. **20**, 165.

AUST, K.T., 1981, Structure and Properties of Grain Boundaries, in: Chalmers Anniversary Volume, Prog. Mater. Sci., eds. J.W. Christian, P. Haasen and T.B. Massalski (Pergamon Press, London) p. 27.

BALLUFFI, R.W., 1980, Grain Boundary Structure and Kinetics (ASM, Metals Park, OH).

BARNES, R.S., G.B. REDDINS and A.H. COTTRELL, 1958, Phil. Mag. **3**, 97.

BECK, P.A., 1954, Phil. Mag. **3**, 245.

BECKER, R., 1938, Ann. Phys. **32**, 128.

BEERÉ, W., 1978, Phil. Mag. **A38**, 691.

BHATTACHARYA, S.K., and K.C. RUSSELL, 1976, Metallurg. Trans. **7A**, 453.

BIRKENBEIL, H.J., and R.W. CAHN, 1962, Proc. Phys. Soc. **79**, 831.

BISHOP, G.H., and B. CHALMERS, 1968, Scripta Metall. **2**, 133.

BJORKLUND, S., L. DONASHEY and M. HILLERT, 1972, Acta Metall. **20**, 867.

BLEIBERG, M.L., and J.W. BENNET, 1977, in: Radiation Effects in Breeder Reactor Structural Materials (Met. Soc. AIME, Warrendale, PA) p. 211.

BOLLMANN, W., 1970, Crystal Defects and Crystal Interfaces (Springer, Berlin).

BOLLMANN, W., and H. NIESSEN, 1968, Acta Cryst. **24**, 546.

BONISSENT, A., and B. MUTAFTSHIEV, 1981, Crit. Rev. Solid State & Mater. Sci. **14**, 297.

BONISSENT, A., E. GAUTHIER and J.L. FINNEY, 1979, Phil. Mag. **B39**, 49.

BOURRET, A., and J. DESSAULT, 1979, Phil. Mag. **39**, 412.

BOYD, A., and R.B. NICHOLSON, 1971, Acta Metall. **19**, 1370.

BRANDON, D.G., B. RALPH, S. RANGANATHAN and M.S. WALD, 1964, Acta Metall. **12**, 813.

BRISTOWE, P.D., A. BROKMAN, F. SPAEPEN and R.W. BALLUFFI, 1980, Scripta Metall. **14**, 943.

BROWN, N., 1959, Phil. Mag. **4**, 695.

CAHN, J.W., and J.E. HILLIARD, 1958, J. Chem. Phys. **28**, 258.

CHADDERTON, L.T., E. JOHNSON and T. WOHLENBERG, 1976, Comm. Solid State Phys. **VII, 5**, 105.

CHALMERS, B., and H. GLEITER, 1971, Phil. Mag. **23**, 1541.

CHANG, R., 1976, Scripta Metall. **10**, 861.

CHEN, H.S., and S.Y. CHANG, 1974, Phys. Stat. Sol. **25**, 581.

CLINE, H., 1971, Acta Metall. **19**, 481.

COCKS, G., and D. BORLUND, 1975, Met. Sci. **5**, 384.

COOPER, S.P., and J. BILLINGHAM, 1980, Met. Sci. J. **14**, 225.

CULLITY, B.D., 1972, Introduction to Magnetic Materials (Addison–Wesley, London) p. 357 and 565.

CYROT-LACKMANN, F., 1968, J. Phys. Chem. Solids **29**, 1235.

DARLING, D.F., and B.D. FIELD, 1973, Surf. Sci. **36**, 630.

DAVIS, C.K., P. NASH and R. STEVENS, 1980a, Acta Metall. **28**, 179.

DAVIS, J.R., T.A. COURTNEY and M.A. PRZYSTUPA, 1980b, Metallurg. Trans. **11A**, 323.

DE FONTAINE, D., 1973 Scripta Metall. **7**, 463.

DELAEY, L., and H. WARLIMONT, 1975, in: Shape Memory Effects in Alloys, ed. J. Perkins (Plenum, New York) p. 89.

DOHERTY, R.D., 1982, Met. Sci. J. **16**, 1.

ECOB, R., and B. RALPH, 1981, Acta Metall. **29**, 1037.

ERB, U., W. ABEL and H. GLEITER, 1982, Scripta Metall. **16**, 1317.

ESTRIN, Y., and K. LÜCKE, 1982, Acta Metall. **30**, 983.

EVANS, J.H., 1971, Nature **229**, 403.

EVANS, J.H., 1983, J. Nucl. Mater., in press.

EWING, R.H., 1971, J. Cryst. Growth **11**, 221.

FERRANTE, M., and R.D. DOHERTY 1979, Acta Metall. **27**, 1979.

FLETCHER, N.H., 1975, J. Cryst. Growth **28**, 325.

FLETCHER, N.H., and K.W. LODGE, 1975, Epitaxial Growth, ed. J.W. Matthews (Academic, New York) vol. 13. p. 530.

FÖLL, O., and D. AST, 1981, Phil. Mag. **A43**, 441.

FRANK, F.C., 1950, Symp. on Plastic Deformation of Crystalline Solids (Carnegie Mellon Inst. of Techn., Pittsburgh, PA) p. 150.

GASTALDI, J., and J. JOURDAN, 1979, Phys. Stat. Sol. (a) **52**, 139.

GAUDIG, W., and H. WARLIMONT, 1969, Z. Metallk. **60**, 488.

GEGUZIN, Ya. E., and M.A. KRIVOGLAZ, 1973, Migration of Microscopic Inclusions in Solids (Consultants Bureau, New York) p. 157.

GIFKINS, H., 1967, Mater. Sci. Eng. **2**, 181.

GLEITER, H., 1969, Phil. Mag. **20**, 821.

GLEITER, H., 1971, Phys. Stat. Sol. (b) **45**, 9.

GLEITER, H., 1977, Scripta Metall. **11**, 305.

GLEITER, H., 1979, Acta Metall. **27**, 1754.

GLEITER, H., 1980, Radex Rundschau **1**, 51.

GLEITER, H., 1981, Chalmers Anniversary Volume, Prog. Mater. Sci., eds. J.W. Christian, P. Haasen and T.B. Massalski (Pergamon Press, Oxford).

GLEITER, H., 1982, Mater. Sci. Eng. **52**, 91.

GLEITER, H., and B. CHALMERS, 1972, Prog. Mater. Sci. **16**, 145.

GLEITER, H., S. MAHAJAN and K.J. BACHMANN, 1980, Acta Metall. **28**, 1603.

GOODHEW, P., 1980, in: Grain Boundary Structure and Kinetics, ed. R.W. Balluffi (ASM, Metals Park, OH) p. 155.

GORLIK, S.S., L. KOVALEVA and M. BLAUTER, 1972, Fiz. Met. Metalloved. **33**(3), 658.

GOTTSCHALK, C., K. SMIDODA and H. GLEITER, 1980, Acta Metall. **28**, 1653.

GRAHAM, L.D., and R.W. KRAFT, 1966, Metallurg. Trans. **236**, 94.

GREENWOOD, G.W., 1956, Acta Metall. **4**, 243.

GREENWOOD, G.W., H. JONES and J.H. WESTBROOK, 1975, Phil. Mag. **31**, 39.

GRONSKI, W., and G. THOMAS, 1977, Scripta Metall. **11**, 791.

GUBANOV, A.I., 1979, Sov. Phys. Solids **21**, 1566.

GULDEN, M.E., 1969, J. NUCL. MATER. **30**, 30.

GUST, W., B. PREDEL and K. STENZEL, 1978, Z. Metallk. **69**, 721.

GUYOT, C., and M. WINTENBERGER, 1974, J. Mater. Sci. **9**, 614.

HAESSNER, F., S. HOFFMANN and H. SEKEL, 1974, Scripta Metall. **8**, 299.

HENDERSON, D., W. JOST and M. McLEAN, 1978, Met. Sci. J. **12**, 113.

HERRING, C., 1950, J. Appl. Phys. **21**, 301.

HERRMANN, G., H. GLEITER and G. BAERO, 1976, Acta Metall. **24**, 353.

HILLERT, H., 1961, Acta Metall. **9**, 525.

HILLERT, M., 1965, Acta Metall. **13**, 227.

HIRABAYASHI, M., 1959, J. Phys. Soc. Jap. **14**, 149.

HIRAGA, K., 1973, Phil. Mag. **27**, 1301.

HO, F., and C.G. WEATHERLY, 1975, Acta Metall. **23**, 1451.

HO, P.S., and J.K. KIRKWOOD, 1974, J. Appl. Phys. **45**, 3229.

HOLT, D.B., 1974, J. Phys. Chem. Solids **27**, 1053.

HORNBOGEN, E., and U. KÖSTER, 1982, Recrystallization of Metallic Materials, ed. F. Haessner (Riederer Verlag, Stuttgart) p. 159.

HORNSTRA, J., 1958, J. Phys. Chem. Solids **5**, 129.

HORTON, C.A.P., J.M. SILCOCK and G.R. KEGG, 1974, Phys. Stat. Sol. **A26**, 215.

HOUGHTON, D.C., and D. JONES, 1978, Acta Metall. **26**, 695.

HU, H., 1963, Recovery and Recrystallization of Metals, ed. L. Himmel (Interscience, New York) p. 311.

JAIN, S.C., and A.E. HUGHES, 1978, J. Mater. Sci. **13**, 1611.

JESSER, W.A., and J.W. MATTHEWS, 1968, Phil. Mag. **17**, 461.

JOHNSON, R.A., and M.G. LAM, 1976, Phys. Rev. **B13**, 434.

JOHNSON, W.C., and J.K. LEE, 1979, Metallurg. Trans. **10A**, 1141.

JONES, D.R., and G.J. MAY, 1975, Acta Metall. **23**, 29.

JOURDAN, C., and J. GASTALDI, 1979, Scripta Metall. **13**, 55.

JUNG, P., and K. TRENZINGER, 1974, Acta Metall. **22**, 123.

JUNG, R.H., 1976, Scripta Metall. **10**, 861.

KAHLWEIT, H., 1975, Adv. Colloid and Interface Sci. **5**, 1.

KHATCHATURYAN, A.G., 1969, Phys. Stat. Sol. **35**, 119.

KHATCHATURYAN, A., and G. SHATALOV, 1969, Sov. Phys. Solid State JETP **11**, 118.

KIKUCHI, R., 1972, J. Chem. Phys. **57**, 4633.

KIKUCHI, R., and J.W. CAHN, 1962, J. Chem. Phys. **33**, 137.

KIKUCHI, R., and J.W. CAHN, 1980, Phys. Rev. **B21**, 1893.

KIRCHNER, H., 1971, Metallurg. Trans. **3**, 2861.

KIRCHNER, H., 1974, Acta Metall. **22**, 553.

KLUGE-WEISS, P., and H. GLEITER, 1979, Acta Metall. **26**, 117.

KNOWLES, K.M., D.A. SMITH and W. CLARK, 1982, Scripta Metall. **16**, 413.

KÖSTER, U., 1979, Adv. Colloid and Interface Sci. **10**, 129.

KONTSKY, J.A., A.G. WALTON and E. BAER, 1966, J. Polymer Sci. **A4**, 611.

KRISHAN, K., 1982, Rad. Eff. **66**, 121.

KRIVANEK, D., T.M. SHAW and G. THOMAS, 1979, J. Appl. Phys. **50**, 4223.

KRONBERG, M.L., and F.H. WILSON, 1949, Trans. AIME **185**, 501.

KRUPP, J., and W. SCHNABEL, 1973, J. Adhesion **5**, 296.

KUCZYNSKI, G.C., G. MATSUMURA and B.D. CULLITY, 1960, Acta Metall. **8**, 209.

LANGER, J.S., and R. SEKERKA, 1975, Acta Metall. **23**, 1225.

LEE, Y., and H.I. AARONSON, 1980, Acta Metall. **28**, 539.

LEMMLEIN, G.G., 1952, Dokl. Akad. Nauk SSSR **85**, 325.

LI, H.S., E. EDWARDS, J. WASHBURN and E. PARKER, 1953, Acta Metall. **1**, 223.

LI, J.C.M., 1961, J. Appl. Phys. **32**, 525.

LI, J.C.M., 1969, Trans. Met. Soc. AIME **245**, 1591.

LIFSHITZ, I.M., and V.V. SLYOZOV, 1961, J. Phys. Chem. Solids **19**, 35.

LIVINGSTON, J.D., 1971, J. Mater. Sci. **7**, 61.

LIVINGSTON, J.D., and J.W. CAHN, 1974, Acta Metall. **22**, 495.

LORIMER, G.W., and R.B. NICHOLSON, 1969, Acta Metall. **13**, 109.

LORMAND, G., J. ROUAIS and C. EYRAND, 1974, Acta Metall. **22**, 793.

LOUAT, N.P., 1974, Acta Metall. **22**, 721.

MALIS, T., and H. GLEITER, 1979, J. Appl. Phys. **50**, 4920.

MANTOVANI, S., and S. VALERI, 1978, Phil. Mag. **A37**, 17.

MARCINKOWSKI, M.J., and K. JAGANNADHAM, 1978, Phys. Stat. Sol. **50**, 601.

MARTIN, G., 1977, J. Physique Coloq. **C7-38**, 419.

MARTIN, J.W., and R.D. DOHERTY, 1976, Stability of Microstructure in Metallic Systems (Cambridge University Press) p. 154.

MASAMURA, R.A., and M.E. GLICKSMAN, 1974, Can. Met. Quest. **13**, 43.

McCALDIN, J.O., and T.C. McGILL, 1980, Ann. Rev. Mater. Sci. **10**, 65.

McLEAN, M., 1973, Phil. Mag. **27**, 1235.

McLEAN, M., 1978, Met. Sci. J. **12**, 113.

McLEAN, M., 1982, Met. Sci. J. **16**, 31.

McQUEEN, H., 1977, Metallurg. Trans. **8A**, 807.

MEIJERING, J.L., 1966, Acta Metall. **14**, 251.

MIEDEMA, A., and J.O. DEN BROEDER, 1979, Z. Metallk. **70**, 14.

MIEKK-OJA, H., and V. LINDROOS, 1972, Surf. Sci. **31**, 422.

MIGAZAKI, T., K. NAKAMURA and H. MORI, 1979, J. Mater. Sci. **14**, 1827.

MORI, T., P. CHENG, M. KATO and T. MURA, 1978, Acta Metall. **26**, 1435.

MORRALL, J.E., and N.P. LOUAT, 1974, Scripta Metall. **8**, 91.

MOTT, N.F., 1948, Proc. Phys. Soc. (London) **60**, 391.

MULLINS, W.W., 1956, Acta Metall. **4**, 421.

MURR, L.E., 1975, Interface Phenomena in Metals (Addison–Wesley, Reading, MA) p. 280.

NES, E., 1974, Acta Metall. **22**, 81.

NEUHÄUSER, H.J., and W. PITSCH, 1971, Z. Metallk. **62**, 792.

NICHOLS, F.A., 1976, J. Mater. Sci. **11**, 1077.

OLSON, G.B., and M. COHEN, 1979, Acta Metall. **27**, 1907.

ORIANI, R.A., 1964, Acta Metall. **12**, 1399.

OROWAN, E., 1970, J. Franklin Inst. **290**, 493.

OZAWA, T., and Y. ISHIDA, 1977, Scripta Metall. **11**, 835.

PASHLEY, D.W., M.H. JAKOBS and J.T. VIETZ, 1967, Phil. Mag. **16**, 51.

PEREPEZKO, J.H., and T.B. MASSALSKI, 1978, Scripta Metall. **6**, 743.

PERKOVIC, V. C.R. PURDY and L.M. BROWN 1979, Acta Metall. **27**, 1075.

POIRIER, J., and J.M. DUPOUY, 1979, Proc. Int. Conf on Irradiation Behaviour of Metallic Materials for Reactor Core Compounds, Ajaccio, Corsica (publ. by CEA–DMCEN, 91190, Gif-sur-Yvette, France).

POND, R.C., D. SMITH and V. VITEK, 1978, Scripta Metall. **12**, 699.

POTAPOV, L.P., B.F. GLOWIN and P.H. SHIRYAEV, 1971, Fiz. Met. Metalloved. **32**, 227.

PUMPHREY, P., 1972, Scripta Metall. **6**, 107.

RALPH, B., P.R. HOWELL and T.F. PAGE, 1977, Phys. Stat. Sol. (b) **55**, 641.

RAYLEIGH, LORD, 1878, Proc. Lond. Math. Soc. **10**, 4.

READ, W.T., and W. SHOCKLEY, 1950, Phys. Rev. **78**, 275.

RHODES, C.G., and N.E. PATON, 1979, Metallurg. Trans. **10A**, 1735.

RIGSBEE, J.M., and H.I. AARONSON, 1979, Acta Metall. **27**, 351.

ROGERS, J.T., H.M. FLOWERS and R. RAWLINGS, 1975, Met. Sci. **9**, 32.

ROY, A., U. ERB and H. GLEITER, 1982, Acta Metall. **30**, 1847.

SATO, H., and R.S. TOTH, 1961, Phys. Rev. **124**, 1833.

SAUTHOFF, G., 1976, Scripta Metall. **10**, 557.

SEEGER, A., and G. SCHOTTKY, 1959, Acta Metall. **7**, 495.

SHEWMON, P., 1964, Trans. AIME **230**, 134.

SHIH, K.K., and J.C.M.C. LI, 1975, Surf. Sci. **50**, 109.

SILCOCK, J.M., and W.T. TUNSTALL, 1964, Phil. Mag. **10**, 361.

SKINNER, S.M., R.L. SAVAGE and J.E. RUTZLER, 1953, J. Appl. Phys. **24**, 439.

SMIDODA, K., Ch. GOTTSCHALK and H. GLEITER, 1978, Acta Metall. **26**, 1833.

SMITH, C.S., 1948, Trans. AIME **175**, 15.

SMITH, C.S., 1954, Met. Rev. **9**, 1.

SMITH, D.A., and R.C. POND, 1976, Internat. Met. Rev. **205**, 61.

SPAEPEN, F., 1975, Acta Metall. **23**, 729.

STIEGLER, J.O., and K. FARRELL, 1974, Scripta Metall. **8**, 651.

STRANSKI, I., and I. KRASTANOV, 1938, Monatsh. Chemie **71**, 351.

SUN, C., and R.W. BALLUFFI, 1979, Scripta Metall. **13**, 757.

SUTTON, A.P., and V. VITEK, 1983, Phil. Trans. Roy. Soc. (London) **309**, 1.

TIAPKIN, YU. D., N.T. TRAVINA and T.V. YEVTSUSHENKO, 1976, Scripta Metall. **10**, 375.

TIEN, J., and S. COPLEY, 1971, Metallurg. Trans. **2**, 215.

TILLER, W.A., and R. SCHRIEFFER, 1974, Scripta Metall. **8**, 487.

TURNBULL, D., 1951, Trans. AIME **191**, 661.

TURNBULL, D., 1964, in: Physics of Non-Crystalline Solids, ed. P. Prins (Delft) p. 46.

TYLER, S.K., and P.J. GOODHEW, 1980, J. Nucl. Mater. **92**, 201.

VAN DER MERWE, J.H., 1973, Treatise on Materials Science and Technology, vol. 2 (Academic, New York) p. 1.

VAN LANDUYT, J., G. VAN TENDELOO, M. VAN SANDE, L. DELAEY and S. AMELINCKX, 1981, Metallurg. Trans. **12A**, 715.

VAN LEEUWEN, C., P. BENNEMAN and D. VAN DIJK, 1974, Acta Metall. **22**, 687.

VAN TENDELOO, G., and S. AMELINCKX, 1975, in: Electron Microscopy in Materials Science, part III, eds. E. Ruedl and M. Valdre (Commission of the European Communities, Luxembourg) p. 773.

VÖLKL, J., 1972, Ber. Bunsen Gesell. **76**, 797.

WAGNER, C., 1961, Z. Elektrochem. **65**, 581.

WARLIMONT, H., and G. THOMAS, 1970, Met. Sci. J. **4**, 47.

WEATHERLY, G.C., and Y.G. NAKAGAWA, 1971, Scripta Metall. **5**, 777.

WEINS, M., H. GLEITER and B. CHALMERS, 1971, J. Appl. Phys. **42**, 2639.

WERT, J., 1976, Acta Metall. **24**, 65.

WHITMAN, W.D., 1926, Amer. J. Sci., Ser. 5, **11**, 126.

WINGROVE, M., and D.M. TAPLIN, 1969, J. Mater. Sci. **4**, 789.

WINTER, A., 1973, Scripta Metall. **7**, 49.

WIRTH, R., and H. GLEITER, 1981a, Acta Metall. **29**, 1825.

WIRTH, R., and H. GLEITER, 1981b, J. Mater. Sci. **16**, 557.

WOODRUFF, D.P., 1973, The Solid–Liquid Interface (Cambridge University Press) p. 39.

Further reading

For further reading we refer to the review articles mentioned in the various sections.

CHAPTER 11

TRANSMISSION ELECTRON MICROSCOPY

M. RÜHLE and M. WILKENS

Max-Planck-Institut für Metallforschung
7000 Stuttgart, FRG

R.W. Cahn and P. Haasen, eds.
Physical Metallurgy; third, revised and enlarged edition
© *Elsevier Science Publishers BV, 1983*

1. Introductory remarks

In the fifties, when transmission electron microscopes became commercially available, their potentialities for enabling applied and fundamental research in physical metallurgy and materials science were realized soon. Within a few years the resolution limit for a direct imaging of structural details of solids – up to that time limited by the light-wavelength in optical microscopy to some fraction of a μm at best – was reduced to about one nm; and in the course of this rapid development the horizon was opened for completely new aspects of research with a spatial resolution to nearly an atomic level. However, at that time it was quickly realized that transmission electron microscopy (TEM) differs from the classical optical microscopy significantly in the sense that TEM, in particular when applied to crystalline specimens, requires a much more profound knowledge of the interaction of the imaging (electron) waves with matter than in the case of optical microscopy. This holds for the imaging of crystal inhomogeneities (lattice defects, precipitates etc.) by TEM via *elastic* interaction of the imaging electrons with the specimen atoms. But it holds also for a local material analysis via various processes of *inelastic* interactions.

The present article attempts to present a brief, and necessarily incomplete, introduction (i) to a number of methods for imaging different kinds of lattice defects and precipitates by *diffraction contrast*, constituted mainly by elastic interaction, and (ii) to problems of the new field of *analytical electron microscopy*, based on inelastic interactions.

Because of the restricted space available, the references quoted are necessarily incomplete and, perhaps, not altogether free of arbitrariness. Other, more special aspects of TEM such as, e.g., Lorentz microscopy of ferromagnetic domains and special aspects of high-voltage electron microscopy (e.g., the critical voltage effect) are not dealt with at all.

In order to facilitate the step into the topics of this chapter the reader is recommended to study first the Appendix, *Elements of kinematical diffraction theory*, which may provide him with the basic knowledge necessary for an understanding of the content of the present chapter. This appendix may also be useful as an introduction to ch. 12.

2. The instrument

The technology of modern electron microscopes has been developed so far that nowadays commercially available instruments and the sophisticated attachments fulfill practically all requirements necessary for studying crystalline and non-crystal-line thin films. Some essential properties of the instrument are sketched in this section.

The *resolution* of an electron microscope is governed by errors of the magnetic lenses, in particular by the *spherical aberration* of the objective lens. The ultimate resolution r_{min} can be reached for an *optimum objective aperture angle* α_{opt}, with

$$\alpha_{opt} = A\lambda^{1/4}C_s^{-1/4}, \qquad r_{min} = B\lambda^{3/4}C_s^{1/4}, \tag{1}$$

where λ is the wavelength of the incident electrons and C_s the constant of spherical aberration. A and B are constants, their actual values depend on the way in which different contributions to lens errors are combined (HIRSCH *et al.* [1977]).

High-resolution instruments (with accelerating voltages of 200 kV or 300 kV) possess a point-to-point resolution of $\leqslant 0.25$ nm. If ultimate resolution has to be reached then stringent requirements are necessary for the stabilities of the high voltage and the lens currents. The pole piece of the objective lens possesses a narrow gap and small borings, so that in such instruments the specimens can be manipulated only in a very limited range.

Usually, ultimate resolution is not necessary for electron microscopy studies in materials science. For these studies it is more important that the specimen can be shifted and tilted over large ranges and that different signals of scattered electrons and X-rays can be detected in analytical microscopy studies. The lenses of the standard instruments possess pole pieces with larger boring which allow specimen manipulations and the mounting of detectors for analytical purpose. Thereby, the resolution of the instrument is reduced to ~ 0.4 nm. This resolution is, however, sufficient for most TEM studies in materials science.

An electron microscope can be split into three components according to its function: (i) the illumination system composed of the electron gun and the condensor lenses produces a fine electron beam to "illuminate" the specimen; (ii) the objective lens, which immediately follows the specimen, produces the diffraction pattern and a first magnified image of the specimen; (iii) the magnification system produces the final image. In addition to the optical components the microscope encloses also a specimen chamber (specimen handling system) and a recording system (HIRSCH *et al.* [1977] and HREN *et al.* [1979]).

The illumination system provides a beam of adjustable size, intensity and convergence angle at the specimen, resulting in a limited coherency. The term coherence refers to the range of phase differences in the illuminating beam as it approaches the specimen. If the electrons come from a single point source, then all the waves in the incident beam are in phase with each other and the illumination is coherent. On the other hand, if the source of electrons is so large that there is *no* phase relation between the incident waves, the illumination is completely incoherent. In reality, the filament in an electron microscope is somewhere between these two extremes and the incident illumination is defined as partially coherent (SPENCE [1981]).

In TEM the dimensions of the region on the specimen, a, over which the illumination appears coherent is related to the angular aperture of the illumination, α_i, by (GEISS [1979]):

$$a = \frac{\lambda}{2\alpha_i}. \tag{2}$$

References: p. 788.

Field emission guns possess a very small α_i which results in a large coherence length.

Charged electrons interact strongly with the transmitted specimen, the scattering cross-section σ_e for electrons is rather large compared to the cross-section of neutrons or X-rays (see appendix). Specimen thicknesses are required in the range of 10 nm to 1 μm depending on the imaging mode and on the voltage of the TEM. Recipes exist for electrochemical thinning of conducting materials (THOMPSON-RUSSELL and EDINGTON [1977]) as well as for ion beam etching of insulators (TIGHE [1976]).

Different kinds of electrons and electromagnetic waves are emitted from a specimen which is irradiated with high-energy electrons. The different waves result from elastic or inelastic scattering processes. Different signals (fig. 1) are used for different imaging modes. Information on the crystal structure and on defects in the specimen can be obtained by studying the elastically scattered electrons (in micrographs inelastically scattered electrons are also present and contribute to the background intensity) whereas investigations of inelastically scattered electrons and of other waves leaving the specimen allow the determination of chemical composition and topology of the specimen surface.

The microscope can be operated in different modes as described briefly in the following. For more details the reader is referred to textbooks on electron microscopy given in the list of references.

In *standard or conventional transmission electron microscopy* (TEM) mode the microscope is operated to form images by bright field (BF), dark field (DF), or lattice image (phase) contrast, see fig. 2. A BF (DF) image is formed when only the direct (one diffracted) beam is used for image formation. The objective aperture prevents all other beams to pass to the recording system. Usually, the specimen is oriented so that the Bragg condition is nearly fulfilled for a set of lattice planes. Then one reflected beam is strongly excited besides the incident beam (see §4). A

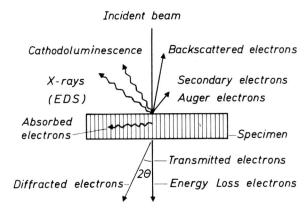

Fig. 1. Electrons and electromagnetic waves emitted from a transmitted specimen as a result of elastic and inelastic scattering or diffraction of the incident electron waves.

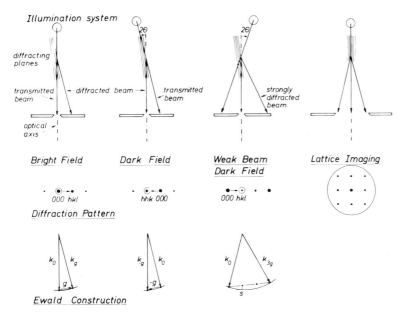

Fig. 2. Ray diagrams (including Ewald sphere construction) for: (a) a conventional two-beam bright-field (BF) image; (b) dark-field (DF) image; (c) weak-beam dark-field (WBDF) image; (d) lattice image. The gun of the electron microscope is tilted by the appropriate angle in going from (a) to (b) or from (a) to (c).

weak-beam dark-field (WBDF) image is produced if a weakly excited DF beam is used for imaging (COCKAYNE [1978]).

A *lattice image* is formed by the interference of at least two beams in the image plane of the objective lens. Lattice fringes can be observed if a row of systematic beams (reflected at the lattice planes in question) is used for imaging, while a structure image is formed by using many beams present in a low-indexed Laue zone. Special adjustments of the microscope are required for the formation of the high resolution electron microscope images (SPENCE [1981] and THOMAS and GORINGE [1979]), see §9.

The objective lens produces a *diffraction pattern* of the specimen in its backfocal plane (see fig. 3). The first image of the object is rotated by 180° against the diffraction pattern. The diffraction pattern and the first image are magnified by the subsequent intermediate lenses and projector lenses. The information obtainable from the diffraction pattern is summarized in §3.

In the *scanning transmission electron microscopy* (STEM) mode, the electron beam is focused as a fine probe on the specimen by the prefield of the objective lens. The beam probe is scanned over the specimen (by scanning coils) and the transmitted intensity is recorded.

The STEM mode is usually applied in materials science for analytical microscopy (see §10), where the probe is fixed on a selected small area and either the energy

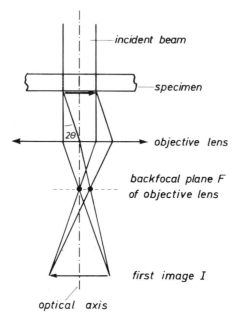

Fig. 3. Ray diagram in the area of the objective lens of an electron microscope. A diffraction pattern is formed in the backfocal plane F of the objective lens, whereas the (first) image I of the object O lies in the plane I. The first image of the object is rotated by 180° relative to the diffraction pattern.

losses of the transmitted electrons are studied (EELS) or the X-rays emitted from the specimens are investigated (usually by EDS) for the determination of the chemical composition of the specimen. The use of a very small probe size ($<$ 10 nm) is often limited by a strongly enhanced contamination rate (HREN [1979]).

In the STEM mode backscattered electrons can be collected as well as secondary electrons. These scanning micrographs are similar to those obtained by regular scanning electron microscopy (SEM). Information on the topography of the specimen surface can be obtained.

3. Information from the diffraction pattern

3.1. Diffraction spot pattern

The diffraction pattern provides crystallographic information on a qualitative phase identification and on the orientation-relations between crystals and the direction of the incoming electron beam. Kikuchi patterns (see § 3.2) can be used for the exact determination of the orientation, whereas the convergent-beam technique allows statements on crystal symmetry and determination of the foil thickness.

The possibilities and the accuracy of analysis of diffraction patterns are discussed in many textbooks on electron microscopy and special papers (e.g., ANDREWS *et al.* [1971]). Important factors for the accuracy are: (i) the shape factor described in the appendix which determines the intensity distribution in the reciprocal space; (ii) instrumental alignment and beam divergence; (iii) specimen perfection; (iv) curvature of the Ewald sphere and its orientation with respect to the foil; (v) double diffraction.

3.1.1. Double diffraction

From the structure factor it follows that certain reciprocal lattice points are not present (zero intensity) for certain crystal symmetries. However, each diffracted beam (within the crystal) can act as an incident beam and can diffract electrons to a reciprocal lattice point forbidden by the structure-factor rules, especially in orientations where several different reflections are excited simultaneously. For example, in the diamond cubic structure the (002) reflection is not allowed, but this reflection can be excited in a [110] foil via double diffraction: if a $(1\bar{1}1)$ reflection is excited then this reflected beam can act as a primary beam for $(\bar{1}11)$ planes; this gives a total reflection $g_1 + g_2 = (1\bar{1}1) + (\bar{1}11) = (002)$.

3.1.2. Patterns from ordered crystals

The symmetries of ordered crystal structures are often changed compared to the disordered crystal structure. This results in the appearance of superlattice reflections at positions that are forbidden for the disordered structure. The intensities of the superlattice reflections correspond to the difference between the atomic scattering factors of the different atoms, in contrast to the intensities of the fundamental reflections, which are related to the sum of the scattering factors. As an example, the B2 superlattice is selected. It is based on the bcc structure of the CsCl lattice with one kind (A) of atoms at 000 and other (B) at $\frac{1}{2}\frac{1}{2}\frac{1}{2}$. The structure factors are (for complete ordering):

$$F = f_A + f_B \quad \text{for } h + k + l = \text{even: fundamental reflections,}$$

$$F = f_A - f_B \quad \text{for } h + k + l = \text{odd: superlattice reflections.} \tag{3}$$

The corresponding diffraction pattern is shown in fig. 4a. In general, superlattices can be identified from their diffraction pattern, either by comparison with structure-factor calculations for different possible superstructures, or by an analytical method which can be viewed as the reversal of the structure-factor calculations (KHACHATURYAN [1974]). In this method the ordered lattice is represented by a superposition of concentration waves. Theoretically, it allows unequivocally the determination of the real space lattice from the complete set of experimentally determined superlattice diffraction vectors.

This method by Khachaturyan can be used to identify superlattices in substitutional (DAS *et al.* [1973]) and interstitial solutions. However, it must be carefully observed that superstructures cannot always be identified by diffraction patterns alone. If, as in many disordered cubic alloys, an ordered structure has non-cubic

References: p. 788.

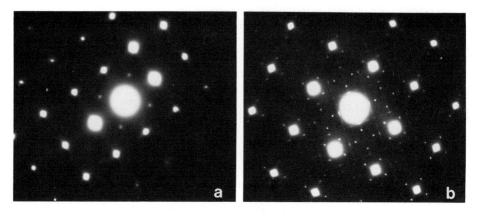

Fig. 4. Diffraction patterns from ordered crystals: (a) diffraction pattern of an ordered β-AlNi alloy (B2 superlattice), [100] zone axis, superlattice reflections are visible; (b) Diffraction pattern of an ordered Ta–O alloy, [110] zone axis, variants of different orientations contribute to the pattern.

symmetry a number of orientational variants may exist. Figure 4b shows, as an example, a (110) pattern of an ordered Ta–O interstitial phase. The superlattice spots arise from very small ordered domains. If the selected area contributing to the diffraction pattern is large compared to the domain size, then the different domain variants contribute to the diffraction pattern. It is then impossible to determine the superstructure from the diffraction pattern alone. The size, shape, and the number of the different variants of the ordered domains can be observed, however, from different DF images taken with superlattice reflections.

3.2. Kikuchi lines

Electrons can be scattered inelastically by interaction with the atoms of the specimen. Those electrons lose energies in the range of about a hundred eV. The inelastically scattered electrons can subsequently be diffracted coherently when Bragg's law is fulfilled at a suitable set of reflection planes. Since the (primary) inelastic scattering process occurs in different directions, the loci of the different subsequent coherent scattering are cones with semivertex angles of $(90° - \theta)$ to each side. The two cones are bisected by the reflection plane. The lines are, therefore, produced in pairs which are in contrast to the background. A *deficiency line* of less intensity than the background occurs nearer the origin of reciprocal space than its associated *excess line* with intensity above the background. Two conditions must be fulfilled so that these *Kikuchi lines* are observed. One is that the crystal is thick enough, so that enough inelastic scattering processes occur, the second condition is that the crystal must be nearly perfect, especially not bent. The width of the lines indicates the curvature range of the crystal planes over the thickness traversed. If this becomes excessive, the lines disappear into the background as their intensity is spread over a larger angle.

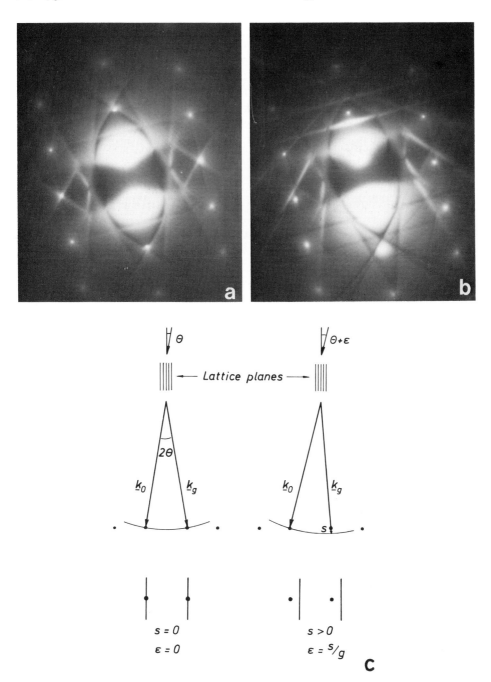

Fig. 5. Kikuchi lines on a diffraction pattern: (a) excitation error $s \approx 0$; (b) $s > 0$. (c) Sketch showing shift in Kikuchi lines produced by a tilt ϵ.

The Kikuchi line pattern can be used to determine the orientation of the crystal with respect to the incoming electron beam. There exist two ways for doing this. Either three pairs of Kikuchi lines have to be indexed and then the orientation can be calculated, or the observed Kikuchi pattern has to be compared to Kikuchi maps (THOMAS and GORINGE [1979]). The orientation of the specimen with respect to the electron beam can be determined with an accuracy of better than 0.3°. The excitation error s (cf. §4) can also be determined from the relative position of Kikuchi lines compared to the diffraction spots as demonstrated in fig. 5.

3.3. Convergent-beam diffraction

The size of the area giving rise to the diffraction pattern can be substantially reduced if – similarly as in STEM – the electron beam is focused onto the specimen. Under this condition is is practically impossible to maintain the nearly parallel illumination condition. Some convergence of the beam is introduced. As a result, the diffraction "spots" become "discs". For a convergence angle $\alpha < 2\theta_B$ this does not introduce problems since the discs do not overlap (θ_B is the Bragg angle).

In the intensity distribution of those diffraction "discs" much information is available (STEEDS [1979]):

(i) Each diffraction disc is produced from exactly the same small area (microdiffraction) without any shift introduced by lens errors (HIRSCH et al. [1977]). Therefore, these diffraction patterns can be used for the determination of the orientation and the crystal structure of the small illuminated area.

(ii) Each disc contains the intensity diffracted by this same area of crystal for a range of incident orientations. That means that diffraction discs (convergent-beam electron diffraction pattern – CBED) are two-dimensional maps of diffraction intensities as a function of inclination between the incident electrons and a particular crystal direction.

The lattice parameters of a crystal can be determined very accurately from the fine structure of CBED patterns. A change in Bragg angle $\Delta\theta$ results in a change of the positions of lines within a pattern. The method is very strong in measuring *relative* changes in lattice parameters. Absolute numbers do not have a high accuracy.

If the change of lattice parameters of an alloy or compound is directly and unambiguously related to its chemical composition, then the chemical composition may be deduced from lines observable in CBED patterns. As an example, for dual-phase steels the local concentration of carbon could be determined with an accuracy of < 0.1 at% (STEEDS [1981]). The spatial resolution (including beam broadening) is governed just by the geometry of the electron probe.

Local strains (STEEDS [1981]) and also the foil thickness (KELLY et al. [1975]) can be measured from CBED patterns. Furthermore, CBED patterns allow the determination of the symmetry and of the space group of the crystals (STEEDS [1981]).

3.4. Moiré pattern

Moiré patterns (see fig. 8c for an example) occur from overlapping crystals as in composite films or in two- (or more) phase systems. Two general cases must be considered:

(i) Parallel moiré fringes are formed if two parallel planes of different spacings are reflecting. The lattice spacings ($d_1 = 1/g_1$ and $d_2 = 1/g_2$) differ only in magnitude. Fringes can be observed with distances $d = 1/\Delta g = 1/|g_1 - g_2|$.

(ii) A rotational moiré pattern is formed when planes with equal spacing d, but rotated through an angle α, diffract together. For this situation the moiré spacing d_r is given by $d_r = 1/g\sin\alpha$.

Sometimes moiré patterns have to be distinguished from other periodic defects in the crystals, e.g., a set of parallel dislocations. This can always be done best by imaging the same area with different diffraction vectors. The direction of the moiré lines is usually perpendicular to the diffraction vector.

4. Theory of diffraction contrast

4.1. Introduction

Diffraction contrast of defects in crystalline specimens is mainly a problem of high-energy electron diffraction in non-perfect crystals. It will turn out later that, by intrinsic reasons, for the imaging of lattice defects (dislocations, stacking faults etc.) an electron–optical resolution of about 1 nm is in general sufficient. Accordingly, lens errors of the objective lens can be neglected. We assume that the objective lens is focused onto the lower specimen surface through which the electrons leave the specimen. Then it suffices for the purpose of this section to calculate the electron wavefunction at the lower specimen surface since the electron–optical imaging system is assumed to be perfect.

In a first part, we deal with the diffraction in a perfect crystal specimen. In a second part, it will be outlined how the diffraction theory must be extended for specimens containing lattice defects. Electron refraction effects, due to the mean inner potential of the crystal, are neglected throughout.

4.2. Specimen, reciprocal lattice and excitation error

We consider a specimen of constant thickness t of the order of 100 nm. A Cartesian coordinate system is introduced with its origin in the upper specimen surface and with the z-axis (unit vector e_z) perpendicular to the specimen plane and pointing downwards. The lateral dimensions L_x, L_y of the specimen are orders of magnitude larger than t. According to the appendix, this means that the intensity distributions $|F(\kappa)|^2$ at the reciprocal lattice points g are rod-shaped or spike-shaped with the spike axis parallel to e_z and a spike length of the order of $1/t$. This is indicated in fig. 6, where also the wavevector k_0 of the incident wave and the Ewald

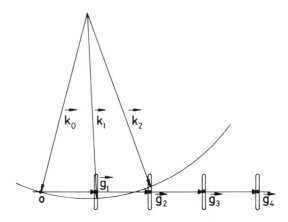

Fig. 6. The Ewald sphere and the reciprocal space. The intensity distributions $|F(\kappa)|^2$ around the reciprocal lattice points are spike-shaped with spike lengths inversely proportional to the specimen thickness. The excitation error s is positive for $\boldsymbol{g} = \boldsymbol{g}_1$ and negative for the other $\boldsymbol{g}$.

sphere are inserted. Note that this figure is not to scale: assuming a modulus of $(0.2$ nm$)^{-1}$ for the low-order diffraction vector $\boldsymbol{g}_1$, and $k_0 = 1/\lambda = (3.7$ pm$)^{-1}$ (100 keV electrons), we have $k_0/g_1 = 54$. Having this in mind, one realizes that near the low-order reflections the Ewald sphere is so flat that, if the sphere cuts through the spike of one of the reciprocal lattice points, this will happen also for the spikes of other adjacent reciprocal lattice points. Accordingly, in high-energy electron diffraction, in general several Bragg reflections are excited simultaneously; besides the primary wave a number of diffracted plane waves leave the crystal. However, in general the specimen can be orientated so that only one diffracted wave is strong. Then, we speak about a *two-beam case* (primary plus diffracted beam). Images taken with either of these two beams are called *strong-beam images*. On the other hand, dark-field images taken with an extremely weakly excited beam are called *weak-beam images*.

The direction of incidence of the primary beam with respect to the specimen can be characterized by the *excitation error* s_g, or simply s, which is given by the distance between the reciprocal lattice point $\boldsymbol{g}$ considered, and that point on the intensity spike where the Ewald sphere cuts through it. s is positive (negative) if the point $\boldsymbol{g}$ lies inside (outside) the Ewald sphere. If θ is the glancing angle between the direction of k_0 and the lattice planes belonging to $\boldsymbol{g}$ and if θ_g is the corresponding Bragg angle, then

$$s = g\Delta\theta, \quad \text{with} \quad \Delta\theta = \theta - \theta_g. \tag{4}$$

4.3. Outline of the dynamical diffraction theory

The essential points of the dynamical diffraction theory, in contrast to the kinematical theory as outlined in the appendix, are that diffractions between all plane waves involved have to be treated as being equivalent and that, in the absence of absorption effects, conservation of intensity must be fulfilled. There are several ways for formulating the dynamical theory for a perfect crystal. Here we refer very briefly to the classical way first developed by BETHE [1928]. Another way will be outlined later when crystals with lattice defects are considered.

Following Bethe, the time-independent Schrödinger equation with a periodic potential is solved in terms of independent "eigen solutions" or Bloch waves ψ_B. Generally, Bloch waves can be written in the form

$$\psi_B(r) = b(r) \exp(2\pi i K \cdot r), \tag{5}$$

where the wavevector K has to be found for a given electron energy and a given direction of K. The function $b(r)$ is periodic with the crystal periodicity. In the two-beam case, to which we restrict ourselves, there are two independent Bloch waves belonging to a given tangential component of K parallel to the electron entrance surface of the crystal. We assume that the two-beam diffraction vector g is perpendicular to e_z and that the origin of the coordinate system lies on a reflecting lattice plane. Before the solutions are presented we introduce some terms which will be used repeatedly later. One important diffraction parameter is the *extinction length* ξ_g,

$$\xi_g = \frac{k_0 V_e \pi}{F_s(g)}, \tag{6}$$

where V_e is the volume of the elementary cell and F_s is the structure amplitude, see appendix. For low-order reflections ξ_g is of the order of some 10 nm. Besides ξ_g we use the "wavenumber" notations

$$1/\xi_g = \sigma_0, \qquad \sigma \equiv \sigma(w) = \sigma_0 \cdot (1 + w^2)^{1/2}, \qquad w = s\xi_g. \tag{7}$$

w is the "normalized" excitation error and σ is the reciprocal of the effective extinction length $\xi_{g,eff}$ as a function of w. The wanted solutions, expressed in these terms, are (e.g., HIRSCH et al. [1977]):

$$\left. \begin{aligned} \psi_B^{(1)} &= c_0^{(1)} \exp\left[2\pi i\left(K_0^{(1)} \cdot r\right)\right] + c_g^{(1)} \exp\left[2\pi i\left(K_g^{(1)} \cdot r\right)\right], \\ \psi_B^{(2)} &= c_0^{(2)} \exp\left[2\pi i\left(K_0^{(2)} \cdot r\right)\right] + c_g^{(2)} \exp\left[2\pi i\left(K_g^{(2)} \cdot r\right)\right]. \end{aligned} \right\} \tag{8}$$

$$\left. \begin{aligned} c_0^{(1)} &= c_g^{(2)} = \frac{1}{\sqrt{2}}\left[1 - \frac{w}{(1 + w^2)^{1/2}}\right]^{1/2}, \\ c_g^{(1)} &= -c_0^{(2)} = \frac{1}{\sqrt{2}}\left[1 + \frac{w}{(\sqrt{1 + w^2})^{1/2}}\right]^{1/2} \\ K_0^{(l)} &= k_0 + \Delta k^{(l)}, \qquad K_g^{(l)} = K_0^{(l)} + g, \quad l = 1, 2, \\ \Delta k^{(1)} &= \tfrac{1}{2}(s + \sigma)e_z, \qquad \Delta k^{(2)} = \tfrac{1}{2}(s - \sigma)e_z. \end{aligned} \right\} \tag{9}$$

References: p. 788.

The $\Delta k^{(l)}$ are the "eigen values" and the $c_n^{(l)}$ ($n = 0$, g) are the components of the "eigen vectors" of the Schrödinger equation. The relation between eqs. (5) and (8) is easy to realize if the phase factor $\exp(2\pi i K_0^{(l)} \cdot r)$ is put in front of the two terms of $\psi_B^{(l)}$ in eq. (8).

If the ψ_B are known, a linear combination of the $\psi_B^{(l)}$,

$$\psi = \varphi^{(1)} \psi_B^{(1)} + \varphi^{(2)} \psi_B^{(2)}, \tag{10}$$

has to be found which satisfies the boundary conditions at the specimen surface at $z = 0$ where both partial waves with the wave vector K_0 have to add up to unity so that at $z = 0$ they fit to the incident primary wave:

$$\psi_0 = \phi_0 \exp[2\pi i(k_0 \cdot r)], \qquad \phi_0 = 1 \text{ for } z < 0. \tag{11}$$

Further, both partial waves with wave vectors K_g have to cancel at $z = 0$. In our case, this leads to

$$\varphi^{(1)} = c_0^{(1)}, \qquad \varphi^{(2)} = c_0^{(2)}. \tag{12}$$

At the lower specimen surface at $z = t$, the Bloch waves decompose into their partial waves, and those having the same subscript, 0 or g, interfere and constitute a plane wave below the specimen. Thus, we obtain for $z > t$:

$$\psi_0 = \phi_0(t) \exp[2\pi i(k_0 \cdot r)], \qquad \psi_g = \phi_g(t) \exp[2\pi i(k_g \cdot r)],$$

with

$$k_g = k_0 + s e_z + g, \qquad |k_g| = |k_0|, \tag{13}$$

and

$$\phi_0(t) = \cos \pi \sigma t - i \frac{w}{(1 + w^2)^{1/2}} \sin \pi \sigma t, \qquad \phi_g(t) = i \frac{1}{(1 + w^2)^{1/2}} \sin \pi \sigma t. \tag{14}$$

4.4. Normal and anomalous absorption

High-energy electrons, when passing through a crystal, experience, besides the elastic scattering at the atom potential, also inelastic scattering, e.g. by interaction with the thermal vibration of the crystal atoms (phonons) or with the crystal electrons (plasmons, inner-shell excitation). By these events energy is transferred between high-energy electrons and the crystal, which leads to a loss of coherency of the wave fields of the elastically and inelastically scattered electrons. This effect can formally be described as an "absorption" (although, of course, the inelastically scattered electrons are not really absorbed). This "absorption" is different for different Bloch waves, depending on the high-energy electron density distribution $|\psi_B|^2$ with respect to the atom positions (HASHIMOTO et al. [1960]). From eqs. (8) and (9) it is easy to derive that $|\psi_B^{(1)}|^2$ reveals a maximum electron density at the lattice planes characterized by g and a minimum in between; for $|\psi_B^{(2)}|^2$ the reverse is true:

$$|\psi_B^{(1)}|^2 = 1 + \frac{1}{(1+w^2)^{1/2}} \cos 2\pi(g \cdot r),$$

$$|\psi_B^{(2)}|^2 = 1 - \frac{1}{(1+w^2)^{1/2}} \cos 2\pi(g \cdot r). \tag{15}$$

Accordingly, $\psi_B^{(1)}$ interacts more strongly with the crystal atoms and is thus more strongly absorbed than $\psi_B^{(2)}$. We subdivide the absorption into *normal* absorption, which a high-energy electron would experience when travelling through the crystal far away from any Bragg reflection, and *anomalous* absorption, which takes the structure of $|\psi_B^{(l)}|^2$ into account. Normal absorption is accounted for by adding a common factor $\exp(-\mu_0 z/2)$, where μ_0 is usually expressed by the "normal" absorption length ξ_0' with $\mu_0 = 2\pi/\xi_0'$. The anomalous absorption is introduced by adding a positive imaginary part to $1/\xi_g$,

$$1/\xi_g \rightarrow \frac{1}{\xi_g} + i\frac{1}{\xi_g'}, \tag{16}$$

where typically $\xi_g' \approx (10-20)\xi_g$ (RADI [1970]). Accurate values of ξ_0' are not well known since they depend, e.g., on the size of the objective aperture. Normal absorption acts only as a scaling factor, independently of the actual diffraction conditions. Therefore, accurate values of ξ_0' are not required, and often $\xi_0' = \xi_g'$ is used for intensity calculations.

Working through the abbreviations introduced in eq. (7) leads in first order of ξ_g/ξ_g' to the substitution

$$\sigma \rightarrow \sigma + i\sigma', \qquad \sigma' = \frac{1}{\xi_g'(1+w^2)^{1/2}}. \tag{17}$$

This finally gives:

$$\psi_B^{(l)} \propto \exp\left[-\tfrac{1}{2}\mu^{(l)}z\right], \quad l = 1, 2,$$

with

$$\mu^{(1)} = \mu_0 + 2\pi\sigma', \qquad \mu^{(2)} = \mu_0 - 2\pi\sigma', \tag{18}$$

i.e., the absorption of $\psi_B^{(1)}$ ($\psi_B^{(2)}$) is enhanced (reduced). (ξ_g is usually left uncorrected where entering into the $c_n^{(l)}$.)

4.5. Dynamical bright-field and dark-field intensities

The same substitution as eq. (17) must be applied to the argument $\pi\sigma t$ in eq. (14). After some algebraic operations, we find for the bright-field (I_0) and dark-field (I_g) intensities:

$$I_0 = \exp(-\mu_0 t)\left[\cosh 2\pi\sigma't + \frac{w \sinh 2\pi\sigma't}{(1+w^2)^{1/2}} - \frac{\sinh^2\pi\sigma't + \sin^2\pi\sigma t}{1+w^2}\right],$$

References: p. 788.

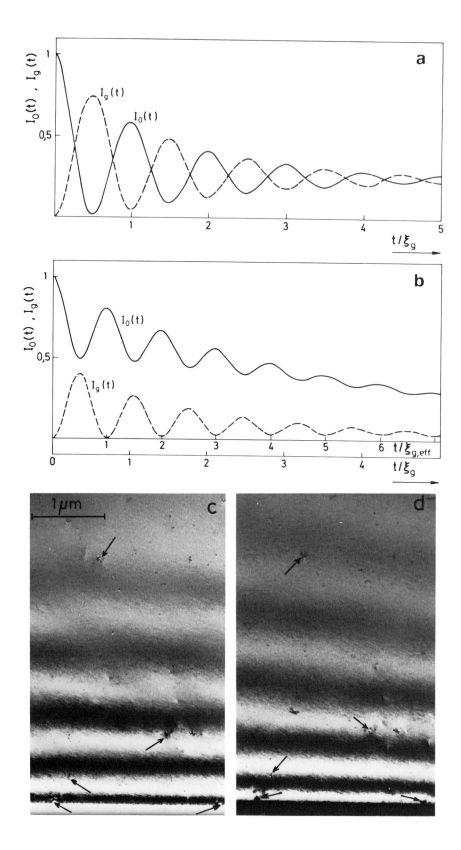

$$I_g = \exp(-\mu_0 t) \frac{\sinh^2 \pi \sigma' t + \sin^2 \pi \sigma t}{1 + w^2}. \tag{19}$$

In fig. 7a, b we have plotted $I_0(t)$ and $I_g(t)$ as a function of t for $w = 0$ and $w = 1$ (with $\xi_0' = \xi_g'$, $\xi_g' = 10\xi_g$). We see that the total intensity oscillates between I_0 and I_g, a maximum in I_0 corresponds to a minimum in I_g and vice-versa ("Pendellösung"). These oscillations are due to the fact that the z-components of the wavevectors of the Bloch waves $\psi_B^{(1)}$ and $\psi_B^{(2)}$ differ by σ, which leads to a beating of the partial waves constituting ψ_0 and ψ_g, respectively. The full oscillation period $\Delta t = \xi_{g,\text{eff}} = \sigma^{-1}$ and the oscillation amplitude decreases with increasing $|w|$. Further, the oscillations are damped with increasing t which is a consequence of the anomalous strong absorption of $\psi_B^{(1)}$; if $\psi_B^{(1)}$ has decayed, a beating between partial waves is no longer possible. On wedge-shaped specimens the Pendellösung-oscillations give rise to "thickness fringes" or "thickness contours" along lines of constant specimen thickness. An example is shown in fig. 7c, d.

In Fig. 8a, b we show I_0 and I_g as a function of w for some values of t. Both terms show oscillations with varying w ("bend contours"), which decrease in amplitude with increasing t. Whereas I_g is symmetric in w, this is not true for I_0: the maximum in I_0 (i.e., best transmittivity!) occurs at $w > 0$. A complicated system of bend contours is visible in fig. 8c.

4.6. The column approximation

We consider in fig. 9 the point C at the lower specimen surface. The lines through A and C and through B and C are parallel to the wavevectors k_0 and k_g of the primary and diffracted wave, respectively. Triangle ABC is known as the *Takagi-tri-angle*. It has been shown (TAKAGI [1962], HOWIE and BASINSKI [1968]) that the wavefunctions ψ_0 and ψ_g at point C are determined in very good approximation only by the specimen parameters within this triangle. With specimen parameters we mean local specimen thickness, local orientation, i.e., local excitation error, and local displacements of atoms from their positions in a perfect lattice. For high-energy electrons the Takagi triangle is very narrow: The angle at C is $2\theta_g$ with the Bragg angle θ_g being about 1° or less. Taking $t = 100$ nm, it turns out that the distance A–B is some nm at most. Accordingly, if variations of the specimen parameters over such a distance are sufficiently small, then ψ_0 and ψ_g at point C can be calculated under the assumption that the specimen parameters along the "column" above C, i.e., along the z-axis in our case, are the same for the entire specimen. This means that for calculation of ψ_0 and ψ_g the "column" coordinate is the only intrinsic variable, whereas the lateral coordinates (x, y in our case) act only as parameters. This is the *column approximation* introduced by HIRSCH et al. [1960].

Fig. 7. (a, b) Two-beam thickness contours calculated for $\xi_g' = \xi_0' = 10\xi_g$ as a function of specimen thickness t: solid line = bright-field intensity I_0, dashed line = dark field intensity I_g, with (a) excitation error $w = 0$, and (b) $w = 1$. (c, d) Thickness contours in copper, $g = (111)$, $w \approx 0$, in (c) bright field, and (d) dark field. Arrows indicate equivalent points on the images. The lower arrows point to the specimen edge.

References: p. 788.

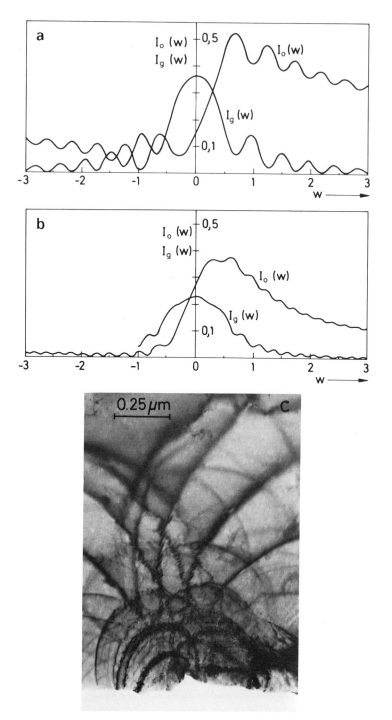

Fig. 8. (a, b) Two-beam bend contours calculated for $\xi_g' = \xi_0' = 10\xi_g$ as a function of w, with (a) $t = 2.5\xi_g$, and (b) $t = 5\xi_g$. (c) Bright field bend contours in copper. The dark lines correspond to specimen orientations where a certain set of lattice planes is in Bragg orientation. The moiré patterns in the centre of the figure are due to a thin oxide layer on the specimen surface.

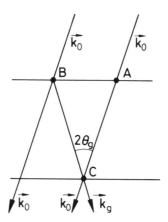

Fig. 9. The Takagi triangle. The wavefunctions ψ_0 and ψ_g at point C are determined by the specimen parameters within triangle ABC.

4.7. Diffraction at imperfect crystals

4.7.1. The displacement field

Lattice defects cause displacements $R(r_n) \equiv R_n$ of the atoms from their positions r_n in the defect-free reference lattice *. In general, $|R_n|$ is of the order of, or smaller than, the interatomic distances. Here we assume for simplicity that the displacements do not vary appreciably over the atom positions within the elementary cell so that the structure-amplitude F_s is unaffected by the lattice defects. Further we confine ourselves to cases where R is a continuous function in space, giving thus rise to "strain contrast". Contrast due to stacking faults and other planar defects will be considered briefly in §8.

4.7.2. The kinematical approach

A first insight in the intensities $I_0(x, y)$ and $I_g(x, y)$ for perfect and imperfect crystals may be obtained by the kinematical diffraction theory outlined in the appendix. We start from eq. (A. 46), where we neglect, as usual, the term $s \cdot R$ in the exponent. Thus, the kinematical diffraction amplitude $F(s)$ follows as:

$$F(s) = \frac{F_s(g)}{V_e} \int_{V_c} \exp\{-2\pi i[g \cdot R(r) + s \cdot r]\} \, d^3r, \tag{20}$$

where the integration runs over the specimen volume $V_c = L_x L_y t$ with $t \ll L_x, L_y$. The diffracted intensity follows by inserting eq. (20) into the integral of eq. (A. 35). We assume that g is perpendicular to the z-axis and make use of the fact that – because of the smallness of the Bragg angle – the Ewald sphere near g is (nearly)

---

* Regarding the notation R, cf. the footnote in §5.2.

References: p. 788.

parallel to the x–y plane. Thus, the differential df_E in eq. (A. 35) can be replaced by $ds_1 ds_2$ [the coordinate s_3 in the appendix is identical with the excitation error s in eq. (4)]. Now having in mind that, within the column approximation, the terms x, y in $R(x, y; z)$ are not coordinates but only parameters, it turns out that all integrations in eq. (A. 35) with $F(s)$ according to eq. (20) can be carried out, except those over the z-axis. After dividing the result by the specimen area we get for the diffracted intensity per unit area:

$$I_g(x, y) = \left(\frac{F_s}{kV_e} \right)^2 \left| \int_0^t \exp\{-2\pi i[g \cdot R(z) + sz]\} \, dz \right|^2. \tag{21}$$

Thus, with eq. (6), the amplitude ϕ_g follows as:

$$\phi_g(x, y; t) = \frac{i\pi}{\xi_g} \phi_0 \int_0^t \exp\{-2\pi i[g \cdot R(x, y; z) + sz]\} \, dz. \tag{22}$$

Here we have added the amplitude ϕ_0 of the primary wave, which is constant ($|\phi_0| = 1$) within the kinematical approach. Equation (22) is the *kinematical contrast integral* derived by HIRSCH et al. [1960] who have shown that the imaginary unit i should be added.

The argument in the exponent of eq. (22) can be re-interpreted as

$$g \cdot R(z) + sz = \int_0^z s_\ell(\zeta) \, d\zeta, \tag{23a}$$

with

$$s_\ell(z) = s + \frac{d(g \cdot R(z))}{dz} \tag{23b}$$

being the *local* excitation error experienced by the primary wave as due to the *local* orientation of the reflecting lattice planes. Diffraction from ϕ_0 into ϕ_g is especially strong where $s_\ell(z)$ is small (COCKAYNE et al. [1969]). For $R = 0$ (perfect crystal) eq. (22) can be integrated and yields, with $|\phi_0| = 1$,

$$I_g = \frac{1}{\xi_g^2} \frac{\sin^2 \pi ts}{s^2}, \tag{24}$$

to which the "dynamical" solution eq. (14) degenerates if absorption is neglected and $|s\xi_g| = |w| \gg 1$. Thus, the range of applicability of eqs. (21)–(24) is restricted to large values of $|w|$, for which $I_g \ll 1$, for instance to the weak-beam imaging mode (COCKAYNE et al. [1969], and COCKAYNE [1978]), where the diffracted beam taken for the image formation is excited with $|w| \gg 1$.

Equation (22) can be rearranged in order to separate the defect-induced part of the contrast integral. By partial integration we get

$$\phi_g = \phi_g' + \phi_g'', \tag{25}$$

with

$$\phi_g' = \frac{i\pi}{\xi_g}\phi_0 \left.\frac{\exp\{-2\pi i[\boldsymbol{g}\cdot\boldsymbol{R}(z)+sz]\}}{-2\pi i s}\right|_{z=0}^{t}, \tag{26a}$$

$$\phi_g'' = -\frac{i\pi}{\xi_g}\phi_0\frac{1}{s}\int_0^t \frac{d(\boldsymbol{g}\cdot\boldsymbol{R}(z))}{dz}\exp\{-2\pi i[\boldsymbol{g}\cdot\boldsymbol{R}(z)+sz]\}\,dz. \tag{26b}$$

If $\boldsymbol{g}\cdot\boldsymbol{R}(t)$ and $\boldsymbol{g}\cdot\boldsymbol{R}(0)$ are neglected in eq. (26a), then ϕ_g' represents the "background amplitude" with $|\phi_g'|^2$ identical to (24). ϕ_g'' is the defect-induced part of ϕ_g. Since the integrand of eq. (26b) is proportional to the displacement derivative $d(\boldsymbol{g}\cdot\boldsymbol{R}(z))/dz$, the integration limits can in general be extended to $\pm\infty$. In the dark-field intensity $I_g = |\phi_g|^2$ the interference term between ϕ_g' and ϕ_g'' is often neglected (cf. e.g. HIRSCH *et al.* [1960] and WILKENS and HORNBOGEN [1964]):

$$I_g(x, y) = |\phi_g'|^2 + |\phi_g''(x, y)|^2. \tag{27}$$

Then adjusting to conservation of intensity gives the bright-field intensity:

$$I_0(x, y) = \left(1 - |\phi_g'|^2\right) - |\phi_g''(x, y)|^2, \tag{28}$$

i.e., the kinematical contrast in dark field (bright field) is always bright (dark). Later we will see that this is not true if $|w|$ is not $\gg 1$.

4.7.3. Dynamical diffraction theory in terms of plane waves

In §4.3 we have outlined that one of the prerequisites of a dynamical diffraction theory is that all plane waves involved must be treated equivalently, i.e., diffraction between all plane waves must be taken into account. Equation (22) suggests intuitively one way by which this condition can be met: Both sides of eq. (22) are differentiated with respect to t, then we set $t = z$ and concede that also ϕ_0 may be z-dependent. In a next step we construct an equivalent equation, describing transition from the diffracted into the primary wave, i.e., $\boldsymbol{k}_g$ and $\boldsymbol{k}_0$ change their roles. This requires a change of the signs of g and s. Then we end up with a set of coupled differential equations:

$$d\phi_g/dz = i(\pi/\xi_g)\phi_0(z)\exp\{-2\pi i[\boldsymbol{g}\cdot\boldsymbol{R}(z)+sz]\},$$
$$d\phi_0/dz = i(\pi/\xi_g)\phi_g(z)\exp\{+2\pi i[\boldsymbol{g}\cdot\boldsymbol{R}(z)+sz]\}. \tag{29}$$

These equations are indeed one form of the differential equations established by HOWIE and WHELAN [1961] in a more detailed way for describing strain contrast by dynamical diffraction in imperfect crystals. These equations have to be integrated down to $z = t$ with the boundary condition $\phi_0 = 1$, $\phi_g = 0$ at $z = 0$. For $\boldsymbol{R} = 0$ (perfect crystal) they can be integrated analytically; the result is identical to that given in eq. (14).

4.7.4. Dynamical diffraction theory in terms of Bloch waves

A different approach for deriving dynamical diffraction in imperfect crystals

References: p. 788.

starts from the Bloch-wave solution of the perfect reference lattice as given in §4.3 (WILKENS [1964], HÄUSSERMANN *et al.* [1973], WILKENS *et al.* [1973]). A trial solution, in the two-beam case given by

$$\psi = \varphi^{(1)}(z)\psi_B^{(1)} + \varphi^{(2)}(z)\psi_B^{(2)}, \tag{30}$$

with z-dependent Bloch-wave amplitudes $\varphi^{(l)}$ is inserted into the Schrödinger equation which now contains a potential, the periodicity of which is perturbed by the atomic displacement field $R(r)$. This leads in the column approximation to a set of ordinary differential equations for the $\varphi^{(l)}$. In the two-beam case one possible representation is given by:

$$d\varphi^{(1)}/dz = i\pi \frac{d(g \cdot R)}{dz} \frac{1}{(1+w^2)^{1/2}} \varphi^{(2)}(z) \cdot \exp\left\{ -2\pi i\left[\frac{s}{\sigma} \frac{d(g \cdot R)}{dz} + \sigma z\right]\right\},$$

$$d\varphi^{(2)}/dz = i\pi \frac{d(g \cdot R)}{dz} \frac{1}{(1+w^2)^{1/2}} \varphi^{(1)}(z) \cdot \exp\left\{ +2\pi i\left[\frac{s}{\sigma} \frac{d(g \cdot R)}{dz} + \sigma z\right]\right\}.$$

$$\tag{31}$$

These differential equations describe the defect-induced transition from Bloch-state (2) into Bloch-state (1) (first equation) and in the opposite direction (second equation). This transition is proportional to the displacement derivative $d(g \cdot R)/dz$ and is essentially controlled by the phase factors $\exp(\pm 2\pi i\sigma z)$. Sufficiently far away from the defect, where $d(g \cdot R)/dz$ vanishes, the differential equations obey trivial solutions, $\varphi^{(1)}$ and $\varphi^{(2)}$ are constant. Once eq. (31) is integrated down to $z = t$ with $\varphi^{(l)}(0) = c_0^{(l)}$ the wanted amplitudes $\phi_n(t)$ ($n = 0$, g) are obtained as outlined in §4.3 with $\varphi^{(l)}(t)$ inserted into eq. (10). Anomalous absorption is taken into account by substituting σ in the exponents of eqs. (8) and (31) according to eq. (17). Normal absorption can be added subsequently.

Both sets of differential equations, eqs. (29) and (31), are in principle equivalent (WILKENS *et al.* [1973]). However, one consequence of the special form of the equations (31) is that they are especially suitable for deriving semiquantitative analytical solutions (e.g., WILKENS [1964], CHIK *et al.* [1967], WILKENS and RÜHLE [1972] and KATERBAU [1981]).

4.7.5. Properties of strain contrast in strong-beam images

Figure 10 shows strong-beam images in bright and dark field of dislocations traversing the specimen from the top to the bottom surface. Near the surface the dislocation contrast reveals characteristic bright–dark oscillations, which are "in phase" in bright and dark field near the top surface and which are "in anti-phase" near the bottom surface. Further, the bright–dark oscillations are reversed if the sign of g is changed. In the middle of the specimen the contrast is mainly dark in both bright and dark field. These phenomena, which are of quite a general nature, will be explained by a qualitative discussion of eq. (31). For this purpose we re-define the Bloch-wave amplitudes $\varphi^{(l)}$ into $\hat{\varphi}^{(l)}$ by incorporating the absorption terms of eq.

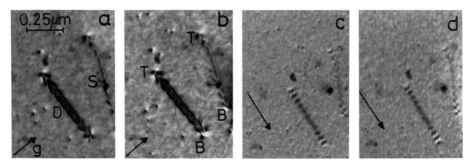

Fig. 10. Diffraction contrast of a single dislocation (S) and a narrow dislocation dipole (D) in copper traversing the specimen from the top (T) to the bottom (B) surface $\boldsymbol{g} = \langle 220 \rangle$. (The black–white dots in the background are due to ion damage (cf. §6.2.3) inside the microscope, as caused by an insufficient vacuum in the microscope column.) (a) Bright field $(\boldsymbol{g} \cdot \boldsymbol{b}) = 2$; (b) dark field $(\boldsymbol{g} \cdot \boldsymbol{b}) = 2$; (c) bright field $(\boldsymbol{g} \cdot \boldsymbol{b}) = 0$; (d) dark field $(\boldsymbol{g} \cdot \boldsymbol{b}) = 0$.

(18), which are incorporated in the usual procedure when going from the $\varphi^{(l)}(t)$ to $\phi_n(t)$,

$$\hat{\varphi}^{(l)}(z) = \varphi^{(l)}(z) \exp - \frac{\mu^{(l)}}{2} z, \qquad l = 1, 2, \tag{32}$$

and restrict ourselves to dynamical diffraction, i.e., $w = 0$. The results, however, are valid also for $|w| \lesssim 1$. In a perfect crystal, where $\varphi^{(1)}$ and $\varphi^{(2)}$ are constant, $\hat{\varphi}^{(1)}(z)$ decreases rapidly with z, whereas $\hat{\varphi}^{(2)}$ is only weakly damped ($\xi_0' < \xi_g'$). We assume a fairly thick specimen, so that $\hat{\varphi}^{(1)}$ has already decayed significantly in the middle of the specimen, cf. fig. 11. We consider the three regions (1), (2) and (3), indicated in fig. 11, separately. Now concerning contrast formation by a defect (e.g., a dislocation segment in fig. 10), we consider one particular column close to the defect, and the depth position z_0 of the latter is varied over the regions (1), (2), and (3).

If z_0 lies in region (1), where $\hat{\varphi}^{(1)}$ and $\hat{\varphi}^{(2)}$ are still of about equal strength, the scattering within a narrow interval near z_0 will increase (or decrease) $|\hat{\varphi}^{(1)}|$ and at the same time decrease (or increase) $|\hat{\varphi}^{(2)}|$, depending on the sign of $d(\boldsymbol{g} \cdot \boldsymbol{R})/dz$ *and* on the phase factors $\exp(\pm 2\pi i \sigma z_0)$ on the right-hand sides of eq. (31). The phase factor is periodic in z_0 with period $\xi_{g,\mathrm{eff}}$. Below the defect, the $\varphi^{(l)}$ in eq. (31) are constant again and the $\hat{\varphi}^{(l)}$ follow the decay as described by eq. (32). Then, going down to $z = t$, $\hat{\varphi}^{(1)}$ has decayed irrespective of what happened to $\hat{\varphi}^{(1)}$ at, or near to, z_0. Thus, the amplitudes $\phi_0(t)$ and $\phi_g(t)$ at $z = t$ are both determined solely by $\hat{\varphi}^{(2)}(t)$. And since the modulus of the latter oscillates with the period $\Delta z_0 = \xi_{g,\mathrm{eff}}$, we get bright–dark depth oscillations in both bright field and dark field, which are "in phase": bright (dark) contrast in bright field corresponds to bright (dark) contrast in dark field.

In region (2) we have already $|\hat{\varphi}^{(1)}| \ll |\hat{\varphi}^{(2)}|$. Accordingly, for defects with z_0 within this region the scattering goes essentially only in one way from $\hat{\varphi}^{(2)}$ to $\hat{\varphi}^{(1)}$, since there is (nearly) nothing to scatter from $\hat{\varphi}^{(1)}$ to $\hat{\varphi}^{(2)}$. So $|\hat{\varphi}^{(2)}|$ is decreased

References: p. 788.

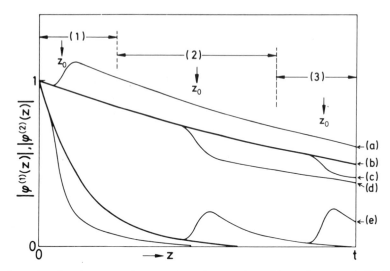

Fig. 11. Properties of strain contrast in strong-beam images taken with $w = 0$, schematically. Shown are the moduli of the Bloch-wave amplitudes $\hat{\varphi}^l(z)$, $l = 1$, 2, for defect depth-positions z_0 in either of the regions (1), (2) or (3), for details see text. (a): $|\hat{\varphi}^{(2)}(t)|$, z_0 in (1); (b): $|\hat{\varphi}^{(2)}(t)|_{bg}$; (c): $|\hat{\varphi}^{(2)}(t)|$, z_0 in (3); (d): $|\hat{\varphi}^{(2)}(t)|$, z_0 in (2); (e): $|\hat{\varphi}^{(1)}(t)|$, z_0 in (3).

irrespective of the actual value of z_0. On the way down to $z = t$, $\hat{\varphi}^{(1)}$ has again decayed, and the amplitudes $\phi_0(t)$ and $\phi_g(t)$ are, as in region (1), solely determined by $\hat{\varphi}^{(2)}(t)$. Since now $(|\hat{\varphi}^{(2)}(t)| < |\hat{\varphi}^{(2)}(t)|_{bg}$, where the subscript bg refers to the corresponding value in the background far away from the defect, we obtain a dark contrast in both bright field and dark field, in striking contrast to the kinematical approach, cf. eqs. (27) and (28).

If z_0 lies in region (3), the scattering occurs even more than in region (2) only from $\hat{\varphi}^{(2)}$ to $\hat{\varphi}^{(1)}$. However, now $\hat{\varphi}^{(1)}$, on its enhanced level below z_0, can "survive" during the short distance from z_0 to t, along which absorption may be negligible. Consequently, the amplitudes ϕ_0 and ϕ_g at $z = t$ are determined by the interference of partial waves as described in §4.3. The mutual phase shifts of these partial waves are given by $\exp[\pm 2\pi i\sigma(t - z_0)]$, and since absorption can be disregarded over the distance $t - z_0$, the depth oscillations in bright field and dark field must be complementary or in "antiphase". Of course, in practice, these three regions are not sharply separated. Depending on the actual specimen thickness, we expect depth oscillations, which are "in phase" in bright field and dark field for defects at positions z_0 close to the top surface of the specimen. These depth oscillations are damped out with increasing z_0. For thick, or moderately thick, specimens they disappear, or nearly disappear, for z_0 in the interior of the specimen, resulting in only a dark contrast in bright and dark field. Finally, they reappear in "antiphase" for z_0 close to the lower specimen surface, see fig. 10.

4.7.6. Structure-factor contrast

Coherent precipitates may reveal a mismatch between the lattice parameters in the precipitate and the surrounding matrix. This mismatch gives rise to a space-dependent displacement field and, accordingly, to strain contrast as described by eqs. (22), (29) or (31). If, in addition, the structure-amplitude F_s inside the precipitate differs from that of the matrix, e.g., by a change of the chemical composition, an additional contrast, named *structure-factor contrast* may be caused. The reason is that now the extinction length ξ_g (proportional to $1/F_s$) becomes space-dependent, $\xi_g = \xi_g(r)$. This can be incorporated into eqs. (22) and (29) by setting $1/\xi_g = 1/\xi_g(x, y; z)$ and taking $1/\xi_g$ in eq. (22) under the integral (cf. ASHBY and BROWN [1963] and WILKENS [1981]). For eq. (31) an appropriate extension for including structure-factor contrast was given by WILKENS *et al.* [1977].

4.8. Practical applications of the differential equations

Standard programs are available for the numerical integration of the differential equations (29) or (31) by electronic computers. The user has only to take care for subroutines for computing the displacement field $\mathbf{R}(x, y; z)$ or its derivative $\partial \mathbf{R}(x, y; z)/\partial z$. If the diffraction contrast of a particular defect is to be calculated as a function of the specimen thickness t and the depth position z_0 of the defect centre, considerable computer time can be saved by making use of the method of "generalized cross-section" (HEAD *et al.* [1973]), referring to eq. (29), or of the "scattering matrix" method (HÄUSSERMANN *et al.* [1973], and KATERBAU [1980]), referring to eq. (31). In many cases computer time can additionally be saved by application of symmetry relations inherent in the particular diffraction contrast problem or in the displacement field of the defect (HOWIE and WHELAN [1961], BALL [1964], POGANY and TURNER [1968] and KATERBAU [1980]).

5. Dislocations

5.1. Introduction

Dislocations and dislocation distributions, e.g., in deformed crystal, are generally best investigated in the two-beam bright-field mode operated at a sufficiently positive excitation error, which ensures best transmittivity, cf. §4.5. This means a maximum specimen volume accessible by TEM and avoidance of pronounced black–white depth oscillations for dislocations close to the specimen surfaces (§4.7.5), which may perturb the image. On the other hand, if details of the dislocation structure, e.g., splitting into partials etc., are of interest, the weak-beam technique $|w| \gg 1$ is superior (COCKAYNE *et al.* [1969]), at the cost of transmittivity.

5.2. The displacement field

We assume elastic isotropy and introduce the displacement field $\mathbf{R}$ of a straight dislocation in its own (right-handed) coordinate system x', y', z'. The dislocation line

References: p. 788.

runs along the y'-axis with its line unit vector $\boldsymbol{u}$ pointing from $y' < 0$ to $y' > 0$. The Burgers vector $\boldsymbol{b}$ lying in the x'–y' plane can be split according to $\boldsymbol{b} = \boldsymbol{b}_s + \boldsymbol{b}_e$, where the screw component $\boldsymbol{b}_s$ is parallel, and the edge component $\boldsymbol{b}_e$ is perpendicular to $\boldsymbol{u}$. Then $\boldsymbol{R}$ is given by (e.g., HIRSCH et al. [1977]) *:

$$\boldsymbol{R} = \boldsymbol{R}_a + \boldsymbol{R}_s, \tag{33a}$$

$$\boldsymbol{R}_a = \frac{1}{2\pi}\left[\boldsymbol{b}\,\mathrm{artan}\frac{z'}{x'} + \boldsymbol{b}_e\frac{1}{2(1-\nu)}\frac{x'z'}{\hat{r}^2}\right], \tag{33b}$$

$$\boldsymbol{R}_s = -\frac{1}{2\pi}(\boldsymbol{b} \times \boldsymbol{u})\left[\frac{1-2}{2(1-\nu)}\ln \hat{r}/r_0 + \frac{1}{4(1-\nu)}\cdot\frac{x'^2 - z'^2}{\hat{r}^2}\right], \tag{33c}$$

with $\nu =$ Poisson's ratio, $\hat{r}^2 = x'^2 + z'^2$, $r_0 =$ inner cut-off radius. Note that $\boldsymbol{R}_a$ is antisymmetric and $\boldsymbol{R}_s$ is symmetric in x', z'. Further, $\boldsymbol{R}$ changes its sign if the sign of either $\boldsymbol{b}$ or $\boldsymbol{u}$ is changed. This is obvious for $\boldsymbol{R}_s$ but must be noticed also for $\boldsymbol{R}_a$.

5.3. Contrast profiles of single perfect dislocations

We assume that $\boldsymbol{b}$ is a translation vector of the crystal structure ($\boldsymbol{b}$ is a "perfect" Burgers vector) so that $\boldsymbol{g} \cdot \boldsymbol{b}$ is integer. Regarding the contrast profiles of such dislocations we have to distinguish between the cases $\boldsymbol{g} \cdot \boldsymbol{b} \neq 0$ and $\boldsymbol{g} \cdot \boldsymbol{b} = 0$.

5.3.1. The $\boldsymbol{g} \cdot \boldsymbol{b} \neq 0$ contrast

In case of $\boldsymbol{g} \cdot \boldsymbol{b} \neq 0$ the contrast is mainly governed by the component $\boldsymbol{R}_a$ of eq. (33b). This component causes an S-shaped bending of the reflecting lattice planes as schematically indicated in fig. 12. We assume $s \neq 0$ and recall the fact that diffraction contrast is especially strong (weak) where the local excitation error $s_\ell(z)$ is decreased (increased) as compared to the background value s, cf. §4.7.2, in other words where the reflecting lattice planes are bent by the dislocation displacement field towards (away from) the exact Bragg orientation. Consequently, for $s \neq 0$ the centre of gravity of a dislocation-contrast profile does not coincide with, but is shifted with respect to the image position of the dislocation line. Assuming a given direction of the line unit vector $\boldsymbol{u}$ the direction of this lateral contrast shift depends on the sign of $(\boldsymbol{g} \cdot \boldsymbol{b})s$, as will be demonstrated below in connection with the images of dislocation dipoles.

The kinematical contrast integral ϕ_g'', cf. eqs. (26)–(28), was evaluated for different types of dislocations by HIRSCH et al. [1960] and GEVERS [1962]. It turned out that the width of the kinematical dislocation contrast is about $(1/3 - 1/2)\xi_K$, where $\xi_K = s^{-1}$ denotes the kinematical extinction length. If dynamical diffraction has to be taken into account ($|w| \lesssim 1$) this result remains essentially valid, with ξ_K substituted by $\xi_{g,\mathrm{eff}} = \sigma^{-1}$ [eq. (17)] (HOWIE and WHELAN [1962]). It should be added

---

* In the TEM literature it is world-wide customary to denote the displacement field vector by $\boldsymbol{R}$ and the dislocation line unit vector by $\boldsymbol{u}$. Here we take over the same notation, although in ch. 12 the symbol $\boldsymbol{u}$ is used for the displacement vector and $\boldsymbol{R}$ is used for denoting particle radii in various meanings.

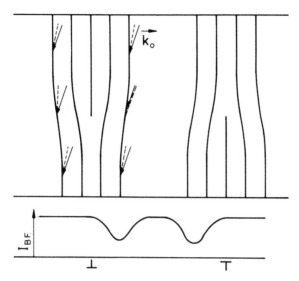

Fig. 12. Diffraction contrast of an edge dislocation for $(\boldsymbol{g}\cdot\boldsymbol{b})s \neq 0$, $s > 0$, schematically. Solid arrows represent the direction of incidence of the primary beam. Dashed lines represent local directions of incidence which would fulfill the Bragg condition. The angle between the two types of arrows is a measure of $s_l(z)$. Bright field intensity is denoted by I_{BF}.

that the contrast of a dislocation line is always single-lined for $|\boldsymbol{g}\cdot\boldsymbol{b}| = 1$ but may be (asymmetrically) double-lined for $|\boldsymbol{g}\cdot\boldsymbol{b}| = 2$ and $0 < |w| \lesssim 1$.

Under normal strong-beam (bright-field) conditions, $\xi_{g,eff}$ can be as large as several 10 nm, whereas under weak-beam conditions $\xi_K = s^{-1}$ can be kept as small as 5 nm (COCKAYNE *et al.* [1969] and COCKAYNE [1978]). Consequently, dislocation images are much sharper in the latter case, cf. fig. 13 where the same specimen area is imaged under strong-beam and weak-beam imaging conditions, respectively. Of course, the gain in resolution is paid for by a reduction of the useful specimen thickness.

5.3.2.   The $\boldsymbol{g}\cdot\boldsymbol{b} = 0$ contrast

In case of $\boldsymbol{g}\cdot\boldsymbol{b} = 0$ the dislocation contrast is completely extinguished ($\boldsymbol{g}\cdot\boldsymbol{R} = 0$) for screw dislocations and also for edge dislocations if in the latter $\boldsymbol{g}$ is parallel to the dislocation line. For $\boldsymbol{g}\cdot\boldsymbol{b} = 0$ but $|\boldsymbol{g}\cdot\boldsymbol{b} \times \boldsymbol{u}| \neq 0$ a "residual" contrast due to the displacement component $\boldsymbol{R}_s$ in eq. (33c) is produced, which is symmetric with respect to the image position of the dislocation. This residual contrast is controlled in strength by the modulus $|\boldsymbol{g}\cdot\boldsymbol{b} \times \boldsymbol{u}|$ and is in general significantly weaker than the $\boldsymbol{g}\cdot\boldsymbol{b} \neq 0$ contrast and can thus be distinguished from the latter. Depending on the strength of $|\boldsymbol{g}\cdot\boldsymbol{b} \times \boldsymbol{u}|$ the contrast may consist of a single, a double or a triple contrast line, cf. e.g., HOWIE and WHELAN [1962] and HIRSCH *et al.* [1977].

Typical dislocation images for $\boldsymbol{g}\cdot\boldsymbol{b} \neq 0$ and $\boldsymbol{g}\cdot\boldsymbol{b} = 0$ are shown in fig. 10. Note that the depth-oscillations where the dislocations approach the specimen surfaces (§4.7.5)

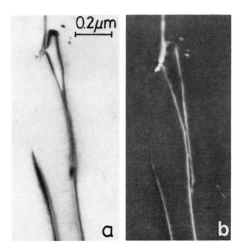

Fig. 13. Dislocations in silicon: (a) strong-beam bright field image, $w > 0$; (b) the same area imaged under dark-field weak beam conditions, $w \gg 1$.

show different symmetries for $g \cdot b \neq 0$ and $g \cdot b = 0$. These differences are occasionally helpful for discriminating between the two cases.

For dislocation of mixed type, complete contrast extinction is not possible at all, since in such a case the terms $g \cdot b$, $g \cdot b \times u$ and $g \cdot b_e$ cannot be zero simultaneously. If the first two terms are zero but $g \cdot b_e \neq 0$ [cf. eq. (33b)] an asymmetrical residual contrast is produced. This is demonstrated in fig. 14 where a curved dislocation segment, which changes in type from screw to edge, is imaged under $g \cdot b = 2$

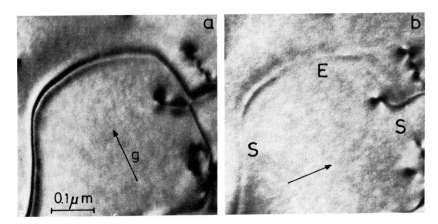

Fig. 14. Strong-beam images of a curved dislocation segment of Burgers vector $b = \frac{1}{2}[110]$: (a) $g = (220)$, $(g \cdot b) = 2$, dislocation is in strong contrast; (b) $g = (2\bar{2}0)$, $(g \cdot b) = 0$, the dislocation contrast is extinguished only at the edge- (E) and the screw (S) orientations. (From KORNER and KARNTHALER [1980].)

conditions (fig. 14a, strong symmetrical double-line contrast) and $\boldsymbol{g} \cdot \boldsymbol{b} = 0$ conditions (fig. 14b). In the latter case the dislocation is out of contrast in the pure screw and the pure edge orientation but reveals an easily detectable asymmetric contrast around the "45°-orientation", where $\boldsymbol{g} \cdot \boldsymbol{b}$ and $(\boldsymbol{g} \cdot \boldsymbol{b} \times \boldsymbol{u}) = 0$, but $\boldsymbol{g} \cdot \boldsymbol{b}_e \neq 0$. Here $\boldsymbol{b}_e$ refers to the component of $\boldsymbol{b}$ perpendicular to the *local* line direction $\boldsymbol{u}$.

5.4. Contrast of dislocation pairs

Two parallel dislocations having opposite Burgers vectors $\boldsymbol{b}$ constitute a dislocation dipole. Another description is that $\boldsymbol{b}$ is the same for both dislocations but their line vectors $\boldsymbol{u}$ are opposite. The most common representative is a dipole constituted by two pure edge dislocations. If such a dipole is imaged with $s \neq 0$ and $\boldsymbol{g} \cdot \boldsymbol{b} \neq 0$, then $(\boldsymbol{g} \cdot \boldsymbol{b})s > 0$ for one and $(\boldsymbol{g} \cdot \boldsymbol{b})s < 0$ for the other dislocation. Consequently, the contrasts of the two dislocations are displaced into opposite directions: The distance between the two contrast lines is either smaller or larger than the true projected distance between the dislocations. If $\boldsymbol{g}$ is changed into $-\boldsymbol{g}$, while leaving the sign of s unchanged, the two cases are interchanged. This phenomenon is called inside–outside contrast. An example is shown in fig. 15a, b.

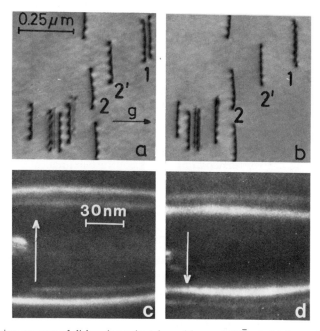

Fig. 15. Diffraction contrast of dislocation pairs taken with $g = \pm(20\bar{2})$: (a, b) Strong-beam bright-field images of dislocation dipoles in copper, taken with $w > 0$. Dipole 1 is clearly resolved in (a) but unresolved in (b). The distance between the dipole dislocations 2 and 2′ is narrow in (a) and wide in (b). (c, d) weak-beam images of dislocations in silver which are split into partials. The dislocation at the top (bottom) is named D_1 (D_2) in the text. (From KORNER and KARNTHALER [1981].)

References: p. 788.

In other cases, the two parallel dislocations may show up the same sign of $g \cdot b$. This may occur in an ordered alloy where two dislocations with the same perfect Burgers vector b of the disordered lattice constitute a split superdislocation ($2b$ = perfect Burgers vector of the ordered alloy) with an antiphase boundary between them. Another example refers to a perfect dislocation which is split into partial dislocations (Burgers vectors b_p) and where the signs of $g \cdot b_p$ are the same for both partials. If in such a case the distance between the two dislocations becomes of the order of, or smaller than, $\xi_{g,eff}$ (which may be $\xi_K = 1/s$ in the weak-beam case) the contrast of one of the two dislocations increases in strength and the contrast of the other decreases, depending on the signs of the ($g \cdot b_p$) (WILKENS and HORNBOGEN [1964], STOBBS and SWORNE [1971] and COCKAYNE [1978]). This is demonstrated in fig. 15c, d, showing the weak-beam images of an edge-dislocation dipole in Ag where the individual dislocations D_1 and D_2 are split into partials. For both dislocations the two partials give rise to the same sign of $g \cdot b_p$, which, however, is opposite for D_1 and D_2. Accordingly, the sequence "strong-weak" is opposite for D_1 and D_2. Further, the sequence is changed when changing the sign of g (indicated by the arrows).

Below a critical distance the contrast of the weakly imaged dislocation disappears in the contrast tail of the strongly imaged one. This effect limits the resolution of dislocation pairs having the same sign of ($g \cdot b$) even on weak-beam images to about 2 nm. This lower limit is important for the evaluation of stacking-fault energies from the measurement of equilibrium distances of split dislocations, cf., e.g., STOBBS and SWORNE [1971].

5.5. Determination of the dislocation Burgers vectors and the dislocation densities

The determination of the Burgers vector b of individual dislocations requires a number of images of the corresponding specimen area taken under different two-beam conditions. If a given dislocation shows contrast extinction or only residual ($g \cdot b = 0$) contrast for two (non-parallel) diffraction vectors, say g_1 and g_2, then its Burgers vector b is perpendicular to g_1 and g_2 (regarding the sign of b see below). The Burgers vector analysis is considerably facilitated if the general crystallographic direction of b can be anticipated, for instance $b = \frac{1}{2}\langle 110 \rangle$ in a fcc lattice. In this case three images taken with three diffraction vectors $g = \{111\}$ are sufficient for indexing all dislocations with $b = \frac{1}{2}\langle 110 \rangle$, since the six significantly different vectors b of this kind give rise to a different contrast-extinction behaviour for the three $g = \{111\}$ (HIRSCH et al. [1977]). The series of micrographs shown in fig. 16 stems from a deformed and subsequently annealed Ni crystal and was taken from a specimen parallel to the primary slip plane (111) with $g_a = (11\bar{1})$, $g_b = (\bar{1}11)$, $g_c = (1\bar{1}1)$, where the subscripts a, b, c refer to figs 16a, b, c, respectively. In the central part of figs. 16b,c a network is visible constituted by three types of dislocation segments, as indicated in the figures. The segments (1) give rise to a $g \cdot b \neq 0$ contrast on fig. 16c and to a residual ($g \cdot b = 0$) contrast on fig. 16b and (scarcely to see) on fig. 16a.

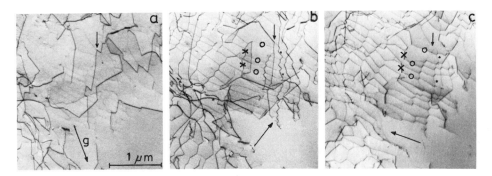

Fig. 16. Dislocation network in nickel. Two-beam bright-field images of the same specimen area, specimen normal (111). Three types of segment directions (see text) of the network are indicated by open circles (1), crosses (2), and dots (3). (a) $g = (11\bar{1})$, (b) $g = (\bar{1}11)$, (c) $g = (1\bar{1}1)$. The small arrows point to the same position on the three images.

Accordingly, we have $b_1 = \pm\frac{1}{2}[101]$. The segments (2) show $g\cdot b \neq 0$ contrast on figs. 16b and c, but not on fig. 16a. This leads to $b_2 = \pm\frac{1}{2}[1\bar{1}0]$. The segments (3) are in $g\cdot b \neq 0$ contrast only on fig. 16b, thus $b_3 = \pm\frac{1}{2}[011]$. Taking always the upper sign, we have $b_2 + b_3 = b_1$ as it is required for dislocation networks. Other dislocation segments in figs. 16a–c can be indexed in the same way.

For a full indexing of a dislocation a discrimination between $+b$ and $-b$ (for a given choice of the line direction u) is required. This can be achieved by making use of the fact that the lateral shift of $(g\cdot b)s \neq 0$ contrast lines is indicative for the sign of the S-shaped bending of the reflecting lattice planes from which the signs of u and b can be determined by physical arguments. In this context, certain contrast pecularities due to surface-stress relaxation effects may also be helpful, cf., e.g., SIEMS *et al.* [1962], TUNSTALL *et al.* [1964], WILKENS *et al.* [1967] and HAZZLEDINE *et al.* [1975].

The dislocation density ρ is defined as the (average) dislocation length per unit volume or, in a somewhat misleading way, as the number of dislocations per unit area. A full and reliable evaluation of ρ requires rather extensive experimental work. Here we stress the attention to one aspect only: On a given set of micrographs taken with a given two-beam diffraction vector g dislocations of some slip systems may be fully in contrast ($g\cdot b \neq 0$). Dislocations of other slip systems may be visible in residual contrast ($g\cdot b = 0$) only or may be completely invisible. This fact suggests immediately that any reliable determination of ρ requires a careful evaluation of different sets of micrographs of the same specimen area taken with different g-vector, cf., e.g., STEEDS [1966], ESSMANN [1966].

5.6. Elastic anisotropy

Experience has shown that regarding the fundamental properties of the dislocation contrast of dislocations, elastic isotropy is a useful approximation even for moderately anisotropic crystals like copper. However, for strongly anisotropic materials such as β-brass the contrast rules, described above on the base of elastic isotropy, break down. This holds in particular for the discrimination between $g \cdot b \neq 0$ and $g \cdot b = 0$ contrast. In such cases a Burgers vector analysis requires the comparison of observed contrast figures, in particular of those parts showing depth oscillations, with computer-simulated images for modelled dislocation types, cf. HEAD et al. [1973] and HUMBLE [1978].

6. Point-defect agglomerates, radiation damage

6.1. Introduction

Irradiation of crystals with energetic particles (e.g., electrons, neutrons, or ions) leads to the formation of interstitials and vacancies. Point defects may also be created by plastic deformation or by quenching-in of thermal vacancies. If these point defects are mobile, they may cluster together, forming point-defect agglomerates such as dislocation loops. In fcc metals they may also form stacking-fault tetrahedra. This holds especially for vacancies, but in principle also for interstitials. Vacancies may also agglomerate into cavities (bubbles, voids). One of the problems to be solved by TEM is the determination of the crystallographic nature of such agglomerates and the determination of their type, vacancy (V) or interstitial (I), i.e., whether they are produced by an agglomeration of vacancies or of interstitials. In this section some of such methods are briefly outlined. For a review see WILKENS [1978].

6.2. Dislocation loops

6.2.1. Formation of loops

Dislocation loops are formed by agglomeration of point defects into plates on densely packed lattice planes. For instance, a monolayer (diameter D) of agglomerated vacancies on a $\langle 111 \rangle$-plane in a fcc metal gives rise to an intrinsic stacking fault surrounded by a dislocation loop (diameter D) with a partial Burgers vector $b_F = \frac{1}{3}\langle 111 \rangle$ of Frank type, perpendicular to the loop plane. Agglomeration of interstitials on $\langle 111 \rangle$ gives rise to an extrinsic stacking fault over the loop area. If the loop size exceeds a critical value, it becomes energetically more favourable to eliminate the stacking fault area by sweeping a Shockley partial $b_S = \frac{1}{6}\langle 112 \rangle$ over the loop area to convert the Frank partial into a perfect Burgers vector b, e.g.,

$$b_F + b_S = b, \tag{34a}$$

$$\tfrac{1}{3}[111] + \tfrac{1}{6}[11\bar{2}] = \tfrac{1}{2}[110]. \tag{34b}$$

There is evidence that similar two-step mechanisms for the formation of loops with perfect Burgers vectors are existing also for bcc (EYRE and BULLOUGH [1965], JÄGER and WILKENS [1975]) and for hcp metals (FÖLL and WILKENS [1977]).

6.2.2. Analysis of large dislocation loops

If the loop diameter D is sufficiently large compared to $\xi_{g,eff}$ then the loop nature is clearly visible on the micrograph and the Burgers vector b of the loop can be determined by the contrast-extinction rules outlined in §5.5. Approximate information about the habit plane of the loop can be obtained by following the change of the projected shape and width of the loop when tilting the specimen around an axis parallel to the operating g-vector (for details see, e.g., MAHER and EYRE [1971]).

Segments of a dislocation loop which are opposite to each other have the same direction of b, but opposite line direction u. Their contrast behaviour is therefore similar to that of a dislocation dipole, cf. §5.4. Accordingly, if the loop is imaged with $(g \cdot b)s \neq 0$, the loop is imaged either as inside contrast (loop contrast inside the true projected loop position) or as outside contrast, depending on the sign of $(g \cdot b)s$. The question, inside- or outside contrast, can best be clarified by comparing images taken with g and $-g$ and leaving the sign of s unchanged, cf. fig. 17 where dislocation loops of interstitial type in electron-irradiated molybdenum are shown; the apparent sizes of the loop contrasts change remarkably when going from g to $-g$. Then, the loop type, V or I, can be determined if the inclination of the loop plane with respect to the primary beam (direction of k_0) and the operating g-vector is known (HIRSCH et al. [1977]).

In application to practical cases the inside–outside method suffers from a number of pitfalls which may lead to the wrong answer regarding the loop type. Recipes have been worked out in order to avoid these pitfalls (MAHER and EYRE [1971], and FÖLL and WILKENS [1975]).

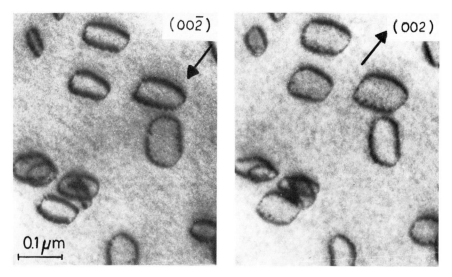

Fig. 17. Dislocation loops of interstitial type in electron-irradiated molybdenum. Two-beam bright-field images taken with $w > 0$. Note the apparent change in the loop size when changing the sign of g. For details see text.

References: p. 788.

6.2.3. Small dislocation loops

If the loop diameter D becomes smaller than $\xi_{g,eff}$, dislocation loops are no longer imaged "as loops". On kinematical strong-beam images the loop contrast degenerates to a black-dot contrast containing very little information on details of the loop (RÜHLE [1967]). Even under weak-beam conditions the inside–outside contrast method breaks down for $D \leq 7$ nm. (HÄUSSERMANN *et al.* [1973]). For dislocation loops below this limit the black–white contrast method becomes applicable when the specimen is imaged under two-beam dynamical conditions with $w = 0$, in bright or dark field (RÜHLE [1967]). If under such an imaging condition a small dislocation loop is located within the surface-near regions of depth-oscillation (§4.7.5) it gives rise to a characteristic black–white contrast figure. An example is shown in fig. 18 referring to a Cu specimen containing mainly small Frank dislocation loops of V-type (produced by irradiation with 30 kev Cu-ions) in a very surface-near layer close to the bottom surface of the specimen. Such black–white contrast figures may be characterized by a black–white vector l, pointing from the centre of the black to the centre of the white lobe. Because of the very nature of the depth oscillation contrast, the black–white contrast of a loop is inverted, i.e., bright is changed into dark and vice versa, if either the loop type, V or I, is changed or if the loop depth-position z_0 is shifted towards $z_0 \pm \frac{1}{2} \xi_{g,eff}$. Accordingly, in order to discriminate between loops of V or I type we need information about the sign of $(g \cdot l)$ *and* of the depth position z_0 of the loop. The latter information can be obtained by careful stereo measurements (e.g., RÜHLE [1967] and RÜHLE and WILKENS [1967]).

Additional information about the direction of the Burgers vector and the loop-plane normal n can be obtained from the fine structure in the centre of a

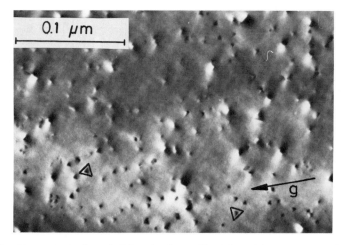

Fig. 18. Black–white contrast of small dislocation loops (Frank loops) in a copper specimen irradiated with 30 keV copper ions. Dynamical dark field image taken with $w = 0$, specimen normal (110), $g = (002)$. The inserted triangles indicate small stacking-fault tetrahedra.

black–white contrast figure (KATERBAU [1976] and EYRE *et al.* [1977]) and from the outer shape of the black–white contrast figures by comparison of experimentally obtained and calculated contrast figures. For elastically isotropic, or nearly isotropic, materials the shape of the contrast figure and in particular the angle between *l* and *g* depend in a characteristic manner on the direction of *b* and *n* with respect to k_0 and *g*, respectively. These dependencies have been worked out by numerical integration of the differential equations (29) or (31) (e.g., RÜHLE [1967], KATERBAU [1976], EYRE *et al.* [1977] and ENGLISH *et al.* [1980]) or by an analytical first-order perturbation integration of eq. (31) (e.g., WILKENS and RÜHLE [1972]).

The latter was successfully applied to the analysis of small dislocation loops in ion-irradiated tungsten (HÄUSSERMANN *et al.* [1972] and JÄGER and WILKENS [1975]) and cobalt (FÖLL and WILKENS [1977]). More recent analytical calculations by WILKENS and KIRCHNER [1981] have shown that the shapes of the black–white contrasts of small loops are sensitive to elastic anisotropy.

6.3. Stacking-fault tetrahedra

Frank dislocation loops in fcc metals can dissociate into *stacking-fault tetrahedra* (SFT) constituted by stacking faults on the four ⟨111⟩-type tetrahedra faces interconnected by stair–rod dislocations with $b = \frac{1}{6}\langle 110\rangle$ at the edges of the tetrahedra. This transformation is favoured in particular in metals of low stacking-fault energy such as gold, silver or copper.

One consequence of the small strength of the stair–rod dislocations bounding the SFT is that their strain contrast is rather weak. Accordingly, the contrast of a SFT is predominantly determined by the stacking-fault areas (which may give rise to a fringe pattern if the SFT is larger than the extinction length (CHIK [1966]), i.e., the contrast shape of a SFT is in general close to the shape of the SFT projected onto the image plane. Some SFT, as produced by ion-damage in Cu, are indicated in fig. 18 by a symbol reflecting their outer shapes, as expected for a specimen orientation close to (110).

In spite of the weakness of the strain field, SFT may reveal black–white contrast. For large SFT with edge lengths of the order of, or larger than, $\xi_{g,eff}$ the black–white contrast degenerates to the so-called Ashby–Brown contrast (ASHBY and BROWN [1963]) where the depth oscillations are suppressed due to surface-stress relaxation (McINTYRE and BROWN [1966] and CHIK *et al.* [1967]). Under suitable conditions even small SFT may reveal black–white contrast similar to that of small dislocation loops (SALDIN *et al.* [1978]). However, in contrast to small loops, black–white vector *l* points always parallel or anti-parallel to *g* (because the strain field does not show up a pronounced preferential direction). The latter property is sometimes helpful in order to discriminate between small loops and small SFT.

6.4. Cavities

Cavities (voids, bubbles) are best imaged under two-beam conditions with $s = 0$. Then cavities act like a local reduction of the specimen thickness t. Thus, in a

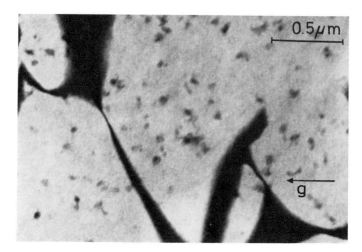

Fig. 19. Dark-field image taken with a superlattice reflection $g = (110)$ of a fully ordered Cu_3Au specimen irradiated with 30 keV copper ions. The dark dots represent zones of reduced long-range order as produced by the displacement cascades of the incident ions. The dark bands are due to antiphase boundaries.

specimen with foil thickness t in that range where thickness fringes are observable the contrast of a cavity is dark on the front flank of a bright thickness contour and bright on the rear side (VAN LANDUYT *et al.* [1965]). If t is beyond the region of thickness fringes, the contrast is bright but decreases rapidly with decreasing diameter d of the cavity. Finally, if d is below a critical value of some nm, cavities are no longer visible on in-focus images. Then the contrast is considerably improved by an appropriate defocusing of the objective lens (RÜHLE and WILKENS [1975]).

6.5. Displacement cascades and disordered zones

Energetic ions (in the case of fast neutron irradiation the primary knocked-on atoms) deposit their kinetic energy in a crystal in so-called cascades, within which a large number of atomic replacements takes place. In an ordered alloy these replacement events lead to a zone of reduced long-range order which reflects size and structure of the cascade. Such disordered zones can be made visible on dark-field images taken with a superlattice diffraction vector g (JENKINS and WILKENS [1976]). An example of disordered zones in Cu_3Au irradiated with Cu^+-ions is shown in fig. 19.

7. Precipitates

The precipitation of a second phase can be pursued by TEM, which was done successfully since the early days of TEM of materials (HIRSCH *et al.* [1977]).

Depending on the structure of the interface, we talk about coherent, partially coherent or incoherent precipitates. A *partially coherent* particle may possess one coherent interface and one where coherency is lost (i.e., is semi-coherent or incoherent). This can be caused either by different structures in the precipitate and the matrix or by a large displacement along the interface (e.g., OLSON and COHEN [1979]). An incoherent particle has a crystal structure different from the matrix. Often there exist no orientation relationships between the two phases. A precipitate can give rise to TEM contrast for two reasons: (i) due to the alteration of the electron waves passing through the particle (*precipitate contrast*) and (ii) due to alteration of the electron waves passing through columns near the particle where the crystal has been distorted due to the presence of the precipitate (matrix contrast or strain contrast).

The interpretation of the *matrix contrast* is straightforward and can be done in a similar way as for radiation-induced defects or dislocations. The strain contrast has to be observed for different foil orientations (and different diffraction vectors) under well-defined dynamical two-beam or well-defined kinematical conditions (see §4). If a strain contrast can be observed then contrast calculations have to be performed for different strain distributions surrounding the precipitate in a thin foil. Matching the results of the calculations with the observations gives a qualitative and sometimes even quantitative model of the precipitate (ASHBY and BROWN [1963]).

MCINTYRE and BROWN [1966] and CHIK *et al.* [1967] showed that black–white contrasts (BW contrasts) can be observed if certain conditions for the size and magnitude of the strain are fulfilled. The strain is thereby expressed in terms of a dimensionless quantity,

$$Q = \epsilon r_0^3 \cdot g \cdot \frac{1}{\xi_g^2}, \tag{35}$$

where r_0 is the radius of the particle, g the modulus of the diffraction vector, ξ_g the extinction length, and ϵ a parameter describing the constrained strain of the particle (ASHBY and BROWN [1963]). BW contrasts are expected for certain combinations of r_0 and Q (CHIK *et al.* [1967]). Small values of r_0 result in BW contrasts with depth oscillation similar to those of radiation-induced defects (§6), whereas for large values of r_0 and Q the depth oscillations of the BW contrasts are suppressed by the stress relaxations at the foil surfaces (Ashby–Brown contrast). In this case the sign of the displacement field can be determined by DF images unambiguously (ASHBY and BROWN [1963]). Very large defects produce no BW contrast at all (CHIK *et al.* [1967]). The calculation of TEM contrast was performed for inclusions of different shapes and included also elastic anisotropy (see e.g. LEPSKI [1974]). The main problem in doing such computer simulations is the determination of the displacement field of the precipitate placed in a thin foil.

Spherical precipitates form in Cu–Co alloys (fig. 20) and the sizes depend on the annealing treatment (MCINTYRE and BROWN [1967]). The typical *coffee-bean contrast* can be observed. A "line-of-no-contrast" is perpendicular to the diffraction vector *g*.

References: p. 788.

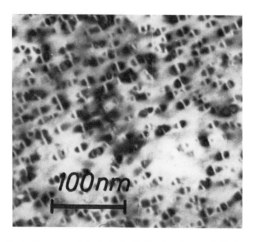

Fig. 20. Contrast from spherically symmetrical strain fields due to precipitations in a Cu–Co alloy. The coffee-bean type contrast is visible.

The width of the lobes measured perpendicular to g is a measure of the size of the precipitate.

The small plate-like precipitates in Al–Cu also produce a strain contrast. The visibility depends on the operating diffraction vector since the displacement field is strongly anisotropic. Coherent Ag precipitates in Al–Ag alloys do not form a strain contrast, since there exists (nearly) no constrained strain around the particle (see fig. 21a).

Semicoherent precipitates may produce a strain contrast which can be evaluated similarly as for coherent precipitates. This was demonstrated for small Mo_2C precipitates in Mo by LEPSKI and BURCK [1981, 1982]. HIRSCH et al. [1977] showed that coherent, semicoherent, or incoherent precipitates can be studied by utilizing the strain contrast (DF and BF techniques). If the symmetry of the precipitate is different from the symmetry of the matrix, then additional reflections in the diffraction pattern can be observed (fig. 21e). The shape of the precipitate is revealed by DF images taken with such a reflection belonging to the precipitate (fig. 21c, d).

The *precipitates* themselves can be made visible (i) if difference in the structure factor in the two phases ("structure-factor contrast"), of which an example is shown in fig. 21, (ii) if the orientation of the foil is such that certain planes in the precipitate are near the exact Bragg condition (strong reflection) while no planes in the matrix are in such a position ("orientation contrast"), (iii) if the matrix displacements induced by the precipitate cause an abrupt phase-change at the precipitate ("stacking-fault contrast"), or (iv) if a moiré pattern is formed due to different lattice parameters in the matrix and precipitate. The contrast caused for the different cases is already extensively described by HIRSCH et al. [1977].

Particles of a second phase change the *diffraction pattern* of the pure matrix because: (i) there are extra reflections due to the diffraction pattern from the

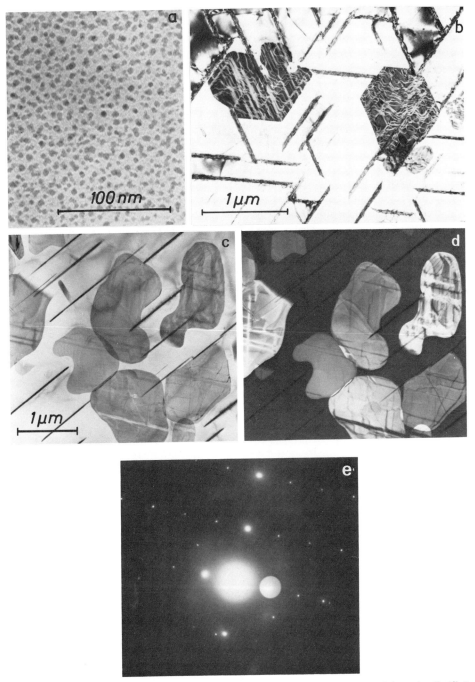

Fig. 21. Contrast of precipitates. (a) Structure-factor contrast of small coherent precipitates in Al–6% Ag alloys; no strain contrast is visible. (b) Structure-factor contrast of incoherent (large) precipitates in Al–6% Ag alloys annealed for 1000 min at 400°C (θ'' precipitates); foil orientation ~ (110); interface dislocations are visible between the Al matrix and the Ag precipitates. (c) Contrast of incoherent Al–4% Cu alloys; structure-factor contrast; foil orientation (106), BF image. (d) DF image with a reflexion of the Cu precipitate. Only Cu precipitates of one variant are in contrast. (e) Diffraction pattern of figs. (c, d).

References: p. 788.

precipitate itself, (ii) the second-phase particles exert an influence on the matrix diffraction spots, (iii) there is the possibility of double diffraction (if the particle is embedded in the matrix), and (iv) since the precipitates are usually small, the shape of the diffraction spots is reciprocal to the shape of the (small) particles.

8. Structure of grain boundaries and interfaces

Internal surfaces determine many properties of materials. For an understanding of the properties it is essential to know the structure of the defects, which are actually the regions in space at which two crystals meet. Interfaces between dissimilar materials are called *heterophase boundaries* (or just interfaces). Interfaces between crystals differing only in relative orientation and/or translation are called *homo-*

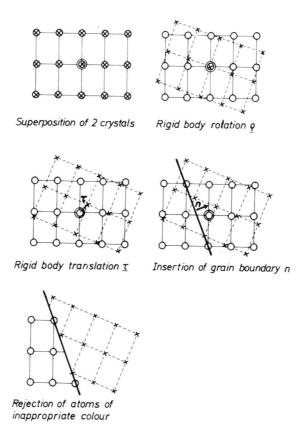

Superposition of 2 crystals   Rigid body rotation ϱ

Rigid body translation τ Insertion of grain boundary n

Rejection of atoms of
inappropriate colour

Fig. 22. The idealized construction of a crystalline interface: (a) superposition of the two crystals; (b) imposition of rigid body rotation (four parameters); (c) imposition of rigid body translation (three parameters); (d) insertion of surface S of the interface (three parameters); (e) rejection of inappropriate atoms at the interface.

phase boundaries. Homophase boundaries include grain boundaries, stacking faults, twins, and antiphase boundaries in ordered alloys. In the first part of this section the possibilities for revealing the structure of homophase boundaries will be described. The second part deals with some observations on heterophase boundaries.

KALONJI and CAHN [1982] manifested that ten parameters are required for the geometrical description of an interface, see fig. 22. In this concept one assumes two interpenetrating crystals which are then misoriented (four parameters) and shifted against each other (three parameters). Three additional parameters are required to specify the location of a plane interface in the interpenetrating crystals. Finally, atoms of one crystal are removed from one side of the surface and those of the second crystal from the other. In this way, the *symmetry* of the interface can be described very elegantly by means of group theory (GRATIAS *et al.* [1979] and KALONJI and CAHN [1982]). Stacking faults and antiphase boundaries are pure translation interfaces, whereas grain boundaries represent general homophase boundaries. The geometric parameters are potentially capable of undergoing relaxation (ch. 10).

8.1. Transmission electron microscopy of pure translation interfaces

At a pure translation interface (stacking faults, antiphase boundaries) two perfect crystal parts are shifted against each other. Usually, the plane of the interfaces coincides with a close-packed plane. For example, the translation vector is $\tau = \frac{1}{6}\langle 112\rangle$ for a stacking fault (STF) in fcc materials, whereas τ is a lattice vector of the disordered crystal structure for antiphase boundaries in an ordered structure. TEM contrast is expected in the projected area of the (usually) inclined translation interface. The depth position of the interface may be t_1. Then the crystal part lying below the interface is shifted against the upper reference crystal by the translation vector τ which defines also the sign of τ.

The diffraction contrast can easily be calculated by utilizing the so-called "matrix-method" introduced by AMELINCKX and VAN LANDUYT [1978]. With this method the contrast can be calculated for a general n-beam situation. We restrict ourselves to the two-beam case which takes into account only one scattered beam ϕ_g besides the transmitted beam ϕ_0. The amplitudes of the scattered beam ϕ_g and of the transmitted beam ϕ_0 are represented by a column vector

$$\psi = \begin{pmatrix} \phi_0 \\ \phi_g \end{pmatrix}. \tag{36}$$

AMELINCKX and VAN LANDUYT [1978] described the changes of the amplitudes after passing through a perfect crystal of thickness t [normalized excitation error w, cf. eq. (7)] by:

$$\begin{pmatrix} \phi_0(t,w) \\ \phi_g(t,w) \end{pmatrix}_{\text{out}} = \boldsymbol{M}(t,w) \begin{pmatrix} \phi_0 \\ \phi_g \end{pmatrix}_{\text{in}}, \tag{37}$$

References: p. 788.

where the subscripts "in" and "out" refer to the incoming and outgoing waves for a perfect crystal, respectively. The initial values are of course $\phi_0 = 1$, $\phi_g = 0$. $M(t, w)$ represents a "response matrix" given by:

$$M(t, w) = \begin{pmatrix} \phi_0^0 & \phi_g^{0-} \\ \phi_g^0 & \phi_0^{0-} \end{pmatrix},$$
(38)

with [cf. eq. (14)]:

$$\phi_0^0(t, w) = \cos \pi \sigma t - i \frac{w \sin \pi \sigma t}{(1 + w^2)^{1/2}}, \qquad \phi_g^0(t, w) = \frac{i \sin \pi \sigma t}{(1 + w^2)^{1/2}},$$
(39)

anomalous absorption is included, which means σ is complex, whereas normal absorption in neglected. The normalized excitation error w has to be replaced by $-w$ in eq. (39) to form ϕ_0^{0-} and ϕ_g^{0-} of eq. (38).

The influence of a planar defect included in a transmitted specimen on the amplitude distribution of the different waves can be described by a response matrix of the defect M^d. This matrix is called M^α for a pure translation interface, with

$$M^\alpha = \begin{pmatrix} 1 & 0 \\ 0 & e^{i\alpha} \end{pmatrix},$$
(40)

and $\alpha = 2\pi g \cdot \tau$ (g = diffraction vector, τ = translation of the perfect crystal below the defect with respect to the perfect crystal in which the electrons enter).

The amplitudes of the waves transmitted through a specimen (total foil thickness t) containing such a translation interface (depth position $t_1(x)$, see §4) are determined by three contributions: (i) the contribution of the perfect crystal [foil thickness $t_1(x)$] lying above the planar defect, described by a response matrix $M(t_1, w)$, [eq. (38)]; (ii) the contribution of the planar defect itself [response matrix M^α, eq. (40)]; and (iii) the contribution of the perfect crystal (thickness $t_2 = t - t_1$) lying below the defect [response matrix $M(t_2, w)$].

The amplitudes of the waves at the lower foil surface are just expressed by

$$\begin{pmatrix} \phi_0(t) \\ \phi_g(t) \end{pmatrix} = M(t_2, w) \cdot M^\alpha \cdot M(t_1, w) \begin{pmatrix} \phi_0(0) \\ \phi_g(0) \end{pmatrix}.$$
(41)

The contrast caused by an inclined defect can be calculated by an evaluation of eq. (41) for different depth positions t_1.

The following results can be obtained for an inclined STF (for details see AMELINCKX and VAN LANDUYT [1978]):

(i) Bright and dark fringes are expected in the projected area of the STF.

(ii) With increasing thickness new fringes are created in the centre of the foil.

(iii) The fringes are parallel to the closest surface.

(iv) The BF fringe pattern is symmetrical with respect to the foil centre, whereas the DF image is similar to the BF image close to the top surface but complementary close to the bottom surface.

Figure 23 shows an example of the contrast of a stacking fault in a Cu–10 at% Al

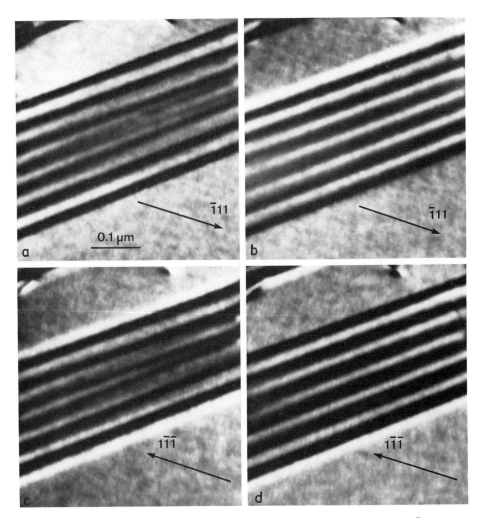

Fig. 23. Images of a stacking fault in Cu–10 at% Al, intrinsic stacking fault: (a) BF, $g = (\bar{1}11)$; (b) DF, $g = (\bar{1}11)$; (c) BF, $g = (1\bar{1}\bar{1})$; (d) DF, $g = (1\bar{1}\bar{1})$. The rule of GEVERS *et al.* [1963] is fulfilled. (Courtesy A. KORNER and H.P. KARNTHALER.)

alloy. The image of a stacking fault (STF) is characterized by the value of $\alpha = 2\pi g \cdot \tau$. In fcc materials stacking faults are predominantly produced on {111} planes by a shear of $\tau = \frac{1}{6}\langle 112 \rangle$ or by removal or insertion of a plane of atoms. This may happen when vacancies or interstitial atoms condense on close-packed planes. In fcc materials the STF are classified as intrinsic or extrinsic.

The determination of the type of STF is identical with the determination of the sign of α. We know from the symmetry rules that the sign of the contrast fringe in BF and DF at the top of the transmitted foil is positive (bright fringe) for $\alpha > 0$

References: p. 788.

(thick foil). From the BF and Df images of a STF (see fig. 23) we can determine the top surface and the bottom surface. Since we know the sign of α from the edge fringe of the BF image, we have the information necessary to determine the sense of τ. This method was first given by HASHIMOTO et al. [1962]. GEVERS et al. [1963] pointed out that the type of the fault can be determined from a DF image alone; the sense of inclination need not be known. GEVERS et al. showed that τ can be determined by the following simple method. The diffraction vector g is drawn as an arrow with its origin at the centre of contrast fringes on the DF image. The nature of the stacking fault is intrinsic (extrinsic) if the limiting fringe on the side of the arrow of g is dark (bright). This rule is valid in fcc materials for $\{111\}$, $\{220\}$ and $\{400\}$ reflexions while it is reversed for $\{200\}$, $\{222\}$ and $\{440\}$ reflexions. The contrast of the STF vanishes for $g \cdot \tau$ = integer. The direction of τ can be determined from two images taken with different diffraction vectors on which the STF is out of contrast.

The contrast of domain boundaries, twins, antiphase boundaries can also be calculated with the matrix method, see AMELINCKX and VAN LANDUYT [1978].

8.2. Transmission electron microscopy of grain boundaries

Grain boundaries (GBs) have been the object of intensive TEM studies for many years, and in that time many papers and review lectures have appeared (eg., CHADWICK and SMITH [1976], CLAREBROUGH and FORWOOD [1978] and BALLUFFI [1980]. It is well recognized that the structure of GBs is important for the under-standing of the problems of segregation, recrystallization texture and intergranular embrittlement, and of course the bonding across the boundary also governs those properties. In the papers quoted above it is shown that much information can be obtained by TEM diffraction contrast studies, diffraction studies and recently also by direct lattice imaging.

By TEM diffraction contrast studies, information on the intrinsic structure of GBs can be obtained; mainly dislocations can be analyzed. For special situations the geometrical parameters can be determined by TEM work. Diffraction studies allow the determination of the "width" and symmetry of GBs, whereas direct imaging by means of high-resolution TEM allows an insight into the atomic structure of the boundary.

In ch. 10B it is explained that GBs may be described in different ways: the dislocation model, the plane-matching model, and the coincidence-site model. All models will summarize the relaxation phenomena at the GB in different configura-tion of defects. The models assume that there exist certain misorientations which possess a low GB energy, and these misorientations are characterized by a low Σ value of the coincidence-site lattice *.

If the symmetry of a boundary and the included dislocations are determined, then

---

* The CSL can be obtained by allowing the two misoriented crystal lattices adjoining the boundary to interpenetrate and translate so that lattice points of each crystal coincide. The space lattice made up of the coincident lattice points is called the CSL. The fraction of lattice points (in one crystal) in good coincidence is defined as $1/\Sigma$. Coincidence models of GBs are discussed in ch. 10B, §2.2.1.3.

the GB is completely specified. The parameters included in the description can be determined by TEM in principle by comparing experimental micrographs taken under well defined diffraction conditions with results of computer simulations carried out using the dynamical theory of electron diffraction. For the computer simulations the displacement of the atoms (lattice planes) due to relaxation as well as many experimental parameters such as the thickness, orientation of the interface, and extinction- and absorption lengths must be known. In addition, experimental diffraction parameters, such as the number of beams excited and their s value, must be established accurately.

The contrast calculations can be very complicated. Each beam excited in the upper crystal is incident on the lower crystal and can give rise to further beams in that crystal. Thus, the total number of beams propagating in the lower crystal can be substantial, and the coupling of the beams is strongly influenced by the crystallographic relationship of the two crystals. There are three experimental conditions which allow a more straightforward interpretation:

(i) Two-beam diffraction in one crystal and negligible diffraction in the other. Either the upper or lower crystal can be oriented for two-beam diffraction, and the non-diffracting crystal is regarded as a block in which normal but not anomalous absorption occurs. The contrast behaviour is similar to thickness fringes. This diffraction condition can only be obtained approximately, since weak beams are inevitably excited in the "non-diffracting" crystal, and these may be coupled to some extent with the beam selected for image formation. This was demonstrated by HUMBLE and FORWOOD [1975] who compared microdensitometer traces taken across experimentally obtained GB thickness fringes to computer profiles. Humble and Forwood observed that the "non-diffracting" crystal does not behave simply as an absorbing wedge, and that no simple function could be found which would adequately describe the attenuation in this grain.

(ii) Simultaneous two-beam diffraction in the two crystals. In this mode the specimen is exactly oriented so that only one diffracted beam is strongly excited in the upper crystal – and in such a way that this (excited) beam does not excite further strong beams in the lower crystal. At the same time, only one beam is strongly excited in the lower crystal by the incoming beam. Usually, only BF images are taken (HUMBLE and FORWOOD [1975]).

(iii) In cases where the crystallography permits, two-beam or systematic diffraction by sets of planes with identical spacing and orientation in the adjacent crystals may occur. Such sets of planes are referred to as common, and this case is a special instance of condition (ii). This orientation has been used for the measurement of the relative shift of the two adjacent crystals.

Experimentally, the orientation-relation between the two adjacent grains of an interface and the normal on the interface can be obtained by three micrographs and accompanying diffraction patterns taken under different, well established orientations. The lateral shift τ can be measured for special configurations (MATTHEWS and STOBBS [1977] and POND [1979]).

The TEM contrast of GB dislocations can be treated similarly as for lattice

References: p. 788.

dislocations. However, for the GB dislocations further parameters, including the geometry of the interface and the diffraction conditions pertaining to both crystals must be considered. The direction of the Burgers vector b of the GB dislocation can be determined by using the $g \cdot b = 0$ criterion. However, the accuracy of this semi-quantitative method is small, since the magnitude of the Burgers vector of secondary GB dislocations is usually small.

Boundaries between two crystals are assumed to have a low-energy structure for certain misorientations (e.g., BROKMAN and BALLUFFI [1981]). This low-energy structure can be thought to exist of finely spaced arrays of dislocations, the so-called "primary" dislocations. Any deviation from such low-energy orientation relations is accommodated by a network of dislocations, the "secondary" dislocations. Experimental observations on those dislocations were carried out by Balluffi and coworkers (e.g. SCHOBER and BALLUFFI [1969]) mainly on "artificial" (001) twist boundaries in Au. The TEM studies reveal that a grid of undissociated secondary dislocations is present, see fig. 24. The distance of dislocations with the same Burgers vectors depends on the deviation $\Delta\theta$ from the exact coincidence position. The observations are in agreement with the predictions of the theory (BROKMAN and BALLUFFI [1981]). Secondary dislocations can split into partial secondary dislocations and stacking-fault-like structures. This is observed not only for metals but also for semiconductors (BACMAN et al. [1981]).

Lattice dislocations can interact with grain boundaries during yielding, creep and recrystallization (SMITH [1976]). Many TEM observations on reactions of lattice dislocations with GB dislocations can be explained on the basis of the dislocation model for GB structures. For the reactions of the lattice dislocations with grain

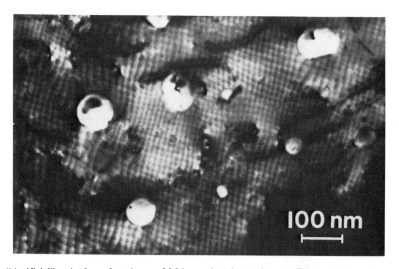

Fig. 24. "Artificial" twist boundary in a gold bicrystal, twist angle near $\Sigma = 5$ (36.9°). Square grids of secondary screw grain-boundary dislocations can be observed, Burgers vector $b = (a/10)\langle 310 \rangle$. The dislocations accommodate the deviations from the exact $\Sigma = 5$ misorientation. (Courtesy T. SCHOBER and R.W. BALLUFFI.)

boundaries one has to observe that Burgers vectors are conserved and dislocation lines can end only on other dislocations or at a free surface.

8.3. Diffraction studies on the structure of grain boundaries

SASS and BRISTOWE [1980] demonstrated that diffraction techniques also in the TEM can answer questions concerning the atomic structure of GBs. Each GB represents a periodic arrangement of strains (misfit) and good coincidences. Electrons and X-rays are scattered by this periodic grid which possesses a unit cell which corresponds to the CSL. If the (periodic) displacements at the GBs are known, then the scattering factor of such boundaries (mostly twist boundaries) can be calculated for the different reflections caused by the GBs. The reciprocal lattice, e.g., of a twist boundary, exists of thin rods, the integral intensity in the rod depends on the scattering factor (see appendix). The length of the rod is proportional to the inverse of the "thickness" of the disturbed region near the GB. This grain-boundary "thickness" approximately equals the distance of the dislocations present in the GB.

8.4. Direct imaging of grain boundaries

High-resolution electron microscopy (HREM) allows the direct imaging of certain GBs. In HREM the structure of the specimen must be periodic in the direction of

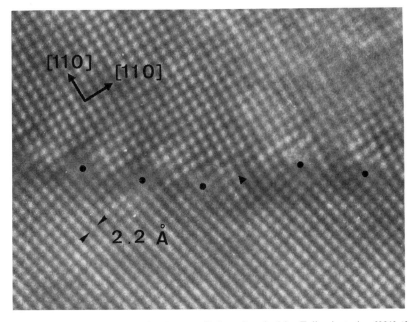

Fig. 25. High-resolution image of a $\Sigma = 41$ pure tilt boundary in Mo. Foil orientation [001] (for both grains). (Courtesy A. BOURRET and J.M. PENISSON.)

References: p. 788.

the transmitted electron beam. Therefore, only tilt boundaries can be studied where the tilt axis is parallel to the beam direction. Since the strong periodicity is disturbed in the core region of the boundaries, the point-to-point resolution of the instrument must be good enough so that information on the relaxation of atoms is transferred through the objective lenses despite the still rather high spherical aberration of the best lenses available to date.

Tilt boundaries in silicon (BOURRET and DESSEAUX [1979]), germanium (KRIVANEK *et al.* [1977]) and molybdenum (PENISSON *et al.* [1982]) were studied by HREM. For these studies the specimen thickness has to be below 15 nm. Figure 25 shows a HREM micrograph of a tilt boundary in molybdenum. For the determination of the positions of the atoms close to the GB, contrast simulations have to be performed. In the simulation work one assumes a certain atomic configuration near the tilt boundary. The simulated micrographs have to be compared with the experimentally observed pictures for different defocusing values. The atomic arrangements have to be modified until a complete fit between the observed and calculated images is reached.

8.5. TEM contrast of heterophase boundaries

Heterophase boundaries are formed when two materials of different structure and/or different chemical composition meet. If, for example, any type of phase transformation occurs then a heterophase boundary is present where the different phases meet. This is true for the interface of a martensitic phase transformation where two materials with the same chemical composition but different structures meet, as well as for an interface of thermally grown precipitate.

The importance of the structure of these heterophase boundaries for the nucleation and growth process of the precipitate is recognized. However, only few systematic TEM studies were performed investigating the structure of such interfaces. The studies would require experimental imaging of the inclined interface under different diffraction conditions under which reflections from both crystal structures are excited simultaneously or one after the other. The observations have to be compared with contrast simulations. General expressions were derived even in the framework of anisotropic elasticity theory for the elastic displacement and stress fields by BONNET [1981]. The results, however, have as yet not been applied to contrast simulations of an interface.

The geometry of the heterophase interfaces can be described by a generalization of the geometry of grain boundaries (BALLUFFI *et al.* [1982]). These models are essentially fit–misfit models in which the regions of a good "fit" are patched where partial lattice matching across the boundary is achieved, and the regions of 'misfit' are boundary line defects which possess the character either of a dislocation or of a boundary step (facette). (See also ch. 10B, § 2.4.1.)

The model has been applied to interfaces between two cubic crystals – copper and silver (LAFFONT and BONNET [1982]) – and for hexagonal materials (BONNET *et al.* [1981]). A metal–metal-carbide interface was studied by different authors (DAH-

MEN *et al.* [1981] and FLORJANCIC *et al.* [1982]). FLORJANCIC *et al.* studied in detail the interface between Mo and Mo_2C precipitates which forms after cooling from a supersaturated solution. In TEM micrographs (fig. 26) a dislocation-type contrast

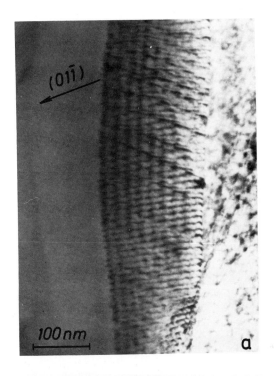

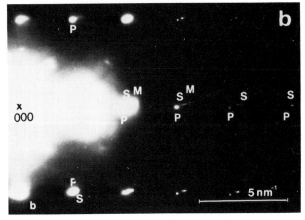

Fig. 26. Interface between Mo and Mo_2C: (a) dislocation contrasts are visible, the Burgers vector cannot be analyzed unambiguously; (b) diffraction pattern of the same interface in an edge-on configuration, additional "streaks" are observable due to the "interface" crystal.

References: p. 788.

can be observed. The determination of the Burgers vector by means of the simple $g \cdot b = 0$ rule is not unambiguously possible. The contrast behaviour suggests that the Burgers vector is of type $\frac{1}{2}\langle 111 \rangle$, diffraction patterns yield the orientation relation between Mo and Mo_2C. Dense packed planes of the Mo lattices are about parallel to dense-packed planes of Mo_2C (Burgers relation). Careful diffraction studies were performed for an edge-on configuration of the interface, fig. 26. It was found that besides the reflections of Mo and Mo_2C, streaks can also be observed lying between them. The formation of such additional streaks can simply be explained with the assumption that an interface crystal is present between the (pure) Mo and Mo_2C. From the maximum streak length the minimum thickness of the interface crystal can be determined to within nine lattice planes of the Mo lattice.

9. High-resolution TEM

9.1. Introduction

By high-resolution TEM we understand all attempts of utilizing modern electron microscopes up to the ultimate resolution limit. The latter is determined by the wave aberrations of the objective lens – spherical aberration, chromatic aberration, astigmatism etc. – under optimal adjustments of size and position of the objective aperture, of the direction of the incident electron beam with respect to the optical axis and of the actual focusing of the objective lens, cf. also §2. Under such optimum conditions a point-to-point resolution of about 0.2 nm and a lattice-fringe resolution of ≤ 0.1 nm are achievable by modern microscopes specialized for high-resolution work. At the present time, high-resolution TEM plays only a marginal role in physical metallurgy, but this may change in the near future when the modern generation of electron microscopes becomes wide-spread available in laboratories concerned with physical metallurgy. Therefore, we present here only a brief outline of the basic principles of high-resolution microscopy. In the following we restrict ourselves to spherical aberration as the most important lens error in the high-resolution work. For more extended introductions to high-resolution TEM we refer to the references in the bibliography.

9.2. The optical transfer function

We assume that the specimen is orientated perpendicular to the optical axis of the microscope and introduce a Cartesian coordinate system in the lower specimen surface with the z-axis (unit vector e_z) pointing downwards, i.e., towards the objective lens. Axial illumination is assumed, i.e., the incident beam is parallel to e_z. A space vector in the plane perpendicular to e_z will be denoted by $\hat{r}$. The objective lens may be focused onto the plane $z = \delta$ where $\delta > 0$ ($\delta < 0$) means overfocusing (underfocusing) with respect to the lower specimen surface ($z = 0$). We denote the electron wavefunction in the plane $z = 0$ by $\psi_0(\hat{r})$ *. By propagating from $z = 0$ to the plane $z = \delta$, $\psi_0(\hat{r})$ is modified by Fresnel diffraction to $\psi_\delta(\hat{r})$. Note that for $\delta > 0$, the wavefunction $\psi_\delta(\hat{r})$ is really existing at the plane $z = \delta$, whereas for $\delta < 0$, $\psi_\delta(\hat{r})$ means a virtual wavefunction, which would merge into $\psi_0(\hat{r})$ at $z = 0$ when propagating from $z = \delta < 0$ to $z = 0$ in an empty space, i.e, in the absence of the specimen.

The propagation of the electron wave through the imaging system of the microscope is considered in terms of partial waves or Fourier waves of amplitudes $\tilde{\psi}(p)$, where the Fourier waves $\tilde{\psi}_0$ and $\tilde{\psi}_\delta$ are assumed to emerge either from the plane $z = 0$ or from the plane $z = \delta$, respectively,

$$\tilde{\psi}_j(p) = \int \psi_j(\hat{r}) \exp(-2\pi i p \cdot \hat{r}) \, d^2\hat{r}, \qquad j = 0, \delta. \tag{42}$$

p is a "space frequency" vector perpendicular to e_z, starting from the optical axis. Since p has the dimension of a reciprocal length, it is a vector in reciprocal space. $\tilde{\psi}_0$ and $\tilde{\psi}_\delta$ are interlinked by the Fresnel diffraction theorem,

$$\tilde{\psi}_\delta(p) = \tilde{\psi}_0(p) \cdot \exp -i\chi_\delta(p), \tag{43}$$

with

$$\chi_\delta(p) = \pi\lambda\delta p^2, \tag{44}$$

with λ = electron wavelength.

The partial wave, belonging to the space frequency vector p and making an angle $\alpha \approx p/k$ ($k = 1/\lambda$) with the optical axis, suffers when passing through the objective lens an additional phase shift $\chi_s(p)$ caused by the spherical aberration of this lens,

$$\chi_s(p) = \frac{\pi}{2} C_s \lambda^3 p^4, \tag{45}$$

where C_s is the spherical aberration constant, typically of the order of some mm. Then, in the backfocal plane of the objective lens (subscript "b"), we get the amplitude distribution

$$\tilde{\psi}_b(p) = \tilde{\psi}_0(p) \cdot \exp -i\chi(p), \tag{46}$$

with the wave aberration function

$$\chi(p) = \chi_f + \chi_s = 2\pi\left[\tfrac{1}{2}\lambda\delta p^2 + \tfrac{1}{4}C_s\lambda^3 p^4\right]. \tag{47}$$

The objective aperture in the backfocal plane (assumed to be circular in shape) cuts off all partial waves making an angle $\alpha > \alpha_{max}$ with the optical axis. With $\alpha = p/k$, see above, we introduce an aperture function $A(p)$ by

$$A(p) = 1 \quad \text{for } p \le p_{max} = k\alpha_{max},$$

$$A(p) = 0 \quad \text{for } p > p_{max}. \tag{48}$$

---

* In this section the subscript of ψ refers to the z-coordinate.

References: p. 788.

Thus, immediately behind the objective aperture we are left with

$$\tilde{\psi}_b(\boldsymbol{p}) = \tilde{\psi}_0(\boldsymbol{p}) \cdot T(\boldsymbol{p}), \qquad T(\boldsymbol{p}) = A(\boldsymbol{p}) \cdot \exp{-i\chi(\boldsymbol{p})}. \tag{49}$$

$T(p)$ is called the optical transfer function. The subsequent imaging system (intermediate lenses, projector lens) can be assumed to be aberration-free. Thus the final image amplitude on the viewing screen (or on the photographic plate) is found from $\tilde{\psi}_b(\boldsymbol{p})$ according to eq. (49) by an inverse Fourier transformation,

$$\psi_m(\hat{\boldsymbol{r}}) = \int \tilde{\psi}_0(\boldsymbol{p}) \cdot T(\boldsymbol{p}) \exp\left(-2\pi i \frac{\boldsymbol{p} \cdot \hat{\boldsymbol{r}}}{M}\right) d^2p, \tag{50}$$

where the index "m" stands for "magnified" image, M = electron–optical magnification. [The same sign of the exponents of the first, eq. (42), and of the inverse, eq. (50), Fourier transformations accounts for the 180° rotation between the diffraction pattern and the image, cf. §2.]

9.3. Consequences of the wave aberration

By the objective aperture all partial waves $\tilde{\psi}_0(\boldsymbol{p})$ with $p > p_{max}$ are cut off. These partial waves are produced by structural details of $\psi_0(\hat{\boldsymbol{r}})$ of "wavelengths" $\leqslant 1/p_{max}$. Accordingly, these structural details are completely suppressed in $\psi_m(\hat{\boldsymbol{r}})$. Moreover, the phases of the partial waves $\tilde{\psi}_0(\boldsymbol{p})$ with $p \leqslant p_{max}$ are shifted by the wave-aberration term $\chi(p)$ so that, after recombination of these partial waves in the image plane, the "structure" of $\psi_m(\hat{\boldsymbol{r}})$ may be significantly different from $\psi_0(\hat{\boldsymbol{r}})$ even for structures of wavelength $> 1/p_{max}$. For illustration, we calculate $\chi(p)$ assuming $C_s = 3$ mm, $\lambda = 3.7$ pm, $\delta = 0$ (exactly focused objective lens), and $p = p_1 = (1 \text{ nm})^{-1}$ and $p_2 = (0.7 \text{ nm})^{-1}$. From eq. (47) we find $\chi(p_1) = 13.7°$ and $\chi(p_2) = 57°$. Accordingly, in this case the wave aberration is probably negligible for the imaging of structures of dimension of 1 nm and above, but it becomes important near 0.7 nm or below. Obviously, the deteriorating influence of $\chi(p)$ on the image formation can be reduced for a certain p-interval if both terms of $\chi(p)$ act against one another: Since C_s is always > 0, it is expedient to operate the microscope with $\delta < 0$, i.e., with an appropriately underfocused objective lens. For a special case this will be quantified in the next section.

9.4. The weak-phase object approximation

At present, high-resolution images with an intensity distribution $I_m(\hat{\boldsymbol{r}}) = |\psi_m(\hat{\boldsymbol{r}})|^2$, which are directly interpretable in terms of structural details of the specimen, are only obtainable from extremely thin specimens of thickness $t \lesssim 10$ nm depending on the composition of the specimen. In such cases the weak-phase object approximation may be applicable. It can be shown that, assuming axial illumination, the wavefunction $\psi_0(\hat{\boldsymbol{r}})$ of sufficiently thin specimens can be represented by

$$\psi_0(\hat{\boldsymbol{r}}) \approx \exp\left[+i\omega_0(\hat{\boldsymbol{r}})\right] \approx 1 + i\omega_0(\hat{\boldsymbol{r}}), \tag{51}$$

where $\omega_0(\hat{\boldsymbol{r}})$, being real and of modulus $\ll 1$, is proportional to the electrostatic potential $V(\hat{r}, z)$ in the specimen projected along the electron beam direction ($= z$-axis, origin in the lower specimen surface!):

$$\omega_0(\hat{r}) \propto \int_{-t}^{0} V(\hat{r}, z)\, dz. \tag{52}$$

Then, the formalism outlined in the preceding section leads to:

$$\psi_m(\hat{r}) = 1 + \omega_m^{(r)}(\hat{r}) + i\omega_m^{(i)}(\hat{r}) \tag{53}$$

with

$$\omega_m^{(r)}(\hat{r}) = \int \tilde{\omega}_0(p) \cdot A(p) \cdot \sin \chi(p) \cdot \exp\left(-2\pi i \frac{p \cdot \hat{r}}{M}\right) d^2p. \tag{54}$$

For $\omega_m^{(i)}$ the same equation is applied with $\sin \chi$ substituted by $\cos \chi$. From $\chi(p) = \chi(-p)$, $A(p) = A(-p)$, and $\omega_0(\hat{r})$ real it follows by symmetry arguments that $\omega_m^{(r)}$ and $\omega_m^{(i)}$ are real as well. Accordingly, in linear approximation of the "perturbation" term $\omega_0(\hat{r})$ we get the image intensity

$$I_m(\hat{r}) \approx 1 + 2\omega_m^{(r)}(\hat{r}), \tag{55}$$

i.e., the only phase-modulated wavefunction $\psi_0(\hat{r})$ at the specimen [eq. (51)], which would give rise to no contrast in a perfect microscope ($|\psi_0(\hat{r})|^2 = 1$), is converted by the wave aberration term $\sin \chi(p)$ into an amplitude-modulated wavefunction $\psi_m(\hat{r})$ at the image plane, eq. (55).

In order to keep an utmost similarity between the observable structure of $I_m(\hat{r})$ and the unknown structure of $\psi_0(\hat{r})$, we have to adjust the focusing parameter and the size of the objective aperture in such a way that the partial waves of a maximum range of space frequencies p are transferred through the imaging system by the $\sin \chi(p)$ term with a reasonable value close to 1 or -1 and with the same sign of $\sin \chi(p)$. This is achieved by the socalled *Scherzer focus*, δ_0, which correlates δ to C_s and λ by:

$$\delta_0 = -\left(\tfrac{3}{2}C_s\lambda\right)^{1/2}. \tag{56}$$

Figure 27 displays the term $\sin \chi(p)$ for three values of δ assuming $C_s = 3$ mm and $\lambda = 3.7$ pm. In the case of $\delta = \delta_0$ (solid curve) we find a broad band-pass with $\sin \chi(p)$ close to -1 (the shallow dent near $p = 1.8$ (nm)$^{-1}$ is tolerable) and with the first zero at $p = p_1 = 2.5$ (nm)$^{-1}$. This means that all partial amplitudes of space frequencies with $p < p_1$ are transferred with the same sign, i.e., they may contribute to a correct reconstruction of the image. The partial amplitudes associated to space frequencies $p > p_1$ change in sign due to the $\sin \chi(p)$ term more and more rapidly with increasing p. So their contribution to the final image may be confusing rather than constructive (e.g., they may be washed out by a finite beam divergence). Therefore, the size of the objective aperture should be chosen so that p_{max} (eq. 48) coincides approximately with p_1, thus cutting off the oscillating part of $\sin \chi(p)$. In this way a resolution limit of $1/p_1$ (≈ 0.4 nm in fig. 27) is achieved.

If δ is reduced by 20% to $0.8\delta_0$ (dashed curve) we find a reduction of the first zero

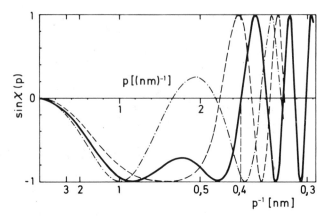

Fig. 27. The transfer function $\sin \chi(p)$ for $C_s = 3$ mm. Solid curve: $\delta = \delta_0 =$ Scherzer focus; dashed curve: $\delta = 0.8\delta_0$, dashed-dotted curve: $\delta = 1.2\delta_0$.

to $p_1 = 2.2$ (nm)$^{-1}$ which corresponds to a reduction of the resolution limit to 0.45 nm. If, on the other hand, δ is increased by 20% to 1.2 δ_0 (dashed-dotted curve) the shallow dent near $p = 1.8$ (nm)$^{-1}$ becomes so deep that it crosses the abscissa. As a consequence, the broad band-pass of the solid curve is completely disturbed and the resolution becomes drastically worse. We learn from these examples that fully utilizing the resolving power of an electron microscope requires a precise knowledge of the spherical aberration constant C_s and a precise control over the actual defocusing value δ.

In the meantime several methods have been developed in order to make the partial waves of space frequencies beyond p_1 also useful for the image interpretation. Here the key-word "image reconstruction" must be sufficient, cf., e.g., HAWKES [1980].

9.5.   Some remarks to the high-resolution images of crystalline specimens

The weak-phase object approximation, originally developed for the study of non-crystalline specimens, is valid also for crystalline specimens, provided they are sufficiently thin. The space frequency spectrum $\tilde{\psi}(p)$ of a perfect crystalline weak-phase object consists of a discrete set of sharp Bragg diffraction spots. If such a specimen is carefully oriented with the incident beam along a low-order zone axis and if the lattice constant is large compared to that of pure metals or alloys, a large number of diffraction spots may pass through the objective aperture. In the frame of the weak-phase object approximation they form an image which reveals many details on an atomic scale of the (projected) crystal structure. An example is shown in fig. 28. In particular, complicated stacking or shear variants of otherwise comparatively simple crystal structures, which are hardly, or not at all, determinable by X-ray or neutron diffraction techniques, may become easy to analyze on

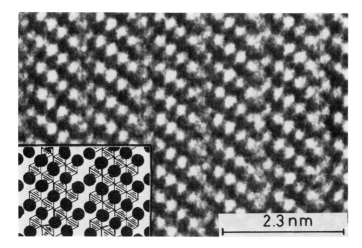

Fig. 28. High-resolution image of $Ba_5Nb_4O_{15}$. (hexagonal unit cell, $a = 0.572$ nm, $c = 1.172$ nm). Projection along $\langle 10\bar{1}0 \rangle$. The insert shows the projected structure: solid circles indicate positions of Ba atoms, hatched diamonds indicate NbO_6 octahedra. (Courtesy J.L. HUTCHISON; inset from SHANNON and KATZ [1970].)

high-resolution TEM. Regarding stacking variants of ordered alloys (antiphase structures) we refer as an example to VAN TENDELOO and AMELINCKX [1977, 1978]. Various applications of high-resolution TEM to crystal-structure research in mineralogy and anorganic chemistry may be found in a book · edited by WENK [1976].

Silicon is a substance especially suitable for high-resolution TEM because of its simple structure and because of its comparatively large lattice constant. Detailed information on an atomic scale of split dislocation configurations and of the structure of dislocation cores have been obtained, cf., e.g., SPENCE and KOLAR [1979] and BOURRET *et al.* [1982].

One point of special interest in physical metallurgy concerns the imaging of a local variation of lattice-plane distances as a consequence of a local variation of the chemical composition, e.g., in the course of a spinodal decomposition. SINCLAIR *et al.* [1976], studying a spinodally decomposed Ni_3Au alloy, found indeed a periodic modulation of the lattice plane fringes, in accordance with the expectation.

However, subsequent model calculations of COCKAYNE and GRONSKY [1981] have clearly demonstrated that, due to the wave aberration $\chi(p)$, the spatial modulation of the lattice fringes observed on the image may be significantly different from the spatial modulation of the lattice plane spacings in the specimen. Even the number of lattice fringes per modulation period may be different from the corresponding number of lattice planes in the specimen.

In conclusion it is worthwhile to emphasize that at the present state of the art all kinds of high-resolution work, in particular that concerning lattice defects, must be

References: p. 788.

accompanied by extended theoretical work, i.e., by corresponding model calculations. This holds even more if one crosses the border of the restricted regime of
applicability of the weak-phase object approximation.

10. Analytical electron microscopy

10.1. Basic considerations

Electron scattering can be divided into two categories: elastic and inelastic
scattering. When elastic scattering occurs, the direction of the electron velocity v is
changed, but the magnitude $|v|$ remains constant, so that the kinetic energy,
$E = \frac{1}{2}m_e v^2$ (m_e = electron mass) is unchanged.

During an inelastic scattering event, energy is transferred to the target atoms and
electrons, and the kinetic energy of the beam electron decreases.

Inelastic scattering can happen by: (i) plasma excitation; (ii) excitation of
conducting electrons leading to secondary electron (low-energy) emissions; (iii)
deceleration of the electron beam in the Coulomb field of an atom (*Bremsstrahlung*);
(iv) excitation of phonons; (v) ionization of the inner shells of atoms. Signals arising
by the latter process can be used for analytical studies (fig. 29).

In the ionization process of inner shells, a sufficiently energetic electron can
interact with an atom and cause the ejection of a tightly bound inner-shell electron,
leaving the atom in an ionized and highly energetic state. The energy transferred to
the bound electrons must be at least the energy of the bound state of the electron in
a shell of the atoms. Subsequent decay of this excitation state results in the emission
of characteristic X-rays and Auger electrons. The X-ray yield is plotted in fig. 30 for
different elements. Qualitative and quantitative information on the presence of the
different elements can be obtained from the wavelength of a characteristic X-ray and
from its intensity. A detailed treatment of the properties of characteristic X-rays is
found in the literature (e.g., BERTIN [1975] and GOLDSTEIN *et al.* [1981]).

In *electron energy loss spectroscopy* (EELS) the inelastic scattering of the incident
beam is studied directly. The intensity of the inelastically scattered beam is measured

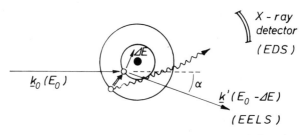

Fig. 29. Inelastic scattering of incoming electrons at electrons of inner shells (schematic drawing). The
characteristic X-rays and the energy losses are used for analytical purposes.

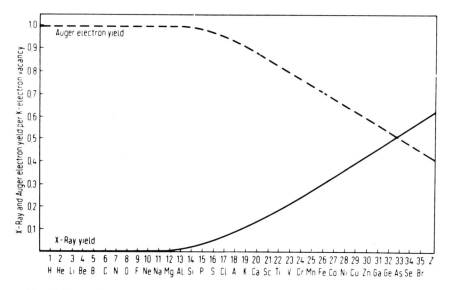

Fig. 30. X-ray yield and Auger-electron yield for K-shell excitation for different elements.

as a function of energy loss by spectral analysis. At characteristic energy losses the intensities of the inelastically scattered electrons increase due to the ionization of inner shells. From the position of the edge and the increase in intensity, information is again available on the chemical composition. EELS is most powerful for light elements (atomic number $Z < 12$), whereas the analysis of the characteristic X-rays is possible for $Z > 9$.

The cross-section for the inelastic processes (i) to (v) has been calculated (see GOLDSTEIN *et al.* [1981]) for different metal targets as a function of energy. All of the cross-sections are observed to decrease with increasing energy. Considering a range of atomic numbers, inelastic scattering is favoured at low atomic numbers and elastic scattering at high atomic numbers.

Inelastic scattering occurs by a variety of discrete processes, with a variable amount of energy transferred to the solid, depending on the strength of each interaction. Cross-sections for the individual processes are difficult to obtain for all targets of interest. It is useful in many calculations to consider all inelastic processes grouped together to give a "continuous energy loss" (BETHE [1933]).

It is found experimentally that an appreciable fraction of the beam electrons which strike a target subsequently escape where the electrons enter the solid (backscattered electrons). Backscattering electrons provide an extremely useful signal for imaging in scanning electron microscopy and scanning transmission electron microscopy. For proper image interpretation, it is necessary to understand the properties of the backscattered electrons as a function of the parameters of the beam and the characteristics of the specimen (for a detailed review see NIEDRIG [1978]).

References: p. 788.

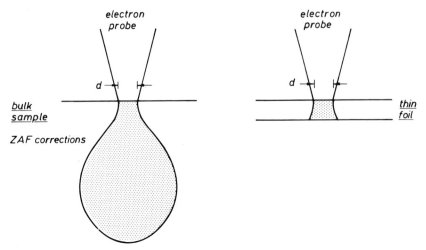

Fig. 31. Schematic representation of the interaction of a high-energy electron beam with a bulk sample and a thin foil, respectively. To the first approximation absorption and fluorescence effects can be ignored in the thin specimen.

It is well established by experiments and by Monte Carlo calculations that the volume of interaction between a high-energy electron beam and a solid possesses the shape of a pear (fig. 31). The width of the neck of the pear is mainly determined by the shape of the electron beam, while the length of the neck depends on the energy of the electrons as well as on the material investigated. The diameter of the pear can exceed several microns (μm). Therefore, studies with high spatial resolution can only be performed in thin foils.

Those studies are preferentially performed in a conventional TEM fitted with a STEM unit, appropriate detectors for X-rays and energy loss spectra.

10.2. Quantitative analytical electron microscopy of thin foils – analysis of X-rays

In X-ray microanalysis the detector is as close as possible to the specimen. Usually, the detectors are energy-dispersive devices, which offer the advantages of speed of operation and ease of attachment to the system. Crystal spectrometers (wavelength-dispersive devices) are usually preferred for quantitative studies. However, it is very cumbersome to attach those to a transmission electron microscope. An example of an EDS X-ray microanalysis spectrum in the STEM mode of a TEM is shown in fig. 32.

10.2.1. Cross-section for inner-shell ionization

Numerous cross-sections for inner-shell ionization can be found in the literature; this has been reviewed by POWELL [1976]. The number of X-ray photons produced

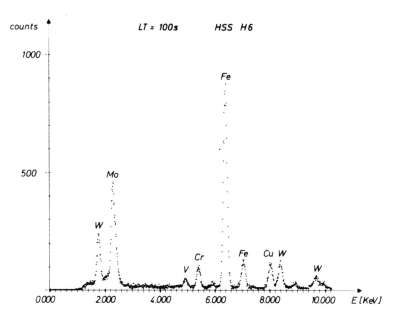

Fig. 32. STEM X-ray spectrum from a low-carbon steel. The Cu peak is caused by the Cu grid of the TEM.

per incident electron in a thin foil of thickness Δx can be predicted from

$$n_x = \sigma w N_0 \frac{1}{A} \rho \Delta x, \tag{57}$$

where σ is the ionization cross-section, w the fluorescence yield (see fig. 30), N_0 Avogadro's number, A the atomic weight, and ρ the density of the material. Experimental measurements of the X-ray yield (absolute efficiency) give a range of $\sim 0.11 \times 10^{-4}$ for Mg to $\sim 0.933 \times 10^{-4}$ for Ni in units of X-ray photons per electron and per angular unit.

10.2.2. Thin-film approximation

If the sample is sufficiently thin to carry out quantitative transmission electron microscopy at $\geqslant 100$ kV, the activated volume is approximately a cylinder equal to the beam diameter (see fig. 31); that means a high lateral resolution can be achieved. This high lateral resolution, however, results in a disadvantage in the use of thin specimens in that the activated volume for X-ray production is small compared to a bulk sample; X-ray counting rates are low and hence the potential accuracy is inferior to that generally accepted for bulk specimens in scanning electron microscopy.

CLIFF and LORIMER [1975] showed that for a thin foil, to a first approximation X-ray absorption and fluorescence in the specimen can be neglected. Therefore, the

References: p. 788.

ratio of two observed X-ray intensities I_A/I_B can be related to the corresponding weight fraction ratio c_A/c_B by the equation

$$c_A/c_B = k_{AB} I_A/I_B, \tag{58}$$

where k_{AB} is a constant at a given accelerating voltage and is independent of specimen thickness and composition. A normalization procedure, e.g. $\Sigma c_n = 1$, must be used to convert the ratios of the weight fractions into weight percentages. In mineral specimens, which are frequently used for calibration, assumptions must also be made concerning oxidation states, e.g., it is impossible to differentiate between Fe_3O_4 and Fe_2O_3 if ratios are measured, and oxygen cannot be detected (LORIMER et al. [1981]).

For quantitative analysis the parameters k_{AB} in eq. (58) have to be determined experimentally and also compared to theoretical results. There are discussions in the literature on the reliability of different k_{AB} values available (e.g. GEISS [1981]). Furthermore the effects of absorption of the X-rays and fluorescence in the specimen have to be considered for a reliable quantitative analysis (see § 10.2.4).

10.2.3. Beam-spreading in the specimen

Beam-spreading in thin foils is currently an active field of research in both experimental investigations and theoretical analysis (LORIMER et al. [1981] and GEISS [1981]).

A simple approach to the problem of beam-spreading has been proposed by GOLDSTEIN et al. [1977] who assumed that a single elastic scattering event occurs at the centre of the foil, and defined the X-ray source as that volume in which 90% of the electron trajectories lie. Experimental observations surprisingly show good agreement with the simple theory by GOLDSTEIN et al. [1977]. The beam-spreading limits the spatial resolution of analytical TEM, as shown in table 1.

10.2.4. Errors limiting the data of X-ray analysis

X-ray counting statistics are usually assumed to obey Gaussian behaviour and at

Table 1

Spatial resolution for X-ray microanalysis at 120 kV for incident electron probe sizes defined by $d = 0$ nm and $d = 5$ nm (after LORIMER et al. [1981]).

Foil thickness (nm)	d (nm)	Spatial resolution			
		C	Al	Cu	Au
40	0	–	1	4	10
	5	22	22	22	23
100	0	4	6	17	38
	5	22	22	26	42
200	0	11	18	47	107
	5	24	27	50	108
400	0	30	50	132	302
	5	35	53	134	302

the 2σ confidence level the relative error in the number of counts I is $2\sqrt{I}$. Using eq. (58) a ratio of two counts is converted into a weight-fraction ratio via the constant k_{AB}. Thus it is necessary to add the total relative errors in I_A, I_B and k_{AB} to obtain the relative error in the weight fraction c_A/c_B. If $\sim 10\,000$ counts were obtained for both I_A and I_B, and k_{AB} were known to an accuracy of $\pm 2\%$, the total relative error in c_A/c_B would be 6%. Unfortunately, X-ray counts are often a premium in thin specimens and it may be necessary to accept only a few hundred counts for one element. If, for example, I_A contained only 900 counts and I_B still equalled $10\,000$, then the relative error in the c_A/c_B ratio would be $\pm 10\%$. The statistical error was often not taken into account in quantitative analytical electron microscopy (AEM). Therefore, materials-science interpretation of AEM work is based on weak or incorrect foundations.

In order to make corrections for absorption, fluorescence and beam-spreading, it is necessary to know the thickness of the sample. Various parallax techniques can be used, including the contamination spots formed on the top and the bottom of the foil during the analysis. However, it seems that the most accurate technique is that of convergent-beam diffraction as described by AMELINCKX [1964] and KELLY *et al.* [1975]. This enables specimen thickness to be determined with an accuracy of $\pm 2\%$.

Many investigators have been aware that the measured X-ray spectrum may contain X-rays generated from other than the sample region excited by the focused electron beam. These additional X-rays are called 'spurious' or 'extraneous' radiation. This problem has received much attention (cf. GOLDSTEIN and WILLIAMS [1981]). The spurious radiation can be avoided by a correct experimental arrangement of the specimen in the analytical electron microscope. The absence of spurious radiation can be checked by a hole count.

10.2.5. Examples

Since about 1979 reliable results obtained by AEM appeared. CHAMPNESS *et al.* [1982] determined the partitioning of various alloying additions during the austenite–pearlite transformation in eutectoid steels. The composition of different precipitates in a variety of steels was obtained and first results on segregation of impurities at grain boundaries and interfaces were reported. More results are published in the proceedings of recent workshops and conferences on AEM (HREN *et al.* [1979], LORIMER *et al.* [1981] and GEISS [1981]).

10.3. Quantitative analytical electron microscopy of thin foils – electron energy loss spectroscopy

A transmission microscope fitted with an electron spectrometer can be used to produce energy-filtered images (KRAHL *et al.* [1981]) or for electron energy-loss spectroscopy (EELS) (JOY [1981]). The latter can be used for measurements of inner-shell losses for quantitative microanalysis of light elements. Those studies are especially important for the determination of light elements.

There are two instrumental principles used nowadays. They are based on (i) the

References: p. 788.

use of a magnetic analyzer below the camera chamber of a conventional TEM or a TEM with STEM attachments (KRIVANEK and SWANN [1981]) and (ii) the use of an analyzer between the objective and the intermediate lens in a conventional TEM (ZANCHI et al. [1977]). Figure 33 shows schematically the energy spectrum of 100 kV electrons after transmission through a specimen of about 25 nm thickness. The elastically or (by phonons) quasi-elastically scattered electrons give rise to a zero-loss peak whose width provides an indication of the instrumental energy resolution. For small energy losses (≤ 100 eV) surface and bulk plasmon losses are observed (JOUFFREY et al. [1978]). For higher energy losses E, inelastic scattering is caused at electrons of the outer atomic shells (e.g., valence electrons). The intensity of the inelastically scattered electrons decays rapidly, approximately as AE^{-r}, where A is a constant and r is between 2 and 6. At an energy loss equal to the ionization energy E_k of an inner atomic shell k (where $k =$ K, L, M) the energy loss intensity increases rather abruptly, followed by a slower decay. By determining A and r from a region just preceding the ionization edge, the outer-shell background can be subtracted (by a computer, or manually using a log–log plot). The area $I_k(\alpha, \Delta)$ above the background is measured up to an energy loss $E_k + \Delta$ (see fig. 33). The number of atoms per unit area of the corresponding element is then given by (JOY [1981])

$$N = \left[I_k(\alpha, \Delta)/I_1(\alpha, \Delta) \right]/\sigma_k(\alpha, \Delta), \tag{59}$$

where $\sigma_k(\alpha, \Delta)$ is a partial cross-section for the ionization of shell k within an energy range Δ and for scattering angles up to α. The angle α is determined by the collecting angle of the spectrometer. For a quantitative analysis $\sigma_k(\alpha, \Delta)$ can be determined experimentally or by calculations (EGERTON [1979] and JOY [1981]).

Unlike X-ray or Auger microanalysis, energy-loss spectroscopy therefore provides a convenient standardless method for determining the absolute number N of atoms of light elements. In addition, the ratio of two (or more) elements may be determined from the appropriate ionization edge, provided an equal integration range Δ is chosen for both elements. For that case $I_1(\alpha, \Delta)$ will cancel in eq. (59) so that the low-loss region needs not to be measured.

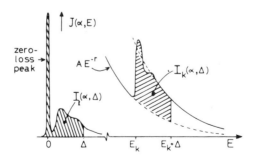

Fig. 33. Schematic electron energy-loss spectrum of the signal intensity $I(E)$ versus energy loss E. The hatched area close to the energy E_K is proportional to the number of atoms present in the specimen.

As the specimen thickness increases, multiple-scattering contributions to the background beneath an inner-shell edge cause the background to increase faster than the inner-shell "signal", so that the signal/background ratio falls, which reduces the visibility of an edge and may make the background-fitting and subtraction process insufficiently accurate (Joy [1981]). Therefore, judging by the criterion of signal/background ratio, the specimen should be as thin as possible within the analyzed region.

However, by making the sample very thin we reduce the amount of valence-electron- and inner-shell scattering, so that the relative noise level in both signal and background is increased. Consequently, the signal/noise ratio (due to the finite number of electrons detected within the energy window chosen for analysis) initially increases with thickness and then goes through a maximum at a sample thickness of the order of Λ_i, the total mean free path for inelastic scattering. This last statement however ignores the practical problem of separating the signal from the background (i.e., background-fitting and subtraction) which generally becomes more difficult as the thickness increases and the signal/background ratio deteriorates. In practice it is generally found that the optimum specimen thickness is closer to $\Lambda_i/2$, i.e., 60 nm for 100 keV electrons (Egerton [1979, 1981]), 50–100 nm for 200 keV, and 100–200 nm for 1000 keV incident energy (Jouffrey *et al.* [1978]).

The sensitivity of a microanalytical technique is an important factor in determining its usefulness. For EELS, as for EDS, the limiting condition will be the statistical requirement for a minimum signal-to-noise ratio between the edge and the background. Because of the dominance of the background in the spectrum the sensitivity will depend very much on the experimental parameters such as beam current, recording time and acceptance angle. Consequently, detailed calculations are necessary in order to obtain realistic results. Joy and Maher [1980] calculated the sensitivity for different atoms distributed in a carbon matrix, under a variety of experimental conditions typical for STEM operation.

Although the absolute detection limits are very good, typically 10^{-19} g, this represents, however, a mass- or atomic fraction of only between 0.5 and 5% in most cases. This indicates that EELS is best suited for studies of precipitates, segregation effects and similar situations where the local mass fraction is high or can be made so by choosing the probe diameter. It can also be seen that much of the potential gain in microanalytical sensitivity derived from EELS operation is sacrificed when the normal sequential mode of spectrum recording is used, since the analysis time is only of the order of a few hundred milliseconds per channel compared with 100 s or more for EDS. However, recent developments in parallel detector arrays which acquire data simultaneously in many channels will ultimately remove this disability and yield a substantial gain in sensitivity.

10.3.1. Examples

EELS is applied mainly to ceramic specimens since it is the only technique for the determination of the distribution of light elements; an example is shown in fig. 34, below. Grain-boundary phases could be detected and analyzed chemically (Geiss

References: p. 788.

[1981], RÜHLE and PETZOW [1981]). Ion implantation is sometimes employed to introduce light-element dopants into semiconductors. EELS could be used to measure local dopant concentrations, if the latter exceed $\sim 0.1\%$ (JOY and MAHER [1980]). Light elements occur in certain metal specimens in the form of nitride or carbide precipitates; these materials have also been analyzed by the EELS technique (ROSSOUW *et al.* [1976], GEISS [1981]).

Acknowledgement

The authors would like to express their sincere thanks to all their colleagues in and outside Stuttgart who have helped them in preparing the present article by critical comments and/or by providing them with suitable micrographs. The latter holds in particular for their colleagues Dr. Bourret, Dr. Hutchison and Dr. Karnthaler.

Appendix. Elements of the kinematical diffraction theory

A.1. Introduction

In materials science, scattering or diffraction experiments using some kind of waves of wavelengths λ comparable to, or smaller than, interatomic distances play a key-role for the study of the atomistic structure of solids *. This holds in particular for solids of more or less perfect crystalline structure. Such experiments are carried out either by *X-rays*, as provided by conventional X-ray generators or, more recently, by synchrotron radiation of electron- or positron storage rings, or by the de Broglie waves of thermalized *neutrons*, as provided by nuclear reactors or, more recently, by spallation sources or by the de Broglie waves of high-energy *electrons* as used in a transmission electron microscope (TEM).

One of the basic theories which describe the interaction of the above-mentioned radiation with matter is the so-called *kinematical diffraction theory* which can be derived as a first Born approximation, for X-rays from the Maxwell equations, and for neutron and electron waves from the Schrödinger equation. The kinematical diffraction theory is applicable under the following conditions:

(i) The scattering at individual atoms is *elastic*, which means that the wavelength of the scattered wave is the same as the wavelength of the incoming wave.

(ii) The scattering at atoms occurs *coherently*, i.e., the phase relationship between the scattered wave and the incoming wave is always the same for a given kind of atoms.

(iii) The scattering at individual atoms is so *weak* that a second scattering of the

---

* In the following the term *scattering* is used for interaction of *individual* scattering centres, as e.g. individual atoms, with radiation. On the other hand, we speak about *diffraction* if the coherent superposition of scattered waves of *more* than one scattering centre is considered.

already scattered wave at other atoms can be neglected.

(iv) The *total diffraction* at an ensemble of atoms remains so *weak* that the intensity of the incoming wave is practically not affected, i.e., all the atoms of the ensemble (specimen) are irradiated with the same intensity.

Under these assumptions a fairly sophisticated kinematical diffraction theory has been developed and applied – using X-ray and neutron waves – to various problems in crystallography and materials science, as set out in ch. 12. However, it turns out that this kind of theory is only of restricted use for TEM investigations of crystalline material (ch. 11): Conditions (iii) and (iv) are in general strongly violated. Therefore, in TEM the theory must be extended to the so-called *dynamical diffraction theory*. Nevertheless, a number of elements of the kinematical diffraction theory will be needed also for understanding TEM of crystalline materials. Therefore, we give here a brief introduction to the general concept of the kinematical diffraction theory, which should be understood as an introduction to the more detailed reports in chs. 11 and 12.

The amplitudes of X-rays are vectors, because X-rays are electromagnetic waves, whereas the amplitudes of neutron and electrons are scalar. This gives some marginal differences in the formulation of the kinematical diffraction theory for these two kinds of radiation. For simplicity we consider here waves of scalar amplitudes only.

A.2. Fundamental equations

The *incident plane wave* $A(r, t)$ is given by

$$A(r, t) = A_0 \exp\left[2\pi i(k_0 r - vt)\right], \tag{A.1}$$

where r is the space vector, t the time coordinate, k_0 the wave vector with $|k_0| = k = 1/\lambda$, λ the wavelength and v the wave frequency. Further, A and A_0 are scalar terms with $|A_0|^2 =$ intensity per unit area perpendicular to k_0. From

$$k_0 \cdot r - vt = \text{const.} \tag{A.2}$$

we obtain the *phase velocity* v in direction of k_0,

$$v = v/k = v \cdot \lambda. \tag{A.3}$$

Since we consider only elastic scattering, where the wavenumber k and the frequency v remain unchanged by scattering events, we can omit the time-dependent part of A. Thus, in the following we start with

$$A(r) = A_0 \exp(2\pi i k_0 \cdot r) \tag{A.4}$$

as the primary wave incident on a number of N atoms. For the moment these atoms are assumed to be point-like. They are characterized by atomic scattering amplitudes f_n and are located at positions r_n near the origin $r = 0$; $n = 1 \cdots N$. At all these atoms, the primary wave excites the emission of spherical waves in coherency with the primary wave. Thus the sum of the scattered waves can be represented by $A_s(r)$,

References: p. 788.

with

$$A_s(r) = -\sum A(r_n) \cdot f_n \cdot \frac{\exp[2\pi i k|r - r_n|]}{|r - r_n|},$$ (A.5)

On the righthand side the term $A(r_n)$ represents amplitude and phase of the incident wave at the positions of the atoms. The term behind f_n represents a spherical wave emerging with phase π from the atom positions. It has the dimension of a reciprocal length. Thus, since A_s and A must be of the same dimension, the atomic scattering amplitude f_n must have the dimension of a length. Accordingly, in neutron diffraction f_n is called the "scattering length", b_n.

A detector for receiving the resultant intensity of the scattered, or diffracted, waves may be placed at a position $r = R$ so far away from the N atoms that in the denominator of eq. (A.5) the approximation

$$|R - r| \approx |R| = R$$ (A.6)

is applicable. This is the condition for *Frauenhofer diffraction*. Further, we assume that near the detector all spherical wave fronts can be approximated by plane waves with a common wave vector k_s parallel to R. Thus, near the detector, we have

$$k_s \cdot (R - r_n) = k|R - r_n| \cos \gamma, \qquad |k_s| = k,$$ (A.7)

where γ is the angle between k_s and $R - r_n$. Since $\gamma \to 0$ for $R \to \infty$, we set $\cos \gamma = 1$. Then we can rearrange eq. (A.5) with eqs. (A.6) and (A.7) to the form

$$A_s(R) = A_0 \frac{1}{R} F(\kappa) \exp(2\pi i k_s \cdot R),$$ (A.8)

with

$$\kappa = k_s - k_0, \qquad |\kappa| = 2k_0 \sin \theta$$ (A.9)

and

$$F(\kappa) = \sum f_n \exp(-2\pi i \kappa \cdot r_n).$$ (A.10a)

κ is called the *diffraction vector* (in neutron diffraction, κ is often used for $4\pi k \sin \theta$). θ is half the angle between k_0 and k_s, and $F(\kappa)$ may be called the *diffraction amplitude* of the ensemble of scattering atoms. Note that information about this ensemble (r_n, f_n) is only contained in $F(\kappa)$ and that F depends only on κ but not explicitly on the moduli and directions of κ_0 and κ_s. Equation (A.10a) may easily be extended to a continuous distribution of the atomic scattering amplitude. If $\rho_f(r)$ denotes the scattering amplitude per unit volume at the point r then eq. (A.10a) is modified to

$$F(\kappa) = \int \rho_f(r) \exp(-2\pi i \kappa \cdot r) \, d^3r.$$ (A.10b)

The detector may receive a diffracted intensity I_s via a window of area Q, with $Q/R^2 \ll 1$. Then I_s is given by:

$$I_s(\kappa) = |A_s(R)|^2 Q = |A_0|^2 |F(\kappa)|^2 \frac{Q}{R^2}.$$ (A.11)

$Q/R^2 = \Delta\Omega$ is the solid-angle interval under which the detector receives radiation from the scattering atoms. Thus, $|F(\kappa)|^2$, which has the dimension of an area, will be called the *differential diffraction cross-section* of the ensemble, i.e., the cross-section per unit solid angle, $d\sigma/d\Omega$, which is a function of κ only. Accordingly, the significance of $|F(\kappa)|^2$ is rather general, and it is in particular free of "instrumental" parameters of the experiment such as the actual values of A_0, R and Q. Therefore, in the following we concentrate mainly on a more detailed evaluation of $F(\kappa)$ or $|F(\kappa)|^2$.

A.3. Real space and reciprocal space, description of perfect crystal structures

We assume now that the atoms are periodically distributed, i.e., they form a perfect crystal lattice. The elementary cell of the lattice is given by three non-coplanar basis vectors a_1, a_2, a_3, or briefly a_j, $j = 1, 2, 3,$. For simplicity we assume here that the crystal is shaped like a parallel epiped, i.e. in the direction of a_j the elementary cells are repeated N_j times so that the lattice consists of $N_1 N_2 N_3$ unit cells. The elementary cell contains M atoms, associated with atomic scattering amplitudes f_m, $m = 1 \cdots M$. Then the positions of the lattice atoms are given by:

$$r_{nm} = r_n + r_m,\qquad\qquad (A.12)$$

where r_n denotes the position of the elementary cell,

$$r_n = \sum_j n_j a_j, \qquad 1 \leqslant n_j \leqslant N_j, \qquad\qquad (A.13)$$

and r_m denotes the position of the mth atom within the elementary cell. We express r_m in dimensionless coordinates ξ_j related to the a_j as:

$$r_m = \sum_j \xi_j^m a_j, \qquad 1 \leqslant m \leqslant M \qquad\qquad (A.14)$$

Besides the basis vectors a_j we introduce so-called *reciprocal basis vectors* which constitute the *reciprocal lattice*:

$$b_1 = \frac{a_2 \times a_3}{V_e}, \qquad b_2 = \frac{a_3 \times a_1}{V_e}, \qquad b_3 = \frac{a_1 \times a_2}{V_e}, \qquad\qquad (A.15)$$

where $\times$ means the vector product and V_e the volume of the elementary cell. The b_j are related to the a_j by:

$$a_j \cdot b_{j'} = \delta_{jj'}, \qquad\qquad (A.16)$$

where

$$\delta_{jj'} = 1 \text{ for } j = j',$$
$$= 0 \text{ for } j \neq j'.$$

Note that the b_j have the dimension of a reciprocal length, as is also true for the wave vectors k_0, k_s and the scattering vector κ. So κ can be expressed by a linear

References: p. 788.

combination of the b_j,

$$\kappa = \sum_j h_j b_j, \tag{A.17}$$

where the h_j are dimensionless numbers. Within the κ-space, or reciprocal space, the reciprocal lattice points given by h_j = integers play a special role. We denote them by g or, if necessary, by g_{hkl}, with

$$g = g_{hkl} = h b_1 + k b_2 + l b_3, \qquad h, k, l = \text{integers}. \tag{A.18}$$

The integers h, k, l are the well-known *Miller indices* of a given set of lattice planes. In standard text books of crystallography it is shown that g_{hkl} is perpendicular to the set (hkl) of lattice planes and that

$$|g_{hkl}| = 1/d_{hkl}, \tag{A.19}$$

where d_{hkl} is the repetition distance of the lattice planes (hkl).

In the following we will denote reciprocal lattice points, depending on the context, by g_{hkl}, or g, or simply by (hkl). If the h, k, l refer to the ensemble of crystallographically equivalent reciprocal lattice vectors we use the symbol $\langle hkl \rangle$. If a particular one is meant we write (hkl). For instance, concerning a crystal of cubic symmetry, $\{100\}$ comprises six g-vectors, namely $\pm(100)$, $\pm(010)$, and $\pm(001)$. In quite a similar way we will denote vectors in real space in an abbreviated form by $r = [uvw]$ with the meaning

$$r = u a_1 + v a_2 + w a_3. \tag{A.20}$$

If the ensemble of all crystallographically equivalent vectors r is meant, we write $r = \langle uvw \rangle$. For instance, in a cubic crystal the symbol $\langle 100 \rangle$ means all vectors of the kind $\pm[100]$, $\pm[010]$, and $\pm[001]$. Sets of different lattice planes (hkl) with a common direction in real space, e.g., r_z, are called a zone, and r_z is the zone axis. The corresponding vectors g_{hkl} constitute a plane in the reciprocal lattice with $g_{hkl} \cdot r_z = 0$. In a cubic crystal, $r_z = [100]$, for instance, is the zone axis for all lattice planes given by $(0kl)$. Note that for crystals of cubic symmetry a real space vector $r = [uvw]$ is parallel to a reciprocal lattice vector $g = (hkl)$ with $u = h$, $v = k$, $w = l$. For crystals of lower symmetry this is, in general, not the case. Considering, for instance, a crystal of tetragonal symmetry $(|a_3| = c \neq |a_1| = |a_2| = a)$, it turns out that the real space vector $r = [101]$ is not parallel to the reciprocal lattice vector $g = (101)$. Accordingly, if crystallographic elements of crystals of lower than cubic symmetry have to be denoted, a careful distinction between vectors r in real space and lattice plane normals g in reciprocal space is necessary.

A.4. The kinematical diffraction amplitude $F(\kappa)$ of a perfect crystal

Applying the coordinates of the crystal atoms as given by eqs. (A.12)–(A.14), eq. (A.10a) can be written as

$$F(\kappa) = F_L(\kappa) \cdot F_s(\kappa) \tag{A.21}$$

with

$$F_L(\boldsymbol{\kappa}) = \sum_n \exp(-\pi i \boldsymbol{\kappa} \cdot \boldsymbol{r}_n), \tag{A.22}$$

where the summation extends over all n_1, n_2, n_3, i.e., over all unit cells, and with

$$F_s(\boldsymbol{\kappa}) = \sum_m f_m \exp(-2\pi i \boldsymbol{\kappa} \cdot \boldsymbol{r}_m). \tag{A.23}$$

The subscript "L" stands for "lattice amplitudes". Accordingly, F_L reflects the outer shape of the crystal and is independent of details of the structure of the elementary cell. The subscript "s" stands for "structure amplitude" by which the structure of the elementary cell is taken into account. Both terms have to be considered separately. First we derive F_L. For simplicity we assume an orthogonal elementary cell where the $\boldsymbol{a}_j$ are parallel to $\boldsymbol{b}_j$ and $|\boldsymbol{b}_j| = 1/|\boldsymbol{a}_j|$. (This restriction is not necessary, but facilitates the interpretation of the final result.) We consider the environment of a particular diffraction vector $\boldsymbol{g}$ and write:

$$\boldsymbol{\kappa} = \boldsymbol{g} + \boldsymbol{s}, \qquad \boldsymbol{s} = \sum_j s_j \boldsymbol{b}_j / |\boldsymbol{b}_j| = \sum_j s_j a_j \boldsymbol{b}_j. \tag{A.24}$$

Then, with (A.13)–(A.18),

$$\boldsymbol{\kappa} \cdot \boldsymbol{r}_n = [n_1 h + n_2 k + n_3 l] + \sum_j n_j s_j a_j. \tag{A.25}$$

The term in square brackets is integer and can be omitted in the exponent of eq. (A.22). Thus:

$$F_L(\boldsymbol{\kappa}) = F_L(\boldsymbol{s}) = \sum_{\substack{n_j=1 \\ j=1,2,3}}^{N_j} \exp\left(-2\pi i \sum_j n_j s_j a_j\right). \tag{A.26}$$

For $s_j a_j \ll 1$, the argument in the exponent varies smoothly with varying the integers n_j. Thus, the summations can be replaced by an integration

$$F_L(\boldsymbol{s}) = \frac{1}{V_e} \int_{x_j=0}^{L_j} \exp\left(-2\pi i \sum_j s_j x_j\right) dx_1 \, dx_2 \, dx_3 \tag{A.27}$$

$$= \frac{\sin \pi s_1 L_1}{\pi s_1 a_1} \frac{\sin \pi s_2 L_2}{\pi s_2 a_2} \frac{\sin \pi s_3 L_3}{\pi s_3 a_3}, \tag{A.28}$$

with $L_j = N_j a_j$ denoting the length of the crystal in the direction of $\boldsymbol{a}_j$ and $V_e = a_1 a_2 a_3$. In eq. (A.28) a phase factor was omitted, since only $|F_L|^2$ is accessible by experiment.

An indication of the "structure" of the lattice factor $|F_L|^2$ in the reciprocal space is obtained by considering the square of one of the three factors of F_L, e.g.,

$$I_1(s_1) = \frac{\sin^2 \pi s_1 L_1}{\pi^2 s_1^2 a_1^2}. \tag{A.29}$$

References: p. 788.

The following properties of I_1 can be recognized: $I_1(s_1)$ is sharply peaked at $s_1 = 0$ where I_1 reaches the value N_1^2. In the tails I_1 oscillates and decreases proportional to s_1^{-2}. The first zero on both sides occurs at $|s_1| = 1/L_1 = 1/N_1 a_1$. Accordingly, the half-width of I_1 is about $1/N_1 a_1$. Thus, one may suppose that

$$\int I_1(s_1) ds_1 = \frac{N_1}{a_1}, \qquad (A.30)$$

which is indeed the case. (If eq. (A.26) is summed exactly, it turns out that the terms $\pi s_j a_j$ in the denominator of eq. (A.28) have to be replaced by $\sin \pi s_j a_j$. This small "error" in (A.28) is, however, without any practical relevance in general.)

Having understood the structure of $I_1(s_1)$, it is easy to understand the three-dimensional structures of $|F_L|^2$,

$$|F_L|^2 = I_1(s_1) \cdot I_2(s_2) \cdot I_3(s_3). \qquad (A.31)$$

Around every reciprocal lattice point g the intensity of $|F_L|^2$ is sharply peaked, and the shape of the peak is reciprocal to the shape of the crystal: parallel to a direction where the crystal is thin (L_j small), $|F_L|^2$ is broad, and parallel to a direction where the crystal is large (L_j large) $|F_L|^2$ is narrow. For instance, a plate-like crystal gives a rod-like structure of the peaks of $|F_L|^2$ and vice versa.

Now we proceed to the term $F_s(\kappa)$, cf. eq. (A.23). We recall that for N_1, N_2, $N_3 \gg 1$, the lattice factor $|F_L|^2$ is essentially $\neq 0$ only for κ close to g, or for $(h_1 h_2 h_3)$ close to (hkl). Further, we realize from eqs. (A.14) and (A.23) that F_s is, comparative to F_L, a smooth function of κ [or $(h_1 h_2 h_3)$]. Therefore, considering κ close to g it is allowed to approximate F_s by

$$F_s(h_1 h_2 h_3) \approx F_s(hkl) = \sum_{m \approx 1}^{M} f_m \exp\left[-2\pi i(h\xi_1^m + k\xi_2^m + l\xi_3^m)\right]. \qquad (A.32)$$

We consider $F_s(hkl)$ for some simple cubic lattices.

(i) face-centred cubic (fcc) lattice; four equivalent atoms in the unit cell are located at $r = [000]$, $\frac{1}{2}[011]$, $\frac{1}{2}[101]$, $\frac{1}{2}[110]$. Thus:

$$F_s(hkl) = f\{1 + \exp[-i\pi(k+l)] + \exp[-i\pi(h+l)] + \exp[-i\pi(h+k)]\}$$
$$= 4f \quad \text{for } h, k, l \text{ unmixed, i.e. all even or all uneven,}$$
$$= 0 \quad \text{for } h, k, l \text{ mixed.}$$

(ii) body-centred cubic (bcc) lattice; two equivalent atoms at $r = [000]$, $\frac{1}{2}[111]$. Then:

$$F_s(hkl) = 2f \quad \text{for } h + k + l = \text{even,}$$
$$= 0 \quad \text{for } h + k - l = \text{uneven.}$$

For these two types of Bravais lattices, F_s takes either full value (f multiplied with the number of atoms per unit cell) or vanishes.

(iii) Ordered lattice of type $L1_2$ (e.g. Cu_3Au); one atom of kind A in $r = [000]$, three atoms of kind B in $r = \frac{1}{2}[011]$, $\frac{1}{2}[101]$, $\frac{1}{2}[110]$. This gives:

$$F_s(hkl) = f_A + 3f_B \quad \text{for } hkl \text{ unmixed,}$$

$$= f_A - f_B \quad \text{for } hkl \text{ mixed.}$$

Lattice plane of the first category are called *fundamental* lattice planes and those of the second category are *superlattice* planes. The F_s-values of the latter are in general much smaller than those of the former.

A.5.   The Ewald sphere and Bragg's law

In order to decide whether a crystal gives rise to a diffracted beam for a given direction and a given wavelength of the incident radiation we introduce the so-called *Ewald Sphere* in the reciprocal lattice. Figure 35 gives a two-dimensional representation. A reciprocal lattice is schematically drawn and the wave vector k_0 of the primary beam is inserted in such a way that k_0 ends at the origin of the reciprocal lattice. A sphere, the Ewald sphere, is drawn around the starting point of k_0 (point C) with $|k_0| = k$ as radius. All vectors starting from C and ending on the Ewald sphere represent possible wave vectors k_s of diffracted waves of intensity $|F(\kappa)|^2$, with $\kappa = k_s - k_0$. If the Ewald sphere cuts a reciprocal lattice point g where $|F(\kappa)|^2$ takes high values a strong intensity will be diffracted in the direction of the particular wave vector k_s, named k_g, pointing from C to g. We denote the angle between k_0 and k_g by $2\theta_{hkl}$. Then we have:

$$|g_{hkl}| = 2k \sin \theta_{hkl}, \tag{A.33}$$

or with eq. (A.19):

$$\lambda = 2d_{hkl} \sin \theta_{hkl}. \tag{A.34}$$

This is *Bragg's law* with θ_{hkl} being the Bragg angle of the set of lattice planes (hkl).

These *Bragg peaks* (or "Bragg reflections") are not infinitely sharp but rather reveal a certain finite width (reciprocal to the crystal dimensions). Therefore, appreciable intensity will be diffracted not only for *one* discrete direction of k_0 but for a (more or less) small interval of directions. In the same way the wave vectors k_s of the diffracted beam will cover a similarly small interval of directions. Consequently, for a particular direction of k_0 the diffracted intensity I_{hkl} is given by a two-dimensional integration,

$$I_{hkl} = \int |F(\kappa)|^2 \frac{df_E}{k^2} \tag{A.35}$$

over the Ewald sphere in the neighbourhood of g_{hkl}. df_E/k^2 is a differential solid angle $d\Omega$ with df_E = differential area on the Ewald sphere.

In a practical diffraction experiment the crystal will be rocked with respect to k_0 over an angular interval so that the Ewald sphere is swept over the peak at the reciprocal lattice point under consideration. If effective source size and detector aperture are sufficiently large to capture all the intensity belonging to g, the

References: p. 788.

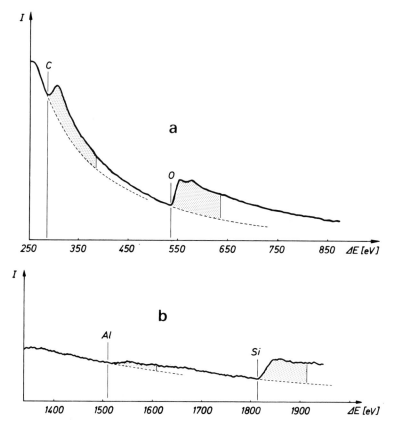

Fig. 34. Electron energy-loss spectrum of a 25 nm thick amorphous area in a silicon nitride ceramic. Edges in the spectrum are found at characteristic energy losses. The concentration of the different elements can be determined from the hatched areas: a) Energy losses 250–850 eV. b) Energy losses 1350–1950 eV. (From BISCHOFF [1983].)

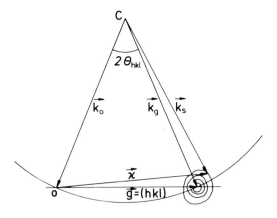

Fig. 35. The Ewald sphere and the intensity distribution $|F(\kappa)|^2$ in the reciprocal space.

diffracted intensity I_{hkl} is proportional to the integral over the diffraction spot,

$$I_{hkl} \propto \int |F(\kappa)|^2 \, d^3\kappa = \frac{N}{V_e} |F_s(hkl)|^2, \tag{A.36}$$

cf. § A.4, where the integration runs over the neighbourhood of g_{hkl}, N is the number of unit cells and $|F_s(hkl)|^2$ is the structure factor of the Bragg reflection (hkl).

A.6. The atomic scattering amplitudes and the Debye–Waller factor

In § A.1 we had assumed that the atoms are point-like scattering centres and that, consequently, the atomic scattering amplitudes, or atomic scattering lengths, are constants which are characteristic for the kind of atoms considered.

This assumption is a very good approximation for nuclear scattering of thermal neutrons having wavelengths of the order of 0.1 nm. Nuclear scattering occurs at the atomic nuclei the diameters of which are of the order of some 10^{-14} m, i.e., smaller by a factor of $\sim 10^4$ than the neutron wavelengths. In neutron diffraction physics it is customary to denote the atomic scattering length by the symbol b. In general b is positive and of the order of 10^{-14} m; however, for some isotopes b may be negative. Considered as a function of the atomic number Z or the atomic mass A, no smooth dependence of b on Z or A exists. The values of b may even vary considerably for different isotopes of a given element. However, apart from these variations the general trend is that b increases roughly proportional to $A^{1/3}$, i.e., to the size of the nuclei.

X-rays are (nearly) exclusively scattered by the electrons constituting the electron cloud of an atom. From Maxwell's equations it follows that a single electron scatters X-rays of wavelength of the order of 0.1 nm like a point-like scattering centre with a scattering amplitude f_0 with

$$f_0 = e^2 / (m_0 c^2) \approx 2.8 \times 10^{-15} \text{ m}, \tag{A.37}$$

where e is the elementary charge, m_0 is the rest mass of the electron and c is the velocity of light. Around an atomic nucleus, located at $r = 0$, the electrons are distributed according to a density function $\rho_e(r)$. If the atom of atomic number Z is neutral,

$$\int \rho_e(r) d^3r = Z. \tag{A.38}$$

Applying eq. (A.10b) we get for the atomic scattering amplitude

$$f_X = f_0 f_a(\kappa),$$

with

$$f_a(\kappa) = \int \rho_e(r) \exp(-2\pi i \kappa \cdot r) \, d^3r. \tag{A.39}$$

The index "X" stands for X-rays. The term f_a is named the *atomic form factor* and is tabulated in general as a function of $|\kappa|/2 = \sin\theta/\lambda$. Obviously, we have $f_a = Z$ for

References: p. 788.

$\sin \theta/\lambda = 0$. With increasing $\sin \theta/\lambda$, f decreases monotonously. In a very rough approximation it decreases to about half its maximum value for $\sin \theta/\lambda \approx 1/d_A$ where d_A is the atomic diameter.

Transmission electron microscopes operate at accelerating voltages U of 100 kV or higher. Taking $U = 100$ kV, we get the corresponding de Broglie wavelength from

$$\lambda = \frac{h}{\left[2m_0 eU \left(1 + \frac{eU}{2m_0 c^2} \right) \right]^{1/2}}, \tag{A.40}$$

giving $\lambda = 3.7$ pm (h = Planck's constant). The wavelengths of such electrons are thus smaller by a factor of about fifty than the wavelengths normally used in X-ray and neutron diffraction work. Because of Bragg's law [eq. (A.34)] the Bragg angles θ_{hkl} are also smaller by about the same factor. Electrons are scattered at an atom by the atomic electrostatic potential $V(r)$ built up by the charge $+Ze$ of the atomic nucleus and by the charge distribution $-e\rho_e(r)$ of the surrounding electron cloud. Since charge distribution and potential are linked by Poisson's equation,

$$\nabla^2 V(r) = 4\pi e \cdot \rho_e(r), \tag{A.41}$$

($\nabla^2 = \partial^2/\partial x^2 + \partial^2/\partial y^2 + \partial^2/\partial z^2$), the atomic scattering amplitudes for electrons are closely related to f_a. The result is

$$f_e(\sin \theta/\lambda) = \frac{m_0 e^2}{2h^2} \frac{Z - f_a(\sin \theta/\lambda)}{(\sin \theta/\lambda)^2}, \tag{A.42}$$

with $m_0 e^2/2h^2 = 2.39 \times 10^8/$m. f_e decreases rapidly (more rapidly than f_a) for small values of $\sin \theta/\lambda$ but only slowly, $\propto Z/(\sin \theta/\lambda)^2$, for large $\sin \theta/\lambda$, where f_a becomes small compared to Z. The value $f_e(0)$ will not be discussed here.

Diffracted intensities are proportional to the square of the atomic scattering amplitudes. In order to compare the different scattering strengths for neutron-, X-ray- and electron waves, we choose as a representative example the 200 Bragg reflection of a copper crystal. With $\sin \theta_{200}/\lambda = 1/2d_{200}$ we get for copper $\sin \theta_{200}/\lambda = 2.76$ nm^{-1}. Taking tabulated values for b, f_a and f_e we obtain:

neutron waves: $b^2 = 5.8 \cdot 10^{-29}$ m^2,

X-rays: $f_X^2 = 3.10^{-27}$ m^2,

electron waves: $f_e^2 = 8.7 \cdot 10^{-20}$ m^2.

It is obvious that neutrons are least effectively scattered and that electron scattering is orders of magnitude stronger than X-ray scattering. For Bragg reflections of high order ($|g_{hkl}|$ large or d_{hkl} small), the difference between neutron and X-ray scattering becomes less spectacular, because f_X decreases, but not b, with increasing $\sin \theta/\lambda$.

There is another effect which reduces the intensities of Bragg reflections with increasing $|g|$ (or decreasing d) even for "perfect" crystals: The atoms are not at rest because of thermal vibrations. This leads to an additional "smearing-out" in space of the scattering power of the individual atoms. If $\langle u_t^2 \rangle$ is the mean square displacement of an atom from its ideal lattice position by thermal vibration the atomic scattering amplitudes f have to be multiplied by a factor e^{-M}, with

$$M = 8\pi^2 \langle u_t^2 \rangle \frac{\sin^2 \theta}{\lambda^2}. \tag{A.43}$$

Of course, $\langle u_t^2 \rangle$ increases with temperature T. For $T > \Theta_D$, where Θ_D is the *Debye temperature* (for copper, $\Theta_D = 320$ K), $\langle u_t^2 \rangle$, and thus M, increases about linearly with T. The diffracted intensities are damped by the factor e^{-2M}. Because $M \propto g^2$, this damping is particularly effective for high-order reflections. The factor e^{-M} is named Debye-Waller factor.

A.7. Imperfect crystals

The Debye–Waller factor as an unavoidable consequence of thermal vibrations is but one example for the effect of displacements of atoms from ideal lattice positions. Apart from thermal displacements, "static" displacements are usually encountered with lattice defects, e.g., stacking faults, point defects, dislocations (including solute atoms), clusters and coherent precipitates. Displacements will generally vary with the position in the crystal. Let r_n denote the position for the nth unit cell of the ideal reference lattice and $R_n = R(r_n)$ the displacement of the first atom in this cell, R_{nm} are the corresponding displacements from the other ideal positions r_{nm} in the nth cell. A factorization of $|F(\kappa)|^2$ as in eq. (A.21) is now no longer possible. Instead, we can write:

$$F(\kappa) = \sum_n F_{sn}(\kappa) \exp(-2\pi i \kappa \cdot r_n) \exp(-2\pi i \kappa \cdot R_n), \tag{A.44}$$

with

$$F_{sn}(\kappa) = \sum_m f_{nm} \exp(-2\pi i \kappa \cdot r_{nm}) \exp\left[-2\pi i \kappa \cdot (R_{nm} - R_n)\right] \tag{A.45}$$

for the structure amplitude of the nth cell.

Equation (A.45) shows that *positional disorder* alone leads to different structure amplitudes for different cells. Furthermore, eq. (A.45) also shows the general effect of *compositional* disorder (chemical disorder), as f_{nm} reflects exactly the occupation of the various sites by different atoms. In the special case, where compositional disorder is not considered and where the displacement vector R_{nm} can be regarded as constant for all atoms of the elementary cell, the structure amplitude $F_s(\kappa)$ remains unchanged, and using eqs. (A.24) and (A.25) the lattice amplitude F_L can be written in the integral form:

$$F_L(\kappa) = \frac{1}{V_e} \int_{V_s} \exp\{-2\pi i [g \cdot R(r) + s \cdot r + s \cdot R(r)]\} \, d^3 r, \tag{A.46}$$

where the integration runs over the sample volume V_s. In many cases the term $s \cdot R$

References: p. 788.

can be neglected. These general expressions are the basis for more detailed evaluations in chs. 11 and 12 where several special cases are discussed.

References

AMELINCKX, S., 1964, The Direct Observations of Dislocations (Academic, New York).

AMELINCKX, S., and J. VAN LANDUYT, 1978, in: Diffraction and Imaging Techniques in Material Science, eds. S. Amelinckx, R. Gevers and J. Van Landuyt (North-Holland, Amsterdam) vol. I, p. 107.

AMELINCKX, S., R. GEVERS and J. VAN LANDUYT, eds., 1978, Diffraction and Imaging Techniques in Material Science, vols. I and II (North-Holland, Amsterdam).

ANDREWS, K.W., D.J. DYSON and S.R. KEOWN, 1971, Interpretation of Electron Diffraction Patterns (Adam Hilger, London).

ASHBY, M.F., and L.M. BROWN, 1963, Phil. Mag. **8**, 1093 and 1649.

BACMAN, J.-J., G. SILVESTRE and M. PETIT, 1981, Phil. Mag. **A43**, 189.

BALL, C.J., 1964, Phil. Mag. **9**, 541.

BALLUFFI, R.W., ed., 1980, Grain-Boundary Structure and Kinetics (ASM, Metals Park, OH).

BALLUFFI, R.W., A. BROKMAN and A.H. KING, 1982, Acta Metall. **30**, 1453.

BERTIN, E.P., 1975, Principles and Practice of X-Ray Spectrometric Analysis (Plenum, New York).

BETHE, H.A., 1928, Ann. Phys. (Leipzig) **87**, 55.

BETHE, H.A., 1933, Handbuch der Physik, vol. 24 (Springer, Berlin) p. 273.

BISCHOFF, E., 1983, unpublished.

BONNET, R., 1981, Phil. Mag. **A43**, 1165.

BONNET, R., E. COUSINEAU and D.H. WARRINGTON, 1981, Acta Cryst. **A37**, 184.

BOURRET, A., and J. DESSEAUX, 1979, Phil. Mag. **A39**, 405.

BOURRET, A., J. DESSEAUX and A. RENAULT, 1982, Phil. Mag. **A45**, 1.

BROKMAN, A., and R.W. BALLUFFI, 1981, Acta Metall. **29**, 1703.

CHADWICK, G.A., and D.A. SMITH, eds., 1976, Grain-Boundary Structure and Properties (Academic, London).

CHAMPNESS, P.E., G. CLIFF and G.W. LORIMER, 1982, Ultramicroscopy **8**, 121.

CHIK, K.P., 1966, Phys. Stat. Sol. **16**, 685.

CHIK, K.P., M. WILKENS and M. RÜHLE, 1967, Phys. Stat. Sol. **23**, 113.

CLAREBROUGH, L.M., and C.T. FORWOOD, 1976, in: Proc. 9th Int. Congress on Electron Microscopy, ed. J.M. Sturgess (Microscopical Society of Canada, Toronto) vol. II p. 38.

CLIFF, G., and G.W. LORIMER, 1975, J. Microsc. **103**, 203.

COCKAYNE, D.J.H., 1978, in: Diffraction and Imaging Techniques in Material Science, eds. S. Amelinckx, R. Gevers and J. Van Landuyt (North-Holland, Amsterdam) vol. I, p. 153.

COCKAYNE, D.J.H., and R. GRONSKY, 1981, Phil. Mag. **A44**, 159.

COCKAYNE, D.J.H., I.L.F. RAY and M.J. WHELAN, 1969, Phil. Mag. **20**, 1265.

DAHMEN, U., K.H. WESTMACOTT and G. THOMAS, 1981, Acta Metall. **29**, 627.

DAS, S.K., P.R. OKAMOTO, P.M.J. FISHER and G. THOMAS, 1973, Acta Metall. **21**, 913.

EGERTON, R.F., 1979, Ultramicroscopy **4**, 169.

EGERTON, R.F., 1981, in: Analytical Electron Microscopy 1981, ed. R.H. Geiss (San Francisco Press, San Francisco) vol. I, p. 154.

ENGLISH, C., B.L. EYRE and S.M. HOLMES, 1980, J. Phys. **F10**, 1065.

ESSMANN, U., 1966, Phys. Stat. Sol. **17**, 725.

EYRE, B.L., and R. BULLOUGH, 1965, Phil. Mag. **12**, 31.

EYRE, B.L., D.M. MAHER and R.C. PERRIN, 1977, J. Phys. **F7**, 1359 and 1371.

FLORJANCIC, M., M. RÜHLE and S.L. SASS, 1982, in: Proc. 10th Int. Congress on Electron Microscopy, (Deutsche Gesellschaft für Elektronenmikroskopie, Frankfurt) vol. 2, p. 359.

FÖLL, H., and M. WILKENS, 1975, Phys. Stat. Sol. (a) **31**, 519.

Föll, H., and M. Wilkens, 1977, Phys. Stat. Sol. (a) **39**, 561.

Geiss, R.H., 1979, in: Introduction to Analytical Electron Microscopy, eds. J.J. Hren, J.I. Goldstein and D.C. Joy (Plenum, New York) p. 43.

Geiss, R.H., ed., 1981, Analytical Electron Microscopy 1981, vols. I and II (San Francisco Press, San Francisco).

Gevers, R., 1962, Phil. Mag. **7**, 59 and 651.

Gevers, R., A. Art and S. Amelinckx, 1963, Phys. Stat. Sol. **3**, 1563.

Gevers, R., J. Van Landuyt and S. Amelinckx, 1965, Phys. Stat. Sol. **11**, 689.

Goldstein, J.I., and D.B. Williams, 1981, in: Quantitative Microanalysis with High Spatial Resolution, eds. G.W. Lorimer, M.H. Jacobs and P. Doig (The Metals Society, London) p. 5.

Goldstein, J.I., J.L. Costley, G.W. Lorimer, and S.J.B. Reed, 1977, in: Scanning Electron Microscopy 1977, ed. O. Johari (IIT Research Inst., Chicago, IL) vol. I, p. 315.

Goldstein, J.I., D.E. Newbury, P. Echlin, D.C. Joy, C. Fiori and E. Lifshin, 1981, Scanning Electron Microscopy and X-Ray Microanalysis (Plenum, New York).

Gratias, D., R. Portier, M. Fayard and M. Guymot, 1979, Acta Cryst. **A35**, 885.

Häussermann, F., M. Rühle and M. Wilkens, 1972, Phys. Stat. Sol. (b) **50**, 445.

Häussermann, F., K.H. Katerbau, M. Rühle and M. Wilkens, 1973, J. Microsc. **98**, 135.

Hashimoto, H., A. Howie and M.J. Whelan, 1960, Phil. Mag. **5**, 967.

Hashimoto, H., A. Howie and M.J. Whelan, 1962, Proc. Roy. Soc. **A269**, 80.

Hawkes, P.W., ed., 1980, Computer Processing of Electron Microscope Images, Topics in Current Physics, vol. 13 (Springer, Berlin).

Hazzledine, P.M., H.P. Karnthaler and E. Wintner, 1975, Phil. Mag. **32**, 81.

Head, A.K., P. Humble, L.M. Clarebrough, A.J. Morton and C.T. Forwood, 1973, Computer Electron Micrographs and Defect Identification (North-Holland, Amsterdam).

Hirsch, P.B., A. Howie and M.J. Whelan, 1960, Phil. Trans. Roy. Soc. **A252**, 499.

Hirsch, P.B., A. Howie, R.B. Nicholson, D.W. Pashley and M.J. Whelan, 1977, Electron Microscopy of Thin Films (Krieger, Huntington, NY).

Howie, A., and Z.S. Basinski, 1968, Phil. Mag. **17**, 1039.

Howie, A., and M.J. Whelan, 1961, Proc. Roy. Soc. **A263**, 217.

Howie, A., and M.J. Whelan, 1962, Proc. Roy. Soc. **A267**, 206.

Hren, J.J., 1979, in: Introduction to Analytical Electron Microscopy, eds. J.J. Hren, J.I. Golstein and D.C. Joy (Plenum, New York) p. 481.

Hren, J.J., J.I. Goldstein and D.C. Joy, eds., 1979, Introduction to Analytical Electron Microscopy (Plenum, New York).

Humble, P., 1978, in: Diffraction and Imaging Techniques in Material Science, eds. S. Amelinckx, R. Gevers and J. Van Landuyt (North-Holland, Amsterdam) vol. I, p. 315.

Humble, P., and C.T. Forwood, 1975, Phil. Mag. **31**, 1011 and 1025.

Jäger, W., and M. Wilkens, 1975, Phys. Stat. Sol. **32**, 89.

Jenkins, M.L., and M. Wilkens, 1976, Phil. Mag. **34**, 1155.

Jouffrey, B., Y. Kihn, J.P. Perez, J. Sevely and G. Zanchi, 1978, in: Proc. 9th Int. Congress on Electron Microscopy, ed. J.M. Sturgess (Microscopical Society of Canada, Toronto) vol. III, p. 292.

Joy, D.C., 1981, in: Quantitative Microanalysis with High Spatial Resolution, eds. G.W. Lorimer, M.H. Jacobs and P. Doig (The Metals Society, London) p. 127.

Joy, D., and D.M. Maher, 1980, Ultramicroscopy **5**, 333.

Kalonji, G., and J.W. Cahn, 1982, J. Physique **C6**, 25.

Katerbau, K.H., 1976, Phys. Stat. Sol. (a) **38**, 463.

Katerbau, K.H., 1980, Phys. Stat. Sol. (a) **59**, 211.

Katerbau, K.H., 1981, Phil. Mag. **A43**, 409.

Kelly, P.M., A. Jostsons, R.G. Blake and J.G. Napier, 1975, Phys. Stat. Sol. (a) **31**, 77.

Khachaturyan, A.G., 1974, in: Order–Disorder Transformations in Alloys, ed. H. Warlimont (Springer, Berlin) p. 114.

Korner, A., and H.P. Karnthaler, 1980, Phil. Mag. **A42**, 753.

KORNER, A., and H.P. KARNTHALER, 1981, Phys. Stat. Sol. (a) **68**, 19.

KRAHL, D., K.-H. HERMANN and W. KUNATH, 1978, in: Proc. 9th Int. Congress on Electron Microscopy, ed. J.M. Sturgess (Microscopical Society of Canada, Toronto) vol. I, p. 42.

KRIVANEK, O.L., and P.R. SWANN, 1981, in: Quantitative Microanalysis with High Spatial Resolution (The Metals Society, London) p. 136.

KRIVANEK, O.L., S. ISODA and K. KOBAYASHI, 1977, Phil. Mag. **36**, 331.

LAFFONT, A., and R. BONNET, 1982, Acta Metall. **30**, 763.

LEAPMAN, R.D., S.J. SANDERSON and M.J. WHELAN, 1978, Met. Sci. **23**, 215.

LEPSKI, D., 1974, Phys. Stat. Sol. (a) **24**, 99.

LEPSKI, D., and P. BURCK, 1981, Phys. Stat. Sol. (a) **64**, 625.

LEPSKI, D., and P. BURCK, 1982, Phys. Stat. Sol. (a) **70**, 571.

LORIMER, G.W., M.H. JACOBS and P. DOIG, eds., 1981, Quantitative Microanalysis with High Spatial Resolution (The Metals Society, London).

MAHER, D.M., and B.L. EYRE, 1971, Phil. Mag. **23**, 409.

MATHEWS, J.W., and W.M. STOBBS, 1977, Phil. Mag. **36**, 373.

MCINTYRE, K.G., and L.M. BROWN, 1966, J. Physique **27**, C3-178.

NIEDRIG, H., 1978, Scanning **1**, 17.

OLSON, G.B., and M. COHEN, 1979, Acta Metall. **27**, 1907.

PENISSON, J.M., R. GRONSKY and J.B. BROSSE, 1982, Scripta Metall. **16**, 1239.

POGANY, A.P., and P.S. TURNER, 1968, Acta Cryst. **A24**, 103.

POND, R.C., 1979, Phil. Mag. **37**, 699.

POWELL, C.J., 1976, in: National Bureau of Standards, Spec. Publ. 460, eds. K.K.J. Heinrich, D.E. Newbury and H. Yakowitz (National Bureau of Standards, Washington) p. 97.

RADI, G., 1970, Acta Cryst. **A26**, 41.

ROSSOUW, C.J., R.F. EGERTON and M.J. WHELAN, 1976, Vacuum **26**, 427.

RÜHLE, M., 1967, Phys. Stat. Sol. **19**, 263 and 279.

RÜHLE, M., and G. PETZOW, 1981, in: Surface and Interfaces in Ceramic and Ceramic–Metal Systems, eds. J. Pask and A. Evans (Plenum, New York) p. 167.

RÜHLE, M., and M. WILKENS, 1967, Phil. Mag. **15**, 1075.

RÜHLE, M., and M. WILKENS, 1975, Cryst. Lattice Defects **6**, 129.

SALDIN, D.K., A.Y. STATHOPOULOS and M.J. WHELAN, 1978, Inst. Phys. Conf. Ser. No. **41**, 350.

SASS, S.L., and P.D. BRISTOWE, 1980, in: Grain-Boundary Structure and Kinetics, ed. R.W. Balluffi (ASM, Metals Park, OH) p. 71.

SCHOBER, T., and R.W. BALLUFFI, 1969, Phil. Mag. **20**, 511.

SHANNON, J., and L. KATZ, 1970, Acta Cryst **B26**, 102.

SIEMS, R., P. DELAVIGNETTE and S. AMELINCKX, 1962, Phys. Stat. Sol. **2**, 421.

SINCLAIR, R., R. GRONSKY and G. THOMAS, 1976, Acta Metall. **24**, 789.

SMITH, D.A., 1976, in: Grain-Boundary Structure and Properties, eds. G.A. Chadwick and D.A. Smith (Academic, London) p. 321.

SPENCE, J.C.H., 1981, Experimental High-Resolution Electron Microscopy (Clarendon Press, Oxford).

SPENCE, J.C.H., and H. KOLAR, 1979, Phil. Mag. **A39**, 59.

STEEDS, J.W., 1966, Proc. Roy. Soc. **A292**, 343.

STEEDS, J.W., 1979, in: Introduction to Analytical Electron Microscopy, eds. J.J. Hren, J.I. Goldstein and D.C. Joy (Plenum, New York) p. 481.

STEEDS, J.W., 1981, in: Quantitative Microanalysis with High Spatial Resolution, eds. G.W. Lorimer, M.H. Jacobs and P. Doig (The Metals Society, London) p. 210.

STOBBS, W.M., and C.H. SWORNE, 1971, Phil. Mag. **24**, 1365.

TAKAGI, S., 1962, Acta Cryst. **15**, 1310.

THOMAS, G., and M.J. GORINGE, 1979, Transmission Electron Microscopy of Materials (Wiley, New York).

THOMPSON-RUSSELL, K.C., and J.W. EDINGTON, 1977, in: Practical Electron Microscopy in Materials Science, vol. 5 (Mac Millan, London).

TIGHE, N.J., 1976, in: Electron Microscopy in Mineralogy, ed. H.R. Wenk (Springer, Berlin).

TUNSTALL, W.J., P.B. HIRSCH, and J.W. STEEDS, 1964, Phil. Mag. **9**, 99.

VAN LANDUYT, J., R. GEVERS and S. AMELINCKX, 1965, Phys. Stat. Sol. **10**, 319.

VAN TENDELOO, G., and S. AMELINCKX, 1977, Phys. Stat. Sol. (a) **43**, 553.

VAN TENDELOO, G., and S. AMELINCKX, 1978, Phys. Stat. Sol. (a) **50**, 53.

WENK, H.R., 1976, Electron Microscopy in Mineralogy (Springer, Berlin).

WILKENS, M., 1964, Phys. Stat. Sol. **6**, 939.

WILKENS, M., 1978, in: Diffraction and Imaging Techniques in Material Science, eds. S. Amelinckx, R. Gevers and J. Van Landuyt (North-Holland, Amsterdam) vol. I, p. 185.

WILKENS, M., 1981, Phys. Stat. Sol. (a) **69**, 123.

WILKENS, M., and E. HORNBOGEN, 1964, Phys. Stat. Sol. **4**, 557.

WILKENS, M., and H.O.K. KIRCHNER, 1981, Phil. Mag. **A43**, 139.

WILKENS, M., and M. RÜHLE, 1982, Phys. Stat. Sol. (b) **49**, 749.

WILKENS, M., M. RÜHLE and F. HÄUSSERMANN, 1967, Phys. Stat. Sol. **22**, 689.

WILKENS, M., K.H. KATERBAU and M. RÜHLE, 1973, Z. Naturf. **28a**, 681.

WILKENS, M., M.L. JENKINS and K.H. KATERBAU, 1977, Phys. Stat. Sol. (a) **39**, 103.

ZANCHI, G., J. SEVELY and B. JOUFFREY, 1977, in: Proc. 5th Int. Conf. on High Voltage Electron Microscopy, Kyoto, eds. T. Imura and H. Hashimoto (Japanese Society for Electron Microscopy, Tokyo) p. 117.

General bibliography for transmission electron microscopy

Textbooks

Amelinckx, S., R. Gevers and J. Van Landuyt, eds., 1978, Diffraction and Imaging Techniques in Material Science, vols. I and II (North-Holland, Amsterdam).

Bethge, H., and J. Heydenreich, eds., 1982, Elektronenmikroskopie in der Festkörperphysik (Springer, Berlin).

Cowley, J.M., 1975, Diffraction Physics (North-Holland, Amsterdam).

Head, A.K., P. Humble, L.M. Clarebrough, A.J. Morton and C.T. Forwood, 1973, Computer Electron Micrographs and Defect Identification (North-Holland, Amsterdam).

Hirsch, P.B., A. Howie, R.B. Nicholson, D.W. Pashley and M.J. Whelan, 1977, Electron Microscopy of Thin Crystals (Krieger, Huntington, NY).

Hornbogen, E., 1971, Durchstrahlungs-Elektronenmikroskopie fester Stoffe (Verlag Chemie, Weinheim).

Reimer, L., 1967, Elektronenmikroskopische Untersuchungs- und Präparationsmethoden (Springer, Berlin).

Thomas, G., and M.J. Goringe, 1979, Transmission Electron Microscopy of Materials (Wiley, New York).

Evaluation of diffraction patterns

Andrews, K.W., D.J. Dyson and S.R. Keown, 1971, Interpretation of Electron Diffraction Patterns (Adam Hilger, London).

Observation of dislocations

Amelinckx, S., 1964, The Direct Observation of Dislocations (Academic, Oxford).

Amelinckx, S., 1979, Dislocations in Particular Structures, in: Dislocations in Solids, ed. F.R.N. Nabarro (North-Holland, Amsterdam) vol. II, ch. 6.

TEM of grain boundaries

Balluffi, R.W., 1980, Grain-Boundary Structure and Kinetics (ASM, Metals Park, OH).

Chadwick, G.A., and D.A. Smith, eds., 1976, Grain-Boundary Structure and Properties (Academic, London).

Analytical electron microscopy

Geiss, R.H., ed., 1981, Microbeam Analysis 1981, vols. I and II (San Francisco Press, San Francisco).

Goldstein, J.I., D.E. Newbury, P. Echlin, D.C. Joy, C. Fiori and E. Lifshin, 1981, Scanning Electron Microscopy and X-Ray Microanalysis (Plenum, New York).

Hren, J.J., J.I. Goldstein and D.C. Joy, eds., 1979, Introduction to Analytical Electron Microscopy (Plenum, New York).

Lorimer, G.W., M.H. Jacobs and P. Doig, eds., 1981, Quantitative Microanalysis with High Spatial Resolution (The Metals Society, London).

High-resolution electron microscopy

Hawkes, P.W., ed., 1980, Computer Processing of Electron Microscope Images, Topics in Current Physics, vol. 13 (Springer, Berlin).

Spence, J.C.H., 1981, Experimental High-Resolution Electron Microscopy (Clarendon Press, Oxford).

Microscopy of Minerals

Wenk, H.-R., 1976, Electron Microscopy in Mineralogy (Springer, Berlin).

CHAPTER 12

X-RAY AND NEUTRON SCATTERING

G. KOSTORZ

Institut für Angewandte Physik
Eidgenössische Technische Hochschule
Zürich, Switzerland

R.W. Cahn and P. Haasen, eds.
Physical Metallurgy; third, revised and enlarged edition
© *Elsevier Science Publishers BV, 1983*

1. Introduction

The list of textbooks and monographs on X-ray and neutron scattering is long (see the selection at the end of this chapter), and the number of publications is immense. This short chapter cannot give a complete account of the history or the current state of the field. The basic theory, standard methods and many of the more classical applications are well described in various textbooks (a brief compendium of fundamentals of scattering and crystallography is given in ch. 11, appendix). The main purpose of the present chapter will be to demonstrate that there is much more we can "learn from scattering experiments besides the average structure" (SCHWARTZ and COHEN [1977], Ch. 7).

One immediate question concerns the range of stability of a given structure, and scattering experiments are helpful to locate phase transformations. There are classical methods (e.g. powder diffraction) and very sophisticated recent techniques (e.g. quasi-elastic neutron scattering) to study transformations and phase separation in metallic systems. Some examples will be discussed. Much space, however, will be devoted to studies of inhomogeneities, i.e. deviations from the average structure (point defects, clusters, short-range order, precipitates, etc.).

In §2, some remarks on scattering from crystalline material containing defects are followed by a discussion of X-rays and neutrons as the two types of radiation now commonly used for scattering studies of essentially bulk materials. Scattering of low-energy electrons, important in the investigation of surfaces and surface phenomena, will not be covered. High-energy electron diffraction is discussed in ch. 11.

In §2 and subsequent sections, scattering intensities are expressed in terms of scattering cross-sections (differential cross-sections without energy analysis, double-differential cross-sections for scattering experiments with energy analysis, mostly applicable to both X-rays and neutrons). The reader should not underestimate the difficulties in converting measured intensities to absolute cross-sections. Calibration, absorption, background, polarization and other corrections may introduce considerable errors. These problems and questions of instrument design and optimization can only be mentioned occasionally.

§§3–6 cover recent applications, and the subject matter has been divided according to simple criteria. Diffraction and elastic scattering, at and near Bragg peaks, between Bragg peaks and near the incident beam are treated in §§3–5, and §6 gives a few examples for inelastic and quasi-elastic scattering. Like any formal pattern, this one has its deficiencies, too, but it is hoped that some coherency prevails. Theoretical expressions are kept to a minimum but some are required to demonstrate the main effects. There are several systematically elegant and quite general schemes to describe the same scattering phenomena (starting, e.g., from lattice sums, correlation functions or convolutions). No formal elaboration of this type will be attempted. Results of the kinematical theory and of first-order Born approximation adapted to simple but manageable cases will mostly be relied upon. Dynamic diffraction theory as the basis of transmission electron microscopy is discussed in ch. 11, and related X-ray and neutron applications can be found there.

2. Scattering from real crystals

2.1. General predictions of the kinematical theory

As can be seen in ch. 11, eq. (A.29), the kinematical scattering theory for an otherwise perfect, but finite crystal yields Bragg peaks whose width $\Delta\kappa_g$ equals $1/L_\kappa$ where L_κ is the linear dimension of the crystal parallel to κ. As $\Delta\kappa_g$ is independent of the magnitude of g, this "finite size effect" broadening can be recognized by comparing the width of different Bragg peaks (at Bragg angles θ_{hkl}). For powders, we thus have a method of determining crystallite sizes, as a constant $\Delta\kappa$ means:

$$2\Delta\theta_{hkl} \approx \frac{\lambda}{L \cos \theta_{hkl}}, \tag{1}$$

with L as the average crystallite diameter. However, experimental conditions will severely limit the range where peak widths are controlled by the crystallite size according to eq. (1). If L is too large ($\geq 1\ \mu$m), we may reach the resolution limit of the experiment, and if L is too small (≤ 100 Å $= 10$ nm), it becomes difficult to separate the diffraction lines (see, e.g., BARRETT and MASSALSKI [1980] for a detailed discussion). For large bulk samples, the size broadening may be ignored, and the differential cross-section for Bragg scattering may be written as [cf. eq. (A.36), ch. 11]:

$$\left(\frac{d\sigma}{d\Omega}\right)_B = N|F_s|^2 \frac{\delta(\kappa - g)}{V_c}, \tag{2}$$

where $\delta(\kappa - g)$ is the delta function and V_c is the unit-cell volume. Nevertheless, a line or peak broadening is frequently found in real crystals – caused by imperfections.

We discuss the consequences of imperfections on the scattering pattern starting from the general expressions given in §A.7 of ch. 11. If defects are present in a crystal, the displacements u_n and the structure amplitudes F_{sn} will be different in different cells. For specific defects it is useful to express these quantities in terms of the properties of individual defects and their mutual arrangement. If t denotes all possible positions for a defect, and u_{tn} is the displacement vector at position n related to the defect at t, the total displacement u_n may be expressed as

$$u_n = \sum_t c_t u_{tn}, \tag{3}$$

where

$$c_t = \begin{cases} 1 & \text{if a defect is present at site } t, \\ 0 & \text{if } no \text{ defect is present at site } t. \end{cases} \tag{4}$$

This simple superposition is certainly justified for low defect concentrations but may be questionable in the case of concentrated alloys.

The corresponding expression for the structure amplitude of the nth cell reads

$$F_{sn} = F_{s0} + \sum_t c_t \Delta F_{stn}, \tag{5}$$

References: p. 847.

where F_{s0} is the structure amplitude of the defect-free crystal. Replacing u_n and F_{sn} in eq. (A.44), ch. 11 by eqs. (3) and (5), the mean value for $|F(\kappa)|^2$, i.e. the scattering cross-section $d\sigma/d\Omega$ of the scattering ensemble, calculated for a random distribution of defects of concentration c, is (see KRIVOGLAZ [1969]):

$$\frac{d\sigma}{d\Omega} = \sum_{n,n'} \left\{ \exp\left[-2\pi \, i\kappa \cdot (r_n - r_{n'}) \right] \right\} e^{-\mathcal{T}}$$

$$\times \left\{ |\bar{F}_s|^2 + c \sum_t \Delta F_{stn} \Delta F_{stn'}^* \exp\left[-2\pi \, i\kappa \cdot (u_{tn} - u_{tn'}) \right] \right\}, \tag{6}$$

where

$$\mathcal{T} = c \sum_t \left\{ 1 - \exp\left[-2\pi \, i\kappa \cdot (u_{tn} - u_{tn'}) \right] \right\} \left[1 + \frac{1}{F_{s0}} \left(\Delta F_{stn} + \Delta F_{stn'} \right) \right], \tag{7}$$

and $\bar{F}_s$ is the average structure amplitude of the crystal with defects:

$$\bar{F}_s = F_{s0} + c \sum_t \Delta F_{stn}. \tag{8}$$

It is now possible to split $d\sigma/d\Omega$ into two terms, a Bragg-like term with sharp maxima at the Bragg positions, and a second term describing scattering for all other scattering vectors. Taking into account that for the Bragg peaks, $d\sigma/d\Omega$ from the double sum of eq. (6) is controlled by terms corresponding to large distances $\rho = |r_n - r_{n'}|$, we may write:

$$\left(\frac{d\sigma}{d\Omega} \right)_B = N |\bar{F}_s|^2 \, e^{-2M} \frac{\delta(\kappa - g)}{V_c}, \tag{9}$$

where $2M$ is the real part of $\mathcal{T}$ according to eq. (7) for $\rho \to \infty$:

$$2M = c \lim_{\rho \to \infty} \sum_t \left\{ 1 - \cos\left[2\pi\kappa \cdot (u_{tn} - u_{tn'}) \right] \right\} \left[1 + \frac{\Delta F_{stn} + \Delta F_{stn'}}{F_{s0}} \right]. \tag{10}$$

Equation (9) defines a generalized Debye–Waller factor e^{-M}. The reciprocal lattice vectors g occurring in eq. (9) are defined in the average lattice *containing* defects. Defects may cause a shift of Bragg peaks because the average lattice constant changes, but also a reduction in intensity due to the factor e^{-2M} [eqs. (9) and (10)]. As long as $2M$ remains finite, Bragg peaks will still be present, but there are cases where $2M$ tends to infinity.

If we subtract the Bragg intensity according to eq. (9) from the total scattering cross-section, eq. (6) we obtain the *diffuse scattering* cross-section

$$\left(\frac{d\sigma}{d\Omega} \right)_d = \frac{d\sigma}{d\Omega} - \left(\frac{d\sigma}{d\Omega} \right)_B. \tag{11}$$

The cross-section $(d\sigma/d\Omega)_d$ contains no δ-function but varies smoothly with κ, even for an infinitely large crystal. KRIVOGLAZ [1969] distinguishes two types of defects depending on whether or not the Bragg intensities are reduced to zero [eq. (9) with $2M \to \infty$]. The limiting behaviour of $2M$ [eq. (10)] may be discussed by considering

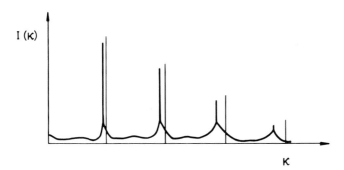

Fig. 1. Scattering from a crystal containing defects. The Bragg positions of a perfect crystal are indicated by thin vertical lines.

a displacement u_{tn}i that falls off rapidly towards zero with increasing distance between t and n. Then, only one of the displacements u (and one of the ΔF_s) is markedly different from zero, and:

$$M = c \sum_t \left[1 - \cos(2\pi\kappa \cdot u_{tn})\right] \left(1 + \frac{\Delta F_{stn}}{F_{s0}}\right). \tag{12}$$

The convergence of the sum depends on the contributions from large distances between n and t. There, u_{tn} is small and the cosine can be expanded, so that $1 - \cos(2\pi\kappa \cdot u_{tn}) = (2\pi\kappa \cdot u_{tn})^2/2$, and if one writes u_{tn} as a continuous function of $r' = r_t - r_n$, the convergence of the integral $\int (\kappa \cdot u_{tn})^2 \, d^3r'$, $\infty \geq r' > r'_0$ ($\gg$ lattice constant), will assure a finite value of M. We see that for a large class of defects where $u \propto (r')^{-2}$ (see ch. 17), M remains finite. Others, e.g. straight dislocations, small-angle grain boundaries and stacking faults, cause e^{-2M} to decrease to very small values for large crystals, and the total scattering is diffuse although it will be concentrated, but not in a δ-like fashion, near the original Bragg positions (*line broadening*).

The distinction between Bragg intensity [eq. (9)] and diffuse intensity (line broadening and scattering far away from Bragg peaks), discussed here for systems with a random distribution of equivalent defects, will not always be possible experimentally, as the width of the Bragg peak is also affected by the resolution function of the instrument. Correlations in the arrangement of defects may reduce long-range displacements and modify the expected effect, as will the presence of different types of defects. Figure 1 shows schematically, how the scattering of an ideal crystal is modified by defects.

2.2. X-rays and neutrons

Apart from electrons (see ch. 11) X-rays (and γ-rays) and thermal neutrons are frequently used for structure determination and the study of defects as they provide the appropriate range of wavelengths for such investigations. Table 1 gives some of the important properties of both types of radiation. For the wavelengths of interest in normal diffraction work (0.5 to 20 Å), corresponding photon energies are in the range of about 1–40 keV whereas neutron energies are between 0.85 and 400 meV. Excitations in condensed matter (phonons, magnons etc.) are in the range of a few meV. The relative energy change of X-rays scattered inelastically (with energy loss or gain) by the sample is then very small ($\leq 10^{-6}$) and cannot normally be resolved (except if Mössbauer sources or synchrotron radiation combined with backscattering techniques are used).

In contrast, neutrons can suffer an appreciable relative change in energy, so that elastic (no energy change) and inelastic scattering can be distinguished (see below, §2.4). Another important difference arises from the magnetic moment of the neutron which interacts with the local magnetization density. This leads to *magnetic scattering* which has very important applications as a sensitive probe in the study of magnetic substances (see §2.3). Finally, absorption differs appreciably for the two types of radiation. (Measurements of absorption can also yield considerable insight in the structure of matter, e.g. in EXAFS = extended X-ray absorption fine structure, see §5.4.) The linear absorption coefficient Σ_t is defined by

$$\ln(I/I_0) = -\Sigma_t D_s, \tag{13}$$

where I_0 and I are the intensities of incident and transmitted beam, respectively, and D_s is the sample thickness. The absorption coefficient has the dimension of 1/length or area/volume, and can be understood as a total macroscopic removal cross-section, as is common in neutron scattering. In the X-ray literature, a mass absorption coefficient is defined by Σ_t/ρ with ρ = density. Its dimensions are area/mass, and values are independent of the state of the matter.

All beam-attenuating processes (including coherent and incoherent scattering) are included in Σ_t, but for X-rays the excitation of fluorescence radiation can be singled out as the most important true absorption mechanism. When the energy of the

Table 1
Some properties of X-rays and neutrons.

Property	Value [a]	
	For X-rays (photons)	For neutrons
mass [kg]	0	1.675×10^{-27}
momentum	h/λ	$h/\lambda = mv$
energy	hc/λ	$h^2/2m\lambda^2$
scattering length	Zf_0 (for $\kappa \to 0$)	b (nuclear)
absorption	$\propto Z^4\lambda^3$ (strong)	$\propto \lambda$ (mostly weak)
v [m/s] [b]	c	$437\, E^{1/2}$
λ [Å] [b]	$12.4/E$	$3956/v$
magnetic moment	0	$-1.913\mu_n$
frequency ν [s^{-1}] [b]	$2.42 \times 10^{17}E$	$2.42 \times 10^{11}E$

[a] With h = Planck's constant, c = velocity of light, μ_n = nuclear magneton.
[b] For photons, E in [keV]; for neutrons, E in [meV].

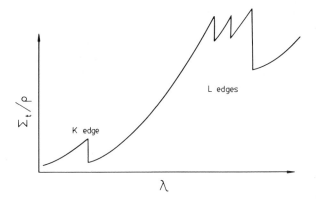

Fig. 2. Mass absorption coefficient Σ_{t}/ρ for X-rays as a function of wavelength near the K and L edges of an element.

incident X-rays approaches a resonance energy in the electronic states, an absorption edge is observed, corresponding to the excitation of electrons in the K, L, etc. levels (see fig. 2 where the mass absorption coefficient is shown as a function of wavelength). The electrons associated with the absorption move out of phase from the others, and a destructive interference results that reduces the atomic scattering factor by the equivalent of twice the number of resonance electrons (e.g., at least a total of four at the K edge). The atomic scattering factor has to be corrected according to

$$f_{a} = f_{a0} + f' + i f'', \tag{14}$$

where f' and f'' are the real and the imaginary part of the *Hönl corrections*. The wavelength dependence of f' and f'' is shown schematically in fig. 3 (see International Tables, vol. III, pp. 214–216 and vol. IV, p. 148, for tabulated values). As synchrotron radiation sources now provide strong X-ray beams with continuously tunable wavelength, diffraction work in the neighbourhood of absorption edges can take advantage of the variation of specific scattering factors.

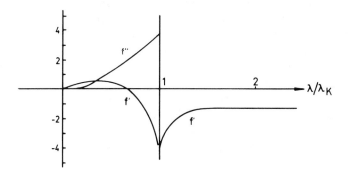

Fig. 3. Variation of the real and imaginary components f' and f'' of the Hönl corrections as a function of X-ray wavelength near the K absorption edge (at λ_{K}) of an element. (After Cowley [1981].)

References: p. 847.

Table 2

Linear absorption coefficients for neutrons (true absorption, Σ_a) and X-rays (Σ_t, total removal) and corresponding mass absorption coefficients (values from BACON [1975], and KOSTORZ and LOVESEY [1979]).

Metal	Neutrons Σ_a (cm^{-1}) 1.8 Å	X-rays Σ_t (cm^{-1}) 1.54 Å	Neutrons Σ_a/ρ (m^2/kg) 1.8 Å	X-rays Σ_t/ρ (m^2/kg) 1.54 Å
Be	0.001	2.7	0.00006	0.150
Al	0.0014	131	0.0005	4.86
Cu	0.326	474	0.0036	5.29
Cd	119	2000	1.29	23.1
W	1.22	3320	0.0061	17.2
Au	5.72	4170	0.029	20.8
Pb	0.005	2630	0.00005	23.2

Table 2 gives a comparison of linear (and mass) absorption coefficients for a few metals. According to eq. (13), $\Sigma_t D_s = 1$ corresponds to a reduction in intensity by a factor $1/e$ which gives an estimate for the typical thickness of a sample. Table 2 shows that even Cd, a material frequently used for shielding purposes in thermal neutron work, has a smaller absorption for neutrons than most common metals for X-rays. On the other hand, lead, a good shielding material for X-rays, is almost transparent to neutrons. (See BACON [1975] and SCHWARTZ and COHEN [1977] for more details on the different properties of X-rays and neutrons.)

2.3. Magnetic scattering

Although there is a measurable interaction between photons and electronic magnetic moments, it is too small (cross-sections about six to eight orders of magnitude smaller than for Bragg scattering, see DE BERGEVIN and BRUNEL [1972]) to be used conveniently in the study of magnetic structures.

The magnetic moment of the neutron has a value of $\gamma\mu_n$ (see table 1) with $\gamma = -1.913$. Examination of the dipole interaction between neutron and local magnetic induction (see GUREVICH and TARASOV [1968]) shows that of the Fourier transform of the local magnetization density, $M(\kappa)$, only the component $M^\perp(\kappa)$, perpendicular to the scattering vector κ, contributes to the scattering. Therefore, a *magnetic interaction vector* may be defined by

$$q_M = M^\perp(\kappa)/|M(\kappa)|. \tag{15}$$

The *magnetic scattering length*, commonly denoted by p, is a *vector*:

$$p = pq_M, \tag{16}$$

with p proportional to $|M(\kappa)|$. If we consider magnetic scattering due to unpaired spins (without orbital moments), p is given by

$$p(\boldsymbol{\kappa}) = \frac{e^2}{m_0c^2}|\gamma|Sf_{\text{mag}}(\boldsymbol{\kappa}). \tag{17}$$

Here, $e^2/(m_0c^2)$ is the classical electron radius f_0 known from X-ray scattering $[f_0 = 2.8 \times 10^{-15}$ m, see eq. (A.37), ch. 11], S is the total number of unpaired spins, and $f_{\text{mag}}(\boldsymbol{\kappa})$ is the Fourier transform of the spin density, normalized to $f_{\text{mag}}(0) = 1$. As the number of Bohr magnetons $(\mu_B = eh/m_0c)$ equals $\mu = 2S$, we can write

$$p(\boldsymbol{\kappa}) = 0.27 \mu f_{\text{mag}}(\boldsymbol{\kappa}) \left[10^{-14}\text{m}\right]. \tag{18}$$

For not too large values of κ, p is comparable to the values of the nuclear scattering amplitude b (for the pure elements Fe, Co, Ni one has $b = 0.96$, 0.28, 1.03 and $p(0) = 0.6$, 0.47 and 0.16, respectively, all in units of 10^{-14}m). The magnetic form factor $f_{\text{mag}}(\boldsymbol{\kappa})$ falls off more rapidly with $\sin\theta/\lambda$ than the atomic form factor for X-rays (ch. 11), as only a few electrons in an outer shell contribute to f_{mag}.

The total scattering of a magnetic material will show a combination of nuclear and magnetic scattering and will also depend on the polarization of the incident beam. Figure 4 shows the scattering geometry, and we assume a fully polarized beam with the polarization vector parallel to the z-axis (up: +, down: −). If the scattered beam is analyzed along the same direction, four different scattering cross-sections can be defined ($++$, $+-$, $-+$ and $--$). In an otherwise perfect crystal, the *nuclear* unit-cell structure factor, $F_s(\boldsymbol{\kappa})$ [see eq. (A.32), ch. 11], can be combined with the *magnetic structure factor*,

$$F_M^\perp(\boldsymbol{\kappa}) = \sum_m \boldsymbol{q}_{Mm} p_m \exp(-2\pi i\boldsymbol{\kappa}\cdot\boldsymbol{r}_m), \tag{19}$$

where $\boldsymbol{q}_{Mm}$ [eq. (15)] is defined according to the direction of the moment at site m,

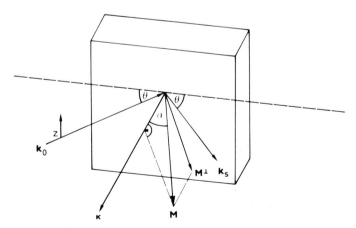

Fig. 4. Scattering geometry for magnetic scattering. The incident neutrons are polarized along the z-axis.

References: p. 847.

and p_m at each site is given by eq. (18). This yields $|F_s + F_{Mz}^\perp|^2$ for $(++)$, $|F_{Mx}^\perp|^2 + |F_{My}^\perp|^2$ for $(+-)$ and $(-+)$, and $|F_s - F_{Mz}^\perp|^2$ for $(--)$, where the $F_{Mi}^\perp$ are the Cartesian components of $F_M^\perp$.

An unpolarized beam can be thought of as being composed of 50% positive and 50% negative polarization, and the scattering cross-section (per atom) without polarization analysis is $d\sigma/d\Omega = |F_s|^2 + |F_M|^2$. For a simple ferromagnet, q_{Mm} is the same for all sites, and with $F_M = q_M F_{mag}$ [see eq. (19)]:

$$\frac{d\sigma}{d\Omega} = |F_s|^2 + \sin^2\alpha |F_{mag}|^2, \tag{20}$$

where α is the angle between κ and M (see fig. 4). By varying α (via the external magnetic field or the scattering geometry), nuclear and magnetic contributions can be separated. Equation (20) also applies to antiferromagnets if we define α relative to the direction of the moment at site one and write $F_{mag} = \Sigma_m \hat{\sigma}_m p_m \exp(-2\pi i\kappa \cdot r_m)$ where $\hat{\sigma}_m$ is either $+1$ or -1 depending on whether or not the moment at site m is parallel or antiparallel to q_1. Figure 5 shows the consequences of ferro- and antiferromagnetic order in the bcc lattice ($\alpha \neq 0$). Additional peaks (magnetic peaks) occur for antiferromagnetic order whereas in ferromagnets the nuclear peaks are enhanced.

If a polarized beam is used, the cross-section for scattering without polarization analysis is the sum of, e.g., $(++)$ and $(+-)$ scattering and contains an interference term between nuclear and magnetic scattering with F_s and $F_M^\perp$ occurring unsquared;

$$\left(\frac{d\sigma}{d\Omega}\right)_{P_0} = |F_s|^2 + 2F_s F_M^\perp \cdot P_0 + |F_M^\perp|^2, \tag{21}$$

where P_0 is a unit vector indicating the direction of polarization. "Flipping" P_0 from

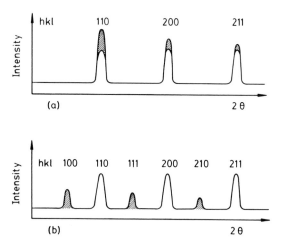

Fig. 5. Schematic neutron diffraction patterns from a bcc polycrystalline (a) ferromagnet and (b) antiferromagnet. The shaded areas represent the magnetic scattering contributions which decrease with θ because f_{mag} decreases. (After SCHWARTZ and COHEN [1977].)

+1 to −1, we have a very sensitive method to measure $F_M^\perp$ and consequently $F_{mag}(\kappa)$, $p_m(\kappa)$ or $f_{mag}(\kappa)$ [cf. eq. (18)]. Equation (21), if generalized as indicated by eq. (8) for structural disorder, is also the basis for a separation of structural and magnetic disorder in alloys.

Finally, we mention the original result of HALPERN and JOHNSON [1939] for paramagnetic scattering, i.e. for a randomly oriented ensemble of identical magnetic moments (spins S). The paramagnetic scattering cross-section (per atom) reads

$$\left(\frac{d\sigma}{d\Omega}\right)_p = \tfrac{2}{3}S(S+1)f_0^2\gamma^2 f_{mag}^2. \tag{22}$$

This scattering is similar to the Laue scattering term in diffuse scattering. Deviations from the simple monotonic κ-dependence are of interest in both cases as they relate to correlations in the atomic or the spin arrangement.

There are many more special features of magnetic scattering than this brief discussion can indicate, and many complex magnetic structures have been studied in recent years (see BROWN [1979], HICKS [1979] and references therein).

2.4. Inelastic and quasi-elastic scattering

As mentioned in §2.2, the energy gain or loss of X-rays scattered from a sample with lattice vibrations (phonons) is too small to be resolved under usual conditions. Other inelastic scattering processes occur near the absorption edge where, simultaneously, incoherent fluorescence radiation is emitted. Compton scattering is another inelastic scattering process of X-rays. From the conservation of energy and momentum for the scattering of a photon from an individual electron, the wavelength shift of Compton-modified radiation is (for electrons assumed at rest):

$$\Delta\lambda\,[\mathring{A}] = 0.0243(1 - \cos 2\theta), \tag{23}$$

independent of the incident wavelength. The scattering is incoherent as there is no fixed phase-relationship between the different inelastic scattering events. The relative contribution of Compton scattering to the total scattering is given by $[1 - \Sigma_j f_{aj}^2/Z]$, where f_{aj} is the form factor (normalized to one) of each of the Z electrons of an atom. Compton scattering increases the background in diffraction experiments, but it can be eliminated experimentally (e.g. with a monochromator in the diffracted beam) or by calculation (see SCHWARTZ and COHEN [1977]). Detailed study of the energy distribution of Compton intensities provides information on the momentum distribution of electrons in condensed matter (see COOPER [1977]), one of the few techniques also applicable to alloys.

Much smaller energy transfers can be detected by neutron scattering, either by analyzing the change in wavelength with a single crystal or the change of neutron momentum by time-of-flight methods. Here, we consider one-phonon scattering only (for a complete account, see e.g. MARSHALL and LOVESEY [1971] and BACON [1975]).

References: p. 847.

Figure 6 shows two possible scattering configurations in reciprocal space. The scattering vector κ can be written as

$$\kappa = k_s - k_0 = g + g, \tag{24}$$

where q is the phonon wavevector, counted from the nearest reciprocal lattice point. With the scattered wavevector k_{s1}, the neutron has lost energy $(k_{s1} < k_0)$, and a phonon has been created. For k_{s2}, a phonon has been annihilated. As the neutron momentum is h/λ, eq. (24) states the conservation of momentum in the scattering process $(\lambda_q = 1/q$ is the phonon wavelength). Simultaneously, the conservation of energy,

$$h^2/2m_n\lambda_0^2 - h^2/2m_n\lambda_s^2 = h\nu_p, \tag{25}$$

defines the energy of the phonon participating in the scattering (λ_0 and λ_s denote the incident and scattered wavelength, respectively). There are only discrete values of ν_p for a given q, and appropriate scans can be designed to obtain directly the phonon dispersion curves of a crystal.

Apart from coherent inelastic scattering processes, analysis of the incoherent inelastic scattering of neutrons may often be interesting. True incoherent scattering processes are due to the interaction of the neutron spin with nuclear spins $I \neq 0$. The scattering length of the compound nucleus depends on its total spin which is $I + 1/2$ or $I - 1/2$. The tabulated values of coherent scattering lengths and incoherent cross-sections for individual isotopes represent properly weighted averages (for unpolarized nuclei). Natural elements are frequently a mixture of different isotopes, each with its own nuclear spin. Coherent scattering lengths and spin-incoherent cross-sections are simply arithmetic averages, but due to the random distribution of nuclei with different coherent scattering lengths over the sites of the sample, another κ-independent terms, $\sigma_i = 4\pi \langle \overline{b^2} - (\overline{b})^2 \rangle$, occurs in complete analogy to the mono-

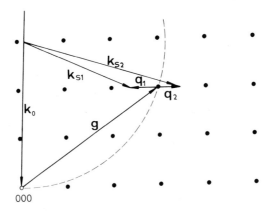

Fig. 6. Two possible inelastic scattering events involving the creation ($\kappa = k_{s1} - k_0$) and the annihilation ($\kappa = k_{s2} - k_0$) of a phonon.

tonic Laue scattering term in diffuse X-ray scattering (see §4). For neutrons, this part is included in the total value of incoherent scattering of an element. Incoherent neutron scattering cross-sections are quite large in several cases, and for coherent scattering experiments (see §2.5), they may be a severe limitation. However, similar to the case of Compton scattering and electrons, energy analysis of the incoherently scattered neutrons will reveal details of the motion of nuclei. The incoherent scattering function can be calculated for different processes (see, e.g., BACON [1975]). If the energy transfer is centred around $h\nu = 0$, i.e. small, the scattering is called quasi-elastic. In condensed matter, the motion of atoms is restricted by the environment, and quasi-elastic neutron scattering has become a widely used technique to study atomic and molecular motion, especially if hydrogen with its high incoherent cross-section is involved (see SPRINGER [1977] and SKÖLD *et al.* [1979] for reviews). In solid Na, too, a study of the quasi-elastic line width helped to identify diffusion mechanisms (see § 6.2).

2.5. Some experimental considerations

Incoherent scattering as a source of background and absorption was already mentioned in §2.4. Extensive discussions on general experimental problems in X-ray and neutron scattering can be found in the book by SCHWARTZ and COHEN [1977], and, more specifically oriented towards defects in crystals, in the articles by SCHMATZ [1969, 1973, 1978]. Some remarks will be found in subsequent chapters, relating to particular applications. Here, we only state a few quite general points.

Laboratory X-ray sources with rotating anodes have been built, the maximum power of 100 kW (see HAUBOLD [1975]) yielding 4×10^{16} quanta/s cm^2 sr (CuK$_\alpha$). Still higher luminosities are obtained (originally as a by-product, now "exploited" in dedicated sources) from electron synchrotrons and electron or positron storage rings. Depending on the energy of the electrons or positrons, synchrotron radiation emerges in a wavelength range from infrared to ~ 0.2 Å. Synchrotron radiation is continuous and very intense (10^{12}–10^{14} quanta/s mrad per 0.1% bandwidth, integrated over the vertical direction). The radiation is highly collimated perpendicular to the orbital plane. In the GeV region, the divergence is $\sim 10^{-4}$ rad. In the plane of the ideal orbit, synchrotron radiation is 100% polarized with the electrical vector parallel to this plane. There is a well-defined time structure of the beam with pulse durations as short as 10^{-10} s with repetition rates of 1 MHz or more. The use of synchrotron radiation for materials studies is just beginning to be explored (see, e.g., WINICK and DONIACH [1980], BIENENSTOCK [1981], SPARKS [1981]).

Compared even with a classical sealed X-ray tube, neutron sources are not very powerful. Figure 7 shows a comparison of several X-ray and neutron sources according to SCHMATZ [1973]. As suggested by MAIER-LEIBNITZ [1966], the momentum space density $p(\mathbf{k}_0)$ is an adequate quantity for comparison, as the count rate $\dot{Z}$ at a detector is proportional to $p(\mathbf{k}_0)$ multiplied by the momentum space elements $d^3\mathbf{k}_0$ and $d^3\mathbf{k}_s$ that can be optimized instrument parameters (within the bounds of k_x, k_y, k_z fixed by the properties of the source), $\dot{Z} \propto p(\mathbf{k}_0)S(\boldsymbol{\kappa}, \nu)\, d^3\mathbf{k}_0\, d^3\mathbf{k}_s$, where

References: p. 847.

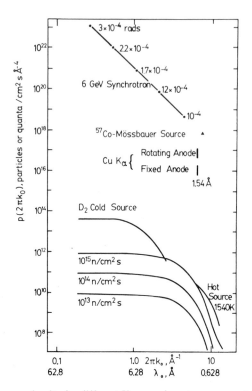

Fig. 7. Momentum space density for different X-ray and neutron sources (after SCHMATZ [1973]).

$S(\kappa, \nu)$ is the scattering law to be studied. We see that $p(k_0)$ for neutrons is several orders of magnitude lower than the values of all X-ray sources. On the other hand, there are restrictions ($\Delta k_0/k_0$ or vertical collimation) for X-rays that are less severe for neutrons where $d^3 k_0$ can be chosen more flexibly to match the resolution requirements imposed by $S(\kappa, \nu)$. This compensates in part for the lower values of $p(k_0)$. The line for synchrotron radiation is typical for a non-dedicated source (DESY, 10 mA current, 6 GeV), where no efforts have been made to obtain a high X-ray intensity. Intensities about four orders of magnitude higher than indicated in fig. 7 may be reached.

Traditionally, thermal neutrons are produced by fission and subsequent moderation, i.e., in a nuclear reactor. A steady-state thermal flux of 10^{15} n/cm^2 is virtually impossible to surpass as heat removal is a limiting factor. With hot and cold sources, the Maxwellian spectrum of neutrons may be shifted to smaller or larger wavelengths (see fig. 7). Pulsed neutron sources may provide a higher peak flux. If the pulsed structure of the neutron beam is maintained after moderation, time-of-flight experiments will be advantageous at pulsed sources because the relevant flux at the sample will be higher than the average flux. Other concepts for the production of neutrons are based on the use of charged particles from accelerators (spallation). A variety of spallation sources are now operational at least in a reduced version. Peak fluxes of 10^{16} n/cm^{2}s are planned (see WINDSOR [1981] for a detailed account).

Apart from film techniques (with a converter foil for neutrons), the *detection* of the scattered radiation is based on electronic counting circuits attached to gas or solid state detectors. For X-rays, gas-filled proportional "counters" and solid-state scintillation "counters" detect the incident quanta via the ionization of a gas or the production of photoelectrons by scintillation photons. The energy resolution is poor for both detector types, typically ~ 20% in the 10 keV range for gas detectors and ~ 50% for scintillation detectors. Solid-state detectors based on electron–hole pair production in doped (Ge or Si with Li) or intrinsic (Ge) semiconductors have a theoretical resolution of about 1% at 10 keV, about 200 eV in practice.

Another important aspect for many experiments is the spatial resolution of large detectors. Linear position-sensitive detectors with a resolution of about 30 μm employ a resistive wire, and peak heights or pulse shapes are analyzed as a function of position of the detected event. Two-dimensional gas-filled detectors for X-rays employ (sets of) mutually perpendicular wires and different electronic techniques to locate the detected event (see, e.g., HENDRICKS [1976] for a survey). The simultaneous measurement of scattering over a large solid angle is of particular importance for weak scattering signals but also for kinetic studies.

Neutrons can only be detected after they have participated in a nuclear reaction with the emission of charged particles or γ-rays. As beam dimensions are usually much larger in neutron scattering than in X-ray scattering, the use of large arrays of individual detectors is feasible without loss of resolution (and with time-of-flight resolution, i.e. energy resolution for each desired detector). Position-sensitive detectors have been developed for diffraction work, planar detectors for small-angle scattering and curved ones for powder patterns.

3. *Bragg peaks and vicinity*

Scattering from real crystals may occur anywhere in reciprocal space but Bragg peaks, though modified, will remain a predominant feature as long as an average lattice can be defined. A diffraction pattern, after all instrumental corrections, reflects the distribution of scattering matter within the (average) unit cell of a substance, and the atomic coordinates (location of the centres of scattering objects) as well as the scattering-length density distribution (electrons with X-rays, nuclei and magnetic moments with neutrons) can be determined from an analysis of Bragg peaks (see, e.g., LIPSON and COCHRAN [1953], WARREN [1969], SCHWARTZ and COHEN [1977]). Particular Bragg peaks occur for different phases in a sample, and diffraction methods are thus essential in the study of phase diagrams and phase transitions. The orientation distribution of Bragg peaks for a polycrystalline sample reveals its texture (see, e.g., BARRETT and MASSALSKI [1980]).

References: p. 847.

3.1. Peak shifts

Changes in peak position may be caused by residual stresses in bulk specimens, by faulting on certain crystallographic planes (WARREN [1969], WAGNER [1966], COWLEY [1981]) or by lattice parameter changes as a function of alloying or of defect concentration. Whereas a lattice parameter change affects all crystallographically equivalent Bragg peaks in the same way, the other two causes may lead to different shifts depending on the orientation of the reflecting planes relative to a preferred axis of the disturbance. Figure 8 illustrates this for a polycrystal with a surface under compression. As residual stresses and applied stresses combined determine load carrying capabilities, X-ray methods in this field have received considerable attention (e.g., BARRETT and MASSALSKI [1980], CULLITY [1977]), and a recent review by JAMES and COHEN [1980] gives a detailed account of procedures and applications.

Gradients of lattice constants may also occur in diffusion couples, e.g. when a plated sample is annealed. The (nondestructive) analysis of such diffusion profiles

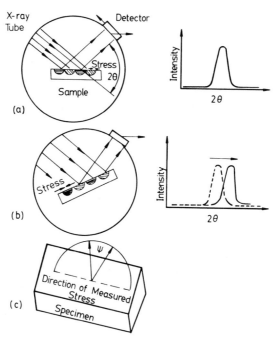

Fig. 8. Residual stress measurements with an X-ray diffractometer for a surface under compression. (a) Bragg's law is satisfied for lattice planes parallel to the surface. These planes are further apart than in the stress-free state (Poisson's effect). Their spacing is obtained from the position of the Bragg peak. (b) The specimen has been tilted, and other grains now present suitable lattice planes for Bragg scattering. As these planes are more nearly perpendicular to the compressive stress, they are less separated than in (a), and the Bragg peak moves to higher angles. (c) The direction of the measured stress is given by the intersection of the circle of tilt and the surface. (After JAMES and COHEN [1980].)

using X-ray diffraction starts from similar ideas and has recently been reviewed by HOUSKA [1980] and MITTEMEIJER and DELHEZ [1980].

Neutron diffraction averages over larger volumes, and coupled with the higher sensitivity for light elements, this may be useful in the study of lattice constants of minority phases (precipitates, inclusions).

3.2 Peak broadening and intensity changes

In §2.1 we have already mentioned a broadening due to sample size that could be relevant for powders [eq. (1)]. However, for bulk samples we have quickly ignored size broadening and written the Bragg cross-section as a delta-function. Thus, for a well collimated X-ray beam of characteristic radiation, the width of a Bragg peak should be controlled by the natural linewidth, as Bragg's law yields:

$$\Delta(2\theta) = 2\frac{\Delta\lambda}{\lambda}\tan\theta. \tag{26}$$

With $\Delta\lambda/\lambda \approx 5 \times 10^{-4}$, $\Delta(2\theta)$ is about one minute of arc at $2\theta \approx 30°$ but increases dramatically for $\theta \to 90°$, and eq. (26) can be confirmed for large perfect crystals. However, quite frequently, the Bragg peaks are much broader (many minutes at moderate Bragg angles), and only crystals with such *mosaicity* will actually approach the predictions of the kinematical theory as may be judged from the integrated reflecting power (which should be $\propto |F_s|^2$). According to DARWIN ([1922], see ZACHARIASEN [1945] and JAMES [1963]) the kinematical theory is valid for an ideal mosaic crystal consisting of small perfect domains which are tilted against each other by small angles (a few minutes). By this concept, the effect of coherent multiple reflection of the same beam can be reduced to just the planes within one *mosaic block* and finally neglected (i.e., primary extinction plays no role). The dynamical theory of diffraction shows (see ch. 11) that the tolerable size of the blocks depends on wavelength. As the extinction length (for Bragg reflections) is proportional to $(\lambda|F_s|)^{-1}$, a sample of given thickness or mosaicity will approach the case of the ideal mosaic crystal with decreasing wavelength.

Mosaicity in a real crystal is a merely formal concept for peak broadening which may be caused by various defects, e.g. dislocations. Referring to crystals containing dislocations in connection with Bragg peaks appears contradictory as eq. (12) and the subsequent discussion imply that dislocations cause Bragg peaks to disappear as their strain fields decrease $\propto (r')^{-1}$. However, this would hold only for a random arrangement of dislocations in a large crystal. As WILKENS [1969] has shown, a random distribution is not a very suitable model for the calculation of X-ray line broadening or of the elastic energy. A so-called restrictedly random distribution of dislocations was used to calculate the line broadening and the peak profile more realistically (WILKENS [1970, 1975]) from the kinematical theory. The linewidth $\Delta\kappa$ is proportional to $g_{hkl}\rho_d^{1/2}\ln M_e$, where ρ_d is the dislocation density. M_e is a parameter influencing the lineshape and given by $M_e = \rho_d^{1/2}R_e$ where R_e is an effective outer cut-off radius, indicating the range over which a random dislocation arrangement

References: p. 847.

can be admitted. Beyond this distance, long-range stresses should compensate each other (see UNGÁR et al. [1982] for a recent application).

An analysis of the static Debye–Waller factor may be useful to determine displacements around defects. In a dilute alloy ($c \ll 1$), eq. (12) simplifies to (see KRIVOGLAZ [1969], DEDERICHS [1973], TRINKAUS [1975]):

$$M = c \sum_n \left[1 - \cos(2\pi\kappa\cdot u_n) \right], \tag{27}$$

or even $2M = c\sum_n (2\pi\kappa\cdot u_n)^2$ if $|\kappa\cdot u_n| \ll 1$. The u_n are displacements caused by a defect taken at the origin, and the summation extends over all cells. In martensite, where interstitially dissolved C causes a tetragonal distortion, M_{002} is expected to be different from $M_{200,020}$, and $\ln(2I_{002}/I_{200,020}) = 2M_{002} - 2M_{200,020}$. P.C. CHEN et al. [1980] have evaluated such (X-ray) intensity ratios for martensite formed in quenched fine-grained Fe–18wt% Ni–(0.9/1.15)wt% C. A similar study of cubic NbH$_x$ was performed by METZGER et al. [1981, 1982] who obtained $u_1 = (0.100 \pm 0.007)$ Å for H occupying tetrahedral sites, a value very close to theoretical calculations using lattice theory.

Neutron and X-ray results for Cu$_3$Au just above or below T_c, the temperature for long-range order, showed a very strong increase of $2M$ when T_c was approached (BARDHAN et al. [1977]). From the difference in the intensity ratios of fundamental and superstructure/diffuse peaks, individual mean-square displacements for Au and Cu (based on an expansion of eq. (27) for M) were calculated, and large displacements of Au near T_c were found. From a wealth of other information including phonon dispersion curves (H. CHEN et al. [1977]) near T_c the authors conclude that these displacements are static and related to a high density of antiphase boundaries within large long-range ordered regions near this first-order transition.

3.3. Diffuse scattering near Bragg peaks

We now turn to the scattering cross-section given formally by eq. (11), i.e., continuous scattering for $\kappa \neq g$. There is no general analytical solution, and approximations have to be introduced to obtain manageable expressions.

As pointed out in §2.4, thermal vibrations (phonons) are always present in a crystal, and their effect on the Bragg intensity is usually contained in the Debye–Waller factor. The diffuse intensity is called thermal–diffuse scattering (TDS) and has been treated extensively (e.g., JAMES [1963], WARREN [1969], BACON [1975], WILLIS and PRYOR [1975]). TDS occurs for all values of κ but is particularly pronounced near reciprocal lattice points. This is also true for static displacements but there are some important differences regarding the symmetry of diffuse scattering in reciprocal space. The theory of diffuse scattering from point defects and clusters has been considered by KRIVOGLAZ [1969], DEDERICHS [1969, 1973] and TRINKAUS [1972]. For small defect concentrations c one obtains from eqs. (6) and (11) the diffuse scattering cross-section:

$$\left(\frac{d\sigma}{d\Omega} \right)_d = cN|F(\kappa)|^2, \tag{28}$$

with $F(\kappa) = \Delta f_B + f_A \sum_n \exp(-2\pi i\kappa \cdot r_n^a) \left[\exp(2 - \pi i\kappa \cdot u_{0n}) - 1\right],$ (29)

where u_{0n} is the displacement at site n due to *one* defect at the origin, r_n^a denotes the position vector in the *average* lattice, and Δf_B, f_A are "scattering lengths" of defect and host atoms (one atom per cell assumed for simplicity), including thermal and static Debye–Waller factors. The value of Δf_B depends on the type of defect (e.g., DEDERICHS [1973]):

$$\Delta f_B = \begin{cases} f_I \exp(-2\pi i\kappa \cdot r_I) & \text{for interstitial impurities,} \\ f_B - f_A & \text{for substitutional impurities,} \\ -f_A & \text{for vacancies,} \\ f_A[2\cos(2\pi\kappa \cdot r_I) - 1] & \text{for split (self-)interstitials,} \end{cases}$$ (30)

where r_I is the position of the interstitial or of one of the split interstitials. For κ close to a Bragg peak ($\kappa = g + s$, and $s \ll g$), but also, with a different reasoning, for any κ if $|2\pi\kappa \cdot u_{0n}| \ll 1$, eq. (29) yields:

$$F(\kappa) = \Delta f_B - 2\pi i f_A \kappa \cdot \sum_n u_{0n} \exp(-2\pi i\kappa \cdot r_n^a),$$ (31)

and finally, for the *Huang scattering* region ($s \ll g$, Δf_B neglected):

$$\left(\frac{d\sigma}{d\Omega}\right)_{Hd} = cN f_A^2 |2\pi g \cdot u(\kappa)|^2,$$ (32)

with $u(\kappa) = \sum_n u_{0n} \exp(-2\pi i\kappa \cdot r_n^a) \approx \frac{1}{V_c} \int u_0(r) \exp(-2\pi i\kappa \cdot r) \, d^3r.$ (33)

The displacements u are generally determined by lattice statics (see, e.g., DEDERICHS *et al.* [1978] and §4.1) relating displacements to forces exerted on atoms around the defect. For large distances from the defect, the asymptotic behaviour of the displacement is given by continuum theory,

$$u_0(r) \propto \frac{1}{r^2} \frac{r}{r}.$$ (34)

(For isotropic materials, the proportionality factor is $\Delta V/4\pi$ with ΔV = volume change per defect in an infinite medium.) Thus, the long-range displacement field is always centrosymmetric, and the Fourier transform can be written as [$u(\kappa)$ is periodic in reciprocal space, and only $s = \kappa - g$ is relevant]:

$$u(\kappa) = u(s) = \frac{i}{sV_c} S(\hat{s}) \cdot [P \cdot \hat{s}].$$ (35)

Here, S is a tensor containing combinations of elastic compliances depending on the orientation of $\hat{s}$ where $\hat{s}$ is a unit vector in the direction of s. The tensor P is the dipole force tensor of the defect (see, e.g., DEDERICHS [1973], SEEGER [1961]) with elements

$$P_{jk} = P_{kj} = \sum_n p_{jn} x_{kn}, \tag{36}$$

where p_{jn} are the components of the forces $\boldsymbol{p}_n$ and x_{kn} the components of the position vectors $\boldsymbol{r}_n$. We note that the volume change caused by defects is proportional to the trace of $\boldsymbol{P}$, and the lattice parameter change $\Delta a / a$ can be obtained from

$$\frac{\Delta V}{V} = 3 \frac{\Delta a}{a} = \frac{c}{V_c} \frac{\mathrm{Tr}\, \boldsymbol{P}}{C_{11} + 2C_{12}} \tag{37}$$

for a cubic crystal with the elastic constants C_{11}, C_{12}. Equation (37) is valid for isotropic *and* anisotropic defects, provided the latter show no preferred orientational arrangement relative to one of the cubic axes (see PEISL *et al.* [1974]).

Substituting eq. (35) into eq. (32), the Huang intensity will be:

$$\left(\frac{\mathrm{d}\sigma}{\mathrm{d}\Omega} \right)_{\mathrm{Hd}} = \frac{cN}{V_c^2} f_A^2 \left(\frac{g}{s} \right)^2 |2\pi \hat{\boldsymbol{g}} \cdot \{ \boldsymbol{S}(\hat{s}) \cdot [\boldsymbol{P} \cdot \hat{s}] \}|^2. \tag{38}$$

We see that Huang scattering has the same general κ dependence as first-order TDS for $\kappa \to g$, especially inversion symmetry around g, but the intensity distribution around a reciprocal lattice point is different, as the intensity depends on $\boldsymbol{g} \cdot \boldsymbol{u}(s)$. For example, an isotropic defect with three equal, mutually perpendicular double forces P_0 in an isotropic cubic crystal has

$$\boldsymbol{u}(s) = \frac{\mathrm{i} P_0 s}{s^2 V_c C_{11}}, \tag{39}$$

and it follows from eq. (32) that there is a zero-intensity plane for s perpendicular to $\kappa \approx g$. Figure 9a (PEISL [1976]) illustrates this case. Double-force tensor, defect configuration and lines of equal intensity in reciprocal space are indicated. In fig. 9b, c, d some other cases are shown where the defect has a preferred axis ("anisotropic" defect, in an isotropic matrix). Because the defect axis can be oriented along several crystallographically equivalent directions, the scattering cross-section [eq. (32) or (39)] has to be averaged over all these orientations. As the orientation of a zero-intensity plane (nodal surface) is determined by the axis of the defect, nodal planes will normally be reduced to a nodal line or disappear entirely, as shown in fig. 10. The isointensity surfaces in anisotropic crystals look deformed and rotated but additional nodal planes can also appear (see DEDERICHS [1973]).

As the Huang-scattering cross-section is proportional to the square of the dipole tensor [eq. (38)], interstitials will scatter considerably more than vacancies (e.g. for Cu, the ratio exceeds 20). A Huang-scattering study of a sample containing Frenkel pairs will therefore yield information predominantly related to interstitials. In a series of experiments on electron irradiated Al and Cu single crystals, EHRHART *et al.* [1974] (see also EHRHART and SCHILLING [1973], EHRHART and SCHLAGHECK [1974]) have analyzed the Huang scattering from as-irradiated and step-annealed samples in terms of single defects and clusters. Clustering of defects leads to an increase of

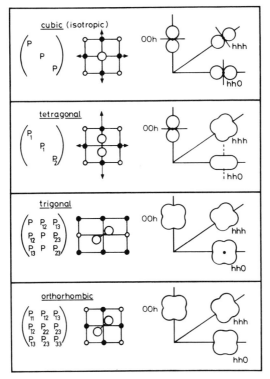

Fig. 9. Schematic isointensity contours for various defect symmetries, averaged over the possible defect orientations (after PEISL [1976]).

Huang scattering [proportional to the number of clustering defects, z, if the dipole strengths superpose linearly, see eq. (38)]. Interstitial clusters ($z \approx 3$) in Al irradiated with fast neutrons at low temperatures (4.6 K) have more recently been reported by

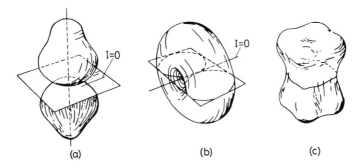

Fig. 10. Types of isointensity surfaces in reciprocal space: (a) double-drop type with one zero-intensity surface; (b) apple-shaped type with one zero-intensity line; (c) single-bubble type. (After TRINKAUS [1972].)

References: p. 847.

V. GUÉRARD *et al.* [1980] who compared Huang scattering from these samples with single-defect scattering after electron irradiation. The analysis yields further details on the size (radius ~ 50 Å) of displacement cascades, the number of defects per cascade (~ 200), overlap at larger irradiation doses and annealing behaviour.

Strong distortions as they may be expected for defect clusters reduce the range of validity of the Huang approximation. This can be seen in neutron-irradiated Al and is also found when clusters form upon recovery of electron-irradiated Al and Cu (EHRHART and SCHILLING [1973], EHRHART and SCHLAGHECK [1974]). Figure 11 shows results for Al. The s^{-4} dependence at somewhat larger s is expected from the theory for strongly distorting defects (Stokes–Wilson approximation, see, e.g., DEDERICHS [1973]). This type of scattering occurs if closely spaced scattered centres introduce large phase shifts [i.e., $2M$ becomes very large, see eqs. (10) and (12)]. The so-called asymptotic distortion scattering is given by ($g \simeq \kappa$):

$$\left(\frac{d\sigma}{d\Omega}\right)_{Ad} = \frac{cN}{V_c^2} f_A^2 \frac{|P||g|}{s^4} \phi(\hat{s}), \tag{40}$$

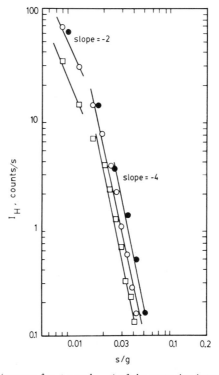

Fig. 11. Symmetrical part (average for $+s$ and $-s$) of the scattering intensity of electron-irradiated Al after annealing at 130 K, measured near the 400 reflection. Open circles: Al I(5×10^{-4} Frenkel pairs), κ parallel to $\langle 100 \rangle$; squares: Al II(3×10^{-4}), κ parallel to $\langle 100 \rangle$; solid circles: Al I, κ parallel to $\langle 110 \rangle$. (After EHRHART and SCHILLING [1973].)

and depends linearly on the modulus of the double-force tensor $\mathbf{P}$ and on g, in contrast to the square dependence for Huang scattering [eq. (37)].

The comparable magnitudes of TDS and Huang scattering by point defects suggest that for X-rays one should work at low temperatures. This is not always possible, as the defects may not be present in the state of interest. METZGER *et al.* [1976] and METZGER and PEISL [1978] have shown that Huang scattering from H in Nb and Ta can be studied at room temperature (where the solubility in the bcc α-phase is sufficiently high), and that after appropriate corrections, especially for the static Debye–Waller factor, the results can be interpreted in terms of single-defect scattering up to surprisingly high concentrations of H in Ta (11% H/Ta, METZGER and PEISL [1978]). The long-range stress field shows cubic symmetry in both systems (with a possible anisotropy of less than 7%), i.e. the distortion caused by H atoms occupying tetrahedral sites is isotropic for large distances. The double-force tensor is found to be $P_{ij} = \delta_{ij} (3.37 \pm 0.1)$ eV for H in Nb and $\delta_{ij} (3.36 \pm 0.16)$ eV for H in Ta. These values are probably more reliable than those obtained with other methods.

As TDS can be separated, neutrons may be advantageous for Huang scattering studies, provided incoherent scattering and absorption are not too high (see BURKEL *et al.* [1979] for an assessment and experiments).

4. *Between Bragg peaks*

If we now extend the range of κ and look for intensity at some distance from the Bragg peaks of a given structure, we will find diffuse intensity from TDS and diffuse scattering from static displacements if defects are present. This scattering (occasionally called structural diffuse scattering or also "Zwischenreflex" scattering) is particularly sensitive to the symmetry of displacements in the immediate vicinity of defects and can help to confirm (or eliminate) certain defect models. In addition to "positional disorder", alloys will also exhibit "compositional disorder". Whereas the Bragg peaks are controlled simply by the average structure factor of the unit cell, diffuse scattering will reflect deviations from a random arrangement (short-range order or clustering). Basic interactions in alloys can thus be studied. Finally, new Bragg peaks may appear when (chemical or magnetic) order or (reconstructive or displacive) phase transformations occur.

The experimental requirements for diffuse scattering between Bragg peaks are somewhat different from those in §3. There, very good resolution near Bragg peaks was desirable. Now, as small intensities are to be monitored over a wide κ range, resolution demands may often be relaxed in favour of higher intensity, and simultaneous observations at various values of κ are advantageous. Multidetector arrangements, position-sensitive detectors or films (for a survey in diffuse scattering and still as an important tool in the study of phase transformation) are therefore used wherever possible.

References: p. 847.

4.1. Displacement scattering

The diffuse scattering for κ not too close to a Bragg peak depends on the displacements in the immediate vicinity of the defect. If we remain in the dilute limit $c \ll 1$, eq. (28) is still valid with $F(\kappa)$ according to eq. (29). But eq. (31) may not be valid for all displacements, and we write

$$F(\kappa) = \Delta f_B + f_A \sum_n \exp(-2\pi \, i\kappa \cdot r_n^a)\left[\exp(-2\pi \, i\kappa \cdot u_{0n}') - 1 + 2\pi \, i\kappa \cdot u_{0n}\right]$$

$$-2\pi \, if_A \kappa \cdot u(\kappa). \tag{41}$$

Thus, if there are any u_{0n} too large to permit an expansion of the exponential, they are taken into account by the second term of eq. (41). If $|\kappa \cdot u_{0n}| \ll 1$, eq. (41) reduces to eq. (31). The u_{0n} may be obtained from lattice statics (see, e.g., DEDERICHS et al. [1978]). A set of (virtual) forces (called *Matsubara–Kanzaki forces*) is assumed to be applied to the neighbouring atoms of a defect in order to produce the displacements u_{0n} within the harmonic approximation, i.e., with the dynamical matrix of the ideal, defect-free crystal. In reciprocal space, we have:

$$f(\kappa) = \phi(\kappa) \cdot u(\kappa), \tag{42}$$

where $f(\kappa)$ is the Fourier transform of the virtual forces f_{0n}, and $\phi(\kappa)$, the dynamical matrix (inverse of the Fourier transform of the lattice Green's function), contains combinations of squares of phonon frequencies. In symmetry directions, $\phi(\kappa)$ can be expressed in terms of the three phonon branch frequencies ν_L^2 and ν_{T1}^2, ν_{T2}^2. The transition to continuum theory ($\nu^2 \propto q^2$) has already been mentioned in §3.3. Although the actual displacements may sometimes be more interesting, the concept of virtual forces has the advantage of giving a more rapidly converging method to calculate the scattering of (model) defects as the relevant forces may be restricted to the immediate surroundings of the defect (see SCHMATZ [1973] and BAUER [1979] for further discussions). EISENRIEGLER [1971] has calculated the scattering cross-sections for dumbbell interstitials in fcc metals (based on values for Cu, SEEGER et al. [1962]) and predicted a very pronounced structure of the diffuse scattering between Bragg peaks (and localized phonon modes). Figure 12 illustrates the sensitivity of diffuse scattering between Bragg peaks to the details of the displacement field near the defect. Experiments with X-rays have first been reported for electron-irradiated Al (HAUBOLD [1975]) and subsequently for Cu (HAUBOLD and MARTINSEN [1978]). These experiments clearly confirmed the dumbbell configuration in $\langle 100 \rangle$ direction (see ch. 17 for a further discussion of the results).

Displacement scattering studies with neutrons have recently been reviewed by BAUER [1979]. Although the incident beam intensities are much smaller than with X-rays, experiments are feasible, and the energy analysis usually achieved with a chopper allows one to extend diffuse scattering measurements to higher temperatures. Dilute alloys with low incoherent scattering cross-sections have so far been studied (Al, Nb, Pb, are favourable solvents). Figure 13 shows diffuse elastic scattering contours for an Al–0.8 at% Cu single crystal (see BAUER [1979]). Whereas

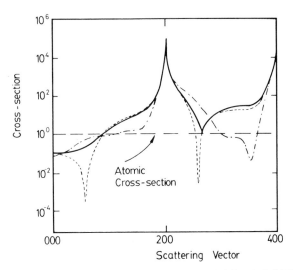

Fig. 12. Calculated cross-sections for diffuse scattering by interstitials in Al. Solid line: $\langle 100 \rangle$ dumbbell, dashed–dotted line: tetrahedral, dotted line: octahedral. (After HAUBOLD [1975].)

the scattering at 300 K shows signs of precipitation, the results at 800 K are indicative of a random distribution of weak distorting defects. Figure 14 shows the scattering cross-sections along the three main symmetry directions, compared with calculated values from a model with radial virtual forces acting on the nearest and next-nearest neighbours of the substitutional Cu solute. As the strength of the dipole force tensor is given by the lattice parameter change and c is known, no adjustable parameters remain in a nearest-neighbour model, and the forces f_0 must be $-4.22 \times$

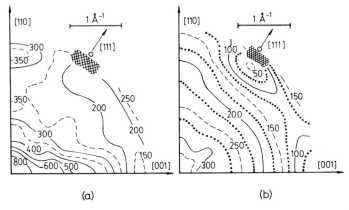

Fig. 13. Lines of equal elastic diffuse scattering cross-section (in mbarns/sr per Cu atom) for Al–0.8 at% Cu in the $(1\bar{1}0)$ plane of the reciprocal lattice for (a) $T = 300$ K and (b) $T = 800$ K. Data in the cross-hatched regions have been omitted. Scale: $1 \ \text{Å}^{-1} = 2\pi\kappa$. (After BAUER [1979].)

References: p. 847.

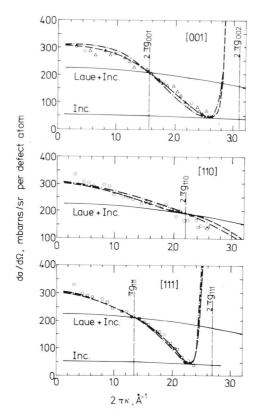

Fig. 14. Comparison of measured cross-sections for elastic diffuse scattering from Al–0.8 at% Cu at 800 K with the results of model calculations. The solid lines marked "Laue + Inc." indicate the expected behaviour without static lattice displacements (but including the Debye–Waller factor). Dashed lines: model with forces on nearest neighbours only; dashed–dotted lines: "best fit" with forces f_1 on nearest and f_2 on next-nearest neighbours, $f_2/f_1 = -0.2^{+0.2}_{-0.1}$. The symbols represent experimental data. (After BAUER [1979].)

10^{-10} N, directed towards the Cu atom (lattice contraction). For this and any other model with centrosymmetric forces (inversion symmetry), the distortion scattering must be zero halfway between the Bragg peaks. For a centrosymmetric defect, one thus obtains just a diffuse scattering contribution from Δf_B [see eq. (41)] at these particular positions. Figure 14 shows that for Cu in Al, inversion symmetry is fully compatible with the results. The nearest-neighbour forces f_0 alone yield quite a satisfactory fit. Detailed analysis of the slope near $\kappa = g/2$ led to the best fit indicated in the figure. Different signs for the radial forces f_1 and f_2 are not in conflict with the oscillatory behaviour of the effective interaction potential in Al (see ch. 3).

Pseudopotential theory has been applied to Mg in Al to calculate diffuse elastic scattering cross-sections, and neutron scattering results obtained at 720 K (Al–3.2 at% Mg) along [110] compare favourably (WERNER *et al.* [1978]). Simple virtual-force models fail in this case, as they do in Al–Zn and, even more so, in Al–Mn (see BAUER [1979]). Another complicated case is Pb–Bi. Alloy crystals with 2 and 4% Bi (and pure Pb) were studied with neutrons (see BAUER [1979]). An unexpected peak at $\kappa = g_{220}/2$ was found, which cannot be attributed to short-range order because a similar peak would then be required at a distance g_{111} from $g_{220}/2$, i.e., at $g_{200}/2$. If displacements are responsible, the inversion symmetry one intuitively expects for a substitutional solute has to be perturbed. The suggested model assumes equal outward forces f_1 on all nearest neighbours and three extra forces f_e pulling three neighbours in one plane closer to the Bi atom (an extension of the $8 - N$ rule).

The diffuse elastic neutron scattering of interstitial hydrogen solutes in niobium (D is used instead of H because H has a very high incoherent scattering cross-section) also shows cubic symmetry for the displacement field (cf. the Huang scattering results mentioned in §3.3, and BAUER [1979]).

4.2. Short-range order *

So far, we have considered dilute solutions of defects and assumed a random distribution. This approach yields simple scattering laws and is sufficient for many cases. However, in concentrated solid solutions, the notion of single defects is difficult to maintain, and additional scattering effects will occur if there is any deviation from a random occupation of lattice sites by the different scattering centres, i.e., short-range order (SRO) occurs.

Much work has been devoted to binary substitutional alloys. If we neglect positional disorder, eq. (28) for diffuse scattering (i.e. $\kappa \neq g$) can be replaced by (KRIVOGLAZ [1969])

$$\left(\frac{d\sigma}{d\Omega}\right)_{SRO} = N|c(\kappa)|^2(f_B - f_A)^2 \qquad (43)$$

for an A–B alloy of concentration $c = c_B$. (We consider alloys with one sublattice only. More general expressions for several sublattices, important for SRO in intermetallic compounds, hydrogen in metals, non-stoichiometric compounds etc., are given, e.g., by HAYAKAWA and COHEN [1975] and BAUER [1979]. For some further discussions including ternary alloys see COHEN [1970] and DE FONTAINE [1971].) In eq. (43), Debye–Waller factors are again included in the scattering lengths f_A, f_B. The term $|c(\kappa)|^2$ contains the Fourier transform of the compositional fluctuations (of component B),

$$c(\kappa) = \frac{1}{\sqrt{N}} \sum_n (c_{Bn} - c_B) \exp(-2\pi i \kappa \cdot r_n^a), \qquad (44)$$

* See chapter 4

References: p. 847.

and c_{Bn} is defined as in eq. (4) to be one if a B atom is present at site n and zero otherwise. In the limit of small concentrations, $N|c(\kappa)|^2 \to Nc$ as in eq. (28). For a random distribution of B atoms of arbitrary concentration, $N|c(\kappa)|^2 \to Nc(1-c)$, and eq. (43) then yields the well-known monotonic Laue scattering $\propto c(1-c) \times (f_B - f_A)^2$. For the theory of alloys, deviations from a random distribution are of course more interesting. If displacements were negligible, $|c(\kappa)|^2$ could be obtained directly from diffuse scattering measurements, but quite frequently, displacements have to be taken into account.

Figure 15 shows a classical experimental result (MOZER et al. [1968]) on a polycrystalline Cu–47.5 at% Ni sample studied with neutrons. A unique possibility offered by neutrons has been exploited here. Some isotopes (see §2.2) have a negative scattering length, and for one (or more, if one changes the isotopic composition of the alloying partners) chemical composition of a binary alloy, it is thus possible to obtain a "null-matrix alloy" with an average scattering length $\bar{f} = 0$. This eliminates Bragg peaks that normally, in the case of polycrystals, severely limit the analysis of diffuse scattering. The alloy used by MOZER et al. [1968] contained natural Cu and Ni enriched to 99% in ^{62}Ni. In fig. 15, only very small Bragg intensities are visible, but a very pronounced modulation of the diffuse scattering indicates a non-random distribution of the alloying elements on the fcc lattice sites.

It is common to describe SRO in terms of the Warren–Cowley parameters α_{0n} (COWLEY [1950], see e.g. SCHWARTZ and COHEN [1977]). They are related to $|c(\kappa)|^2$ by:

$$|c(\kappa)|^2 = c(1-c)\alpha(\kappa), \tag{45}$$

$$\text{where} \quad \alpha(\kappa) = \sum_n \alpha_{0n} \exp(-2\pi i\kappa \cdot r_{0n}), \tag{46}$$

and the α_{0n} are defined using "conditional probabilities" P_{0n}^{AB} (indicating the probability that a B atom is at position n if an A atom is at the origin), P_{0n}^{BB} etc. (see ch. 4):

$$\alpha_{0n} = \frac{P_{0n}^{BB} - c}{1-c} = \frac{c - P_{0n}^{AB}}{c}. \tag{47}$$

Obviously, $\alpha_{00} = 1$, independent of the state of SRO, and for a random distribution, $\alpha_{0n} \equiv 0$ ($n \neq 0$). In cubic structures, the α_{0n} are usually labeled per coordination shell i or with indices lmn referring to all combinations of coordinates for positions within one shell.

For a polycrystalline sample, the diffuse SRO scattering from eqs. (43)–(46), averaged over all orientations (e.g. WARREN [1969]), is

$$\left(\frac{d\sigma}{d\Omega}\right)_{SRO} = Nc(1-c)(f_B - f_A)^2 \sum_i Z_i \alpha_i \frac{\sin 2\pi\kappa r_i}{2\pi\kappa r_i}, \tag{48}$$

where Z_i is the number of neighbours in the ith shell with radius r_i (the sum includes $i=0$). The dashed curve in fig. 15 is a fit according to eq. (48) with only one α_i adjusted ($\alpha_1 = 0.131$). This fit already looks quite reasonable and indicates that

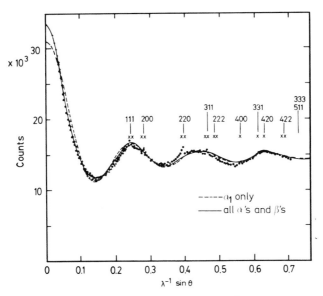

Fig. 15. Diffuse neutron scattering from polycrystalline Cu–47.5 at% Ni, furnace-cooled from 1021°C. The data indicated by crosses were taken with a neutron wavelength $\lambda = 1.951$ Å, those indicated by solid circles with $\lambda = 1.024$ Å. The Bragg positions are marked. The dashed curve is a fit with one SRO parameter only, the solid curve is the "best fit" described in the text. (After MOZER *et al.* [1968].)

short-range clustering is present in this alloy. According to eq. (47), a positive α means more BB pairs than expected from the average concentration. This "negative SRO" leads to a reduction of diffuse scattering (relative to the Laue scattering) between Bragg positions, and an enhancement near Bragg positions (including 000, i.e. $\kappa = 0$). The opposite is true for normal ("positive") SRO where $\alpha_1 < 0$.

The deviations from the simple α_1 fit visible in fig. 15 cannot be explained by contributions of more α_i terms alone (except for κ near zero). As discussed in §3, following eq. (38), displacements from ideal lattice sites introduce Huang scattering (symmetric around Bragg peaks and $\propto s^{-2}$) and "size effect" scattering (antisymmetric around reciprocal lattice points). Both contributions have to be considered in concentrated alloys, and the treatment, even for the approximation of small displacements, becomes rather involved (see, e.g., WARREN [1969] and SCHWARTZ and COHEN [1977]). In the approximation $\exp[-2\pi i\kappa\cdot(u_n - u_{n'})] \approx 1 - 2\pi i\kappa\cdot(u_n - u_{n'})$, neglecting the Huang term [(32), κ is no longer restricted to the vicinity of a Bragg peak], the diffuse scattering can be written (see WARREN [1969]):

$$\left(\frac{d\sigma}{d\Omega}\right)_d = Nc(1-c)(f_B - f_A)^2 \sum_{i,j} (\alpha_i - 2\pi i\beta_i\kappa\cdot r_{ij}) \exp(-2\pi i\kappa\cdot r_{ij}), \qquad (49)$$

where i indicates the shell and j the position in the ith shell, and the "size effect coefficients" are given by

$$\beta_i = \frac{f_A}{f_A - f_B}\left(\frac{1-c}{c} + \alpha_i\right)\epsilon_{AA}^i - \frac{f_B}{f_A - f_B}\left(\frac{c}{1-c} + \alpha_i\right)\epsilon_{BB}^i, \tag{50}$$

where the $\epsilon_{\mu\nu}^i$ are defined as the average relative deviations of the distance between a μ atom at the origin and a ν atom in the ith shell,

$$r_{\mu\nu,i} = r_i^a\left(1 + \epsilon_{\mu\nu}^i\right). \tag{51}$$

Equation (49), averaged for polycrystals, was used to fit the data in fig. 15 (Mozer et al. [1968]). The "best fit", shown by the continuous curve, was obtained with nine adjustable α_i and size effect coefficients for five shells. In this case, $\alpha_1 = 0.121$ and $\alpha_2 = -0.008$, indicating a preference for unlike second-nearest neighbours.

In a more extensive study, Vrijen and Radelaar [1978] investigated Cu–Ni alloys containing 20–80% Ni and were able to quench from thermal equilibrium at various temperatures prior to the neutron scattering measurements at room temperature.

Linear size effect corrections, frequently limited to nearest neighbours, were also used to separate SRO and size effect scattering from single crystals, exploiting the different symmetry of the α- and β-terms in eq. (49) (see Sparks and Borie [1966], Moss and Clapp [1968] and Schmatz [1973] for surveys of experimental results), until Borie and Sparks [1971] and Gragg and Cohen [1971] extended the evaluation to include size-effect contributions up to second order, i.e., starting from

$$\exp\left[-2\pi i\boldsymbol{\kappa}\cdot(\boldsymbol{u}_n - \boldsymbol{u}_{n'})\right] \approx 1 - 2\pi i\boldsymbol{\kappa}\cdot(\boldsymbol{u}_n - \boldsymbol{u}_{n'}) - 2\pi^2\left[\boldsymbol{\kappa}\cdot(\boldsymbol{u}_n - \boldsymbol{u}_{n'})\right]^2. \tag{52}$$

The "Borie–Sparks approach" is fully described in recent textbooks (e.g., Schwartz and Cohen [1977] and Cowley [1981]) and reviews (Hayakawa et al. [1975], Bardhan and Cohen [1976] and H. Chen et al. [1979]). The total diffuse intensity, divided by $Nc(1-c)(f_B - f_A)^2$, can be written in this approximation as (see Schwartz and Cohen [1977]):

$$I_d = I_\alpha + h_1 Q_x + h_2 Q_y + h_3 Q_z + h_1^2 R_x + h_2^2 R_y + h_3^2 R_z + h_1 h_2 S_{xy} + h_2 h_3 S_{yz}$$
$$+ h_3 h_1 S_{zx}, \tag{53}$$

where I_α is the short-range order term,

$$I_\alpha = \sum_{l,m,n} \alpha_{lmn} \exp\left[-2\pi i(h_1 l + h_2 m + h_3 n)\right] \tag{54}$$

(with l, m, n from $-\infty$ to $+\infty$), h_1, h_2, h_3 are the components of the scattering vector in units of the reciprocal lattice vectors $\boldsymbol{b}_i$ [see eq. (A.17), ch. 11] and the l, m, n coordinates are measured in units of the lattice vectors $\boldsymbol{a}_i$. The functions Q are the size effect terms containing corresponding components of the displacements β_{lmn} [see eqs. (50) and (51)] and similarly, the R and S functions contain pair probabilities and squares and products of displacements. All functions Q, R and S also contain ratios of atomic form factors, $f_A/(f_B - f_A)$, $f_B/(f_B - f_A)$, and only if these can be assumed to be constant, Q, R and S are periodic functions in reciprocal space. Figure 16 shows schematically the three contributions along $[h_1 00]$. Using the symmetry properties of Q, R and S, it is now possible to construct a minimum volume in reciprocal space where the diffuse intensity must be measured in order to form appropriate sums and differences for certain sets of reciprocal lattice points that will yield the various terms of eq. (53) separately (see SCHWARTZ and COHEN [1977]). Figure 17 shows the minimum volume in reciprocal space for fcc crystals. It corresponds to about 13% of a unit cell in reciprocal space and has been placed in a region accessible in reflection geometry.

The assumption of constant ratios of the atomic form factors is the main limitation of the Borie–Sparks approach if X-rays are used (see TIBALLS [1975] and GEORGOPOULOS and COHEN [1977a, 1979]), whereas it is ideally suited for neutron scattering studies. After the first application of the method to the clustering system Al–Ag (Al–5 at% Ag, GRAGG and COHEN [1971]), only a few further full applications with X-rays have been reported. The Cu–Au system is certainly the most extensively studied binary system, providing several SRO (and long-range order) effects that have been used to test theoretical ideas at various stages (MOSS and CLAPP [1968], KRIVOGLAZ [1969], MOSS [1969], WILKINS [1970], COWLEY and WILKINS [1972], MOSS and WALKER [1975], WILKINS and SHIRLEY [1975] and DE FONTAINE [1979]). BARDHAN and COHEN ([1976], see also H. CHEN *et al.* [1979]) measured the diffuse scattering of Cu_3Au in a volume of reciprocal space at six temperatures ranging from 2°C above T_c for long-range order (~ 394°C) to 930°C, and used the Borie–Sparks approach to separate the corrected, absolute intensities (including detailed error analysis, also for higher-order displacement terms, see GRAGG *et al.* [1973]). More limited measurements with smaller temperature intervals indicated discontinuous changes in slope of the diffuse intensity versus temperature near specific-heat anomalies reported in the literature. The SRO scattering separated from complete measurements at selected temperatures revealed several new features. Figure 18 shows contours of the SRO intensity (synthesized after separation) at 396, 475 and 930°C. The intensity profiles at 396°C (fig. 18a) show disc-shaped maxima near 100 and 110 as expected (corresponding to the superlattice peaks that develop for the $L1_2$ structure below T_c) and reported in previous studies. A weaker streak of

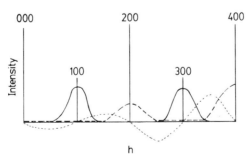

Fig. 16. Schematic of the diffuse intensity components according to eq. (53) (after SCHWARTZ and COHEN [1977]).

References: p. 847.

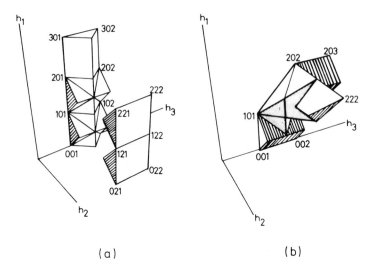

(a)   (b)

Fig. 17. (a) Typical volumes in reciprocal space required to separate the diffuse intensity from a fcc crystal into components due to local order and due to atomic displacements (to second order in the displacements). (b) As (a), after symmetry of intensity in reciprocal space across the planes $h_i = h_j$ has been employed. (After HAYAKAWA et al. [1975].)

intensity near $1 \frac{1}{2} 0$ is characteristic of local order in a material tending to order in the DO_{22} structure (two adjacent unit cells of Ll_2 with an anti-phase boundary on their common $\{100\}$ plane, and the SRO state near T_c seems to contain Ll_2- and DO_{22}-like regions. At 475°C (fig. 18b) the $1 \frac{1}{2} 0$ diffuse peak is weaker but still present. The contours around 110 are reminiscent of the satellites around 110 found in electron diffraction (see ch. 11) but there is a smooth variation of intensity. A ridge of intensity along $\langle 110 \rangle$ near 110 as stipulated by Moss and WALKER ([1975],

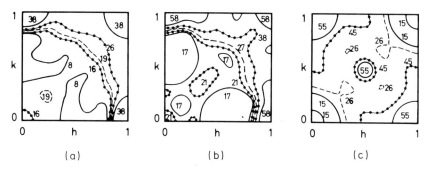

(a)   (b)   (c)

Fig. 18. Short-range order X-ray intensity [absolute intensities, cf. eq. (54)] from Cu_3Au at three different temperatures: (a) 396°C, $(h\,k\,0.1)$ section of the reciprocal lattice, scale: $1 = 1.1 \times 10^{-1}$; (b) 475°C, $(h\,k\,0.1)$ section of the reciprocal lattice, scale: $1 = 5.2 \times 10^{-2}$; (c) 930°C, $(h\,k\,0.5)$ section of the reciprocal lattice, scale: $1 = 1.9 \times 10^{-2}$. (After BARDHAN and COHEN [1976].)

Moss [1969]) for Fermi surface effects influencing SRO scattering cannot be seen. At 930°C, the cross-like pattern around 110 and the $1 \frac{1}{2} 0$ intensity are no longer visible, but a concentration of SRO intensity around $\frac{1}{2} \frac{1}{2} \frac{1}{2}$ occurs (fig. 18c). This type of scattering would result e.g. from alternating Cu- and Au-rich {111} planes.

The local atomic arrangement in SRO structures can be simulated on a computer by rearranging several thousand atoms until sufficient agreement is obtained with a given set of measured SRO parameters (GEHLEN and COHEN [1965], GRAGG *et al.* [1971]). The simulated structure can then be analyzed in terms of specific atomic arrangements. Thus, BARDHAN and COHEN [1976] were able to compare various cluster probabilities (up to quadruplets) in Cu_3Au with CVM (Cluster Variation Method) results and found a greater degree of disorder than predicted. At the highest temperature (930°C) there is a tendency for clustering of Au atoms, with a tendency for ordering in the second shell.

Apart from the classical Cu–Au system and the Al–Ag crystal mentioned above, a few other alloys have been analysed with the Borie–Sparks approach; Ni_4Mo (CHAKRAVARTI *et al.* [1974]), Cu–(9.1–14.8) at% Al (EPPERSON *et al.* [1978a]), Cu–29.8 at% Pd (OHSHIMA *et al.* [1976]) and Au_4Mn (Au–18 at% Mn, FÜRNROHR *et al.* [1980], Au–20.3 at% Mn, H. SUZUKI *et al.* [1982]) with X-rays and Ni_3Fe (LEFEBVRE *et al.* [1980, 1981]) with neutrons. The X-ray study on Cu–Al (EPPERSON *et al.* [1978a], Epperson [1979]), employing a Si(Li) detector, was performed at room temperature, with samples quenched from different temperatures ranging from 150–900°C. The apparent degree of SRO was found to pass through a minimum near 350°C for Cu–14.8 at% Al. The values obtained for samples quenched from higher temperatures do not reflect thermal equilibrium. For some of the equilibrium states (1580 h annealing at 150°C), a computer simulation was performed using the experimental α_i and requiring agreement for the first six α_i. The resulting structures were searched for specific nearest-neighbour configurations (CLAPP [1971]), and fig. 19 shows those found in all conditions investigated. In these configurations, none of the Al atoms are nearest neighbours. The configurations C9, C16 and C17 are particularly frequent in the equilibrium states.

The SRO study on Ni_3Fe (LEFEBVRE *et al.* [1980, 1981]) demonstrates for the first time the ideal suitability of the Borie–Sparks method for the analysis of neutron scattering experiments. Furthermore, the least-squares fitting method developed by WILLIAMS [1972, 1976] which also includes second-order size-effect corrections, is compared with the Borie–Sparks approach, and the experimental results are compared with similar X-ray measurements.

All displacements were found to be very small, in agreement with the small size effect in Ni–Fe (see ch. 4). The α_0 values were always close to one (within 7%, with an uncertainty of 6% attributed to the calibration alone). Pair potentials were calculated in the CLAPP and MOSS [1968] approximation. They show an oscillatory behaviour and a rapid decrease, similar to CuAu (METCALFE and LEAKE [1975]). The ratios V_2/V_1 and V_3/V_1 place Ni_3Fe well within the $L1_2$ stability region, in contrast to Cu_3Au.

Further improvements for the X-ray case have been achieved. As the main

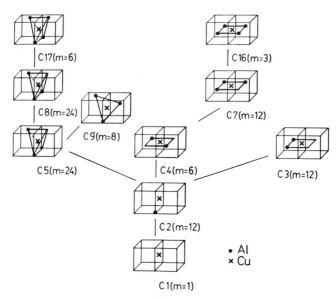

Fig. 19. The nearest-neighbour configurations of Al atoms (solid circles) around Cu atoms (crosses) found in a Cu–14.76 at% Al single crystal annealed for 1 h at 650°C and quenched to room temperature. Two adjacent unit cells are outlined. Not specially marked lattice sites are occupied by Cu atoms. The number of crystallographically equivalent variants of a configuration is indicated by m. (After EPPERSON et al. [1978a].)

problem in the separation of X-ray diffuse scattering data is caused by the frequently substantial variation of the ratios of atomic form factors across the experimental κ range, TIBALLS [1975] has proposed to write the functions Q, R and S of the Borie–Sparks approach as products of these ratios and new functions Q', R' and S' that are *strictly* periodic in reciprocal space. There are now 25 independent periodic functions instead of 10 in the Borie–Sparks method. GEORGOPOULOS and COHEN [1977a, 1979] have developed a new separation method based on this approach. The procedure is a factor of 2.5 more laborious than for the Borie–Sparks method. From a detailed error analysis the authors conclude that the extra effort may be worthwile, especially for clustering systems. Apart from more reliable values for α_i, the method also yields individual (AA, BB, AB) values for the displacement terms. A first application to diffuse scattering from an Al–1.7 at% Cu single crystal aged to contain GPI zones has been reported (AUVRAY et al. [1981]). The resulting α_i have been used to synthesize a model crystal with 108 000 atoms (30^3 fcc cells, with periodic boundary conditions) which was subsequently searched for Cu-rich zones. A mixture of single- and multi-layer zones with {100} faces was found, consisting essentially of pure Cu whereas practically no Cu was found in the matrix. The original model for GPI (GEROLD [1954, 1958]) is a Cu monolayer disc about 5 nm in diameter with the adjacent Al planes collapsing toward the zone. The displacements found by AUVRAY *et al.* [1981] are also different (substantially larger but decreasing more rapidly, similar to the lattice statics results by SEITZ and DE FONTAINE [1976]) from those in Gerold's model. For a recent discussion of these results, see GEROLD and BUBECK [1982] and COHEN and GEORGOPOULOS [1982]. Another application of the TIBALLS–Georgopoulos–Cohen method concerns the defect arrangement in non-stoichiometric β'-NiAl (GEORGOPOULOS and COHEN [1977b, 1981]).

The three-dimensional measurements necessary for a complete separation of diffuse scattering are time-consuming. Quantitative kinetic studies at temperature have therefore been performed with somewhat reduced requirements, e.g. by recording the intensity at a few points in reciprocal space. H. CHEN and COHEN [1977] have reported measurements of continuous ordering at temperatures above T_c (for long-range order) for a variety of alloy single crystals and evaluated the results in terms of the theory of continuous transformations (see COOK [1976]).

No complete separation of SRO in a bcc or non-cubic system has been reported (for limited information, see SEMENOSKAYA [1974] for Fe–Al, SAFRONOVA *et al.* [1977] for hexagonal and fcc Mg–In alloys and MEARDON and KOSTORZ [1975] for a hexagonal Ti–Zr null-matrix alloy).

There are many other studies of SRO where the elaborate procedures described above were not employed. Thus, BOUCHIAT *et al.* [1981] and DARTYGE *et al.* [1982] have found atomic SRO in the spin glass alloy systems A̲g–Mn and A̲g–Fe, respectively, using X-rays. The absence of a small-angle scattering signal for A̲g–Mn (1–24 at% Mn, single crystals quenched from 900°C) coupled with diffuse spots at $1\frac{1}{2}\,0$ indicates ordering but the $D0_{22}$ structure can be ruled out as the basic ordering unit. More complex models are discussed (e.g. $I4_1/amd$) where nearest-neighbour Mn pairs could also be present. As nearest-neighbour Mn atoms are believed to couple antiferromagnetically and next-nearest pairs ferromagnetically, the SRO state has important consequences on the magnetic order (BOUCHIAT *et al.* [1981]), and the same arguments would apply to C̲u–Mn, a system frequently studied with neutrons (see e.g. HICKS [1979]). The Au–Fe system shows a tendency for clustering (DARTYGE *et al.* [1982]), and the authors propose Fe-rich platelets parallel to {420} in quenched single crystals containing 14.4, 15.4 and 19 at% Fe (compositions just spanning the spin-glass/ferromagnet transition). SRO in F̲e–V (MIREBEAU *et al.* [1982]) and clustering in C̲r–Fe (KAJZAR *et al.* [1981]) have recently been studied with neutrons, the latter investigation employing polarized neutrons and revealing a ferromagnetic coupling of iron moments in clusters, starting from 2.4 at% Fe. The results are in qualitative agreement with a model by FRIEDEL and HEDMAN [1978] for the occurrence of a ferromagnetic component in the magnetic properties of C̲r–Fe at this concentration. For further neutron scattering work on magnetic alloys, see BROWN [1979] and HICKS [1979].

References: p. 847.

4.3. Phase transitions

A phase transition is normally accompanied by a measurable change of the scattering function, and X-rays and neutrons are frequently used to monitor structural and other transitions.

In liquids and amorphous solids, the atomic arrangement is not spatially periodic, and the diffraction pattern shows no Bragg peaks but just diffuse intensity due to the combined effect of positional and compositional disorder. The evaluation of these structures is beyond the scope of this chapter (see, e.g. WAGNER [1978] for a survey, NOLD et al. [1981] and LARIDJANI and SADOC [1981] for examples of structural studies on amorphous Fe–B and Gd–Y). Crystallization, i.e. long-range positional order, introduces Bragg peaks in the scattering pattern.

Quite similar observations, though primarily related to the compositional scattering term, can be made when a long-range ordered (LRO) structure develops in a sample with SRO (see COHEN [1970], COWLEY [1981]). Sharp superlattice peaks indicate that large, fully ordered domains are present, eventually separated by antiphase boundaries (see ch. 14). If these antiphase boundaries occur with any kind of periodicity (not necessarily commensurate with the basic lattice), the superlattice peaks will split according to the long-period repeat distance (CuAuII, see ch. 11). In fact, if the resolution is high enough, splitting may also be observed in SRO crystals (see ch. 11, for X-rays: Moss [1966] and COWLEY [1981]), giving rise to the so-called microdomain model of SRO.

Apart from substitutional or interstitial (see, e.g., Moss [1982]) ordering, the appearance of new commensurate or incommensurate structures due to displacements and related precursor effects have become a subject of intense research, for three-dimensional systems (see ch. 15, Moss [1977]; GOBIN and GUENIN [1978] for martensites, SANCHEZ and DE FONTAINE [1977] and PYNN [1978] for the ω-transformation) and especially in two- and one-dimensional systems (see COWLEY et al. [1979], COMÈS and SHIRANE [1979], ALCACER [1980] and AXE [1983]). Here, diffuse

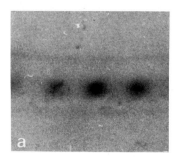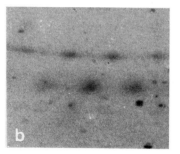

Fig. 20. Enlarged sections from X-ray diffuse scattering patterns of KCP, showing the buildup of three-dimensional order at low temperature: (a) at room temperature: one-dimensional scattering; the diffuse scattering occurs in a continuous diffuse satellite line. (b) at 77 K: the intensity on the diffuse line has condensed half-way between two successive Bragg spots. (From COMÈS et al. [1973].)

scattering and new diffraction peaks are due to the establishment of discrete patterns of static or dynamic displacements. Figure 20 (COMÈS *et al.* [1973]) shows details of two X-ray scattering patterns of KCP [$K_2Pt(CN)_4 Br_{0.3} \cdot xH_2O$], a compound with one-dimensional metallic properties. In fig. 20a, bands of diffuse scattering can be seen at a distance of $2k_F(k_F =$ Fermi wavevector) above and below a layer line of Bragg spots. These diffuse lines correspond to a one-dimensional modulation of the platinum chains. Below 120 K, the diffuse scattering starts concentrating at reciprocal lattice vectors of the type ($1/2a$, $1/2a$, $2k_F$), corresponding to an increasing coupling of the phases of the modulations of neighbouring chains. X-rays cannot distinguish between static and dynamic modulations, and neutrons are frequently used to study the dynamics of modulated structures and displacive transitions (see COMÈS and SHIRANE [1979], CURRAT and PYNN [1979], and §6).

5.   *Near the incident beam*

This section will be mostly concerned with the region around the origin of the reciprocal lattice, i.e., $\kappa \ll g_m$ where g_m is the modulus of the smallest reciprocal lattice vector. This field is commonly called low- or small-angle scattering which means diffuse scattering for small κ, not just Bragg diffraction at small angles as in the electron microscope or with γ-rays. After a summary of the principles of small-angle scattering, some applications to the study of inhomogeneities in alloys and of defect clusters will be presented. Finally, some other effects and methods for $\kappa \approx 0$ will be discussed.

5.1. Small-angle scattering

Small-angle scattering (SAS) is caused by the variation of scattering length density over distances exceeding the normal interatomic distances in condensed matter. If κ is the maximum value of the scattering vector accessible in a SAS experiment, details on a scale smaller than about $1/\kappa_{max}$ will not be resolved, and the discrete arrangement of scattering centres (atoms or nuclei) can be replaced by a continuous distribution of scattering length over volumes of about $1/\kappa_{max}^3$. Sums may then be replaced by integrals (cf. eq. (A10.b), ch. 11), and the theory of SAS specializes on the evaluation of these integrals for a variety of cases. For a full account of the theoretical principles, developed for X-rays but equally valid for neutrons, see GUINIER and FOURNET [1955], BEEMAN *et al.* [1957], GUINIER [1963], GEROLD [1967] and POROD [1982], for neutrons see SCHMATZ [1976, 1978] and KOSTORZ [1979]. The basic expression for the SAS cross-section is

$$\frac{d\sigma}{d\Omega} = |\int_{V_s} \rho_f(r) \exp(-2\pi i\kappa \cdot r) \, d^3r|^2, \tag{55}$$

where the integration extends over the sample volume, V_s, and $\rho_f(r)$ is the scattering

References: p. 847.

length density, locally averaged as indicated above. It is also useful to write

$$\rho_f(r) = \Delta\rho_f(r) + \bar{\rho}_f,$$ (56)

where $\bar{\rho}_f$ is averaged over distances much larger than $1/\kappa_{min}$, and κ_{min} is the smallest κ value accessible in the experiment. For the κ range considered, only $\Delta\rho_f(r)$ will contribute to the scattering, i.e.:

$$\frac{d\sigma}{d\Omega} = |\int_{V_s} [\Delta\rho_f(r)] \exp(-2\pi i\kappa \cdot r) \, d^3r|^2.$$ (57)

Equations (55) or (57) may be used as a starting point for analytical or numerical calculations of scattering for model distributions. With the help of the equations of §2.3, magnetic SAS may also be included for the case of neutrons.

The simplest and very widely used approach to SAS is based on the two-phase model, assuming small particles with a homogeneous scattering length density ρ_{fp} embedded in a homogeneous matrix of scattering length density ρ_{fm} ($\rho_{fm} = 0$ covers the case of small particles in vacuo). If there are N_p identical particles without spatial correlations (dilute limit), but – if they are anisometric – all aligned in the same direction:

$$\frac{d\sigma}{d\Omega} = N_p(\rho_{fp} - \rho_{fm})^2 V_p^2 S(\kappa),$$ (58)

where V_p is the volume of one particle and $S(\kappa)$, the *single-particle scattering function*, is given by:

$$S(\kappa) = \left| \frac{1}{V_p} \int_{V_p} \exp(-2\pi i\kappa \cdot r) \, d^3r \right|^2, \qquad S(0) = 1.$$ (59)

$S(\kappa)$ can be calculated for a variety of particle shapes (see POROD [1982]) and depends on the direction of κ relative to any given axis, except for spheres. For all other particle shapes, $S(\kappa)$ has to be averaged for a given orientational distribution. Only if the orientational distribution is isotropic, κ can be replaced by κ for anisometric particles.

In many real scattering systems, the single-particle approach is not valid as particle sizes and possibly particle shape as a function of size may vary and spatial and orientational correlations must be considered. Generalized cases can only be treated by finite-element methods, but several approximations have been suggested, e.g., evaluation of size distributions of spheres or other uncorrelated particles of known shape, or linear distance distributions of polydisperse spheres (GUINIER [1963]). These problems are extensively discussed by POROD [1982] and GLATTER [1982a, b]. If eq. (58) can be used (possibly after correction for interparticle interference), the evaluation of SAS yields important parameters of the scattering systems. We summarize some general properties.

a. Extrapolation to $\kappa = 0$. If the extrapolation can be performed reliably (experimental problems at very small angles may interfere), eq. (58) yields [because

$S(0) = 1$]:

$$\frac{d\sigma}{d\Omega}(\kappa \to 0) = N_p(\rho_{fp} - \rho_{fm})^2 V_p^2. \tag{60}$$

Three parameters determine $d\sigma/d\Omega(\kappa \to 0)$: number of particles (i.e. particle density $n_p = N_p/V_s$), contrast and particle size. Combined with information from other parts of the scattering curve, they may be obtained separately.

b. Guinier approximation. For any particle shape, the scattering function at small values of κa (where a is the relevant size of the particle) can be approximated by an exponential function (GUINIER [1939, 1963]),

$$S(\kappa) = \exp(-4\pi^2\kappa^2 R_\kappa^2), \tag{61}$$

where R_κ is the radius of gyration of the particle defined by

$$R_\kappa^2 = \frac{1}{V_p} \int_{V_p} r_\kappa^2 q(r_\kappa) \, dr_\kappa, \tag{62}$$

where $q(r_\kappa)$ is the geometrical cross-section of the particle at a distance r_κ measured along the direction of κ from the origin inside the particle, defined by $\int r_\kappa q(r_\kappa) \, dr_\kappa = 0$. The scattering function reflects the anisometry of a particle as its decrease with increasing κ is more rapid for larger R_κ. For randomly oriented particles:

$$S(\kappa) = \overline{S(\kappa)} = \exp(-4\pi^2\kappa^2 R_G^2/3), \tag{63}$$

with the *average* radius of gyration R_G defined by

$$R_G^2 = \frac{1}{V_p} \int_{V_p} r^2 \, d^3r. \tag{64}$$

The quantity R_G is also called *Guinier radius*. For a sphere of radius R_s, $R_G^2 = 3R_s^2/5$, for an ellipsoid with axes $2a$, $2b$, $2c$, $R_G^2 = (a^2 + b^2 + c^2)/5$. For other particle shapes, see e.g. GLATTER [1982a].

The Guinier approximation results from an expansion of the exponential function in eq. (59) and a reinterpretation of the resulting series for $S(\kappa)$ as an exponential [eq. (63)]. The term proportional to κ^2 in the Guinier approximation is exact for any particle shape. For spheres, the term with κ^4 from eq. (63) is correct to better than 10%, and higher-order terms are in fair agreement. The Guinier approximation is therefore acceptable for $2\pi R_G\kappa \lesssim 1.2$. For not too strongly anisometric particles, a wider range may even be possible, whereas for extremely anisometric particles (e.g. rods or platelets) the higher-order terms will contribute at smaller values of κ (see, e.g., POROD [1982]).

c. Integrated intensity. From eq. (57):

$$Q = \frac{1}{V_s} \int \frac{d\sigma}{d\Omega}(\kappa) \, d^3\kappa = \overline{\{\Delta\rho_f(r)\}^2}, \tag{65}$$

References: p. 847.

where the integration extends over the entire reciprocal space ($0 \leqslant \kappa \leqslant \infty$) and the bar denotes averaging over the sample. As Q represents the mean-square fluctuation of the system which is insensitive to detailed structural features, it is sometimes (see POROD [1982]) called 'invariant'. In the two-phase model:

$$Q = (\rho_{fp} - \bar{\rho}_f)(\bar{\rho}_f - \rho_{fm}) \tag{66a}$$

$$\text{or} \quad Q = C_p(1 - C_p)(\rho_{fp} - \rho_{fm})^2, \tag{66b}$$

where $C_p = N_p V_p / V_s$ is the volume fraction of particles. The invariant is, as eq. (65) indicates, the Fourier transform of the scattering cross-section for $r = 0$, i.e., a special value $\gamma(0)$ of a correlation function $\gamma(r)$ (see POROD [1982]) which, however, has a simple meaning only for dilute isotropic systems.

d. Characteristic length. An average correlation length L_c can be defined by (the bar denotes an average of all directions of κ if the system is anisotropic):

$$L_c = \frac{2\pi}{V_s Q} \int \kappa \overline{\frac{d\sigma}{d\Omega}}(\kappa) \, d\kappa, \tag{67}$$

with Q as defined in eq. (65), for any scattering system. In the two-phase model, L_c can be interpreted as the mean length of all lines passing through all points in all directions. The average of all the chords is L_p, the *characteristic length*, given by

$$L_p = 2\pi V_p \int \kappa \overline{S(\kappa)} \, d\kappa. \tag{68}$$

e. Porod approximation. For scattering systems with well-defined internal surfaces (see POROD [1951, 1982]), the final slope of the scattering function is proportional to κ^{-4}. For particles of any shape (κ must be larger than the inverse of the shortest dimension of the particle):

$$\overline{S(\kappa)} \simeq (2\pi)^{-3} A_p V_p^{-2} \kappa^{-4}, \tag{69}$$

where A_p is the surface area of the particle. Inserting eq. (69) into eq. (58), we get:

$$\frac{d\sigma}{d\Omega} = (2\pi)^{-3} N_p A_p (\rho_{fp} - \rho_{fm})^2 \kappa^{-4}; \tag{70}$$

the cross-section becomes proportional to the total surface area of the scattering particles.

The advantage of the Guinier approximation is that the radius of gyration, i.e. a size parameter, can be determined from uncalibrated SAS data [cf. eqs. (61) and (63), inserted into eq. (58)]. The combination of several of the above relationships [(60) and (61) or (63), (66), (68) and (70)] allows one to evaluate shape, size, number and composition of uniform particles from precise measurements over a sufficiently large range of κ. For example, eqs. (66b) and (70) yield the surface-to-volume ratio of particles, again without calibration of the measured intensities.

Although X-rays are more widely available than neutrons, the use of neutrons in SAS studies of metallic systems is basically more universal. As SAS is measured in transmission geometry, the most severe restriction for X-rays stems from the absorption properties of materials (see §2.2, table 2). For CuK_α radiation, the optimum thickness [see eq. (13), $\Sigma_t D_s = 1$] of a pure Al sample is $D_s = 76$ μm, but less than 10 μm for many other metals (atomic numbers 23–27 and above 41, except 55). With MoK_α, Al of 713 μm thickness is ideal, but for most heavier metals, 20–100 μm should not be exceeded. Although with more powerful sources or yet shorter wavelengths somewhat thicker samples may be used, the sample volume may still not be representative of the bulk material. Undesired scattering from surface irregularities (ROTH [1977], KOSTORZ [1976], PARKER [1972]) and sample environment (windows, heat shields etc.) will be more perturbing with X-rays than with neutrons. Another difficulty arises from double Bragg scattering which can obscure the SAS effects and sometimes exceed them. The general remedy, increasing the incident wavelength above the Bragg cut-off, works well for neutrons but not for X-rays where only properly oriented single crystals can eliminate this problem. Finally, inelastic scattering may be appreciable at high sample temperatures, and if a separation is required, neutrons must be used.

The applications of SAS of X-rays and neutrons to metallurgical problems are numerous and have recently been extensively reviewed (GEROLD and KOSTORZ [1978] and KOSTORZ [1979, 1982]). From a simple verification of sample homogeneity to the determination of sizes, size distribution and interparticle interference effects, the degree of complexity of evaluation procedures varies from simple analytical methods to very involved computer routines. Here, only a few examples of SAS research related to alloys and defects can be given.

5.2. Alloys

GUINIER [1938, 1939] was the first to report SAS results from various Al-rich alloys, e.g. Al–Cu and Al–Ag, and found evidence for the existence of very small coherent precipitates, now known as *Guinier–Preston zones* (GP zones). An important problem which still has not been solved completely is the question how phase separation is initiated and progresses during the early stages when large parts of the sample are still in a supersaturated state (see ch. 14). The SAS technique is sensitive to small (in scale and in amplitude) compositional variations, bridging the domains accessible by field-ion microscopy and transmission-electron microscopy. Many SAS experiments have therefore been performed to study phase separation, but also coarsening reactions, particle parameters in relation to other properties, and dissolution of precipitates (see the reviews quoted above). For X-rays, Al-rich alloys are most suitable, and very few other systems have been studied. Initial experiments with neutrons concentrated on Al alloys too, but attention to other systems has continuously increased.

As an example, fig. 21 (MESSOLORAS [1974]) shows a set of SAS curves obtained for a polycrystalline Al–6.8 at% Zn alloy (neutron measurements in a cryostat at

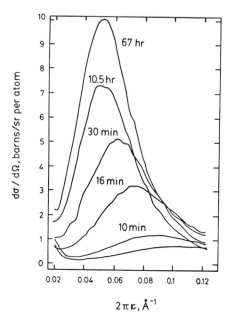

Fig. 21. Neutron SAS cross-sections as a function of $2\pi\kappa$ for an Al–6.8 at% Zn alloy quenched from 310°C into ice water and aged at room temperature for the indicated periods (from MESSOLORAS [1974]).

4.2 K). As the scattering did not depend on the direction of κ, the SAS cross-sections (calibration with the incoherent scattering of vanadium) are given as a function of the modulus of κ. A peak of the SAS intensity at a value $\kappa_m \neq 0$ is quite common for decomposing or decomposed alloys containing – in their fully decomposed metastable or stable state – a few percent of precipitates ($C_p \to 7\%$ in the present example). An early appearance of a peak has sometimes been taken as evidence for the mechanism of spinodal decomposition (see ch. 14) but this feature of SAS alone is insufficient to distinguish between concentration fluctuations and well-defined homogeneous particles. Quantitative kinetic measurements with a variation of important parameters (initial concentration, quenching conditions, ageing conditions) are necessary and must be compared with specific predictions of the different theoretical models. A SAS peak will of course also occur in a two-phase system as the first maximum of the interparticle interference function (see GUINIER and FOURNET [1955], LASLAZ et al. [1977a] and GLATTER [1982b]), and many other cases can be constructed, e.g., a "three-phase" system representing particle, surroundings depleted of the alloying element, and supersaturated matrix (WALKER and GUINIER [1953]). Figure 22 shows measurements obtained at a synchrotron (LURE–DCI, Orsay) with $\lambda = 1.54$ Å, revealing a SAS peak at very small κ for Al–6.8 at% Zn aged at 135°C, a temperature which is definitely above any spinodal at this composition.

Considerable progress has been made in recent years in the theoretical description

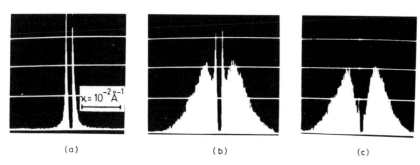

(a)   (b)   (c)

Fig. 22. Multichannel analyzer display of SAS patterns obtained with a linear position-sensitive detector. The centre was covered by a beam stop. (a) Pure Al; (b) Al–6.8 at% Zn, aged for 7 h at 135°C; (c) difference between alloy and pure Al (long white lines in the centre are artefacts). Measuring time 100 s, intensity range (full scale) 51 200 counts. (From NAUDON *et al.* [1979].)

of the decomposition of alloys (see ch. 14, and MARTIN [1978] for a review), in the metastability (nucleation) and in the instability (spinodal) regimes. The Al–Zn system (on the Al-rich side) is an ideal candidate for an experimental verification of many theoretical predictions as the matrix is almost elastically isotropic and the Zn-rich GP zones are fully coherent with the matrix and initially spherical because of a small size effect (see ch. 4). Under these circumstances, scattering length density changes can be exclusively attributed to compositional changes (displacement effects, small according to eq. (32), can be neglected), and a comparison with coarse-grained models, cluster dynamics theories and computer simulations is more easily achieved. In a series of experiments, Guyot and coworkers (LASLAZ *et al.* [1977a, b], HENNION *et al.* [1982], GUYOT and SIMON [1982]) have investigated the kinetics of decomposition of slightly supersaturated Al–Zn alloys (poly- and single crystals) at various temperatures by neutron SAS. In the range of 5.3–12.1 at% Zn, the rate of decomposition at constant temperature increases dramatically with increasing supersaturation. If the supersaturation is very small, a slowing-down is noticeable. The overall kinetics compares favourably with the nucleation theory for fluids by LANGER and SCHWARTZ [1980]. A linear spinodal behaviour (exponential growth of SAS intensity and time-invariant cross-over of the scattering function) is not found (peak intensity and peak position follow power laws). However, a nonlinear spinodal process cannot be ruled out. Figure 23 shows a standard plot suggested by the linear theory, with $\Re(2\pi\kappa, t)/(2\pi\kappa)^2$ as a function of $(2\pi\kappa)^2$, where

$$\Re(2\pi\kappa, t) = \frac{\partial \ln \hat{S}(2\pi\kappa, t)}{\partial t}, \tag{71}$$

and $\hat{S}$ is the normalized scattering function. The linear theory predicts one straight line for a plot as in fig. 23, whereas the experimental results show pronounced curvature and a change with time, in qualitative agreement with the mean-field

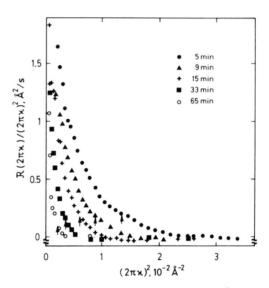

Fig. 23. Evolution of the amplification factor $\mathcal{R}(2\pi\kappa)$, divided by $(2\pi\kappa)^2$, versus $(2\pi\kappa)^2$, upon ageing of an Al–12.1 at% Zn alloy at 20°C. The vertical arrows indicate the positions of the SAS peak (cf. figs. 21, 22) for the various ageing times indicated. (After GUYOT and SIMON [1982].)

theory of LANGER *et al.* [1975] (see GUYOT and SIMON [1982]). With the average zone size as the relevant length scale (FURUKAWA [1979]), the more advanced stages for all alloys can be scaled according to

$$\hat{S}(2\pi\kappa, t) = |2R_s(t)|^3 \, \mathcal{F}(4\pi\kappa R_s), \tag{72}$$

with an average zone radius R_s and a unique scaled function $\mathcal{F}$. This type of scaling is suggested by Ising model computer simulations (MARRO *et al.* [1979], see HENN-ION *et al.* [1982], and LEBOWITZ *et al.* [1982]). In the same ageing regime, a standard analysis based on the two-phase model yields consistent results, and coarsening according to the Wagner–Lifshitz–Slyozov theory sets in.

The Zn concentrations in the Al–Zn studies discussed above cover the metastable and unstable regime (the spinodal at room temperature is suggested to pass near 7.6 at% Zn, RUNDMAN and HILLIARD [1967]), but no distinct difference in the decomposition behaviour was found. It may be inferred that the instability regime occurs at higher concentrations of Zn. The Pt–40% Au alloy studied by SINGHAL *et al.* [1978] (see also KOSTORZ [1983]) was chosen because of the almost symmetrical miscibility gap in this system. Neutron SAS results for samples aged at $T/T_c = 0.4$–0.6 ($T_c \approx 1100°$C) show the same general behaviour, i.e. power laws for κ_m and the peak intensity, curvature of the '$\mathcal{R}$-plots' [eq. (71)] and scaling (at least for $T/T_c = 0.6$, see LEBOWITZ *et al.* [1982]) at the later stages of decomposition ($t > 30$ min).

The earliest stages of decomposition, in favourable cases well accessible with the

SAS technique, are still not well understood. The role of quenched-in vacancies deserves further experimental attention and theoretical consideration. For example, the more concentrated Al–Zn alloys studied by ACUÑA [1980] with X-ray SAS show a reduced rate of decomposition, probably because of a smaller amount of quenched-in vacancies. Besides quenching, unconventional methods of reaching non-equilibrium states in alloys may be helpful, e.g., neutron transmutation or ion implantation (see DELAFOND *et al.* [1981] for $Zn^{+(+)}$ implantation in Al and GP zones studied by X-ray SAS).

Some more applied SAS studies with neutrons on technical alloys have been summarized (KOSTORZ [1979]). In a recent investigation of microstructural changes in a nickel-base superalloy, 713 LC, SCHWAHN *et al.* [1981] observed a coarsening of the γ' precipitates with increasing creep deformation to a larger plate-like shape with the shorter axis preferring alignment along the stress axis, and an increasing volume fraction of voids and microcracks near the fracture surface. A neutron time-of-flight SAS study on a superconducting multifilament composite wire allowed the ageing behaviour to be determined nondestructively (OSAMURA *et al.* [1982b]). The Ti-rich Ti–Nb–Ta–Zr alloy embedded in Cu showed α precipitation when aged at 643 K.

Decomposition processes in amorphous alloys (with and without crystallization) have received particular attention. SAS of X-rays has been reported for a variety of substances (see OSAMURA *et al.* [1981a, b, 1982a], FLANK *et al.* [1981] and NAUDON and FLANK [1982]), and fig. 24 shows an example of a rolled and subsequently heat-treated sample of $Fe_{90}Zr_{10}$. The drastic change of the SAS intensity is attributed to fine-scale separation (~ 60 Å) into α-Fe and $Fe_3Zr/Fe_{23}Zr_6$ (OSAMURA *et al.* [1983]). No Bragg peaks are found with X-rays or electrons.

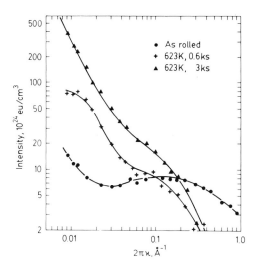

Fig. 24. X-ray SAS for amorphous $Fe_{90}Zr_{10}$ after rolling (as rolled) and subsequent annealing as indicated (after OSAMURA *et al.* [1982a]).

References: p. 847.

Compositional fluctuations and clustering above the critical temperature for phase separation may also be studied by SAS techniques. For large-scale fluctuations, i.e. those relevant for the SAS signal, the continuum theory of fluctuation waves (see KRIVOGLAZ [1969]) is appropriate, and one can write [starting from eq. (43)] for a binary alloy (v_a is the atomic volume):

$$\frac{d\sigma}{d\Omega} = \frac{NkT}{v_a}(f_B - f_A)^2 \left(g'' + 4\pi^2 B\kappa^2 \right)^{-1},$$ (73)

$$\text{as} \quad \overline{|c(\kappa)|^2} = \frac{kT}{v_a}\left(g'' + 4\pi^2 B\kappa^2 \right)^{-1},$$ (74)

with $g'' = d^2g/dc^2$ and g = Gibbs free energy density, and B = gradient energy term. The free energy density g may contain, apart form the chemical term g_0, a strain energy term g_δ taking into account the elastic strain energy around a cluster (see ch. 14). Defining a correlation length ξ by

$$\xi^2 = \frac{B}{g_0'' + g_\delta''}$$ (75)

$$\text{and} \quad \frac{d\sigma}{d\Omega}(0) = \frac{NkT(f_B - f_A)^2}{v_a(g_0'' + g_\delta'')},$$ (76)

one can write:

$$\frac{d\sigma}{d\Omega}(\kappa) = \frac{d\sigma}{d\Omega}(0)\frac{1}{1 + 4\pi^2\xi^2\kappa^2}.$$ (77)

According to eqs. (75) and (76), $d\sigma/d\Omega(0)$ and the correlation length diverge if $g_0'' + g_\delta'' \to 0$, i.e. when an coherent critical point is approached. This has been confirmed by SCHWAHN and SCHMATZ [1978] for Al–Zn of the critical composition $c = 39.5$ at% Al. The stable phase diagram shows a critical temperature of 351.5°C, but neutron SAS measurements (at temperature) indicated no special behaviour at this temperature. Upon further cooling, large changes occurred between 324 and 322°C, corresponding to the coherent critical point at 323°C. A depression of the coherent spinodal by 28 K is well understood on the basis of CAHN's [1961] formulation of the elastic energy term.

The kinetics of clustering in Cu–Ni alloys (see §4 for diffuse scattering) has been followed by neutron SAS, too, to complete the diffuse scattering results (see VRIJEN et al. [1980]). Equation (77) gives the scattering intensity for equilibrium at any temperature above a miscibility gap. COOK [1969] derived an expression for the time evolution of SAS based on the linear theory of spinodal decomposition developed by CAHN (see ch. 14 and CAHN [1968]) [the formalism can be extended to larger κ by using a discrete lattice model for diffusion (COOK et al. [1969])]:

$$\frac{d\sigma}{d\Omega}(\kappa, t) = \frac{d\sigma}{d\Omega}(\kappa, 0) - I_\infty(\kappa) \exp[2\Re(2\pi\kappa)t] + I_\infty(\kappa),$$ (78)

where $I_\infty(\kappa)$ denotes the equilibrium value [eq. (77)] and $\Re(2\pi\kappa)$ is the amplification factor [cf. eq. (71)] which is independent of time in the linear theory and of course negative for temperatures outside the spinodal. The linearization of the diffusion equation is better justified in the single-phase region than in the unstable regime, and it seems that SAS studies above the miscibility gap can yield more reliable values of the parameters (diffusion coefficient, strain energy, gradient energy) appearing in the theory. Figure 25 shows the SAS during relaxation of clustering in Ni–32 at% Cu (AALDERS [1982]) and the $\mathcal{R}$ values obtained according to eq. (78). If $I_\infty(\kappa)$ can be reached for a series of temperatures, and the inverse correlation length obtained from an Ornstein–Zernike–Debye plot [reciprocal intensity versus κ^2, see eq. (71)] is plotted as a function of temperature, extrapolation to $\xi^{-2} = 0$ yields the critical temperature (e.g. $T_c = 500$ K for Ni–32% Cu, 675 K for Ni–30% Cu–5% Fe, AALDERS [1982]).

Magnetic clusters and precipitates can be studied with neutron SAS. The magnetic structure factor, eq. (19), can, in analogy to nuclear scattering, be reinterpreted by introducing an integration over fluctuations of the local magnetization density

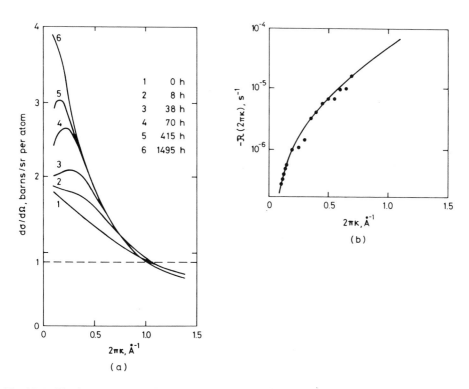

Fig. 25. (a) Elastic neutron scattering cross-section as a function of $2\pi\kappa$ for different annealing times for a Ni–32 at% Cu alloy annealed at 650 K (quenched from 975 K). The dashed line indicates the Laue scattering (random alloy). (b) The (negative) amplification factor $\mathcal{R}(2\pi\kappa)$ as a function of $2\pi\kappa$ obtained from (a). (After AALDERS [1982].)

rather than discrete magnetic moments,

$$M(\kappa) = \frac{1}{V_s} \int_{V_s} M(r) \exp(-2\pi i \kappa \cdot r) \, d^3 r. \tag{79}$$

A homogeneously magnetized sample will therefore not show any magnetic SAS, but fluctuations in the orientation and/or the magnitude of $M(r)$ will be revealed (see GEROLD and KOSTORZ [1978], SCHMATZ [1978], HICKS [1979] and KOSTORZ [1979]).

5.3. Defects

Here, we discuss the SAS from dislocations and clusters of point defects as further examples of inhomogeneities revealed by this technique, and some other defect scattering results.

In an otherwise homogeneous material, dislocations yield a SAS signal according to eq. (57) because of local density changes which can be described by elastic continuum theory. This scattering is very small, and as the presence of dislocations simultaneously increases the probability of double Bragg scattering, early attempts to reveal SAS from dislocations with X-rays failed. ATKINSON [1959] and ATKINSON and LOWDE [1957] used neutrons of long wavelength and finally found true SAS of the correct intensity from deformed metals. Theoretical work by ATKINSON and HIRSCH [1958a, b] and Seeger and coworkers (SEEGER and KRÖNER [1959], SEEGER [1959], KRONMÜLLER et al. [1963], SEEGER and RÜHLE [1963]) for isotropic cubic crystals and by SEEGER and KRÖNER [1959] and SCHMATZ et al. [1974], who considered elastic anisotropy, has been reviewed by SCHMATZ [1975] along with the (scarce) experimental results. The SAS cross-sections are so small that even for high dislocation densities, not many specific dislocation arrangements have been studied, and surface irregularities or a few large inclusions or pores may easily obscure the scattering pattern.

In magnetic crystals, magnetoelastic coupling leads to an additional SAS term (for unpolarized neutrons), and deformed single crystals of Ni (SCHEUER [1977]) and Fe (GÖLTZ [1976]) (see SCHMATZ [1978] and KOSTORZ [1979]) have been studied making use of the additional intensity and its symmetry properties near magnetic saturation. Despite the magnetic scattering, experiments of this type are very tedious and require a high incident neutron flux.

The agglomeration of point defects should lead to more easily measurable SAS effects as the scattering contrast is much higher. An extensive study of the structure and annealing behaviour of voids in Al single crystals, produced by irradiation with fast neutrons (see HENDRICKS et al. [1977], LINDBERG et al. [1977] and references therein) has recently been summarized (KOSTORZ [1979, 1982]). X-rays, neutrons, transmission electron microscopy and positron annihilation were combined to obtain a rather complete picture of the microstructure of these samples. From the SAS point-of-view, the two-phase model can be employed, and no interparticle interference effects are visible at volume fractions of about 1% and void sizes of several hundred Å.

Whereas the voids in irradiated Al showed faceting attributed to truncated octahedra, voids formed in quenched and annealed β'-NiAl single crystals of strictly stoichiometric composition showed faceting on $\langle 110 \rangle$ planes, forming a rhombic dodecahedron (EPPERSON *et al.* [1978b]). Figure 26 shows an example obtained with a two-dimensional detector. The crystallographic symmetry of the faceted voids is reflected in the scattering pattern. SAS at smaller angles than shown in the figure is "isotropic", and a radius of gyration $R_G \approx 240$ Å can be determined for this particular case.

The void concentrations in the studies mentioned above, about 0.1–1%, were easily measurable in otherwise perfect single crystals. Among the factors influencing mechanical properties of metals and alloys, void formation during fatigue or high-temperature creep presents a major problem, and it is desirable to recognize void formation as early as possible. SAS, especially with neutrons because bulk samples can be examined without further preparation, is a useful method if other scattering contributions are not prohibitively large (see WALTHER and PIZZI [1980]). Grain boundary cavitation in fatigued Cu was studied by PAGE *et al.* [1982] who found cavities in the range of 100–900 Å and estimated a detection limit at a volume fraction of about 5×10^{-7} in an otherwise homogeneous sample. YOO *et al.* [1982] measured neutron SAS from fatigued polycrystalline Ni of commercial purity. Figure 27 shows size distributions (spherical voids were assumed) obtained from the SAS curves (radially averaged two-dimensional data and Guinier and Porod extrapolations to smaller and larger κ values), using the method of FEDOROVA and SCHMIDT

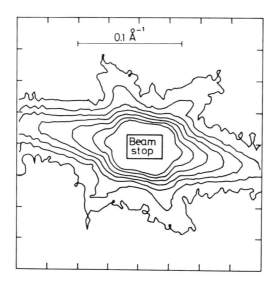

Fig. 26. Isointensity lines of neutron SAS measured for a β'-NiAl single crystal containing faceted voids. The crystal was annealed at 1600°C, quenched and aged for 30 min at 650°C. The [110] direction was parallel to the incident beam. A 64×64 cm^2 position-sensitive detector was placed 2.5 m away from the sample, the neutron wavelength was 6.64 Å. Scale: 0.1 Å$^{-1} = 2\pi\kappa$. (After EPPERSON *et al.* [1978b].)

References: p. 847.

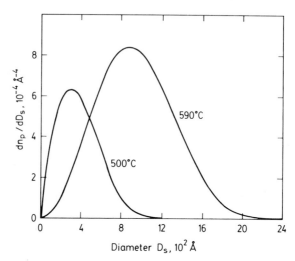

Fig. 27. Size distributions of spherical cavities obtained from neutron SAS of polycrystalline Ni after fatigue at 500 and 590°C (after Yoo *et al.* [1982]).

[1978]. The fatigue tests were performed in vacuo with a fully reversed stress amplitude of 55 mPa to 10^5 cycles. A strong influence of temperature on void formation can be seen. HVEM results show that the average void size may be larger than obtained from SAS, possibly because of uncertainties in the extrapolation to smaller κ values (the smallest measured κ was $\sim 10^{-3}$ Å^{-1}).

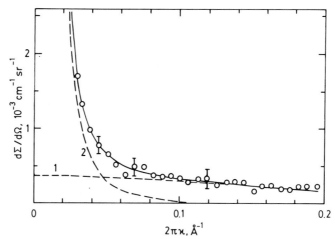

Fig. 28. Neutron SAS increment between a $\langle 111 \rangle$ Cu single crystal fatigued to about 80% of its expected fatigue life and another $\langle 111 \rangle$ crystal fatigued to only 20% (peak hardened). The circles represent experimental values, the solid curve is the sum of curve 1 (void scattering) and curve 2 (dislocation scattering). (After KETTUNEN *et al.* [1981].)

Small voids, about 20 Å, in diameter, have been seen by neutron SAS after fatigue deformation of $\langle 111 \rangle$ oriented Cu single crystals (KETTUNEN *et al.* [1981]). Figure 28 shows the SAS increment between a late and early state of fatigue life. A major scattering contribution at low κ must be attributed to dislocations, but at higher κ, voids (or small dislocation loops) are present (volume fraction $\sim 2 \times 10^{-5}$). The existence of small vacancy clusters in the persistent slip bands of fatigued Cu has been confirmed by positron annihilation (LEPISTÖ *et al.* [1981]).

Finally, large-scale inhomogeneities have been found in a number of amorphous alloys, e.g. in $Pd_{80}Si_{20}$ (K. SUZUKI *et al.* [1981]), corresponding to $R_G \approx 10$ μm. Cold working reduces this "very-small angle" scattering. In amorphous $Fe_{40}Ni_{40}C_{14}P_6$, GÖLTZ and KRONMÜLLER [1980] infer the presence of stress centres corresponding to quasi-dislocation dipoles, based on magnetic neutron SAS results.

5.4. Special topics

A special case of small κ scattering is Bragg diffraction from structures with large lattice constants or large-scale periodicity. The flux line lattice of type II superconductors with a lattice constant typically around 1000 Å and first revealed by neutron scattering by CRIBIER *et al.* [1964], has been studied in great detail for many different materials and conditions. The situation is fully reviewed in the literature (SCHMATZ [1976], GEROLD and KOSTORZ [1978], HICKS [1979]). Periodic and near-periodic multilayers can also be studied in 'specular reflection' near the critical angle of total reflection (see CROCE and NÉVOT [1976], HAYTER [1976], SEGMÜLLER [1979]). Such investigations are essential in the development of X-ray and neutron mirrors.

At small angles, multiple refraction in two-phase systems may obscure scattering, especially for neutrons of large wavelength and for thick samples (see BACON [1975], SCHMATZ [1978], KOSTORZ [1979]). A separation of refraction and scattering is in principle possible by varying the incident wavelength. Strong multiple neutron refraction from magnetic domains has been evaluated by GALOTTO *et al.* [1976] (see KOSTORZ [1979] and HICKS [1979] for further examples).

A very simple method to monitor changes in the microstructure of a sample is to measure its transmission. As indicated by eq. (13), the transmission is a function of the total removal cross-section, i.e. intensity scattered anywhere outside the range covered by the transmission monitor acts like additional absorption. The method has been proposed for nondestructive testing of materials containing large inhomogeneities, e.g. cavities (PALACIOS *et al.* [1981]). With a very highly collimated beam, and if SAS is the only source of additional/variable scattering, a change in the transmission corresponds to the integrated SAS intensity change as given by eq. (65), or, for isotropic scattering

$$Q = \frac{4\pi}{V_s} \int_0^\infty \kappa^2 \frac{d\sigma}{d\Omega}(\kappa) \, d\kappa. \tag{80}$$

In reality, the lower limit of the integral will be finite, κ_m. It is also possible to work

References: p. 847.

with a fixed acceptance angle $4\theta_a$ for transmission measurements and vary the wavelength of the incident radiation, thus testing the value of the integral of eq. (80) as a function of its lower limit $\kappa_m \approx 2\theta_a/\lambda$ (see ENGELMANN *et al.* [1979] for an experiment with ultracold neutrons). As many details of the scattering function will thus be lost, angular-resolved measurements are preferred if the intensity is high enough.

The extended X-ray absorption fine structure (EXAFS), i.e., the energy dependence of absorption up to about 1000 eV above the absorption edge (e.g. the K edge, see fig. 2) can now be measured with sufficient accuracy. The basic physical process leading to oscillations of the absorption coefficient is the modification of the final state of the photoelectron of the excited atom by neigbouring atoms (see, e.g., STERN [1974]). The effect of different chemical species on phase and amplitude of the oscillations is rather complex, but in principle specific for each type of atom. Nearest neighbours of the excited atom have the most pronounced influence, and the EXAFS technique is thus a promising tool, complementary to scattering studies in all areas discussed and mentioned in this chapter. Some recent applications to dilute Al alloys containing solute atoms, clusters or zones may serve as an introduction to this expanding field (FONTAINE *et al.* [1979], MIMAULT *et al.* [1981], RAOUX *et al.* [1981]).

6. *Energy transfers*

As mentioned in §2.4, coherent inelastic neutron scattering is a versatile method to study phonons (eqs. (24) and (25)] whereas incoherent energy-resolved quasi-elastic scattering of neutrons reveals diffusive motion. A few examples will now be given.

6.1. **Phonons in real crystals**

The dynamic properties of crystals are very sensitive to lattice defects and change dramatically near phase transitions. Phonons and defects have been discussed by NICKLOW [1979] and phonons and phase transformations by CURRAT and PYNN [1979]. As an example, fig. 29 (NICKLOW *et al.* [1979]) shows the frequency distribution for several phonon wavevectors in a Cu single crystal irradiated with thermal and fast neutrons to produce Frenkel pairs (concentration $\sim 1.3 \times 10^{-4}$). The measured phonon peaks are shifted relative to those measured for defect-free Cu, and an additional component on the high-frequency side occurs. Subsequent annealing results in an elimination of the peak shifts (72 K), but the additional high-frequency structure is only removed at 800 K. Part of the results can be explained by a resonant coupling of phonons to the librational modes of the split interstitial, but other defects, possibly small vacancy clusters, also contribute.

The phonon spectra of one-dimensional systems frequently show phonon anomalies at temperatures well above the transformation temperatures. For KCP, the

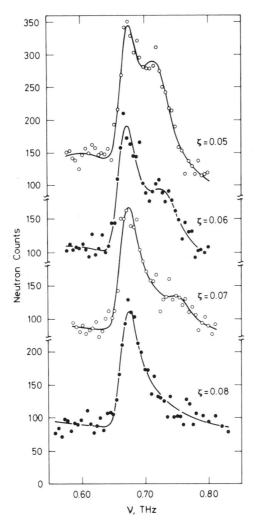

Fig. 29. The frequency distributions of neutrons scattered from irradiated Cu at 4 K for $q = (0, 0, \zeta)/a$. Open and solid circles are experimental data, the lines are fits including resonant coupling of librational modes of the split interstitial. (After NICKLOW *et al.* [1979].)

example already presented in §4.3, fig. 30 shows the phonon dispersion surface for acoustic phonons travelling along the chain direction. The anomaly for the longitudinal modes is related to the special shape of the Fermi surface which is restricted, in the one-dimensional case, to a pair of points. Because of the electron–phonon coupling, phonon anomalies are expected (KOHN [1959]) for scattering processes involving opposite sides of the Fermi surface connected by the wavevector $2k_F$ (k_F is the Fermi wavevector), i.e. energy conservation of the electrons. In the one-dimen-

References: p. 847.

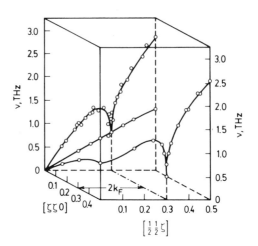

Fig. 30. Room-temperature dispersion surface of KCP for acoustic phonons propagating along the chain direction. A giant $2k_F$ anomaly is clearly visible for the longitudinal mode. (After COMÈS and SHIRANE [1979].)

sional case, the electronic susceptibility diverges for a wave-vector $2k_F$, and a "giant" Kohn anomaly as seen in fig. 30 results. The displacive transformation at lower temperature (see § 4.3) may be interpreted as a condensation of this Kohn anomaly into a pattern of static displacements, leading to a modulation of period $1/2k_F$ (see COMÈS and SHIRANE [1979] for a detailed discussion).

6.2. Diffusive motion

The use of incoherent quasi-elastic neutron scattering (see § 2.4) to study the motion of hydrogen in metals has been reviewed, e.g., by SKÖLD et al. [1979]. Here, another example using the same principles will be presented.

With a backscattering spectrometer (BIRR et al. [1971]) changes of neutron energies can be detected down to 10^{-7}–10^{-8} eV, corresponding to atomic motion on a time scale of 10^{-7}–10^{-9} s, or diffusion coefficients as low as 10^{-8}–10^{-6} cm^2/s. Self-diffusion in solid metals can thus be studied at temperatures not too far below the melting point if the incoherent scattering cross-section is high and the absorption is low. GÖLTZ et al. [1980] have studied self-diffusion in Na(bcc), using quasi-elastic neutron scattering, at temperatures between 323 and 370.2 K (melting point 370.9 K). Figure 31 shows the quasi-elastic line width along three crystallographic directions as a function of κ, including some earlier data by AIT-SALEM et al. [1979], and two sets of theoretical curves. The monovacancy mechanism with nearest-neighbour jumps seems to fit very well, but if the neutron results are to agree with tracer diffusion data (MUNDY [1971]), a divancy contribution has to be assumed.

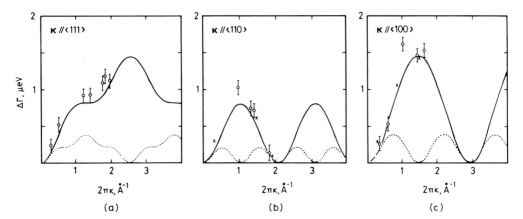

Fig. 31. Quasi-elastic line width $\Delta\Gamma$ (full width at half-maximum) as a function of $2\pi\kappa$ for κ along the indicated crystallographic directions, measured for Na at 369.2 K (circles: data of GÖLTZ *et al.* [1980], crosses: AIT-SALEM *et al.* [1979]). Dotted lines: theoretical values assuming a monovacancy diffusion mechanism with $\langle 111\rangle$ jumps, solid lines: theoretical values of monovacancy diffusion with nearest-neighbour jumps. (After GÖLTZ *et al.* [1980].)

Acknowledgements

The author is grateful to many colleagues, especially Drs. J.B. Cohen, A. Freund and L.H. Schwartz, for helpful comments on the manuscript and to Dr. R. Comès for the originals of figure 20.

References

AALDERS, J., 1982, thesis, Utrecht Univ.

ACUÑA, R.J., 1980, J. Mater. Sci. **15**, 20.

AIT-SALEM, M., T. SPRINGER, A. HEIDEMANN and B. ALEFELD, 1979, Phil. Mag. **39**, 797.

ALCACER, L., ed., 1980, The Physics and Chemistry of Low-Dimensional Solids (Reidel, Boston).

ATKINSON, H.H., 1959, J. Appl. Phys. **30**, 637.

ATKINSON, H.H., and P.B. HIRSCH, 1958a, Phil. Mag. **3**, 213.

ATKINSON, H.H., and P.B. HIRSCH, 1958b, Phil. Mag. **3**, 862.

ATKINSON, H.H., and R.D. LOWDE, 1957, Phil. Mag. **2**, 589.

AUVRAY, X., P. GEORGOPOULOS and J.B. COHEN, 1981, Acta Metall. **29**, 1061.

AXE, J.D., 1983, Physica B **120**, 256.

BACON, G.E., 1975, Neutron Diffraction (Clarendon Press, Oxford).

BARDHAN, P., and J.B. COHEN, 1976, Acta Cryst. **A32**, 597.

BARDHAN, P., H. CHEN and J.B. COHEN, 1977, Phil. Mag. **35**, 1653.

BARRETT, C.S., and T.B. MASSALSKI, 1980, Structure of Metals (Pergamon Press, Oxford).

BAUER, G.S., 1979, Diffuse Elastic Neutron Scattering, in: Neutron Scattering, ed. G. Kostorz (Academic, New York) p. 291.

BEEMAN, W.W., P. KAESBERG, J.W. ANDEREGG and M.B. WEBB, 1957, Size of Particles and Lattice Defects, in: Handbuch der Physik, ed. S. Flügge, vol. 32 (Springer, Berlin) p. 321.

BIENENSTOCK, A., 1981, Materials Research at Stanford Synchrotron Radiation Laboratory, in: EXAFS Spectroscopy, eds. B.K. Teo and D.C. Joy (Plenum, New York) p. 185.

BIRR, M., A. HEIDEMANN and B. ALEFELD, 1971, Nucl. Instr. and Meth. **95**, 435.

BORIE, B., and C.J. SPARKS, 1971, Acta Cryst. **A27**, 198.

BOUCHIAT, H., E. DARTYGE, P. MONOD and M. LAMBERT, 1981, Phys. Rev. **B23**, 1375.

BROWN, P.J., 1979, Neutron Crystallography, in: Neutron Scattering, ed. G. Kostorz (Academic, New York) p. 69.

BURKEL, E., B. V. GUÉRARD, H. METZGER, J. PEISL and C.M.E. ZEYEN, 1979, Z. Phys. B35, 227.

CAHN, J.W., 1961, Acta Metall. **9**, 795.

CAHN, J.W., 1968, Trans. AIME **242**, 166.

CHAKRAVARTI, B., E.A. STARKE, JR., C.J. SPARKS and R.O. WILLIAMS, 1974, J. Phys. Chem. Solids **35**, 1317.

CHEN, H., and J.B. COHEN, 1977, J. Physique **38**, C7-314.

CHEN, H., J.B. COHEN and R. GHOSH, 1977, J. Phys. Chem. Solids **38**, 855.

CHEN, H., R.J. COMSTOCK and J.B. COHEN, 1979, Ann. Rev. Mater. Sci. **9**, 51.

CHEN, P.C., B.O. HALL and P.G. WINCHELL, 1980, Metallurg. Trans. **11A**, 1323.

CLAPP, P.C., 1971, Phys. Rev. **B4**, 255.

CLAPP, P.C., and S.C. MOSS, 1968, Phys. Rev. **171**, 754.

COHEN, J.B., 1970, The Order–Disorder Transformation, in: Phase Transformations (ASM, Metals Park, Ohio) p. 561.

COHEN, J.B., and P. GEORGOPOULOS, 1982, Scripta Metall. **16**, 1107.

COMÈS, R., and G. SHIRANE, 1979, X-Ray and Neutron Scattering from One-Dimensional Conductors, in: Highly Conducting One-Dimensional Solids, eds. J.T. Devreese, R.P. Evrard and V.E. van Doren (Plenum, New York) p. 17.

COMÈS, R., M. LAMBERT and H.R. ZELLER, 1973, Phys. Stat. Sol. **58**, 587.

COOK, H., 1969, J.Chem. Solids **30**, 2427.

COOK, H.E., 1976, Mater. Sci. Eng. **25**, 127.

COOK, H.E., D. DE FONTAINE and J.E. HILLIARD, 1969, Acta Metall. **17**, 765.

COOPER, M., 1977, Contemp. Phys. **18**, 489.

COWLEY, J.M., 1950, J. Appl. Phys. **21**, 24.

COWLEY, J.M., 1981, Diffraction Physics, 2nd Ed. (North-Holland, Amsterdam).

COWLEY, J.M., and S. WILKINS, 1972, Derivation of Long-Range Interaction Energies from Diffuse Scattering in Diffraction Patterns, in: Interatomic Potentials and Simulation of Lattice Defects, eds. P.C. Gehlen, J.R. Beeler and R.I. Jaffee (Plenum, New York) p. 265.

COWLEY, J.M., J.B. COHEN, M.B. SALAMON and B.J. WUENSCH, eds., 1979, Modulated Structures – 1979, Proc. Conf. Kailua Kona, Hawaii 1979 (AIP, New York).

CRIBIER, D., B. JACROT, L. MADHAV RAO and B. FARNOUX, 1964, Phys. Lett. **9**, 106.

CROCE, P., and L. NÉVOT, 1976, Rev. Phys. Appl. **11**, 113.

CULLITY, B.D., 1977, Elements of X-ray Diffraction (Addison–Wesley, Reading, MA).

CURRAT, R., and R. PYNN, 1979, Phonons and Phase Transitions, in: Neutron Scattering, ed. G. Kostorz (Academic, New York) p. 131.

DARTYGE, E., H. BOUCHIAT and P. MONOD, 1982, Phys. Rev. **B25**, 6995.

DARWIN, C.G., 1922, Phil. Mag. **43**, 800.

DE BERGEVIN, F., and M. BRUNEL, 1972, Phys. Lett. **39A**, 141.

DEDERICHS, P.H., 1969, Phys. Rev. **188**, 1175.

DEDERICHS, P.H., 1973, J. Phys. **F3**, 471.

DEDERICHS, P.H., C. LEHMANN, H.R. SCHOBER, A. SCHOLZ and R. ZELLER, 1978, J. Nucl. Mater. **69/70**, 176.

DE FONTAINE, D., 1971, J. Appl. Crystallogr. **4**, 15.

DE FONTAINE, D., 1979, Solid State Phys. **34**, 74.

DELAFOND, A., A. NAUDON and C. TEMPLER, 1981, Nucl. Instr. and Meth. **182/183**, 379.

EHRHART, P., and W. SCHILLING, 1973, Phys. Rev. **B8**, 2604.

EHRHART, P., and U. SCHLAGHECK, 1974, J. Phys. **F4**, 1589.

EHRHART, P., W. SCHILLING and H.-G. HAUBOLD, 1974, Adv. Solid State Phys. **14**, 87.

EISENRIEGLER, E., 1971, Cryst. Lattice Defects **2**, 181.

ENGELMANN, G., A. STEYERL, A. HEIDEMANN, G. KOSTORZ and H. MUGHRABI, 1979, Z. Phys. **B35**, 345.

EPPERSON, J.E., 1979, J. Appl.Crystallogr. **12**, 351.

EPPERSON, J.E., P. FÜRNROHR and C. ORTIZ, 1978a, Acta Cryst. **A34**, 667.

EPPERSON, J.E., K.W. GERSTENBERG, D. BERNER, G. KOSTORZ and C. ORTIZ, 1978b, Phil. Mag. **A38**, 529.

FEDOROVA, I.S., and P.W. SCHMIDT, 1978, J. Appl. Crystallogr. **11**, 405.

FLANK, A.-M, M. LARIJDANI and A. NAUDON, 1981, C.R. Acad. Sci. (Paris) **292**, 995.

FONTAINE, A., P. LAGARDE, A. NAUDON, D. RAOUX and D. SPANJAARD, 1979, Phil. Mag. **B40**, 17.

FRIEDEL, J., and L.E. HEDMAN, 1978, J. Physique **39**, 1225.

FÜRNROHR, P., J.E. EPPERSON and V. GEROLD, 1980, Z. Metallk. **71**, 403.

FURUKAWA, H., 1979, Phys. Rev. Lett. **43**, 136.

GALOTTO, C.P., P. PIZZI, H. WALTHER, V. ANGELASTRO, N. CERULLO and G. CHERUBINI, 1976, Nucl. Instr. and Meth. **134**, 369.

GEHLEN, P.C., and J.B. COHEN, 1965, Phys. Rev. **139**, A844.

GEORGOPOULOS, P., and J.B. COHEN, 1977a, J. Physique **12**, C7-191.

GEORGOPOULOS, P., and J.B. COHEN, 1977b, Scripta Metall. **11**, 147.

GEORGOPOULOS, P., and J.B. COHEN, 1979, Direct Methods of Analyzing Diffuse Scattering, in: Modulated Structures – 1979, Proc. Conf. Kailua Kona, Hawaii 1979, eds. J.M. Cowley, J.B. Cohen, M.B. Salamon and B.J. Wuensch (AIP, New York) p. 21.

GEORGOPOULOS, P., and J.B. COHEN, 1981, Acta Metall. **29**, 1535.

GEROLD, V., 1954, Z. Metallk. **45**, 593, 599.

GEROLD, V., 1958, Acta Cryst. **11**, 236.

GEROLD, V., 1967, Application of Small-Angle X-Ray Scattering to Problems in Physical Metallurgy and Metal Physics, in: Small-Angle X-Ray Scattering, Proc. Conf. Syracuse University, 1965, ed. H. Brumberger (Gordon and Breach, New York) p. 277.

GEROLD, V., and E. BUBECK, 1982, Scripta Metall. **16**, 1101.

GEROLD, V., and G. KOSTORZ, 1978, J. Appl. Crystallogr. **11**, 376.

GLATTER, O., 1982a, Data Treatment, in: Small-Angle X-Ray Scattering, eds. O. Glatter and O. Kratky (Academic, London) p. 119.

GLATTER, O., 1982b, Interpretation, in: Small-Angle X-Ray Scattering, eds. O. Glatter and O. Kratky (Academic, London) p. 167.

GOBIN, P.F., and G. GUENIN, 1978, Martensitic Transformation: an Approach to the Martensitic Nucleation Problem, in: Solid State Phase Transformations in Metals and Alloys (Les Editions de Physique, Orsay) p. 573.

GÖLTZ, G., 1976, dissertation, Univ. Stuttgart.

GÖLTZ, G., and H. KRONMÜLLER, 1980, Phys. Lett. **77A**, 70.

GÖLTZ, G., A. HEIDEMANN, H. MEHRER, A. SEEGER and D. WOLF, 1980, Phil. Mag. **A41**, 723.

GRAGG, J.E., JR., and J.B. COHEN, 1971, Acta Metall. **19**, 507.

GRAGG, J.E., JR., P. BARDHAN and J.B. COHEN, 1971, The "Gestalt" of Local Order, in: Critical Phenomena in Alloys, Magnets and Superconductors, eds. R.E. Mills, E. Ascher and R.I. Jaffee (McGraw–Hill, New York) p. 309.

GRAGG, J.E., M. HAYAKAWA and J.B. COHEN, 1973, J. Appl. Crystallogr. **6**, 59.

GUINIER, A., 1938, Nature (London) **142**, 569.

GUINIER, A., 1939, Ann. Phys. (Paris) [11] **12**, 161.

GUINIER, A., 1963, X-Ray Diffraction, transl. P. Lorrain and D. Lorrain (Freeman, San Francisco).

GUINIER, A., and G. FOURNET, 1955, Small-Angle Scattering of X-Rays, transl. C.B. Walker (Wiley, New York).

GUREVICH, I.I., and L.V. TARASOV, 1968, Low-Energy Neutron Physics, transl. eds. R.I. Sharp and S. Chomet (North-Holland, Amsterdam).

GUYOT, P., and J.P. SIMON, 1982, in: Studies of Clustering During Decomposition by Neutron Small Angle Scattering, Proc. Int. Conf. Phase Transformations, Pittsburgh 1981, eds. H.I. Aaronson, D.E. Laughlin, R.F. Sekerka and C.M. Wayman (ASM, Metals Park, OH) p. 325.

HALPERN, O., and M.H. JOHNSON, 1939, Phys. Rev. **55**, 898.

HAUBOLD, H.-G., 1975, J. Appl. Crystallogr. **8**, 175.

HAUBOLD, H.-G., and D. MARTINSEN, 1978, J. Nucl. Mater. **69/70**, 644.

HAYAKAWA, M., and J.B. COHEN, 1975, Acta Cryst. **A31**, 635.

HAYAKAWA, M., P. BARDHAN and J.B. COHEN, 1975, J. Appl. Crystallogr. **8**, 87.

HAYTER, J.B., 1976, Recent Developments in Polarized Neutrons, in: Proc. Conference on Neutron Scattering, Vol. II, Gatlinburg 1976, ed. R.M. Moon (US Dept. Commerce, Springfield, VA, CONF 76061-P2) p. 1074.

HENDRICKS, R.W., 1976, Trans. Am. Crystallogr. Assoc. **12**, 103.

HENDRICKS, R.W., J. SCHELTEN and G. LIPPMANN, 1977, Phil. Mag. **36**, 907.

HENNION, M., D. RONZAUD and P. GUYOT, 1982, Acta Metall. **30**, 599.

HICKS, T.J., 1979, Magnetic Inhomogeneities, in: Neutron Scattering, ed. G. Kostorz (Academic, New York) p. 337.

HOUSKA, C.R., 1980, The Investigation of Composition Variations by Diffraction, in: Treatise on Materials Science and Technology, vol. 19 (Experimental Methods, Part A) ed. H. Herman (Academic, New York) p. 63.

International Tables for Crystallography, vol. I (1952), vol. II (1959), vol. III (1962), ed. K. LONSDALE, vol. IV (1974), eds. J.A. IBERS and W.C. HAMILTON (Kynoch Press, Birmingham).

JAMES, M.R., and J.B. COHEN, 1980, The Measurement of Residual Stresses by X-Ray Diffraction Techniques, in: Treatise on Materials Science and Technology, vol. 19 (Experimental Methods, Part A), ed. H. Herman (Academic New York) p. 2.

JAMES, R.W., 1963, The Optical Principles of the Diffraction of X-Rays, 3rd Ed. (Bell, London).

KAJZAR, F., G. PARETTE and B. BABIC, 1981, J. Phys. Chem. Solids **42**, 501.

KETTUNEN, P.O., T. LEPISTÖ, G. KOSTORZ and G. GÖLTZ, 1981, Acta Metall. **29**, 969.

KOHN, W., 1959, Phys. Rev. Lett. **2**, 393.

KOSTORZ, G., 1976, Z. Metallk. **67**, 704.

KOSTORZ, G., 1979, Small-Angle Scattering, in: Neutron Scattering, ed. G. Kostorz (Academic, New York) p. 227.

KOSTORZ, G., 1982, Inorganic Substances, in: Small-Angle X-Ray Scattering, eds. O. Glatter and O. Kratky (Academic, London) p. 467.

KOSTORZ, G., 1983, Physica B **120**, 387.

KOSTORZ, G., and S.W. LOVESEY, 1979, Neutron Scattering – General Introduction, in: Neutron Scattering, ed. G. Kostorz (Academic, New York) p.1.

KRIVOGLAZ, M.A., 1969, Theory of X-Ray and Thermal Neutron Scattering by Real Crystals, translated from Russian, ed. S.C. Moss (Plenum, New York).

KRONMÜLLER, H., A. SEEGER and M. WILKENS, 1963, Z. Phys. **171**, 291.

LANGER, J.S., and A.J. SCHWARTZ, 1980, Phys. Rev. **A21**, 948.

LANGER, J.S., M. BAR-ON and H.D. MILLER, 1975, Phys. Rev. **A11**, 1417.

LARIDJANI, M., and J.F. SADOC, 1981, J. Physique **42**, 1293.

LASLAZ, G., G. KOSTORZ, M. ROTH, P. GUYOT and R.J. STEWART, 1977a, Phys. Stat. Sol. (a) **41**, 577.

LASLAZ, G., P. GUYOT and G. KOSTORZ, 1977b, J. Physique **38**, C7-406.

LEBOWITZ, J.L., J. MARRO and M.H. KALOS, 1982, Acta Metall. **30**, 297.

LEFEBVRE, S., F. BLEY, M. BESSIÈRE, M. FAYARD, M. ROTH and J.B. COHEN, 1980, Acta Cryst. **A36**, 1.

LEFEBVRE, S., F. BLEY, M. FAYARD and M. ROTH, 1981, Acta Metall. **29**, 749.

LEPISTÖ, T., J. YLI-KAUPPILA, P. KETTUNEN and P. HAUTOJÄRVI, 1981, Phys. Stat. Sol. (a) **67**, K93.

LINDBERG, V.W., J.D. MCGERVEY, R.W. HENDRICKS and W. TRIFTSHÄUSER, 1977, Phil. Mag. **36**, 117.

LIPSON, H. and W. COCHRAN, 1953, The Determination of Crystal Structures (Bell, London).

MAIER-LEIBNITZ, H., 1966, Nukleonik **8**, 61.

MARRO, J., J.L. LEBOWITZ and M.H. KALOS, 1979, Phys. Rev. Lett. **43**, 282.

MARSHALL, W., and S.W. LOVESEY, 1971, Theory of Thermal Neutron Scattering (Oxford Univ. Press, London and New York).

MARTIN, G., 1978, The Theories of Unmixing Kinetics of Solid Solutions, in: Solid State Phase Transformations in Metals and Alloys (Les Editions de Physique, Orsay) p. 337.

MEARDON, B., and KOSTORZ, 1975, ILL-Annexe to the Annual Report (Grenoble) p. 207.

MESSOLORAS, S., 1974, Ph.D. thesis, Univ. of Reading.

METCALFE, E., and J.A. LEAKE, 1975, Acta Metall. **23**, 1135.

METZGER, H., and H. PEISL, 1978, J. Phys. **F8**, 391.

METZGER, H., J. PEISL and J. WANAGEL, 1976, J. Phys. **F6**, 2195.

METZGER, H., H. BEHR and J. PEISL, 1981, Solid State Commun. **40**, 789.

METZGER, H., H. BEHR and J. PEISL, 1982, Z. Phys. **B46**, 295.

MIMAULT, J, A. FONTAINE, P. LAGARDE, D. RAOUX, S. SADOC and D. SPANJAARD, 1981, J. Phys. **F11**, 1311.

MIREBEAU, I., M.C. CADEVILLE, G. PARETTE and I.A. CAMPBELL, 1982, J. Phys. **F12**, 25.

MITTEMEIJER, E.J., and R. DELHEZ, 1980, Determination of Compositional Variations by X-Ray Diffraction Line Profile Analysis, in: Proceedings of Symposium on Accuracy in Powder Diffraction, Gaithersburg, MD, June 1979 (NBS Special Publication 567) p. 271.

MOSS, S.C., 1966, Local Order in Solid Alloys I, in: Local Atomic Arrangements Studied by X-Ray Diffraction, eds. J.B. Cohen and J.E. Hilliard (Gordon and Breach, New York) p. 95.

MOSS, S.C., 1969, Phys. Rev. Lett. **22**, 1108.

MOSS, S.C., 1977, J. Physique **38**, C7-440.

MOSS, S.C., 1982, Structure and Phase Transitions in $V_2 D$ and $V_2 H$, in: Proc. Int. Symp. on the Electronic structure and Properties of Hydrogen in Metals, Richmond, VA, 1982, eds. P. Jena and C.B. Satterthwaite (Plenum, New York) in press.

MOSS, S.C., and P.C. CLAPP, 1968, Phys. Rev. **171**, 764.

MOSS, S.C., and R.H. WALKER, 1975, J. Appl. Crystallogr. **8**, 96.

MOZER, B., D.T. KEATING and S.C. MOSS, 1968, Phys. Rev. **175**, 868.

MUNDY, J.N., 1971, Phys. Rev. **B3**, 2431.

NAUDON, A., and A.-M. FLANK, 1982, Study by Small-Angle Scattering of X-Rays of Concentration Fluctuations in Some Metallic Glasses, in: Proc. 4th Int. Conf. on Rapidly Quenched Metals, Sendai 1981 (Japan. Inst. Met., Sendai) p. 425.

NAUDON, A., M. LEMONNIER and F. ROUSSEAUX, 1979, C.R. Acad. Sci. (Paris) **288**, 21.

NICKLOW, R.M., 1979, Phonons and Defects, in: Neutron Scattering, ed. G. Kostorz (Academic, New York) p. 191.

NICKLOW, R.M., W.P. CRUMMET and J.M. WILLIAMS, 1979, Phys. Rev. **B12**, 5034.

NOLD, E., P. LAMPARTER, H. OLBRICH, G. RAINER-HARBACH and S. STEEB, 1981, Z. Naturf. **36a**, 1032.

OHSHIMA, K.-I., D. WATANABE and J. HARADA, 1976, Acta Cryst. **A32**, 883.

OSAMURA, K., K. SHIBUE, R. SUZUKI, Y. MURAKAMI, S. TAKAYAMA, 1981a, J. Mater. Sci. **16**, 957.

OSAMURA, K., K. SHIBUE, R. SUZUKI and Y. MURAKAMI, 1981b, Colloid and Polymer Sci. **259**, 677.

OSAMURA, K., R. SUZUKI, and Y. MURAKAMI, 1982a, SAXS Study on the Structure of Amorphous Metallic Alloys, in: Proc. 4th Int. Conf. on Rapidly Quenched Metals, Sendai 1981 (Japan. Inst. Met., Sendai) p. 431.

OSAMURA, K., H. TSUNEKAWA, Y. MURAKAMI, M. ONO, H. YOSHIDA, S. OKAMOTO, Y. MONJU and T. FUKUZUKA, 1982b, J. Appl. Crystallogr. **15**, 611.

OSAMURA, K., S. OCHIAI and S. TAKAYAMA, 1983, J. Mater. Sci., to be published.

PAGE, R., J.R. WEERTMAN and M. ROTH, 1982, Acta Metall. **30**, 1357.

PALACIOS, J., D. SCHWAHN and H. RAUCH, 1981, NDT International, August 1981, 189.

PARKER, B.A., 1972, J. Appl. Crystallogr. **5**, 372.

PEISL, H., 1976, J. Physique **37**, C7-47.

PEISL, H., R. BALSER and H. PETERS, 1974, Phys. Lett. **46A**, 263.

POROD, G., 1951, Kolloid–Z. **124**, 83.

POROD, G., 1982, General Theory, in: Small-Angle X-Ray Scattering, eds. O. Glatter and O. Kratky (Academic, London) p. 17.

PYNN, R., 1978, J. PHYS. **F8**, 1.

RAOUX, D., A. FONTAINE, P. LAGARDE and A. SADOC, 1981, Phys. Rev. **B24**, 5547.

ROTH, M., 1977, J. Appl. Crystallogr. **10**, 172.

RUNDMAN, K.B., and J.E. HILLIARD, 1967, Acta Metall. **15**, 1025.

SAFRONOVA, L.A., A.A. KATSNEL'SON, S.V. SVESHNIKOV and YU. M. L'VOV, 1977, Fiz. Met. Metalloved. 43, 76.

SANCHEZ, J.M., and D. DE FONTAINE, 1977, J. Physique 38, C7-444.

SCHEUER, H., 1977, dissertation, Univ. Bochum.

SCHMATZ, W., 1969, Studies of Point Defects and Defect Clusters by Small-Angle and Diffuse Scattering of X-Rays and Neutrons, in: Vacancies and Interstitials in Metals, Jülich Conf. 1968, eds. A. Seeger, D. Schumacher, W. Schilling and J. Diehl (North-Holland, Amsterdam) p. 589.

SCHMATZ, W., 1973, X-Ray and Neutron Scattering Studies on Disordered Crystals, in: Treatise on Materials Science and Technology, vol. 2, ed. H. Herman (Academic, New York) p. 105.

SCHMATZ, W., 1975, Riv. Nuovo Cim. 5, 398.

SCHMATZ, W., 1976, Neutron Small-Angle Scattering: Experimental Techniques and Applications, in: Proc. Conference on Neutron Scattering, vol. II, Gatlinburg 1976, ed. R.M. Moon (US Dept. Commerce, Springfield, VA, CONF 76061-P2) p. 1037.

SCHMATZ, W., 1978, Disordered Structures, in: Neutron Diffraction, ed. H. Dachs (Springer, Berlin, Heidelberg, New York) ch. 5.

SCHMATZ, W., P.H. DEDERICHS and H. SCHEUER, 1974, Z. Phys. 270, 337.

SCHWAHN, D., and W. SCHMATZ, 1978, Acta Metall. 26, 1571.

SCHWAHN, D., W. KESTERNICH and H. SCHUSTER, 1981, Metallurg. Trans. 12A, 155.

SCHWARTZ, L.H., and J.B. COHEN, 1977, Diffraction from Materials (Academic, New York).

SEEGER, A., 1961, Phys. Stat. Sol. 1, 670.

SEEGER, A., and E. KRÖNER, 1959, Z. Naturf. A14, 74.

SEEGER, A., and M. RÜHLE, 1963, Ann. Phys. (Leipzig) 11, 216.

SEEGER, A., E. MANN and R.v. JAN, 1962, J. Phys. Chem. Solids 23, 639.

SEEGER, A.K., 1959, J. Appl. Phys. 30, 629.

SEGMÜLLER, A., 1979, Small-Angle Interferences of X-Rays Reflected from Periodic and Near-Periodic Multilayers, in: Modulated Structures – 1979, Proc. Conf. Kailua Kona, Hawaii 1979, eds. J.M. Cowley, J.B. Cohen, M.B. Salamon and B.J. Wuensch (AIP, New York) p. 78.

SEITZ, E., and D. DE FONTAINE, 1976, UCLA Report No. 34, P201-17, Eng. 7690 (Univ. of California, Los Angeles).

SEMENOSKAYA, S.V., 1974, Phys. Stat. Sol. (b) 64, 291.

SINGHAL, S.P., H. HERMAN and G. KOSTORZ, 1978, J. Appl. Crystallogr. 11, 572.

SKÖLD, K., M.H. MUELLER and T.O. BRUN, 1979, Hydrogen in Metals, in: Neutron Scattering, ed. G. Kostorz (Academic, New York) p. 423.

SPARKS, JR., C.J., 1981, Phys. Today, May 1981, p. 49.

SPARKS, C.J. and B. BORIE, 1966, Methods of Analysis for Diffuse X-Ray Scattering Modulated by Local Order and Atomic Displacement, in: Local Atomic Arrangements Studied by X-Ray Diffraction eds. J.B. Cohen and J.E. Hilliard (Gordon and Breach, New York) p. 5.

SPRINGER, T., 1977, Molecular Rotations and Diffusion in Solids, in Particular Hydrogen in Metals, in: Dynamics of Solids and Liquids by Neutron Scattering, eds. S.W. Lovesey and T. Springer (Springer, Berlin, Heidelberg, New York) p. 255.

STERN, E.A., 1974, Phys. Rev. B10, 3027.

SUZUKI, H., J. HARADA, T. NAKASHIMA and K. ADACHI, 1982, Acta Cryst. A38, 522.

SUZUKI, K., K. DOI and K. KOHRA, 1981, Japan. J. Appl. Phys. 20, L271.

TIBALLS, J.E., 1975, J. Appl. Crystallogr. 8, 111.

TRINKAUS, H., 1972, Phys. Stat. Sol. (b) 51, 307.

TRINKAUS, H., 1975, Z. Naturf. 28a, 980.

UNGÁR, T., H. MUGHRABI and M. WILKENS, 1982, Acta Metall. 30, 1861.

V. GUÉRARD, B., D. GRASSE and J. PEISL, 1980, Phys. Rev. Lett. 44. 262.

VRIJEN, J., and S. RADELAAR, 1978, Phys. Rev. B17, 409.

VRIJEN, J., J. AALDERS, C. VAN DIJK and S. RADELAAR, 1980, Phys. Rev. B22, 1503.

WAGNER, C.N.J., 1966, Analysis of the Broadening and Changes in Position of Peaks in an X-Ray Powder Pattern, in: Local Atomic Arrangement Studied by X-Ray Diffraction, eds. J.B. Cohen and J.E. Hilliard (Gordon and Breach, New York) p. 219.

WAGNER, C.N.J., 1978, J. Non-Cryst. Solids **31**, 1.

WALKER, C.B., and A. GUINIER, 1953, Acta Metall. **1**, 568.

WALTHER, H., and P. PIZZI, 1980, Small Angle Neutron Scattering for Nondestructive Testing, in: Research Techniques in Nondestructive Testing, vol. IV, ed. R.S. Sharpe (Academic, London) p. 341.

WARREN, B.E., 1969, X-Ray Diffraction (Addison–Wesley, Reading, MA).

WERNER, K., W. SCHMATZ, G.S. BAUER, E. SEITZ, A. BARATOFF and H.J. FENZL, 1978, J. Phys. **F8**, L207.

WILKENS, M., 1969, Acta Metall. **17**, 1155.

WILKENS, M., 1970, Phys. Stat. Sol. (a) **2**, 359.

WILKENS, M., 1975, J. Appl. Crystallogr. **8**, 191.

WILKINS, S., 1970, Phys. Rev. **B2**, 3935.

WILKINS, S.(W.) and C.G. SHIRLEY, 1975, J. Appl. Crystallogr. **8**, 107.

WILLIAMS, R.O., 1972, ORNL Report No. 4828 (Oak Ridge National Laboratory, Oak Ridge, TN).

WILLIAMS, R.O., 1976, ORNL Report No. 5140 (Oak Ridge National Laboratory, Oak Ridge, TN).

WILLIS, B.T.M. and A.W. PRYOR, 1975, Thermal Vibrations in Crystallography (Cambridge Univ. Press, London).

WINDSOR, C.G., 1981, Pulsed Neutron Scattering (Taylor and Francis, London).

WINICK, H. and DONIACH, S., eds., 1980, Synchrotron Radiation Research (Plenum, New York).

YOO, M.H., J.C. OGLE, B.S. BORIE, E.H. LEE and R.W. HENDRICKS, 1982, Acta Metall. **30**, 1733.

ZACHARIASEN, W.H., 1945, Theory of X-Ray Diffraction in Crystals (Wiley, New York).

Further reading

General

The books referred to in the text and contained in the list of references are recommended for general reading, in particular the books by SCHWARTZ and COHEN and by COWLEY and, more extensively covering real crystals, the book by KRIVOGLAZ. A long list of current crystallographic books (1970–1981), edited by J.H. Robertson, has appeared in J. Appl.Crystallogr. 15 (1982) 640–676.

Neutron scattering

In addition to the books referred to, G.L. Squires, Introduction to the Theory of Thermal Neutron Scattering (Cambridge Univ. Press, 1978) may be consulted. Several chapters in G. Kostorz, ed., Neutron Scattering, vol. 15, Treatise in Materials Science and Technology (H. Herman, series ed., Academic, New York, 1979) contain more details about metallurgical applications than could be presented here.

Diffuse scattering

Beyond the coverage of the subject in the book by SCHWARTZ and COHEN [1977], BAUER'S [1979] (see references) chapter and the reviews by H. CHEN *et al.* [1979] and by GEORGOPOULOS and COHEN [1979] will be most useful. Many review and research papers can be found in J. Appl. Crystallogr. 8, 1975 (proceedings of the Jülich Conference on Lattice Distortions and Atomic Disorder) and in Suppl. C-7 to J. Physique **12**, 1977 (proceedings of the Colloque International "Order and Disorder in Solids", Paris 1977).

Small-angle scattering

The classical monograph by GUINIER and FOURNET [1955] is now complemented by "Small-Angle X-ray Scattering", eds. O. Glatter and O. Kratky (Academic, London, 1982) which gives a solid theoretical background and more current methods and applications. Neutrons are covered by KOSTORZ [1979] (see references). Reviews and research papers of the 1977 Gatlinburg Small-Angle Scattering Meeting can be found in J. Appl. Crystallogr. 11 (1978).

CHAPTER 13

INTERFACIAL AND SURFACE MICROCHEMISTRY

E.D. HONDROS and M.P. SEAH

Division of Materials Applications
National Physical Laboratory
Teddington, Middlesex, UK

R.W. Cahn and P. Haasen, eds.
Physical Metallurgy; third, revised and enlarged edition
© *Elsevier Science Publishers BV, 1983*

1. Introduction – The chemistry of interfaces and physical metallurgy

Writing nearly a hundred years ago, one of the progenitors of modern physical metallurgy, ROBERTS-AUSTEN [1888], stated: "One thousandth part of antimony converts first rate best selected copper into the worst conceivable". Although it was well known at that time that small amounts of certain elements could provoke remarkable changes in the physical and mechanical properties of metals – for example, the improvement in the strength of iron by carbon and the reduction in the electrical conductivity of copper by impurities – the above refers to the dramatic embrittlement of an otherwise ductile metal, associated with intergranular fractures. This is a cogent illustration of the subject matter in the present chapter, in which we shall be concerned with how the chemical constitution of the various interfaces in polycrystals influences the physical metallurgical properties. Observations on the transformation of ductile metals to intergranularly brittle matter clearly implicate the chemical constitution of the grain boundaries and point to the existence of basic, underlying mechanisms which lead to interfacial regions having highly localized and altered chemistry. In this chapter, the generic term *interfacial microchemistry* denotes the science and practice of those phenomena in polycrystalline materials which give rise to zones of chemical heterogeneity. This may occur from either the equilibrium or the non-equilibrium partitioning of those solutes from solid solution which are present as alloying elements or as residual impurities.

In metallurgical practice, the term *segregation* is used in its original sense to denote the build-up of concentrations of elements during crystallization from casting. In more recent times, metallurgists studied, by indirect procedures, various effects which implied very local chemical-concentration changes at grain boundaries. These latter concentrations were thought to be the origin of metallurgical problems such as *hot cracking* or *temper-embrittlement* in low alloy steels, as demonstrated by increases in the ductile-to-brittle transition temperature during impact testing. Such indirect observations associated with the presence of certain residual impurities at grain boundaries were commonly referred to as "segregation" in metallurgical circles (McLEAN [1975]) and although common usage dictates that we shall continue to use this term in the context of interfacial microchemistry, we clearly distinguish between the phenomena which give rise to these types of equilibrium segregation and the phenomena which give rise to the original solidification segregation. Indeed, as will be demonstrated, this redistribution of solutes by *equilibrium segregation* is truly reversible as analyzed by thermodynamic procedures, and it is quite analogous to the chemisorption or adsorption phenomena long studied by surface chemists for gas atoms interacting with free solid surfaces. Although the terms "segregation" and "adsorption" have acquired historically these specific usages in their respective disciplines, in order to emphasize the fact that the basic phenomena involved are identical, we shall apply the terms "segregation" and "adsorption" interchangeably to both the *external interface*, such as the free surface and the *internal interface*, such as the grain boundary.

In addition to grain boundaries which are the principal interfaces with metallurgical consequences, interfacial microchemistry embraces a variety of interfaces in polycrystalline materials, among them free surfaces, the interfaces between various constituent phases in the solid, stacking faults, and precipitate/matrix interfaces. From a macroscopic point of view of this theme, we underline that all these interfaces behave essentially in a similar way in spite of widely differing, often very complex structures at the atomic level – the same thermodynamic analyses are applicable to all these types of interface, which may be described by the classical concepts of surface adsorption chemistry; indeed similar adsorption isotherms hold, the conditions for the existence of any particular form and the magnitude of the adsorption parameters depending on the nature of the interface alone.

Interfacial microchemical phenomena in polycrystals can be visualized by aid of the schema in fig. 1. The multicomponent solid mass is held at equilibrium in an isothermal enclosure and at a temperature which permits rapid thermal transport. The chemical potentials of all species, assumed here to be in solid solution, are constant throughout the system. Instead of a random distribution of solute species,

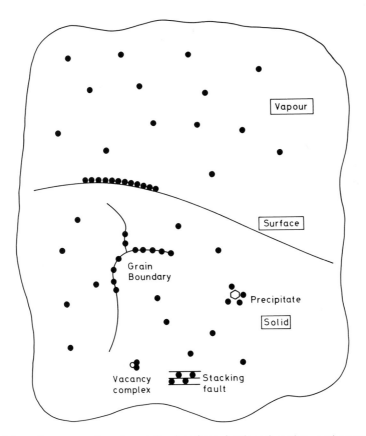

Fig. 1. Schematic representation of crystalline interfaces showing adsorption or microsegregation.

References: p. 928.

as in an ideal single crystal, it is found that at equilibrium there is a heterogeneous partitioning which results in the enrichment of interfaces by certain surface-active species, as shown diagrammatically in fig. 1. The levels of the enrichment are defined only by the system parameters at equilibrium and not by the history of the material. The chemical enrichment at any interface can be reproduced simply by re-establishing the identical physicochemical conditions. It is in this sense that the segregation is truly reversible.

An essential condition of equilibrium segregation, whether at a free surface, a grain boundary or precipitate/matrix interface, is that the width of matter over which it builds up is influenced by the structural width of the interface. The field of structural perturbation of a grain boundary should not extend beyond a few atom distances, and it has now been experimentally confirmed that the space occupied by the segregation is constrained to within the structurally perturbed region of the interface (§ 3.2). Hence a distinguishing feature of equilibrium segregation is that it be localized to within one or two atom distances of the plane of the interface. Thus we speak of a fractional monatomic layer level of segregation at grain boundaries and other interfaces, by which we mean, by analogy with the concepts of mono-molecular adsorbed layers in surface chemistry, that a fraction of a single equivalent atomic layer consisting of a sheet of close-packed atoms lies along the interface. Of course this is an idealization, and in practice monatomic layers of this nature probably do not form. However, it is a convenient way of visualizing the extent of segregation and of quantifying it, whether this is expressed as a fraction of a monatomic layer or as several such layers.

In contrast to this equilibrium segregation, various phenomena exist in which the apparent levels of segregation build-up may extend to distances of as much as several μm across grain boundaries. This effect is sensitive to the rate of cooling from a high temperature. The earliest effect of this type was announced by Westbrook and his collaborators (WESTBROOK [1964]) in a series of experiments in which they claimed to detect such an effect through changes in indentation micro-hardness profiles across grain boundaries in certain dilute alloys. Although falling within the scope of a general treatment of interfacial microchemistry, this phenome-non must be distinguished from that involving equilibrium segregation, which is probably the most ubiquitous form of interfacial enrichment in solid systems. The origin of the former segregation is also believed to be entirely different from that involving reversible segregation – namely, during a temperature fall, vacancies flow to the grain-boundary sinks in order to preserve their thermal equilibrium value. A solute concentration is thus built up about the boundary because of the dragging of vacancy–solute pairs. Although highly system-specific, the phenomenon may be of consequence in certain metallurgical operations and this, together with other related manifestations, will be considered later in this chapter. To distinguish this phenome-non from reversible segregation, we refer to it as *non-equilibrium segregation*.

In order to understand the impact of interfacial microchemistry on physical metallurgical processes, our aim in this chapter is to provide descriptions of the equilibrium and non-equilibrium segregation phenomena in terms of basic physical, chemical and kinetic parameters, and then to relate such segregation to changes in mechanical properties, embrittlement in particular. Indeed, the manner by which a narrow sub-monatomic layer of a foreign species along a grain-boundary path may so affect bulk mechanical properties as to convert a tough metal into a fragile one, has been the point of departure of many intriguing basic studies. However, it is beyond the scope of this chapter to enlarge in detail on all the mechanical effects that have been scrutinized in recent years in terms of the role of interfacial microchemistry.

2. *Thermodynamic features of interfacial adsorption*

The thermodynamic property possessed by all interfaces in common is a free energy, which is a measure of the unsatisfied atomic bonding in the relatively disordered structure of the interface. In liquids, where it is referred to as *surface tension*, this free energy is easily demonstrated to be able to do work, as testified by many conventional capillarity phenomena, such as droplet formation or the shapes of soap bubbles. Foreign species may accumulate at these interfaces in order to satisfy better the atomic bonding, and hence to reduce the free energy: this is in simple terms the basic motivation for the segregation of foreign atoms at interfaces. It is in this way that soap added to water reduces its surface tension. This free energy is the central thermodynamic function which characterizes all interfaces whether in solids or liquids, and because its magnitude depends on temperature, crystalline orientation and the presence of foreign species, its determining presence is felt in many physical phenomena in nature and in turn in the mechanical and chemical properties of materials.

The fundamental connection between surface free energy and the chemical state of the surface was first demonstrated in the last century by GIBBS [reprinted 1948] in an elegant and generalized treatment. This treatment and the mathematical derivations are shown in detail in a number of textbooks on surface chemistry to which the reader is referred (e.g., DEFAY *et al.* [1966]). In his classical derivation of the fundamental theorem relating the "surface of tension" of a fluid to bulk composition and the excess of species at the surface, Gibbs introduced for convenience the device of a mathematical "dividing surface" which was placed arbitrarily in order to make the surface concentration of the solvent species vanish; however, for internal interfaces such as grain boundaries which were not considered by Gibbs, there are conceptual difficulties in locating this mathematical dividing surface in a manner that corresponds to a physical surface of separation, because the physicochemical properties vary continuously from one homogeneous phase to the adjoining phase. Therefore, in the treatment of adsorption processes at internal interfaces it is now customary to adopt the convenient approach of GUGGENHEIM [1950], in which the interface is considered as a separate phase of finite thickness, and where the thermodynamic relations so derived are independent of the thickness of the phase separating the two adjoining phases which may be two crystals or a crystal in

References: p. 928.

contact with a vapour. For a multicomponent solid, following the approach of §9 leading to eq. (69), ch. 6, but replacing the surface tension, σ, by the scalar interfacial free energy γ, the Gibbs adsorption isotherm may be derived. In the dilute approximation, which is that of general interest, for a bulk solute molar concentration $X_c \ll 1$, in which Henry's Law holds, this becomes:

$$\frac{d\gamma}{d \ln X_c}\Big|_T = -RT\,\Gamma_2, \tag{1}$$

where Γ_2 is the interfacial excess of the solute species expressed in mol/m^2. This is the most useful form of the *Gibbs Adsorption Theorem* for a dilute binary system and in this basic form it has been used experimentally to relate changes in composition of the bulk to the changes in both the free energy and the surface excess composition for all interfaces in solids and in liquids. (See also ch. 6, §9.1.).

To illustrate the use of the Gibbs Adsorption Theorem in the dilute form in order to measure interfacial excesses, fig. 2 shows for three interfaces in pure iron – the liquid surface, the solid surface and the average grain boundary – the variation in

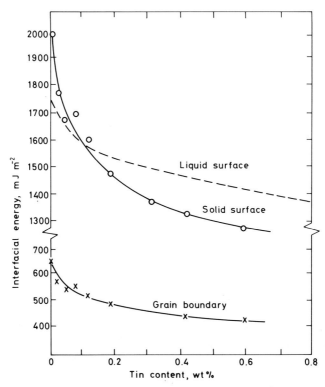

Fig. 2. Isotherms for interfacial free energies in the dilute binary system Fe–Sn: data for the liquid surface from KOZAKEVITCH and URBAIN [1961].

the interfacial free energy as a function of the bulk tin content (SEAH and HONDROS [1973]). The three interfaces behave similarly in the general form of the dependence of interfacial energy on bulk composition, in that there is an early rapid fall in the isotherm, followed by a gradual weakening of the effect as the composition increases. This is typical of the behaviour that has been encountered in many such binary systems studied experimentally. The interfacial tensions for the pure metal are also typical in that the free energy of the solid surface is significantly greater than that of the liquid surface, while the grain boundary free energy is approximately one third of that of the surface free energy. The data shown in this figure are analyzed by application of eq. (1) to the results pertaining to the specific temperature of the experiment. The amount of interfacial excess expressed by Γ_2 is in terms of moles of the solute species per unit area. In fig. 3 these quantities have been transformed into equivalent monatomic layers, and the surface composition is shown as a function of the bulk tin content for the three interfaces in question. The behaviour of the liquid surface is more ideal, in that it shows the approach towards a saturation adsorption of tin at the liquid iron surface, at a level of about a single monatomic layer. With increasing bulk content, the interfacial excesses shown for

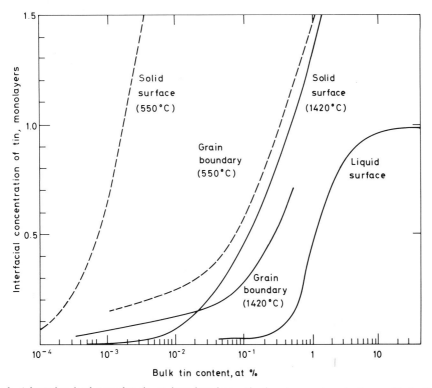

Fig. 3. Adsorption isotherms for tin at iron interfaces: the low temperature isotherms (dashed) are measured directly by AES; the others are derived from the interfacial energy data shown in fig. 2.

References: p. 928.

the grain boundary and for the solid surface increase, but in this particular system and in the conditions of this experiment, there is no apparent sign of saturation adsorption. In fact, for the system iron–tin the behaviour in the solid state is not typical in that there occurs multiple layer segregation (SEAH and HONDROS [1973]).

In the case of iron containing dilute amounts of phosphorus, which typifies the behaviour of iron in the presence of a number of species, including sulphur and oxygen, the dependence of the grain boundary free energy on the bulk phosphorus content is shown in fig. 4 (HONDROS [1965]). From the slopes of the surface tension isotherm at 1450°C, the grain boundary excesses are calculated and the resulting adsorption isotherm is superimposed on the same figure. At the saturation part of the isotherm, the calculated grain boundary excess of phosphorus is 0.65×10^{19} atoms/m² which corresponds to approximately a third of a monatomic layer of phosphorus at grain boundaries, assuming the phosphorus atoms to be hard spheres spread out evenly and compactly across the interface. This compares with 1.4×10^{19} atoms of phosphorus per m² for the saturation coverage of the free surface which, in turn, corresponds to about 0.75 atoms of phosphorus per outermost atom of iron.

We note that until the advent of the sophisticated modern surface spectroscopies for measuring surface composition, the only quantitative means available for detecting and measuring this was through the use of the above Gibbs adsorption approach. The slope of the surface tension isotherm at infinite dilution (the *surface activity*) has been used conventionally in surface chemistry as a measure of the propensity of the solute to reduce the surface energy and thus to segregate. The quantity defined as

$$\eta_s = \frac{d\gamma_s}{dX_c}\bigg|_{X_c \to 0} \tag{2}$$

(the *interfacial* activity), is a useful notion in that it permits rapid, quantitative comparisons to be made between systems displaying a wide diversity of behaviour.

A remarkable and fundamental feature of surface microchemistry is its specificity, a feature which is revealed by a glance at some of the values for measured surface or interfacial activities. Thus, in an early application of these surface chemistry notions to the solid state, HONDROS and MCLEAN [1968] demonstrated that the interfacial activity for silicon at solid iron surfaces is 0.13 J/m² per atom percent of solute, compared with 3.2 J/m² for phosphorus and the extraordinary value 10 kJ/m² for oxygen. This remarkable system sensitivity of interfacial segregation is illustrated in fig. 5 for the grain boundary segregation in copper of three elements, gold, antimony and bismuth, and for comparison, the grain boundary segregation of phosphorus in iron (HONDROS [1969]). In the alloys of copper, the wide variation in the initial slopes of the grain boundary energy isotherms reflect this variation in interfacial activity and hence the widely differing tendencies of the solute atoms to segregate to the boundaries. It will not have passed unnoticed that the system Cu–Bi, with the highest interfacial activity, is also the system long associated with metallurgical problems.

As will be shown later, there has been an enormous stimulus to the study of interfacial microchemistry in both binary systems as well as multicomponent en-

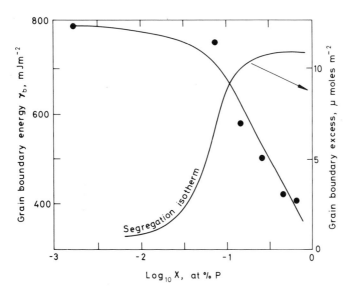

Fig. 4. Grain-boundary energy and segregation isotherms for phosphorus in iron (after HONDROS [1965]).

gineering alloys as a result of the advent of the modern surface spectroscopy techniques which permit the direct measurement of segregation. In order to build up a body of reliable data, it is useful that the quantities determined by the different approaches be made compatible. Thus we have extended to all interfaces the notion of an *Interfacial Enrichment Factor*, β_s, defined as the ratio between the *interfacial* concentration, X_s, (in mole fraction of a monatomic layer) and the *bulk solute*

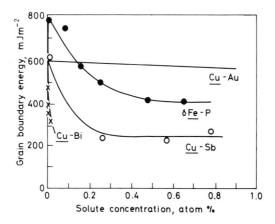

Fig. 5. Grain-boundary energy as a function of bulk solute concentration in four dilute binary systems: the solvent element is underlined in each case.

References: p. 928.

concentration, X_c, (expressed as mole fraction). Thus:

$$\beta_s = \frac{X_s}{X_c} = \frac{\Gamma_s}{\Gamma_s^0 X_c},$$ (3)

where Γ_s is the Gibbs excess defined earlier as Γ_2 and expressed as mol/m^2 and Γ_2^0 is the quantity of solute in moles constituting a close packed monatomic layer of unit area. This can be shown to be related to the measure of interfacial activity defined earlier from eqs. (1) and (2) as:

$$\beta_s = \frac{X_s}{X_c} = -\frac{1}{RT\Gamma_s^0} \frac{d\gamma_s}{dX_c}\bigg|_T = -\frac{1}{RT\Gamma_s^0}\eta_s,$$ (4)

In this way comparisons can be made between enrichment levels obtained by the Gibbs technique and those obtained directly using spectroscopy techniques.

3. Methods of measuring the microchemistry of interfaces

There now exists a copious technical literature on the subject of the detection and measurement of interfacial segregation, and one will remark on the wide range of imaginative approaches which were deployed during the past fifty years in attempts, mostly qualitative, to detect the suspected contaminants at grain boundaries which gave rise to various metallurgical effects. These mostly indirect techniques include: electrode potential measurements on grain boundary fracture surfaces; a number of subtle metallographic features observed at grain boundaries; variations in X-ray lattice parameter measurements with different grain sizes; internal friction measurements; micro-indentation hardness measurements; the spectrographic analysis of material carefully extracted from the grain boundary region; auto-radiography; and deductions made from anomalous grain growth behaviour. From the point of view of furthering this subject matter and offering a deeper insight, these past methods are not recommended to the reader as vital to the pursuit of the theme. The interested reader will find them fully covered in the reviews by INMAN and TIPLER [1963] and more recently by HONDROS [1976], but for most purposes these early techniques can be relegated to studies of the historical evolution of the subject: in one respect it is interesting to read these accounts as a testament to the highly ingenious approaches that the tenacious research worker is forced to adopt in those frequently encountered situations where the available tools are inadequate to satisfy his curiosity and sense of scientific exploration. These methods have been effectively superseded with the development in recent years of a range of sophisticated direct surface analysis techniques, based upon a variety of electron and ion emission processes – these and other significant techniques are considered below.

3.1. The interfacial energy or Gibbsian approach

Not only is there a requirement for data on interfacial energies in alloys as quantities in the modelling of various metallurgical processes, but as we saw above, a knowledge of the dependence of the interfacial free energy on bulk composition yields a quantitative measure of the amount of the species concentrated at that interface. This is the classical Gibbsian approach to the problem, and its most serious disadvantage is that since it is an indirect procedure, one requires an *a priori* knowledge of the relevant species procuring the change in the interfacial energy. Thus it finds its greatest applicability in binary systems where one knows in advance the elements involved. This inability to detect chemical species is a serious disadvantage in the study of, say, a multicomponent steel where one must presuppose a knowledge of the surface active species from prior general metallurgical observations.

The demand for relevant interfacial free energy data for the solid state arising, for example, from studies of grain growth or nucleation phenomena, has stimulated a variety of measurement approaches such as heat of solution calorimetry or controlled cleavage of the crystal. Most of these have been found inadequate or intrinsically not convenient for studying adsorption effects. For the measurement of the surface free energy of a metal, the most successful technique, and indeed the only one to have supplied data on Gibbsian segregation, is that described as the *Zero Creep Technique* in which the surface energy is deduced from a knowledge of the critical externally applied force necessary to counter-balance the capillarity forces which tend to shrink, at high temperature, samples with a high surface-to-volume ratio. This, as well as other measurement techniques are described in detail by HONDROS [1970]. The idea that at high temperature a solid will measurably shrink in order to reduce its surface area has been used in various forms by investigators, but we note that its main limitation is that because the shape change depends on solid-state diffusion, the technique is limited in practice to temperatures generally above $0.7\ T_m$. In a common experimental approach, the specimens consist of a set of fine filaments, each displaying a "bamboo structure", that is, the grain boundary surfaces are aligned normal to the long axis of the wire. The specimen set, containing a range of loads, is suspended in a cell, held at temperature for a known time in a controlled atmosphere and the deformation changes in the wires are measured. In another form of this technique HONDROS [1965] introduced a cylindrical foil specimen arrangement which allowed the measurement of creep displacements by X-ray shadowgraphy *in situ* in alloy specimens held in an opaque enclosure which ensured chemical equilibrium. This approach also improved the sensitivity of measurement of the creep changes, because much thinner foils may be used. Considering a polycrystalline foil of grain size d freely suspended under a uniform load and with grain boundaries intersecting the surfaces normally, a stress analysis shows that at equilibrium (i.e., zero displacement rate),

$$F = \gamma_s w - \frac{t\, w \gamma_b}{2d}, \tag{5}$$

where F is the applied force, w the width of the foil, t its thickness, γ_s the surface free energy, and γ_b the grain boundary free energy.

A typical specimen assembly for a series of alloys and suitable for fine creep

References: p. 928.

deformation measurements by X-ray radiography is shown in fig. 6. Here the thin specimen foil, shaped into a tube, is loaded with weights at five intervals so as to constitute one of a set of specimen elements progressively stressed over a range of stresses. With such an assembly, four alloy specimens of different composition can be studied under identical conditions of temperature and environment while changes in the dimensions of all specimens can be measured simultaneously on the same X-ray plate. The equilibrium stress, F/wt, for zero displacement rate is deduced from the intercept of the strain rate/stress curve, as shown in fig. 7. This is the equilibrium stress appropriate to eq. (5), and from the specimen dimensions the surface energy can be deduced. (In general, with the grain structures present in such specimens, the grain boundary term in the above equation is negligible compared with the surface energy term, so the grain-boundary energy need not be known.) In the most refined version of the Zero Creep Technique and with experimental precautions which ensure the attainment of chemical equilibrium, measurements can be reproduced to an accuracy of $\pm 5\%$. A further refinement of this foil technique is that it can be applied on samples having a sharp orientation texture and therefore a measurement is made of the surface energy for a particular orientation.

A compilation of surface free energy values for solid metals, citing in each instance the atmosphere and experimental method, has recently been published by KUMIKOV and KHOKONOV [1983].

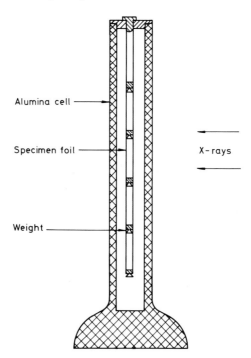

Fig. 6. Specimen configuration for measuring the solid state surface energy of an alloy by the Zero Creep Technique using foils in conjunction with X-ray radiographic measurements of the creep displacements.

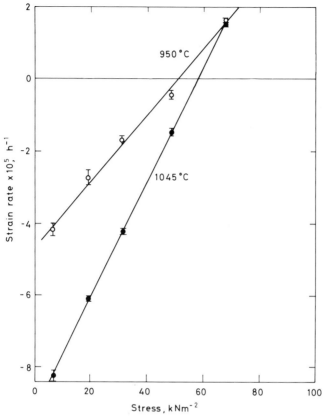

Fig. 7. Typical plots of specimen strain rates as a function of stress to define the equilibrium stress value for zero creep rate by interpolation; this provides a measure of the surface free energy.

As in the case of free surfaces, a wide range of techniques has been explored in order to measure grain-boundary free energies. These include isothermal calorimetry but in practice, most techniques are restricted to the determination of the grain-boundary energies for the pure metal. The only systematic data on the compositional dependence of grain-boundary energies have come through the application of polyphase equilibria techniques, which yield a *relative* grain-boundary/surface free energy value. The simple procedure is based on the observation that at high temperatures, the kinetics of mass transport allow intersecting interfaces to assume equilibrium configurations consistent with a minimum of energy, in which the local surface tensions can be analyzed as if in vectorial balance (SMITH [1948]). This idea has been used for a variety of situations and, in the case of grain boundaries, the microtopography of a grain boundary intersecting a free surface (fig. 8) is a distinct groove along the intersection of the boundary with the surface. This configuration indicates a balance in the tensions between the two crystalline surfaces and that of the grain boundary and in these conditions, assuming the surfaces to be isotropic,

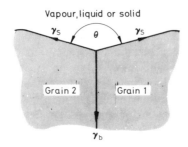

Fig. 8. Equilibrium configuration for a grain boundary intersecting the free surface, showing the dihedral angle.

the equilibrium is given by:

$$\gamma_b = 2\gamma_s \cos \frac{\theta}{2}, \tag{6}$$

where θ is the dihedral angle formed by the groove. In practice, the polycrystalline sample is equilibrated in physicochemical conditions which duplicate those in which γ_s, the reference value, is measured by the Zero Creep Technique. After a prolonged period of heating at temperature, which allows the equilibrium geometry to be attained, dihedral angles are measured on about 50 intersecting boundaries using optical interferometry or some other suitable technique. In this way, errors arising from the anisotropy of interfacial energies, which lead to rotational torque terms (HERRING [1953]) can be neglected, since it has been shown that eq. (6) is adequate if the grain-boundary/surface energy ratios are averaged statistically over a large number of observations.

3.2. Modern surface analysis techniques

The stimulus for much of the present day work on surface and interface microchemistry arises from the ease of use and interpretation of measurements made with the recently developed surface analysis techniques. To give some idea of the problems involved in this analysis, suppose a typical metal is fractured in air to provide a clean surface. This will be covered by a monolayer of oxygen atoms in a time of the order of one nanosecond. Thus, to study the surface or interface chemistry and reactions over a reasonable timescale, vacua of the order of 10^{-13} atm (10^{-10} Torr, 10 nPa or 100 fbar) are required to keep the environmental contamination under control. This technical capability became generally available only with the development of ultra-high vacuum (UHV) technology, in the mid-1960s. Thus, it was not until the 1970s that the surface analysis techniques became firmly established as tools for materials studies.

There are four main techniques, Auger electron spectroscopy (AES), X-ray photoelectron spectroscopy (XPS), ion scattering spectroscopy (ISS) and secondary ion mass spectroscopy (SIMS), the first three of which have been used to study segregation and each of which provides slightly different information. In general, the techniques are operated in UHV and are used to study the free surfaces of solids. The solid may be cleaned by argon ion sputtering, and the free surface segregation studied as a function of time, temperature, ambient environment or a combination of these. For the study of grain boundaries, these are exposed by fracture in the UHV of the instrument, using a suitable fracture stage. If the segregant embrittles the grain boundary, this fracture may be achieved fairly readily either at room temperature or by cooling the sample to liquid nitrogen temperatures. In the absence of intrinsic embrittlement, the grain boundary may be parted in some materials by impact after cathodically charging the solid with hydrogen (SMIALOWSKI [1962]) to promote hydrogen embrittlement. Of course, for grain boundary studies, unlike those on free surfaces, a fresh sample must be prepared for each heat-treatment time and temperature. The relative ease of studying free surfaces explains, to some extent, the high level of effort devoted to free surfaces compared with that for grain boundaries.

The analysis of the prepared surface in UHV is usually undertaken with the most powerful and popular of the techniques, AES (BRIGGS and SEAH [1983]). In this, a focused electron beam of 1–30 keV energy is used to excite atoms in the surface layer of an appropriate area of the target, creating holes in their inner core energy levels. The atoms subsequently decay by emission of either a characteristic X-ray (which is the basis of bulk chemical analysis) or by the emission of a characteristic Auger electron, which is the basis for surface analysis. We show in fig. 9(i) the inner core level diagram for an element heavier than neon as an example. The initial core hole may be created in level K which is then filled by a higher energy electron from, say, L_3 with the energy balance taken by, say, a second L_3 electron which is ejected from the atom with an energy E_A and is known as an Auger electron. E_A is characteristic of the particular atom and in this case is given approximately by:

$$E_A = E_K - E_{L_3} - E_{L_3}. \tag{7}$$

Fortunately, of the very many transitions that may occur, only a few are strong for each element and these enable the surface atoms to be clearly identified from the emitted electron energy spectrum. Atoms from depths greater than a few monolayers (1 nm) also eject Auger electrons but these do not escape easily and so do not contribute to the emitted line spectrum. Thus AES is characteristic of the outermost atomic layers of a solid and, by focusing the electron beam, we may now localize the composition of heterogeneous surfaces to a resolution across the surface that currently approaches 100 nm. Elements, except for H and He, are generally detected with sensitivities in the range one part in 100 to 1000.

An example which illustrates the use of AES is the analysis of the segregation giving rise to the temper brittleness in the $3Cr\frac{1}{2}Mo$ steel rotor which initiated a well known failure at a power station (KALDERON [1972]). The fracture of this material is fully intergranular as shown by the scanning electron micrograph of fig. 10. AES analysis of a sample taken from the vicinity of the original crack, and fractured in

References: p. 928.

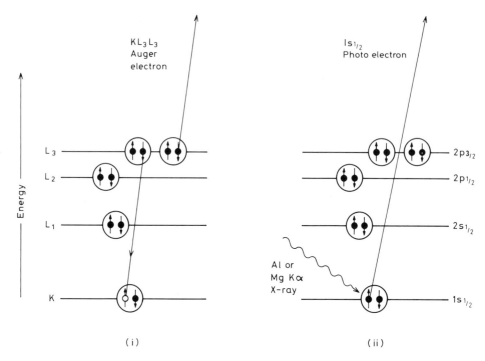

Fig. 9. Schematic transition level diagram for electrons in (i) AES and (ii) XPS.

the UHV AES system, shows 45% of a monatomic layer of phosphorus at the grain boundary. The spectrum shown in fig. 11 also identifies the alloying elements present and the carbides at the grain boundary.

That the segregant is located in the grain boundary zone may be demonstrated by slowly peeling away the surface atoms, using *in situ* argon ion sputtering and monitoring the surface composition by AES. In this way a composition–depth profile may be obtained for all elements present. Measurements for many segregants at grain boundaries are shown in fig. 12 where it is seen that the results agree with the solid curve predicted on the hypothesis that the segregant atoms are on the outermost atom plane of the fracture surface and hence associated with the precise atom plane of fracture.

A particular attribute of AES is the ability to achieve a fine localization on the free or fracture surface with the focused electron beam. This allows anisotropy effects between different crystals and the segregation at inclusion–matrix interfaces to be analyzed with comparative ease.

The second of the techniques, XPS (BRIGGS and SEAH [1983]) has some advantages over AES although it lacks spatial resolution. In XPS, as shown in fig. 9(ii), electrons are ejected from the surface atom core levels by the characteristic X-rays of energy $h\nu$ from a metal target, usually Al or Mg. The *emitted electron energy*, E_x is

Fig. 10. Scanning electron micrograph of the service failure of a temper-brittle $3Cr\frac{1}{2}Mo$ rotor steel, showing the fully intergranular fracture surface (field of view approximately 200 μm) (from SEAH [1975]).

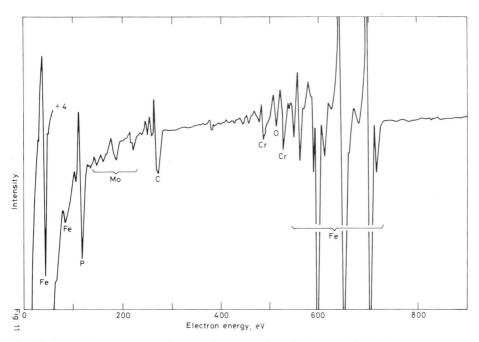

Fig. 11. Auger electron spectrum from the fracture surface of fig. 10, exhibiting 0.45 monolayers of phosphorus segregated at the grain boundary (after SEAH [1975]).

References: p. 928.

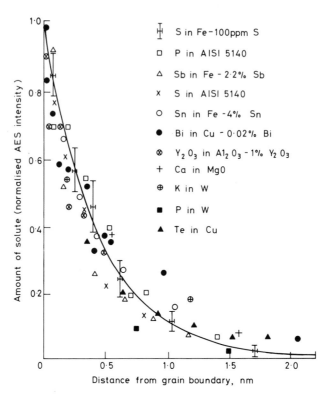

Fig. 12. Localization of segregant atoms at the grain boundary in many systems by AES with argon ion etching (after SEAH [1980a], based on MARCUS *et al.* [1972]).

given in the example of fig. 9ii by:

$$E_x = h\nu - E_{1s}.$$ (8)

Thus, each of the lines in the emitted photo-electron spectrum directly reflects the core level positions, identifying the emitting atoms which, for the same reasons as given for AES, are those in the outermost 1 nm of the surface. The precise position and shape of the photo-electron line depends on the chemical state of the surface atoms, and so XPS can be used to probe the chemical state of the segregant atoms and to separate out those elements which are in micro-precipitates on the surface. For instance, in fig. 13 details are shown of the 2p (or L_{23}) line for phosphorus on the free (100) surface of an iron single crystal. The various curves show: (1) a true segregant; (2) phosphorus segregated plus Fe_3P precipitates where the phosphorus level is above the solubility limit during the heat treatment; and (3) the dotted curve from solid Fe_3P.

During the past few years, a veritable plethora of alternative surface analysis techniques has emerged. Of these, the only one that has been used for segregation

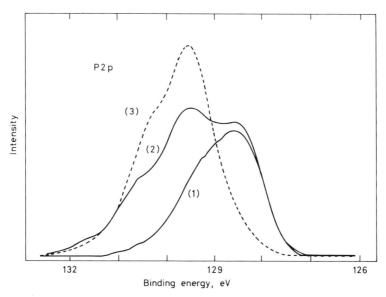

Fig. 13. X-ray photoelectron 2p core line of phosphorus: (1) segregated on Fe (100); (2) segregated with Fe$_3$P precipitates; (3) from solid Fe$_3$P. (After EGERT and PANZNER [1982].)

studies is ion-scattering spectroscopy (ISS). In ISS (BAUN *et al.* [1976]) the mass of atoms in the surface atom layer is determined by recording the energy loss of ions bounced off those atoms as if in a billiard-ball collision. Using a detector at an angle θ to the incident beam of ions of mass M_i and energy E_i, it is easy to show that surface atoms of mass M will reflect those ions into the detector with an energy E_M where:

$$M = M_i \left[\frac{E_i + 2\sqrt{E_i E_m}\ \cos \theta + E_m}{E_i - E_M} \right]. \tag{9}$$

This allows the analysis of the surface atoms. However, it will be seen from eq. (9) that high masses are all found bunched in a small energy range near E_i and thus, because of energy blurring terms which give rise to peak broadening, it is difficult to distinguish adjacent masses heavier than copper. ISS has, however, two main advantages over AES and XPS which are very pertinent to studies of surface segregation, especially in applications related to adsorption and catalysis. These are that by using neon ions of 1 keV energy, the analysis is limited to the outermost atom layer only and by suitably directing the beam at a single crystal surface, atom site positions can be determined very accurately by shadowing effects.

    SIMS, as a surface analysis technique, has not been used to study segregation but could well supply useful information. As with ISS, the surface is interrogated by an ion beam, usually argon with an energy in the range 1–3 keV, with a flux of some

nA/cm^2 (BENNINGHOVEN et al. [1982]). Secondary ions that are then emitted may be mass analyzed to determine the atom groupings on the surface since these groupings are reflected in the total mass of the clusters detected. Complex atom groupings of twenty or more atoms can be observed which represent bonding arrangements at surfaces (BRIGGS [1982]) and so, in principle, the interactions of co-segregants could be studied. SIMS has other advantages of detecting hydrogen and of being much more sensitive than AES or XPS; however, it is very difficult to quantify the spectra and hence it has not yet become popular as a technique to study segregation.

3.3. Microscopical techniques

Three microscopical techniques have been used in the study of grain-boundary segregation, and although each has its own unique advantages, as noted below, none can be used for the parallel study of surface segregation. These three techniques have the crucial advantage over the techniques discussed above that, in addition to being analytical, they can provide measurements for boundaries that will not undergo fracture. They thus enable a new range of systems to be studied.

The most popular of the microscopical techniques is ion microprobe analysis or, as it is sometimes known, *secondary ion microscopy*. In this technique, a mass spectrometer is used to construct emitted-ion images of the surface bombarded by a primary ion beam. The grain boundary is arranged normal to the surface being imaged, so it intersects the surface in a line that does not move as the surface is eroded by the primary ion beam. In this way, a trace of the boundary can be imaged using the segregant atoms, with a resolution of a few μm (WALSH and KEAR [1975]). Isotopes can be separated, and the elements hydrogen and helium, not observed in AES or XPS, may be clearly imaged.

Another microscopical technique which has unique advantages is the *scanning transmission electron microscope* (STEM) with X-ray analysis (DOIG et al. [1981]). Here a thin section of material is prepared with the grain boundary again perpendicular to the surface and the sample is then imaged in the electron microscope. The segregant is measured using a nondispersive X-ray detector with the electron beam on the boundary. The technique has the advantage that small precipitates and inclusions on the boundary can also be analyzed by X-rays and electron diffraction, but it has the disadvantages of not being able to analyze the light elements ($Z < 10$) and of requiring careful specimen preparation (see also ch. 11, §§ 2, 10).

The third microscopical technique is *atom-probe field ion microscopy* (MILLER and SMITH [1977], KARLSSON et al. [1982]). Here the atoms on the end of a sharp tip of the material may be imaged with atomic spatial resolution. Selected atoms may then be removed from the tip, using (electric) field evaporation, and mass-analyzed. Thus, in principle, individual atoms around a grain boundary or a precipitate–matrix interface may be analyzed and counted. In an alternative variant of the instrument, atoms of selected masses may be field-desorbed and imaged. In this way images of the trace of a grain boundary may be constructed with near atomic resolution, as shown in the example of molybdenum with oxygen segregated at the grain boundaries,

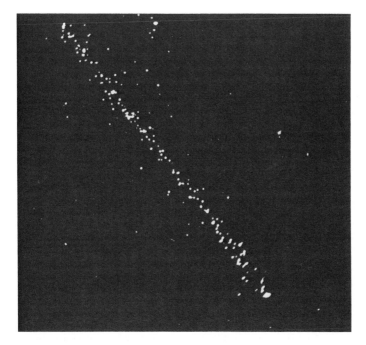

Fig. 14. Field desorption image of the trace of a grain boundary in molybdenum, using oxygen atoms. The field of view, approximately 20 nm wide, shows how uniformly the oxygen segregates. (From WAUGH [1978].)

in fig. 14. This highly resolved image shows that the oxygen is not present in precipitates at the boundary but as a uniformly segregated layer.

4. Theory of segregation processes

4.1. Introduction: equilibrium and non-equilibrium segregation

In this section we are concerned with the theory of microsegregation in two forms: equilibrium and non-equilibrium. Equilibrium segregation occurs, as noted earlier, as a result of inhomogeneities in the solid giving rise to sites for which solute atoms have a lower free energy. These sites occur at interfaces such as the free surface, grain boundaries and phase interfaces as well as at defect sites, dislocations and stacking faults. All of these regions have concentrations of solute atoms which differ from each other and from that of the bulk materials as shown schematically in fig. 1. At any given temperature, there is a unique solute concentration for each of these sites that is asymptotically approached as time goes to infinity and at a rate governed by diffusion.

References: p. 928.

On the other hand, non-equilibrium segregation depends on rate processes and kinetic events and, in general, disappears as time approaches infinity if diffusion processes are allowed to reach full equilibrium. There are a number of discrete routes for producing this form of segregation, which include moderate rate quenching of samples from a high temperature, the growth of precipitates, the effect of stress at temperature, etc, which are dealt with in more detail in §4.6. Here we concentrate on equilibrium segregation which not only is the more common form, but also has been studied more comprehensively.

The free energies of the sites for equilibrium segregation may be represented as shown in fig. 15, where each site has both enthalpy and entropy contributions. In the dilute limit of element A segregating in a matrix of element B, one may consider the relative concentrations $C_1(A)$ and $C_2(A)$, at different sites, 1 and 2, to obey the Maxwell–Boltzmann relation:

$$\frac{C_1(A)}{C_2(A)} = \exp - \frac{\Delta G_{12}}{RT}, \tag{10}$$

where ΔG_{12} is the free energy difference between sites 1 and 2. Although eq. (10) provides a feel for what may generally occur in dilute systems, it greatly oversimplifies the problem. In the sections that follow we consider the various adsorption theories for non-dilute systems, which have been established as direct analogues or developments of theories well known in the field of gas adsorption on the free surfaces of solids. The theories will be presented as a series with successively more complex segregation conditions. The free energy term giving rise to segregation will then be analyzed and finally the kinetics of the segregation process will be presented.

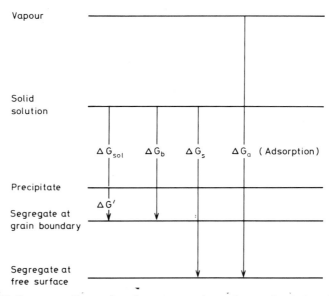

Fig. 15. Free energy diagram for solutes segregated at surfaces and grain boundaries.

4.2. The Langmuir–McLean theory

The earliest derivation was made specifically for grain boundaries, (McLean [1957]), but it is also valid for free surfaces. In this classical derivation, McLean proposed a model of P solute atoms distributed at random amongst N lattice sites and p solute atoms distributed at random amongst n independent grain boundary sites. The total free energy due to the solute atoms is then

$$G = pe + PE - kT\left[\ln n!N! - \ln(n-p)!p!(N-P)!P!\right], \qquad (11)$$

where E and e are the energies of the solute atom in the lattice and in the grain boundary respectively and the term in k is the configurational entropy for the arrangement of the solute atoms in the bulk and grain boundary. The equilibrium state of the system occurs at the minimum value of G. This may be determined by differentiating G with respect to p, noting that the sum of p and P remains constant. Corresponding to this minimum, the grain boundary analogue of Langmuir adsorp-

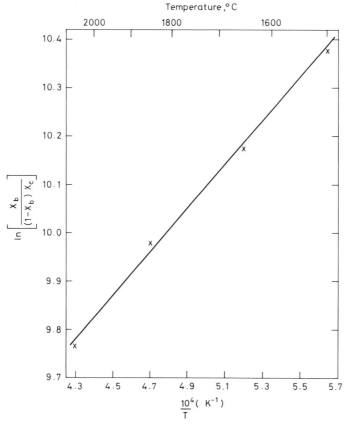

Fig. 16. Langmuir–McLean plot for oxygen grain-boundary segregation measured by AES in molybdenum (after Kumar and Eyre [1980]).

References: p. 928.

tion at free surfaces is obtained:

$$\frac{X_b}{X_b^0 - X_b} = \frac{X_c}{1 - X_c} \exp \frac{-\Delta G}{RT}, \qquad \text{Langmuir–McLean,} \qquad (12)$$

where the notation of HONDROS and SEAH [1977a] is now used: here X_b^0 is the fraction of the grain boundary monolayer available for segregated atoms at saturation, X_b is the actual fraction covered with segregant, X_c is the bulk solute molar fraction and ΔG is the free energy of segregation per mole of solute. ΔG contains all the entropy terms such as vibrational and anharmonic, but not the configurational term which is written separately in eq. (11). Segregation measurements obeying the form of eq. (12) have been reported for several systems at both free surfaces and grain boundaries. Figure 16, for example, reproduces the measurements by KUMAR and EYRE [1980] which show that the Langmuir–McLean relation is obeyed for the segregation of 8–12 at ppm of oxygen to grain boundaries in molybdenum over a wide temperature range. For convenience eq.(12) has been rearranged as follows to obtain a linear plot: X_b^0 is assumed to be unity and $X_c \ll 1$ so that:

$$-\frac{\Delta G}{RT} = \ln \frac{X_b}{(1 - X_b) X_c}. \qquad (13)$$

We recognize the basic features of segregation behaviour from this form: the element segregation increases as the bulk solute content, X_c, increases or as the temperature, T, falls. In this simple model, solute atoms are not interacting at the grain boundary and never exceed the saturation segregation level of one monolayer. At this point, we require some way of estimating the value of ΔG for segregation to both grain boundaries and free surfaces. This is discussed in the next sections.

4.2.1. Prediction of the free energy of segregation to grain boundaries

The value of ΔG_b was estimated by MCLEAN [1957] from the elastic strain energy, E_{el}, of the solute in the lattice, all of which is assumed to be released on segregation. For a solute atom of radius r_1 in a site of radius r_0, the elastic energy associated with one mole of solute is given by (WYNBLATT and KU [1979]):

$$E_{el} = \frac{24\pi NKG \, r_0 r_1 (r_1 - r_0)^2}{3Kr_1 + 4Gr_0}, \qquad (14)$$

where K is the solute bulk modulus, G is the solvent or matrix shear modulus and N is Avogadro's number. Two examples of the values for segregants in copper computed by MCLEAN [1957] are shown in table 1. The final column shows the experimental values.

Values estimated by this approach are generally correct to within a factor of two. However, much higher accuracy is required for the quantitative prediction of segregation behaviour. This was provided in the treatment by SEAH and HONDROS [1973]. Using the (BET) gas adsorption theory of BRUNAUER et al. [1940], they write

Table 1

Values of the elastic distortion energy, E_{el}, for Sb and Bi in Cu.

Element	K (GN/m^2)	r_1 (nm)	$(r_1 - r_0)/r_1$	E_{el} (kJ/mol)	ΔG_b (kJ/mol)
Sb	41	0.1528	+0.194	37	65
Bi	31.4	0.157	+0.266	66	100

the solid-state analogue as

$$\frac{X_b}{X_b^0 - X_b} = \frac{X_c}{X_c^0} \exp \frac{-\Delta G'}{RT}, \qquad \text{(Truncated BET)}, \qquad (15)$$

where X_c^0, the solid solubility, is the important parameter. For slightly soluble substances, $X_c^0 = \exp(\Delta G_{sol}/RT)$ so that the Langmuir–McLean and Truncated BET theories are in fact identical in the dilute limit with

$$\Delta G_b = \Delta G' + \Delta G_{sol}, \qquad (16)$$

as shown in the energy level diagram of fig. 15. The importance of the Truncated BET form is that one may define as a useful parameter the enrichment ratio, β_b, which represents the ratio X_b/X_c in the dilute limit. Since X_b^0 generally turns out to be unity, we find:

$$\beta_b = \frac{K}{X_c^0} \qquad \text{where } K = \exp \frac{-\Delta G'}{RT}. \qquad (17)$$

The usefulness of eq. (17) was first noted by SEAH and HONDROS [1973] who produced the earlier version of fig. 17 incorporating only the points shown by dots. This figure shows a compilation of measurements of grain-boundary enrichment ratios, β_b, (estimated by the grain-boundary energy and surface-analysis approaches), in relation to the solubilities of the segregant at the measurement temperature. Thus the grain-boundary enrichment for systems in which no measurements are available may be accurately estimated from handbooks of phase diagrams (SMITHELLS [1976]; HANSEN [1958]). The original prediction has been confirmed by all the later measurements shown starred in fig. 17. It is clear that, in the dilute limit, eq. (17) provides the theoretical description of the experimental data of fig. 17 quite accurately. Indeed it is seen that whilst ΔG_{sol} ranges from zero to -80 kJ/mol, $\Delta G'$ has a mean value of -10 kJ/mol with a standard deviation of only 6 kJ/mol. Thus,

$$\Delta G_b = \Delta G_{sol} - 10 \pm 6 \text{ kJ/mol}. \qquad (18)$$

Equation (15) is valid only for $X_c < X_c^0$. If excess solute is present, so that a second phase appears, the solute content is limited to X_c^0 and eq. (15) becomes

$$\frac{X_b}{X_b^0 - X_b} = \exp \frac{-\Delta G'}{RT}. \qquad (19)$$

References: p. 928.

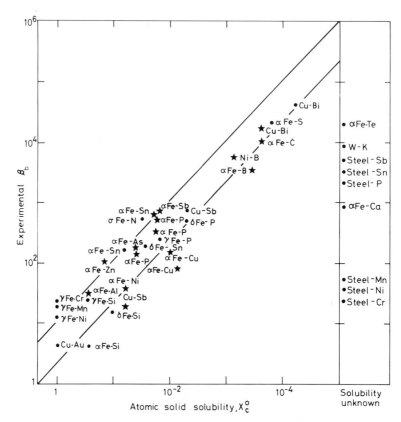

Fig. 17. Correlation of measured grain-boundary enrichment ratios with the atomic solid solubility. The points denoted by stars represent measurements published since the first correlation was made.

The translation from eq. (15) to eq. (19) as the solubility limit is reduced through the solute level, is illustrated by the measurements for sulphur in iron by SEAH and HONDROS [1973], shown in fig. 18. Equation (15) is shown for the higher temperatures, where the solubility is high, and eq. (19) at the lower temperatures.

4.2.2. Prediction of the free energy of segregation to surfaces

The theory for the free energy of surface segregation, ΔG_s, has developed along less phenomenological lines than that for grain boundaries although both are merely special cases of one general effect. Each of the two approaches leads to a reasonably accurate prediction for the case to which it pertains. The reader may blend the two approaches to gain a greater insight into the nature of the contributions to the free energy, however, at the present time it does not lead to a greater accuracy in calculation.

The treatment for free surfaces is based on the derivation of WILLIAMS and

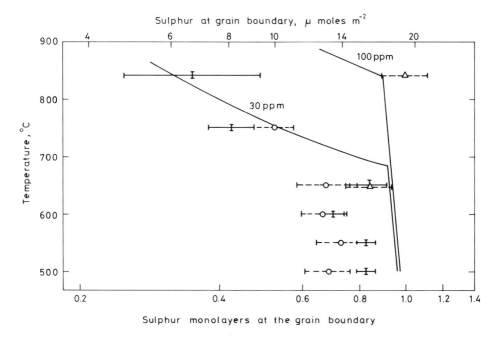

Fig. 18. AES measurements of sulphur grain-boundary segregation in iron as a function of temperature for two bulk compositions (after HONDROS and SEAH [1977b]).

NASON [1974] who use a layer-by-layer model of the surface region, with solute A atoms replacing the solvent B atoms substitutionally at the surface. They find that this model gives the Langmuir–McLean adsorption eq. (12) for the fractional coverage of A on the surface, which allows the calculation of ΔG_s. The basic model adopts the quasi-chemical approach, shown in fig. 19, where the nearest neighbour bond energies are given by ϵ_{AA}, ϵ_{BB} and ϵ_{AB} between AA, BB and AB neighbours respectively. ΔG_s is calculated as the energy released on removing an A atom from a lattice site and exchanging it for a B atom on the free surface. The energy required to remove A from the bulk is:

$$-(Z_1 + 2Z_v)\left[X_c\epsilon_{AA} + (1 - X_c)\epsilon_{AB}\right],\tag{20}$$

where Z_1 is the atomic coordination number in the layer and Z_v is the atomic coordination to one of the adjacent layers. The energy to replace A at the surface is similarly:

$$Z_1\left[X_s\epsilon_{AA} + (1 - X_s)\epsilon_{AB}\right] + Z_v\left[X_c\epsilon_{AA} + (1 - X_c)\epsilon_{AB}\right].\tag{21}$$

Equivalent terms occur for the B atom moving in the reverse direction so that by using the *regular solution approximation* in which

$$\epsilon_{AB} = 1/2(\epsilon_{AA} + \epsilon_{BB}) + \omega,\tag{22}$$

References: p. 928.

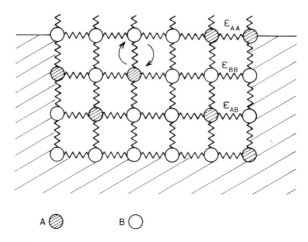

Fig. 19. Schematic substitutional model for the quasi-chemical segregation theory.

we find that the free energy of surface segregation per atom, $\Delta G_s/N$, is given by

$$\Delta G_s/N = \tfrac{1}{2}Z_v(\epsilon_{BB} - \epsilon_{AA}) + 2\omega\{Z_l(X_c - X_s) + Z_v(X_c - 1/2)\}. \tag{23}$$

In Williams and Nason's theory successive layers away from the surface are considered and for nonzero values of ω the composition of the second and further layers can also differ from that of the bulk. For instance, if ω is negative, there is a perceptible oscillation of composition decaying away from the surface in addition to the surface segregation. Here, however, to simplify the analysis and because it has not been possible to observe such small oscillations in practice, it will be assumed that all of the compositional variation occurs in the topmost atom layer.

Numerical evaluation of eq.(23) may proceed in several ways. Following WYN-BLATT and KU [1979] the bond strengths ϵ_{AA} and ϵ_{BB} may be derived from the molar surface energies of the two constituents. At absolute zero these energies may be expressed as follows:

$$\gamma_A^s = -\tfrac{1}{2}Z_v\epsilon_{AA}N; \qquad \gamma_B^s = -\tfrac{1}{2}Z_v\epsilon_{BB}N. \tag{24}$$

The regular solution parameter, ω [eq. (22)], may then be calculated from tabulated values (HULTGREN et al. [1973]) of the enthalpy of mixing, H^m:

$$\Omega = N\omega = H^m/ZX_c(1 - X_c), \tag{25}$$

where Z is the total coordination number. Williams and Nason in their original paper evaluated ϵ_{AA} and ϵ_{BB} from the molar sublimation enthalpies, H^{sub}, where

$$H_i^{sub} = -\tfrac{1}{2}Z\epsilon_{ii}N, \tag{26}$$

where i stands for A or B. The above terms now give some insight into the kinds of elements that will segregate to free surfaces. If the regular solution parameter can be ignored, it is seen from eqs. (23) and (24) that, other things being equal, the element with the lower surface energy enriches the surface of a binary system. Alternatively, from eqs. (23) and (26), this will also be the element of lower sublimation enthalpy.

The above is particularly true for liquid binary metallic systems as shown by HONDROS [1980]. However, for solids McLean's strain term given in eq. (14) is also important. The strain term is only significant for excess-sized solute atoms. TSAI *et al.* [1977] point out that, as there is little relaxation around vacancies, the strain energy associated with $r_0 < r_1$, must be much less than the converse.

Using the above approach, SEAH [1979] gained an overall view of surface segregation by combining eqs. (23) and (24) and adding the strain term of eq. (14). From what we have seen in § 3.2.1, this term will be of the order of $2.6 \times 10^{35} \times r_0(r_1 - r_0)^2$. In fact, using regression analysis of published data, Seah found for dilute binary systems:

$$-\Delta G_s = \left(\gamma_B^S - \gamma_A^S\right) + 1.8\Omega + M\, 2.66 \times 10^{35} r_0 \left(r_1 - r_0\right)^2, \tag{27}$$

where M is unity for $r_1 > r_0$ and zero for $r_1 < r_0$. The r values are the atom sizes given

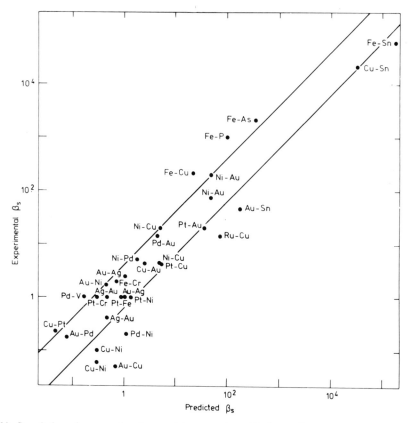

Fig. 20. Correlation of measured surface enrichment ratios with the predicted values from eq. (27) (after Seah [1979]).

by $\rho N(2r)^3 = A$, where ρ is the bulk density and A the atomic weight of the element. Figure 20 shows the resulting correlation for an improved version of eq. (27), using the relation $\beta_s = X_s/X_c = \exp(-\Delta G_s/RT)$, and the experimental data for the surface enrichment ratio. This analysis confirmed the correctness of simply adding the bond and strain energy terms directly and that the latter is significant only for $r_1 > r_0$. Thus we may write:

$$\Delta G_s = [\text{bond term, eq. (23)}] + M[\text{strain term, eq. (14)}]$$
$$- T(\text{entropy terms discussed below}). \tag{28}$$

4.2.3. Segregation with adsorbate–adsorbate interactions

In the above we have concentrated on evaluating ΔG in the limit of dilute X_b, X_s and X_c to compare the overall behaviour with experiment. To study the effect of higher levels of segregation we may rewrite eq. (23) simply:

$$\Delta G_s = \Delta G_s^0 - 2Z_1 N\omega X_s, \tag{29}$$

where $\Delta G_s^0 = NZ_v(\epsilon_{BB} - \epsilon_{AB})$ does not depend on the segregation level. This equation is based on the substitutional segregation model shown in fig. 19, which is a good description for many free surfaces and grain boundaries. A completely different description, valid only for free surfaces, is the *Fowler theory* in which adsorbed atoms on top of the free surface have, simply, the interaction energy ϵ_{AA}. In this case:

$$\Delta G_s = \Delta G_s^0 + Z_1 N\epsilon_{AA} X_s. \tag{30}$$

This is seen to be the same as the result for eq. (29) if the top atom layer B atoms are replaced by vacancies.

Using either of the above equations, if the presence of a segregated A atom enhances the probability of the next site being occupied by an A atom, ΔG becomes more negative as the segregation proceeds. As ϵ_{AA} becomes more and more negative, the segregation shows progressively sharper rises as the temperature falls until eventually the rise in segregation becomes discontinuous at a temperature given by the solution of

$$C = -4RT, \tag{31}$$

where C is the coefficient of X_s in eqs. (29) and (30). Measurements illustrating this form of segregation are shown in fig. 21 for Se and Te segregation in pure iron. There is also shown the simple Langmuir–McLean case with $C = 0$ and a case in which a discontinuous rise occurs from a low to a high segregation level. As seen from the labelling of the ordinate, the lowest segregations occur at low bulk solute contents, X_c, and high temperatures, T.

4.2.4. Anisotropy of segregation

In the above we considered that all sites are equivalent prior to segregation. This is generally not the case either at free surfaces or at grain boundaries. The simplest

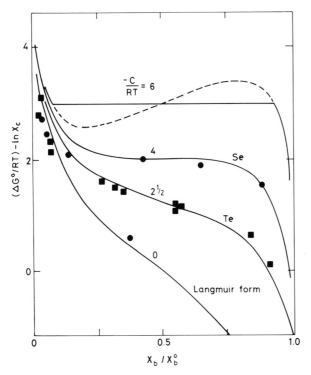

Fig. 21. Grain boundary Fowler isotherms with the AES measurements of PICHARD *et al.* [1975] (after HONDROS and SEAH [1977a]).

case to understand is that of free surfaces. The driving force for segregation is the lowering of the overall system free energy. If the surface energy is already low as in the case of the low-index surfaces (111), (110) and (100), we should expect that the segregation here would be lower than that for a high index surface. Little direct work has been reported, but measurements by JOHNSON *et al.* [1978] for Au segregation on Ni generally confirm this. Considerably more work has, however, been completed on the influences of the anisotropy of surface segregation on the anisotropy of surface energy, because of the technological significance, and this is discussed in §5.1.

For grain boundaries, one has the relative orientations of both crystals to the grain-boundary plane to take into account and so the problem is much more complex. In a neat study by SUZUKI *et al.* [1981] of phosphorus grain-boundary segregation in iron, they show that after fracture, the level of phosphorus observed may be associated with the Miller indices of the fracture surface, as shown in fig. 22a. The measurements of the segregation in relation to the stereographic triangle are shown in fig. 22b. It is clear that the lower segregations are associated with the lower index poles since, as one may expect, the boundaries involving these surfaces are more ordered than the general high-index boundaries. In general, the more the

References: p. 928.

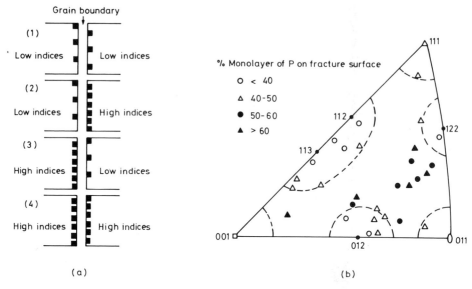

Fig. 22. The anisotropy of phosphorus grain-boundary segregation in iron–1% phosphorus showing (a) the segregant atoms (dark squares) in relation to the fracture process and (b) the level of segregation in relation to the relative orientation of each grain to the grain boundary (after SUZUKI et al. [1981]).

segregation, the greater the effect in metallurgy, and hence most studies have concerned the high-index boundaries rather than the more ordered cases. However, work is now in hand to study this complex problem in Professor Gleiter's laboratory (ROY et al. [1982]); HASHIMOTO et al. [1982], SUTTON and VITEK [1982] and LARTIGUE and PRIESTER [1983] have also made a promising start. BRIANT [1983] has shown that variations in grain-boundary structure can lead to variability of ±30% from average in the extent of segregation in a given system.

4.2.5. Temperature dependence of the free energies of segregation

The temperature dependence of segregation occurs mainly through the explicit temperature term in eq. (15). As the temperature rises the segregant "boils off" leading to a lower value. However, the free energy itself is temperature dependent through the customary relation:

$$\Delta G = \Delta H - T\Delta S \tag{32}$$

where ΔS is the entropy change on segregation to a grain boundary or free surface. SEAH and LEA [1975] write ΔS as the sum of three terms, ΔS_v, ΔS_a and ΔS_m. ΔS_v is associated with the changes in the vibrational behaviour on segregation, ΔS_a with the anharmonicity of the potential of the segregant atom site and ΔS_m with site multiplicity. The vibrational entropy term is given, in the Einstein model, as:

$$S_v = 3R\left[1 + \ln(kT/h\nu)\right], \tag{33}$$

where $kT \gg h\nu$, ν being the Einstein frequency. $h\nu$ may be rewritten $k\theta_E$ or $0.775k\theta_D$ where θ_E and θ_D are the Einstein and Debye temperatures (KITTEL [1956]) so that

$$\Delta S_v = 3R \ln(\theta_D/\theta_D^*), \tag{34}$$

where θ_D and θ_D^* are the Debye temperatures for the solute atom in the matrix and at the distorted site of the grain boundary or free surface. Owing to the greater vibrational amplitude of atoms at surfaces, θ_D^*/θ_D has been calculated for tin surface segregation in iron to be approximately 2/3. In this way, taking into account the matrix atom exchanging places with the segregant atom, ΔS_v is about $3.5R$ for the free surface and $3.3R$ at grain boundaries.

In a similar manner, the two further entropy contributions, ΔS_a, due to the anharmonicity of the atomic potential at the termination of a lattice, either by the surface or by a grain boundary (EWING [1971]), and ΔS_m, due to the possible site

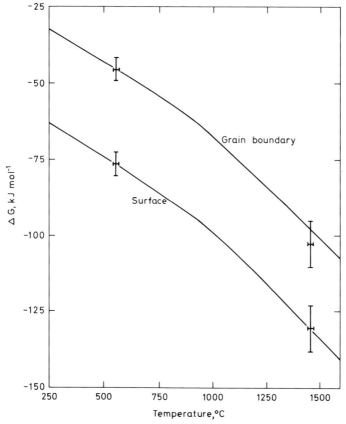

Fig. 23. The predicted temperature dependence of the free energies of surface- and grain-boundary segregations of tin in iron, together with the experimental data at 550°C and 1420°C (after SEAH and LEA [1975]).

References: p. 928.

multiplicity for the segregating atoms, may be calculated. Both terms are much smaller than ΔS_v and so will not be treated here.

The correlation of the above full prediction of the temperature dependence of ΔG with the experimental data for tin in iron is shown in fig. 23 for both surface and grain-boundary segregations. This figure also serves to emphasize the generally observed fact that surface segregation at moderate temperatures is generally much greater than segregation at grain boundaries.

4.3. Segregation in simple ternary systems – site competition

Site competition in a ternary system occurs where there are two segregants which can fill the same sites at the free surface or grain boundary. Each segregant obeys the appropriate adsorption theory with the available empty sites reduced by the segregation of the other species. At saturation segregation, this leads to the situation where the sum of the segregants is constant at one monolayer. This has been observed on the free surface of iron for Sn, Sb and O in competition with S. Generally the Sn, Sb or O segregate rapidly to an equilibrium level but, with time at temperature, S (which may be present at only a few ppm in solution), will replace much of the Sn, Sb and O. Such a competition is not generally expected at grain boundaries since the bond energy terms can continue to be reduced until two total monolayers are segregated, and this latter level of segregation is rarely reached. Grain boundary site competition between N and S has been reported (TAUBER and GRABKE [1978]) in iron but not under all conditions (JONES *et al.* [1981]). More importantly, P is displaced by C (ERHART and GRABKE [1981]). This is of great significance in steels, as discussed in §6.3.

4.4. Segregation in complex metallurgical systems

In 1975 GUTTMANN extended the Fowler theory to allow for coupling interactions between two co-segregating species in multicomponent systems. This development, vital to explain the segregation behaviour resulting in intergranular failures in engineering materials, gives the analogue to the Langmuir–McLean equation,

$$\frac{X_{bi}}{X_{bi}^0} = \frac{X_{ci} \exp -\Delta G_i / RT}{1 + \Sigma_{j=1}^2 X_{cj} \left[\exp(-\Delta G_j / RT) - 1 \right]}, \tag{35}$$

where X_{b1} and X_{b2} are the molar fractional monolayers segregated by a noxious impurity and by an alloying element of bulk contents X_{c1} and X_{c2} respectively. The ΔG's are given by equations of the form of eqs. (29) or (30) but depend not on the level of self-segregation but on each other through the equations:

$$\Delta G_1 = \Delta G_1^0 + \alpha'_{12} X_{b2}, \qquad \Delta G_2 = \Delta G_2^0 + \alpha'_{12} X_{b1}, \tag{36}$$

where ΔG_1^0 and ΔG_2^0 are the free energies of segregation of the impurity and alloying elements separately in the matrix. The interaction coefficients α'_{12} refer to the changes in nearest neighbour bond energies in forming the alloy–impurity bonds and can be obtained from measurements of the effects of the alloying elements on the solubilities of the impurities. Figure 24 shows the effects of a range of solutes on the solubility of phosphorus in α-Fe at 1000°C, from which the calculated $-\alpha'_{12}$ values are 30 kJ/mol for the interaction of phosphorus with nickel and 67, 105, 146, 176, 180, 223 and 258 kJ/mol for phosphorus with Mn, Cr, V, W, Mo, Ti and Zr, respectively (GUTTMANN [1976]). The stronger the reduction in solubility, the stronger the coupling of the alloy element to the impurity and the more the alloying addition enhances the impurity segregation.

In a similar manner to that of the Fowler isotherm, as α'_{12} becomes more and more negative the curves exhibit a more pronounced S shape and eventually attain a region in which the segregation shows a discontinuous increase from a low to a high level. The general effect of Guttmann's coupling can be seen by reference to fig. 17. Alloy element additions with a negative value of α'_{12} cause the impurity element solubility to fall. Simultaneously, through eqs. (35) and (36), the segregation level rises. Thus, the addition of the alloying element causes the point for the original binary system in fig. 17 to move diagonally upwards to the right but to stay within the general correlation (GUTTMANN and McLEAN [1979]).

The general behaviour of this model is now well accepted and allows an accurate

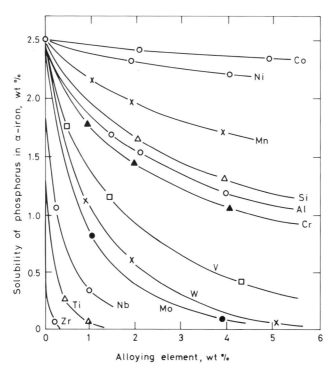

Fig. 24. The effect of alloying elements on the solubility of phosphorus in α-Fe at 1000°C (after KANEKO *et al.* [1965]).

References: p. 928.

description of some of the behaviour observed in embrittlement problems. The increase in the free energy of segregation of one species by a second, described in eq. (36), has been validated in careful experiments on grain-boundary segregation in steel by GAS et al. [1982]. Although high $-\alpha'$ values lead to a high enrichment ratio, the result in practice often will be a low segregation. This is because the reduction in solubility and hence the number of solute atoms available to segregate make the rate of build-up of the segregant at the surface or grain boundary very slow indeed so that, with practical heat treatments, a negligible segregation occurs. This is precisely the case, for example, with the addition of manganese to remove the sulphur embrittlement in steels. The problem of the kinetics of segregation is very important in practice and this is considered in the next section.

Guttmann's original theory was modified by SEAH [1977] to remove the site competition between alloy elements and impurities which had not been observed in practice. In eq. (35) the sum over the j terms is simply replaced by the ith term. This simplifies the calculations and gives a better description of the experimental results as discussed in §6.3. Several more complex theories are detailed by GUTTMANN and MCLEAN [1979] and by GUTTMANN [1980].

4.5. The kinetics of segregation

Most models of the kinetics of segregation follow MCLEAN's [1957] approach. Solute atoms are assumed to segregate to a grain boundary from two infinite half crystals of uniform solute content or to a surface from one infinite half crystal. Diffusion in the crystals is described by Fick's Laws and the ratio of the solute in the grain boundary to that in the adjacent atom layer of the bulk is given by the enrichment ratio, β, assumed to be constant and independent of the actual values of X_b and X_c. The kinetics of the segregation are thus described by:

$$\frac{X_b(t) - X_b(0)}{X_b(\infty) - X_b(0)} = 1 - \exp\frac{FDt}{\beta^2 f^2} \operatorname{erfc}\left[\frac{FDt}{\beta^2 f^2}\right]^{1/2}, \tag{37}$$

where $F = 4$ for grain boundaries and 1 for the free surface, $X_b(t)$ is the boundary content at time t, D is the solute bulk diffusivity, and f is related to the atom sizes b and a of the solute and matrix, respectively, by $f = a^3 b^{-2}$. For short times, eq. (37) approximates to

$$\frac{X_b(t) - X_b(0)}{X_b(\infty) - X_b(0)} = \frac{2}{\beta}\frac{b^2}{a^3}\left[\frac{FDt}{\pi}\right]^{1/2}. \tag{38}$$

Equations (37) and (38) are, in fact, limiting extremes of a general problem. In practice β is only constant for dilute systems with low segregation levels. As segregation proceeds β generally falls as a result of saturation in X_b. If β starts high and falls rapidly as the segregation saturates, eq. (38) is valid up to saturation (LEA and SEAH [1977]). A detailed analysis for the saturation occurring in the Langmuir–McLean adsorption theory has been presented by ROWLANDS and

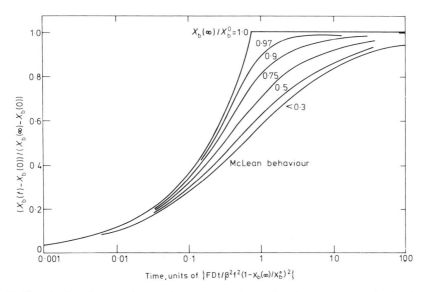

Fig. 25. The kinetics of segregation in binary systems for varying degrees of saturation in the final equilibrium level (after ROWLANDS and WOODRUFF [1979]).

WOODRUFF [1979]. Their analysis, re-interpreted in fig. 25, shows how the time dependence of the segregation changes from eq. (37) to eq. (38) as the final equilibrium segregation level $X_b(\infty)$ approaches the saturation level X_b^0. Calculations for particular systems in relation to temper brittleness are given in §6.3.

The more complex problem of the kinetics of segregation in ternary systems has also been studied by TYSON [1978]. Tyson uses McLean's approach but incorporates Guttmann's theory to define the grain boundary concentration. For a ternary system with a dilute impurity and a non-dilute alloying element he finds that eq. (38) is often a good description if the final segregation level is near saturation and similarly eq. (37) is valid if the final level is low. However, for certain critical cases, in which the two interacting species have similar values of $D\beta^{-2}$, the segregation curves exhibit an intermediate plateau.

The kinetics of desegregation have, in the past, been considered as much faster than the kinetics of segregation. This should not be so. The relationships are as given in eqs. (37) and (38), with $X_b(0)$ and $X_b(\infty)$ transposed.

4.6. Non-equilibrium segregation

The above segregation process leads to a well defined equilibrium value of the segregation as time approaches infinity if the temperature and constituents are kept constant. This equilibrium is approached at a rate defined by the relevant diffusion processes as discussed in the previous section.

References: p. 928.

In non-equilibrium segregation phenomena, the enrichment disappears as time approaches infinity but it may be very significant at intermediate times. These non-equilibrium segregations arise through a number of discrete processes but all depend ultimately on the fact that changes in the materials environment cause the chemical potential of one of the constituents to vary from place to place at a given concentration. This constituent then redistributes at a rate governed by diffusion theory, concentrating in certain regions in order to attain a constant chemical potential everywhere. In the meantime the spatial dependence of the chemical potential generally weakens also at a rate governed by diffusion theory, so that the constituent, having segregated, disperses again to become homogeneous throughout the material. This type of segregation is thus transient and is termed non-equilibrium but, in fact, includes many different separate mechanisms. (See also ch. 8, §8). Another important point is that each of these mechanisms leads to segregation in a zone of considerably greater width around the appropriate interface than occurred with the equilibrium mechanism discussed earlier. Depending on the mechanism, this zone may range from nm to μm. It should now be recognized that, having established a zone of enrichment, equilibrium partitioning between this zone and the interface will inevitably occur so that the real situation will incorporate contributions from both equilibrium and non-equilibrium segregations. Below, the non-equilibrium aspects are discussed but the above caveat should be borne in mind.

4.6.1. Solute pile-up at growing precipitates

An early form of non-equilibrium segregation concerns the solute pile-up at the face of a growing carbide in steels. Owing to their low solubility in carbides, certain solutes such as Sn and Sb will be rejected as the carbide grows and will pile up on the matrix side of the matrix–precipitate interface. Immediately this happens, the excess atoms start to diffuse into the matrix. Thus, if the carbide grew at a constant rate, the solute pile-up would grow asymptotically to a steady level. However, the carbide precipitate growth rapidly slows down and stops so that the pile-up disperses eventually to zero. In a practical situation, with the carbides growing as the material cools, the pile-up may be "frozen in". Precise calculations are difficult since the extent of the pile-up has been shown, by RELLICK and McMAHON [1974], to be critically dependent on the cooling rate, the carbide growth rate and the solute partitioning between the carbide and the matrix. With large, rapidly grown carbides, enrichments as high as a factor of 100 may be encountered although much weaker effects are likely to be observed in practice.

4.6.2. Quench-induced segregation

Another form of non-equilibrium segregation which also occurs at interfaces has been analyzed by WILLIAMS et al. [1976] on the basis of a model proposed by AUST and WESTBROOK [1965]. In this model, cooling of the material causes the equilibrium vacancy concentration to fall so that vacancies flow to interfaces where they may be readily annihilated. Because solute atoms in the crystal lattice have an associated strain energy, as discussed in §3.2.1, which may be relieved by pairing the solute atom with a vacancy, the vacancy flow has an associated solute flow. In their calculations for boron segregation during the quenching of 316 steel (17% Cr, 11% Ni stainless steel) from solution temperatures in the range 900–1360°C, WILLIAMS *et al.* write the vacancy concentration as:

$$v = k_v \exp(-E_f/kT), \tag{39}$$

where $k_v (= 4)$ contains geometric and entropy terms and E_f, the vacancy formation energy is 1.4 eV (1 eV per atom = 96.5 kJ/mol). The concentration of boron–vacancy complexes, v_B, obeys a similar relation but also depends on v and the boron bulk concentration, B.

$$v_B = Bv \, k_c \exp(E_B/kT), \tag{40}$$

where $k_c (= 12)$ contains geometric and entropy terms and E_B, the vacancy–solute binding energy, is 0.5 eV. In this system a significant population of complexes occurs at 1350°C but not at 900°C and, since the diffusivity of the boron–vacancy complexes is higher at all temperatures than that of the vacancies or the boron atoms, significant boron segregation from the bulk level of 90 at ppm could be observed by autoradiography, as shown in fig. 26, for the higher temperature quenches at 50 K/s.

More recently, detailed calculations for Cr segregation in $2\frac{1}{4}$Cr1Mo steel by DOIG and FLEWITT [1981] show that, in that case, narrow distributions for Cr enrichment are obtained around the grain boundary for quench rates in excess of 2000 K/s with significant segregation occurring for quenches from temperatures in the range

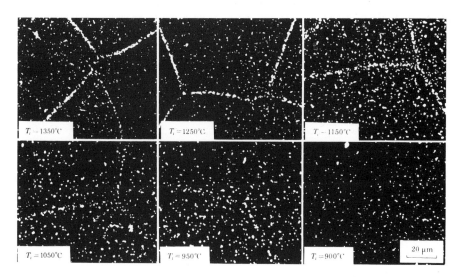

Fig. 26. Optical autoradiograph of austenitic 316 stainless steel containing 90 ppm boron solution heated at 1350°C for 1/2 hour, furnace-cooled to the temperature T_i in the range 900 to 1350°C, held for 1/2 hour and cooled at 50 K/s to room temperature. Strong boron non-equilibrium grain-boundary segregation is visible for the higher temperature quenches. (After WILLIAMS *et al.* [1976].)

References: p. 928.

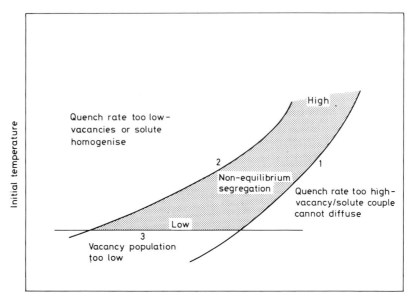

Fig. 27. Diagram of the limiting conditions for appreciable non-equilibrium segregation as a function of quench rate and temperature prior to quenching.

1300–1400 K. Experiment and theory agree in indicating an excess Cr level of some 2% over a zone of 5 nm on either side of the boundary. The limiting conditions for the quench-induced segregation are presented in fig. 27 as a function of the initial temperature before quench and the quench rate. At quench rates above line 1 there is insufficient time for the solute–vacancy pairs to diffuse an adequate distance, whereas at quench rates below line 2 there is sufficient time for the solute to diffuse away from the segregation region and so outside these lines little segregation will be observed. Again, at initial temperatures below line 3 there is neither sufficient kinetics or sufficient vacancy population for the segregation to be significant. No high temperature limit is appropriate if the quench goes through the temperature range to line 3. Observations of significant quench-induced segregations are reviewed by AUST *et al.* [1968] and by HARRIES and MARWICK [1980] and include quench rates from 0.05 to 50 K/s for Mg in Al, Al and Cd in Zn, Pb in S, and In, Sn, Ag and Au in Pb.

4.6.3. Stress-induced segregation

A third form of non-equilibrium segregation occurs when the vacancy flux is not produced from a change in temperature but from an applied stress at constant temperature. The vacancy flux is directed by the stress to relieve the strain and consequently it in turn directs excess solute atoms, by the vacancy–solute coupling discussed above, to grain boundaries parallel to the stress axis. The source of the solute atoms is thought to be the other grain boundaries rather than the lattice, since the activation energy for grain boundary diffusion is much lower than that for lattice diffusion. In steels the problem is complicated by the stress-assisted dissolution and reprecipitation of grain-boundary carbides which produces the first non-equilibrium segregation mentioned above due to pile-up. Changes in grain-boundary phosphorus segregation as a function of tensile and compression stresses in $2\frac{1}{4}$ Cr steels have been observed and interpreted by SHINODA and NAKAMURA [1981] although, at present, the interpretative model is not fully complete.

4.6.4. Radiation-induced segregation
This topic is treated in chapter 8, § 8.3 and chapter 17, § 4.4.

5. *Segregation-related physicochemical properties*

The influence of the interfacial microchemical state on physical metallurgical properties, such as creep-rupture life and temper embrittlement, operates through associated effects on certain basic physicochemical properties which in turn determine the metallurgical behaviour. The main physicochemical properties which are influenced by segregation processes fall into three categories: interfacial energetics, kinetics and cohesion. These are considered in turn below. Wherever these basic interfacial parameters are found to be involved with metallurgical phenomena, clearly these phenomena are influenced by segregation even though no explicit mention of the fact may occur in this chapter or, indeed, elsewhere.

5.1. Interfacial energetics

The close association between interfacial free energies and interfacial composition is discussed in § 2 in terms of the Gibbs Adsorption Theorem. We note that the thrust of much of the effort on the determination of interfacial free energies was originally intended to derive the values for interfacial composition. Both this thermodynamic approach and the new direct spectroscopy techniques can now be used interchangeably by way of parameters such as the interfacial activities or enrichment ratios, through which patterns of enrichment behaviour for a wide range of systems and for various interfaces may be compared and interrelated.

However, there are situations where the treatment of a microstructural or metallurgical problem requires a knowledge of the exact interfacial energy values relevant to the conditions which prevail. Examples of this are the nucleation of precipitates or second phases at grain boundaries, where a determining parameter is the actual interfacial free energy between the boundary plane and the second phase that is being nucleated. Again, in the study of the nucleation and stabilization of cavities formed along grain boundaries during creep, an important quantity is the value of the surface free energy pertaining to the cavity wall. The surface and grain-boundary

References: p. 928.

free energies of most pure metals have been measured experimentally by the techniques discussed earlier and fair assessments have been made for others, on the basis of a knowledge of bulk thermochemical properties with which empirical relationships exist. These have been summarized elsewhere (HONDROS [1969, 1978]). We note, as expected from eqs. (24) and (26), that $\gamma_s = 0.16 H_{sub}$ at around 1500°K, where γ_s and H_{sub}, the heat of sublimation, are measured per mole (OVERBURY et al. [1975]). At 0 K γ_s increases to 0.25 H_{sub}, as expected (TYSON [1975]).

In multi-component crystalline solids, the main determinants of the interfacial energies are the presence of segregants, the temperature, and the crystalline orientation. The evaluation of the interfacial free energy relevant to the modelling of a metallurgical event is difficult because of its sensitivity to the above parameters, in particular, adsorption of solute species. The direct experimental determination of that quantity is technically often very difficult and indirect.

For binary dilute alloys, reasonable experimental data exist for several systems on the change in absolute surface free energies with increasing bulk content of the alloying element: these are summarized in fig. 28 (HONDROS and McLEAN [1974]). The depression in γ_s up to the limit of solid solubility is system dependent, however, the estimate usually adopted is about 40%. Furthermore, we note that the data were measured on polycrystalline samples and therefore they refer strictly to the average surface free energies. The anisotropy of surface energy is small for pure metals, but it may be quite significant for alloys in which surface enrichment is involved.

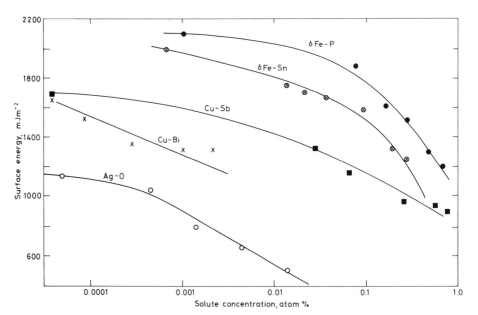

Fig. 28. Dependence of the surface free energy on bulk composition for a number of dilute binary systems: the host element is shown first in each pair.

In some cases, extremely low quantities of very surface-active elements in the vapour phase may produce significant effects on the interfacial free energies. Figure 29 shows as an example, the sensitivity of the surface free energy of Fe–3% Si at two temperatures to the potential of oxygen in the vapour phase. In order to obtain and hold such low values of oxygen potential, it is required to work with complex gas phase mixtures involving H_2O in H_2. Furthermore, these experiments were conducted on foils showing a (100) texture so that the values refer substantially to this crystal plane. (See also ch. 25, §4.3.2.)

In a subsequent study aimed at providing fundamental data on the surface-energy driven secondary crystallization in sheet alloy, MILLS *et al.* [1973] showed that the surface energies of crystals exposing the principal poles differed in a complex but significant manner as a function of temperature and oxygen adsorption, so that by manipulating these variables, each of the textures (111), (110) or (100) could be controllably grown.

For the effect of temperature on the interfacial free energy, considering a single component isotropic solid, eq. (68), ch. 6 reduces to:

$$-\frac{d\gamma}{dT} = S^\sigma, \qquad (41)$$

where S^σ is the interfacial entropy. Thus for pure elements, the temperature dependence of the interfacial free energy is negative. Theoretically, this is computed to be about $-0.5 \text{ mJ/m}^2 \text{K}$ which is close to the value conventionally adopted from experimental data, $-0.33 \text{ mJ/m}^2 \text{ K}$ (HONDROS [1969]).

In contrast to the above, fig. 29 clearly shows that in a system of more than one component the temperature dependence of the surface free energy can be positive. This is consistent with the thermodynamics of surfaces. By differentiating eq. (68), ch. 6 with respect to T, a complex expression may be obtained containing two terms which describe the temperature dependence of the interfacial free energy in a binary system. The first term, relating to entropy, is always negative, while the second term relates to adsorption and is positive. (The latter term refers to the effect of "boiling off" of a segregate with increasing temperature, where it is expected that the amount of adsorption would decrease with increasing temperature, i.e., d Γ/dT is negative.) This shows that in a system of more than one element, the interfacial energy may *increase* or decrease with increasing temperature, depending on the relative strengths of the two terms of entropy and adsorption.

The above discussion indicates the complexities involved in assessing the precise interfacial free energy value for a given physicochemical situation. There are very few systems for which this quantity has been determined at the level of rigour shown in fig. 29. For more complex interfaces, such as those between a second phase and the matrix, the experimental problems are even more severe. As a general guideline for binary systems, a knowledge of the amount of surface excess of an identified species from a known bulk concentration provides an estimate of the associated change in interfacial energy, through the application of the Gibbs Adsorption Theorem in a reversed manner.

References: p. 928.

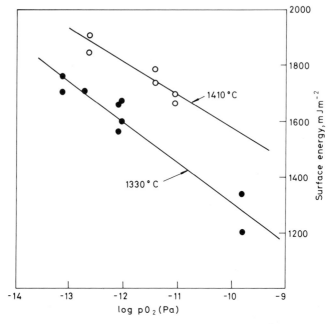

Fig. 29. Dependence of the surface free energy of the (100) plane in Fe–3% Si on oxygen potential and temperature (after HONDROS and STUART [1968]).

Where the form of the adsorption is known, an approach that has been used for both free surfaces and grain boundaries is to integrate the isotherm. Thus, if the Langmuir isotherm holds, this may be combined with the Gibbs Adsorption Theorem, which for a dilute system yields the equation for grain boundary free energy:

$$\gamma_b = \gamma_b^0 + RT\,\Gamma_b^0\,\ln\!\left(1 - \frac{\Gamma_b}{\Gamma_b^0}\right), \tag{42}$$

where the quantities in Γ are defined as above and γ_b^0 is the grain boundary energy of the pure metal. This approach has been used by PETCH [1956] in a similar form (but retaining the gas pressure term), in order to determine the effect of adsorbed hydrogen in lowering the surface energy of iron in a theory of hydrogen-induced fracture, and also by SEAH [1980], in a study of impurity-aided creep cavitation embrittlement. The enrichment quantity Γ_b required for eq. (42) may be obtained directly by spectroscopic measurements or assessed through the enrichment factor β_b and its dependence on the inverse of the solid solubility (see eq. (17) and fig. 17). This yields a change in free energy $\Delta\gamma$ which in many modelling studies is often the quantity required: an absolute value of γ for the appropriate conditions is assessed by referring to the standard state value for the energy of the pure component.

5.2. Surface and grain boundary kinetics

The free surfaces of solids offer rapid diffusion paths for the transport of matter. For example, the grooves that are formed at the intersection of grain boundaries with free surfaces when metals are held at high temperature [commonly referred to as "thermal etching" (see fig. 8)], owe their origin to the interchange of matter by surface diffusion. In general, this mechanism predominates in solid state phenomena where the microstructural features involve dimensions of the order of μm. Thus surface diffusivity is an important mechanism in the early stages of sintering, where the necking of the spherical particles takes place.

Considering the effects of surface-adsorbed elements, a good body of evidence affirms that adsorption will generally accelerate the surface diffusivity, while in some specific cases suppression will occur (GJOSTEIN [1966]). The interesting data in fig. 30 for example, compiled by DELAMARE and RHEAD [1971] show the effects of a number of impurities, either arriving from the vapour phase or segregating from the bulk, on the surface diffusivities of copper, gold and silver. The Arrhenius plots for the pure metals are shown as solid curves, whereas each of the broken curves refers to the metal substrate containing an adsorbed layer of impurity under controlled conditions. The second element of each pair denotes the adsorbed species. Clearly, in some cases such adsorbed layers induce spectacular increases in the self-diffusivity of the substrate metal and at the highest temperatures, these values can approach a

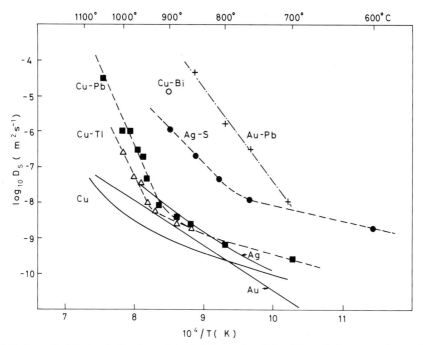

Fig. 30. Surface self-diffusion in Cu, Au and Ag (solid curves) and the effects of adsorption of a number of species (broken curves) (after DELAMARE and RHEAD [1971]).

References: p. 928.

factor of 10^4 above that of the clean substrate. As yet there is no agreement on the mechanism for this remarkable effect: one theory proposes that the uppermost atomic layer of the surface consists of a mixture of adsorbate and adsorbent, constituting in effect a two-dimensional compound with liquid-like properties. From this theory, it follows that adsorbates which form compounds with low melting points should lead to this accelerated surface diffusivity. An earlier theory proposed a "skating" mechanism in which the substrate atom is thought to climb on top of the adsorbed layer, where it may migrate freely with long jump distances of the order of 100 atom spacings, a hypothesis which could explain increases in surface diffusivities of the order of 10^4. This overlayer model of adsorption diffusion now appears to be superseded by the mixed layer or two-dimensional liquid model, which is seemingly supported by recent Low-Energy Electron Diffraction (LEED) studies on adsorbed monolayers of lead and bismuth on copper.

Whereas the copious studies on surface self-diffusion (ch. 8, § 7.4) fall within the context of a fundamental understanding of mechanisms probably relevant to the important process of catalysis, the somewhat fewer studies of the effect of segregation on grain-boundary self-diffusivity have a more immediate applicability to physical-metallurgical phenomena. We now turn to consider the latter.

Grain boundaries are paths for rapid self-diffusion and it is commonly understood that the transport of matter along such interfaces should be rate-controlling in a number of important metallurgical processes, in particular in temperature regimes of about $0.5T_m$ or below. In general, grain-boundary diffusivity data which refer to the pure elements have been employed in the modelling of various processes in metallurgy. Clearly, the use of such readily available data could introduce serious distortions if transport along grain boundaries were to be sensitive to the microchemical aspects of the interface. Below we examine the theory and evidence for the role of solute segregation on grain-boundary diffusivities.

A pure grain boundary is characterized by a high free energy, being a structural zone with a low volume density of matter compared with the bulk lattice. From such simplistic considerations, we might expect that this should lower the activation energy barrier for substitutional self diffusion, so that atom transport is easier along these paths than in the bulk crystalline lattice. This concept has been expressed in a semi-quantitative manner by GIBBS and HARRIS [1969] who related the activation energy for grain-boundary transport Q_b to that for volume diffusion Q_v by the expression

$$Q_b = Q_v - N\alpha'\gamma_b a^2, \tag{43}$$

where a^2 is the cross-sectional area of an atom*, N is Avogadro's Number and α' a structure factor which depends on whether diffusion is substitutional or interstitial. This predicts sensibly that increasing γ_b will lower the activation energy for grain-boundary transport and that for a highly coherent interface such as a twin boundary, with a low free energy, the activation energy for diffusion would be little different from that of the lattice.

* In this chapter the atom size, a, is derived from $\rho N a^3 = M$, where ρ is the bulk density and M the atomic weight of the solid (see ch. 2, §4.1).

Consider the presence of a solute in the base solvent with accompanying high grain-boundary enrichment of solute. If the segregation-associated change in grain-boundary energy is $\Delta\gamma_b$, it follows that the activation energy for grain-boundary diffusivity in the presence of segregation, Q_b^{seg}, is related to that for the pristine boundary by:

$$Q_b^{seg} = Q_b + N\alpha'a^2\Delta\gamma_b. \tag{44}$$

Hence, according to this general model, segregation increases the activation energy for grain-boundary diffusion compared with the pure state. In effect, the segregation permits the sites of high compression and tension to be relaxed, reducing the net free energy of the boundary and increasing the volume density of the boundary by the occupation of vacant sites. Thus, from the diffusional point of view, the material in the boundary zone approaches the character of the material in the bulk lattice. The above approach allows estimates of the magnitude of the effect. Thus, when phosphorus segregates to the grain boundaries of pure iron, the grain-boundary energy is reduced by about 400 mJ/m^2 at its maximum (HONDROS [1965]); substituting in the above equation and including a value of 2 for the structure factor appropriate to vacancy diffusion, the activation energy for grain-boundary diffusion in pure iron is raised from 175 kJ/mol to 200 kJ/mol.

The above account is probably satisfactory for rough estimates of expected effects, and supports the view that the consequence of segregation is the elimination of the boundary sites having a high degree of disorganization, thereby decreasing grain-boundary transport with respect to that in a pure boundary. The subject has now been developed analytically by BERNARDINI *et al.* [1982] who derived a more rigorous expression linking the change in diffusivity to the amount adsorbed at the grain boundary. This treatment takes as its point of departure the theory of BORISOV *et al.* [1964] who derived the basic relationship between grain-boundary energy and grain-boundary diffusivity, given by the expression

$$\gamma_b = \frac{kT}{2\,a_{sv}^2}\cdot m\cdot\left[\ln\frac{D_b\delta}{D_v a_{sv}} - \ln m\right], \tag{45}$$

where D_b is the grain boundary diffusivity, D_v is the volume bulk diffusivity, a_{sv} is the size of the solvent atom, δ is the width of the grain boundary, and $\delta = ma_{sv}$. This equation is transformed by expressing γ_b in terms of Γ_b, the amount of segregation. By combining eqs. (43) and (45), we effectively extend the Borisov treatment to a binary system in which grain boundary segregation occurs. This yields:

$$\frac{D_b^*}{D_v^*} = \frac{D_b}{D_v}\left[1 - \Gamma_b/\Gamma_b^0\right]^{2a_{sv}^2/ma_{su}^2}, \tag{46}$$

where D_b^* is the grain-boundary self-diffusion coefficient in the presence of segregation, D_v^* is the coefficient due to the presence of the solute in the bulk, D_b and D_v are the corresponding values in the pure solvent, a_{su} is the atomic size of the solute in the particular solvent, and m is the quantity, retained from the Borisov equation (45), which relates to the number of effective atom layers in the boundary. The

References: p. 928.

above equation has now been confirmed experimentally in iron containing tin, by directly measuring the diffusivity constants using radio-tracer techniques and also by determining the amount of grain-boundary segregation using Auger electron spectroscopy on exposed grain-boundary surfaces. Figure 31 shows how the measured grain-boundary self-diffusivity of iron decreases with increasing levels of tin present at the boundary, at 615°C. Similar data were obtained for a number of temperatures and for both solvent and solute diffusivities along the boundary. In the same figure, the straight line indicates the effect predicted by the application of eq. (46), the treatment necessarily restricting the prediction to the dilute approximation.

Equation (46) may be simplified further by expressing D_v^* as a linear function of the bulk concentration of solute, X_c, following a number of theoretical and experimental investigations on systems involving substitutional self-diffusion, as discussed in ch. 8, §4.1.3:

$$D_v^* = D_v\left(1 + b_v X_c\right), \tag{47}$$

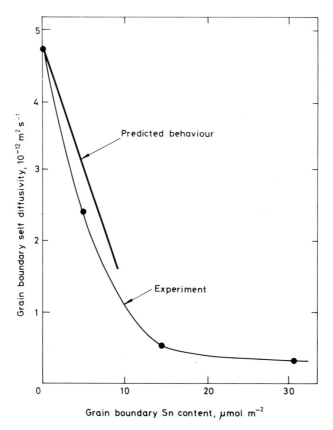

Fig. 31. The measured and predicted dependence of the grain-boundary self-diffusivity of iron–tin alloys at 615°C on the amount of tin segregated at the boundary (after BERNARDINI *et al.* [1982]).

where b_v is a constant generally positive and of the order of 10–100 for the many binary systems in which it has been measured (LE CLAIRE [1975]). Thus eq. (46) can now be expressed as

$$D_b^* = D_b \left[1 + (b_v - 2\alpha) X_c \right],$$ (48)

where α is a concentration ratio. This defines the quantity actually measured in boundary diffusion measurements in the presence of segregation as $\alpha D_b \delta$, and not the standard $D_b \delta$ where δ is the boundary width. To express eq. (48) in a more accessible form, we introduce the grain-boundary enrichment factor defined earlier, β_b [eq. (17)], which is closely related to α by:

$$\alpha = \beta_b \frac{a_{sv}^2}{m \, a_{su}^2}.$$ (49)

Therefore, the overall effect may be expressed by:

$$D_b^* = D_b \left[1 + \left(b_v - \frac{2}{m} \frac{a_{sv}^2}{a_{su}^2} \beta_b \right) X_c \right].$$ (50)

In summary, this equation expresses the effect of segregation (contained in the enrichment factor β_b) on grain-boundary diffusivity. This is offset by the effect of the solute on volume self-diffusivity. The equation then predicts that grain-boundary transport of both solvent and solute atoms may be reduced or increased depending on the balance between the opposing effects implicit in β_b and b_v. Since b_v is generally of the order of 10–100 and β_b for highly surface active species is of the order of 1000–10 000, in general, the effect of the high enrichment factor will dominate in the presence of strongly segregating species and this will reduce the grain-boundary diffusivity.

The ability to predict the effect of segregation on grain-boundary diffusivities is a development which permits the quantitative examination of a number of metallurgical phenomena in which these kinetics are known to be rate-determining: some of these applications will be considered in §6.

5.3. Grain-boundary cohesion

As was noted in the introduction, historically the most important manifestation of grain-boundary segregation has been the effects on grain-boundary cohesion as expressed in a number of well known forms of intergranular fragility. This continues to provide much of the focus for work in this field. The central problem is the role of solute atoms on atomic cohesion at the interface. This is now recognized to be a wider issue, extending to aspects of *ad* hesion (i.e. cohesion between dissimilar pieces of matter), as in that between a metal and an oxide or another phase such as a precipitate or even a polymer.

The theoretical and experimental framework for understanding adhesion in such systems and the role of interfacial microchemical interactions is hardly developed and this section will be restricted to grain-boundary cohesion which is now quite well advanced. However, in connection with adhesional phenomena in metals, HONDROS [1980] has attempted to systematize the data available for metals adhering to oxides and other phases, and it appears that the classical concept of *work of adhesion*, expressed in the formulation of Young and Dupré as the algebraic sum of the two free surface energies and the interfacial energy, may be applied to these solid state systems. This would predict that segregation to metal–oxide interfaces, by decreasing the interfacial energy should increase the work of adhesion but scant data are available to test this hypothesis.

Because of its technological importance, much of the work on grain-boundary cohesion has been concerned with effects of additions in iron, and it is now well established that the elements shown on the dotted ground in fig. 32 all cause intergranular weakness in iron. A similar set also weaken copper and nickel. We now consider the two questions "why do certain elements weaken grain boundaries?" and "what is the relative embrittling potency of these elements?".

A number of theories have been proposed to account for the effect of segregants on grain-boundary cohesion. All have a common approach but differ in their interpretation of the way to carry out the numerical calculations. In 1957 McLEAN first proposed that in low temperature intergranular fracture, the total work of fracture is the sum of the ideal work of fracture, γ, representing the energy to disrupt the bonds across the interface, and the irreversible plastic work of deformation, γ_p, which is absorbed in the crystal lattice as dislocations and phonons over a region well away from the boundary. Although γ_p is much larger than γ it is easy to see that if γ is increased, the forces at a crack tip must also be increased to propagate the fracture and hence γ_p will increase. Thus, for a given grain boundary, γ and γ_p are directly related. The precise relation will depend on the orientations of the two grains and the grain boundary to the stress axis as well as on the microstructure. Indeed, recent analyses by McMAHON and VITEK [1979] and by JOKL *et al.* [1980]

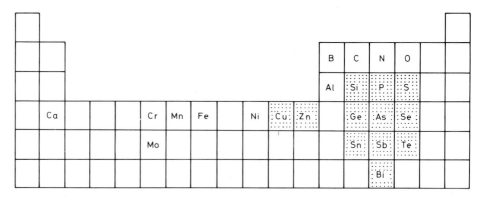

Fig. 32. Table of elements observed, by AES, to segregate in iron. Those known to cause embrittlement are shown on a dotted ground. (After BRIGGS and SEAH [1983].)

show that γ_p is proportional to γ^n where n is in the range 2–5. Thus, to answer the above questions we must understand the effects of segregants on the ideal work of fracture of the grain boundary.

The ideal work of fracture of a clean grain boundary with energy γ_b^0 was given by McLEAN [1957] as:

$$\gamma^0 = 2\gamma_s^0 - \gamma_b^0, \tag{51}$$

where γ_s^0 is the fracture surface energy of the clean material. An analysis of γ_s^0 and γ_b^0 values for many metals by McLEAN and HONDROS (SEAH and LEA [1975]) shows that, typically, $\gamma_b^0 \approx \gamma_s^0/3$ so that the ideal work of fracture of clean grain boundaries is approximately 5/6 of that of an average plane in the crystal. This does not mean that the grain boundaries will always fail in preference to cleavage, since the orientation of the slip planes and the surface energy of the low-index cleavage planes make cleavage generally more likely than intergranular failure in clean bcc metals (HONDROS and McLEAN [1976]).

More important than the choice of brittle fracture modes is the balance between brittle and ductile failure. The fracture behaviour of a 0.2% carbon steel, as a function of the test temperature, is shown schematically in fig. 33. At high tempera-

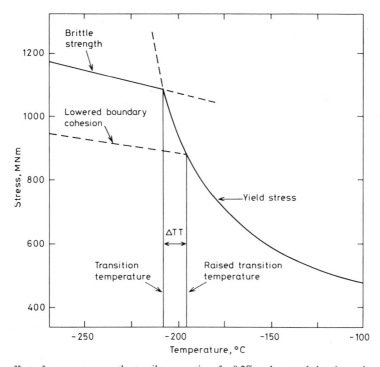

Fig. 33. The effect of temperature on the tensile properties of a 0.2% carbon steel showing, schematically, the lowering of grain-boundary cohesion and the resultant increase in the ductile–brittle transition temperature.

References: p. 928.

tures, where dislocations move easily, the yield stress is low and the steel fails in a ductile manner. As the test temperature is reduced, the dislocation movement, governed by a term of the form $(\exp -Q/RT)$, becomes more difficult and the material eventually fails in a brittle manner. The temperature at which this occurs is the ductile–brittle transition temperature (DBTT). If the grain boundaries contain the segregants shown in fig. 32, the boundary cohesion may be sufficiently lowered so that the transition temperature is raised and the otherwise ductile material becomes brittle.

An analysis of the ideal work of fracture of grain boundaries with segregants, γ, has been made by HIRTH and RICE [1980] using thermodynamic arguments. They show that the reduction in the ideal work of fracture, where there is no redistribution of the segregant species, is given by:

$$\gamma = \gamma^0 - \int_0^{\Gamma_b} \left[\mu_b(\Gamma) - \mu_s(\Gamma/2) \right] d\Gamma, \tag{52}$$

where $\mu_{b,s}(\Gamma)$ are the chemical potentials of the solute species in equilibrium with a level of segregation Γ mol/m² at the grain boundary and the free surface, respectively. In the dilute limit, this relation may be re-expressed:

$$\gamma = \gamma^0 + \Gamma_b(\Delta G_s - \Delta G_b - RT \ln 2), \tag{53}$$

where Γ_b is the segregation level at the grain boundary, and the terms in ΔG refer to the binding energies of segregants, which, it should be noted, are negative quantities. Thus we see that the ideal work of fracture falls linearly at first with the level of segregation, and that elements which segregate more strongly to free surfaces than to grain boundaries reduce the ideal work of fracture and vice versa.

An alternative approach which gives the same result in the quasi-chemical pair bonding approximation has been given by SEAH [1980b]. In this approach the actual bond energies across the boundary before and after fracture are calculated in the manner described in §4.2.2. In this way:

$$\gamma = \gamma^0 + \Gamma_b \left\{ \frac{Z_g}{Z\Gamma_b^0} \right\} \left\{ H_A^{sub*} - H_B^{sub*} - \frac{Z\Omega}{a_A^2} \right\}, \tag{54}$$

where the terms are as described in §4.2.2. and, in addition, Z_g corresponds to Z_v across the grain boundary (approximately $\frac{5}{6} Z_v$), Γ_b^0 is the value of Γ_b at one monolayer, a_A is the atomic diameter of the segregation atom A and H_A^{sub*} is the sublimation enthalpy of A atoms in J/m². Calculations may be easily carried out for eq. (54) in the regular solution approximation, but only small errors are involved if Ω is ignored. In this case it is clear that the lower the value of H_A^{sub*} for the solute, the more will a segregant embrittle. Figure 34 shows a compilation of H^{sub*} values for all elements. It is clear that the well recognized segregants, Sb, Sn, S, P, Si and Cu all with H^{sub*} values below that of iron shown by the dashed horizontal line, will all embrittle iron, whereas Mo and C will improve the cohesion; this is confirmed experimentally (SEAH [1981, 1982]).

As will be shown in the next section, it is not sufficient to consider solely the

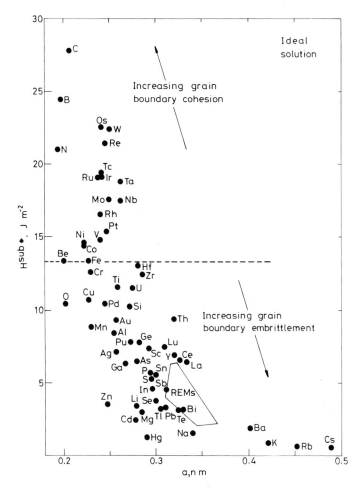

Fig. 34. The general embrittlement–ductility plot for matrix and segregant elements in the ideal solution approximation. Any element may be chosen as matrix and then those elements with higher values of H^{sub*} increase the grain-boundary cohesion and vice versa. As an example iron may be taken as the matrix material. (After SEAH [1980b].)

effect of segregants on the ideal work of fracture, as described above. At a crack tip it is the choice between dislocation emission and bond breaking that decides whether ductility or brittle fracture occurs. It can be shown that embrittling segregants increase the ease of dislocation emission at the crack tip, so offsetting the total embrittling effect discussed above. The correction is small but allows the correct prediction of the absolute embrittlement of copper by bismuth (SEAH and HONDROS [1982]).

References: p. 928.

6.   Metallurgical phenomena affected by segregation

Interfacial segregation influences metallurgical phenomena through its impinge-
ment on several basic physicochemical properties, involving the energetics, kinetics
or the cohesion of the interfaces, which were treated in the previous section. This is
illustrated schematically in fig. 35. For example, grain-boundary segregation will in
general retard the boundary diffusivity and this in turn will affect the rate of
diffusion creep or the rate of grain-boundary cavity growth involved in creep
embrittlement. Again, because it retards grain-boundary ionic mobility in polycrystalline oxides, this should also inhibit the rate of surface oxide growth. In some
instances, the particular metallurgical property may be affected through changes in
more than one of the basic physicochemical properties considered: for example, the
rate of oxidation of nickel alloys containing aluminium may be affected through the
kinetics of ion transport across or through the boundaries, and in addition the
integrity of the oxide layer is enhanced by improved interfacial adhesion resulting
from the presence of segregated species at the metal–oxide interface.

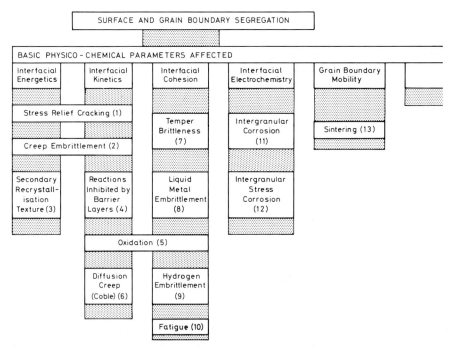

Fig. 35. Some metallurgical phenomena affected by the physicochemical parameters influenced by
surface- and grain-boundary equilibrium segregation. Key references for the interested reader are: (1)
BATTE et al. [1980]; (2) TIPLER [1980]; (3) MILLS et al. [1973]; (4) NICOLET [1978]; HAYES and GRIEVESON
[1975]; (5) WHITTLE and STRINGER [1980]; (6) HONDROS and HENDERSON [1982]; (7) McMAHON [1978];
(8) NICHOLAS and OLD [1979]; (9) LATANISION and OPPERHAUSER [1974]; (10) SURESH et al. [1981]; (11)
KUPPER et al. [1981]; (12) LEA and HONDROS [1981]; (13) NANNI et al. [1976].

As fig. 35 clearly indicates, numerous metallurgical and microstructural phenomena in alloys are influenced by interfacial microchemistry: in some cases this may be a determining factor while in others it may be simply one of a number of contributory factors. In the space of this chapter, we cannot consider all of these phenomena in detail and so some key references are cited in the caption of fig. 35. Below we consider for each of the important basic physicochemical properties treated in §5 (i.e., the first three columns in fig. 35) a significant example of its impact in physical metallurgy, following which we mention briefly a number of other metallurgical phenomena for which evidence is accumulating of effects related to microchemistry.

6.1. Surface free energy change: role in creep cavitation

In microstructural terms, the creep rupture life of alloys serving at high temperature under stress may be controlled by the nucleation, growth and coalescence of microcavities which develop at grain boundaries, in general those normal to the stress axis. A number of contending micromechanisms have been proposed for the nucleation of these cavities, and while there is very strong evidence that in certain engineering alloys these are initiated at sites where slip planes intersect second phase particles such as carbides or manganese sulphide inclusions, cavities have nevertheless been observed in quite pure metals. Many observations in the literature strongly affirm that impurity adsorption at both the grain boundary and the surface of the cavity wall will affect creep rupture properties. Depending on the temperature and stress regime, grain-boundary segregation may affect the process of cavity growth through its influence on the grain-boundary diffusivity, but in addition, because segregation to the inner surface of the cavity reduces its surface energy, it will also affect the nucleation propensity.

Among the many examples, we cite the work of TIPLER and McLEAN [1970] who showed metallographically and by creep measurements that small quantities of antimony in copper increase the amount of grain-boundary cavitation and also lower the creep rupture life compared with that of the pure material. KRAAI and FLOREEN [1964] showed that the ductility of nickel is reduced by a factor of ten by the presence of sulphur of up to 20 ppm in the bulk, while THOMAS and GIBBONS [1980] demonstrated the remarkable effects of trace impurities on the creep performance of nickel-base superalloys. Figure 36 shows the important reduction of creep rupture ductility in these alloys caused by ppm levels of lead and tellurium. At the maximum impurity level shown in this figure, the deleterious effect of each impurity was associated in every case with a much higher level of grain-boundary cavitation, of the order of 5–10 times greater than that observed in the pure alloy. In Nimonic 105 containing 34 ppm of lead, the amount of grain-boundary damage as measured by the number of cavities per mm^2 was ten times greater than in the alloy with the base composition.

In addition to the considerable metallurgical evidence in which impaired creep life is associated with the presence of impurities, which presents circumstantial

References: p. 928.

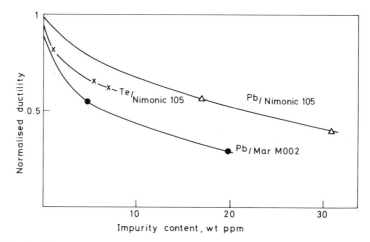

Fig. 36. Reduction in creep rupture ductility in nickel-base superalloys induced by trace levels of impurities.

evidence for an effect through the interfacial microchemistry, there are important observations using Auger Electron Spectroscopy on the creep grain-boundary fracture surface which show a considerable accumulation of the suspected contaminant. An elegant example of selective segregation through the application of high resolution (0.2 μm) Auger spectroscopy is shown in fig. 37 (FRANZONI *et al.* [1981] for a commercial $2\frac{1}{4}$Cr1Mo steel, creep tested at 600°C and subsequently fractured at liquid nitrogen temperature for examination. The figure shows the high magnification scanning electron image of a grain boundary area and the corresponding Auger spectroscopy maps for the elements Sn and Sb, indicating a simultaneous segregation of these elements only on the cavity surfaces. The non-cavitated areas of the boundary showed only P which was in turn significantly lower within the cavity.

In considering the role of interfacial microchemistry on cavitation, we assume that the cavities have been successfully nucleated while the precise mechanism for nucleation will not concern us. We consider an applied tensile stress, σ, which performs an amount of work $\frac{4}{3}\pi r^3\sigma$ in generating a spherical cavity of radius r. The associated surface energy of the cavity is $4\pi r^2\gamma$ and it is simple to show that as a cavity grows from a very small size, the net energy that has to be supplied first increases and then, after reaching a balance point, decreases, at which critical point the radius is given by r_c, where

$$\sigma = 2\gamma_s/r_c. \tag{55}$$

At this value, the competition between the surface energy which tends to sinter the pore and the applied stress is in balance. When the pore radius reaches a value greater than r_c, energy will be saved as it grows to a microscopical cavity. If the surface segregation of the active species is sufficiently rapid, a pore nucleus with a

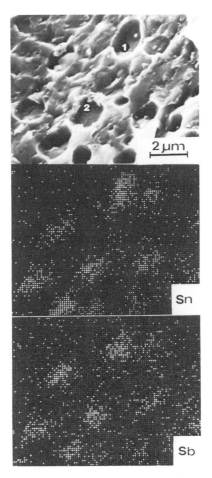

Fig. 37. SEM image of a creep cavitated grain-boundary area in $2\frac{1}{4}$Cr1Mo steel and the corresponding Auger electron spectroscopy maps for Sn and Sb showing segregation on cavity surfaces (after FRANZONI *et al.* [1981]).

radius smaller than r_c may survive according to the above equation, because of the reduction in γ_s, typically by a factor of two. The net effect of this impurity segregation is that a greater density of nuclei per unit area of grain boundary will achieve stability and hence they will be able to grow: the experimental evidence cited above in connection with the incidence of segregation to cavity walls strongly affirms this view.

The detailed mechanism of surface-energy induced cavitation damage has been analyzed recently by McLEAN [1981], specifically for the alloy Nimonic 80A. The steep function of the curve reproduced in fig. 38 shows the quantity N, the number of grain-boundary cavities in a cubic millimetre of material per 1% creep strain, as a

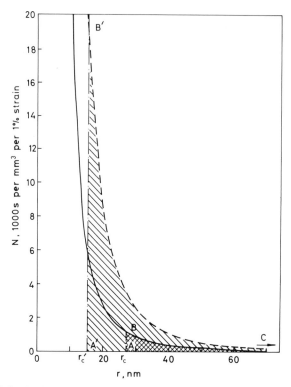

Fig. 38. Theoretical distributions for the density of cavities, N, in Nimonic 80A as a function of the cavity radius, r, indicating the areas (hatched) in which cavities will contribute to the creep damage. [Note, there are approx. 100 mm² of grain boundary per mm³ of material here (McLean, private commun.).]

function of r, the cavity radius. For the pure alloy, substituting for γ_s at a stress of 150 MPa, the critical value of r is 27 nm. At this stress, the cavities which are stable and which will contribute to the creep damage are those which fall to the right of r_c under the solid line, shown as the cross-hatched area ABC in the diagram. McLean integrated the equation representing the curve between $r_c = 27$ nm and $r = \infty$, and found that the number of cavities in this area is about $1.6 \times 10^{13}/\text{m}^3$ per 1% strain. In the first instance, segregation to the cavity wall surface affects this process as we have seen by reducing γ_s, thereby reducing the critical stable pore size to r'_c. This is marked in the diagram at 15.6 nm, corresponding to a 42% reduction in γ_s. There is also a second effect to be considered, associated with segregation to the grain boundary itself. The consequent reduction in grain-boundary energy leads to a reduction in intergranular cohesion [eq. (51)], and, irrespective of the precise mechanism of nucleus generation, a lower stress concentration is required to nucleate a cavity in a segregated boundary than in a clean boundary (Hondros and McLean [1974]) so that more cavities will be generated for a unit strain. Thus the curve for nucleation of cavities in the presence of grain-boundary segregation lies at

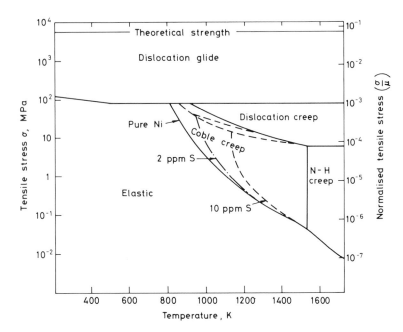

Fig. 39. Theoretical deformation map as a function of tensile stress and temperature where Coble creep dominates and the effect of low levels of sulphur on the boundaries (broken lines), for a grain size of 32 μm, and a strain rate of 10^{-8} s.

a high value and is shown as the dashed curve in fig. 38. The two effects of segregation are cumulative with respect to cavity stabilization, and all cavities which fall in the hatched area A′B′C to the right of r_c' now contribute to the creep damage. It is difficult to ascribe accurately the position of the dashed curve representing the role of grain-boundary segregation and the ease of decohesion. For an order of magnitude increase in the creep cavity density in the presence of a segregant, the dashed curve corresponds to N values about three times those associated with the solid curve. Thus, while at this stage the model appears somewhat qualitative, the quantities are plausible and consistent with some experimental observations.

6.2. Grain-boundary diffusivity: role in diffusion creep

It is now well established that at lower temperature regimes and under light stresses, the predominant mode of deformation of polycrystals is through diffusional creep dominated, in this case, by mass transport along the grain boundaries. In the course of studying sintering mechanisms in alumina, COBLE [1963] recognized this deformation mode and accordingly modified the equation for diffusional creep associated with the names of NABARRO [1948] and HERRING [1950] in which volume diffusivity dominates: this is analogous to the Herring equation and is of the form

$$\dot{\epsilon} = \frac{B_2 \sigma \Omega \delta D_b}{d^3 kT}. \tag{56}$$

Here $\dot{\epsilon}$ is the strain rate, σ the tensile stress, Ω the atomic volume, d the grain size, and B_2 a numerical constant which varies with grain geometry. It is appreciated that both lattice- and grain-boundary diffusion contribute independently to diffusional creep, and the general equation involving contributions from both volume- and grain-boundary diffusion is given by:

$$\dot{\epsilon} = \frac{\sigma \Omega}{d^2 kT} \left(B_1 D_v + \frac{B_2 \delta D_b}{d} \right). \tag{57}$$

Clearly because the activation energy for boundary diffusion is less than that for lattice diffusion and because of a greater sensitivity to grain size, the *Coble creep* mechanism predominates at the lower temperatures and in fine grained material. ASHBY [1972] showed that a generalized deformation mechanism map may be produced by plotting stress as a function of homologous temperature (see ch. 20, §2.3). Applying a version of the above constitutive equation, the *Ashby map* indicating the fields of predominance for various deformation mechanisms is reproduced in fig. 39 and shown as solid lines, for nickel. This indicates clearly the important tracts where Coble creep predominates. Such maps have been computed on a basis of diffusional data derived from pure metals. If impurity species in the bulk alter the lattice diffusivity, or more importantly, if by enriching at the grain boundaries they affect the boundary transport, this should be reflected in significant shifts in the boundaries on such maps. We examine here, to what extent the Coble creep mechanism is affected by the presence of interfacially active impurities and how this is reflected in the positions of the boundaries on the Ashby map.

The predictive eq. (50) developed earlier shows the dependence of grain-boundary diffusivity on grain-boundary segregation as expressed in the enrichment factor β_b. We insert this into eq. (57) above and limit it to the deformation regime where grain-boundary transport is rate-determining.

From these equations we compare the strain rates $\dot{\epsilon}$ and $\dot{\epsilon}^*$ resulting from a change of D_b to D_b^* and D_v to D_v^*; hence:

$$\frac{\dot{\epsilon}^*}{\dot{\epsilon}} = 1 + b_v X_c - \frac{2}{m} \frac{a_{sv}^2}{a_{su}^2} \beta_b X_c, \tag{58}$$

where the symbols are as defined in §5.1. This may be simplified further: noting that in general b_v has a value of 10^2 and considering very dilute concentrations of highly surface-active species (X_c of the order of 10^{-4}), the second term containing b_v may be ignored in this instance. Hence in a binary system in which the second component is very dilute and also very surface-active, the grain-boundary diffusion creep rate at a given temperature is related to the diffusional creep rate of the pure solvent in the first approximation by:

$$\frac{\dot{\epsilon}^*}{\dot{\epsilon}} = 1 - \frac{2}{m}\frac{a_{sv}^2}{a_{su}^2}\beta_b X_c. \tag{59}$$

There exist practical systems in which the dilute approximation implicit in the above equation should apply. For example, consider the effect of small impurity additions of sulphur on the nickel deformation map shown in fig. 39 in connection with the boundaries of the Coble creep mechanism. For the application of eq. (59), it is required to know the solid solubility of the impurity in the parent lattice at the temperature of interest, and also the relevant atomic sizes. Thus the quantity β_b is derived by substitution in the solubility law of eq. (17) described earlier. In the case of nickel, a number of dilute impurities at the ppm level may introduce significant effects on Coble creep rates. The computed effect of trace additions of sulphur on the extent of the Coble creep regime in nickel is superimposed on the Ashby map in fig. 39 as the dashed lines, here specifically for a grain size of 32 μm and a critical strain rate of $10^{-8}/s$. This shows that by introducing quantities as low as 2 and 10 ppm of sulphur in nickel, the boundaries of the Coble creep regimes are shifted substantially. These large effects predicted for sulphur, magnesium and other dilute impurities (HONDROS and HENDERSON [1982]) demonstrate the important role of interfacial microchemistry on grain-boundary diffusion phenomena and how in this particular case, the impurities induce a beneficial effect by inhibiting grain-boundary transport.

6.3. Interfacial cohesion: role in temper-brittleness

Temper-brittleness is one of the oldest known forms of brittle intergranular failure. It occurs in low alloy steels incorporating alloying elements such as Cr, Ni and Mn when they are slowly cooled from temperatures above 500°C. High-purity alloys do not exhibit this embrittlement and it has been shown that the cause can generally be associated with the adventitious levels of P, Sn, Sb and As impurity, which are typically in the 50–200 ppm range (LOW [1968]; SCHULZ and MCMAHON [1972]). More recently it has been recognized that Cu is also deleterious (HASEGAWA *et al.* [1975]) and this is important since much present day low alloy steel has copper contents as high as 0.15%. Analyses of commercial steels (HONDROS *et al.* [1976]) show that temper-brittleness is, in practice, mainly caused by the grain-boundary segregation of phosphorus whereas in nickel-containing steels, tin also contributes. The phosphorus comes from the original steel making, and is expensive to remove to very low levels. The tin arises from recycled scrap plated steel.

It is instructive to consider the analysis of one very well documented instance of temper brittleness investigated some years ago at the Watertown Arsenal (CARR *et al.* [1953]). As we have mentioned earlier, as segregation increases in a steel, the ductile–brittle transition temperature (DBTT) also increases until it rises above the ambient temperature and brittle failure will occur in service. Studies of the DBTT through Charpy impact measurements therefore provide a characterization of the heat treatments that will cause temper brittleness. Figure 40 shows the DBTT measurements for SAE 3140 steel (1.26% Ni, 0.77% Cr, 0.39% C, 0.015% P) heated to 675°C and water-quenched, followed by isothermal heat treatments at increasing times in the critical temperature range 375–575°C.

In fig. 40 we observe several of the characteristic features of temper-brittleness. The embrittlement occurs most rapidly around 500–550°C, and reheating above 600°C rapidly removes the embrittlement. Material quenched through the temperature range 600°C–400°C will not be embrittled, whereas large section castings or forgings necessarily cooled slowly through this range will be severely embrittled. The embrittlement is often called reversible temper-brittleness since samples embrittled through slow cooling can be de-embrittled by reheating above 600°C followed by a quench, and then again embrittled by a slow cooling treatment.

The reconstruction of fig. 40 has been made by a calculation of the segregation of phosphorus in the steel using Guttman's modified theory as described at the end of §4.4. SEAH [1977] used this approach with $\Delta G_{Ni}^0 = 11.5$, $\Delta G_P^0 = 44.0$ and $\alpha'_{NiP} = 26.0$ kJ/mol to predict a low phosphorus equilibrium segregation above 525°C but rapidly rising to near the saturation of one monolayer at 475°C. Combined with this prediction are the kinetics of segregation discussed in §4.5 with $D_P = 1.58 \times 10^{-4} \times \exp(-219\,000/RT)$ m^2/s. These permit the generation of the segregation contours of fig. 41 which correlate very closely with the DBTT curves. This correlation shows the dramatic DBTT shift of 275 K per monolayer of segregated phosphorus.

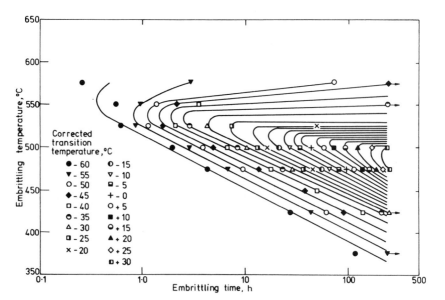

Fig. 40. The time–temperature diagram for embrittlement of SAE 3410 steel corrected to constant hardness (after CARR et al. [1953]).

Recently an alternative to the above interpretation of temper-brittleness via the alloy–impurity coupling model of Guttmann, has been proposed. Studies of phosphorus segregation in pure iron, and alloys with up to 0.1% carbon and 2.2% chromium by ERHART and GRABKE [1981] show that the phosphorus segregation in pure iron is as high as customarily observed in steels but that carbon, if present, will also segregate, reducing the phosphorus segregation through site competition, and improving the cohesion as described in §5.3. The action of added chromium is shown to precipitate the carbon, so that it no longer segregates and hence the phosphorus segregation returns to the initial high level. Thus, in steels, the presence of chromium appears to enhance the phosphorus segregation, but in reality it is the carbon which the chromium influences and this, in turn, affects the phosphorus segregation. This view is supported by BRIANT [1981] who also finds that the alloying elements have no effect on phosphorus segregation in 0.3% carbon steels. If this model is correct, the lower part of fig. 41, below 450°C, should remain largely unaltered but the top part above 500°C, should rise as a result of carbon competitive segregation deriving from, say, dissolution of carbides at temperatures above 500°C. This is clearly not the situation in figs. 40 and 41 since the Cr can only precipitate a small fraction of the C in the steel. We conclude that, for the SAE 3140 steel, we must be concerned with Guttmann's alloy–impurity coupling. However, it is possible that in higher Cr steels such as $2\frac{1}{4}$Cr1Mo, with lower carbon contents, the Erhart and Grabke mechanism may operate. In other steels both mechanisms may be important.

Finally, such steels as the Mo-containing $2\frac{1}{4}$Cr1Mo and 3Cr$\frac{1}{2}$Mo alloys incur additional effects in that Mo and P react readily to form $(FeMo)_3P$ precipitates. Thus, in untempered steels quenched from above 850°C, there is little P segregation and most of the Mo is in solution. As a function of time in the tempering range 450–650°C, the Mo that is free in solution couples with the P and according to the Guttmann theory this leads to high equilibrium segregation. However, the coupling is strong, causing the formation of Mo_3P microprecipitates so that free P level is low, thereby considerably retarding the rate of build-up to high segregation at grain

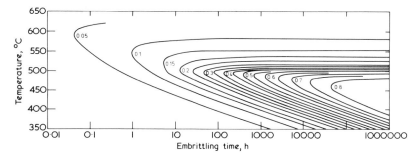

Fig. 41. The time–temperature diagram for the segregation of P in the SAE 3410 steel of CARR *et al.* [1953]. The numbers against the curves denote the P segregation occurring as a result of the embrittling treatment, i.e., in excess of the 0.06 monolayers segregated during 675°C temper. (After SEAH [1977].)

References: p. 928.

boundaries. This is clear from eqs. (37) and (38) where the initial rate of segregation is proportional to the free solute content. In addition, GRUZIN and MURAL [1964] show that 0.5% of Mo retards the diffusivity of P in pure iron by an order of magnitude at these temperatures. Thus Mo initially retards the segregation of P. With time at temperature, the Mo nucleates Mo_2C carbides which precipitate and release the locked-up P. Thus, as time evolves the P segregation may eventually return to the level expected in Mo-free steels, as observed in practice (MCMAHON *et al*. [1977]). The initial retarding effect of Mo improves as the Mo content of the steel increases but reaches an optimum in the range 0.4–0.7%, after which the embrittlement deteriorates again (POWERS [1956], DUMOULIN *et al*. [1980], YU and MC-MAHON [1980]). Part of the initial improvement is, as discussed above, due to the reduced P segregation. An additional effect arises through the improvement in cohesion caused by Mo segregation predicted in fig. 34 and observed by DUMOULIN *et al*. [1980]. However, as the Mo content increases, the propensity to Mo_2C precipitation increases and above 0.7% content the remedial effect disappears.

6.4. Further examples of metallurgical phenomena influenced by microchemical processes

The case studies of metallurgical properties affected by microchemical processes presented above are being increasingly supported by a growing body of theoretical and experimental studies. Some of these are now fairly mature examples. As fig. 35 (above) indicates, there exist many other examples of metallurgical phenomena at various stages of understanding and different levels of significance, which are being progressively scrutinized in terms of the contribution of the interfacial microchemistry. Below we consider, in brief, a selection of case studies which are being currently expanded by work in several laboratories and which represent, to a certain extent, fresh directions in the understanding of traditional metallurgical problems.

6.4.1. Microchemical barrier layers

There is a category of metallurgical phenomena in which interfacial microchemistry induces its effect through an impedance layer across the interface. The phenomena refer mostly to ripening or microstructural shape modification processes (ch. 10B, §3.2.2; ch. 14, §2.4), which depend on the ease with which atoms can transfer across the interface between solid phases, but they may also operate at a free surface (as in nitridation or carburization from gas phase equilibria), involving atom transfer across the free surface from the vapour to the interior of the solid.

Consider second phase particles or precipitates in a solid matrix at service or processing temperatures. There exists an inherent tendency for such particles or precipitates to coarsen in order to reduce the total interfacial free energy associated with them. The rate-determining step in normal ripening processes is the volume diffusivity, however in the presence of segregants at this type of interface, the atom transfer step may become rate-determining. This may lead to a significant retardation in the kinetics of ripening.

There exists much indirect evidence for the segregation of impurities to these interfaces. BOYD and NICHOLSON [1971] showed that the addition of 0.1% cadmium to an aluminium–4% copper alloy produced a remarkable reduction in the ageing kinetics of θ' precipitates at 200°C as indicated by the rate of growth of the mean particle size with time. In addition, they were able to measure by isothermal calorimetry a considerable reduction in interfacial free energy, from 1530 mJ/m^2 to 250 mJ/m^2, produced by the cadmium additive. This is clear evidence for the segregation of the cadmium to the interface. This subject has been considered in most detail for the ripening of γ'-Fe$_4$N precipitates in an iron–nitrogen alloy. Low bulk additions of antimony, oxygen, phosphorus and tin produce a remarkable inhibition in the rate of coarsening of the nitride. This is illustrated in the recent work of MILLER [1979] in fig. 42 in which the increasing bulk tin content is seen to reduce the mean nitride particle coarsening rate by an order of magnitude compared with the behaviour in pure iron.

In considering the theory of the segregation-induced retardation of ripening, the starting point is the *Lifshitz–Wagner equation* (LIFSHITZ and SLYOZOV [1961]; WAGNER [1961]) for volume-diffusion controlled growth of a dispersion of particles of initial mean radius r_0:

$$r^3 - r_0^3 = \frac{B_1 \gamma_i V^2 C_0 D_v}{RT}(t - t_0), \tag{60}$$

where r is the mean particle radius after a time $(t - t_0)$, γ_i the interfacial free energy, V the molar volume of precipitates, C_0 the molar concentration of solute in equilibrium with a particle of infinite size and B_1 is a numerical parameter which can vary according to the shape of the precipitates. Segregation to such interfaces will reduce γ_i typically by about 50%. However, much larger inhibitions in coarsening rates have been observed, and a reduction in interfacial energy cannot in itself account for the observed behaviour. It is believed that the most likely mechanism is that the segregate inhibits the rate of transfer of solute atoms across the interface. In this situation the relevant ripening equation becomes:

$$r^2 - r_0^2 = \frac{B_2 \gamma_i V^2 C_0 Q}{RT}(t - t_0), \tag{61}$$

where Q is a reaction rate parameter associated with the ease of transferring a species across the interface. Thus, according to this theory, the mean particle size varies as $t^{1/3}$ for volume-diffusion control and with $t^{1/2}$ for interface-reaction control. In studies of this nature it has not been easy to make a clear distinction in the mechanisms on the basis of this time-dependent growth behaviour because these functions both lie within the experimental scatter. Thus, although these studies do not give a clear confirmation of this mechanism, neither do they negate it. Recently MILLER [1979] has re-examined the theory and has shown that it predicts a time invariant size distribution profile depending on the above growth mechanisms and that the data shown in fig. 42 can be fitted more closely to the particle size profile predicted for interface control.

References: p. 928.

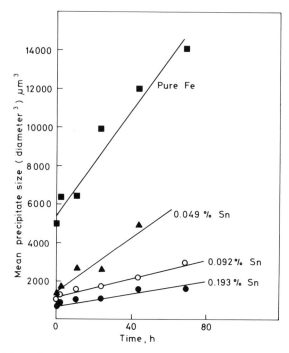

Fig. 42. The effect of increasing bulk tin content on the rate of coarsening of nitride precipitates in iron at 370°C.

The surface-active elements which inhibit the ripening of precipitates are now shown to be able to form barrier layers at iron surfaces, thereby strongly retarding nitridation and carburization reactions. The inhibition can be quite significant as demonstrated by GRABKE *et al.* [1977] with sulphur impurity adsorption up to a level of a monolayer. In this type of atom transfer process, the alloying species is initially present in a molecular form, as CO_2, CH_4 or NH_3, in the vapour phase, and for its entry into the metal the basic mechanism is the stepwise catalytic dissociation of the surface-adsorbed molecule, allowing the C or N ions to penetrate into the interior. The strongly bound impurities at the surface impair the dissociation step, as in a poisoning reaction. In the reverse process, the surface denudation of nitrogen or carbon in iron alloys has also been shown to depend strongly on the existence of chemical barrier layers which inhibit the formation of the molecular species at the free surface. The precise mechanisms appear to be strongly related to the catalytic poisoning of surfaces by impurities, which operate in these instances in a manner that effectively retards the rate of ingress or expulsion of the elements.

6.4.2. Creep-embrittlement

It was noted earlier that as a consequence of surface segregation, the rate of grain-boundary creep cavity generation is increased, leading to a deterioration in creep rupture life. This pertains to typical weldable creep-resistant steels of the Cr–Mo–V series where the impurities present in the bulk exercise their role in the heat-affected zone of the weld, following a stress-relief heat treatment at temperatures of the order of 700°C. Thus in a stress-relief operation in the average commercial UK steel of the type $\frac{1}{2}$Cr$\frac{1}{2}$Mo$\frac{1}{4}$V (impurities in ppm: P, 170; Sn, 120; Sb, 30: As, 160; Cu, 1200; Ni, 1200), the most active embrittling impurities are Sn, Cu, As, Sb and P in that order with relative fragility potencies given by the ratios 3 : 2.5 : 2 : 1 : 1, respectively (LEA *et al.* [1980]).

We consider now these alloys in service conditions, where stress and temperatures are lower than in the above, and under longer-term creep durations. Analysis of existing data by SEAH [1980c] reveals a different effect. Here it appears that the rate-determining mechanism is the transport of matter or vacancies along the grain boundaries in order to feed the growing cavities. For a given strain associated with cavity growth, a high density of small cavities is much more harmful than a lower density of large cavities. The former condition may be promoted either by increasing the cavity nucleation rate (which we have seen is induced by surface segregation to the cavity walls) but it may also be promoted by retarding the growth rate. These effects are noted in the analysis of creep cavitation by SKELTON [1975], and are

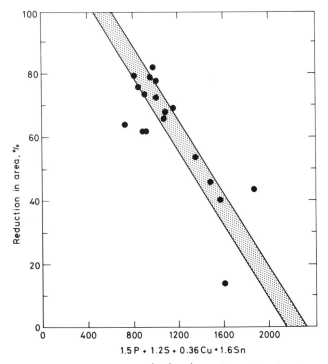

Fig. 43. Regression analysis of creep ductility in $\frac{1}{2}$Cr$\frac{1}{2}$Mo$\frac{1}{4}$V steels as a function of a combined impurity parameter involving P, S, Cu and Sn (after SEAH [1980c]).

References: p. 928.

described by the equation

$$\epsilon_r = \frac{0.65}{d} \left[\frac{2\pi D_b \delta \sigma \Omega}{NkT} \right]^{1/5}, \tag{62}$$

where ϵ_r is the strain to rupture, d is the average grain diameter, D_b is the grain-boundary diffusivity and N the continuous rate of creation of cavities; the other symbols have been defined earlier.

A regression analysis on the effects of various impurities on the rupture ductilities during long-term creep at $550°C$ on $\frac{1}{2}Cr\frac{1}{2}Mo\frac{1}{4}V$ commercial steels has shown a decrease in the rupture ductility with increasing impurity content as indicated in fig. 43 (SEAH [1980c]). The dependence of rupture ductility upon impurities is given by:

$$-\Delta(\text{rupture ductility}) \propto 1.5P + 0.36Cu + 1.6Sn + 1.2S, \tag{63}$$

where the element symbols refer to solute concentrations in the bulk. For the above typical commercial-purity steel, the relative damaging potencies of the impurities are different from that of the stress-relief case of embrittlement mentioned above: the order is now Cu, P, Sn and S with relative fragilities of $2.5 : 1.5 : 1 : 1$, respectively.

Thus, in both forms of creep embrittlement pertaining to the generation and growth of grain boundary cavities, such as those illustrated by stress-relief cracking or long-term creep-embrittlement, the impurity sensitivity arises from different modes of interfacial segregation. This difference appears to be associated with the very different strain rates that are experienced.

6.4.3. Intergranular stress-corrosion cracking

The notions of interfacial microchemistry and the effects on interfacial cohesion are being applied currently to explain various forms of intergranular cracking in the presence of both stress and a corrosive environment. Thus, pure iron is resistant to stress-corrosion cracking in nitrate environments, however in commercial carbon steels, failure is invariably intergranular. Many attempts have been made to trace the role of alloying elements, for example carbon, aluminium, and chromium, but there is seemingly little systematic behaviour. The importance of the impurity contents of these commercial steels has now been recognized. In a recent study (LEA and HONDROS [1982]), samples were prepared from high-purity mild steel stock, each sample containing a single impurity at a dilute level comparable with that found in commercial material. Here the free residual sulphur, which is very active, was first rendered harmless by the addition of manganese. Each impurity element was added separately at a bulk level which was predicted to give rise to a grain-boundary segregation content of about 20% of a monatomic layer following an isothermal heat treatment. The samples were tested to failure in a controlled environmental cell containing ammonium nitrate, at a constant strain rate. In each case, a control sample was tested under exactly the same conditions except for a neutral solution. Here it was seen that every specimen exhibited stress corrosion in the nitrate environment, failing in a shorter time than that in the control environment. The copious data shown diagrammatically in fig. 44 refer to the time for intergranular

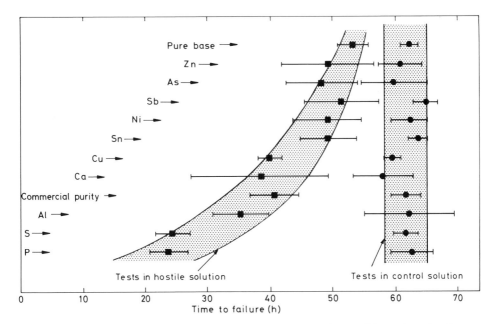

Fig. 44. The times to failure of 11 specimens of carbon steel, each containing a different impurity element, stress-corrosion tested in ammonium nitrate solution at a constant strain rate. The control tests in a neutral environment are shown to the right. (After LEA and HONDROS [1982]).

failure for alloys stress-corroded at a constant strain rate, noting that the data on the right-hand side of the diagram refer to the tests in the controlled solution, here paraffin. In the nitrate solution the fracture was almost always entirely intergranular, while in the control solution ductile fracture predominated. The figure shows that in the aggressive environment, with all other conditions identical, the reduction in life depends on the impurity present. Taking the time to failure under constant strain-rate testing, normalized to the value in a benign environment as the measure of the reduction in the resistance of the steel to cracking, the data can be presented in the form

$$-\Delta R = 20P + 1.9Cu + 1.0Sn + 0.9Sb + 0.9(\text{others}). \tag{64}$$

Here the element symbols represent the bulk content in wt%. The changes in R thus provide a ranking order of the potent segregating impurities which affect the stress-corrosion propensity. We note that in commercial steels S, Ca and Al are mainly present as precipitates. To optimize the performance of carbon steel in nitrate environments, the clearest metallurgical guideline from this is a reduction in bulk impurity levels, particularly that of residual phosphorus.

Although the detailed micromechanism for this effect awaits elaboration, the principal observations can be described fairly adequately by a dissolution model in which the grain-boundary material is preferentially removed, the driving force for this being the divergence of the segregant's electrochemical potential from that of iron. In an oxidizing environment such as aqueous ammonium nitrate, the driving force for atomic dissolution is related to the potential difference between the matrix and the segregants, which form a galvanic cell. Thus for segregants which have a more positive potential than iron, these atoms themselves are dissolved more rapidly and a very sharp grain-boundary crack is exposed for further dissolution. On the other hand, for segregants having a more negative potential than iron, atoms adjacent to the boundary are dissolved, thus enhancing the intergranular corrosion but with a different crack tip profile.

6.4.4. Intergranular hydrogen-embrittlement

An aspect of the ubiquitous problem of the hydrogen-embrittlement of steels is of interest here. This is the intergranular mode of failure, which has been considered recently in relation to the microchemical nature of the grain boundaries. Thus LATANISION and OPPERHAUSER [1974] proposed that hydrogen penetration along the grain-boundary regions should be promoted by hydrogen-recombination poisons which are present as grain-boundary segregants. These elements, such as P, S, As and Sb, which have a strong tendency to segregate to grain boundaries in steel also have a stronger intrinsic binding to hydrogen than does iron. A probable effect of this is that following the dissociation of a hydrogen molecule which arrives from the vapour or from solution, the stronger bonding available at the solute atom sites causes the hydrogen to reside at these sites for much longer times than at normal iron sites, and therefore there is a greater chance for the hydrogen to be absorbed into the lattice. Hence the role of these solute species is effectively to increase the amount of hydrogen occluded along the grain boundary zones. If the mechanism of hydrogen-embrittlement requires the concentration of hydrogen in the metal just ahead of the crack tip, the above grain-boundary segregants should therefore aid this embrittlement.

6.4.5. Inhibition of surface oxidation in alloys

In certain alloys, especially those containing aluminium, surface oxidation can be inhibited by the introduction of dopants which both reduce the rate of growth of the oxide and also inhibit "breakaway" oxidation by improving the scale adhesion at the metal–metal-oxide interface. This complex subject has been reviewed in detail, for example by WHITTLE and STRINGER [1980] who assessed various mechanisms for the improvement in performance. Several microchemical phenomena have been proposed to account for this. One proposal, which requires experimental verification but which is consistent with the analysis given in §5.2, is that the dopant segregates to the oxide grain boundaries, thereby reducing the boundary diffusivity. In their study of oxidation behaviour of γ–γ'-Cr_2C_2 eutectic composite containing additions of yttrium at a low level, BULLOCK *et al.* [1974] observed a remarkable improvement (i.e. reduction) in oxidation weight gain at 1100°C and in addition showed by Auger electron spectroscopy that the yttrium level increased with distance in the oxide bulk and reached a peak level at a depth which suggested that the interface between the

oxide and the alloy was enriched in yttrium. In addition to the probable improvements in growth kinetics by segregation to the boundaries, it was considered that the
formation of a microchemical barrier layer at the metal–metal-oxide interface
improved the adhesion of the alumina in the mixed metal oxide scale to the metal
substrate and hence increased the resistance to oxide scale spalling.

A third possibility for inhibited high-temperature corrosion is through the formation of a microchemical barrier layer at the metal oxide–vapour interface. The
presence of boron in the vapour phase is known to improve greatly the oxidation
resistance of chromium-containing steels by increasing the time to "breakaway"
oxidation. LEA [1979] showed by Auger electron spectroscopy that the boron was
present essentially only at the outer oxide surface layer and it was also accompanied
by a high chromium enrichment. The mechanism for this type of inhibition thus has
similarities with the processes considered above (§6.4.1). In particular, it was
considered that the introduction of O–B–O covalent bonds in the outer oxide
surface structure would impede the transfer of O ions onto the lattice, thus forming a
film which in turn allows slowly diffusing protective chromium from the alloy to
reach the free surface.

7. Interfacial microchemistry and alloy design theory

All the important themes of physical and chemical metallurgy contribute collectively to the theory of alloy design – including the thermochemistry of phase
equilibria, crystal defect theory, fracture theory, oxidation and corrosion resistance
and so on. This chapter has placed emphasis on the importance of the relatively new
subject of interfacial microchemistry for a wide diversity of metallurgical properties,
and the insight and information now made available should be viewed in terms of its
contribution to alloy design. Here we distinguish between deliberate additions of
specific elements which procure beneficial effects on certain properties, and the
planned control of known elements which are detrimental. The advanced knowledge
in this field provides many opportunities to manipulate alloy properties, often in the
context of "fine tuning" but equally often to gain significant improvements in
service life. In the past decade, several lines of advance have been made in this
subject matter which are valuable to alloy design theory: (i) the identification of
potent impurity species (both harmful and beneficial); (ii) the basic mechanisms
(sometimes only partly understood) by which they operate; (iii) the enrichment levels
as well as bulk contents at which the effects are significant.

This chapter provides several guidelines. Thus, on the basis of a retardation of
grain-boundary transport, or on improved interfacial cohesion, certain types of
element can be beneficial – as in the improvement of oxidation characteristics or in
the rate of Coble creep. Certain elements can be predicted to offer an improvement
in sintering behaviour through a segregant stabilization of fine grain structure. In a
recent example of benefit to mechanical properties, WHITE *et al.* [1981] demonstrated that the room-temperature strength and ductility of a Pt/Rh/W alloy can be

References: p. 928.

improved by the addition of 75 wt ppm of B which was shown to enrich, in a typical manner, the grain boundaries.

Where the impurities produce deleterious effects, clearly the alloy design aspects involve the elimination of the impurities or, more practicably, their control to within tolerance levels. The identification of potent surface-active species and the assigning of bulk tolerance levels have been the specific objectives of many studies in this field. The information is couched often in formulae of the type presented above for intergranular stress-corrosion cracking [eq. (64)] or creep rupture ductility [eq. (63)]. This permits the design of alloys of closely controlled composition for improved performance in the defined conditions of use.

In a previous discussion (HONDROS and SEAH [1977b]), we presented a number of procedures which might offer a control over the effects of harmful impurities – including the judicious use of the principles of competitive segregation, the selection of remedial segregants, the thinning out of the embrittling species by spreading them out over a large interfacial area, i.e. a very fine grain size, reducing the kinetics of the embrittling species, and the used chemical fixation or precipitation reactions. In the meantime, at least one of the above approaches has been explored in depth, in connection with affording a simple and economical control over temper-embrittlement. SEAH et al. [1979] demonstrated that temper-embrittlement induced by P and Sn in $2\frac{1}{4}$Cr1Mo and $3\frac{1}{2}$Ni–Cr–Mo–V steels can be reduced by additions of La or Ce at a predicted level. The selection of La, Ce and mischmetal (approx. 50% Ce, 25% La, 25% other rare-earth metals) are based on a comprehensive thermochemical assessment of the possibility of forming stable microprecipitates in order to reduce the bulk levels of active P and Sn. The optimum addition of La required to remove the embrittling effects of P and Sn is given by the formula

$$La = 8.7S + 2.3Sn + 4.5P, \tag{65}$$

where the element symbols represent the wt% of the element in the steel. Figure 45, taken from this work, shows the high DBTT for a pure $2\frac{1}{4}$Cr1Mo steel with 0.017% P added. The further addition of various levels of La lower the transition temperature significantly, to the limit of a high purity material.

There is an aspect of the general subject matter of this chapter which has wider ramifications in the context of metals recycling, and which implies that it will be a subject of growing importance in the future. It is clear that because of geo-political, economic and social factors there will be in the future a greater emphasis on the recycling of used materials in industrialized countries. This will reduce their vulnerability to external sources of raw materials and also, there are inherent energy savings in reclaiming metals from used articles rather than obtaining them from raw supplies of ore. Because of the complex mechanical systems used by industry and society and the wide combination of metals involved, inevitably metals derived from recovered scrap will contain certain unwanted residuals which bypass the refinement process (HONDROS [1980b]). This chapter has underlined that such small quantities of noxious elements can provoke remarkable effects on physical and mechanical properties, and more specifically the accumulation of residual elements, such as

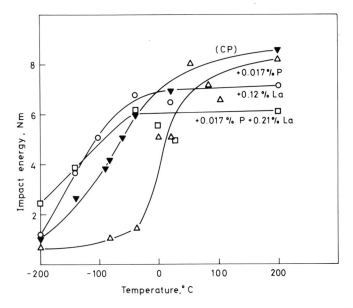

Fig. 45. Improvement in the ductile–brittle transition temperature in a steel susceptible to temper embrittlement, resulting from low level additions of lanthanum which combat the effect of phosphorus (after SEAH *et al.* [1979]).

copper and tin in steel from scrap, will have effects on the performance. Thus, an increased effort on the recycling of metals will, in general, exacerbate the effects of unwanted tramp elements on the properties of alloys aimed for particular end uses. Based upon better metallurgical understanding, there will be effort devoted to a control of tramp element effects, involving remedial measures, of the type discussed above.

However, we envisage the need for a broader perspective, leading to a new metallurgical or engineering subject matter encompassing the theory of design involving recycling. In this global approach, we consider the final end use of the alloy as the primary parameter, and recyclability should be built in to the design of the final alloy. Thus we may plan for the evolution of secondary alloy products which may not be adequate for the original property requirements, but which may be suitable for other applications. An interesting example of this is a carbon steel with high levels of tin and copper arising from the use of scrap containing much tin plate – this has been demonstrated to have an improved corrosion resistance associated with the presence of these elements in sub-scale layers. Such an alloy may not have adequate mechanical properties for the original purposes, however it can be used in situations where the improved corrosion resistance is advantageous. Thus, in this theory of design with recycling we can envisage recovery epicycles in which certain grades of alloy might be blended together to produce new alloys which are more suitable for specific applications. The science of interfacial microchemistry will

References: p. 928.

make basic contributions in the future in connection with alloy design in the context of metals recycling, improved reliability and advances in performance.

References

ASHBY, M.F., 1972, Acta Metall. **20**, 887

AUST, K.T., and J.H. WESTBROOK, 1965, Lattice Defects in Quenched Metals (Academic Press, London) p. 771.

AUST, K.T., R.E. HANNEMAN, P. NIESSEN and J.H. WESTBROOK, 1968, Acta Metall. **16**, 291.

BATTE, A.D., J.M. BREAR, S.R. HOLDSWORTH, J. MYERS and P.R. REYNOLDS, 1980, Phil. Trans. Roy. Soc. **A295**, 253.

BAUN, W.L., N.T. McDEVITT and J.S. SOLOMON, 1976, Surface Analysis Techniques for Metallurgical Applications, Am. Soc. Testing Mater., Spec. Tech. Publ. **596**, 86.

BENNINGHOVEN, A., J. GIBER, J. LASLO, M. RIEDEL and H. WERNER, eds., 1982, Springer Series in Chemical Physics, **19**, Secondary Ion Mass Spectroscopy, SIMS III (Springer, Berlin).

BERNARDINI, J., P. GAS, E.D. HONDROS and M.P. SEAH, 1982, Proc. Roy. Soc. **A379**, 159.

BORISOV, V.T., V.M. GOLIKOV and G.V. SCHERBEDINSKIY, 1964, Phys. Met. Metallogr. **17**, 80.

BOYD, J.D., and R.B. NICHOLSON, 1971, Acta Metall. **19**, 1379.

BRIANT, C.L., 1981, Scripta Metall. **15**, 1013.

BRIANT, C.L., 1983, Acta Metall. **31**, 257.

BRIGGS, D., 1982, Surf. and Interface Anal. **4**, 151.

BRIGGS, D., and M.P. SEAH, 1983, Practical Surface Analysis by Auger and Photo-Electron Spectroscopy (Wiley–Heyden, London).

BRUNAUER, S., L.S. DEMING, W.E. DEMING and E.J. TELLER, 1940, J. Am. Chem. Soc. **62**, 1723.

BULLOCK, E., C. LEA and M. McLEAN, 1979, Met. Sci. **13**, 373.

CARR, F.L., M. GOLDMAN, L.D. JAFFE and D.C. BUFFUM, 1953, Trans. AIME **197**, 998.

COBLE, R.L., 1963, J. Appl. Phys. **34**, 1679.

DEFAY, R., I. PRIGOGINE, A. BELLOMANS and D.H. EVERETT, 1966, Surface Tension and Adsorption (Longmans, London).

DELAMARE, F., and G.E. RHEAD, 1971, Surf. Sci. **28**, 267.

DOIG, P. and P.E.J. FLEWITT, 1981, Acta Metall. **29**, 1831.

DOIG, P., D. LONSDALE and P.E.J. FLEWITT, 1981, Metallurg. Trans. **12A**, 1277.

DUMOULIN, P.H., M. GUTTMANN, M. FOUCAULT, M. PALMIER, M. WAYMAN and M. BISCONDI, 1980, Met. Sci. **14**, 1.

EGERT, B., and G. PANZNER, 1982, Surf. Sci. **118**, 345.

ERHART, H., and H.J. GRABKE, 1981, Met. Sci. **15**, 401.

EWING, R.H., 1971, Acta Metall. **19**, 1359.

FRANZONI, U., H. GORETZKI and S. STURLESE, 1981, Scripta Metall. **15**, 743.

GAS, P., M. GUTTMANN and J. BERNARDINI, 1982, Acta Metall. **30**, 1309.

GIBBS, G.B., and J.E. HARRIS, 1969, In: Interfaces, ed. R.C. Gifkins (Butterworths, London) p. 53.

GIBBS, J.W., reprinted 1948, Collected Works, Vol. 1 (Yale University Press) p. 219.

GJOSTEIN, N.A., 1966, Proc. 13th Sagamore Army Materials Research Conference, Raquette Lake, NY, eds. J.J. Burke, N.L. Reed and V. Weiss (Syracuse University Press).

GRABKE, H.J., W. PAULITSCHKE, G. TAUBER and H. VIEFHAUS, 1977, Surf. Sci. **63**, 377.

GRUZIN, P.L., and V.V. MURAL, 1964, Fiz. Metal. Metalloved. **17** (3) 62.

GUGGENHEIM, E.A., 1950, Thermodynamics, 2nd Ed. (North-Holland, Amsterdam) p. 35.

GUTTMANN, M., 1975, Surf. Sci. **53**, 213.

GUTTMANN, M., 1976, Met. Sci. **10**, 337.

GUTTMANN, M., 1980, Phil. Trans. Roy. Soc. **A295**, 169.

GUTTMANN, M., and D. McLEAN, 1979, Proc. ASM Materials Science Seminar, Interfacial Segregation, eds. W.C. Johnson and J.M. Blakely (ASM, Metals Park, OH) p. 261.

HANSEN, M., 1958, Constitution of Binary Alloys, also Suppl. 1, Elliott, R.P., 1965, and Suppl. 2, Shunk, F.A., 1969 (McGraw–Hill, New York).

HARRIES, D.R., and A.D. MARWICK, 1980, Phil. Trans. Roy. Soc. **A295**, 197.

HASEGAWA, M., N. NAKAJIMA, M. KUSUNOKI and K. SUZUKI, 1975, Trans. Japan. Inst. Met. **16**, 641.

HASHIMOTO, M., Y. ISHIDA, R. YAMAMOTO, M. DOYAMA and T. FUJIWARA, 1982, Scripta Metall. **16**, 267.

HAYES, P. and P. GRIEVESON, 1975, Met. Sci. **9**, 332.

HERRING, C., 1950, J. Appl. Phys. **21**, 437.

HERRING, C., 1951, in: Physics of Powder Metallurgy, ed. W.E. Kingston (McGraw–Hill, New York).

HERRING, C., 1953, Structure and Properties of Solid Surfaces (Univ. of Chicago Press) p. 5.

HIRTH, J.P. and J.R. RICE, 1980, Metallurg. Trans. **11A**, 1501.

HONDROS, E.D., 1965, Proc. Roy. Soc. **A286**, 479

HONDROS, E.D., 1967, Met. Sci. **1**, 36.

HONDROS, E.D., 1969, in: Interfaces, ed. R.C. Gifkins (Butterworths, London) p. 77.

HONDROS, E.D., 1970, Surface Energy Measurements, in: Physicochemical Measurements in Metals Research, Techniques in Metals Research Vol IV, ed. R.A. Rapp (Wiley, New York) Part 2, p.293.

HONDROS, E.D., 1976, in: Grain Boundary Structure and Properties, eds. G.A. Chadwick and D.A. Smith (Academic, London) p. 265.

HONDROS, E.D., 1978, Precipitation Processes in Solids, Proc. TMS–AIME Meeting 1976, Eds. K.C. Russell and H.I. Aaronson (Metallurg. Soc. of AIME, Warrendale, PA) p. 1.

HONDROS, E.D., 1980a, Scripta Metall. **14**, 345.

HONDROS, E.D., 1980b, Phil. Trans. Roy. Soc. **A295**, 9.

HONDROS, E.D., and P.J. HENDERSON, 1983, Metallurg. Trans. **14A**, 521.

HONDROS, E.D., and D. MCLEAN, 1968, Surface Phenomena of Metals, Monograph (Society of Chemical Industry, London) No. 28, p. 39.

HONDROS, E.D., and D. MCLEAN, 1974, Phil. Mag. **29**, 771.

HONDROS, E.D., and D. MCLEAN, 1976, in: Grain Boundary Structure and Properties, eds. G.A. Chadwick and D.A. Smith (Academic, London) p. 353.

HONDROS, E.D., and M.P. SEAH, 1977a, Metallurg. Trans. **A8**, 1363.

HONDROS, E.D., and M.P. SEAH, 1977b, Int. Met. Rev. **22**, 262.

HONDROS, E.D., and L.E.H. STUART, 1968, Phil. Mag. **17**, 711.

HONDROS, E.D., M.P. SEAH and C. LEA, 1976, Met. Mater. (Jan.) p. 26.

HULTGREN, R., P.A. DESAI, D.T. HAWKINS, M. GLEISER and K.K. KELLY, 1973, Selected Values of the Thermodynamic Properties of Binary Alloys (ASM, Metals Park, OH).

INMAN, M.C., and H.R. TIPLER, 1963, Met. Rev. **8**, 105.

JOHNSON, W.C., N.G. CHARKA, R. KU, J.L. BOMBACK and P.P. WYNBLATT, 1978, J. Vac. Sci. Technol. **15**, 467.

JOKL, M.L., V. VITEK and C.J. MCMAHON, 1980, Acta Metall. **28**, 1479.

JONES, R.H., S.M. BRUEMMER, M.T. THOMAS and D.R. BAER, 1981, Metallurg. Trans. **12A**, 1621.

KALDERON, D., 1972, Proc. Inst. Mech. Eng. **186**, 341.

KANEKO, H., T. NISHIZAWA, K. TAMAKI and A. TANIFUJI, 1965, J. Japan. Inst. Met. **29**, 166.

KARLSSON, L., H-O. ANDREN and H. NORDEN, 1982, Scripta Metall. **16**, 297.

KITTEL, C., 1956, Introduction to Solid State Physics (Wiley, New York).

KOZAKEVITCH, P., and G. URBAIN, 1961, Mém. Sci. Rev. Métallurg. **6**, 401.

KRAAI, D.A., and S. FLOREEN, 1964, Trans. AIME **230**, 833.

KUMAR, A., and B.L. EYRE, 1980, Proc. Roy. Soc. **A370**, 431.

KUMIKOV, V.K., and KH. B. KHOKONOV, 1983, J. Appl. Phys. **54**, 1346.

KUPPER, J., H. ERHART and H.J. GRABKE, 1981, Corros. Sci. **21**, 227.

LARTIGUE, S., and L. PRIESTER, 1983, Acta Metall., in press.

LATANISION, R.M., and H. OPPERHAUSER, 1974, Metallurg. Trans. **5**, 483.

LEA, C., 1979, Met. Sci. **13**, 301.

LEA, C., and E.D. HONDROS, 1982, Proc. Roy Soc. **A377**, 477.

LEA, C., and M.P. SEAH, 1977, Phil. Mag. **35**, 213.

LEA, C., M.P. SEAH and E.D. HONDROS, 1980, Mater. Sci. Eng. **42**, 233.

LE CLAIRE, A.D., 1975, Thin Solid Films **25**, 1.

LIFSHITZ, I.M., and V.V. SLYOZOV, 1961, Phys. Chem. Solids **19**, 35.

LOW, J.R., 1968, Trans. AIME **242**, 14.

MARCUS, H.L., L.H. HACKETT and P.W. PALMBERG, 1972, Temper Embrittlement of Alloy Steels, Am. Soc. Testing Mater., Spec. Tech. Publ. **499**, 90.

MARWICK, A.D., 1981, Nucl. Instr. and Meth. **182/183**, 827.

MCLEAN, D., 1957, Grain Boundaries in Metals (Oxford Univ. Press).

MCLEAN, D., 1981, Metals Forum **4**, 45.

MCMAHON, C.J., 1968, Temper-Embrittlement in Steel, Am. Soc. Testing Mater., Spec. Tech. Publ. **407**, 127.

MCMAHON, C.J., and V. VITEK, 1979, Acta Metall., **27**, 507.

MCMAHON, C.J., A.K. CIANELLI and H.C. FENG, 1977, Metallurg. Trans. **8A**, 1055.

MILLER, D., 1979, Doctor of Philosophy Thesis, Univ. of Strathclyde.

MILLER, M.K., and G.D.W. SMITH, 1977, Met. Sci. **11**, 249.

MILLS, B., M. MCLEAN and E.D. HONDROS, 1973, Phil. Mag. **27**, 361.

NABARRO, F.R.N., 1948, Report of Conference on Strength of Solids, (Phys. Soc., London) p. 75.

NANNI, P., C.T.H. STODDART and E.D. HONDROS, 1976, J. Mater. Chem. **1**, 297.

NICHOLAS, M.G., and C.F. OLD, 1979, J. Mater. Sci. **14**, 1.

NICOLET, M.A., 1978, Thin Solid Films **52**, 415.

OVERBURY, S.H., P.A. BERTRAND and G.A. SOMORJAI, 1975, Chem. Rev. **75**, 547.

PETCH, N.J., 1956, Phil. Mag. **1**, 331.

PICHARD, C., M. GUTTMANN, J. RIEU and C. GOUX, 1975, J. Physique **36**, C4-151.

POWERS, A.E., 1956, Trans. ASM **48**, 149.

RELLICK, J.R., and C.J. MCMAHON, 1974, Metallurg. Trans. **5**, 2439.

ROBERTS-AUSTEN, W.C., 1888, Phil. Trans. Roy. Soc. **A179**, 339.

ROWLANDS, G. and D.P. WOODRUFF, 1979, Phil. Mag. **40**, 459.

ROY, A., U. ERB and H. GLEITER, 1982, Acta Metall. **30**, 1847.

SCHULZ, B.J., and C.J. MCMAHON, 1972, Temper Embrittlement of Alloy Steels, Am. Soc. Testing Mater., Spec. Tech. Publ. **499**, 104.

SEAH, M.P., 1975, Surf. Sci. **53**, 168.

SEAH, M.P., 1976, Proc. Roy. Soc. **A349**, 535.

SEAH, M.P., 1977, Acta Metall. **25**, 345.

SEAH, M.P., 1979, J. Catal. **57**, 450.

SEAH, M.P., 1980a, J. Phys. **F10** 1043.

SEAH, M.P., 1980b, Acta Metall. **28**, 955.

SEAH, M.P., 1980c, Phil. Trans. Roy. Soc. **A295**, 265.

SEAH, M.P., 1981, Mater. Sci. Club. Bull. **64**, 2.

SEAH, M.P., 1983, in: Practical Surface Analysis by Auger and Photo-Electron Spectroscopy, eds. D. Briggs and M.P. Seah (Wiley–Heyden, London) ch. 7.

SEAH, M.P., and E.D. HONDROS, 1973, Proc. Roy. Soc. **A335**, 191.

SEAH, M.P., and E.D. HONDROS, 1982, Proc. NATO Advanced Research Institute, Atomistics of Fracture May 1981, San Bastiano, Corsica, ed. R.M. Latanision (Plenum, New York) to be published.

SEAH, M.P., and C. LEA, 1975, Phil. Mag. **31**, 627.

SEAH, M.P., P.J. SPENCER and E.D. HONDROS, 1979, Met. Sci. **13**, 307.

SHINODA, T. and T. NAKAMURA, 1981, Acta Metall. **29**, 1631 and 1637.

SKELTON, R.P., 1975, Met. Sci. **9**, 192.

SMIALOWSKI, I.M., 1962, Hydrogen in Steel (Pergamon Press, New York).

SMITH, C.S., 1948, Trans. AIME **175**, 15.

SMITHELLS, C.J., 1976, Metals Reference Book, 5th Ed. (Butterworths, London).

SURESH, S., G.F. ZAMISKI and R.O. RITCHIE, 1981, Metallurg. Trans. **12A**, 1435

SUTTON, A.P., and V. VITEK, 1982, Acta Metall. **30**, 2011.

SUZUKI, S., K. ABIKO and H. KITAMURA, 1981, Scripta Metall. **15**, 1139.

TAUBER, G., and H.J. GRABKE, 1978, Ber. Bunsen Gesell. Phys. Chem. **82**, 298.

THOMAS, G.B., and T.B. GIBBONS, 1980, Superalloys 1980, Proc. Seven Springs Conference, eds. G.K. Tien *et al.* (ASM, Metals Park, OH) p. 99.
TIPLER, H.R., 1980, Phil. Trans. Roy. Soc. **A295**, 213
TIPLER, H.R., and D. MCLEAN, 1970, Met. Sci. **4**, 103.
TSAI, N.H., G.M. POUND and F.F. ABRAHAM, 1977, J. Catal. **50**, 200.
TYSON, W.R., 1975, Can. Met. Quart. **14**, 307.
TYSON, W.R., 1978, Acta Metall. **26**, 1471.
WAGNER, C., 1961, Z. Electrochem. **65**, 581.
WALSH, J.M., and B.H. KEAR, 1975, Metallurg. Trans. **6A**, 226.
WAUGH, A.R., 1978, J. Phys. **E11**, 49.
WESTBROOK, J.H., 1964, Met. Rev. **9**, 415.
WHITE, C.L., J.R. KEISER and D.N. BRASKI, 1981, Metallurg. Trans. **12A**, 1485.
WHITTLE, D.P., and J. STRINGER, 1980, Phil. Trans. Roy. Soc. **A295**, 309.
WILLIAMS, F.L., and D. NASON, 1974, Surf. Sci. **45**, 377.
WILLIAMS, T.M., A.M. STONEHAM and D.R. HARRIES, 1976, Met. Sci. **10**, 14.
WYNBLATT, P., and R.C. KU, 1979, Proc. ASM Materials Science Seminar Interfacial Segregation, eds. W.C. Johnson and J.M. Blakely (ASM, Metals Park, OH) p. 115.
YU, J., and C.J. MCMAHON, 1980, Metallurg. Trans. **11A**, 277.

Further reading

Czanderna, A.W., ed., 1975, Methods of Surface Analysis (Elsevier, New York).
Fiermans, L., J. Vennik and W. Dekeyser, Eds., 1978, Electron and Ion Spectroscopy of Solids, NATO Advanced Study Institute Series B (Plenum, New York).
Gleiter, H., and B. Chalmers, 1972, High Angle Grain Boundaries, Prog. Mater. Sci. **16**, 1.
Johnson, W.C., and J.M. Blakely, eds., 1979, Interfacial Segregation (ASM, Metals Park, OH).
Kelly, A., D.W. Pashley, E.D. Hondros and C. Lea, eds., 1980, Residuals, Additives and Materials Properties Proc. Conf. (The Royal Society, London); also appears as Phil. Trans. Roy. Soc. **A295**, 1–341.
McLean, D., 1957, Grain Boundaries in Metals (Oxford Univ. Press).

SUBJECT INDEX